MW00611477

Regional and Petroleum Geology of the Black Sea and Surrounding Region

Edited by
A. G. Robinson

AAPG Memoir 68

Published by
The American Association of Petroleum Geologists
Tulsa, Oklahoma, U.S.A. 74101

Published 1997
Printed and bound in the United States of America

ISBN: 0-89181-348-9

Regional and petroleum geology of the Black Sea and surrounding region
/ edited by A.G. Robinson.
p. c.m. - - (AAPG memoir : 68)
Includes bibliographic references (p.) and index.
ISBN 0-89181-348-9 (alk. paper)
1. Petroleum- -Geology- -Black Sea Region. I. Robinson, A. G.
(Andrew G.) II. Series.
TN875.R396 1997
553.2'8'0916389- -dc21 97-42045
CIP

Association Editor: Neil F. Hurley
Science Director: Richard Steinmetz
Publications Manager: Kenneth M. Wolgemuth
Special Projects Editor: Anne H. Thomas
Production: Custom Editorial Productions, Inc., Cincinnati, Ohio

This books and other AAPG publications are available from:

The AAPG Bookstore
P.O. Box 979
Tulsa, OK 74101-0979
Telephone: (918) 584-2555;
or (800) 364-AAPG (U.S.A.—book orders only)
Fax: (918) 584-2652
or (800) 898-2274 (U.S.A.—book orders only)

Geological Society Publishing House
Unit 7, Brassmill
Enterprise Centre
Brassmill Lane
Bath BA1 3JN
United Kingdom
Tel 1225-445046
Fax 1225-442836

Australian Mineral Foundation
AMF Bookshop
63 Conyngham Street
Glenside, South Australia 5065
Australia
Tel (08) 379-0444
Fax (08) 379-4634

Canadian Society of Petroleum Geologists
160, 540-5th Ave. SW
Calgary, Alberta T2P 0M2
Canada
Tel (403) 264-5610

About the Editor

Andrew Robinson studied geology at Oxford and Toronto Universities and subsequently at Reading University, where he obtained a Ph.D. degree.

Andrew began his work in the oil industry with Shell, then moved in 1984 to BP. During five years in BP Research, he worked on problems of reservoir quality and sandstone diagenesis. Out of this work came the books *Inorganic Geochemistry: Applications of Petroleum Geology* and AAPG Studies in Geology 36, *Diagenesis and Basin Development*. For this work, the Geological Society awarded Andrew the William Smith Fund.

In 1990, Andrew moved to BP Exploration and worked on international new ventures, one of which involved the Turkish sector of the Black Sea. At this point, his longstanding interest in the petroleum and regional geology of the Black Sea began.

Since leaving BP in 1994, Andrew has worked for JKX Oil & Gas as Chief Geologist, where he has continued to publish papers about two of his great research interests: clastic diagenesis and the regional geology of Eurasia.

AAPG
Wishes to thank the following
for their generous contributions
to

Regional and Petroleum Geology of the Black Sea and Surrounding Region

◆

Amoco Production Company

◆

Petroconsultants (U.K.) Ltd.

◆

R. W. Jones

◆

Contributions are applied against the production costs of publication, thus directly reducing the book's purchase price and making the volume available to a greater audience.

Table of Contents

Robinson, A.G., 1997, Introduction: tectonic elements of the Black Sea Region, *in* A.G. Robinson, ed., Regional and petroleum geology of the Black Sea and surrounding region: AAPG Memoir 68, p. 1–6.

Chapter 1

Introduction: Tectonic Elements of the Black Sea Region

Andrew G. Robinson
JKX Oil & Gas plc
Guildford, United Kingdom

INTRODUCTION

In 1967 and 1969, two oceanographic cruises were made in the Black Sea under the guidance of the Woods Hole Oceanographic Institute: The cruises included scientists from many countries and disciplines. Their aims were to determine the recent geological and geochemical evolution of the Black Sea, to map the shallow structure of the basin, and to study the interaction between the oxidized surface waters and the anoxic waters beneath them. The results were published 23 years ago, as AAPG Memoir 20 (Ross and Degens, 1974). During the 1969 cruise, the vessel *Atlantis II* collected 40 piston cores, which formed the basis of most of the subsequent geological studies that were restricted to very recent sedimentation. Speculations concerning the origin of the basin and the relationship of the geology offshore to that exposed around the margins of the Black Sea were rooted in pre-plate tectonic concepts of basin formation and were in any case hampered by a lack of relevant data (Brinkmann, 1974).

In 1976, the *Glomar Challenger* visited the Black Sea on Leg 42B of the Deep Sea Drilling Project and drilled and cored three deep-water sites (379, 380, and 381). Well 381 north of the Bosporus encountered sediments as old as Miocene, including some apparently deposited in shallow water (Ross, 1978).

The next major volume in Western literature to deal with the Black Sea was published a decade later, collecting papers presented two years earlier at a conference in Yalta. In this volume, a number of seismic reflection lines—shot in 1975 by an Italian vessel—were published and, for the first time, the scientific community had a picture of the deeper structure of the Black Sea (Finetti et al., 1988). The interpretation of the seismic data, however, was still impeded by the small number of wells drilled in the Black Sea to which the lines could be tied, by the ambiguity of even these few ties, and by the presence of numerous multiples. By this time, the Black Sea was nonetheless widely regarded as a marginal basin developed to the north of the northward-subducting Tethyan oceanic plate, apparently rifting during the mid-Cretaceous (Görür, 1988; Manetti et al., 1988). There was also the hint that the Black Sea had originated not as a single basin, but as two—an eastern and a western Black Sea—that had coalesced during their postrift phases to form the single depocenter observed today.

The volumes referred to above did not reflect even a small part of the total geological work carried out on the Black Sea. Unfortunately, the vast volume of Soviet literature was inaccessible and, although often of good quality, was just as often difficult for a Western reader to understand. This was also largely true of the Turkish literature, although research—mainly on the Pontides—by the group at İstanbul Technical University was widely disseminated. None of the countries around the Black Sea made information obtained from petroleum exploration programs available either to each other or to the scientific community. It was even impossible to obtain geological maps from the surrounding onshore areas (other than old 1:500,000 geological maps of northern Turkey). As much as any sedimentary basin, the Black Sea suffered from the cold war.

During the first few years of the 1990s, however, the profound political changes that took place in Eastern Europe began to have an equally profound effect on the quantity and quality of geological work carried out in the Black Sea region. Romania, Bulgaria, Ukraine, Georgia, and Russia became independent sovereign states and, to a greater or lesser extent, opened their offshore areas to exploration by Western oil companies (see Benton, this volume). In doing so, they made available a large amount of well and seismic data that had until that time been regarded as state secrets. The new petroleum exploration programs led to the acquisition of new high-multiplicity marine reflection seismic data and to the drilling of new exploration wells in Bulgarian, Romanian, and Ukrainian offshore areas. At the same time, previously secret detailed geological maps of excellent quality became available for all of the former Soviet and Eastern European states (although, for the most part, these remain difficult to obtain). It also became possible to visit these countries more or less independently, to carry out field studies, and to talk without hindrance to their scientists. Meanwhile, in the southern part of the Black Sea, the early 1990s saw the licensing of much of the Turkish offshore sector to Western companies for petroleum exploration. No new wells have been drilled in the licensed areas, but a large amount of reflection seismic data has been acquired, interpreted, and in part published (Robinson et al., 1996). It is unfortunate that detailed geological maps of Turkey are still considered secret and remain unpublished.

As a result of this activity, a large amount of new high-quality geological work has been carried out on the Black Sea and surrounding areas. Much of this is published in this volume for the first time. The contributions to the volume cover most of the major tectonic elements in and around the Black Sea. They do not do so evenly, and are biased principally toward those areas that have received the most attention by oil companies, and toward northern Turkey, where Turkish geologists have been active for many years. The chapters not only cover different areas but also encompass very different types of study, based on different kinds of data. Thus, papers on the Pontides are essentially based on field mapping; those on the offshore shelf areas are based on seismic and well data. Perhaps not surprisingly, different workers using different databases sometimes come up with quite different and even opposing and incompatible conclusions. In editing this volume, I have made no attempt to resolve such differences or to sweep them under the carpet; I wish to draw attention to them on the basis that the identification of a problem is the first step to its solution. The volume begins with a series of chapters that deal with general aspects of the development of the Black Sea; subsequent chapters are organized in an essentially counterclockwise fashion, beginning with Romania and ending in the Gulf of Odessa (Ukrainian offshore). There are notable gaps at Thrace (although the Thrace Basin is well documented in literature elsewhere; see later), the Greater Caucasus, the Russian margin of the Eastern Black Sea, the Azov Sea, and onshore Crimea.

To those not particularly familiar with the Black Sea area, the complexity of the geology and the volume of literature available (although often inaccessible) can prove somewhat daunting. This chapter is therefore intended to serve not just as a background and introduction to the Memoir and the chapters in it, but also to the main tectonic elements in the Black Sea region. I hope that this will help the reader put the other chapters into a regional context quickly. The complexity of the area is such that it is impossible to write an uncontroversial review, and this chapter inevitably reflects my prejudices. Where others have very different prejudices, I have tried to point this out. Indeed, a second aim of this chapter is to indicate where there are major differences of interpretation.

Following, I give a brief description of the main tectonic elements in the Black Sea region, explaining how these are covered in this Memoir. For detailed reference lists, the reader should look in these chapters. I illustrate the descriptions with reference to a map (Enclosure 1). This is a slightly odd map in that it tries to show a number of attributes, principally basin origin—age and type—but also the latest deformation event. In many areas, the nature and exact positions of the boundaries of sedimentary basins are unclear; the origin of some is disputed; and in some parts of the Black Sea, the map is based on scanty information. It is therefore a somewhat unsatisfactory hybrid and will be open to criticism from those who have detailed knowledge of particular areas. So, after many dark hours with blunted colored pencils during which I many times nearly consigned the map to the bin, I have ended up including it, having convinced myself that it is better to have some map of this kind covering the entire Black Sea region than it would be to have nothing at all. I encourage those who know where it is wrong or misleading to write and tell me.

GENERAL SETTING OF THE BLACK SEA BASINS

The present Black Sea morphology has been produced by the coalescence of two basins during their postrift phases (Robinson et al., 1996). Both formed as extensional basins north of a northward-subducting oceanic plate—the Tethys Ocean. The suture zone where this ocean eventually closed is marked by an ophiolite belt and subduction-accretion complex running from İzmir on the Turkish Mediterranean coast, through Ankara and Erzincan, and into the Sevan region of Armenia. The Western basin is widely accepted as having rifted in the Aptian-Albian. There is plenty of evidence of synrift deposits of this age onshore in Turkey, and of Aptian-Albian synrift geometries on offshore seismic data. The opening of the Eastern Black Sea is harder to date, partly because synrift deposits appear to be absent, but a consensus seems to be emerging that it is younger than the Western Black Sea, within end-Cretaceous to Paleocene. Spadini et al. (this volume) summarize the results of their work modeling the subsidence and sedimentation history of the two basins. They show how Western and Eastern basins appear to have formed on quite different lithospheres with quite different thermal and mechanical properties. They show how these differences influenced the subsequent development of the basins, and how they can explain the absence of synrift deposits in the Eastern basin and the variable thicknesses of the early postrift stratigraphies.

These two most recent Black Sea basins are very much the tip of a marginal-basin iceberg. Back- and intra-arc basins have been opening and closing near the southern margin of the East European continent since at least the beginning of Mesozoic. Examples include the Greater Caucasus basin (Early Jurassic rift) and the Küre-Tavric basin (Triassic), now split between the Central Pontides and Crimea by the spreading of the Western Black Sea (indeed, the Western Black Sea rifted on the site of this older basin). Reconstructing the original settings and geometries of these older basins is not easy and is not helped by a complete lack of plausible paleomagnetic data. Banks and Robinson (this volume) attempt an explanation for the early Mesozoic basins in terms of strike-slip motion along major NW-SE faults such as the Peceneaga-Camena fault in Romania. They envisage a setting behind a zone of oblique subduction, rather like the present-day Andaman Sea.

As the Tethys Ocean finally began to close during the Paleogene, the elevation of the Pontides led to the development of a restricted basin system, partly isolated from the world's oceans and known as Paratethys. At times, Paratethys stretched from the Pannonian basin in the west as far as the South Caspian. Due to widespread provinciality of faunas and flora, the biostratigraphy of Paratethys is a subject in its own right. A digestible review of its stratigraphy is provided by Jones and Simmons (this volume), who attempt their explanation in a global sequence stratigraphic framework.

WESTERN MARGIN OF THE WESTERN BLACK SEA: FROM THE SCYTHIAN PLATFORM TO RHODOPE

The East European, Scythian, and Moesian platforms appear to have had rather similar geological histories and share a common general stratigraphy. The Moesian Platform is described by Tari et al. (this volume). They present a series of seismic lines and regional isopach maps that show that this area was anything but platform-like during its pre-Late Jurassic history. The area was affected by a Hercynian (pre-Permian) deformation and, during the Middle Triassic, E-W trending rift basins developed in northern Bulgaria and southern Romania. Tari et al. describe these as failed arms of the Paleotethys Ocean. During the Norian-Rhaetian, the area was again subjected to compressional deformation. A foreland fold and thrust belt developed in northern Bulgaria, with the effects of the compression dying out to the north in Romania. This thrust belt was presumably the external (northern) part of the Strandzha orogenic belt (Banks, this volume). The disappearance of compressive structures of Late Triassic age to the north is interesting because north of the Peceneaga-Camena fault and the North Dobrogean orogenic belt, on the southern edge of the Scythian Platform, there is another belt of thin-skinned compressive deformation beneath undeformed Upper Jurassic limestones that also appears to be of Triassic age (Odessmorgeologia, unpublished data; see map, Figure 1). These two foldbelts—in north Bulgaria and southern Ukraine—could be juxtaposed by 200–300 km of sinistral strike-slip movement along the Peceneaga-Camena fault during or prior to the Late Jurassic. Such movement is independently proposed by Banks and Robinson (this volume) to explain the development of Late Triassic? extensional basins that closed prior to or during the Middle Jurassic.

During the Late Jurassic and Neocomian (and possibly earlier), a south-facing passive margin developed, on which a carbonate ramp formed. The Upper Jurassic carbonates are of interest from the point of view of petroleum exploration, as they form at least one oil reservoir—at the Tyulenovo oil field on the Bulgarian coast. The sedimentology of the carbonates is described in detail by Harbury and Cohen (this volume). They show a transition between shallow-marine carbonates in the north and deep-marine facies in the south, with the transition trending approximately east-west and passing through Varna in northern Bulgaria. By the Hauterivian, a clastic wedge had developed on the margin. Following a mid-Cretaceous hiatus, presumably reflecting the location of the area at the western margin of the Aptian Western Black Sea rift, Upper Cretaceous facies are outer shelf to bathyal. At this time, the southern margin of the Moesian Platform (where the Balkanides are now) would have been linked to the Western Black Sea. The subsidence and structural history of the Balkanides are the subject of the chapter by Sinclair et al. (this volume). Using a combination of seismic, well, and outcrop data, they show how, at around the end of the Cretaceous, the Jurassic extensional faults on the south-facing passive margin were inverted as compression in the Balkanide region began. Most of the shortening is, however, thin-skinned and of early to middle Eocene age. Compression had ended by the beginning of the Miocene.

The Balkanides are also described by Banks (this volume) in a chapter that attempts to integrate the geological histories of all of the major tectonic units along a north-south transect from the Danube delta to Thrace. Banks describes how the early Mesozoic stratigraphy of the Strandzha Zone (İstranca in Turkish) also restores to a south-facing passive margin, and how the stratigraphy is similar to that exposed in the Balkanides. He suggests a Late Triassic age for the onset of compression (which is the same as that demonstrated by Tari et al. for the Moesian Platform further north), but believes the main deformation to be post-Middle Jurassic. Strandzha has also been affected by Tertiary compression. These relationships suggest that there is little extension associated with the Srednogorie Zone, which contains more than 3 km of Upper Cretaceous marine volcanics and volcaniclastic sediments. The chemistry of the volcanics suggests that the zone principally represents a subduction-related volcanic arc.

SOUTHERN MARGIN OF THE BLACK SEA BASINS: THE PONTIDES, ACHARA-TRIALET BELT, AND ASSOCIATED FORELAND BASINS

The Pontides are a complex belt of compressional deformation that runs from Thrace in the west to Georgia in the east, forming the northern coast of Turkey and extending offshore to affect the postrift fills of both Western and Eastern Black Sea basins. The northern deformation front mainly runs a few tens of kilometers offshore. The Pontides are bounded to the south by a broad subduction-accretion complex with ophiolites that was assembled through the Mesozoic and early Tertiary as the Tethys Ocean closed. The Pontides are in fact geologically quite diverse and include at least three major terranes (and probably other smaller ones): the Western, Central, and Eastern Pontides. Each of these has its own characteristic history of compressive, extensional, and strike-slip deformation, and each incorporates more than one basin type. An overview of the entire province is provided here by Yılmaz et al. (this volume), who summarize years of field studies by Turkish workers. Although this chapter is long and presupposes at least some geographic familiarity with northern Turkey, it includes a tremendous amount of detailed information that has for the most part been published only in Turkish.

The Western Pontides are characterized by an unmetamorphosed Cambrian–Ordovician to Carboniferous sedimentary sequence resting on Precambrian metamorphic basement. On this is superimposed a Triassic rift to passive margin sequence followed by a Late Jurassic carbonate ramp. The similarity to the Moesian Platform is clear. Indeed, it is now widely accepted that the Western Pontides rifted from the Moesian Platform during the Aptian–Albian and moved south to their present position during the Late Cretaceous, leaving behind the Western Black Sea. In north Turkey, the transition from shallow to deep-marine limestones in the Upper Jurassic takes place close to the position of the North Anatolian fault zone. Prior to the Aptian, this area would therefore restore to a position immediately east of the present-day Balkanides. The onshore evidence for Aptian–Albian rifting and Late Cretaceous postrift subsidence is summarized by Görür (this volume). The relevant stratigraphy has been exposed by Tertiary inversion of the mid-Cretaceous extensional faults. Görür and Tüysüz (this volume) provide a summary of the petroleum potential of this part of northern Turkey. Despite many years of onshore, as well as some offshore, exploration, there has been no petroleum discovery in the Pontides despite the presence of several oil and gas seeps (Derman and Iztan, this volume). My guess is that this is due to a timing problem: Source rocks in the Ordovician/Silurian and possibly the Aptian were largely matured during or prior to rifting. Most of the traps are compressional and of principally Eocene age.

The Central Pontides are quite different from the Western Pontides. They have an ophiolitic basement covered by Triassic–Lower Jurassic turbidites and intruded by Mid-Jurassic postcollisional granites. The evolution of this area is covered by Ustaömer and Robertson (this volume). They describe the presence of a late Paleozoic oceanic arc and back-arc basin. The back-arc basin closed before Late Jurassic. What appears to be the same Triassic to Late Jurassic back-arc basin fill can be found in Crimea and in the offshore part of the Ukrainian Black Sea, the two areas having been separated by Late Cretaceous spreading in the Western Black Sea. Banks and Robinson (this volume) accordingly believe that the eastern transform margin of the Western Black Sea runs between the Eastern and Central Pontides, along the western edge of the Mid-Black Sea High, and that the boundary between the Western and Central Pontides can be linked to the Peceneaga-Camena fault in Romania. Görür (this volume) links the southern and northern margins of the Western Black Sea in a different way, joining the Western/Central Pontides boundary to a postulated West Crimean fault west of the Crimean Peninsula (see also Okay et al., 1994).

The Eastern Pontides have been the subject of little attention until recently. Their geological history is described by Okay and Şahintürk (this volume). The pre-Jurassic deposits have a typically Laurasian character, indicating that the boundary with Gondwana lay further to the south. The usual south-facing carbonate-dominated passive margin can be recognized for the Late Jurassic to Barremian period and is located toward the south of the Eastern Pontides. The Eastern Pontides are dominated at outcrop by two more or less coincident ensialic volcanic arcs of Late Cretaceous and Eocene (Lutetian) age. Okay and Şahintürk date the onset of subduction here as Cenomanian–Turonian and suggest that the Eastern Black Sea extensional basin opened in an intra-arc setting during the Maastrichtian, rather earlier than the Late Paleocene suggested by Robinson et al. (1996). There appears to be a consensus emerging that the Eastern Black Sea is not just a separate basin, but is significantly younger than the Western Black Sea.

Further east, the deformation front jumps (or bends) to the north, and the Eastern Pontides merge into the Achara-Trialet Belt in Georgia. Banks et al. (this volume) describe a study of this fold belt and the related Rioni and Kartli foreland basins, incorporating interpretations of geological maps, fieldwork, and seismic and onshore well data. The Achara-Trialet Belt appears to be a Paleogene extensional (back- or intra-arc) basin that began to close during the late Eocene or Oligocene. The stratigraphy is dominated by a very thick deep-marine Eocene sequence, including volcanics and volcanogenic turbidites in the Middle Eocene, the equivalents of the Eastern Pontides Lutetian arc. This sequence—in particular the very thick Eocene—is very similar to the stratigraphy interpreted for the Eastern Black Sea by Spadini et al. (this volume). Indeed, Banks et al. consider that the Achara-Trialet Belt represents the closed eastern end of the Eastern Black Sea. The Rioni and Kartli basins developed mainly during Miocene, by flexure of the northern margin of the Eastern Black Sea—Achara-Trialet Basin (the Shatsky Ridge) beneath the compressional fold belts to the north (Greater Caucasus) and the south. There has been oil exploration onshore in Georgia for around a century, mostly concentrating on the frontal folds of the Achara-Trialet Belt and the Rioni and Kartli basins. The petroleum geology of this area is described by Robinson et al. (this volume). They provide further evidence for the regional development of an Upper Eocene oil-prone source rock (see also Robinson et al., 1996).

NORTHERN MARGIN OF THE BLACK SEA BASINS: GREATER CAUCASUS, CRIMEA, AND GULF OF ODESSA

Regretfully, the northern margins of the Black Sea are not well represented in this volume, or in any accessible literature. The Russian coast is dominated by the Greater Caucasus. This appears from geological maps to represent an Early Jurassic extensional basin that accumulated a great thickness of Jurassic and Cretaceous deep-marine sediments before being closed from the Late Eocene onward (Robinson et al., 1996). It can perhaps thus be considered a forerunner of the Eastern Black Sea. The main foreland basin development is to the north of the mountain belt (Indolo-Kuban Basin), but the Greater Caucasus had an effect on the Kartli Basin (in Georgia) (Robinson et al., this volume) and produced the small flexural Tuapse Trough (offshore Russia).

Toward the northeast, the Greater Caucasus seem to die out. It is tempting to link them with the Crimean fold belt, but the stratigraphy and style of deformation in the Crimea are quite different. Robinson and Kerusov (this volume) describe the seismic stratigraphy of the offshore Gulf of Odessa (known also locally as the North-West Shelf) and relate the offshore to the exposed geology in Crimea. They interpret offshore features and the Crimean Mountains to represent Aptian–Albian half-grabens (developed during Western Black Sea rifting) that were inverted from the middle Eocene onward. The degree of inversion is minor offshore, but very substantial in Crimea. Gas-condensate fields offshore are found in inversion anticlines above Aptian–Albian extensional faults and may have been sourced from the Paleozoic of the Scythian Platform.

ACKNOWLEDGMENTS

I would like to thank JKX Oil & Gas plc for supporting the preparation of this Memoir, in particular Martin Miller. Many other people have been most helpful: I am grateful especially to Alexandru Maftei (Enterprise Oil) and to David Roberts (BP Exploration). İstanbul Technical University wins the award for preparing papers on time. Thanks to Petroconsultants for providing a Black Sea base map.

REFERENCES CITED

Banks, C.J., this volume, Basins and thrust belts of the Balkan Coast of the Black Sea, *in* A.G. Robinson, ed., Regional and petroleum geology of the Black Sea and surrounding region: AAPG Memoir 68, p. 115-126

Banks, C.J., and A.G. Robinson, this volume, Mesozoic strike-slip back-arc basins of the Western Black Sea region, *in* A.G. Robinson, ed., Regional and petroleum geology of the Black Sea and surrounding region: AAPG Memoir 68, p. 53–62

Banks, C.J., A.G. Robinson, and M.P. Williams, this volume, Structure and regional tectonics of the Achara-Trialet Fold Belt and the Adjacent Rioni and Kartli Foreland Basins, Republic of Georgia, *in* A.G. Robinson, ed., Regional and petroleum geology of the Black Sea and surrounding region: AAPG Memoir 68, p. 331–346.

Benton, J., this volume, Exploration history of the Black Sea province, *in* A.G. Robinson, ed., Regional and petroleum geology of the Black Sea and surrounding region: AAPG Memoir 68, p. 7–18.

Brinkmann, R., 1974, Geologic relations between the Black Sea and Anatolia, *in* D.A. Ross and E.T. Degens, eds., 1974, The Black Sea—geology, chemistry, and biology: AAPG Memoir 20, p. 63–76.

Derman, A.S., and Y.H. Iztan, this volume, Results of geochemical analysis of seeps and potential source rocks from Northern Turkey and the Turkish Black Sea, *in* A.G. Robinson, ed., Regional and petroleum geology of the Black Sea and surrounding region: AAPG Memoir 68, p. 313–330.

Finetti, I., G. Bricchi, A. Del Ben, M. Pipan, and Z. Xuan, 1988, Geophysical study of the Black Sea area: Bolletino di Geofisica Teorica ed Applicata, v. 30, p. 197–324.

Görür, N., 1988, Timing of opening of the Black Sea basin: Tectonophysics, v. 147, p. 247–262.

Görür, N., this volume, Cretaceous syn- to postrift sedimentation on the southern continental margin of the Western Black Sea Basin, *in* A.G. Robinson, ed., Regional and petroleum geology of the Black Sea and surrounding region: AAPG Memoir 68, p. 227–240

Görür, N., and O, Tüysüz, this volume, Petroleum geology of the southern continental margin of the Black Sea, *in* A.G. Robinson, ed., Regional and petroleum geology of the Black Sea and surrounding region: AAPG Memoir 68, p. 241–254.

Harbury, N., and M. Cohen, this volume, Sedimentary history of the Late Jurassic–Paleogene of Northeast Bulgaria and the Bulgarian Black Sea, *in* A.G. Robinson, ed., Regional and petroleum geology of the Black Sea and surrounding region: AAPG Memoir 68, p. 129–168.

Jones, R.W., and M.D. Simmons, this volume, A review of the stratigraphy of Eastern Paratethys (Oligocene–Holocene), with particular emphasis on the Black Sea, *in* A.G. Robinson, ed., Regional and petroleum geology of the Black Sea and surrounding region: AAPG Memoir 68, p. 39–52.

Manetti, P., M. Boccaletti, and A. Peccerillo, 1988, The Black Sea: remnant of a marginal basin behind the Srednogorie-Pontides island arc system during Upper Cretaceous–Eocene time: Bolletino di Geofisica Teorica ed Applicata, v. 30, p. 39–51.

Okay, A.I., and Ö. Şahintürk, this volume, Geology of the Eastern Pontides, *in* A.G. Robinson, ed., Regional and petroleum geology of the Black Sea and surrounding region: AAPG Memoir 68, p. 291–312.

Okay, A.I., A.M.C. Şengör, and N. Görür, 1994, Kinematic history of the opening of the Black Sea and its effect on the surrounding regions: Geology, v. 22, p. 267–270.

Robinson, A.G., and E. Kerusov, this volume, Stratigraphic and structural development of the Gulf of Odessa, Ukrainian Black Sea: implications for petroleum exploration, *in* A.G. Robinson, ed., Regional and petroleum geology of the Black Sea and surrounding region: AAPG Memoir 68, p. 369–380.

Robinson, A.G., J.H. Rudat, C.J. Banks, and R.L.F. Wiles, 1996, Petroleum geology of the Black Sea: Marine and Petroleum Geology, v. 13, p. 195–223.

Robinson, A.G., E.T. Griffith, A.R. Gardiner, and A.K. Home, this volume, Petroleum geology of the Georgian fold and thrust belts and foreland basins, *in* A.G. Robinson, ed., Regional and petroleum geology of the Black Sea and surrounding region: AAPG Memoir 68, p. 347–368.

Ross, D.A., 1978, Summary of results of Black Sea drilling: Initial Reports DSDP, XLII (Part 2), p. 1149–1177.

Ross, D.A., and E.T. Degens, eds., 1974, The Black Sea—geology, chemistry, and biology: AAPG Memoir 20, 633 p.

Sinclair, H.D., S.G. Juranov, G. Georgiev, P. Byrne, and N.P. Mountney, this volume, The Balkan thrust wedge and Foreland Basin of Eastern Bulgaria: structural and stratigraphic development, *in* A.G. Robinson, ed., Regional and petroleum geology of the Black Sea and surrounding region: AAPG Memoir 68, p. 91–114.

Spadini, G., A.G. Robinson, and S.A.P.L. Cloetingh, this volume, Thermomechanical modeling of Black Sea Basin formation, subsidence, and sedimentation, *in* A.G. Robinson, ed., Regional and petroleum geology of the Black Sea and surrounding region: AAPG Memoir 68, p. 19–38.

Tari, G., O. Dicea, J. Faulkerson, G. Georgiev, S. Popov, M. Stefanescu, and G. Weir, this volume, Cimmerian and Alpine stratigraphy and structural evolution of the Moesian Platform (Romania/Bulgaria), *in* A.G. Robinson, ed., Regional and petroleum geology of the Black Sea and surrounding region: AAPG Memoir 68, p. 63–90

Ustaömer, T., and A. Robertson, this volume, Tectonic-sedimentary evolution of the North-Tethyan margin in the Central Pontides of Northern Turkey, *in* A.G. Robinson, ed., Regional and petroleum geology of the Black Sea and surrounding region: AAPG Memoir 68, p. 255–290.

Yılmaz, Y., O. Tüysüz, E.Yiğitbaş, S. Can Genç, and A.M.C. Şengör, this volume, Geology and tectonic evolution of the Pontides, *in* A.G. Robinson, ed., Regional and petroleum geology of the Black Sea and surrounding region: AAPG Memoir 68, p. 255–290.

Benton, J., 1997, Exploration history of the Black Sea province, *in* A.G. Robinson, ed., Regional and petroleum geology of the Black Sea and surrounding region: AAPG Memoir 68, p. 7–18.

Chapter 2

Exploration History of the Black Sea Province

Jeremy Benton
Petroconsultants (U.K.) Ltd.
London, United Kingdom

ABSTRACT

The Black Sea Province has an exploration history that dates back more than a century. One of the oldest discoveries, Priozernoye, was made in 1886 on the basis of seeps in the easternmost part of the Crimean Peninsula, within the Indolo-Kuban foreland basin of the Caucasus Province. For many years, due to the aftermath of World War I, exploratory drilling was intermittent. In 1939, the Supsa oil field was discovered in the Rioni Basin of Georgia; the prospect had originally been drilled in 1886, but the flow rates were noncommercial. More systematic exploration was undertaken by newly formed state companies after World War II. The introduction of geophysical techniques led to the identification of thick sedimentary sequences in areas such as the Moesian Platform, previously considered of marginal prospectivity. A gas blowout in 1951 marked the discovery of Tyulenovo, which was to prove to be Bulgaria's largest field. Its coastal location and extension offshore first demonstrated the potential of the Black Sea. Further encouragement was provided in the mid-1950s by the Kamchiya gas discovery and the opening up of the Romanian sector of the Moesian Platform. The gas/condensate play of the Black Sea–Crimea Basin was established in the 1960s, at the time offshore exploration began. Surveying was first undertaken offshore Bulgaria (with Soviet assistance), and by the early 1970s most countries were actively surveying the Black Sea. Drilling began offshore in the 1970s when Westates drilled two dry new-field wildcats in the far west of Turkish waters. The first offshore discovery was Golitsyna in 1975, on the Odessa Shelf, and when brought onstream in 1983 it became the first producing gas field in the Black Sea. Drilling off Romania began in 1976 (the same year that the Turkish state company TPAO made a subcommercial gas discovery with Akçakoca 1) and led to the discovery of the Lebada Est in 1981; oil production started in 1987. The breakup of the Soviet Union and the revolutions of Eastern Europe mark a new phase of exploration, with foreign companies taking a leading role. As yet, no deepwater wildcats have been drilled, and the limited exploration on the western Black Sea shelf has resulted in 14 discoveries (3 oil and 11 gas) and aggregate reserve additions estimated at 630 MMBOE.

BLACK SEA EXPLORATION HISTORY: INTRODUCTION

In the following sections, the exploration history of the Black Sea and adjacent coastal areas is examined by country, basin, and onshore and offshore sector. There is then a discussion of the Black Sea environment, and finally the results of exploration are summarized. First, however, the constituent basins of the Black Sea Province are defined as:

1. The Moesian Platform of coastal Romania and Bulgaria—characterized by a thick and undeformed Paleozoic–Mesozoic section with a thinner Tertiary cover.
2. The coastal parts of the Balkanide fold and thrust belts and associated basins in Bulgaria, including the Kamchiya Basin to the north and Burgas Basin to the south.
3. Pontides Province—a complex Alpine fold and thrust belt that extends along the coast of northern Turkey.
4. Western Black Sea and Eastern Black Sea basins—deepwater extensional basins separated by the Mid-Black Sea High.
5. Rioni Basin of Georgia—a Negoene foreland basin bounded to the north and south by fold and thrust belts.
6. North Black Sea–Crimea Basin of Ukraine—located along the southern margin of the East European Platform. A thick Tertiary sequence in the Karkinit Trough overlies Mesozoic sediments, which onlap northward.
7. Dobrogea Province of the Ukraine and Romania—a geologically complex area north of the Moesian Platform. It comprises a Paleozoic–Mesozoic orogenic belt and foreland basin buried beneath a thin Tertiary cover sequence; offshore Romania, a thicker Tertiary section is present.

Refer to Enclosure 1 for the locations of the basins mentioned in this account. Enclosure 2 illustrates the geography of the Black Sea region and the locations referred to in this chapter.

ROMANIA–BLACK SEA WESTERN MARGIN

Moesian Platform

Onshore

Despite Romania's long history of production from hand-dug shafts, before World War II exploration was directed at the Carpathian basins and the Transylvanian Basin, and the coastal areas bordering the Black Sea were generally regarded as lacking oil and gas potential. After the nationalization of the industry in the late 1940s, surface geological mapping and geophysical surveying helped to reveal the presence of a thick Mesozoic sequence on the Moesian Platform. The discovery of the coastal Tyulenovo field in Bulgaria spurred activity, and in 1955 the state company Petrom made the first Moesian Platform oil find in Romania with well Ciuresti Nord-Birla 105; the field's main reservoir is Lower Cretaceous carbonates. In the early 1960s the introduction of analog seismic techniques led to a series of small gas finds. Digital seismic methods were introduced in 1972, but further finds generally proved disappointing, although more than 140 discoveries were made. In terms of the volume of oil discovered, Upper Miocene clastics (mostly derived from the Carpathian Mountains) are the main reservoir on the Moesian Platform, but there is a range of pre-Tertiary productive horizons from Paleozoic fractured carbonates through reservoirs of Triassic, Jurassic, and Cretaceous ages.

Offshore

Offshore geophysical surveying began in 1969 when the state IPGG (Intreprinderea de Prospectiuni Geologica si Geofizice) was active with the *Voinicul* vessel. The seismic data revealed that the Moesian Platform deepened to the southeast, and had a thin Tertiary cover, downgrading its prospectivity; attention subsequently focused on the area further north toward the Dobrogea promontory. Interest resumed in the late 1980s when four or five wells were drilled, but without success.

Dobrogea Province

Onshore

Onshore areas are largely nonprospective as Hercynian basement crops out or is buried by a thin sedimentary cover.

Offshore

The early results of seismic surveying in the offshore extension of the province showed promise—a thick Tertiary clastic sequence was present with growth faults and large rollover anticlinal traps present. To enable drilling to begin, Romania first built a fleet of jack-up rigs (based on a Sonat offshore *Orion* design and rated to 6000 m depths). With the assistance of the Chernomorneftegazprom administration of the Ukraine, Petromar (the offshore subsidiary of the state Petrom) spudded its first offshore well, Ovidiu 1, in August 1976. The well was eventually abandoned with gas shows in Pontian (Upper Miocene) sands after reaching a depth of 5006 m; it remains the deepest well in the Black Sea. The first discovery was made by the Lebada (Swan) Est 8 well, which was spudded in June 1978 and completed in January 1980. It tested a faulted pre-Upper Cretaceous structural high cut by an Eocene submarine canyon, with updip pinch-outs and rapid lateral facies changes providing a stratigraphic element to trapping. The main (light oil) reservoir was found to be Albian sandstones, with Eocene marls hosting gas. The Lebada Vest field was discovered in July 1985 on the flanks of the same structural high. On May 20, 1987, Lebada Est was brought onstream, and the first oil was produced from the Black Sea. Production was initially from the *Gloria* jack-up rig converted to a production system, but the installation of two more converted jack-ups, the *Fortuna* and *Jupiter*, and water injection allowed output to increase to 15,000 bbl of oil per day (bo/d) by 1989. The crude is transported ashore by shuttle tankers, as the 33 cm diameter/63 km pipeline originally built to transport the crude oil to a terminal at the Navodari refinery, near the port of Midia, has been used to pipe gas. Lebada Vest started production in May 1993 from seven wells, and by June 1993 production was reported as 2860 bo/d and 1980 MCFGD. Following the success of deviated exploratory well Lebada Est G 12 (spudded in 1991, but completed in 1993), which found a nonassociated gas reservoir in Eocene marls (as previously proven in Lebada Vest), a nine-well development drilling program was instigated in 1994, of which four wells had been drilled by mid-1996. Comprehensive statistics have not been released, but in 1995 offshore Romanian oil production averaged 13,988 bo/d, and gas production had risen to 34,150 MCFGD.

In the late 1980s there was a high level of seismic data acquisition, mostly by Russian crews. The *Marea Neagre* (the only Romanian survey vessel) was active on the shelf, as were the *Pitsunda*, *Akademik Fersman*, and *Yuriy Godin*, while the *Topaz* surveyed in waters more than 1000 m deep. In total, 42,441 line-km of 2-D seismic data and 760 km^2 of 3-D seismic data were recorded offshore Romania to end-1990 (Ionescu, 1994). By 1990, 15 exploratory wells had been drilled in offshore Romania and only one further discovery made: Sinoe 30 was completed in 1987 as a gas and condensate well in an Eocene shallow-marine sandstone play. To 1995 five wells (two dry) had been drilled on the structure; appraisal is continuing, and a 12,720 line-km 3-D survey acquired in 1994 will help refine the current reserve estimates of 20–30 million barrels of oil (MMBO).

With the fall of the Ceaucescu regime in 1989, exploratory activity declined, and efforts were made to attract foreign investment. In 1992 Enterprise Oil signed production-sharing contracts for two blocks in the Black Sea (XIII and XV) and became the first foreign company to operate off Romania when it recorded a 6700 line-km seismic survey. In 1994 Enterprise (65%) and its partners, Canadian Occidental (30%) and Ogy Petroleums (5%), began a three-well drilling campaign in its Block XV (also known as the Midia block after the only previous well drilled in it) southeast of the Lebada fields by using the semisubmersible *Ocean Liberator*. The first well, Rapsodia 1, was drilled in 101 m of water to a depth of 3722 m, where it was abandoned with gas shows; it had a Pontian objective. In 1995 Doina 1 was drilled in 85 m of water, targeting a seismic bright spot feature in what was thought to be Pliocene sandstones, but was abandoned with gas shows at a depth of 3025 m. However, the follow-up well, Doina 2 (only 400 m from Doina 1), resulted in a gas discovery after testing up to 17,500 MCFGD of dry gas from a single Pliocene reservoir interval. In an agreement that dates from August 1994, ARCO earned a farm-in option in blocks XIII and XV by participating in two of these wells.

In August 1995 Petromar spudded Cobalescu 75, some 80 km east of Lebada Est in 90 m of water, targeting Pontian and Oligocene objectives. After having problems with overpressuring, it was eventually abandoned in May 1996, with gas shows at a total depth of 4000 m. Its results were, however, sufficiently encouraging for the rig to stay on location and drill Cobalcescu 70 to a depth of 4140 m. Unfortunately, the Oligocene and basal Pontian clastics were water wet, and the well was abandoned with gas shows in May 1997.

Ratification of the new hydrocarbon legislation in 1995 enabled the long-delayed First National Licensing Round to be opened in April 1996 (bid deadline of 30 November) by the newly formed National Agency for Mineral Resources. Included in the bid was the 6202 km^2 EPI-15/Constanta block, which abuts the Bulgarian border and extends offshore into the Black Sea, but failed to receive any bids. In advance of the bid call, Petrom recorded 2959 line-km of 2-D over the open area between Enterprise's Pelican and Midia blocks by using Western Geophysical's *Western Challenger*; however, this area was left out of the bidding round.

In 1997 Enterprise drilled three new-field wildcats in Block XV, with little success, as first Tandala 1 was abandoned dry without testing, then Luceafarul 1 experienced drilling problems and had to be abandoned prematurely. The replacement well (Luceafarul 1A) reached a total depth of 3024 m in the Oligocene, but due to overpressuring only a single test was run, and the well was abandoned with gas shows, as was the final well, Voinicul 1.

BULGARIA

Moesian Platform

Onshore

In the 1920s shows of gas in a water well drilled near Varna, together with surface seeps, triggered the search for hydrocarbons. Shows were also recorded in shallow wells drilled near the Provadija salt dome, where the first geophysical survey was undertaken in 1936. A deeper well, also in the Varna area, reached a depth of 1840 m and tested saltwater from the Cretaceous and gas in the Oligocene. Across the country, a few hundred shallow wells were drilled between the two world wars, but with no commercial success (Vuchev et al., 1994). More systematic exploration began with the nationalization of the industry postwar with Soviet assistance; after gravity and magnetic surveys, a gas blowout in 1951 marked the discovery of the Tyulenovo (Shabla) oil/gas field in a faulted elongate anticline, which extends along the coast for 25 km. Heavy (19°API) oil and gas are reservoired in karstified and fractured Upper Jurassic to Lower Cretaceous dolomitic limestones at a depth of 350–400 m, and there are minor amounts of gas in Oligocene sandstones, which unconformably overlie the Mesozoic. An early indication of the Black Sea's potential was provided when the eastern portion of Tyulenovo was found to extend offshore. Production from Tyulenovo began at a rate of 80–90 bo/d and rose to ~10,000 bo/d in 1968; it has been in decline since then. Cumulative production has now exceeded 21 MMBO from about 400 wells (most are shut-in), and daily production averaged only 258 bo/d and 99 MSCFGD in 1996. Subsequent onshore exploration in the coastal area proved largely disappointing, with many dry wells drilled and only a couple of subcommercial gas discoveries (Bulgarevo and Krapets). Following the large Moesian Platform discoveries in Romania, attention moved further inland; in the 1960s several commercial oil discoveries were found in Triassic carbonates, beginning with the Dolni Dubnik P 1 well in 1962. More recently, improved seismic data have been directed at identifying stratigraphic or combination traps, such as Dolni Lukovit P 1 in 1975, which found oil in Lower Jurassic sandstones and siltstones onlapping the Upper Triassic unconformity surface.

Prompted by Tyulenovo, the first marine seismic survey off Bulgaria was undertaken by the Soviets in 1960 on a 15 km grid along the coast; by 1968 most areas in waters up to 100 m had been surveyed. Due in part to equipment constraints, drilling did not begin until the mid-1980s when the Soviet *Sivash* jack-up rig drilled two wells to the south of Tyulenovo, off Cape Kaliakra. Oil and gas were found in the Paleozoic at depths below 2600 m in at least one well, but for technical and logistical reasons, no tests were undertaken. Following the end of Communist rule in 1989, the country was opened to foreign companies and the UK company Gandalf Explorers was the first to sign technical assistance and risk-sharing agreements with the state Committee of Geology (COMMGEO). These rights were subsequently sold to Edward Callan Interests, which formed Balkan Explorers. Commitment drilling began in 1993 in the Shabla/1 Block, but results were not encouraging: two dry shallow wells were drilled on the North Shabla structure, only 3 km from the Tyulenovo field. In addition, Severna 1 was junked at a depth of 1542 m (short of its planned total depth of 2000 m) after minor gas shows were encountered at shallow depths (Union Pacific acquired 50% interests and operatorship in 1992, but withdrew the following year after drilling Severna 1). A First Round award (Galata/3) was made to Texaco (operator, 40%), Enterprise (40%), and OMV (20%) in 1991; financial commitments totalled $20 million in the initial five-year term. In 1995 Texaco drilled a domal structure associated with the east-west–trending Bliznak fault on the southern margin of the Moesian Platform. Galata 1 tested gas at a rate of 34 MMCFGD from a 25-m thick interval of Eocene sandstones, but appraisal well Bogdanov East 1, on the east flank of the structure, was dry, as was Texaco's next new-field wildcat, Epsilon 1. Nevertheless, Galata may prove commercial; in 1995 Texaco recorded a 2-D/3-D sesimic survey over the discovery and proposed development involving a 50-km pipeline (50 MMCFGD capacity). Texaco also secured an extension to its license, and in November 1996 successfully drilled outpost Galata 2, which tested 40 MMCFGD from a 23-m thick interval of Paleocene algal limestones and Maastrichtian sandstones.

Enterprise was also awarded the 2240 km^2 Kaliakra/2 license in the First Round, and late in 1996 it drilled its first commitment well near the southern limit of the Tyulenovo field. The $2 million new-field wildcat, Bulgarevo East 1, was abandoned dry without testing at a total depth of 1050 m in the Triassic.

In 1995 MMS Petroleum Services, the result of a merger of Gandalf Explorers and the Irish company Marine and Mercantile Securities, acquired Balkan Explorers and reacquired offshore license Shabla/1. An option was negotiated to extend the license to the 200-m isobath and as far north as the Romanian territorial border (when it is defined). MMS fulfilled the work obligations inherited from Edward Callan Interests by shooting 850 km of seismic data in 1995; the survey has helped to define two prospects that it plans to drill, providing it can find farm-in partners.

Bulgaria's Third Licensing Round is under preparation and is expected to involve onshore blocks only; its opening has been delayed pending approval of the new Mineral Resources Law.

Balkanides

Onshore

The first exploratory well in the eastern Balkans was drilled in 1941 near the village of Varbitza, on the basis of a mappable surface anticline. The well tested only saltwater with H_2S and was abandoned at a total depth of 1000 m. The first well in the Kamchiya Basin, drilled near the village of Gorni Bliznak in 1949, was abandoned at a depth of 1305 m with gas shows. Six years later the Kamchiya gas field was discovered when well P 8 tested some 30.8 MMCFGD at a depth of 1569 m from Eocene sandstones. In 1957 gas shows were recorded in the Oligocene in a well on the Samotino structure, but no further discoveries were made. In the early 1980s, six wells targeted Oligocene plays in the northern flank of the Kamchiya depression; short-term gas flows were obtained, but since no commercial discoveries were made, the focus of attention switched offshore. No hydrocarbon exploration wells have been drilled onshore in the Burgas Basin to the south of the Balkanide thrust belt, although a number of water and coal wells (there is a working coal mine) have been drilled to the shallow pre-Tertiary basement.

Offshore

In 1986 the initial offshore well in the Kamchiya Basin, Samotino More 1, made a subcommercial discovery after flowing about 17,600 MCFGD and condensate from Eocene turbidites in a hanging-wall anticline structure. The following year Samotino Iztok 1 encountered gas shows in the thick Paleogene section, but further drilling with the Soviet *Sivash* jack-up rig had to be halted due to the lack of funds. In 1988, deviated well Skorpilovci 79 tested an Eocene play in a structure that straddled the coast, resulting in more gas shows. British Gas was awarded two blocks in the First Licensing Round in 1991, and in 1993 began drilling thrust-related anticlines in the Kamchiya/4 License. Well LA-IV/91 1 bottomed at 3641 m (base of the Paleogene section) and tested water and dissolved gas at 2338–2414 m. Further offshore, the play fairway progressively deepens and new-field wildcat LA-IV/91 2 was drilled to 4609 m, where it was abandoned as dry, as was British Gas's third and final well (Byala LA-IV/91 3), which tested a closure downflank of Samotino More 1. The lack of success led to the relinquishment of the license in 1995.

In 1991 two First Round awards were made over the Burgas Basin and Balkanide thrust belt: the 2850 km^2 Emine/5 license was awarded to Euroil, a subsidiary of Edison Gas, and the 2480 km^2 Ropotamo/6 license was granted to Enterprise (operator, 50%) and Edison Gas (50%). In addition, the 4250 km^2 Burgas/10 onshore license was awarded to British Gas. Several relinquishments have since occurred (Emine/5 in 1994, Burgas/10 in 1995), and Edison Gas has withdrawn from Enterprise's Ropotamo/6 block. Exploration has initially focused on seismic data acquisition, with Enterprise being most active. The Russians previously recorded several surveys off Bulgaria, and in 1991 Halliburton Geophysical acquired 2600 line-km in the Emine/5 block and 1531 line-km in Enterprise's Ropotamo/6. This was followed by further surveys in 1993 when a CGG (Cie Generale Geophysique) crew acquired 1010 line-km in block 6, and in 1995 when a detailed shallow-water survey was run (50 line-km of 2-D lines and 2 km^2 of 3-D seismic data were recorded). Several prospects have been identified, and Enterprise is seeking farm-in partners to spread the drilling risks as it prepares to fulfill its drilling obligations.

TURKEY–BLACK SEA SOUTHERN MARGIN

Pontides Province

Onshore

Exploration in Turkey has historically focused on the continuation of the Zagros fold belt in the southeast part of the country, at the expense of the Black Sea margin. The first recorded onshore well, Boyabat 1, was drilled in the Central Pontides by the Turkish state company TPAO in 1960. Because it and all the following wells (including Gulf's 1966 Badut 1 commitment well in the Bafra Delta) were dry, exploration halted. Drilling did not resume until the late 1980s, when TPAO drilled ten wells along the Black Sea coast. Again all were dry, although two deep new-field wildcats on the flanks of the Boyabat structure encountered gas shows. TPAO maintained a drilling program in the Pontides in the early 1990s, drilling several more dry wells, including Erfelek 1, which bottomed at 4515 m in the Upper Cretaceous, and Gegendere 1, which reached a depth of 3450 m in Devonian carbonates.

Offshore

Since the 1970s TPAO has only drilled two wells in the Black Sea, both in the offshore extension of the Pontides thrust belt. In 1976 Akçakoca 1, located in 50 m of water 150 km east of İstanbul, reached Paleozoic basement at a depth of 2284 m and tested 2.5 MCFGD from Eocene clastics. The test results were sufficiently encouraging for a second new-field wildcat to be drilled 2 km away, but Akçakoca 2 was abandoned dry at a depth of 1643 m. It is of note, however, for being the deepest water exploration well (114 m) yet drilled in the Black Sea. In the early 1990s Texaco (partnered by Enterprise) held the 7500 km^2 Sinop (IP-84) investigation permit in the Central Pontides on the Black Sea shelf. In 1991 it recorded 2040 line-km of seismic data by using a Halliburton crew, but decided not to drill, and the license lapsed in 1995.

Balkanides

Offshore

While the early exploration along the margin of the Black Sea lagged behind its neighbors, Turkey briefly led the way in offshore exploration. In 1969 a joint venture was formed between TPAO and Turkey Westates Petroleum, whereby Westates was awarded 45% interest and operatorship of all the offshore acreage in the Black Sea, which previously had been held solely by TPAO. In 1970–1971 Westates drilled two back-to-back wildcats by using the *Glomar Grand Isle* drill ship in the Burgas Basin, near the Bulgarian offshore boundary. Kara Deniz 1 was spudded in 76 m of water on December 14, 1970, and was abandoned dry in mid-January 1971 at a depth of 2588 m in Cretaceous volcanics after penetrating a sequence of Tertiary clastics and Upper Cretaceous limestones. Igneada 1 was subsequently drilled in 87 m of water on a prospect about 15 km north of Kara Deniz 1. It reached a depth of 3109 m in Eocene marly limestones, where it was abandoned as dry. There are no reports of any shows or formation tests being undertaken, and the licenses were relinquished in 1973.

Western and Eastern Black Sea Basins

In the mid-1970s the *Glomar Challlenger* drill ship was used by the Deep Sea Drilling Project Leg 42B to investigate three sites within the Turkish sector of the Black Sea (Ross, 1978). The first site was selected in the central Black Sea in water depths of 2171 m, but once drilling was started it was realized that the Pleistocene section was too thick to be cored, and the deepest hole was abandoned at 624.5 m. The next site was off the Bosporus in 2115 m of water, where the sedimentary section was expected to be thinner, but the two wells drilled (380 and 380A) were abandoned prematurely because of an injury to a crew member and shale collapse, respectively. The final site in 1751 m of water was selected because unconformities were evident on seismic data and the recent section was thin; the 381 well was continually cored to 503.5 m in Miocene sediments. Of note in this well, at a depth of ~400 m, was Upper Miocene cemented shelly material, interpreted as being deposited in supratidal conditions and indicative of rapid subsidence. Source rock studies indicated that the organic carbon content averaged 1.8% from 12 samples from the deeper section, sufficient for the Miocene sediments to be classed as potential source rocks, albeit immature.

The first attempts to systematically evaluate the deepwater section of the Black Sea were undertaken in the early 1990s, after the technology had evolved to allow drilling in more than 2000 m of water. Under a joint evaluation agreement, BP and TPAO conducted extensive gravity, magnetic, and seismic surveys (18,110 line-km) over an area that encompassed the entire Turkish sector outside the 12 mi (22 km) limit and east of 34°E. Encouraged by the Rize seep off the coast of northeast Turkey, BP also conducted a 60,000 km^2 ALF (airborne laser fluorosensor) over the Eastern Black Sea in an effort to locate further seeps. Integrating all the data, including the results of geochemical analysis of source intervals from around the Black Sea and oil and condensate samples from the producing fields, led to the identification of the upper Eocene as the prime potential source interval (Robinson et al., 1996). Maturation modeling indicated that this interval is in the oil or gas window over much of the Black Sea, at depths of 5500–8000 m below sea level. Long-distance migration from the source kitchen in the Black Sea could also account for charging of the coastal fields of Romania and Bulgaria. Aptian sands in fault-block traps in the Mid-Black Sea High are regarded as having the best potential for giant oil or gas discoveries; however, as the risks associated with the presence of reservoirs, migration paths, and the hydrocarbon phase (oil or gas) are high, no drilling has yet been attempted. Arco was awarded a comparable investigation permit over the western portion of the Black Sea in 1995 and was committed to re-process and evaluate all available data and acquire a further 800 line-km of 2-D seismic with an aim of defining a possible drilling site.

GEORGIA–BLACK SEA EASTERN MARGIN

Rioni Basin

Onshore

In 1886 the first three known wells were drilled by Anglo Belgium Oil on the Supsa prospect in the frontal folds of the Achara-Trialet thrust belt to depths of 220–280 m. Oil flows of up to 6 bo/d were recorded but, as further drilling was unsuccessful, operations were discontinued. In 1930 the state company Gruzneft began more systematic exploratory drilling in the Rioni Basin, and in 1939 tested 22 bo/d of 260°API crude from late Miocene sandstones at Supsa, which is classified as the basin's first discovery. After World War II, drilling targeted anticlines identified by seismic data; initial objectives were Miocene sandstones, but progressively deeper objectives were chased. In 1969 Gruzneft' struck oil at Chaladidi, and recorded flows of up to 365 bo/d of 29° API crude from Upper Cretaceous carbonates. As all other wildcats penetrating Cretaceous sequences were dry or water wet, Tertiary objectives continued to be tested. The Shromisubani discovery was drilled in 1974 when a well tested up to 730 bo/d from upper Miocene clastics. In 1975 Ochamchira 1 encountered subcommercial oil in a Bathonian reservoir. No more discoveries were made, despite the ongoing exploration program, until 1991 when Gruzneft's Okumi 1, drilled east of Ochamchira, tested 126 bo/d from an Upper Jurassic clastic sequence between 1517 m and 1540 m. While the breakup of the Soviet Union brought new freedoms, the ensuing financial crisis forced the new state oil company, Saknavtobi, to curtail its exploration activities and seek new partners. In 1993 Georgian British Oil Company (GBOC), a joint venture between JKX Oil & Gas and Saknavtobi, was granted exploration and production licenses covering much of the Rioni Basin, both onshore and offshore in the Black Sea. In 1995 GBOC started appraisal drilling in the Shromisubani field, which from 1974 to 1993 produced a cumulative 400,000 bo/d from eight Miocene reservoir units. In 1995 Shromisubani 101 was drilled to 3475 m and encountered abundant hydrocarbon indications from an 823-m-thick interval comprising five Miocene sandstone units. After testing, the well was suspended pending a decision on whether to integrate production with the nearby Supsa field. The nature of the commercial risk of operating in the region became apparent in 1997 when cash-flow problems caused through late payment in Ukraine (outside the Black Sea Province) forced JKX to seek a merger. It was later announced that Ramco Energy of the UK, which also held acreage in Georgia, had agreed in principle to acquire JKX in a deal worth about $90 million.

Offshore

The Georgian sector of the Black Sea has been surveyed by Russian seismic vessels, but despite an award to GBOC, it remains undrilled. The best prospects offshore are Tertiary anticlines, which lie in deep waters, but, as they plunge to the northeast, significant closures are rare (Robinson et al., 1996). Like most other foreign operators active in the Black Sea Province, JKX needed partners to spread the risks and costs of its exploration program. Arco was already undertaking a regional evaluation of the Black Sea offshore Turkey and was keen to extend its study eastward. In exchange for running seismic and possibly through drilling the first well offshore Georgia it agreed to farm into the West Georgia Offshore block.

RUSSIA–BLACK SEA NORTHWESTERN MARGIN

Caucasus Province

Onshore

As the Greater Caucasus Mountains border much of the Russian sector of the Black Sea, the coastal margin onshore is of limited prospectivity and is largely undrilled. In contrast, the Indolo-Kuban foreland basin (and other Caucasus basins) to the north of the mountains has a long history of oil and gas production, mainly from Oligocene to Miocene Maykop sands, but also from Mesozoic plays.

Offshore

Although the entire Black Sea Russian shelf is presently undrilled, there has been some recent geophysical activity. In 1995 Soyuzmorgeo began a marine survey in the northern Black Sea over the westward extension of the Blagoveshchenskoye trend of oil fields, and recorded 156 line-km of 120-fold seismic data. It plans to cover the entire Northern Black Sea on the same 5 km × 5 km reconnaissance grid.

Eastern Black Sea Basin and Contiguous Areas

Academic seismic surveys of the Black Sea date from the 1950s. By the late 1980s more than 150 regional common depth point (CDP) seismic lines had been acquired by Russian crews in the deep waters of the Black Sea, but the area has yet to be surveyed by foreign (non-Russian) seismic crews.

UKRAINE–BLACK SEA NORTHERN MARGIN

North Black Sea–Crimea Basin and Contiguous Areas

Onshore

Exploration was initially triggered by the development of the eastern Caucasus Province at the end of the last century; this trend was followed westward toward the Black Sea. The first known discovery in the Black Sea region is Priozernoye, made in 1886 on the basis of seeps in the easternmost part of the Crimean Peninsula (Kerch Peninsula), within the westernmost part of the Indolo-Kuban foreland basin. Until abandonment in 1980 the field produced a cumulative 3 MMBOE from Tertiary clastics at depths of 200 m to 300 m. Subsequent exploration proved to be limited and was disrupted by the world wars. Seismic surveying of the Crimean lowlands began in earnest in the late 1950s, and in 1960 the state company Ukrnafta discovered gas and condensate with Olenevskoye 5 on the Tarkhankut Peninsula, the westernmost part of the Crimean Peninsula. The following year Oktyabr'skoye 1 tested 287 bo/d of 47° API crude from Lower Cretaceous clastics. Further gas, gas/condensate, and oil discoveries, albeit modest in size, were rapidly made in Maykop (mostly Oligocene–Lower Miocene), Paleocene, and Lower Cretaceous reservoirs—in all, several hundred exploratory wells have been drilled onshore, but only a handful of fields have ever produced oil. The focus of exploration subsequently moved offshore. Recently, attention has reverted to the Indolo-Kuban foredeep in the Crimean Peninsula, where Epic Energy has negotiated a licensing agreement. Through its KrymTexasNafta joint venture with the local state exploration operator Krymgeologiya, it has brought onstream the Aktash field at a rate of up to 1000 bo/d from four wells. Fifteen more wells are planned in Aktash; subsequently, drilling is to start in other fields nearby, such as the abandoned Priozernoye.

Offshore

The first offshore reconnaissance seismic surveys on the Black Sea shelf west of the Crimean Peninsula date from 1957; CDP surveys were introduced in the early 1970s, and by the early 1990s the whole northwestern shelf was covered by a 10 × 7 km regional grid, with a 2–3 km grid over the larger prospects. Total coverage of Russian/Ukrainian seismic data in Ukrainian waters is about 90,000 line-km, including 48,000 line-km of CDP seismic, but the pre-middle Cretaceous is poorly imaged.

As with the former Eastern Bloc countries, equipment constraints have historically slowed exploration, the most significant being that drilling operations have entirely been undertaken by the *Sivash* jack-up rig in less than 60 m of water. The Golitsyna prospect, a 27 km × 5 km anticline in the Karkinit Trough, was identified on seismic in 1964, but drilling did not begin until 1971, and it was not until 1975 that Yevpatoriyskaya's (the state drilling unit) Golitsyna 7 well flowed 10–15 MMCFGD from Maykop sandstones, and a discovery was made. When brought onstream by Chernomorneftegas in 1983, Golitsyna was the first producing field in the Black Sea; gas production is from three Maykop sand intervals, and gas/condensate is from Paleocene carbonates.

The next gas discovery was in 1979, when the Schmidt 25 well tested 4836 MCFGD from the Maykop at depths between 450 m and 700 m; a gas/condensate pool was also found in Maastrichtian limestones. Other significant finds include Shtormavaya in 1982 (Shtormavaya 1 tested up to 6713 MCFGD from Paleocene limestones), Arkhangel'skoye in 1987 (gas is reservoired in Paleocene to Miocene sandstones), and Odessa in 1988 (appraisal drilling has since delineated two main reservoir units comprising Paleocene sandstones and Eocene siltstones). Shtormavaya and Arkhangel'skoye have since been brought onstream; field production figures are not available, but 1993 gas production offshore Ukraine totalled some 15.6 bcf.

Foreign involvement in exploration began in 1993 when Crimean Petroleum Company (in which UK independent JKX Oil & Gas holds a 45% stake) was awarded the Delphin Block in an out-of-round award. The western part of the license area originally extended into the disputed Romanian territorial zone, but following protests from the Romanian authorities, an interim license was granted further east, away from the contested area. In 1994 detailed seismic was recorded in the block over a large tilted fault-block structure, and in September 1995 the *Ocean Liberator* semisubmersible drilled Delfin 1. The well was dry, as no viable reservoir was present in the Triassic below the Upper Cretaceous seal; nevertheless, JKX plans to record more seismic data in the block with a view to drilling four other prospects.

In 1994 Western Atlas commenced a 17,000 line-km survey to accompany the First Ukrainian Offshore Licensing Round, which closed in January 1996. Four blocks (each covering about 435 km^2) located south of the Shtormavaya field were subsequently pre-awarded to Pecten (operator), partnered by Shell. No other bids were received, and the remaining 146 blocks remain open. Pecten is in the process of setting up a joint venture company with Chernomorneftegas, but negotiations have been delayed by problems with the Ukrainian tax regime. It is hoped that the introduction of new production-sharing legislation will allow agreement to be concluded. At a promotional meeting in Houston in

Table 1. Indicative Black Sea Exploration Statistics to End-1995*

Country	Area (km²)	Number of NFWs Completed	NFW density (km²/NFW)	Exploration Status	Number of Other Exp. Wells	Post-1990 Seismic (line-km)	Number of Discoveries	Liquid Reserves (MMbbl)	Gas Reserves (Bcf)	Total Reserves (MMBOE)	Finding Rate (MMBOE/NFW)	Number of Producing Fields
Romania	20,000	24	833	Immature	22	23,229	4	109	692	224.3	9.3	2
Bulgaria	40,000	12	3333	Immature	1	13,873	2	0.4	120	20.4	1.7	0
Turkey	170,000	4	42,500	Frontier	0	20,883	1	0	30	5.0	1.3	0
Georgia	25,000	0	-	Frontier	0	0	0	-	-	-	-	0
Russia	50,000	0	0	Frontier	0	≥156	0	-	-	-	-	0
Ukraine	120,000	15	8000	Immature	40	>17,000	7	7.6	2241.5	381.2	27.2	3
Totals	425,000	55	7870	Immature	63	>75,141	14	117	3083.5	630.9	11.7	5

*Excluding the Azov Sea and fields that straddle the coast. Areas are approximate, as maritime boundaries are largely undefined.

Table 2. Checklist of Black Sea Discoveries to End-1996*

Country	Basin/Province	Name	Type	Discovery Year	Original Operator	Oil Reserves (MMbbl)	Condensate Reserves (MMbbl)	Gas Reserves (Bcf)	Total Reserves (MMBOE)	Main Reservoir	Production Status
Bulgaria	Kamchiya Basin	Samotino More 1	Gas/cond	1986	Committee of Geology		0.4	20	3.7	Eocene sandstone	Discovery
Bulgaria	Kamchiya Basin	Galata 1	Gas	1993	Texaco			100	16.7	Eocene limestone and sandstone	Discovery
Romania	Dobrogea Province	Lebada Est	Oil/gas/cond	1981	Ministry of Mining	42	2	242	84.3	Albian sandstone	Producing
Romania	Dobrogea Province	Lebada Vest	Oil/gas	1985	Ministry of Mining	40		200	73.3	Albian sandstone	Producing
Romania	Dobrogea Province	Sinoe 30	Oil/gas	1987	Ministry of Mining	25		50	33.3	Eocene sandstone	Appraising
Romania	Dobrogea Province	Doina 2	Gas	1995	Enterprise Oil			200	33.3	Pliocene sandstone	Discovery
Turkey	Pontides Province	Akçakoca 1	Gas	1976	TPAO			30	5.0	Eocene sandstone	Discovery
Ukraine	North Black Sea	Golitsyna	Gas/cond	1975	Ukrnafta		2.6	550	94.3	Paleocene carbonate	Producing
Ukraine	North Black Sea	Schmidtovskoye	Gas	1979	Chernomorneftegas			404.8	67.5	Oligocene–Lower Miocene sandstone	Discovery
Ukraine	North Black Sea	Krymskoye	Gas	1981	Chernomorneftegas			110	18.3	Oligocene–Lower Miocene sandstone	Discovery
Ukraine	North Black Sea	Golitsyna Yuzhnoye	Gas	1981	Chernomorneftegas			65	10.8	Oligocene–Lower Miocene sandstone	Discovery
Ukraine	North Black Sea	Shtormavaya	Gas/cond	1982	Chernomorneftegas		5	500	88.3	Paleocene carbonate	Producing
Ukraine	North Black Sea	Arkhangel'skoye	Gas	1987	Chernomorneftegas			185	30.8	Oligocene–Lower Miocene sandstone	Producing
Ukraine	North Black Sea	Odessa	Gas	1988	Chernomorneftegas			426.7	71.1	Paleocene sandstone	Appraising
Total Reserves						**107**	**10**	**3083.5**	**630.9**		

*Excluding the Azov Sea and fields that straddle the coast.

early 1996, the Ukrainian Geological Committee announced that the Odessa and Schmidt gas discoveries were to be offered for development; they have aggregate recoverable gas reserves of about 800 bcf. Several other discoveries and prospects in southern Ukraine were also highlighted as possible candidates for future international tenders, including Pridorozhana, Slyusarivs'ka, Tetyanivs'ke, and Povoronoye on the Kerch Peninsula, and the Zheltoyarskoye oil discovery in the Dobrogea Province (see below).

Dobrogea Province

Onshore

Exploration of the Western Soviet Black Sea margin began in the 1950s, and by 1975 a number of Hercynian to Cimmerian anticlinal structures had been mapped. Drilling began in 1976, but the first discovery was not made until 1984, when Sarata-Vostochno 3 tested 308 bo/d, after acidizing, from Devonian limestones and dolomites. The field was fully appraised by 1989 when a total of six wells had been drilled, but it remains shut-in. Although ten other wells encountered hydrocarbon shows in Devonian to Upper Jurassic rocks, only one further small oil discovery (Zheltoyarskoye) was made. In total, 28 exploratory wells had been drilled onshore in the Ukrainian sector to 1990, when drilling halted. No drilling has taken place offshore, although one well, Morskaya 1, was drilled in 1982 from Zmeinyy (serpent or snake) Island, off the Danube delta. It penetrated a few hundred meters of Neogene clastics and bottomed at a depth of 509 m in the Silurian, the oldest rocks yet found "in" the Black Sea.

BLACK SEA ENVIRONMENT

Physiography

The Black Sea covers 423,000 km^2 and has a volume of 534,000 km^3 (Ross et al., 1974). The shelf is typically delimited by the 100 m bathymetric contour and is often <20 km wide, but to the west of the Crimean Peninsula in the region of the Danube fan it is ≤190 km in width. The gradient of the continental slope is often about 10°, but it is about half this figure in the vicinity of the Danube fan. Erosional canyons and slumps are frequent where the gradient is steep, producing an irregular topography, which can degrade seismic data. The abyssal plain below ~2000 m dips gently toward the central part of the Black Sea, which is at a maximum depth of 2206 m (Ross et al., 1974).

The Black Sea is almost entirely encircled by mountain belts: the Pontides to the south, the Caucasus to the north and east, and the Carpathians to the west. Drainage is predominantly from the East European Platform, via the Danube. Because its only link to the Mediterranean is via the silled Bosporus, circulation is restricted and anoxic conditions have developed below ~70 m. Surface salinities are 18‰–20‰, and deeper, denser waters have salinities of 20‰–22‰.

Climate

Although the climate of the Black Sea region is continental, the moderating effect of the Black Sea and the shelter provided by the Caucasus Mountains combine to give the coastal regions relatively mild winters. Average water temperatures along the Northern Black Sea fall close to 0°C in winter, but increase to 20–22°C in summer. Frequent storms and strong N–NE winds accompanied by waves 2–4 m high are characteristic of the winter months; in summer, wave heights are generally less than 1 m. The ports along the Odessa Shelf are usually icebound during January and February.

Territorial Boundaries

Maritime boundaries within the Black Sea are ill-defined, and only the median line between Turkey and the former Soviet Union has been agreed by treaty with the former Soviet Union. The territorial boundary between Romania and Ukraine is a source of contention, as demonstrated by the partial overlap of Enterprise's Romanian Block XIII (Pelican) and JKX's Delfin Block in the Ukraine. The dispute received further publicity in 1995 with a visit to the small Zmeinyy Island by the Ukraine foreign and defense ministers. The island, which is located ~35 km off the Danube delta, was ceded to Soviet jurisdiction under the terms of an agreement signed in 1948. A recently agreed two-year moratorium on exploration and production within the disputed 10,350 km^2 area claimed by both Romania and Ukraine will allow time for continued negotiations. If agreement cannot be reached, the boundary dispute will be referred to the International Court of Justice in The Hague.

SUMMARY

More than 100 exploratory wells (Table 1) have been drilled in the Black Sea, and 14 (Table 2) small- to medium-sized discoveries have been made in Albian, Paleocene, Oligocene–Lower Miocene, and Pliocene plays. The average discovery size to date is estimated at 45 MMBOE, a finding rate of 12 MMBOE per new-field wildcat.

The graphs illustrating the annual amount of exploration (Figures 1, 2) reveal a sharp boom in seismic data acquisition in the early 1990s caused by the opening up of the Black Sea to foreign oil companies. The increase in the drilling effort over the same period has been more gradual, largely because of the high volume of appraisal drilling off Romania. In contrast, the trend in the discovery rate (Figure 3) appears to be downward from a peak reached in the early 1980s, when the Ukrainian gas/condensate fields in the Karkinit Trough were discovered.

Of the five fields that have been developed to date, the Albian sandstone reservoirs of Lebada Est and Vest produce oil and gas, while Paleocene carbonate reservoirs of Shtormavaya and Golitsyna produce gas with small amounts of condensate, and Arkhangel'skoye produces gas from Oligocene–Lower Miocene (Maykop) sandstones.

As the shallow waters (<200 m) of the Black Sea can be regarded as being at an immature stage of exploration, further discoveries can be expected; but most

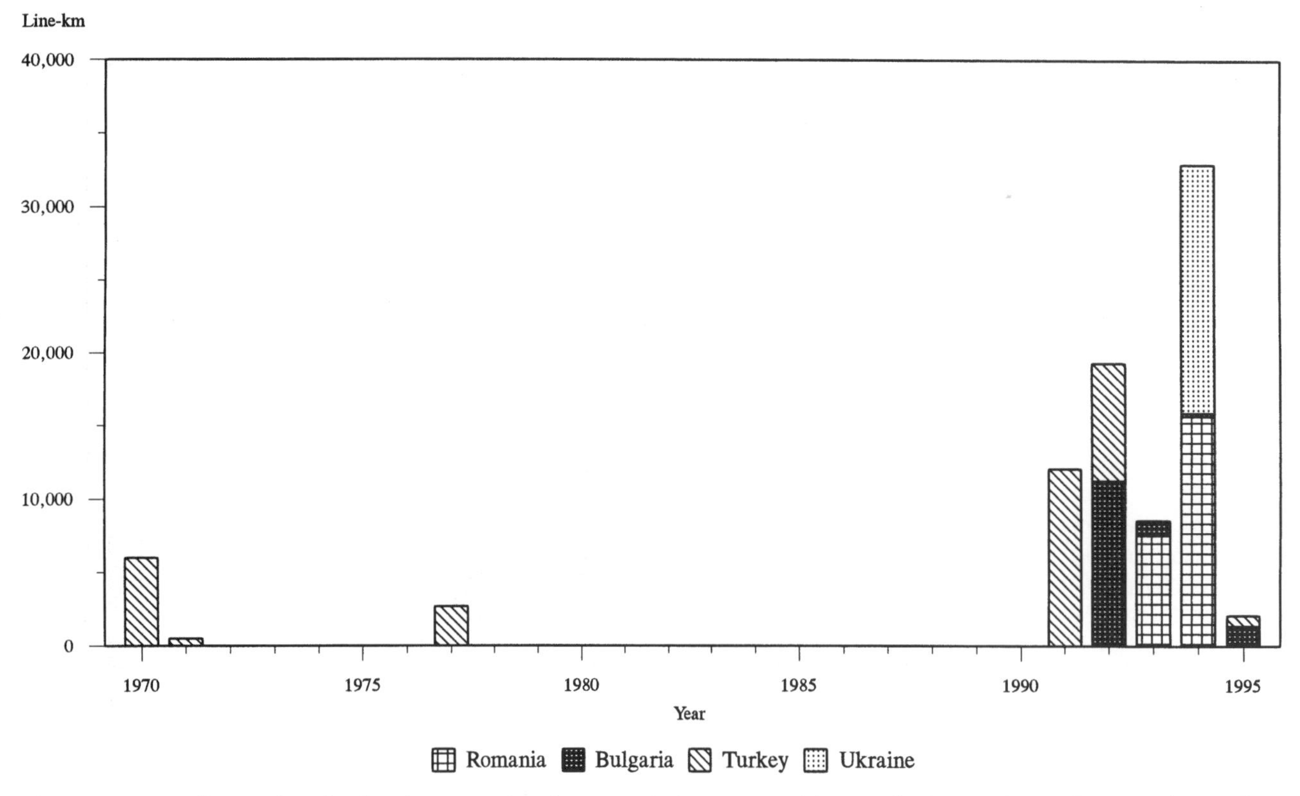

Figure 1. Two-dimensional seismic surveying by completion year. This graph shows the early 1990s boom in surveying in the Black Sea led by foreign companies. Note (1) this graph excludes surveys by Soviet/Russian crews and academic surveys; (2) the 1970 and 1977 survey volumes were estimated from survey duration assuming 1000 line-km per party-month; and (3) no details are available for a 1994 survey in the Delphin Block (Ukraine).

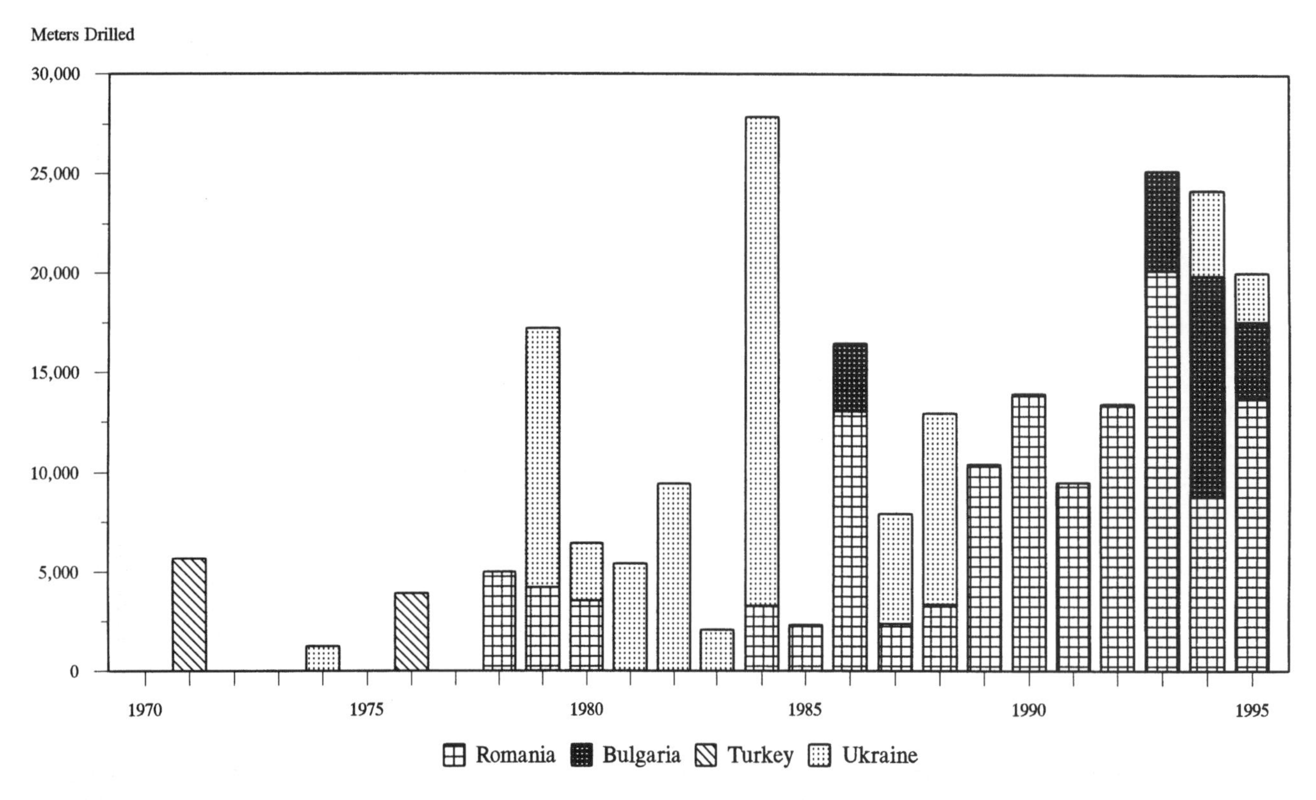

Figure 2. Exploratory well meterage by completion year. This graph shows an irregular but generally rising trend of exploratory drilling over the last two decades. The 1984 peak was caused by appraisal drilling in the Karkinit Trough off Ukraine, and the 1993 peak was due to commitment drilling by foreign companies off Romania and Bulgaria. Note the totals are minimum figures; 18 known Ukrainian wells (including 10 wells drilled in the Golitsyna field in 1984) plus 2 Bulgarian wells have unreported total depths. There has been no drilling in the Russian and Georgian sectors of the Black Sea.

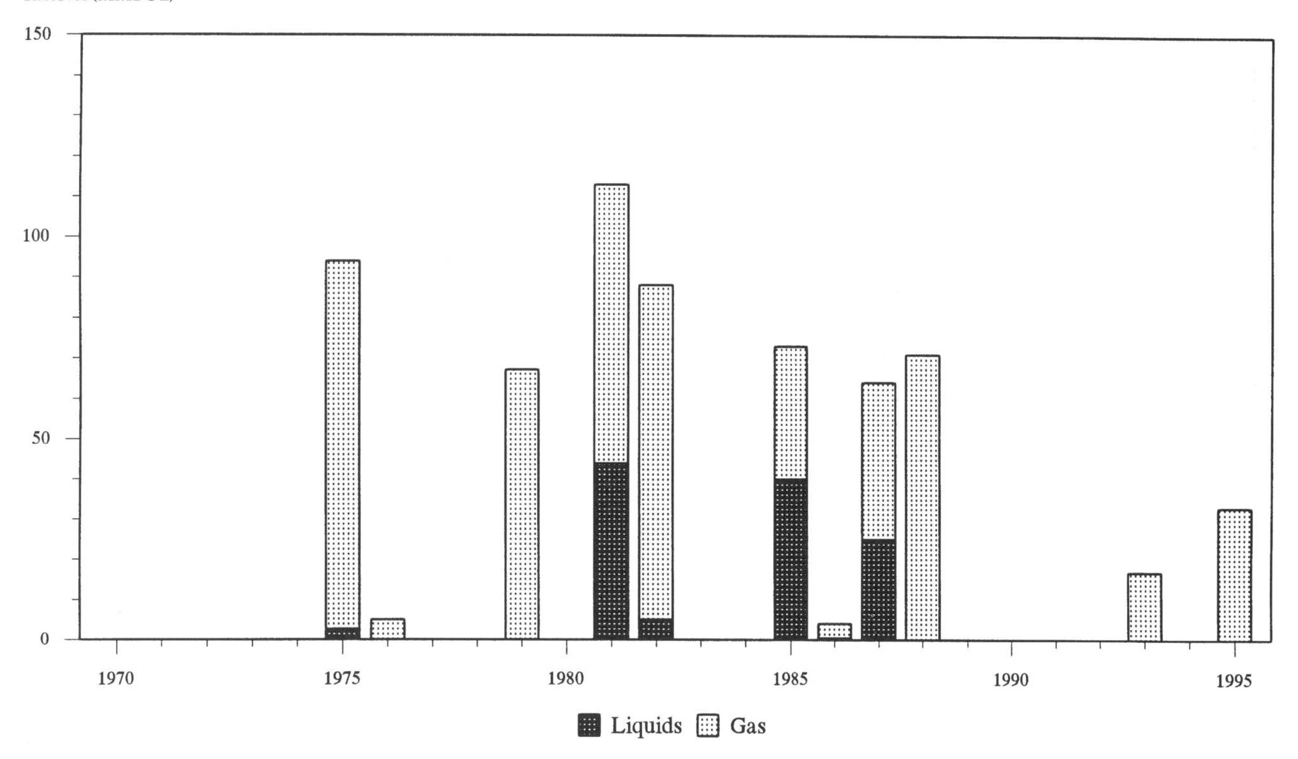

Figure 3. Reserve additions by year. This graph shows the rewards of exploration in the Black Sea, and demonstrates that in barrels-of-oil-equivalent terms, the Black Sea has to date proven to be gas-prone. The graph shows some evidence for declining levels of reserve additions, since a 1981 peak.

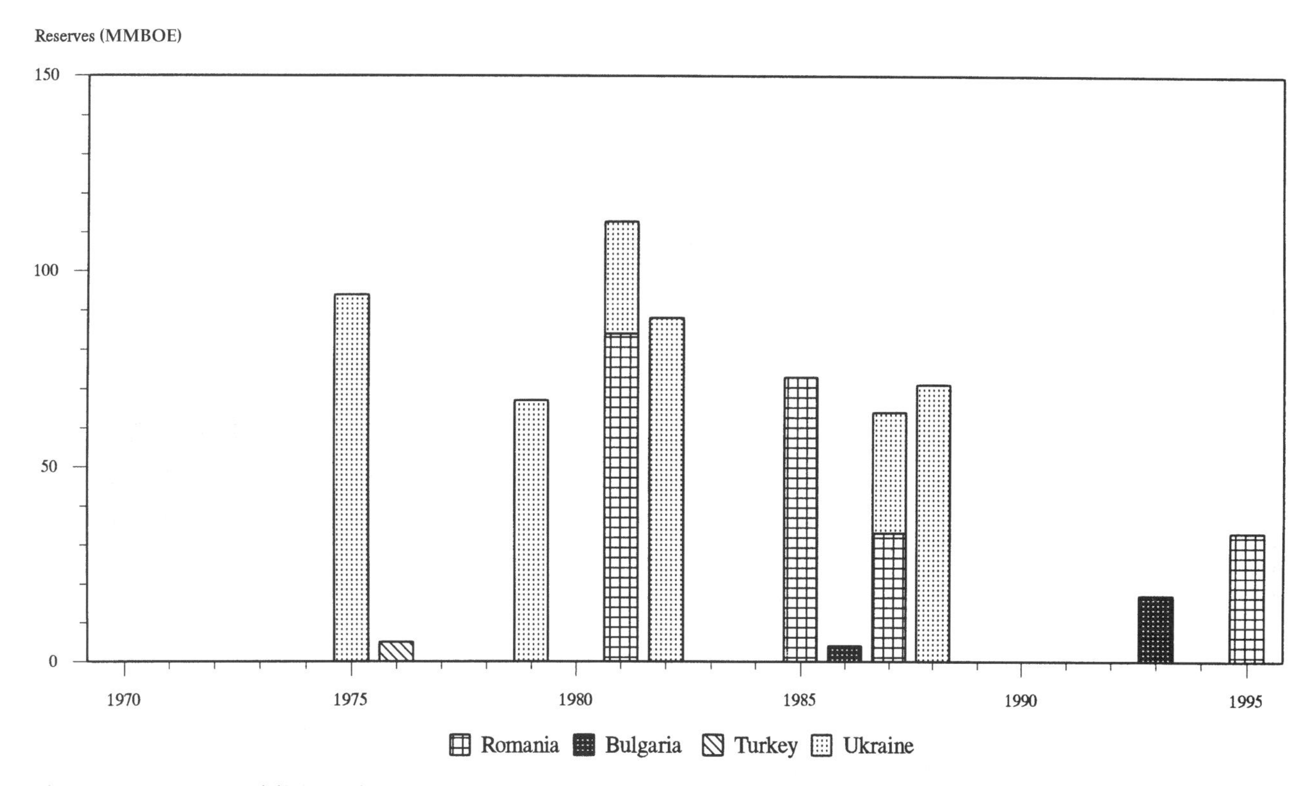

Figure 4. Reserve additions by country by year. This graph shows that the bulk of the discoveries in the Black Sea have been made in the Ukrainian and Romanian sectors. No discoveries have yet been made off Russia or Georgia.

of the obvious structural closures have been drilled, so few large discoveries are predicted. With the exception of some shallow wells of the deep sea drilling projects, the deepwater (>200 m) sector of the Black Sea is undrilled. It is this frontier region that holds the greatest potential for substantial oil and gas finds, and that is likely to become a focus of exploration in the next century (Figure 4).

ACKNOWLEDGMENTS

I would like to thank my colleagues at Petroconsultants who are involved with the production of scouting reports and nonexclusive basin analysis reports, or in maintaining the upstream database, which formed the basis of this review. Thanks are also due to various reviewers, including Andrew Robinson and David Smith.

REFERENCES CITED

Ionescu, N., 1994, Exploration history and hydrocarbon prospects of Romania, *in* B.M. Popescu, ed., Hydrocarbons of Eastern Central Europe: Berlin, Springer-Verlag.

Robinson, A.G., J.H. Rudat, C.J. Banks, and R.L.F. Wiles, 1996, Petroleum geology of the Black Sea: Marine and Petroleum Geology, v. 13, no. 2, p. 195–223.

Ross, D.A., E. Uchupi, K.E. Prada, and J.C. MacIlvaine, 1974, Bathymetry and microtopography of the Black Sea, *in* T.D. Egon and D.A. Ross, eds., The Black Sea—geology, chemistry, and biology: AAPG Memoir 20, p. 1–10.

Ross, D.A., 1978, Summary of results of Black Sea drilling: Initial Report of Deep Sea Drilling Project, XLII, National Science Foundation, v. 2, p. 1149–1177.

Vuchev, V., P. Bokov, B. Monov, A. Atanasov, R. Ognyanov, and D. Tochkov, 1994, Geologic structure, petroleum exploration development and hydrocarbon potential of Bulgaria, *in* B.M. Popescu, ed., Hydrocarbons of Eastern Central Europe: Berlin, Springer-Verlag.

Spadini, G., A.G. Robinson, and S.A.P.L. Cloetingh, 1997, Thermomechanical modeling of Black Sea Basin formation, subsidence, and sedimentation, *in* A.G. Robinson, ed., Regional and petroleum geology of the Black Sea and surrounding region: AAPG Memoir 68, p. 19–38.

Chapter 3

Thermomechanical Modeling of Black Sea Basin Formation, Subsidence, and Sedimentation

Giacomo Spadini[1]
Faculty of Earth Sciences, Vrije Universiteit
Amsterdam, Netherlands

Andrew G. Robinson
JKX Oil & Gas plc
Guildford, United Kingdom

S.A.P.L. Cloetingh
Faculty of Earth Sciences, Vrije Universiteit
Amsterdam, Netherlands

ABSTRACT

We demonstrate the key role of prerift rheology on the kinematics of basin formation and subsidence history in the Western and Eastern Black Sea basins. Constraints on modeling results are provided by a large data set based on >50,000 km of multichannel seismic data, offshore and onshore wells, regional gravity and magnetic surveys, refraction seismic data, and field studies. The western and eastern parts of the Black Sea appear to be two distinct basins, characterized by different evolutionary paths determined by different prerift conditions. The model supports the presence of important differences in the thickness and in the thermal state of the lithosphere, which rifted to form the Western (middle Barremian) and the Eastern (middle Paleocene) Black Sea subbasins. A 200-km thick and an 80-km thick prerift lithosphere appears to have driven the deformation in the Western and in the Eastern Black Sea, respectively. Differences in the geometry and in the mechanical properties of the prerift lithosphere have a strong control on the depth of necking and, thus, on the basin morphology. The model sheds light on paleotectonic and paleogeographic reconstructions, duration of rifting events, location of subsiding areas, and erosional surfaces.

Stratigraphic modeling provides new constraints on the paleowater depth evolution of the basin and associated basement subsidence. The model reproduces and provides explanations for several features of the stratigraphy of

[1]Currently at AGIP, San Donato Milanese, Italy.

the Black Sea: the apparent near absence of synrift strata (other than in the Western Pontides), thin to condensed early postrift sequences in both basins, a thick upper Eocene in the Eastern Black Sea, a relatively thin Oligocene to Miocene and a very thick Quaternary. It also predicts the geometry and depth of the lake that developed in the center of the Black Sea when sea level fell by 1500 m during the late Miocene.

INTRODUCTION

Recently, several dynamic modeling studies have emphasized the role of the prerift rheology in imposing a particular style of rifting. According to Buck (1991), the prerift crustal thickness and the temperature at the base of the crust are likely to be the most effective parameters in driving the deformation to a narrow vs. a wide rift. Bassi (1991) and Bassi et al. (1993) validated Buck's conclusions and introduced the importance of considering a wet vs. a dry rheology during extension. Other parameters, such as the presence of lithospheric weakness zones (Dunbar and Sawyer, 1989) and strain rate (Kusznir and Park, 1987; Bassi, 1995), have been proposed as factors that have to be taken into account for a better understanding of the rifting processes. Recent work by Cloetingh et al. (1995) determined the key role played by the prerift geometries and thermal perturbations in the evolution of a number of Mediterranean and intracratonic basins. In this chapter we focus on prerift lithospheric geometry and thermal structure, and their influence on basin subsidence, presenting the results of a quantitative basin analysis of the Black Sea. Our kinematic modeling, its validation through data sets, and the comparison with rheological models yield constraints on the prerift conditions of the lithosphere, which rifted to form the eastern and western parts of the Black Sea. Furthermore, stratigraphic simulation sheds light on the subsidence history, sedimentation rates, and paleowater depth evolution of the two subbasins.

First, we rationalize lithospheric thinning, crustal deformation, and basin formation in the Black Sea area by using a numerical modeling approach. In order to choose between different isostatic compensation models, we examine the flexural state of the lithosphere by modeling free-air gravity anomalies along two profiles in each basin parallel to the inferred extension directions. We then test different prerift lithospheric conditions and different kinematics that could have driven the deformation. To simulate lithospheric and crustal thinning and basin morphology, we use a pure shear model that calculates basement subsidence from defined crustal stretching factors, initial lithospheric thickness, and depth of necking (Kooi et al., 1992). We compare the kinematic modeling results with the rheological models of the area affected by the rifting process. Second, we model the postrift stratigraphic development of the basins in an attempt to explain variations in sedimentation and subsidence rates. We provide a 2-D reconstruction of the stratigraphic evolution consistent with available data.

Our modeling study of the Black Sea is based on a database of >50,000 km of multichannel seismics (some reprocessed, some newly acquired in the southeast Black Sea); data from 28 offshore wells and from further onshore wells situated around the Black Sea; extensive field studies in all countries surrounding the Black Sea, with the exception of Georgia; regional gravity and magnetic surveys (Robinson et al., 1995a); and Russian refraction seismic data (Belousov et al., 1988). This paper summarises results reported in more detail by Robinson et al. (1995b) and Spadini et al. (1996).

BASIN CONFIGURATION AND TECTONIC SETTING

The Black Sea is located north of Turkey and south of Ukraine and Russia, bordered to the west by Romania and Bulgaria and to the southeast by Georgia (Figure 1). The general geological setting of the basin has been known for many years (Ross et al., 1974; Letouzey et al., 1977; Zonenshain and LePichon, 1986; Manetti et al., 1988; Okay et al., 1994). Lying toward the northern margin of the group of orogenic belts related to the closure of the Tethys Ocean, the Black Sea is generally considered to be a result of back-arc extension associated with northward subduction of the Tethyan plate. Although this basin is primarily of extensional origin, most of the Black Sea margins are characterized by (and have been modified by) compressive deformation: the Pontides in northern Turkey and the Greater Caucasus and Gorni-Crimea mountain belts in Russia and Ukraine. Much of the present basin floor is a flat abyssal plain lying at a depth of 2200 m and appears to reflect the presence of a single basin. However, deep-reflection seismic studies have shown that there are two extensional basins in the Black Sea which have coalesced in their postrift phases (Figures 1, 2). The Western Black Sea opened with the separation of a fragment including the Western and Central Pontides (north Turkey) from the Moesian Platform (Romania and Bulgaria). Rifting began in the Middle Barremian, with major postrift subsidence and probable oceanic crust emplacement in the Cenomanian (Belousov et al., 1988; Finetti et al., 1988; Görür, 1988; Artyushkov, 1992). The postrift consists of ≤13 km of flat-lying Upper Cretaceous to Recent volcanics

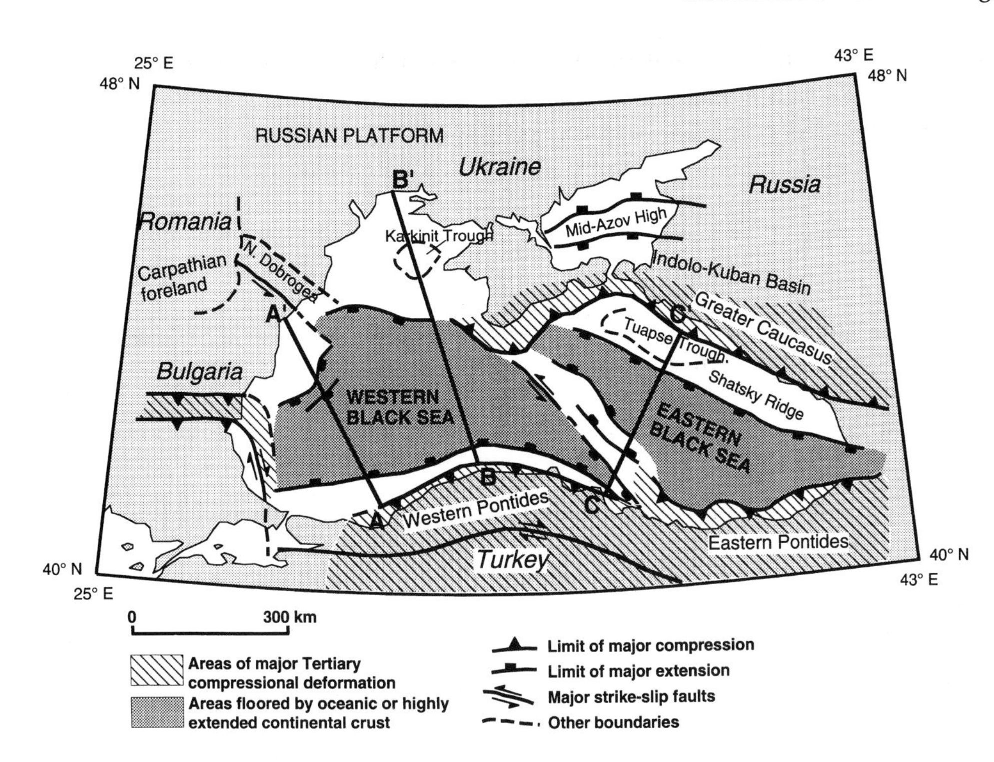

Figure 1. Location map showing major tectonic elements of the Black Sea area and the locations of the modeled profiles shown in Figures 5, 6, and 7.

and sediments. Rifting in the Eastern Black Sea probably began in the late Paleocene with rotation of the Mid-Black Sea High away from the Shatsky Ridge–Caucasus (Russia). Extension and probable oceanic crust emplacement were complete by the middle Eocene, and the upper Paleocene to Recent postrift sequence is ~11 km thick.

The older of the two basins, the Western Black Sea, rifted with the dissection of an Upper Jurassic to Lower Cretaceous carbonate platform that had been established on the southern margin (Moesian Platform) of the northern supercontinent, Laurasia. The limestones are as young as Middle Barremian in the Western Pontides (İnalti Formation), where they are unconformably overlain by Aptian–Albian synrift sediments including shallow-water sandstones, submarine slides, and olistostromes and turbidites (Çağlayan and Ülüs formations). Unconformably overlying the synrift strata is a unit of pelagic carbonates and distal tuffs of Cenomanian age (Kapanboğazı Formation) that is interpreted to mark the change from rift to drift in the Western Black Sea (Görür et al., 1993). Seismic reflection data on the Romanian shelf—the conjugate margin to the Western Pontides—show tilted extensional fault blocks draped by chalks that can be dated as Cenomanian to Maastrichtian (Robinson et al., 1995a). These constraints suggest that rifting took place over a period perhaps as long as 30 m.y., with spreading occupying at most 6–7 m.y. (corresponding to a spreading rate of about 5 cm/yr).

The age of the rifting event in the Eastern Black Sea is not as well documented because relevant stratigraphy is poorly exposed. Modeling of sea floor heat-flow measurements led Golmshtok et al. (1992) to the conclusion that the basin is Jurassic. The presence of a Jurassic marine basin on the southern flank of the Russian Platform is demonstrated by the stratigraphy of the southern slopes of the Greater Caucasus in Russia and Georgia, where Sinemurian mudstones unconformably overlie the Hercynian metamorphic basement. At least in the Middle Jurassic and Upper Cretaceous, this basin lies north of major volcanic arcs exposed now in the Eastern Pontides, and can thus be considered to have formed in a back-arc setting. Nonetheless, despite the apparent existence of a Jurassic–Cretaceous back-arc basin, three lines of evidence suggest that the Eastern Black Sea in its present form rifted after the early Paleocene (Danian). The uppermost part of what offshore seismic data clearly show to be the prerift—the Shatsky Ridge (northern rift shoulder)—has been drilled by numerous petroleum exploration wells in Georgia (e.g., Ochamchira) and shown to be a thick Mesozoic sequence including Middle Jurassic volcanics and volcanoclastic sediments, Upper Jurassic–Lower Cretaceous limestones (locally with evaporites), and an apparently complete Upper Cretaceous to Danian sequence of turbidites and chalks. These are overlain unconformably by upper Eocene mudstones. The same stratigraphic relationship has been found on dredging the sea floor north of the Turkish coast where the conjugate margin of the rift, the Archangelsky Ridge (Mid-Black Sea High), outcrops on the sea floor (Rudat and MacGregor, 1993): Upper Cretaceous volcanics, tuffs, and chalks including tuffaceous material are overlain unconformably by Eocene mudstones. Finally, the upper Paleocene is missing in the Eastern Pontides. Dating of the deepest parts of the postrift fill suggests that spreading in the Eastern Black Sea was completed by the middle Eocene (Robinson et al., 1995a). In summary, in contrast to the

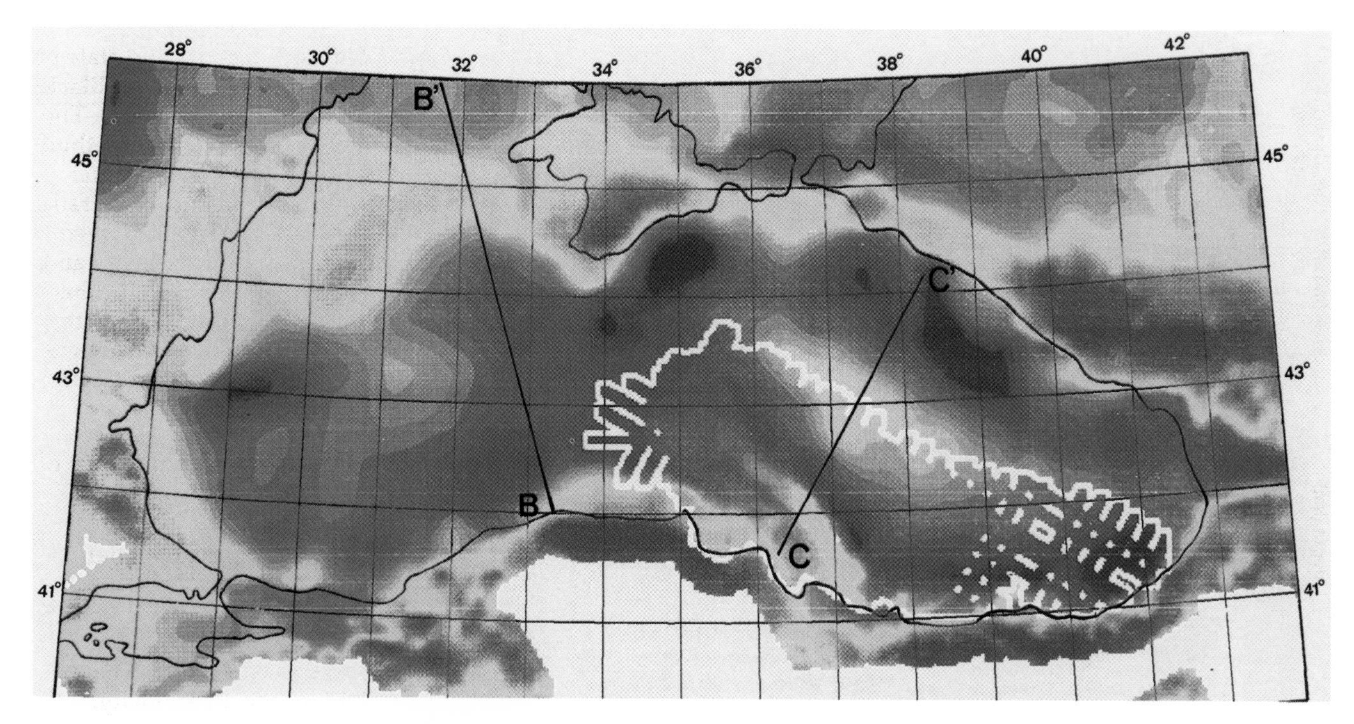

Figure 2. Free-air gravity map of the Black Sea and location of the profiles analyzed by our gravity modeling procedure (Figures 3, 4). Colors indicate values from 230 mGal (bright pink) to –100 mGal (dark blue). See Figures 3 and 4 for free-air gravity anomaly values along the modeled profiles.

situation in the Western Black Sea, where the stable Moesian Platform was rifted, rifting in the eastern basin apparently superimposed a younger (Paleocene) extensional basin on an area that had already been a back-arc basin since the Early Jurassic. The maximum length of time available for opening of the Eastern Black Sea is thus around 11 m.y.

The structure of the crust beneath the Black Sea has been determined by refraction seismic data profiling (Neprochnov et al., 1974; Belousov et al., 1988). Beneath the Western Black Sea, the Moho rises from a depth of 45 km beneath the Pontides mountain belt to ~20 km in the center of the Western Black Sea, falling again to the north to a depth of 40–45 km beneath the Russian Platform. The postrift fill in the Western Black Sea is as deep as 15 km in the basin center, and the crust has a thickness characteristic of oceanic crust. Beneath the Eastern Black Sea, the Moho rises to ~25 km. The base of the postrift lies at a depth of ~13 km, suggesting that the crust in the eastern basin may not be entirely oceanic. The evidence for well-developed magnetic anomalies is absent. This may be due, in part, in the western basin, to the coincidence of spreading with the Late Cretaceous quiet zone, but in both basins could be largely due to the obscuring effect of the huge thickness of postrift sediments.

In the Early Cretaceous, the crust beneath the location of the rift that was to become the Western Black Sea was part of the Moesian/European Platform with a characteristic crustal thickness of ~35 km. It is possible that crust along this southern margin of Laurasia had been thickened during the Middle Jurassic Cimmerian orogeny (Şengör et al., 1980, 1984, 1988; Ustaömer and Robertson, 1994), but the deposition of shelf carbonates during the Late Jurassic and Early Cretaceous (~35 Ma) suggests stabilization of the region. Rifting in the Eastern Black Sea affected the Russian Platform crust with characteristic thickness of 40–45 km (Guterch et al., 1986). However, as the area was already a basin by the time of rift initiation, the crust may have been previously thinned.

LITHOSPHERIC STATE OF FLEXURE: CONSTRAINTS BY GRAVITY MODELING

The tectonic evolution of extensional basins depends on the isostatic compensation of the vertical loads acting on a stretched and thinned lithosphere. Loads resulting from crustal thinning, thermal contraction, and basin fill can be compensated regionally or locally, depending on the capability of the lithosphere to distribute these loads over a broad area. The rigidity of the lithosphere is the key parameter controlling the flexural behavior of a deforming plate. Predictions of basin architecture and subsidence patterns have to take into account these different mechanisms of load compensation since they strongly control the effects of thinning and stretching operating on the lithosphere (Kooi et al., 1992; Spadini et al., 1995). A kinematic model of extension leading to the formation of an overdeep basin (deeper than an isostatic compensated situation) would cause an upward state of flexure; if an underdeep

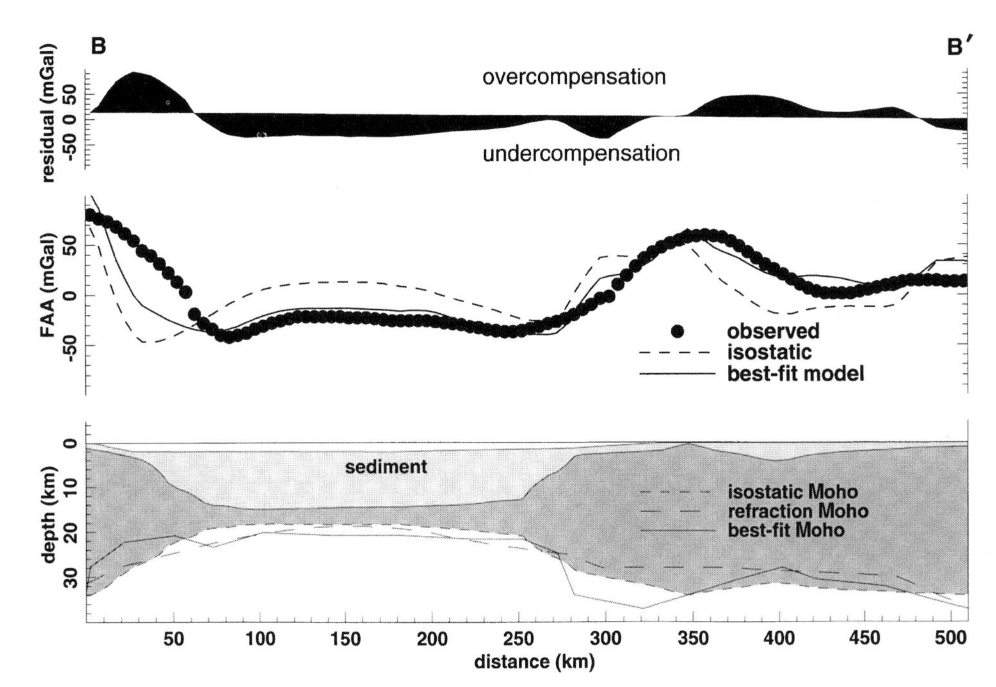

Figure 3. Gravity and state of flexure in the Western Black Sea (BB′ in Figures 1, 2). The figure illustrates the method of calculating the residual gravity anomaly (the difference between the observed free-air gravity anomaly and the anomaly that would be produced if the basin were locally isostatically compensated). The deviation (residual anomaly) from a local isostatic compensation is a measure for the state of flexure of the lithosphere. An upward state of flexure is suggested for the Western Black Sea. Also shown is the Moho shape, which provides the best fit with the measured gravity anomalies. FAA = free-air anomaly.

basin is formed, a downward state of flexure is expected (Braun and Beaumont, 1989; Weissel and Karner, 1989; Kooi et al., 1992). Braun and Beaumont (1989) and Kooi (1991) showed that a deep level of necking (the lithospheric level with no vertical movements during deformation in absence of restoring forces) creates an overdeep surface depression; an upward vertical load is expected in order to restore the isostatic equilibrium. Conversely, a shallow level of necking creates an underdeep surface depression and a downward-compensating vertical load.

Understanding the state of lithospheric flexure is important for modeling basin fill. The depths of necking (or local isostasy) and their state of flexure are not apparent from the shape of the basin, but they have an important expression in the gravity signal (Figure 2), especially in the "isostatic residual anomaly" (Kooi, 1991). The isostatic residual anomaly is defined as the difference between the observed (free air) anomaly and the anomaly predicted if the basin were compensated locally ("isostatic anomaly"). A positive isostatic residual anomaly indicates overcompensation, and a negative isostatic residual anomaly undercompensation. Upward flexure, related to a deep level of necking, is associated with overcompensated basin flanks and an undercompensated basin center; downward flexure and a shallow level of necking are expressed by undercompensated basin flanks and an overcompensated basin center.

We performed gravity modeling of the Western and Eastern Black Sea subbasins along two transects (Figure 2) by applying a 2-D forward and inverse numerical model that is able to simulate the gravity anomaly signature produced by a given distribution of mass. Geometry and densities of large-scale bodies have been defined by the combination of seismic reflection and refraction data (Belousov et al., 1988; Finetti et al., 1988). A velocity-density conversion allows us to assign densities of 2700 kgm^{-3} and 2980 kgm^{-3} to the upper and the lower crust, respectively. For the heavily thinned crust underlying the central areas of the basin, the density has been constrained by refraction seismic data at 2900 kgm^{-3} in the west (possible basaltic layer) and at 2800 kgm^{-3} in the east. The thick sedimentary cover of the Black Sea has been approximated, with a number of horizontal layers (according to seismic data available for the west and for the east) with densities ranging between 2000 and 2600 kgm^{-3}. Seismic velocities indicate a density of 3330 kgm^{-3} for the mantle underlying both the Western and the Eastern Black Sea crust.

We have calculated the isostatic anomaly and the isostatic residual anomaly along two transects, in the Western Black Sea and in the Eastern Black Sea, based on a high-quality regional gravity data set (Figure 2). Both in the Eastern and Western Black Sea, a clear discrepancy exists between the observed and the isostatic anomaly, indicating a nonlocal isostatic compensation of the Black Sea lithosphere (Figures 3, 4). The large wavelength of the residual anomaly indicates that the discrepancy cannot be due to small-scale density variations that are not included in our calculation. It must reflect a regional feature.

The analysis of the sign of the isostatic residual anomaly (Figures 3, 4) reveals an interesting and pronounced difference between the Eastern and the Western Black Sea basins. The Western Black Sea appears to be in an overall upward state of flexure (undercompensated basin center and overcompensated basin flanks), and the Eastern Black Sea is in a downward state of flexure (overcompensated basin center and undercompensated basin flanks). This suggests that

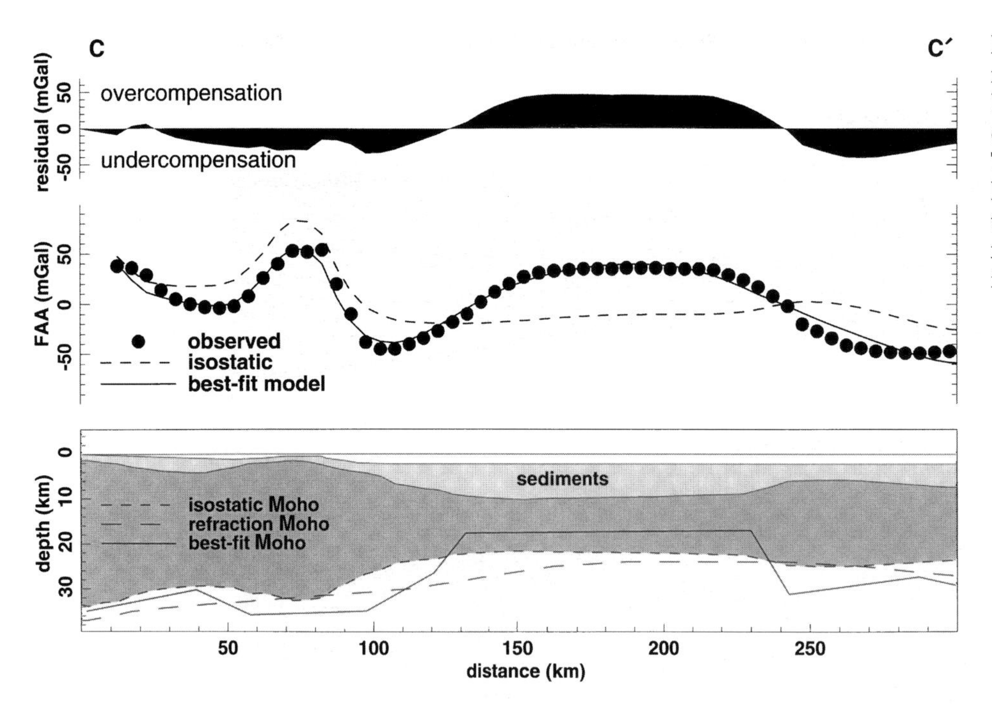

Figure 4. Results of gravity modeling for the Eastern Black Sea suggesting a downward state of flexure. The best-fit Moho ("gravity Moho") is much shallower than the Moho defined by refraction seismic. FAA = free-air anomaly.

the level of necking involved in the deformation is deep in the west but shallow in the east.

Using an inverse gravity modeling procedure, we have also calculated the "best-fit Moho," the Moho that gives the best fit with the observed free-air anomaly signature. The relation between the best-fit Moho and the isostatic Moho (Figures 3, 4) also shows a constant pattern: the best-fit Moho is the deepest below the basin flanks and shallowest below the basin center for the Western Black Sea. The opposite is true in the Eastern Black Sea. Again, a deep level of necking is expected for the west, and a shallow one for the east. The refraction Moho generally follows the best-fit Moho (in the sense that it has the same geometrical relationship with the isostatic Moho), with some important exceptions. In the Western Black Sea between 270 and 340 km (Figure 3) along the analyzed transect, we predict a much deeper Moho than detected by refraction seismic data (Belousov et al., 1988). This difference does not alter our conclusions since it is confined to a relatively small area and is probably the product of a small-scale density contrast within the crust. The central portion of the Eastern Black Sea (130–230 km) (Figure 4) is characterized by a predicted Moho shallower than the seismically defined base of the crust. The shallow Moho (related to the broad positive free-air anomaly at the basin center) is responsible for the overcompensation of the area. A shallower Moho at the basin center seems to be likely to occur since the positive free-air anomaly is a large 3-D feature characterizing the whole central part of the Eastern Black Sea (Figure 2). The refraction seismic data studies could have overestimated the depth of the Moho. This would support the presence of oceanic crust in the Eastern Black Sea, instead of continental stretched crust. This interpretation could have a strong effect on estimates for crustal thinning.

TECTONIC MODELING

We modeled the Black Sea tectonic evolution applying a finite-difference kinematic model of lithospheric thinning (Kooi et al., 1992). We take into account the finite duration of a nonadiabatic rifting and a nonzero strength of the lithosphere, which can compensate changing loads in a regional manner. The flexural rigidity of the lithosphere is controlled by the effective elastic thickness that we consider temperature dependent and defined as the depth to the 400°C isotherm (Watts et al., 1982). The complete set of parameters we use in the model is given in Table 1. We also take into account the presence of a level of necking (Kooi et al., 1992) in order to simulate the dynamic control of a specified lithospheric layer on the kinematics of extension and thinning (Spadini et al., 1995). The state of lithospheric flexure and the imprinting of the

Table 1. Model Parameters.

	Value	Definition
Te	400°C	isotherm describing EET*
$T0$	0°C	surface temperature
Ta	1333°C	asthenosphere temperature
k	7.8 x 10–7 m^2 s^{-1}	thermal diffusivity
α	3.4 x 10–5°C	thermal expansion coefficient
g	9.8 m s–2	gravitational acceleration
ρc	2800 kg m^{-3}	surface density crustal rock
ρm	3330 kg m^{-3}	surface density mantle rock
ρs	2700 kg m^{-3}	sediment grain density
ρw	1030 kg m^{-3}	water density
ϕ_0	0.55	sediment surface porosity
c	0.55 km^{-1}	compaction depth constant

*EET = effective elastic thickness

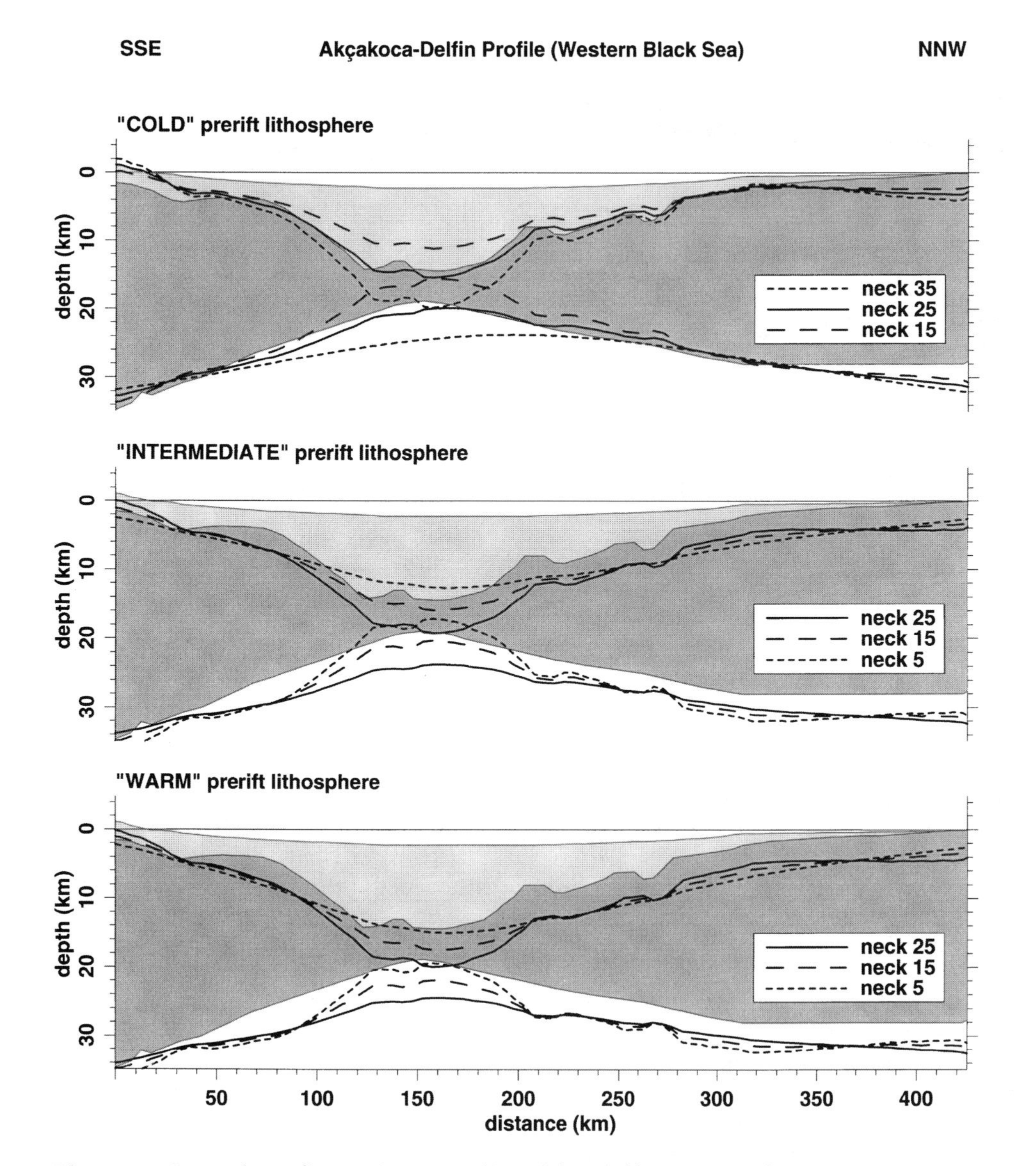

Figure 5. Crustal configurations predicted for different prerift lithospheric geotherms along the profile AA′ (Figure 1) in the Western Black Sea. The base of the lithosphere (1333°C) is fixed at 200 km depth in the "cold" model, 120 km in the "intermediate" model, and 80 km in the "warm" model. Also shown is a sensitivity test on different depths of necking adopted. A cold and thick lithosphere prior to rifting and a medium-deep depth of necking (25 km) yield the best fit with the observed crustal geometry (gray in the figure). Observed sediment thickness is shown in light gray.

necking-related thinning are also taken into account for predictions during the postrift thermal cooling and subsidence. We simulate the presence of oceanic crust in the Western Black Sea, using the concept of a limited β factor, a value beyond which stretching will be superseded by creation of new oceanic lithosphere. Following Keen and Beaumont (1990), we use a β of 5.5 as a reasonable approximation to simulate oceanic thermal subsidence when a uniform-extension model is used.

The analyzed transects (Figures 5, 6, and 7) are divided in a finite number of boxes for which we assign thinning factors. Crustal thinning factors (β) along the three profiles are calculated from the depth-converted reflection seismic data (prerift basement morphology), the Moho depth determined by refraction seismic data (Belousov et al., 1988), and initial crustal thicknesses (taken to be 35 km for both basins). As discussed, we are aware that the refraction seismic data experiments can contain errors in estimating the position of the base of the crust. The choice of using the refraction-defined Moho to estimate thinning factors was driven by the need for a consistency that would permit comparisons between different scenarios (i.e., different initial lithospheric thicknesses and different depth of necking during extension). The thickness of crust prior to rifting and the derived thinning factors influence the

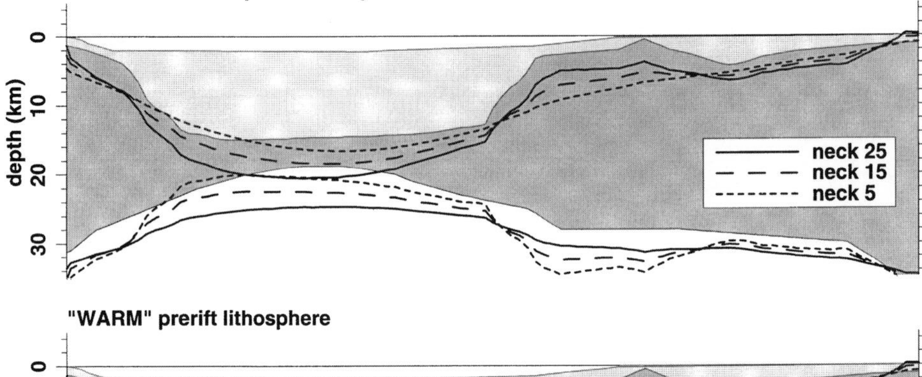

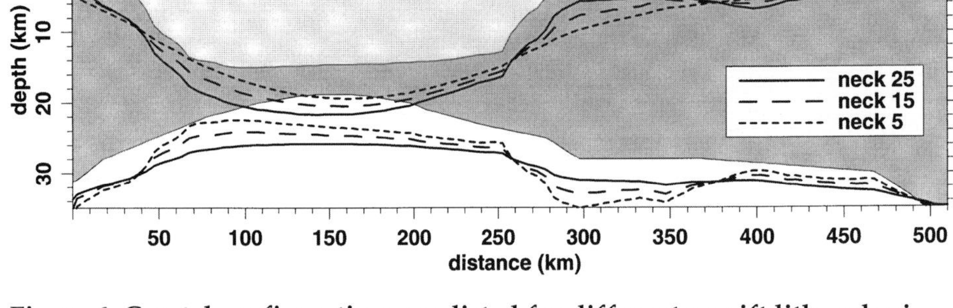

Figure 6. Crustal configurations predicted for different prerift lithospheric geotherms along the profile BB′ (Figure 1) in the Western Black Sea. The base of the lithosphere (1333°C) is fixed at 200 km depth in the "cold" model, 120 km in the "intermediate" model, and 80 km in the "warm" model. Also shown is a sensitivity test on different depths of necking adopted. A cold and thick lithosphere prior to rifting and a medium-deep depth of necking (25 km) give the best fit with the observed crustal geometry. Figure conventions are as in Figure 5.

predicted synrift subsidence. In our model, the base of the lithosphere is considered to be controlled by the 1333°C isotherm. The initial lithospheric thickness also has a strong influence in limiting the synrift subsidence: if the ratio between initial crustal thickness and initial lithospheric thickness is smaller than about 0.15, no subsidence takes place; it will be superseded by uplift (McKenzie, 1978). The depth of necking defines the layer where vertical movements are compensated by horizontal shear; it directly controls the synrift subsidence of the basin and its morphology. Neither initial lithospheric thickness nor depth of necking are known a priori. We, therefore, consider a "cold" (200 km thick), an "intermediate" (120 km), and a "warm" (80 km) prerift lithosphere in order to investigate the role played by the subcrustal thinning in the vertical movements. We also present a sensitivity test on the different depths of necking adopted.

The two sections in the Western Black Sea (AA′ and BB′) (Figures 5, 6) run SSE–NNW (Figure 1), aligned along the direction of extension. The western section (AA′) runs from the offshore exploration well Akçakoca-2 through the deep postrift basin and onto the relatively little extended Moesian Platform of the Romanian Shelf. The eastern section (BB′) runs from the Turkish town of Cide into the postrift basin, across the Kalamit Ridge and Karkinit Trough and onto the southern margin of the Russian Platform in the Gulf of

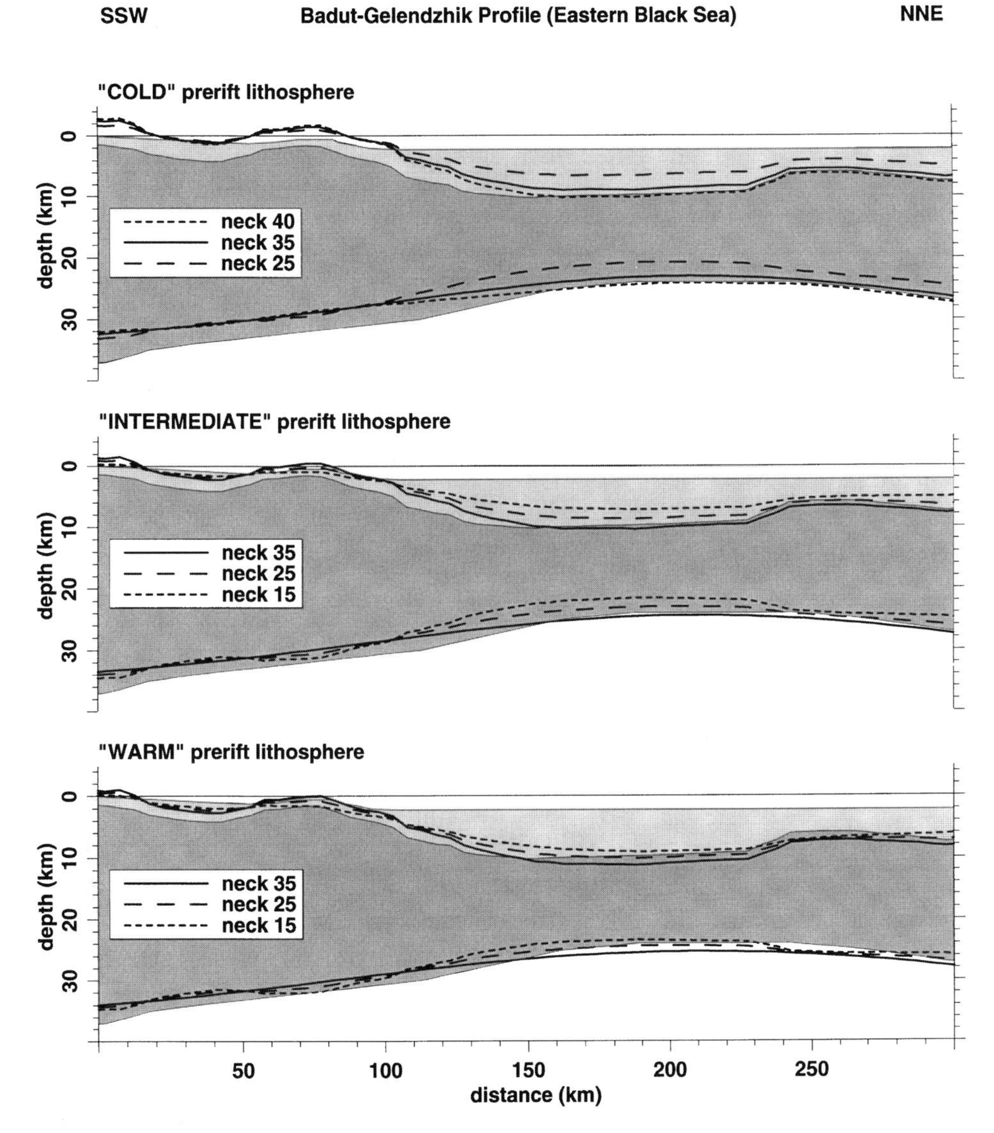

Figure 7. Crustal configurations predicted for different prerift lithospheric geotherms and depths of necking along the profile CC′ (Figure 1) in the Eastern Black Sea. The base of the lithosphere (1333°C) is fixed at 200 km depth in the "cold" model, 120 km in the "intermediate" model, and 80 km in the "warm" model. A warm, thin lithosphere prior to rifting gives the best fit with the observed crustal geometry. The predicted configuration is not very sensitive to different depths of necking within the "warm" scenario. Although the tectonic model cannot discriminate among the different values of depth of necking tested, the result of the gravity modeling (Figure 4) suggests a shallow level of necking. Figure conventions are as in Figure 5.

Odessa (Figure 1). The section that we model in the Eastern Black Sea (CC′; Figure 7) is aligned SSW–NNE, again parallel to the inferred extension direction (Figure 1). This section runs from the Badut petroleum exploration well in North Turkey toward the town of Gelendzhik on the Russian coast, crossing the Sinop Trough, Archangelsky Ridge, Shatsky Ridge, and Eastern Black Sea Basin (Figure 1). The profile was truncated short of the Russian coastline to avoid the shortening and crustal thickening associated with the Caucasus mountain belt.

Prerift Crustal and Lithospheric Thicknesses and Depth of Necking

Figures 5, 6, and 7 show bathymetry, the mapped top of the prerift basement, and the position of the Moho (Belousov et al., 1988) for each of the three modeled sections. As discussed, the thickness of the crust prior to rifting in the two basins is difficult to measure because of the long and complex tectonic history of the region. For crustal thicknesses of 40 and 45 km, the predicted relative amount of synrift subsidence is substantially increased, for which feature there is very little evidence on seismic profiles (Robinson et al., 1995a). As a result, an initial thickness of 35 km was adopted for modeling both basins.

Also shown in Figures 5, 6, and 7 are modeled crustal configurations calculated by using initial lithospheric thicknesses of 80, 120, and 200 km. In the Eastern Black Sea, the best fit to the observed crustal geometry along the CC′ section is for an initial lithospheric thickness of 80 km (Figure 7). The "warm" model appears to provide the best fit, but the differences with the "intermediate" scenario are very small and are probably within the error range of the observed data. For the modeled sections AA′ and BB′, the situation is quite different. With an initial lithospheric thickness of 80 km, there is a large mismatch between predicted and observed crustal structure; the best fit is obtained for a 200 km thick (cold) lithosphere. This result is very robust since the differences between the cold and the warm model are large not only on the margins, where boundary conditions not taken into account in our modeling (i.e., loads from the Pontides orogenic belt) can play a substantial role, but also along the entire transect.

Our calculations show an inverse relationship between prerift lithospheric temperature and sensitivity to the depth of necking selected. In the Eastern Black Sea, where a warm lithosphere is inferred, it is therefore difficult to select the most appropriate position of the necking level. The gravity modeling, nonetheless, shows that a relatively shallow depth of necking (15 km) has to be preferred. In the Western Black Sea, the best-fit model for the AA′ and BB′ profiles provides a well-constrained estimate on the depth of necking: a lower crustal layer (25 km) clearly controls the rifting-related thinning and the flexural response of the lithosphere. The differences in predicted prerift basement depth between the best-fit model (25 km depth of necking) and the other scenarios vary between 2 to 6 km at the center of the basin (Figures 5, 6). These discrepancies are much higher than any possible error in the observation; this makes the conclusion very robust.

IMPLICATIONS FOR THE BLACK SEA LITHOSPHERE EVOLUTION

The model results support the existence of a consistent and substantial difference in the nature of the lithosphere where rifting led to the formation of the Western Black Sea in the Middle Cretaceous and the Eastern Black Sea in the Paleocene. The Western Black Sea was initiated on cold, thick lithosphere (200 km); the Eastern Black Sea on a warm, thin lithosphere (80 km). Besides this difference in the implied lithospheric thickness, the extension in the Western Black Sea appears to be controlled by a deep crustal level of necking (25 km), whereas in the Eastern Black Sea the inferred level of necking is shallow (15 km). This controls the state of flexure of the deformed lithosphere and explains the differences in the gravity field over the studied area.

Differences in the lithospheric depth of necking during extension suggest different mechanical properties characterizing the Eastern and the Western Black Sea lithospheres before and during rifting (Kooi et al., 1992; Cloetingh et al., 1995; Spadini et al., 1995). In fact, the geometry and the thermal state of the prerift lithosphere (which ultimately control its dynamic response) are likely to impose different evolutionary paths on the deforming plate. To investigate the possible dynamic constraints on the kinematic evolution, we calculate the strength profiles that should have characterized the Western and the Eastern Black Sea lithospheres at the beginning of rifting (Figure 8). We adopt different lithospheric thicknesses and geotherms according to the results of the tectonic modeling. Strain rates in the west (2.2×10^{-15} s^{-1}) and in the east (4.9×10^{-15} s^{-1}) were derived from the averaged value of thinning factors on continental lithosphere and from the duration of rifting. Strength profiles based on extrapolation of rock-mechanics data (Carter and Tsenn, 1987) (Figure 8) suggest a pronounced difference in the mechanical properties of the prerift lithosphere between the Western Black Sea and the Eastern Black Sea that could have strongly controlled the overall kinematics of rifting. In the Western Black Sea the inferred strength distribution localizes the depth of necking either at deep crustal levels [combined effects of the upper mantle and crustal strength, the "strong couple" (Spadini et al., 1995)] or below the Moho (key role played by the strong upper mantle) (Kooi et al., 1992). The first hypothesis seems the most appropriate after the comparison of the strength distribution with depth with the best-fit value (25 km) obtained for the depth of necking. In the Eastern Black Sea, the inferred warm state of the lithosphere predicts a very weak mantle: shallow to mid-crustal crustal layers are likely to impose the style of rifting around a shallow level of necking, as confirmed by gravity and tectonic modeling results.

The proposed model (Figure 9) involving rifting of mechanically different lithospheres in east and west is supported by several features of the initiation and development of the Eastern and the Western Black Sea basins (see below).

STRATIGRAPHIC MODELING, METHOD, AND ASSUMPTIONS

In order to investigate the subsidence history of the Black Sea area by using a stratigraphic modeling approach, we need to isolate the tectonic component of the vertical movements. We need to define the parameters controlling the lithospheric thinning and, thus, the tectonic subsidence pattern during the evolution of the basin. Once we have determined the tectonic component, we can predict the water depth evolution, sea level change, and total basement subsidence that can better simulate the depositional history of the Western and Eastern Black Sea basins.

To reproduce the tectonic component of basin subsidence, we use the same numerical model and the same set of parameters (i.e., prerift lithospheric thickness

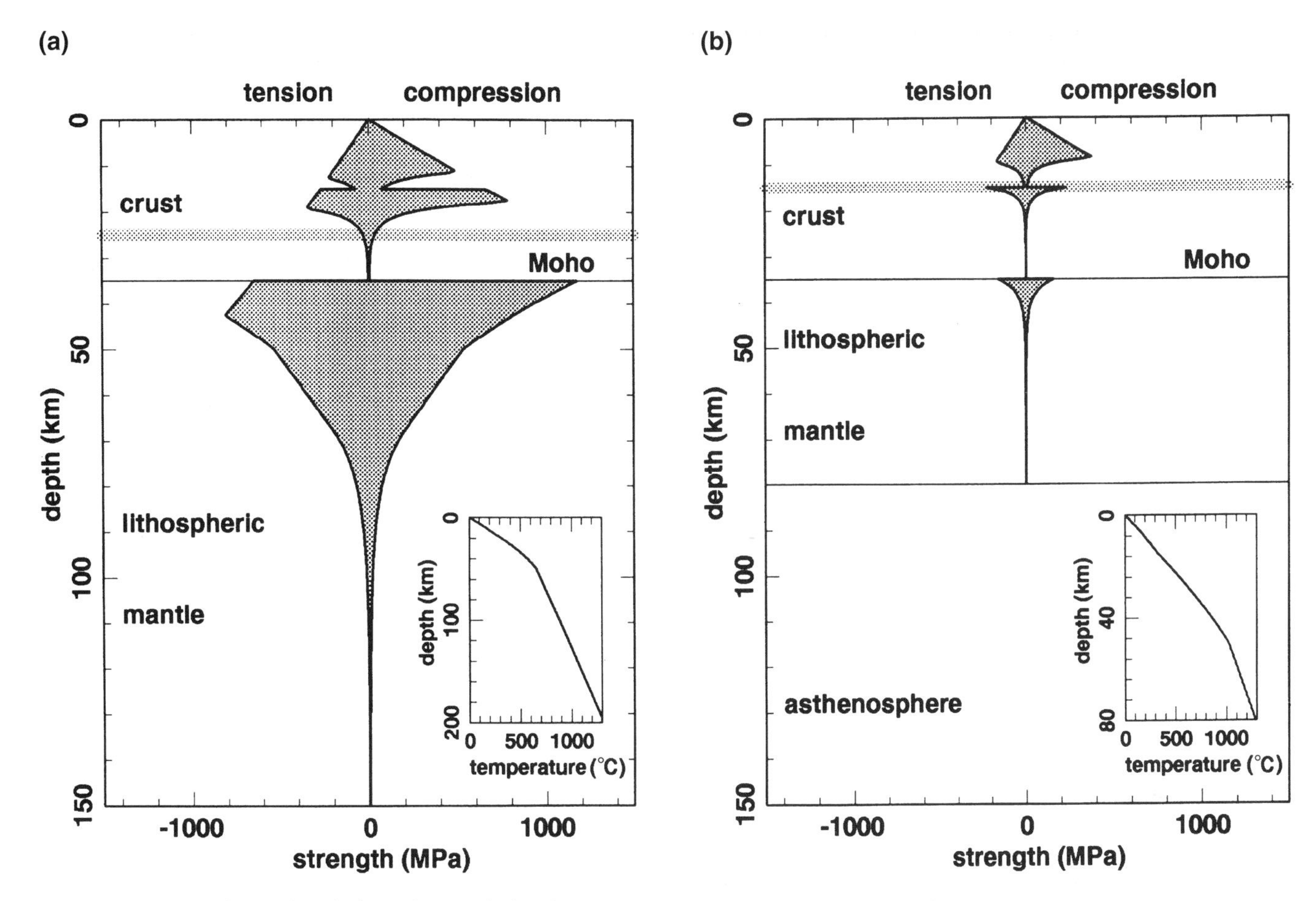

Figure 8. Strength vs. depth for a layered rheology (granite, diorite, and olivine for the upper crust, lower crust, and mantle, respectively) (Banda and Cloetingh, 1992) calculated for (a) the Western Black Sea (WBS) and (b) the Eastern Black Sea (EBS) at the beginning of rifting. For the calculation we use the best-fit geotherms (inset) derived by tectonic modeling. Strain rates in the west (2.2×10^{-15} s^{-1}) and in the east (4.9×10^{-15} s^{-1}) were derived from the averaged value of thinning factors on continental lithosphere and from the duration of rifting. The strength profiles for the lithosphere are based on extrapolation of rock-mechanics data (Carter and Tsenn, 1987). Note that the higher strain rate adopted for the EBS should increase the strength of the ductile layers (e.g., upper mantle). In this case, the strength is mainly controlled by the different geotherms adopted; the EBS lithosphere appears to be much weaker than the WBS lithosphere. Levels of necking predicted through tectonic modeling for the WBS and for the EBS are also shown (horizontal line in light gray). MPa = Megapascal.

and depth of necking) (Table 1) that have been successful in simulating the lithospheric deformation in the Western and Eastern Black Sea basins. This set of parameters constitutes our starting point in investigating the subsidence pattern (tectonic component plus the sediment/water loading) during rift and postrift. With the tectonic component of basin subsidence established, the only variables controlling sediment and water loading and stratigraphy are (1) sediment and water densities, (2) variation of sea level, and (3) paleowater depth. In our approach, subsidence is calculated using a 2-D pure-shear McKenzie (1978)-type model, modified in order to include finite duration of stretching and lateral heat flow during rift and postrift. For each step during basin evolution, the tectonic component of subsidence is calculated by considering the adopted thinning factors and the induced thermal perturbation. The space between the calculated basement position and sea level is then filled by sediments up to a specified paleowater depth profile along the analyzed transect (sediment–water interface). Taking into account sediment compaction, using an exponential porosity–depth relation (Table 1), the tectonic subsidence is corrected to obtain the total basin subsidence (basement subsidence). With a trial-and-error procedure, we then vary the position of the sediment–water interface in order to get the observed thickness for each sedimentary unit deposited during the evolution of the basin (Figures 10, 11). Predictions of the time-dependent water depth values and the corresponding basement subsidence are the goal of our modeling procedure.

When modeling of basement subsidence is performed, including a mechanical compaction of sedimentary units, it is commonly assumed that the thickness and total mass of the unit will decrease as pore fluid is progressively expelled (Sclater and Christie, 1980). For the purpose of

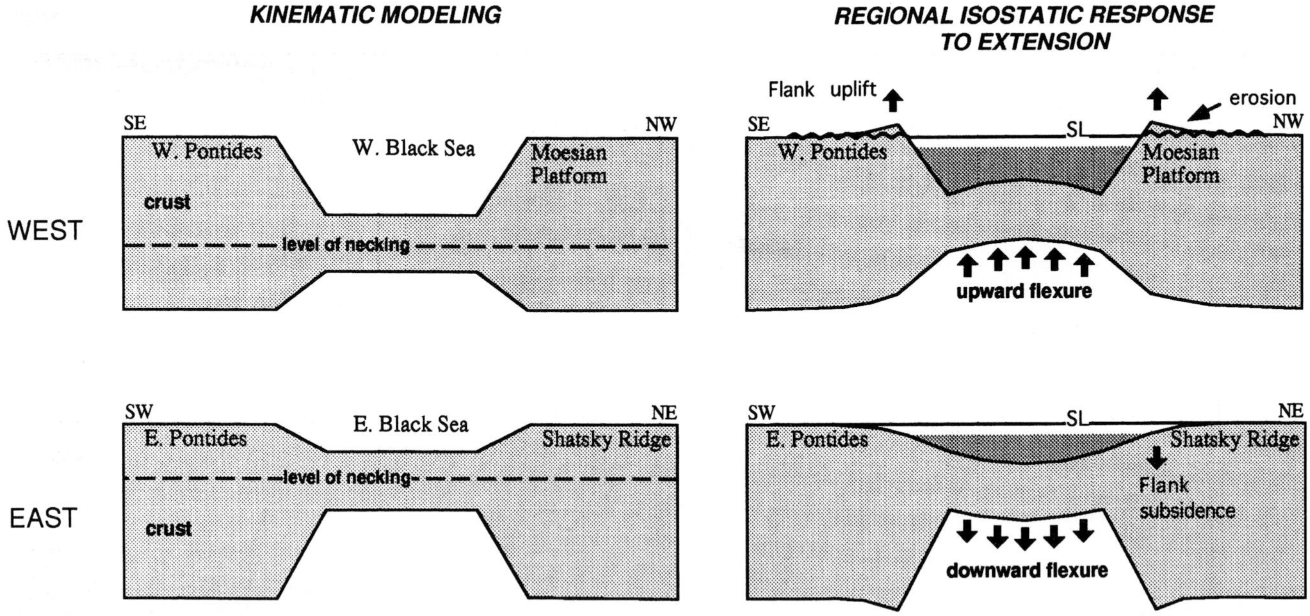

Figure 9. Diagram illustrating a scenario for the large-scale deformation of the Black Sea Basin and the surrounding regions. Our reconstruction is consistent with several observed geological features of the present-day Black Sea and explains different aspects of its tectonic evolution.

numerical modeling, it is convenient to define a simple porosity-depth function as

$$\phi(z) = \phi_0 \exp(-cz) \quad (1)$$

where z is the depth of the considered unit, ϕ_0 denotes surface porosity, and c is the characteristic depth constant (see Table 1 for adopted values). Errors in defining ϕ_0 and c lead to errors in basement subsidence predictions and, thus, in the estimate of paleowater depth values required to fit the observed stratigraphy. An error analysis by Gallagher (1989) pointed out that fluctuations of ±100 m of subsidence curves are possibly within the error range of the adopted porosity–depth relation; thus, they cannot be correctly interpreted without additional constraints. In fact, in the following paragraphs we will not address the problem of identifying and interpreting the small amplitude variations of subsidence trends and of related paleowater depths, especially for deep buried units, for which the error is statistically higher. We will describe and discuss the general trend that defines the evolution of the Western and Eastern Black Sea basins. As a matter of fact, this general trend is relatively insensitive to variations in the porosity–depth function (Watts and Steckler, 1981).

During our modeling procedure, we have assumed that eustatic sea level variations have been small relative to the large water depth changes to which the Black Sea basins have apparently been subjected. Maximum changes on the order of 200 m have been suggested by Haq et al. (1987), and the model is not particularly sensitive to these, particularly in the center of the basin. During the Sarmatian (10 Ma), however, a major sea level fall is inferred by the stratigraphy of the wells of the deep sea drilling project and by major (DSDP) erosive unconformities around the basin margins. This large sea level change has to be incorporated in our model; we now have two variables to fix in order to simulate the stratigraphy at the beginning of the Sarmatian. The water depth during the late Miocene at the basin margin has been estimated between 0 to 100 m from biostratigraphic and paleoenvironmental studies from DSDP 380 and 381 (Ross, 1978; Schrader, 1978). According to our modeling calculations, to explain both the observed thickness of the pre-Sarmatian? Oligocene–Miocene sediments and the suggested water depth of 100 m at the edge of the present bathyal plain, a sea level fall of 1500 m is required. The value, which represents an outcome of our modeling procedure, can be applied to the area; this allows us to constrain, from stratigraphic modeling, the water depth profile for the considered sections at 10 Ma.

STRATIGRAPHIC MODELING RESULTS

Figures 10 and 11 show modeled and observed stratigraphies along one profile in the Western Black Sea (Akçakoca) and one in the Eastern Black Sea (Badut). Taking into account that the paleowater depth was the only free parameter during the modeling procedure, the modeled stratigraphies have to be considered as the best fit. The match of model to observed stratigraphies is always good in the basin centers; on the margins there are some mismatches. The northern part of the modeled stratigraphy on the Akçakoca section shows a sediment package thickening northward toward the Russian Platform, while in reality the Black Sea strata thin and onlap northward.

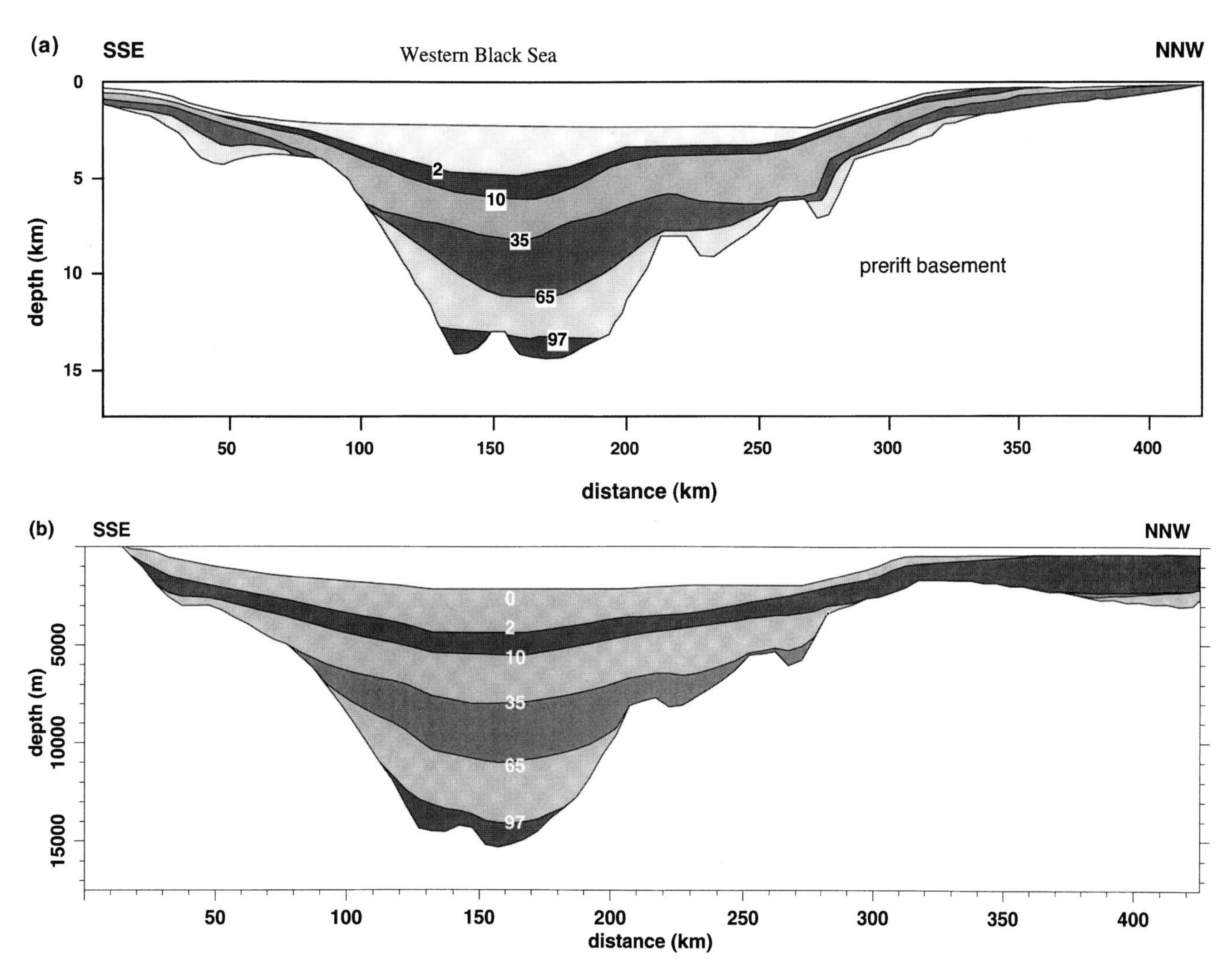

Figure 10. Observed (a) and predicted (b) stratigraphy, Western Black Sea (Akçakoca profile) (Line AA′ in Figure 1). Markers represent end-Albian (97 Ma, end of rifting), end-Cretaceous (65 Ma), end-Eocene (35 Ma), intra-Sarmatian (10 Ma, the age of major sea level fall), and end-Pliocene (2 Ma).

This is probably due to the profile running parallel to a bend in the Moho depth contours of Belousov et al. (1988); the Moho is thus flat along the northern part of the profile, even though the regional pattern is that the Moho falls northward. We thus believe this mismatch to be an artifact of the contouring of the Moho depth. The SSE end of the Akçakoca profile (Figure 10) is located at the boundary with the contractional structures of the Western Pontides (Figure 1). Differences between the observed and predicted stratigraphy are related to compressional deformation of the margin that has not been taken into account in our model. The modeled Badut profile in the Eastern Black Sea (Figure 11) shows an excellent fit with the observed stratigraphy. We have no information on the geometry of the sequence boundaries in the Sinop Trough, the SSW end of the profile. For that area we predict a stratigraphy characterized by synrift deposition (end of rifting at 52 Ma) and by the presence of an erosional unconformity in the Early Sarmatian (10 Ma) as a consequence of the sea level fall.

The model reproduces several notable features of the stratigraphy of the Black Sea: the apparent near absence of synrift strata (other than in the Western Pontides); a thick upper Eocene; a relatively thin Oligocene to Miocene and a very thick Quaternary.

The modeled stratigraphies of Figures 10 and 11 have been fitted to the observations by varying paleowater depth histories. These are calculated assuming no sea level variation until the 1500 m fall during the Sarmatian, with a subsequent return to present-day sea level. Figures 12 and 13 show the basement subsidence, the water-loaded tectonic subsidence, and the paleowater depth profiles that provide the best fits of modeled to observed stratigraphy for points on the margins and in the centers of the Western and Eastern Black Sea basins. The figures show a number of significant features predicted by the modeling:

1. There is rapid basement subsidence during rifting to abyssal depths in the centers of both basins. At the end of rifting, the Western Black Sea was

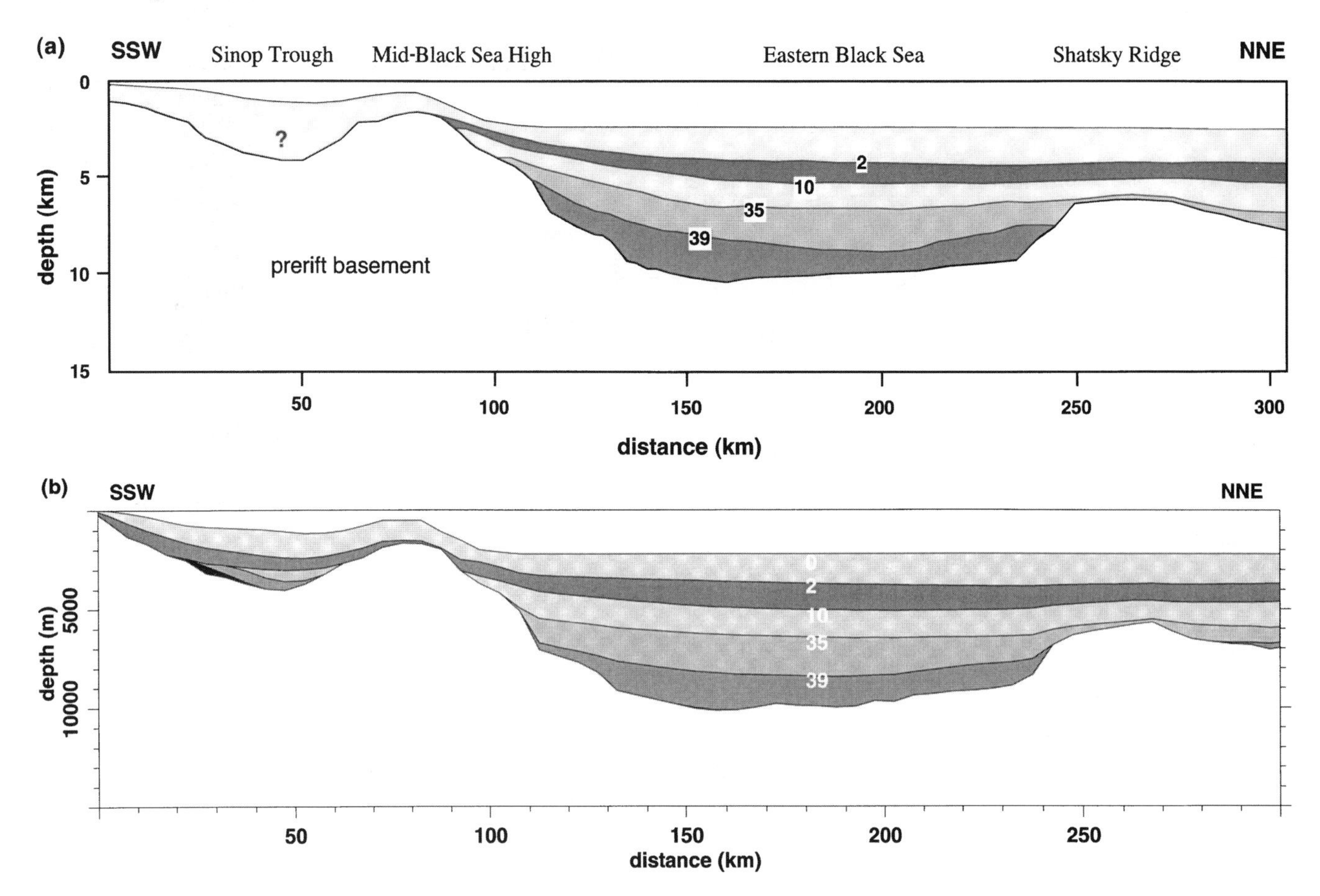

Figure 11. Observed (a) and predicted (b) stratigraphy, Eastern Black Sea (Badut Profile) (Line CC′ in Figure 1). Markers represent end-Early Eocene (52 Ma, end of rifting), end-Middle Eocene (39 Ma), end-Eocene (35 Ma), intra-Sarmatian (10 Ma, the age of major sea level fall), and end-Pliocene (2 Ma).

~5000 m deep, and the Eastern Black Sea 4000 m deep. Such rapid subsidence and great water depths would have favored starvation of the basin. This deduction is therefore consistent with the rather limited development of synrift sediments in both basins other than close to the southern margin of the Western Black Sea in the Western Pontides.

2. After rifting was completed, the water depth generally decreased in the depocenters but increased at the basin margins (Figures 12, 13). This suggests that most sediment was bypassing the basin margins, leading to high sedimentation rates in the basin centers, which were able to compensate for the postrift thermal subsidence. The most dramatic example of this effect is observed in the thick upper Eocene of the Eastern Black Sea. This must reflect an increase in sediment supply sufficient to compensate for the thermal subsidence and to begin to fill up the basin toward sea level. This comes from the analysis of predicted subsidence curves for the Eastern Black Sea (Figure 13). The basement subsidence shows a sharp acceleration between 39 Ma and 35 Ma. On the contrary, the predicted tectonic subsidence does not accelerate, indicating that the feature is related to sediment loading (i.e., increased sedimentation rate). A decrease in water depth from 3600 to 2800 m is implied during the late Eocene. The late Eocene is, in fact, the age of the onset of compressional deformation in the Greater Caucasus; in the Pontides it was a time of major compression and, in the east, volcanic arc development.
3. During the late Miocene, replacing the 1500 m of water that was removed at the beginning of the Sarmatian has the effect of increasing the water-loaded tectonic subsidence and thus basement subsidence (Figures 12, 13). As a result, water depth increases dramatically during the late Miocene and Pliocene to around 2.8 km in the west and to 2.4 km in the east at the beginning of the Quaternary.
4. By the Quaternary, the effect of the replaced water on tectonic subsidence had ceased. Nonetheless, continued basement subsidence is required to accommodate the large thickness of Quaternary sediment. This must be due to an increase in sediment supply and associated loading. Again, a comparison between basement subsidence and water-loaded tectonic subsidence between 2 to 0 Ma highlights the key role of the increasing sedimentation rate in controlling the subsidence rate. The extra sediment may have come into the Black

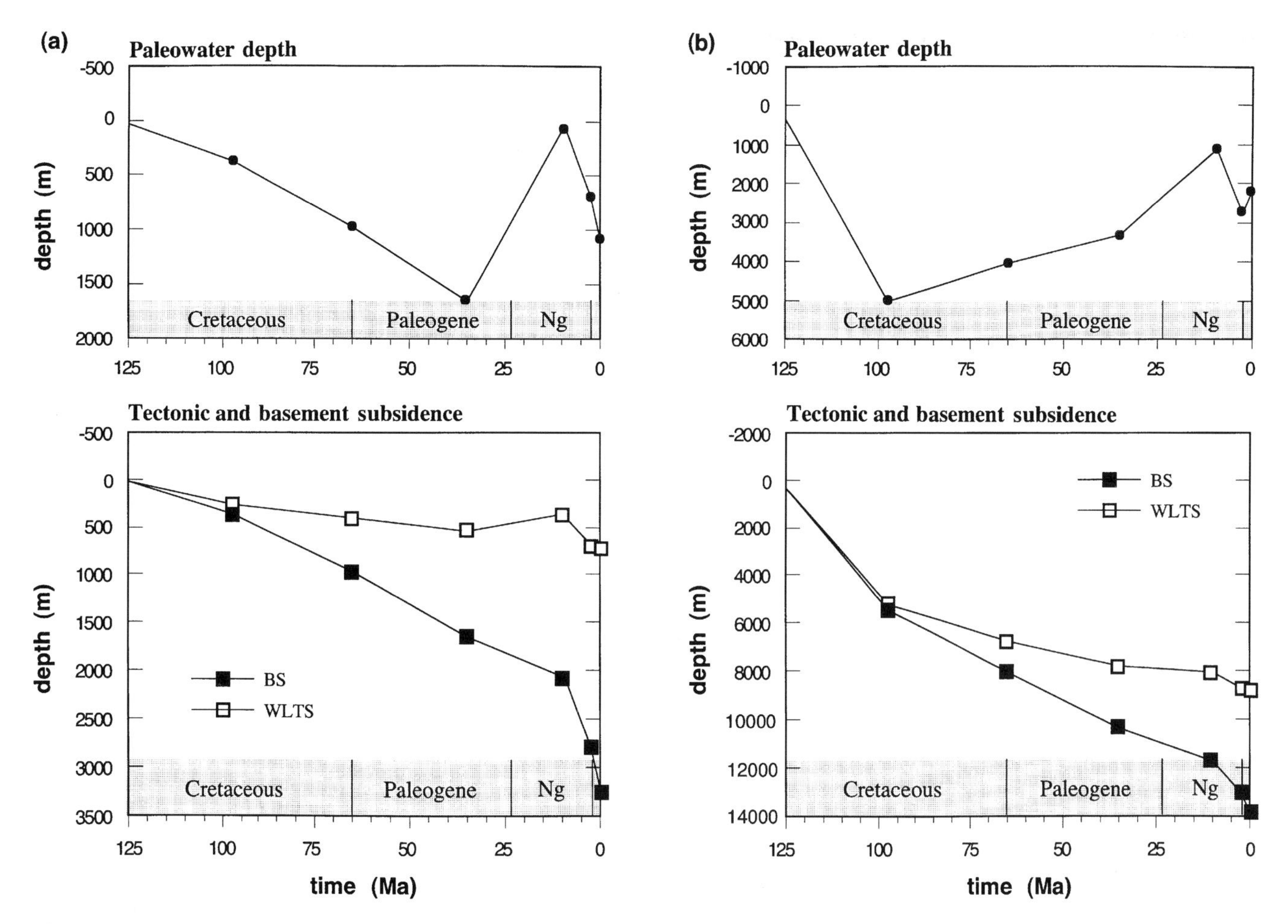

Figure 12. Representative subsidence curves for the Western Black Sea. The curves show the calculated paleowater depth histories (above) and basement subsidence (BS) and water-loaded tectonic subsidence (WLTS) for a point near (a) the basin margin and another in (b) the basin center. Note the difference in vertical scale between the basin margin and the basin center.

Sea due to glaciation of much of the catchment area in Northern Europe. An important role should have been played also by the Danube River, which started to contribute to the Black Sea Basin fill with a large amount of sediment, starting from the late Pleistocene (Wong et al., 1994). The load required actually implies a minor decrease in water depth in the basin center from the end of the Pliocene to today's 2200 m.

DISCUSSION AND CONCLUSIONS

Large-scale modeling of lithospheric and crustal thinning of the Black Sea area has shown that the opening of the Black Sea basins and the crustal thinning of the area can be simulated by pure-shear deformation, taking into account a finite duration of rifting and nonzero lithospheric strength during the rifting and postrift periods (Kooi et al., 1992). The main results of the modeling are that the Western and Eastern Black Sea were initiated on lithosphere with very different thicknesses, geothermal gradients, and associated mechanical properties. The Western Black Sea formed by rifting of thick (~200 km) and therefore cold lithosphere with high mechanical strength and an associated deep depth of necking (~25 km). In contrast, the Eastern Black Sea developed by rifting of thin (~80 km) and therefore hot and weak lithosphere, with a shallower depth of necking (~15 km). The differences in initial lithospheric conditions (Cloetingh et al., 1995) between east and west explain differences in total subsidence and the absence of rift flank uplift in the east.

The existence of two very different types of lithosphere in the Black Sea region prior to rifting is supported by paleogeographic reconstructions. The Western Black Sea developed on the stable continental Moesian Platform in a setting generally considered to be "back-arc" but without any contemporaneous volcanics. The lithosphere in this case would be expected to be both thick and cold. In contrast, the Eastern Black Sea developed on a preexisting back-arc basin, north of an Upper Cretaceous (and a later, Eocene) volcanic arc. The lithosphere in this case would be expected to be both thin and warm.

One of the features predicted for a rift initiated on thick, cold, and therefore strong lithosphere (such as the Western Black Sea) is a substantial associated flank

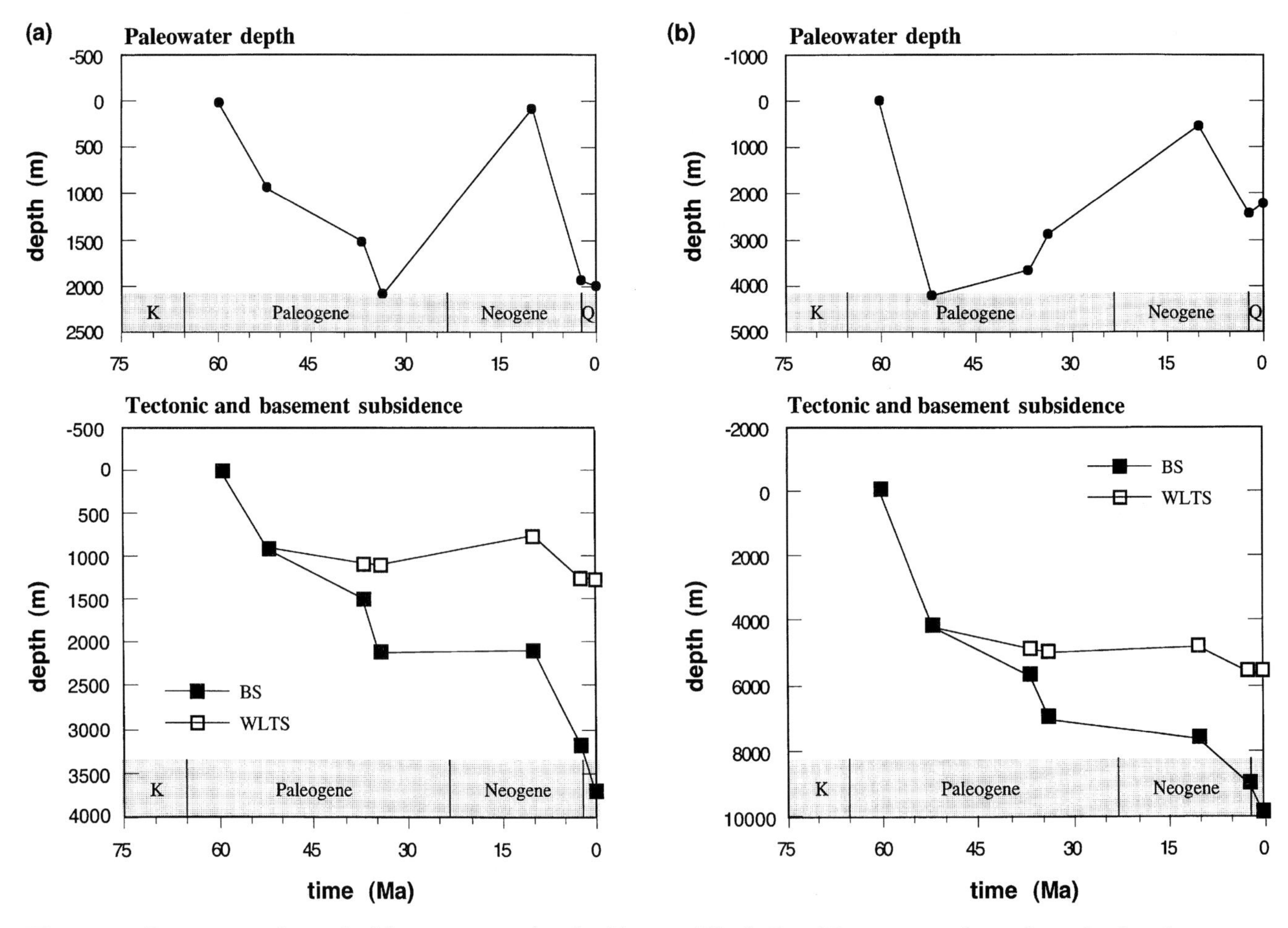

Figure 13. Representative subsidence curves for the Eastern Black Sea. The curves show the calculated paleowater depth histories (above) and basement subsidence (BS) and water-loaded tectonic subsidence (WLTS) for a point near (a) the basin margin and another in (b) the basin center. Note the difference in vertical scale between the basin margin and the basin center.

uplift, a result primarily of the high flexural rigidity of the plate (Figure 9). This tends to produce major rift flank erosion. Such erosion is in fact observed in the Western Pontides where the latest prerift strata—Upper Jurassic–Neocomian limestones—were eroded, karstified, and in places completely removed prior to the Aptian. In contrast, the flanks of rifts initiated on hot, warm, and therefore weak crust (such as the Eastern Black Sea) tend to subside. Seismic lines across the Shatsky Ridge—the northern rift flank of the Eastern Black Sea—show no evidence for synrift erosion (Robinson et al., 1995a).

Basins developed on thick lithosphere involving a larger depth of necking tend to undergo more total subsidence. This provides an explanation for why the Western Black Sea has a thicker sedimentary fill than the Eastern Black Sea. Marginal rift basins developed on a thick lithosphere appear also to generally rift over longer periods than basins developed on thin lithosphere (Cloetingh et al., 1995). Ultimately, the integrated strength of the lithosphere seems to have an important role in controlling the duration of rifting. The strong Western Black Sea lithosphere (Figure 8) apparently rifted for about 30 m.y., while rifting and spreading in the Eastern Black Sea, characterized by a much weaker lithosphere (Figure 8), were completed within 8 m.y.

Figures 14 and 15 summarize the development of the Western and Eastern Black Sea, predicted by the stratigraphic modeling, from the end of rifting to the present day. The Western Black Sea began rifting in the Late Barremian, and by the Cenomanian was a deep (~5000 m) marine basin with oceanic crust and limited synrift sediments toward the basin center. Although water depth decreased somewhat through the Late Cretaceous, Paleocene, and early Neogene, the deep basin persisted until the Sarmatian sea level fall, which reduced the basin to a relatively small lake ~800 m deep in the center. The Eastern Black Sea began rifting in the late Paleocene and subsided rapidly with little rift flank uplift or erosion to form a deep (~4000 m) marine basin. A draping horizon is visible on seismic overparts of the rift margins (e.g., Andrusov Ridge) and may be interpreted as pelagic. During the late Eocene, an increase in sediment supply from compressional belts to the Pontides or possibly the Greater Caucasus led to the deposition of a thick upper Eocene sequence (including oil-prone source rocks) and a consequent decrease in water depth from 3600 to 2800 m. Like its western counterpart, the Eastern

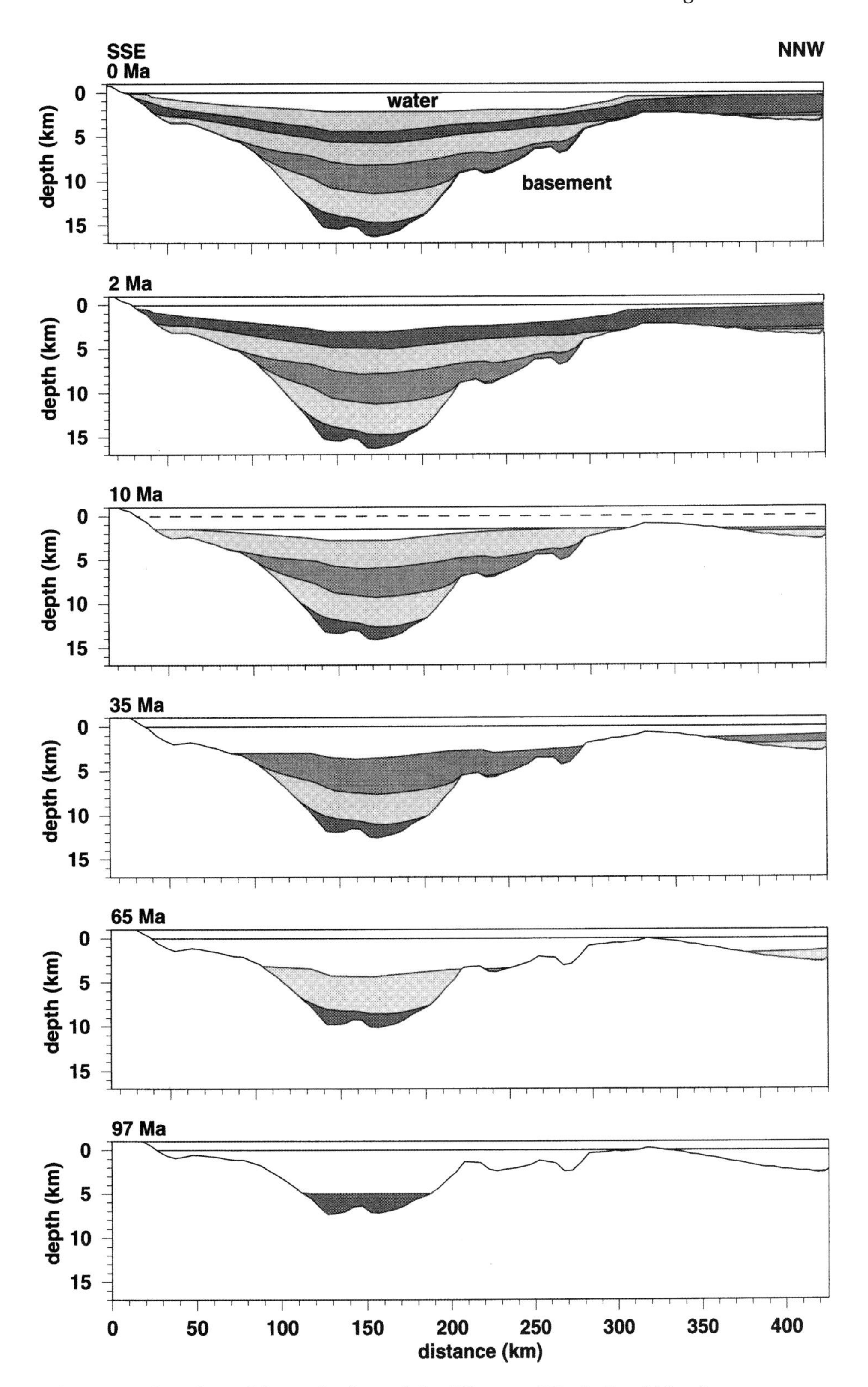

Figure 14. Stratigraphic evolution of the Western Black Sea (Akçakoca profile). The backstripped section (Line AA' in Figure 1) obtained from our forward model shows the prerift basement, water depth, and thickness of each unit (same codes as in Figure 5) during the evolution of the basin. Note that the different units undergo compaction mainly during the early stage of their burial. At 10 Ma we predict a sea level drop of 1500 m compared to today's sea level (dashed line).

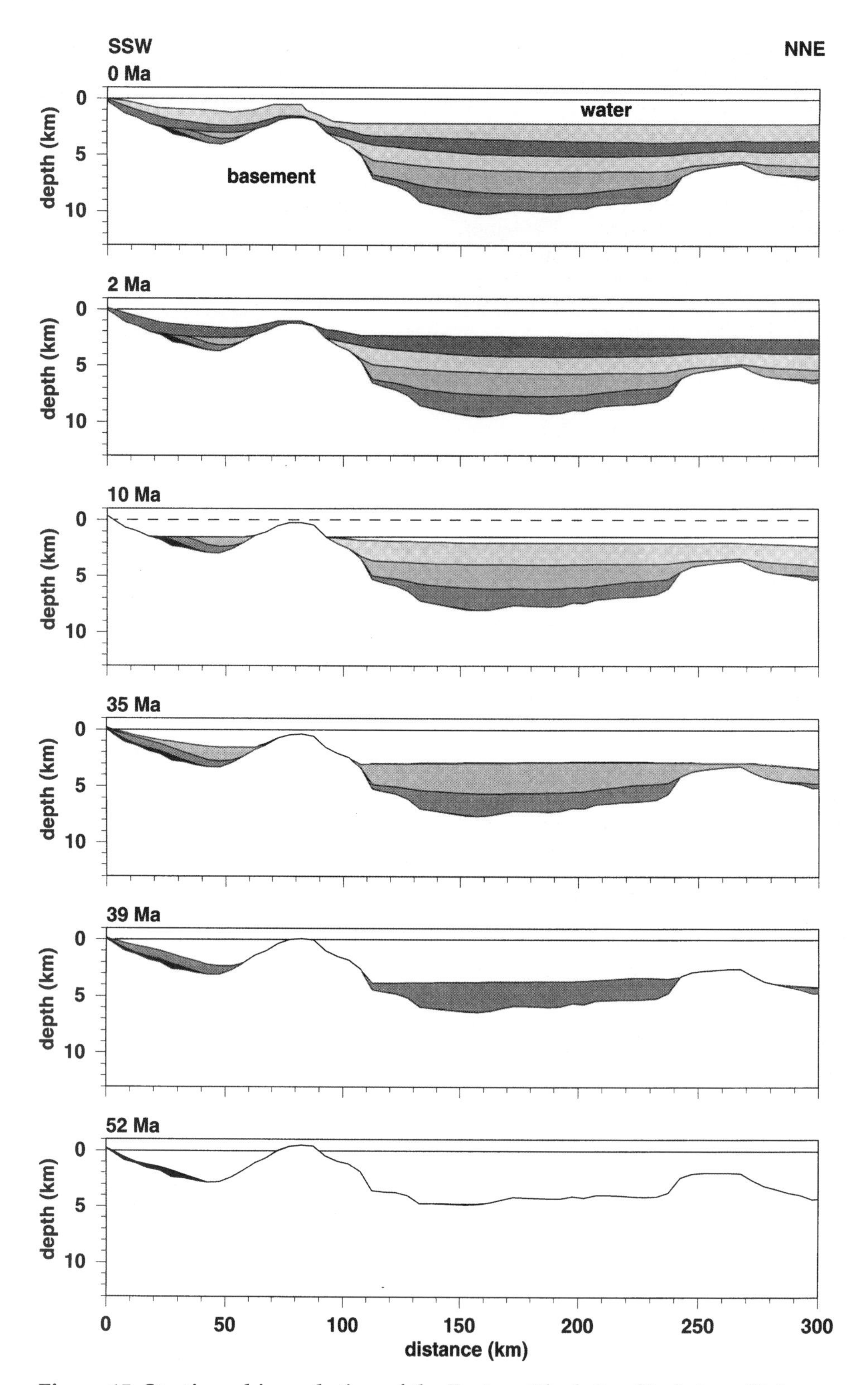

Figure 15. Stratigraphic evolution of the Eastern Black Sea (Badut profile). The backstripped section (Line CC′ in Figure 1) obtained from our forward model shows the prerift basement, water depth, and thickness of each unit (same codes as in Figure 5) during the evolution of the basin. Note that the different units undergo compaction mainly during the early stage of their burial. At 10 Ma we predict a sea level drop of 1500 m compared to today's sea level (dashed line).

Black Sea remained a deep basin until the Sarmatian so that all upper Eocene to middle Miocene sediments will be of deep-water origin. The Eastern Black Sea was also converted into a lake during the Sarmatian, ≤400 m deep on the Badut profile. As sea level returned to normal in the late Miocene, water depth increased dramatically to 2800 m in both eastern and western basins due to the loading effect of the water. During the Quaternary, increased sediment supply led to significant subsidence and sediment accumulation, but the water depth decreased only slightly to the present-day value of 2200 m.

ACKNOWLEDGMENTS

This research was funded through the IBS (Integrated Basin Studies) Project of the European Community (Contract JOU2-CT92-0110). We acknowledge A. Tankard for suggestions and comments on the manuscript.

REFERENCES CITED

Artyushkov, E.V., 1992, Role of crustal stretching on subsidence of the continental crust: Tectonophysics, v. 215, p. 187–207.

Banda, E., and S. Cloetingh, 1992, Physical properties of the lithosphere, *in* D. Blundell, R. Freeman, and S. Mueller, eds., The European Geotraverse, a continent revealed: Cambridge University Press, p. 71–80.

Bassi, G., 1991, Factors controlling the style of continental rifting: insights from numerical modeling: Earth and Planetary Science Letters, v. 105, p. 430–452.

Bassi, G., 1995, Relative importance of strainrate and rheology for the mode of continental extension: Geophysical Journal, v. 122, p. 195–210.

Bassi, G., C.E. Keen, and P. Potter, 1993, Contrasting styles of rifting: models and examples from the Eastern Canadian Margin: Tectonics, v. 12, p. 639–655.

Belousov, V.V., et al., 1988, Structure and evolution of the Earth's crust and upper mantle of the Black Sea: Bollettino di Geofisica Teorica e Applicata, v. 30, no. 117–118, p. 109–196.

Braun, J., and C. Beaumont, 1989, A physical explanation of the relation between flank uplifts and the breakup unconformity at rifted continental margins: Geology, v. 17, p. 760–764.

Buck, W.R., 1991, Modes of continental lithospheric extension: Journal of Geophysical Research, v. 96, p. 20,161–20,178.

Carter, N.L., and M. Tsenn, 1987, Flow properties of continental lithosphere: Tectonophysics, v. 136, p. 27–63.

Cloetingh, S., J.D. van Wees, P.A. van der Beek, and G. Spadini, 1995, Role of prerift rheology in kinematics of extensional basin formation: constraints from thermomechanical models of Mediterranean and intracratonic basins: Marine and Petroleum Geology, v. 12, p. 793–807.

Dunbar, J.A., and D.S. Sawyer, 1989, How pre-existing weaknesses control the style of continental breakup: Journal of Geophysical Research, v. 94, p. 7278–7292.

Finetti, I., G. Bricchi, A. Del Ben, M. Pipan, and Z. Xuan, 1988, Geophysical study of the Black Sea area: Bollettino di Geofisica Teorica e Applicata, v. 30, no. 117–118, p. 197–324.

Gallagher, K., 1989, An examination of some uncertainties associated with estimates of sedimentation rates and tectonic subsidence: Basin Research, v. 2, p. 97–114.

Golmshtok, A.Y., L.P. Zonenshain, A.A. Terekhov, and R.V. Shainurov, 1992, Age, thermal evolution and history of the Black Sea Basin based on heat flow and multichannel reflection data: Tectonophysics, v. 210, p. 273–293.

Görür, N., 1988, Timing of opening of the Black Sea basin: Tectonophysics, v. 147, p. 247–262.

Görür, N., O. Tüysüz, A. Aykol, M. Sakinç, E. Yiğitbaş, and R. Akkök, 1993, Cretaceous red pelagic carbonates of northern Turkey: their place in the opening history of the Black Sea: Eclogae Geologicae Helvetiae, v. 86/3, p. 819–838.

Guterch, A., M. Grad, R. Materzok, and E. Perchuc, 1986, Deep structure of the Earth's crust in the contact zone of the Palaeozoic and Precambrian platforms in Poland (Tornquist-Teisseire Zone): Tectonophysics, v. 128, p. 251–279.

Haq, B.U., J. Hardenbol, and P.R. Vail, 1987, Chronology of fluctuating sea levels since the Triassic: Science, v. 235, p. 1156–1167.

Keen, C.E., and C. Beaumont, 1990, Geodynamics of rifted continental margins, Chapter 9, *in* M.J. Keen and G.L. Williams, eds., Geology of continental margins of Eastern Canada: geological survey of Canada: Geology of Canada, v. 2, p. 391–472.

Kooi, H., 1991, Tectonic modeling of extensional basins: the role of lithospheric flexure, intraplate stress and relative sea-level change: Ph.D. thesis, Vrije Universiteit, Amsterdam, 183 p.

Kooi, H., S. Cloetingh, and J. Burrus, 1992, Lithospheric necking and regional isostasy at extensional basins. 1. Subsidence and gravity modeling with an application to the Gulf of Lions margins (SE France): Journal of Geophysical Research, v. 97, p. 17, 553–17,571.

Kusznir, N.J, and R.G. Park, 1987, The extensional strength of the continental lithosphere: its dependence on geothermal gradient, and crustal composition and thickness, *in* M.P. Coward, J.F. Dewey, and P.L. Hancock, eds., Continental extensional tectonics: Geological Society Special Publication 28, p. 35–52.

Letouzey, J., B. Biju-Duval, A. Dorkel, R. Gonnard, K. Kristchev, L. Montadert, and O. Sungurlu, 1977, The Black Sea: a marginal basin; geophysical and geological data, *in* B. Biju-Duval and L. Montadert, eds., International symposium on the structural history of the Mediterranean basins: Paris, Editions Technip, p. 363–376.

Manetti, P., M. Boccaletti, and A. Peccerillo, 1988, The Black Sea: remnant of a marginal basin behind the Srednegorie–Pontides island arc system during the Upper Cretaceous–Eocene times: Bollettino di Geofisica Teorica e Applicata, v. 30, no. 117–118, p. 39–51.

McKenzie, D.P., 1978, Some remarks on the development of sedimentary basins: Earth and Planetary Science Letters, v. 40, p. 25–32.

Neprochnov, Y.P., A.F. Neprochnova, and Y.G. Mirlin, 1974, Deep structure of the Black Sea Basin, *in* D.A. Ross and E.T. Egens, eds., The Black Sea—geology, chemistry and biology: AAPG Memoir 20, p. 35–49.

Okay, A.I., A.M.C. Şengör, and N. Görür, 1994, Kinematic history of the opening of the Black Sea and its effect on the surrounding regions: Geology, v. 22, p. 267–270.

Robinson, A.G., J.H. Rudat, C.J. Banks, and R.L.F. Wiles, 1995a, Petroleum geology of the Black Sea: Marine and Petroleum Geology, v. 13, p. 195–223.

Robinson, A., G. Spadini, S. Cloetingh, and J. Rudat, 1995b, Stratigraphic evolution of the Black Sea: inferences from basin modelling: Marine and Petroleum Geology, v. 12, no. 8, p. 821–835.

Ross, D.A., E. Uchupi, K.E. Prada, and J.C. MacIlvaine, 1974, Bathymetry and microtopography of Black Sea, *in* D.A. Ross and E.T. Egens, eds., The Black Sea—geology, chemistry, and biology: AAPG Memoir 20, p. 1–10.

Ross, D.A., 1978, Summary of results of Black Sea drilling: Initial Reports DSDP XLII, Part 2, p. 1149–1177.

Rudat, J.H., and D.S. MacGregor, 1993, Unconventional exploration techniques in a high cost deep water basin: a case study from the Black Sea (abs.): Society of Exploration Geophysicists.

Schrader, H.J., 1978, Quaternary through Neogene history of the Black Sea deduced from the palaeoecology of diatoms, silicoflagellates, ebridians and chrysomonads: Initial Reports DSDP XLII, Part 2, p. 789–902.

Sclater, J.G., and P.A.F. Christie, 1980, Continental stretching: an explanation of post mid-Cretaceous subsidence of the central North Sea: Journal of Geophysical Research, v. 85, p. 3711–3739.

Şengör, A.M.C., Y. Yılmaz, and I. Ketin, 1980, Remnants of a pre-Late Jurassic ocean in Northern Turkey: fragments of Permian–Triassic Palaeotethys: Geological Society of America Bulletin, v. 91, p. 599–609.

Şengör, A.M.C., Y. Yılmaz, and O. Sungurlu, 1984, Tectonics of the Mediterranean Cimmerides: nature and evolution of the western termination of Palaeotethys, *in* J.E. Dixon and A.H.F. Robertson, eds., The geological evolution of the Eastern Mediterranean: Geological Society Special Publication 17, p. 7–112.

Şengör, A.M.C., D. Altiner, A. Cin, T. Ustaömer, and K.J. Hsü, 1988, Origin and assembly of the Tethyside orogenic collage at the expense of Gondwanaland, *in* M.G. Audley-Charles and A. Hallam, eds., Gondwana and Tethys: Geological Society Special Publication 37, p. 119–181.

Spadini, G., S. Cloetingh, and G. Bertotti, 1995, Thermomechanical modeling of the Tyrrhenian Sea: lithospheric necking and kinematics of rifting: Tectonics, v. 14, p. 629–644.

Spadini, G., A. Robinson, and S. Cloetingh, 1996, Western versus Eastern Black Sea tectonic evolution: prerift lithospheric controls on basin formation: Techophysics, v. 266, p. 139–154.

Ustaömer, T., and A.H.F. Robertson, 1994, Palaeozoic marginal basin and subduction-accretion, the Palaeotethyan Küre Complex, Central Pontides, northern Turkey: Journal of Geological Society of London, v. 151, p. 291–305.

Weissel, J.K., and G.D. Karner, 1989, Flexural uplift of rift flanks due to mechanical unloading of the lithosphere during extension: Journal of Geophysical Research, v. 94, p. 13.919–13.950.

Watts, A.B., and M.S. Steckler, 1981, Subsidence and tectonics of Atlantic-type continental margins: Oceanologica Acta, v. 4 (suppl. no. SP), p. 143–153.

Watts, A.B., G.D. Karner, and M.S. Steckler, 1982, Lithospheric flexure and the evolution of sedimentary basins: Philosophical Transactions of Royal Society of London, Series A, v. 305, p. 249–281.

Wong, H.K., N. Panin, C. Dinu, P. Georgescu, and C. Rahn, 1994, Morphology and post-Chaudian (Late Pleistocene) evolution of the submarine Danube fan complex: Terra Nova, v. 6, p. 502–511.

Zonenshain, L.P., and X. LePichon, 1986, Deep basins of the Black Sea and Caspian Sea as remnants of Mesozoic back-arc basins: Tectonophysics, v. 123, p. 181–212.

Jones, R.W., and M.D. Simmons, 1997, A review of the stratigraphy of Eastern Paratethys (Oligocene–Holocene), with particular emphasis on the Black Sea, *in* A.G. Robinson, ed., Regional and petroleum geology of the Black Sea and surrounding region: AAPG Memoir 68, p. 39–52.

Chapter 4

A Review of the Stratigraphy of Eastern Paratethys (Oligocene–Holocene), With Particular Emphasis on the Black Sea

R.W. Jones
BP Exploration
Sunbury, Middlesex, United Kingdom

M.D. Simmons
University of Aberdeen
Aberdeen, United Kingdom

ABSTRACT

A synopsis of the stratigraphy of Eastern Paratethys is provided. Particular emphasis is placed on the Black Sea. An attempt is made to place the regional stratigraphy in a (global) sequence stratigraphic framework for the first time.

INTRODUCTION

The Tethyan Ocean began to close in the Eocene as a result of plate collisions along the southern margin of the Eurasian supercontinent that ultimately gave rise to the formation of the mountain chain extending from the Alps in the west to the Himalayas in the east. The initial response to these plate collisions was the formation of a suite of east-west–trending sedimentary basins extending from Austro-Hungary in the west to Central Asia in the east, collectively constituting the intracontinental Paratethyan Basin (Figure 1). Subsequent tectonic uplift (enhanced by eustatic shallowing) through the Miocene–Pliocene led to widespread marginal- to nonmarine sedimentation. Severance of connections to the world's oceans led to the evolution of largely endemic faunas and floras (in particular in Eastern Paratethys, which was more isolated than Central Paratethys). This renders stratigraphic correlation between established Mediterranean and Paratethyan stages extremely difficult.

This chapter provides a synopsis of the stratigraphy of Eastern Paratethys (Figure 1), placing particular emphasis on the Black Sea. Fuller details are given by Jones (1996) and Jones and Simmons (1996). We give an indication of the paleontology of each regional stage. For the sake of brevity and because of their stratigraphic utility, we concentrate on various groups of microfossils, although we acknowledge that macrofossils, especially mollusks, also have stratigraphic utility. We attempt to place the regional stratigraphy in a global framework by calibrating biostratigraphic and magnetostratigraphic data against Central Paratethyan and global standards, and by suggesting possible calibrations between regional sequence boundaries and flooding surfaces and the global sequence stratigraphic framework and eustatic sea-level curve of Haq et al. (1988).

In a hydrocarbon-exploration context, the calibration of the regional stratigraphy against global standards enables better understanding of basin (e.g., source rock burial and maturation) history and the development of predictive stratigraphic play models. It also provides a more readily understood context for regional terminology.

ABSOLUTE CHRONOSTRATIGRAPHY

There is no established comprehensive absolute chronostratigraphic timescale for Eastern Paratethys.

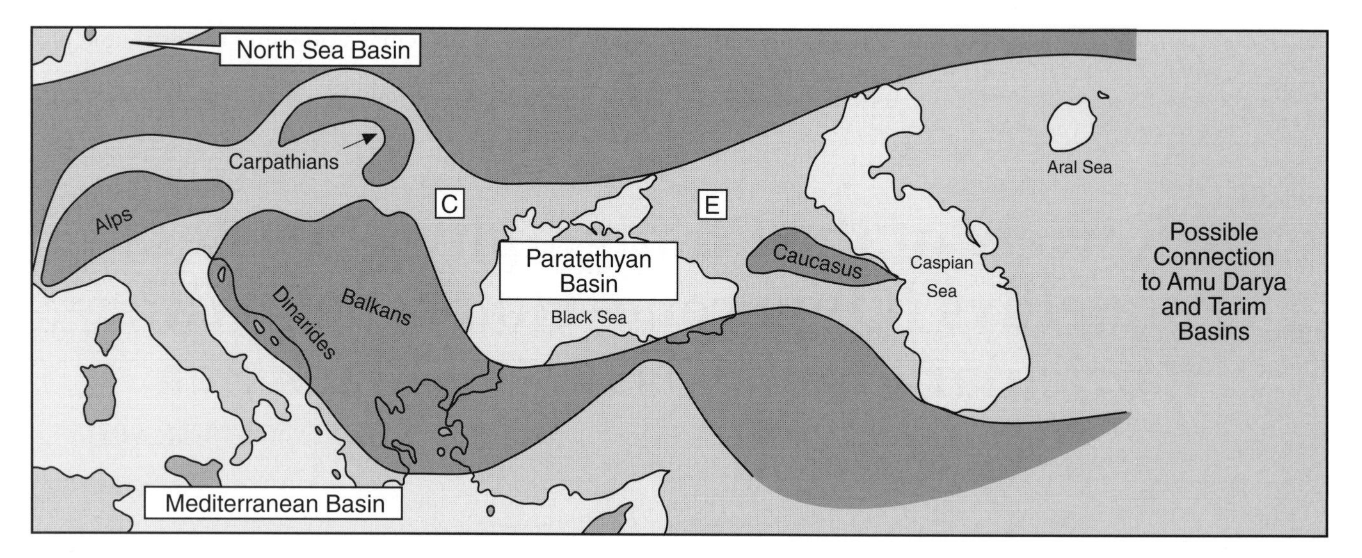

Figure 1. Geological sketch map of the Paratethyan Basin in the Oligocene. C = Central Paratethys; E = Eastern Paratethys. Eastern Paratethys can be considered as including the Pontian (Black Sea) Basin and the Caspian Basin. Throughout most of the Miocene, the eastern limit of the Paratethyan Basin was probably the Caspian Basin, but in the late Pliocene, at least, it was probably further east once more.

Thus, in Eastern Paratethys, absolute chronostratigraphic dating is often only possible by calibration of regional stratigraphic datums against global standards. We have attempted to calibrate regional datums against the Haq et al. (1988) timescale, which is the most up-to-date timescale that conveniently integrates bio-, magneto-, and sequence stratigraphic data. The confidence with which this sort of calibration can be made varies considerably with stratigraphic interval.

MICROPALEONTOLOGICAL BIOSTRATIGRAPHY AND PALEOENVIRONMENTAL INTERPRETATION

Biostratigraphy

Those groups of planktonic organisms traditionally used in the biostratigraphic zonation of the Cenozoic (planktonic foraminifera and calcareous nannoplankton) are restricted in their development in Paratethys. Only locally or periodically [as in the Maykopian, Meotian, and Kuyalnikian/Akchagylian (see "Sequence Stratigraphy" section below)] are they sufficiently well developed to enable ties to global biostratigraphic zonation schemes.

Biostratigraphic zonation in Eastern Paratethys relies largely on facies-dependent benthonic foraminifera and, especially in the marginal- to nonmarine environments of the Miocene–Pliocene, benthonic ostracods and terrestrially derived pollen and spores.

Other locally stratigraphically useful fossil groups include Problematica, siliceous microfossils, and, in nonmarine environments, vertebrate remains (*Camelopardis, Felis, Gazella, Hipparion, Hyaena, Mastodon, Mesopithecus, Rhinoceros,* etc.) and charophytes.

Paleoenvironmental Interpretation

Nonmarine Environments

Nonmarine environments are characterized by freshwater ostracods such as *Aglaiocypris, Candona, Candonella, Cyclocypris, Cypria, Eucypris, Ilyocypris, Pseudostenocypria,* and *Zonocypris,* and terrestrially derived pollen and spores. Pennate diatoms, freshwater gastropods, and terrestrial vertebrate remains may also be found.

Paleoclimate can be inferred from the distribution of vegetation types as inferred from pollen and spores. At the present, the distribution of vegetation types is determined chiefly by climatic factors [temperature (latitude, altitude) and aridity]. Thus, for instance, birches characterize the cold "forest-tundra" of the extreme north, diverse coniferous and deciduous types the "taiga" of the central area, and grasses and shrubs the arid treeless "steppe" and semidesert to the extreme south.

Quasimarine and Marine Environments

Deposition in oligo- to mesohaline [hereafter referred to as "quasimarine" (brackish, reduced salinity)] environments prevailed in the Paratethyan Basin (especially in the Caspian) throughout much of its geological evolution because of its restricted connection to the open ocean. However, water depths and sedimentary regimes may have been similar to those of the normal marine realm; moreover, deposition under normal or near-normal marine conditions did take place at times. Paleosalinity can be inferred from foraminifera, ostracods, and calcareous nannofossils ranging through to the Recent.

Quasimarine environments in the Black Sea and Caspian Sea are characterized by the benthonic foraminiferal genus *Florilus,* and some species of the genera *Ammobaculites, Ammoscalaria, Ammonia,* and

Elphidium (salinity tolerance range 1–5 ppt), and *Miliammina, Haynesina,* and *Rosalina* and some species of *Nonion s.l.* and *Quinqueloculina* (1–26 ppt); the ostracod genera *Cyprideis* (2–14 ppt), *Maetocythere* (4–14 ppt), *Loxoconcha* (5–14 ppt), *Bakunella, Caspiolla,* and *Cytherissa* (11–13/14 ppt), and *Graviacypris* (12–13 ppt), and the calcareous nannofossil genus *Emiliania* (11 ppt).

Normal or near-normal marine environments are characterized by the benthonic foraminiferal genera *Discorbis, Textularia, Bolivina, Bulimina, Brizalina, Cibicides, Gavelinopsis,* and *Trifarina,* and some species of the genera *Ammonia, Nonion s.l.,* and *Quinqueloculina* (salinity tolerance range 11–26 ppt).

CLIMATOSTRATIGRAPHY

Zubakov and Borzenkova (1990) defined a series of climatostratigraphic units called "climathems," some conceptual and some stratotypified (and with representative pollen spectra documented), which they used in the regional correlation of Eastern Paratethys (see also Zubakov, 1993). Of these, "superclimathems" (SCTs), with an average duration of 200 ka (thousand years), are the most useful. SCTs are correlated with half the 370–425 ka cycle of orbital eccentricity, and reflect changes in climate (alternating between "cryo-" and "thermo-" meric, cool and warm, respectively).

Zubakov and Borzenkova (1990) interpreted pollen spectra dominated by steppe and semidesert vegetation as of "warm" aspect (whereas, in fact, they are more characteristic of aridity than high temperature) and those dominated by forest vegetation as of "cool" aspect (whereas, they are in fact more characteristic of humidity than of low temperature). In the Caspian, they found the former to characterize regressions and the latter to characterize transgressions, and therefore correlated regressions with "warm" phases (interglacials) and transgressions with "cool" phases (glacials).

An equally strong case, and one more in keeping with *a priori* expectation from experience in other parts of the world, can be made for correlating regressions with glacials and transgressions with interglacials. One key observation in support of this case is the apparent correlation of the major transgressions not only with warm phases (Skalbdyna, 1985), but also with global transgressions (Haq et al., 1988). Pollen spectra of the "arid" aspect in glacial sediments and of the "humid" aspect in interglacial sediments are explicable in terms of, respectively, contractions and expansions of the forest belt (the former in response to permafrost development). This is also indicated by paleoclimatic reconstructions for the late Valdai Glacial and Mikulino Interglacial (Grichuk, 1984; Savina and Khotinskiy, 1984; Velichko, 1984).

MAGNETOSTRATIGRAPHY

Much magnetostratigraphic data is available from Eastern Paratethys. Theoretically, magnetostratigraphic data should enable a correlation between Eastern Paratethys and the rest of the world (which, as noted above, is difficult to do using the available biostratigraphic data). However, in practice the process is complicated by apparently inconsistent definition and usage of magnetostratigraphic units (polarity epochs). It is beyond the scope of this chapter to address this problem in any more detail (instead, we simply quote the published magnetostratigraphic (polarity epoch) ranges for the various regional stages. It is nonetheless evident that the potential exists for a refined magnetostratigraphic subdivision of critical intervals using short-lived polarity reversal "episodes" within the longer-term epochs.

OXYGEN ISOTOPE STRATIGRAPHY

Theoretically, the ages of the Pliocene-Pleistocene sediments of Eastern Paratethys are resolvable by using oxygen isotope stratigraphic techniques. However, in practice, what data there are exist in widely disseminated form and are not particularly useful.

SEQUENCE STRATIGRAPHY AND PALEOGEOGRAPHY

Introduction

No published sequence stratigraphic schemes exist for the Oligocene–Holocene of Paratethys, although relative sea level changes and associated aspects of sequence stratigraphy are discussed by Rögl and Steininger (1983), Chepalyga (1985, 1991), Demarcq (1985), Krhovsky (1985), Nevesskaya et al. (1985), Pogacsas (1985), Pogacsas and Revesz (1985), Skalbdyna (1985), Zubakov and Borzenkova (1990), Klopovotskaya (1991), Jones (1996), and Jones and Simmons (1996).

This section attempts to place the regional stratigraphy of Eastern Paratethys in a (global) sequence stratigraphic framework. It is written in the form of a geological history. Stratigraphic (bio-, climato-, magneto-, and sequence stratigraphic) data are summarized on Figures 2 and 3. Sketch paleogeographic reconstructions for selected time slices are given by Jones (1996) and Jones and Simmons (1996).

It should be noted that the calibration against the global sequence stratigraphic framework and eustatic sea level curve of Haq et al. (1988) is tentative. Figure 2 demonstrates where biostratigraphic control exists in order to constrain the calibration. In the absence of such constraint, calibration is made by matching patterns of transgression and regression within a looser stratigraphic framework.

The correlation between Eastern Paratethyan and global sequence stratigraphy and eustatic sea level appears good, with all of the global eustatic sea level trends finding their expression in Eastern Paratethys. It could be argued that this apparent correlation is entirely fortuitous. However, the stratigraphic signature of the Mid–Late Cenozoic appears remarkably consistent throughout the world, presumably because at this time it was an "ice-house" world characterized by overriding glacioeustasy (Vail et al., 1991). Indeed,

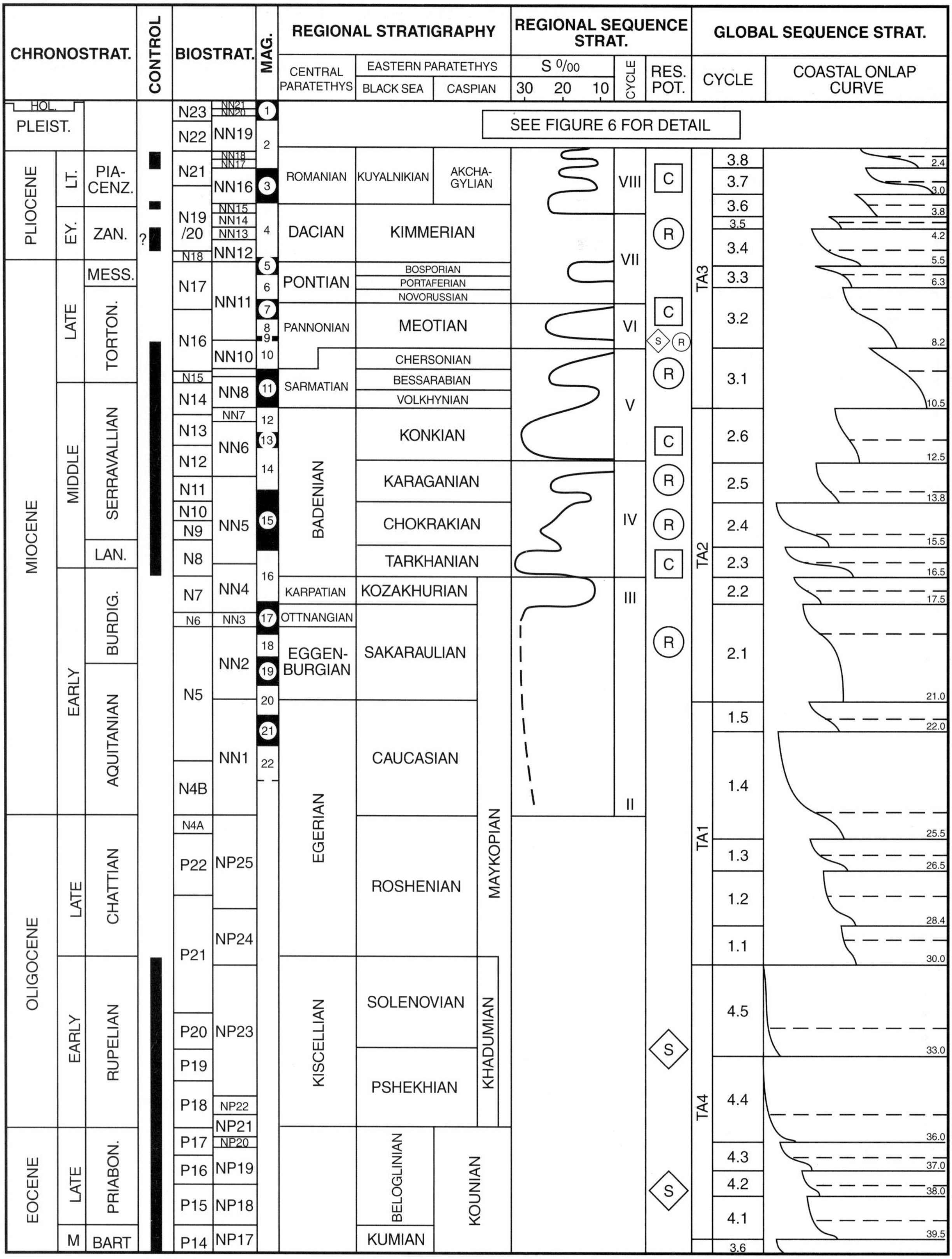

CHRONOSTRAT. | CONTROL | BIOSTRAT. | MAG. | REGIONAL STRATIGRAPHY | REGIONAL SEQUENCE STRAT. | GLOBAL SEQUENCE STRAT.

CENTRAL PARATETHYS | EASTERN PARATETHYS: BLACK SEA, CASPIAN | S 0/00: 30 20 10 | CYCLE | RES. POT. | CYCLE | COASTAL ONLAP CURVE

HOL. PLEIST. | N23 NN21 NN20 1 | N22 NN19 2 | SEE FIGURE 6 FOR DETAIL

PLIOCENE LT. PIA-CENZ. | N21 NN18 NN17 NN16 3 | ROMANIAN | KUYALNIKIAN | AKCHA-GYLIAN | VIII | C | 3.8 2.4 | 3.7 3.0 | 3.6 3.8

EY. ZAN. ? | N19 /20 NN15 NN14 NN13 4 | DACIAN | KIMMERIAN | VII | R | 3.5 4.2 | 3.4 5.5

MIOCENE LATE MESS. | N18 NN12 5 | PONTIAN | BOSPORIAN PORTAFERIAN NOVORUSSIAN | 3.3 6.3 | TA3

TORTON. | N17 NN11 6 7 | N16 8 9 NN10 10 | PANNONIAN | MEOTIAN | VI | C | S R | 3.2 8.2

CHERSONIAN | N15 N14 NN8 11 | SARMATIAN | BESSARABIAN | VOLKHYNIAN | V | R | 3.1 10.5

MIDDLE SERRAVALLIAN | NN7 12 | N13 13 | N12 NN6 14 | BADENIAN | KONKIAN | C | 2.6 12.5

N11 | KARAGANIAN | IV | R | 2.5 13.8

N10 N9 NN5 15 | CHOKRAKIAN | R | 2.4 15.5

LAN. | N8 | TARKHANIAN | C | 2.3 16.5 | TA2

EARLY BURDIG. | N7 NN4 16 | KARPATIAN | KOZAKHURIAN | III | 2.2 17.5

N6 NN3 17 | OTTNANGIAN

N5 NN2 18 19 20 | EGGEN-BURGIAN | SAKARAULIAN | R | 2.1 21.0

AQUITANIAN | NN1 21 22 | EGERIAN | CAUCASIAN | 1.5 22.0 | 1.4 | II

N4B | MAYKOPIAN | 25.5

OLIGOCENE LATE CHATTIAN | N4A | P22 NP25 | ROSHENIAN | TA1 | 1.3 26.5 | 1.2 28.4

P21 NP24 | 1.1 30.0

EARLY RUPELIAN | P20 NP23 | KISCELLIAN | SOLENOVIAN | KHADUMIAN | S | 4.5 33.0

P19 | P18 NP22 | PSHEKHIAN | TA4 | 4.4 36.0

EOCENE LATE PRIABON. | NP21 P17 NP20 | P16 NP19 | BELOGLINIAN | KOUNIAN | S | 4.3 37.0 | 4.2 38.0

P15 NP18 | 4.1 39.5

M BART | P14 NP17 | KUMIAN | 3.6

Figure 2. Stratigraphic summary (Oligocene–Holocene). Chronostratigraphy, biostratigraphy, magnetostratigraphy, global sequence stratigraphy and calibration from Haq et al. (1988). Sequence boundary ages are given as million years ago. Regional stratigraphy is from this report. Regional sequence stratigraphy is modified after Chepalyga (1985). Cycles are regressive (mega) sequences. II–III are equivalent to the "Eoparatethyan," IV to the "Mesoparatethyan," and V–VI to the "Neoparatethyan" of Nevesskaya et al. (1985). The curve shows extent of open marine connection (function of sea level) as inferred from salinity data from paleontological analyses (Sppt). Res. pot. = Resource potential, C = cap rock, R = reservoir, S = source. The correlation of Eastern Paratethyan sequence stratigraphy with the global coastal onlap curve of Haq et al. (1988) is tentative. This is indicated where biostratigraphic control constrains the correlation.

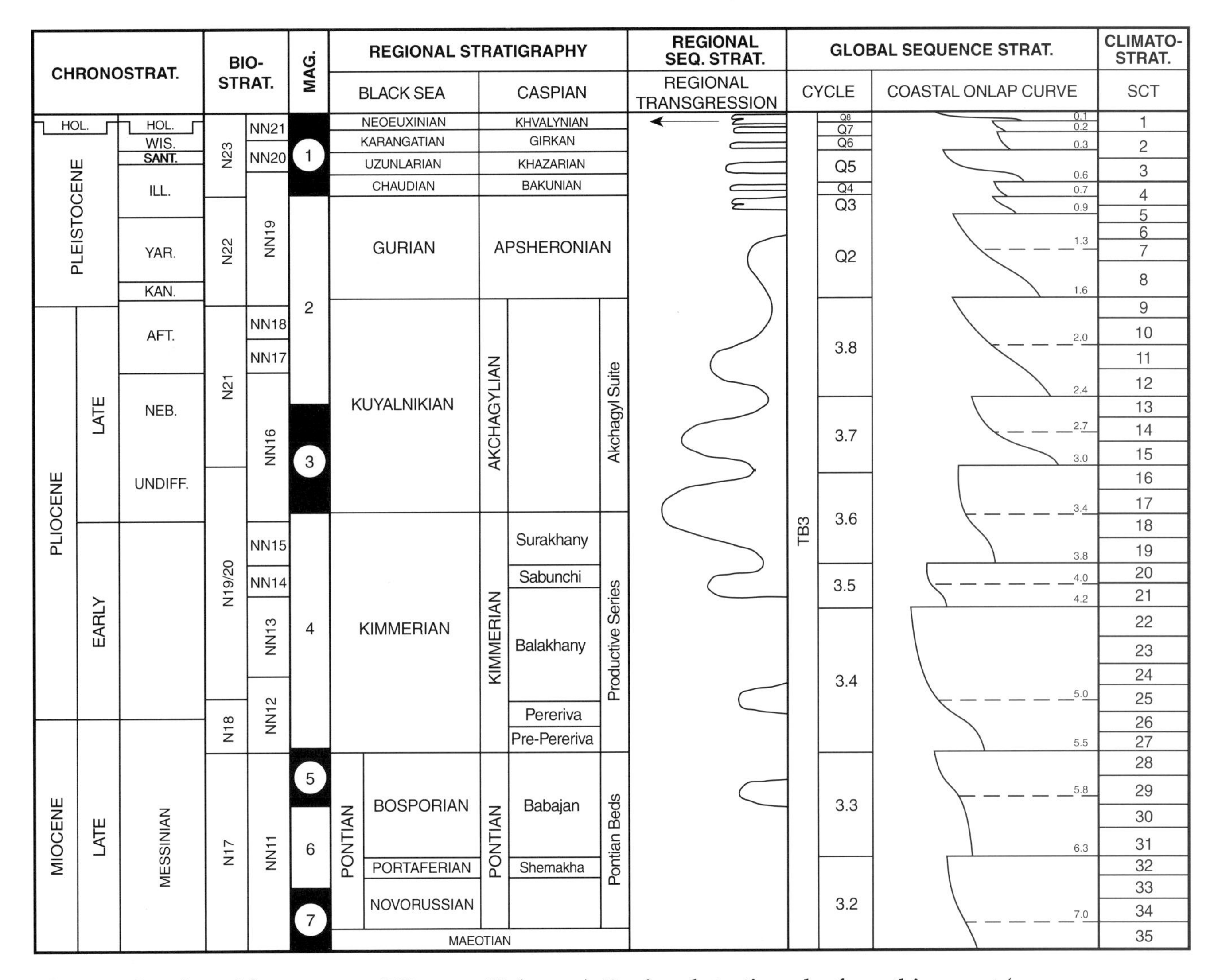

Figure 3. Stratigraphic summary (Pliocene–Holocene). Regional stratigraphy from this report (uppercase = chronostratigraphic, lowercase = lithostratigraphic units). Regional sequence stratigraphy (transgressions) after Skalbdyna (1985). Climatostratigraphy (superclimathems, or SCTs) after Zubakov and Borzenkova (1990). The correlation of Eastern Paratethyan sequence stratigraphy with the global coastal onlap curve of Haq et al. (1988) is tentative. Note that the Chaudian, Uzunlasian, Karangatian, and Neoeuxinian are represented by raised beaches respectively 100 m, 40 m, 13–25 m, and 5 m above the present level of the Black Sea (Fedorov, 1960). The extent of biostratigraphic control constraining the correlation is indicated on Figure 2.

it may be that not only third-order but also higher frequency sea level oscillations are recognizable in areas characterized by a high sedimentation rate.

Maykopian

The Maykopian takes its name from a town in the Caucasus. The term "Maykopian" refers to essentially argillaceous rocks of Oligocene–early Miocene. The Maykopian (in particular, the Khadumian) is an important regional source rock (e.g., Veto, 1987).

Details of Maykopian stratigraphy have been discussed by Muratov (1960), Krasheninnikov and Muzylev (1975), Bolli and Krasheninnikov (1977), Krasheninnikov et al. (1985), Nevesskaya and Nosovsky (1985), Krasheninnikov (1986), Krasheninnikov and Ptukhian (1986), Koshkarly and Baldi-Beke (1987), Gasanov and Kyazymov (1988), and Nagymarosy (1992). Microbiostratigraphic study of the Maykopian is hindered by massive reworking, reflecting deposition in a foreland basin in front of the emerging Caucasus. Maykopian samples can contain >90% reworked (especially Eocene) microfossils.

The Maykopian has been divided into five substages by various authors (Figure 2). In ascending stratigraphic order, these are the Khadumian, Roshenian, Caucasian, Sakaraulian, and Kozakhurian. The Khadumian is dated as early Oligocene on planktonic evidence and can therefore be calibrated against global standard biostratigraphic zonation schemes and absolute chronostratigraphic time scales. In contrast, the Roshenian is dated as late Oligocene and the Caucasian to Kozakhurian as early Miocene essentially only on benthonic evidence (Nevesskaya and

Nosovsky, 1985). The youngest substages of the Maykopian appear to be absent in the Dacian Basin in the Western Black Sea region (Steininger et al., 1987).

The Khadumian is dated as early Oligocene on planktonic (and larger benthonic) foraminiferal and calcareous nannoplankton evidence. Krasheninnikov (1986) recorded planktonic foraminifera indicative of early Oligocene (P18) from immediately below the "Ostracod Horizon" in the Kuban-Kuma Interfluve (North Caucasus). Krasheninnikov et al. (1985) recorded *Globigerina tapuriensis* (early Oligocene, P18–P20) associated with the larger benthonic foraminifer *Nummulites intermedius* (also early Oligocene) from the Khadumian of Armenia. Later, Krasheninnikov and Ptukhian (1986) recorded *Globigerina sellii* (Oligocene, P19–20 to "early" P22) associated with *Nummulites intermedius* (early Oligocene) and the calcareous nannofossil *Helicosphaera reticulata* (Eocene–early Oligocene, zones NP17–NP22) from the Khadumian of Armenia.

Tarkhanian to Konkian

These stages have collectively been correlated with the Badenian of Central Paratethys (Steininger et al., 1987). The Badenian is middle Miocene (planktonic foraminiferal zones N8–N12?; calcareous nannoplankton zones NN5–NN7). Palynologically, it is locally characterized by mangrove elements (Nagy and Kokay, 1991).

The base of the Badenian (the Moravian substage) is defined at the first appearance of the planktonic foraminifer *Praeorbulina* (zone N8). This biostratigraphic control indicates that the base of the Badenian can be correlated with the 16.5 Ma (glacioeustatic) sea level lowstand of Haq et al. (1988) (Figure 2).

The middle part of the Badenian (the Wielician substage) is characterized by marginal-marine sediments (including evaporites). This regressive substage can be tentatively calibrated against planktonic foraminiferal zones N10–N12 or calcareous nannoplankton zones NN5–NN6. The onset of regressive conditions can be tentatively correlated with the 15.5 Ma (glacioeustatic) sea level lowstand of Haq et al. (1988) (Figure 2). The regressive coarse clastics of the Chokrakian and Karaganian in Eastern Paratethys also appear to be associated with this event (although they could be associated with a separate tectonic event). These clastics constitute important reservoirs in the Indolo-Kuban and Terek Caspian foredeeps (Ulmishek and Harrison, 1981). Chepalyga (1985) calibrates the Chokrakian and Karaganian against magnetostratigraphic polarity epochs 15–12, while Zubakov and Borzenkova (1990) calibrate them against polarity epochs 16–14.

The top of the Badenian (the Kosovian substage) is defined below the last appearances of *Globorotalia mayeri/siakensis* (N14) and *Globigerina druryi* (N15). Details of Tarkhanian–Konkian stratigraphy have been discussed by Bogdanowicz (1950a, b, 1965) and Popkhadze (1983). A monograph of polymorphinid foraminifera of this age from Georgia was published by Dzhanelidze (1977).

Tarkhanian

The Tarkhanian takes its name from a promontory in the Crimea. The stratotype section yields middle Miocene (NN5) calcareous nannoplankton (F. Rögl, 1994, personal communication). Only non-age-diagnostic quasimarine, smaller benthonic, and rare planktonic foraminifera were recorded by Bogdanowicz (1950a) from the Tarkhanian of Kuban. These include *Rotalia [Ammonia]* ex gr. *beccarii* (smaller benthonic), which has a cosmopolitan distribution and probably ranges no older than middle Miocene (Jones, personal communication), and *Nonion [Florilus] boueanum* (smaller benthonic) and *Globigerina tarchanensis* (planktonic), both of which have been recorded in the Badenian of Central Paratethys.

Chokrakian

The Chokrakian takes its name from a lake in the Crimea. It is of middle Miocene based on regional evidence. Direct biostratigraphic evidence is lacking. Only non-age-diagnostic, quasimarine, smaller benthonic foraminifera were recorded by Bogdanowicz (1950b) from the Chokrakian of the western Precaucasus and later by Popkhadze (1983) for the Chokrakian of western Georgia. These include *Rotalia [Ammonia]* ex gr. *beccarii,* which has a cosmopolitan distribution and probably ranges no older than middle Miocene (Jones, personal communication), *Nonion [Florilus] boueanum,* and *Miliolina [Quinqueloculina] akneriana* sspp., both of which have also been recorded in the Badenian of Central Paratethys, and *Miliolina caucasica, Sigmoilina tschokrakensis,* and *Tschokrakella longiuscula,* all of which are endemic to Eastern Paratethys. The ostracod *Leptocythere bardrakensis* sp. nov. was recorded by Popkhadze (1984) from the Chokrakian of western Georgia.

Karaganian

The Karaganian takes its name from a locality on the Mangyshlak Peninsula in Kazakhstan. It is middle Miocene based on regional evidence. Direct biostratigraphic evidence is lacking.

Konkian

The Konkian takes its name from a river in the Ukraine (a tributary of the Dniepr). It is of middle Miocene based on regional evidence. Direct biostratigraphic evidence is lacking.

Only non-age-diagnostic, quasimarine, smaller benthonic foraminifera were recorded by Bogdanowicz (1965) from the Konkian of the western Precaucasus. These include *Rotalia [Ammonia]* ex gr. *beccarii,* which has a cosmopolitan distribution and probably ranges no older than middle Miocene, *Articulina gibbosa* and *Miliolina* [*Quinqueloculina*] *haidingerii,* both of which have also been recorded in the Badenian of Central Paratethys, and *Articulina elongata konkensis, Bulimina konkensis,* and *Elphidium nachischevanicus,* all of which are endemic to Eastern Paratethys.

Sarmatian

The Sarmatian of Eastern Paratethys is probably equivalent to the stratotypical Sarmatian of Central

Paratethys (late-middle to early-late Miocene, calcareous nannoplankton zones NN7–NN9; planktonic foraminiferal zones N13?–N15), but may also be equivalent to the lower part of the Pannonian (Slavonian) of that area (late Miocene). Chepalyga (1985) calibrates the Sarmatian of Eastern Paratethys against magnetostratigraphic polarity epochs 10–7, while Zubakov and Borzenkova (1990) calibrate it against epochs 14–9 and Pevzner and Vangengeim (1993) calibrate it against polarity epochs 10–7. The regressive events that characterize the Sarmatian suggest that (within the limits of biostratigraphic control) its base can be correlated with the 10.5 Ma (glacioeustatic) sea level lowstand of Haq et al. (1988).

The Sarmatian of Eastern Paratethys is characterized by areally restricted regressive marginal-marine sediments including coarse clastics and, in the Nakchichevan Depression, evaporites. It has been subdivided into three substages, which are, from oldest to youngest, Volkhynian, Bessarabian, and Chersonian. The "early" Bessarabian and "late" Chersonian marked the culminations of major regressive phases (Chepalyga, 1985), during which the Black Sea first became isolated from the Caspian.

Kojumdgieva (1979, 1983) has argued that the Black Sea desiccated during the "late" Chersonian regressive phase (which she regarded as associated with tectonic uplift). This resulted in the precipitation of evaporites (carbonates, as against the chlorides that would have been expected from waters of normal marine salinity) in the southwestern Black Sea. However, her argument hinges on Unit IVd (variously described as a "gravel," a "pebbly mudstone," or a "bedded dolomite") in deep sea drilling project (DSDP) Site 380 in the southwestern Black Sea being Sarmatian in age, for which there is no fossil evidence. Hsu (1978) and Hsu and Giovanoli (1979) have suggested a probable late Messinian (Pontian or Kimmerian) age (5.5 Ma) for this unit on the basis of lithological and paleontological evidence [the extinction of the *Engelhardtia* fauna (regionally late Tortonian) at the base of underlying Unit V, the disappearance of the endemic marine-brackish foraminiferal fauna (Messinian) at the base of underlying Unit IVe, and the reappearance of marine fauna (earliest Pliocene) at the base of overlying Unit IVc].

Details of the Sarmatian stratigraphy of Eastern Paratethys have been discussed by Maisuradze (1971), Paramonova et al. (1979), Shchekina (1979), Shatilova (1984), and Pevzner and Vangengeim (1993).

Micropaleontology

Only non-age-diagnostic (and largely endemic), quasimarine, smaller benthonic foraminifera and ostracods were recorded from the Sarmatian by Paramonova et al. (1979) from various sites in the Ponto-Caspian region. These include rare cosmopolitan species such as *Streblus [Ammonia] beccarii* and *Elphidium macellum* (foraminifers), which probably range no older than middle Miocene; *Elphidium reginum* (foraminifer) (lower part only), which is also found in the Sarmatian of Central Paratethys and in what is interpreted by Hsu (1978) as the Pliocene of the Black Sea (Gheorghian, 1978); *Nonion* diverse species, *Porosononion* diverse species and *Quinqueloculina consobrina* (foraminifers); and *Cyprideis littoralis, Cythere multistriata, Leptocythere stabilis, Loxoconcha eichwaldi,* and *Xestoleberis lutrae* (ostracods).

Palynology

Pollen spectra from the Sarmatian of the Ukraine are characterized by arid elements (Shchekina, 1979).

Meotian

The Meotian of Eastern Paratethys is equivalent to the Pannonian (late Miocene) of Central Paratethys, [although possibly only the upper part (Serbian)]. Rögl (1985) calibrates it against calcareous nannoplankton zone NN10. Chepalyga (1985) calibrates it against magnetostratigraphic polarity epochs 6–5, while Zubakov and Borzenkova (1990) calibrate it against polarity epochs 10–7. Krakhmalnaya et al. (1993) described a succession at Novaya Emetovka on the Black Sea coast with a good Meotian mammal fauna, which they calibrate against polarity epochs 6 and 5. The Meotian is represented by a transgressive-regressive cycle. The Meotian Sea was probably characterized by reduced salinity. Similar environmental conditions were evidently obtained in the Pannonian of Central Paratethys, where benthonic foraminiferal assemblages are of quasimarine (brackish water) aspect.

Details of Meotian stratigraphy have been discussed by Bogdanowicz (1967, 1969, 1974), Popkhadze (1977), Paramonova et al. (1979), Shatilova (1984), Ananova et al. (1985), Maisuradze (1988), and Naidina (1988).

Micropaleontology and Nannopaleontology

Only non-age-diagnostic, quasimarine, smaller benthonic foraminifera were recorded by Bogdanowicz (1967, 1969) from the Meotian of the Kuban and Western Precaucasus and by Paramonova et al. (1979) from the Meotian of various sites in the Ponto-Caspian. These include *Elphidium macellum*, which has a cosmopolitan distribution and probably ranges no older than middle Miocene, and *Nonion* diverse species.

Some stratigraphically and/or paleoenvironmentally significant ostracods were recorded by Popkhadze et al. (1980) from Abkhazia. These include *Leptocythere biplicata, L. meotica, Loxoconcha meotica, L. tamarindus,* and *L. viridis* (quasimarine).

A range of diatoms, calcareous nannofossils, and ostracods were recorded by Ananova et al. (1985) from the Meotian of the Black Sea. These include *Actinocyclus ehrenbergi, Rhaponeis maeotica,* and *Thalassiosira maeotica* (diatoms), *Braarudosphaera* spp. (calcareous nannofossil), and *Cyprideis torosa* and *Leptocythere* spp. (ostracods).

Palynology

Only non-age-diagnostic palynomorphs have been recorded from the Meotian. The acritarch *Micrhystridium* sp. was recorded by Ananova et al. (1985) from the Meotian of the Black Sea. Pollen spectra from the Late Meotian of the Task-Sunzhenskii region are characterized by relatively high incidences of *Asteraceae* and

Polygonaceae (herbs), *Ephedra* (shrubs) and *Gramineae* (grasses) (Naidina, 1988). This indicates an open, sparsely forested hinterland and an arid climatic regime similar to that of the present-day steppe or semidesert. The locally relatively high incidences of *Gleicheniaceae* (ferns) and *Lycopodiaceae* (club mosses) indicate local development of conditions similar to those of the present-day tundra, forest-tundra, or mountain belt. The presence of *Chenopodiaceae* probably indicates local development of salt marshes.

Pontian

The Pontian takes its name from the ancient name for the Black Sea. It is essentially regressive and is characterized regionally by marginal-marine coarse clastics and shallow-marine carbonates, and locally (Babajan Formation, Bosporian substage) by evaporites. The evaporites associated with the desiccation of the Black Sea (Unit IVd at DSDP Site 380 in the southwestern Black Sea) are arguably at least in part Pontian. Chepalyga (1985) calibrates the Pontian against magnetostratigraphic polarity epoch 4 (Gilbert), while Zubakov and Borzenkova (1990) calibrate it against polarity epochs 6–5. We correlate the Pontian evaporites against those of the stratotypical Messinian, which can be calibrated against magnetostratigraphic polarity epoch 5 (Zubakov and Borzenkova, 1990).

Details of the Pontian stratigraphy of Eastern Paratethys have been discussed by, among others, Sveier (1949), Ramishvili (1969), Chelidze (1973), Karmishina (1975), Vekua (1975), Krstic (1976), Shchekina (1979), Imnadze and Karmishina (1980), Shatilova (1984), Sirenko and Turlo (1986), and Yagmurlu and Helvacì (1994).

Micropaleontology

Only the non-age-diagnostic, quasimarine, smaller benthonic foraminifer *Elphidium stellatum* was recorded by Imnadze and Karmishina (1980) from the Late Pontian (Bosporian substage) of the Black Sea.

Stratigraphically and/or paleoenvironmentally significant ostracods recorded by Karmishina (1975) from the Northern Precaspian and Southeastern Kalmyk (Northern Caspian) and Prechernomore (northern Black Sea), and by Vekua (1975) from Abkhazia (northeastern Black Sea), include *Bakunella dorsoacuata, Caspiolla acronasuta, Pontoniella acuminata,* and *P. loczyi. Bakunella dorsoacuata* and *Caspiolla acronasuta* are quasimarine species. Species of *Leptocythere, Loxoconcha,* and *Xestolebris* also occur.

Palynology

Only non-age-diagnostic palynomorphs have been recorded from the Pontian. Pollen spectra from the Pontian of Georgia are characterized by relatively high incidences of tropical elements such as *Nypa* (palm) (Ramishvili, 1969). Those from the Late Pontian (Bosporian substage) of the Ukraine are characterized initially by thermophilic (warm-temperate) and hydrophilic (moisture-loving) elements such as *Taxodiaceae* (cypresses and swamp cypresses), and later by arid steppe and semidesert elements (Shchekina, 1979; Sirenko and Turlo, 1986).

Kimmerian

The Kimmerian takes its name from an ancient tribe that lived on the shores of the Black Sea. The Dacian (a stage name sometimes used in the Black Sea region) appears synonymous. Semenenko (1979), Pevzner and Vangengeim (1985), Skalbdyna (1985), and Zubakov and Borzenkova (1990) calibrate the Kimmerian against magnetostratigraphic polarity epochs 5–4, while Chepalyga (1985) and Chepalyga et al. (1985) calibrate it against polarity epoch 4 (Gilbert). Essentially on the basis of magnetostratigraphic evidence, we have tentatively calibrated the major unconformity at the base of the Kimmerian against the 5.5 Ma glacioeustatic sea level lowstand of Haq et al. (1988) and apparently coincident uplift (leading to the severance of the connection between the Black Sea and the Caspian).

The Kimmerian was a major regressive phase characterized by the widespread deposition of coarse clastics. The evaporites associated with the desiccation of the Black Sea (Unit IVd at DSDP Site 380 in the southwestern Black Sea) are arguably at least in part Kimmerian. These are essentially dolomites and other carbonates precipitated from waters of reduced salinity. According to Hsu (1978), the overlying quasimarine aragonitic muds (Unit IVc) and alternations of lacustrine chalks or "Seekreide" (units IVb and III) and sideritic muds (Unit IVa) are of undifferentiated Pliocene (i.e., Kimmerian–Kuyalnikian) age, although it should be noted that similar cyclic sedimentation persisted into the Pleistocene. Steppe indices (Traverse, 1978, 1988) seem to suggest that the aragonitic and sideritic muds were deposited during relatively warm intervals, and the lacustrine chalks were deposited during relatively cool intervals. Incidentally, freshwater dinoflagellates are locally so abundant in the chalks as to form oozes (sapropels).

Details of Kimmerian stratigraphy have been discussed by, among others, Sveier (1949), Karmishina (1975), Vekua (1975), Ananova et al. (1985), and Sirenko and Turlo (1986).

Micropaleontology

Only non-age-diagnostic, quasimarine, smaller benthonic foraminifera were recorded by Karmishina (1975) from the Kimmerian of Prechernomore (northern Black Sea). These include *Ammonia beccarii* and *Elphidium incertum.*

Stratigraphically and/or paleoenvironmentally significant ostracods recorded by Karmishina (1975) and Vekua (1975) from the Kimmerian of Prechernomore (northern Black Sea) and Abkhazia (northeastern Black Sea), respectively, include *Bakunella dorsoacuata, Caspiocypris labiata, Caspiolla acronasuta, Cyprideis littoralis/torosa, Leptocythere bosqueti, Mediocythereis apatoica,* and *Pontoniella acuminata. Bakunella dorsoacuata, Caspiolla acronasuta,* and *Cyprideis torosa* are quasimarine species. *Caspiocypris labiata* is a freshwater species. Ostracods recorded by Karmishina (1975) from the

Kimmerian of the Northern Precaspian and Southeastern Kalmyk (Northern Caspian) include *Candona angulata, C. neglecta, C. rostrata, Cyclocypris laevis, Cypria arma, Eucypris naidinae, Ilyocypris bradyi, I. gibba, I. serpulosa,* and *Zonocypris membranae.* These are all freshwater forms.

Nannopaleontology

Stratigraphically significant calcareous nannofossils recorded by Zubakov and Borzenkova (1990) from the Kimmerian include *Discoaster quinqueramus* (NN11) (reworked?) and *Ceratolithus acutus* ("late" NN12) and *C. rugosus* (NN13–NN19?).

Palynology

Only non-age-diagnostic palynomorphs have been recorded from the Kimmerian. However, the results of preliminary analyses have shown pollen spectra from "Thermo"-SCT27 in the Ukraine to be characterized by broad-leaved and subtropical forest elements [*Castanea* (chestnut), *Rhus* (rue), and *Taxodiaceae* (cypress and swamp cypress) (Sirenko and Turlo, 1986)], and those from "Cryo"-SCT26 and "Cryo"-SCT24 to be characterized by steppe elements (Ananova et al., 1985; Zubakov and Borzenkova, 1990). "Thermo"-SCT23 has been shown to be characterized by the quasimarine acritarch palynomorph *Sigmailina* (and the quasimarine diatom *Actinocyclus ehrenbergi*) (Ananova et al., 1985; Zubakov and Borzenkova, 1990).

Kuyalnikian to Neoeuxinian

Details of Kuyalnikian to Neoeuxinian stratigraphy have been discussed by Wall and Dale (1973), Karmishina (1975), Vekua (1975), Kaplin (1977), Shikmus et al. (1977), Schrader (1979), Semenenko and Pevzner (1979), Sirenko and Turlo (1986), Yanko (1990a, b, 1991), Balabanov et al. (1991), and Trubikhin et al. (1991a, b).

Kuyalnikian

The Kuyalnikian takes its name from a locality on the Danube delta. The Romanian appears synonymous. Zubakov and Borzenkova (1990) calibrate it against magnetostratigraphic polarity epochs 3 (Gauss) to 2 (Matuyama). The Kuyalnikian represents a major transgressive episode when Eastern Paratethys was reconnected with the world oceans. During this time, marine plankton were introduced into Eastern Paratethys, enabling calibration to global data.

The quasimarine aragonitic muds (Unit IVc) and alternations of lacustrine chalks or "Seekreide" (Units IVb and III) and sideritic muds (Unit IVa) of DSDP Site 380 in the southwestern Black Sea are arguably at least in part of Kuyalnikian age. Steppe indices (Traverse, 1978, 1988) seem to suggest that the aragonitic and sideritic muds were deposited during relatively warm intervals, and the lacustrine chalks during relatively cool intervals. Freshwater dinoflagellates are locally so abundant in the chalks as to form oozes (sapropels).

Details of Kuyalnikian stratigraphy have been discussed by Karmishina (1975), Vekua (1975), Semenenko and Pevzner (1979), Shatilova (1984), and Sirenko and Turlo (1986).

Micropaleontology

Only the non-age-diagnostic, quasimarine, smaller benthonic foraminifera *Ammonia beccarii* and *Elphidium incertum* were recorded by Karmishina (1975) from the Kuyalnikian of Prechernomore (northern Black Sea).

Stratigraphically and/or paleoenvironmentally significant ostracods recorded by Karmishina (1975) and Vekua (1975) from the Kuyalnikian of Prechernomore (northern Black Sea) and Abkhazia (northeastern Black Sea), respectively, include *Bakunella dorsoacuata, Caspiocypris labiata, Caspiolla acronasuta, Cryptocyprideis bogatschovi, Cypria arma, Leptocythere andrusovi, L. circumsulcata, Loxoconcha eichwaldi, L. petasa, Mediocythereis apatoica,* and *Pontoniella acuminata. Bakunella dorsoacuata, Caspiolla acronasuta,* and *Loxoconcha petasa* are quasimarine species. *Caspiocypris acronasuta* and *Cypria arma* are freshwater species.

Nannopaleontology

Stratigraphically significant calcareous nannofossils recorded by Semenenko and Pevzner (1979) from the Kuyalnikian include *Discoaster pentaradiatus* (NN9?–NN17) and *Reticulofenestra pseudoumbilica* (NN7?–NN15).

Palynology

Only non-age-diagnostic palynomorphs have been recorded from the Kuyalnikian. Pollen spectra from "Thermo"-SCT15 are characterized by polydominance (Shatilova, 1984; Sirenko and Turlo, 1986).

Gurian

The Gurian takes its name from an ancient province of what is now Western Georgia. Zubakov and Borzenkova (1990) calibrate it against magnetostratigraphic polarity epoch 2 (Matuyama).

Chaudian

The Chaudian takes its name from a promontory on the Kerch Peninsula (Crimea). Zubakov and Borzenkova (1990) calibrate it against magnetostratigraphic polarity epochs 2 (Matuyama) to 1 (Brunhes).

Uzunlarian, Karangatian, and Neoeuxinian

The Uzunlarian takes its name from a lake; the Karangatian takes its name from a promontory on the Kerch Peninsula (Crimea); and the Neoeuxinian takes its name from an ancient name for the Black Sea. Zubakov and Borzenkova (1990) calibrate the Uzunlarian, Karangatian, and Neoeuxinian against magnetostratigraphic polarity epoch 1 (Brunhes).

Details of Uzunlarian, Karangatian, and Neoeuxinian stratigraphy have been discussed by Schrader (1979) and Markova and Mikhailesku (1994). Schrader (1979) recorded the paleoenvironmentally significant diatoms *Actinocyclus divisus, A. ochotensis, Cymatopleura solea,* and *Stephanodiscus astraea* (which indicate a paleosalinity range of 0.5–3.0 ppt). Markova and Mikhailesku (1994) recorded the ostracods *Ammcythere cymbula, Callistocythere alfera, C. lopalica, C. mediterrarea,*

C. quinquetuberculata, and *Loxoconcha immodalata* in the stratotypical Uzunlarian.

CONCLUSIONS

We have attempted to place Eastern Paratethyan stratigraphy in a global stratigraphic framework by calibrating regional biostratigraphic and magnetostratigraphic data against global standards. Biostratigraphic calibration is rendered difficult by the restricted development in Paratethys of those groups of planktonic organisms traditionally used in the biostratigraphic zonation of the Cenozoic. This is a function partly of the poor connection between Paratethys and the world's oceans, and partly of the prevalence of quasimarine conditions inimical to the open oceanic plankton.

We have also attempted to place Eastern Paratethyan stratigraphy in a sequence stratigraphic framework by suggesting correlations between regional and global sequence boundaries, flooding surfaces, and eustatic(?) sea level. This is complicated by the paucity of biostratigraphic constraint. Nonetheless, within the limits of resolution, reasonable matches can be made. All global eustatic(?) sea level events over the Oligocene–Holocene appear to find their expression in Eastern Paratethys.

In a hydrocarbon-exploration context, the calibration of the regional stratigraphy against global standards enables better understanding of basin (e.g., source rock burial and maturation) history and the development of predictive stratigraphic play models. It also provides a more readily understood context for regional terminology.

REFERENCES CITED

Ananova, Ye. N., N.S. Volkova, V.A. Zubakov, V.I. Pavlovskaya, and V.N. Remizovsky, 1985, New data on Taman key section of the Mio-Pliocene Black Sea region (in Russian): Doklady Akademii Nauk Soyuza Sotsialistioheskikh Respublik, Leningrad, v. 284(4), p. 925–928.

Balabanov, I., V.V. Yanko, J. İsmaylov, and N. Gey, 1991, The Holocene history of the Black Sea Basin (abs.): XIII INQUA International Congress, Beijing, China, 1991, p. 15.

Bogdanowicz, A.K., 1950a, Stratigraphical subdivision of the Tarkhanian of Kuban on the basis of foraminiferal investigations (in Russian): Trudy Vsesoyuznogo Neftyanago Nauchno-Issledovatel'skogo Geologo-Razvedochnogo Instituta (VNIGRI), Novaya Seriya, Leningrad and Moscow, v. 51, p. 113–128.

Bogdanowicz, A.K., 1950b, Tschokrakian foraminifera of the western Precaucasus (in Russian): Trudy Vsesoyuznogo Neftyanago Nauchno-Issledovatel'skogo Geologo-Razvedochnogo Instituta (VNIGRI), Novaya Seriya, Leningrad and Moscow, v. 51, p. 129–176.

Bogdanowicz, A.K., 1965, New data on Konkian miliolidae from the western Precaucasus (in Russian): Trudy Vsesoyuznogo Neftyanago Nauchno-Issledovatel'skogo Geologo-Razvedochnogo Instituta (VNIGRI), Paleontologicheskii Sbornik 2, Leningrad and Moscow, v. 16, p. 34–49.

Bogdanowicz, A.K., 1967, New types of articuline from the Meotian of Kuban (in Russian): Moscow, Paleontologicheskii Zhurnal, v. 1, p. 131–132.

Bogdanowicz, A.K., 1969, Meotian miliolidae from the western Precaucasus (in Russian): Trudy Vsesoyuznogo Neftyanago Nauchno-Issledovatel'skogo Geologo-Razvedochnogo Instituta (VNIGRI), Paleontologicheskii Sbornik 2, Leningrad and Moscow, v. 19, p. 64–133.

Bogdanovich, A.K., 1974, New miliolids from the Meotian in Western Georgia: Leningrad, Trudy Vsesoyuznyi Nauchno-Issledovatel'skii Geologo-razvedochnyi Neftyanoi Institut (VNIGNI), v. 152, p. 115–125.

Bolli, H.M., and V.A. Krasheninnikov, 1977, Problems in Paleogene and Neogene correlations based on planktonic foraminifera: Micropaleontology, v. 23(4), p. 436–452.

Chelidze, A.L., 1973, Correlation of the Pontian from the Euxinian and Caspian basins (abs.) (in Russian with English abstract): Soobshcheniya Akademii Nauk Gruzinskoi, v. 71(3), p. 645–648.

Chepalyga, A.L., 1985, Climatic and eustatic fluctuations in the Paratethys basins history: Abstracts (abs.): VII Congress, Regional Commission on Mediterranean Neogene Stratigraphy (RCMNS), Budapest, 1985, p. 34–36.

Chepalyga, A.L., 1991, Pleistocene Black Sea level changes and ecological consequences (abs.): XIII INQUA International Congress, Beijing, China, 1991, p. 56.

Chepalyga, A.L., E.L. Korotkevich, V.M. Trubikhin, and T.V. Svellitskaya, 1985, Chronology of the Eastern Paratethys regional stages and Hipparion events according to palaeomagnetic data (abs.): VII Congress, Regional Commission on Mediterranean Neogene Stratigraphy (RCMNS), Budapest, 1985, p. 137–139.

Demarcq, J., 1985, Paleothermic evolution during the Neogene in Mediterranean through the marine megafauna: Abstracts (abs.): VII Congress, Regional Commission on Mediterranean Neogene Stratigraphy (RCMNS), Budapest, 1985, p. 176–178.

Dzhanelidze, O. I., 1977, Polymorphinids of the Miocene of Georgia (in Russian): Tbilisi, "Metsnerieva."

Fedorov, P.V., 1960, Dreunie beregorie linii chernogo Mora na nogeresche Kaukaza: Izvestiya Akademii Nauk SSSR, Seriya Geologicheskaya, v. 1979(2), p. 56–64.

Gasanov, T., and T.M. Kyazymov, 1988, Paleogene and Neogene sediment accumulation in eastern Lesser Caucasus: Moscow, Soviet Geology, v. 1988(3), p. 62–70.

Gheorghian, M., 1978, *in* D.A. Ross, Y.P. Neprochnov, and Micropaleontological investigations of sediments from sites 377, 380 and 381 of Leg 42B. Initial Reports of the Deep Sea Drilling Project, v. 42, p. 783–788.

Grichuk, V.P., 1984, Late Pleistocene vegetation history, *in* A.A. Velichko, ed., Late Quaternary environments of the Soviet Union (English translation): London, Longman, p. 155–178.

Haq, B.U., J. Hardenbol, and P.R. Vail, 1988, Mesozoic and Cenozoic chronostratigraphy and eustatic cycles, *in* C.K. Wilgus ,B.S. Hastings, C.G. St.C. Kendall, H. Posamentier, C.A. Ross, and J.C. Van Wagoner, eds., Sea-level changes: an integrated approach: SEPM Special Publication 42, p. 71–108.

Hsu, K.J., 1978, Stratigraphy of the lacustrine sedimentation in the Black Sea: Initial Reports of the Deep Sea Drilling Project, v. 42, p. 509–524.

Hsu, K.J., and Giovanoli, F., 1979, Messinian event in the Black Sea: Palaeogeography, Palaeoclimatology, Palaeoecology, v. 29(1979), p. 75–93.

Imnadze, Z.A., and G.L. Karmishina, 1980, Comparison of Pliocene Ostracoda complexes in the Northern and Eastern Black Sea region (in Russian): Leningrad, Voprosy Stratigrafii, v. 5, p. 131–148.

Jones, R.W., 1996, Micropalaeontology in Petroleum Exploration: Oxford, University Press, 432 p.

Jones, R.W., and M.D. Simmons, 1996, A review of the stratigraphy of Eastern Paratethys (Oligocene–Holocene): Bulletins of the British Museum (Natural History), Geology, v. 52(1), p. 25–49.

Kaplin, P.A., 1977, Paleogeography and deposits of the Pleistocene of the southern seas of the USSR (in Russian): Moscow, Nauka.

Karmishina, G.I., 1975, Pliocene Ostracoda from the southern (European) USSR (in Russian): Saratov, Izdanie Saratovskogo University.

Klopotovskaya, N.B., 1991, The Caucasus at the coldest time of the last glaciation (abs.): XIII INQUA International Congress, Beijing, China, p. 164–165.

Kojumdgieva, E., 1979, Critical notes on the stratigraphy of Black Sea boreholes (Deep Sea Drilling Project, Leg 42B): Geologica Balcanica, Sofia, v. 9(3), p. 107–110.

Kojumdgieva, E., 1983, Palaeogeographic environment during the desiccation of the Black Sea: Palaeogeography, Palaeoclimatology, Palaeoecology, v. 43(1983), p. 195–204.

Koshkarly, R.O., and M. Baldi-Beke, 1987, Correlation of the Paleogene deposits of Azerbaijan and Hungary by nannoplankton: Acta Geologica Hungarica, v. 30(3–4), p. 289–298.

Krakhmalnaya, T.V., T.V. Svetlitskaya, and A.L. Chepalyga, 1993, New data on stratigraphy, magnetostratigraphy and mammal faunas of the late Miocene locality of Novaya Emetovka (Ukrania): Newsletters on Stratigraphy, v. 29, p. 77–89.

Krasheninnikov, V.A., 1986, The Kuban River sequence (USSR, North Caucasus), *in* Ch. Pomerol and I. Premoli Silva, eds., Terminal eocene events: Amsterdam, Elsevier, p. 137–139.

Krasheninnikov, V.A., and M.G. Muzylev, 1975, Relationship between the zonal scales based on planktonic foraminifera and nannoplankton in Paleogene sections of the north Caucasus (abs.) (in Russian with English abstract): Voprosy Mikropaleontologii, Moscow, v. 1975, p. 212–224.

Krasheninnikov, V.A., M.G. Muzylev, and A.E. Ptukhian, 1985, Stratigraphical subdivision of Paleogene deposits of Armenia by planktonic foraminifers, nannoplankton and nummulites (Pt. 1, reference Paleogene sections of Armenia) (abs.) (in Russian with English abstract): Moscow, Voprosy Mikropaleontologii, v. 1985, p. 130–169.

Krasheninnikov, V.A., and A.E. Ptukhian, 1986, Stratigraphical subdivision of Armenian Paleogene deposits by planktonic microfossils and nummulites (regional stratigraphy, zonal scales by planktonic and benthonic microfossils, their correlation) (abs.) (in Russian with English abstract): Moscow, Voprosy Mikropaleontologii, v. 1986, p. 60–98.

Krhovsky, J., 1985, Central Paratethys ecostratigraphic correlations in relation to the Oligocene sea-level changes: (abs.): VII Congress Regional Commission on Mediterranean Neogene Stratigraphy (RCMNS), Budapest, 1985, p. 333–335.

Krstic, N., 1976, Pontian ostracodes in Paratethys and Tethys: Proceedings: Bratislava, VI Congress Regional Commission on Mediterranean Neogene Stratigraphy (RCMNS), 1975, p. 325–330.

Maisuradze, P.C., 1971, Sarmatian foraminifera of Western Georgia (in Russian): Tbilisi, "Metsnerieva."

Maisuradze, P.C., 1988, Foraminifera of the Meotian of West Georgia (in Russian): Tbilisi, "Metsnerieva."

Markova, A.K., and K.D. Mikhailesku, 1994, Correlation of Pleistocene marine and continental deposits from the northwestern Black Sea region: Stratigraphy and Geological Correlation, v. 2(4), p. 388–394.

Muratov, M.V., 1960, A brief summary of the geological structure of the Crimean Peninsula (in Russian): Moscow.

Nagy, E., and J. Kokay, 1991, Middle Miocene mangrove vegetation in Hungary: Acta Geologica Hungarica, v. 34(1/2), p. 45–52.

Nagymarosy, A., 1992, The response of the calcareous nannoplankton to the Early Oligocene separation of the Paratethys: International Nannoplankton Association Newsletter, v. 13(2), p. 62–63.

Naidina, O.D., 1988, Palynological characteristics of Akchagylian deposits of the Tersko-Sunzhenskii petroleum region (in Russian): Moscow University Geology Bulletin, v. 43(4), p. 69–74.

Nevesskaya, L.A., and M.F. Nosovsky, 1985, Eastern Paratethys, *in* F. Rögl, ed., Mediterranean and Paratethys Neogene: Report on Activity of the RCMNS Working Groups and Bibliography 1979–1984: Budapest, p. 55–58.

Nevesskaya, L.A., V.V. Tikhomirov, and P.V. Fedorov, 1985, Stratigraphy of Neogene–Quaternary deposits of the Euxinian–Caspian area (abs.): VII Congress Regional Commission on Mediterranean Neogene Stratigraphy (RCMNS), Budapest, p. 413–415.

Paramonova, N.P., E.N. Ananova, A.S. Andreeva-Grigorovic, L.S. Belokrys, L.K. Gabunia, K.F. Grusinskaja, S.O. Kondkarian, G.I. Karmishina, T.F. Kozirenco, L.S. Majsuradze, E.Z. Movlazade-Ateava, L.A. Nevesskaya, L.D. Ponomareva, V.N. Roshka, and A.L. Chepalyga, 1979, Paleontological characteristics of the Sarmatian sensu lato, and Meotian of the Ponto-Caspian area and possibilities of correlation to the Sarmatian sensu stricto and Pannonian of Central Paratethys: Annales Géologiques des Pays Helléniques, v. 1979, p. 961–971.

Pevzner, M.A., and E.A. Vangengeim, 1985, Magnetostratigraphy and correlation of biostratigraphic subdivisions of the Paratethyan and Mediterranean Neogene (abs.): VII Congress Regional Commission on Mediterranean Neogene Stratigraphy (RCMNS), Budapest, p. 461–462.

Pevzner, M.A., and E.A. Vangengeim, 1993, Magnetostratigraphic age assignments of Middle and Late Sarmatian mammalian localities of the Eastern Paratethys: Newsletters on Stratigraphy, v. 29(2), p. 63–75.

Pogacsas, Gy., 1985, Seismic stratigraphy as a tool for chronostratigraphy: the Pannonian Basin (abs.): VII Congress Regional Commission on Mediterranean Neogene Stratigraphy (RCMNS), Budapest, p. 465–468.

Pogacsas, Gy., and I. Revesz, 1985, Seismic stratigraphy and sedimentological analysis of Neogene delta features in the Pannonian Basin, Abstracts (abs.): VII Congress Regional Commission on Mediterranean Neogene Stratigraphy, Budapest, p. 469–471.

Popkhadze, L.I., 1977, Meotian microfauna (foraminifera and ostracods) from Western Georgia (in Russian): Tbilisi, Akademii Nauk Gruzenski SSR.

Popkhadze, L.I., 1983, The foraminifera and ostracoda of the Tschokrakian sediments of western Georgia (in Russian): Sobschcheniya Akademii Nauk Gruzenski SSR, v. 110, p. 541–544.

Popkhadze, L.I., 1984, A new representative of the genus *Leptocythere* from the Tschokrakian sediments of western Georgia (in Russian): Sobschcheniya Akademii Nauk Gruzenski SSR, v. 115, p. 337–339 .

Popkhadze, L.I., H.N. Pursteladze, and T.I. Badzoshvili, 1980, On the Meotian sediments of Abkhazia (in Russian): Sobschcheniya Academii Nauk Gruzenski SSR, v. 98, p. 365–368.

Ramishvili, I.Sh., 1969, The description of Black Sea flora of western Georgia and their correlation with present-day flora (in Russian): Tbilisi, "Metsniereva."

Rögl, F., 1985, Late Oligocene and Miocene planktonic foraminifera of the Central Paratethys, *in* H.M. Bolli, J.B. Saunders, and K. Perch-Nielsen, eds., Plankton stratigraphy: Cambridge, University Press, p. 315–328.

Rögl, F., and F.F. Steininger, 1983, Vom Zerfall der Tethys zu Mediterran und Paratethys: Annalen des Naturhistorischen Museums Wien, v. 85/A, p. 135–163.

Ross, D.A., Y.P. Neprochnov et al., eds., 1978, Initial Reports of the Deep Sea Drilling Project, v. 42.

Royden, L.H., and F. Horvath, eds., 1987, The Pannonian Basin: a study in basin evaluation: AAPG Memoir 45.

Savina, S.S., and N.A. Khotinskiy, 1984, Holocene paleoclimatic reconstruction based on the zonal method, *in* A.A. Velichko, ed., Late Quaternary environments of the Soviet Union (English translation): London, Longman, p. 287–296.

Schrader, H.-J., 1979, Quaternary paleoclimatology of the Black Sea: Sedimentary Geology, v. 23, p. 165–180.

Semenenko, V.N., 1979, Correlation of Mio–Pliocene of the Eastern Paratethys and Tethys: Annales Géologiques des Pays Helléniques, v. 1979, p. 1101–1111.

Semenenko, V.A., and M.A. Pevzner, 1979, Biostratigraphic and paleomagnetic correlation of the Miocene and Pliocene in the Pontic-Caspian region (in Russian): Izvestiya Akademii Nauk SSSR, Seriya Geologicheskaya, v. 1979(1), p. 5–15.

Shatilova, I.I., 1984, Late Miocene vegetation of western Georgia (in Russian): Tbilisi, "Metsniereva."

Shchekina, N.A., 1979, The history of flora and vegetation in the south of the European part of the USSR during the Late Miocene–Early Pliocene (in Russian): Kiev, Naukova "Dumka."

Shikmus, K.M., A.V. Komarov, and I.V. Grakova, 1977, Stratigraphy of the Upper Quaternary deep-sea sediments in the Black Sea: Oceanology, v. 17(4), p. 443–446.

Sirenko, N.A., and S.I. Turlo, 1986, Development of the Ukrainian soil and vegetation through the Pliocene and Pleistocene (in Russian): Kiev, Naukova "Dumka."

Skalbdyna, L.N., 1985, Geological events in the history of the Pliocene and Pleistocene of southern and northern seas (in Russian): Moscow, Akademmi Nauk SSSR.

Steininger, F.F., 1987, Correlation of Central Paratethys, Eastern Paratethys and Mediterranean Neogene stages, *in* L.H. Royden and F. Horvath, eds., The Pannonian Basin: a study in basin evaluation: AAPG Memoir 45, p. 69–78.

Sveier, A.V., 1949, Basic morphology and systematics of Pliocene and post-Pliocene ostracods (in Russian): Leningrad and Moscow, Trudy Vsesoyuznogo Neftyanago Nauchno-Issledovatel'skogo Geologo-Razvedochjnogo Instituta (VNIGRI), Novaya Seriya, v. 30, p. 1–106.

Traverse, A., 1978, Palynological analysis of DSDP Leg 42B (1975) cores from the Black Sea: Initial Reports of the Deep Sea Drilling Project, U.S. Government Printing Office, Washington D.C., v. 42B, p. 993–1015.

Traverse, A., 1988, Paleopalynology: Boston, Unwin Hyman.

Trubikhin, V.M., V.I. Bagin, T.S. Gandler, T.B. Nechaeva, and A.G. Fein, 1991a, Late Holocene of west Turkmenia: paleomagnetism, chronology and climatic events (abs.): XIII INQUA International Congress, Beijing, p. 359.

Trubikhin, V.M., T.B. Nechaeva, and A.G. Fein, 1991b, Ponto-Caspian Quaternary deposits: stratigraphy, chronology, fine structure of magnetic field (abs.): XIII INQUA International Congress, Beijing, 1991, p. 359.

Ulmishek, G., and W. Harrison, 1981, Petroleum geology and resource assessment of the middle Caspian Basin, USSR: Argonne National Laboratory (ANL/ES-116).

Vail, P.R., F. Audemard, S.A. Bowman, P.N. Eisner, and G. Perez-Cruz, 1991, The stratigraphic signatures of tectonics, eustasy and sedimentation, *in* G. Einselle, ed., Cycles and events in stratigraphy: New York, Springer-Verlag.

Vekua, M.L., 1975, The Ostracoda of the Kimmerian and Kujalnikian deposits of Abkhazia and their stratigraphic significance (in Russian): Tbilisi, "Metsniereva."

Velichko, A.A., 1984, Late Pleistocene spatial paleoclimatic reconstructions, *in* A.A. Velichko, ed., Late Quaternary environments of the Soviet Union (English translation): London, Longman, p. 281–286.

Veto, I., 1987, An Oligocene sink for organic carbon: upwelling in the Paratethys?: Palaeogeography, Palaeoclimatology, Palaeoecology, v. 60, p. 143–153.

Wall, D., and B. Dale, 1973, Paleosalinity relationships of dinoflagellates in the Late Quaternary of the Black Sea—a summary: Geoscience and Man, v. 7, p. 95–102.

Yagmurlu, F., and C. Helvacì, 1994, Sedimentological characteristics and facies of the evaporite-bearing Kirmir Formation (Neogene), Beyparazi Basin, Central Anatolia, Turkey: Sedimentology, v. 41, p. 847–860.

Yanko, V.V., 1990a, Quaternary foraminifera of the genus *Ammonia* from the Ponto-Caspian: Paleontological Journal, v. 24(1), p. 14–24.

Yanko, V.V, 1990b, Stratigraphy and paleogeography of the marine Pleistocene and Holocene deposits of the southern seas of the USSR: Memorie Societa Geologica Italiana, v. 44, p. 167–187.

Yanko, V.V., 1991, Benthonic foraminifera as a basis of Quaternary detailed stratigraphy and palaeogeography of the southern seas of the USSR (abs.): VII Congress Regional Commission on Mediterranean Neogene Stratigraphy (RCMNS), Budapest, p. 408.

Zubakov, V.A., 1993, Trans-Eurasian correlation and the general climatostratigraphic scale of the Pleistocene: Newsletters on Stratigraphy, v. 29(1), p. 1–19.

Zubakov, V.A., and I.I. Borzenkova, 1990, Global palaeoclimate of the Late Cenozoic: Amsterdam, Elsevier.

Banks, C.J., and A.G. Robinson, 1997, Mesozoic strike-slip back-arc basins of the Western Black Sea region, *in* A.G. Robinson, ed., Regional and petroleum geology of the Black Sea and surrounding region: AAPG Memoir 68, p. 53–62.

Chapter 5

Mesozoic Strike-Slip Back-Arc Basins of the Western Black Sea Region

Chris J. Banks
Royal Holloway University of London
Egham, Surrey, United Kingdom

Andrew G. Robinson
JKX Oil & Gas plc
Guildford, United Kingdom

ABSTRACT

This chapter presents schematic reconstructions of the Black Sea region in Triassic to Cretaceous time. The tectonic evolution of the region during this time was controlled by the northward subduction of the Tethys oceanic plate. The ocean is now closed at a suture extending from Romania to the Aegean and through the whole length of northern Turkey to Iran. The overriding European plate was alternately subjected to extensional and compressive deformation and arc magmatism, resulting in a zone of considerable structural and stratigraphic complexity. The present Western Black Sea opened in the mid-Cretaceous as the microplate comprising what is now the Western and Central Pontides separated from the Moesian and Scythian platforms and moved southeast to leave an oceanic back-arc basin behind it. We identify two regional strike-slip transfer fault zones that constrained the movement of the Pontide microplate. Our restoration enables us to recognize the Peceneaga-Camena fault and its extensions as a key tectonic feature—another major transfer fault—in the earlier Triassic and Jurassic events. We suggest that its displacement was sinistral in the Late Triassic–Early Jurassic, with Moesia moving southeast, leaving an oceanic embayment now occupied by the Pannonian Basin. This phase was generally transtensional, opening a string of back-arc basins in the Black Sea area, which then closed in the Middle–Late Jurassic Cimmeride orogeny.

INTRODUCTION

The Black Sea is widely regarded as an extensional back-arc basin developed along the northern active margin of the Tethys Ocean, which was subducting northward from Triassic–Miocene time (Letouzey et al., 1977; Zonenshain and Le Pichon, 1986; Manetti et al., 1988) The basin has two components with different timing and orientation of extension: the Eastern and Western Black Sea basins (Figure 1; Finetti et al., 1988).

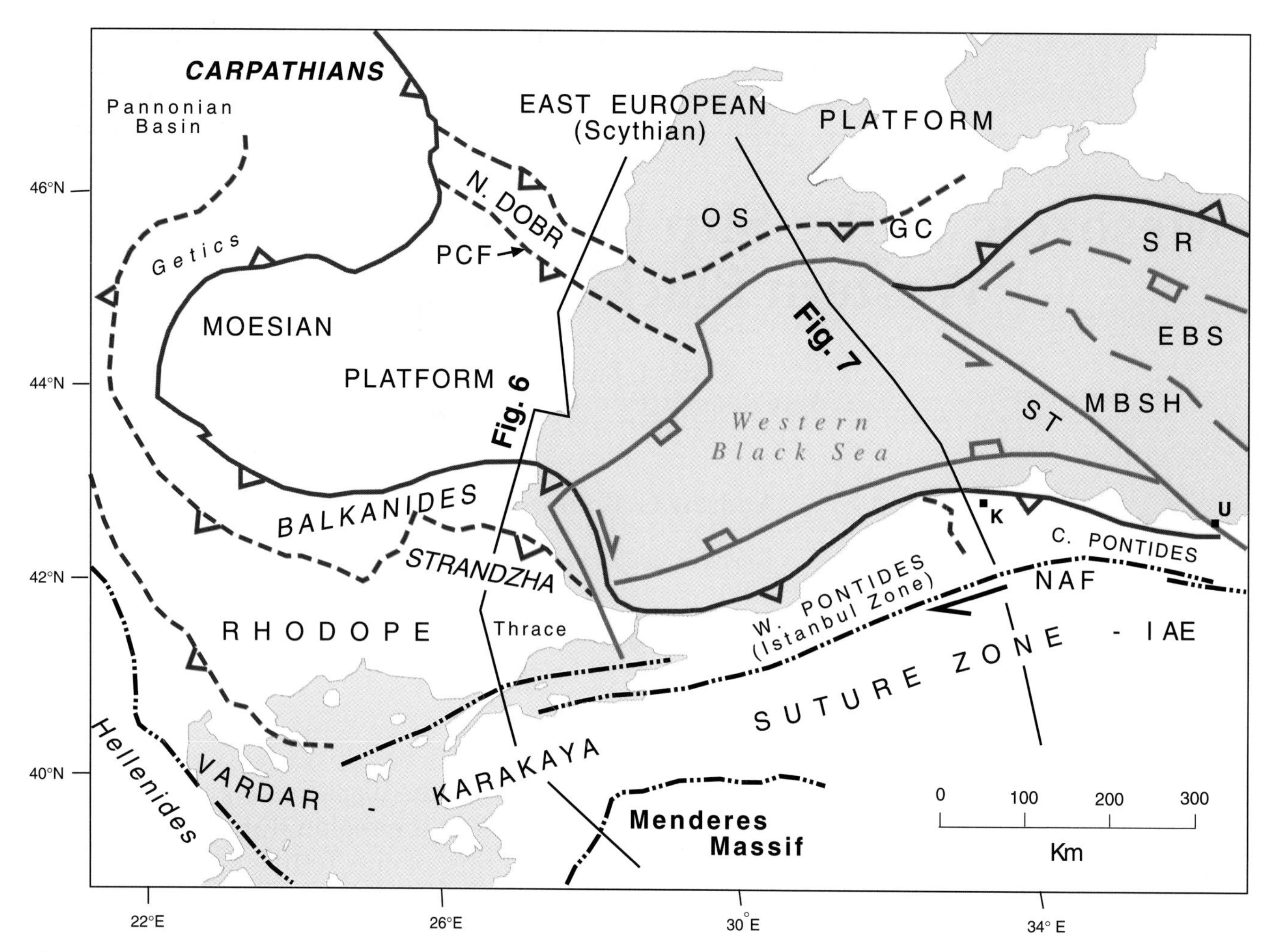

Figure 1. Tectonic elements of the Black Sea, showing locations of cross sections in Figures 6 and 7. Solid lines in red with thrust marks are Alpide (Tertiary) compressive fronts; short-dashed thrusts in purple are Cimmeride (Jurassic). Solid and dashed lines in green in the Black Sea with downthrow marks are the extensional and strike-slip boundaries of the Western and Eastern (EBS) Black Sea oceanic basins. Lines marked dash-double-dot relate to the superimposed Cimmeride (Vardar-Karakaya) and Alpide (İzmir-Ankara-Erzincan, IAE) subduction suture zones and the North Anatolian Fault system (NAF). CP = Central Pontides, MBSH = Mid-Black Sea High, GC = Gorniy Crimea and Greater Caucasus, K = Küre, OS = Odessa Shelf, PCF = Peceneaga-Camena fault, SR = Shatsky Ridge, U = Ünye.

Rifting of the Western Basin began in late Barremian, and spreading continued to the Albian or Cenomanian (Görür, 1988); the age of rifting in the Eastern Black Sea is less certain, but may be mid-Paleocene (Robinson et al., 1995a, 1996). The present single-basin configuration reflects the coalescence of the Eastern and Western basins in their postrift phases in the Pliocene. The coastal regions of the Black Sea basins have been substantially modified by Tertiary compression associated with the closure of the Tethys Ocean.

Okay et al. (1994) have proposed a tectonic model for the opening of the Eastern and Western Black Sea basins. They recognize that the Paleozoic–Triassic stratigraphy of the Western Pontides—the İstanbul Zone—and its Jurassic to Barremian cover is not part of an exotic nappe (as proposed by Şengör et al., 1980, 1984, 1988) but a fragment of the Moesian Platform that rifted from the present Romanian–Ukrainian Black Sea shelf area, leaving the oceanic Western Black Sea basin behind. The argument is based upon the similarity of the stratigraphy of the İstanbul Zone and Moesian Platform (Sandulescu, 1978) and the geometry of the Western Black Sea. We have accepted the general features of this explanation for the origin for the Western Black Sea (Robinson et al., 1996), but disagree on two fundamental issues: (1) the location of the eastern margin of the Western Black Sea and (2) the age of the Eastern Black Sea. Both of these issues are fundamental for, in particular, pre-Cretaceous restorations of the region. In this chapter, we suggest an interpretation of the geometry and the history of opening of the basins in the Black Sea region as far back as the Triassic. This interpretation provides an explanation for the major changes in pre-Late Jurassic geology observed in northern Turkey and in the Romanian and Ukrainian offshore.

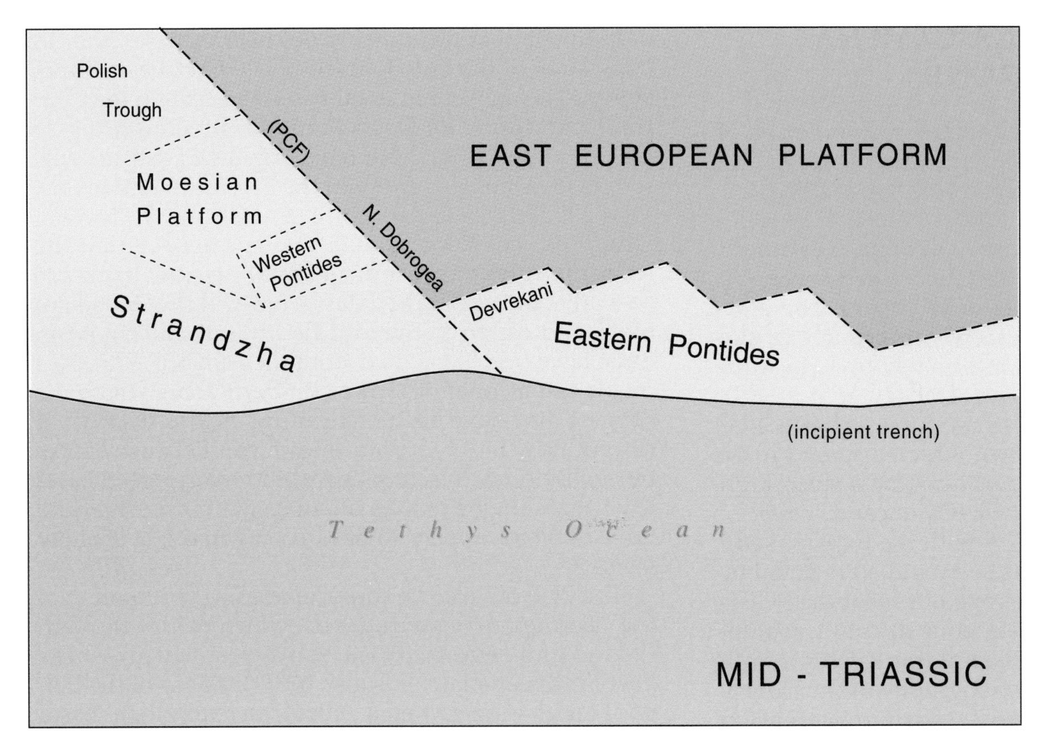

Figure 2. Mid-Triassic reconstruction. This map restores the Black Sea region back prior to displacement on the Peceneaga-Camena fault (PCF) and the opening of the Küre and linked back-arc basins. The East European Platform (in light brown) is regarded as fixed. The area shown in light blue is continental shelf with shallow-marine or non-marine sediments. Dark blue shows ocean or deep basin. Schematic, not to scale.

GEOMETRY AND OPENING OF THE WESTERN BLACK SEA BASIN

The Western-Central Pontide terrane rifted from the Moesian and Scythian platforms in the Barremian to Albian and moved southeast to its present position by the Cenomanian (Figure 1). It subsequently became involved in (mainly late Eocene–Oligocene) compressional deformation (Görür, 1988; Okay et al., 1994). This mode of opening requires the presence of two strike-slip transfer margins on the eastern and western sides of the Western Black Sea. The western (dextral) transfer margin, we believe, passes through Thrace between the Strandzha thrust belt and the İstanbul Zone; its exact location is obscured by Eocene sediments. Its offshore extension in the Black Sea has been overridden and obscured by the Tertiary compressive deformation fronts of Strandzha and the Balkanides (Dachev et al., 1988), so that its original Cretaceous position cannot be accurately determined. At the offshore location mapped by Okay et al. (1994), the fault should be—but to the best of our knowledge is not—visible on seismic data, so we would locate it some distance to the west.

Okay et al. (1994) locate the eastern margin of the Western Black Sea running from the middle of the Odessa shelf through the present-day Western Black Sea depocenter, leaving a large segment of the postrift basin attached to a plate that they show to include Crimea, the Mid-Black Sea High, and the Eastern Black Sea. They do this in order to take it along the eastern margin of the İstanbul Zone in the Pontides and join it with their "Intra-Pontide Suture," thus attempting to explain why the İstanbul Zone disappears going east (their figure 1). No such fault can be recognized on seismic data in the Gulf of Odessa, nor on the Turkish shelf, where it should easily be detected, nor in the deep basin itself.

Our mapping of the rift unconformity in the Black Sea (Robinson et al., 1996, plate 2) suggests that the sinistral margin of the Western Black Sea runs along the southwestern edge of the Mid-Black Sea High, connecting with a faulted margin southwest of Crimea. It continues along the north side of the Sinop Trough, and should meet the Turkish coast somewhere near the town of Ünye (Figure 1). Its onshore continuation is obscured by the Late Cretaceous magmatic arc and subsequent compression (Robinson et al., 1995b). This is ~250 km too far to the east to explain the disappearance of the İstanbul Zone. The Pontide terrane includes both the İstanbul Zone and the very different Central Pontides, where thick, deformed Late Triassic–Early Jurassic flysch overlies a poorly understood basement, which at Küre includes Triassic ophiolite (Ustaömer and Robertson, 1994; Tüysüz et al., 1995). When the Pontides are restored to their prerift position using the boundary transforms suggested, the İstanbul Zone lies adjacent to the Moesian Platform. The Central Pontides were adjacent to the Odessa shelf (which has Triassic to Lower Jurassic Tavrik flysch cover as in Crimea; Robinson and Kerusov, this volume) and close to North Dobrogea, onshore Romania. The Moesian Platform is separated from North Dobrogea by the Peceneaga-Camena fault (PCF) (Figure 2; Banks, this volume). We consider that this fault and its projection offshore and to the Turkish margin of the Black Sea is critical to the understanding of the region.

THE PECENEAGA-CAMENA FAULT ZONE

The PCF appears on the Romanian Committee of Geology maps as a near-straight fault trending approximately NW-SE. To the southwest are Precambrian schists and quarzites, the basement of the Moesian Platform. Further south, Silurian, Devonian, Carboniferous, and Triassic rocks are preserved, all largely undeformed (Pol'ster et al., 1976). The platform was tilted and truncated, apparently in the Callovian, and overlain unconformably by Late–Middle–Upper Jurassic limestones (Dachev et al., 1988). Offshore Romania, there is a Late Jurassic basin containing Tithonian evaporites, which appears to be abruptly terminated to the northeast by a steep fault that may be a branch of the PCF (Catuneanu, 1992).

The relationship of the PCF with the Jurassic sediments of North Dobrogea has been studied in detail by Gradinaru (1984, 1988), who concludes that the PCF is a Middle Jurassic–Early Cretaceous dextral transtensional fault that became a sinistral transpressive fault in the mid-Cretaceous. The stratigraphy of the Dobrogea fold belt as a whole, however, requires extension to near-oceanic depths in the Late Triassic, and compression starting after the deposition of Lower–Middle Jurassic (Nalbant) flysch. A simpler interpretation of Gradinaru's data would be that the PCF was part of a Triassic extensional basin boundary and became a major compressive fault only in the Late Jurassic (near-synchronous with compression in the Strandzha Zone) (Chatalov 1988; Banks, this volume). The actual geometry of the PCF is that of a NE-vergent thrust, dipping about 60° SW and putting Precambrian on top of similarly dipping Kimmeridgian limestones that contain Moesian basement clasts. This implies that the thrust was emplaced on flat-lying Jurassic and subsequently rotated by deformation below it (Banks, this volume, figure 5). There is no conclusive local evidence of the sense of any strike-slip component of these deformations. By the Mid-Early Cretaceous, the whole of the Western Black Sea region had become extensional (so transpression on the PCF at this time seems improbable). By the Cenomanian, postrift sediments started to cover all the truncated compressive structures of Dobrogea.

During the Late Jurassic, the Pontides microplate lay adjacent to the Romanian margin. However, in the Pontides, there is no obvious single fault that can be directly correlated with the PCF. The İstanbul Zone, stratigraphically a good match for the Moesian Platform, disappears in a complex and poorly exposed area at about 30°30'E. To the east, it is replaced by the Küre complex, of Late Triassic–Early Jurassic age, including Akgöl Formation flysch, basic volcanics, and, at Küre, ultrabasics of suprasubduction zone ocean floor origin (Ustaömer and Robertson, 1994). Contrary to some authors (Şengör et al., 1980), our field observations suggest that the Akgöl flysch overlies the İstanbul Paleozoics in normal stratigraphic sequence, although subjected to intense near-surface deformation above a detachment that presumably lies near its base, prior to deposition of the Late Jurassic–Early Cretaceous limestones. The only continental basement seen in the Central Pontides is the Devrekani Massif, consisting of metamorphics thought to have originated as Paleozoic sediments similar to those in the Western Pontides (O. Tüysüz, 1992, personal communication). Following Ustaömer and Robertson (1994), we believe that the Küre complex represents a small oceanic back-arc basin that formed in the Triassic north of the Devrekani block and closed in the Middle Jurassic. Such a basin must have been separated from the İstanbul Zone by a major extensional or strike-slip fault zone, which we suggest may have been the continuation of the PCF. It cannot now be identified in outcrop because it was buried by thick flysch deposits and overprinted by at least three major phases of subsequent deformation, none of which appear to have reactivated it at shallow levels.

The PCF can also be considered as a continuation of the "Tornquist-Teisseire Line," which passes through Poland and represents the southwest margin of the East European plate. It is also the boundary of the Polish Trough (Guterch et al., 1986), an extensional basin of Permian age with a stratigraphy very similar to that of the Moesian Platform.

THE CIMMERIDE PHASE

Following the termination of Hercynian compression, rifting began in the Permian in the Polish Trough and on the Moesian Platform (Ziegler, 1990). More regional subsidence of the southern passive margin of southeast Europe began in the Early Triassic. While most of the area including the Moesian Platform was covered with red-bed clastics, southern Strandzha (Zabernovo Nappe) was already a site of marine sedimentation in the Early Triassic (Chatalov, 1988). In the Middle Triassic (Figure 2), a regional south-facing carbonate platform was established in Strandzha, with a thin shallow-water limestone/dolomite extending north onto the Moesian Platform and through the Western and Central Pontides. The transition to an active margin, located south of Thrace and the Rhodope Massif, probably occurred before the end of the Early Triassic, when the Tethys Ocean and its northwestern extension—the Vardar Ocean—began to subduct to the north.

There is regionally widespread evidence for back-arc extension disrupting this platform in the Late Triassic and Early Jurassic, most notably in the Küre area in the Central Pontides, where there is an ophiolite of Late Triassic age associated with the Akgöl flysch (Ustaömer and Robertson, 1994; Figure 3). There is also an ophiolite in the far Eastern Pontides in the Çoruh valley (off map), and similar basinal sediments (flysch) were deposited in Crimea (Tavrik flysch), Dobrogea (Nalbant flysch), and possibly also in the Balkanides, with thick, deep-water volcanics in places. These back-arc basins have been interpreted as evidence for a "Paleotethys" ocean lying between the Pontides and

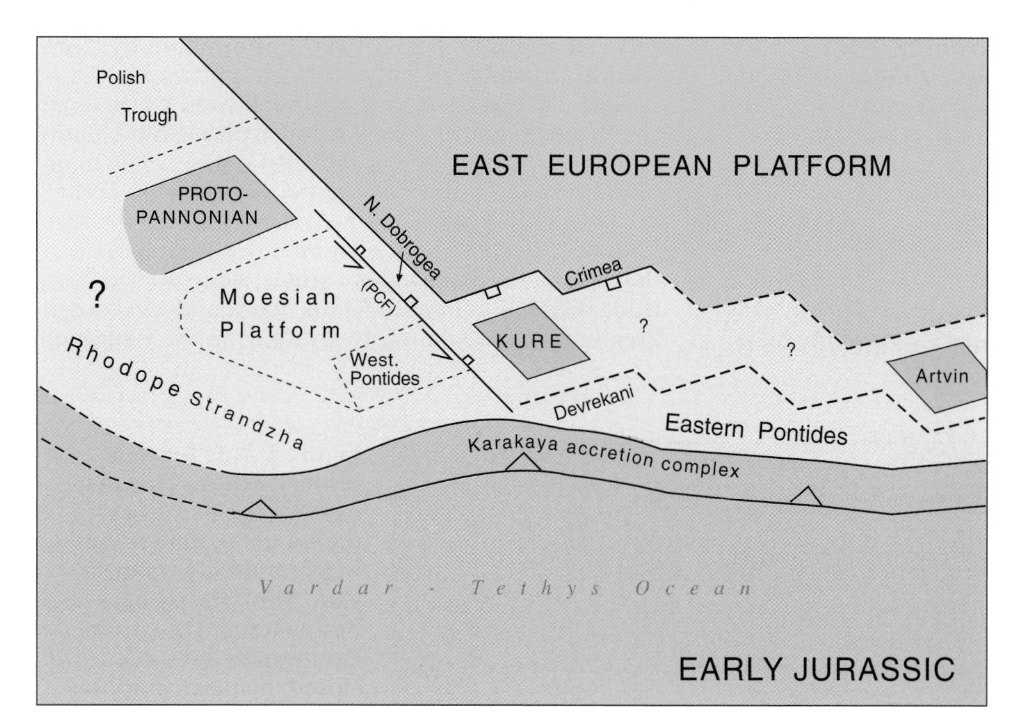

Figure 3. Early Jurassic reconstruction. This map restores the Black Sea region to the time after opening of the Küre and other back-arc basins by sinistral transtensional displacement on the Peceneaga-Camena Fault (PCF) and similar faults. The Karakaya Complex is a subduction-accretion assemblage located south of the Pontide (fore-arc) basement blocks. A basin also opened in the Early Jurassic along the southern edge of the East European platform that was subsequently to become the Greater Caucasus. This basin is not shown on the figure. Color code is as for Figure 2.

the Eastern European continent (Şengör et al., 1980; Nachev, 1991). This interpretation is unlikely, since the Western Pontides are themselves of European, not Gondwanan, origin, and the fore-arc accretion zone (Karakaya Complex) lies to the south of the Pontides. The Karakaya Complex is a southerly vergent imbricated flysch unit of Triassic–Early Jurassic, with radiolarites and olistostromes of Carboniferous–Permian limestones (possibly seamounts), that is interpreted as the major accretion complex that formed as the Tethys Ocean subducted northward (Okay and Mostler, 1994; Ustaömer and Robertson, 1994).

The PCF has a key role in determining the geometry of the Late Triassic extensional basins. The marginal continental strip shown in Figure 2 was displaced to the southeast along the PCF, which acted as a major sinistral transform, offsetting the extensional basins. The basin farthest to the northwest was an oceanic embayment between the Polish Trough and Moesia (which was displaced by ~200–300 km to the southeast) that subsequently became the site of the Pannonian Basin (Dewey et al., 1973). By the end of the Early Jurassic (Figure 3), the basins were fully open and filling with flysch. South of these basins was a fault-disrupted strip of fore-arc continental crust, with Lower–Middle Jurassic flysch/volcanoclastic cover, as seen sporadically through the Eastern Pontides (including the Devrekani Massif). These exposures are all broadly similar to European crust in stratigraphy, and therefore unlikely to be sutured fragments of Gondwana (Robinson et al., 1995b). We see no need to invoke a separate "Sakarya" microcontinent for these fragments, or for an "Intra-Pontide" suture (Şengör and Yılmaz, 1981; Tüysüz et al., 1995). The conclusion of Sarıbudak (1989), based on few inconsistent paleomagnetic data points, that the Pontides were in low lattitudes attached to Africa during the Jurassic (having been part of Laurasia in the Triassic) is unreasonable.

Toward the end of the Early Jurassic, the whole region started to go into compression (the Cimmeride orogeny). It would seem that compression started in the east and migrated westward, reaching Moesia and the Strandzha Zone in the Callovian to late Jurassic, and not deforming North Dobrogea until the Kimmeridgian (Figure 4) (based on Banks, this volume). The Küre Basin closed, mainly by north-vergent thrusting during the Callovian, displacing deformed flysch all around its margins (Ustaömer and Robertson, 1994). There was widespread intrusion of granites and other igneous rocks, and deposition of volcaniclastics, all of subduction-related types (Yılmaz and Boztuğ, 1986). As noted, the PCF in Romania became reactivated as a major compressive fault in the Late Jurassic, and it is possible that such faults had a strike-slip component of deformation at this time. However, a major sinistral displacement, as suggested by the minor thrust orientation in North Dobrogea (Gradinaru, 1988), would not be compatible with the closure of the Küre Basin by north-vergent compression at the same time.

THE ALPIDE PHASE

Toward the end of the Middle Jurassic and following subaerial erosion, the Black Sea region became blanketed with carbonate deposits. Subduction accelerated again toward the end of the Early Cretaceous, renewing arc magmatism, which reached a peak in about Santonian time from the Achara-Trialet Zone in Georgia (Banks et al., this volume), through the

Eastern and offshore of the Western Pontides, to the Srednogorie Zone in Bulgaria. Again, the onset of subduction was associated with back-arc extension. The opening of the present Western Black Sea back-arc basins began in the Early Cretaceous (Barremian–Aptian) and was completed by the Cenomanian (Figure 5). The conjugate extensional margins show a high degree of asymmetry, with faulted margins facing rollover margins (Robinson et al., 1996). Regional cross section (Figure 6) shows this asymmetry schematically, while Figure 7 passes west of the major extension and is therefore still dominated by Cimmeride structures.

Back-arc extension was again followed by regional compression, starting with a minor phase in the Campanian in the Balkanides and the Pontides. The main phase was in the Late Eocene–Oligocene, as Tethys finally closed at the İzmir–Ankara–Erzincan suture (ophiolite belt). This involved modest compression in the Balkanides (Banks, this volume, figure 4) and Pontides (Robinson et al., 1995b, 1996), and also much greater compression eastward (e.g., in the Caucasus

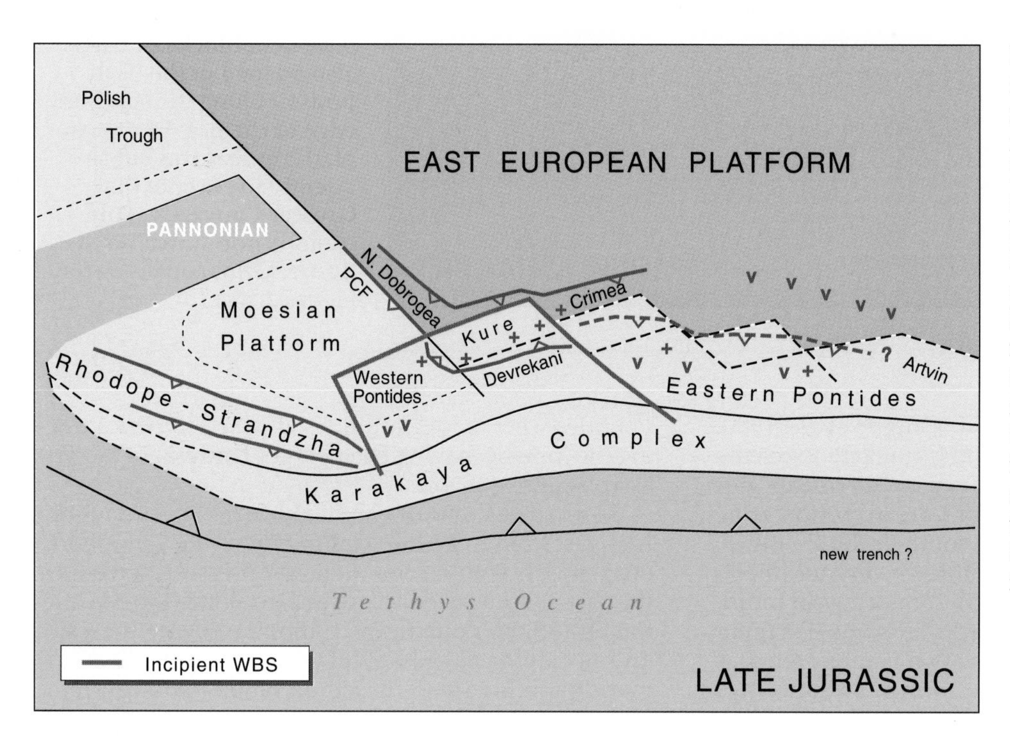

Figure 4. Late Jurassic reconstruction. This map restores the Black Sea region to the time following Cimmeride compression. The Triassic back-arc basins (except the proto-Pannonian) have been closed, displacing ophiolites and flysch onto their margins. Thrusts in red are Cimmeride compressive fronts; v and + are Cimmeride volcanics and intrusives. Green line shows the incipient location of the Western Black Sea (WBS) boundary faults.

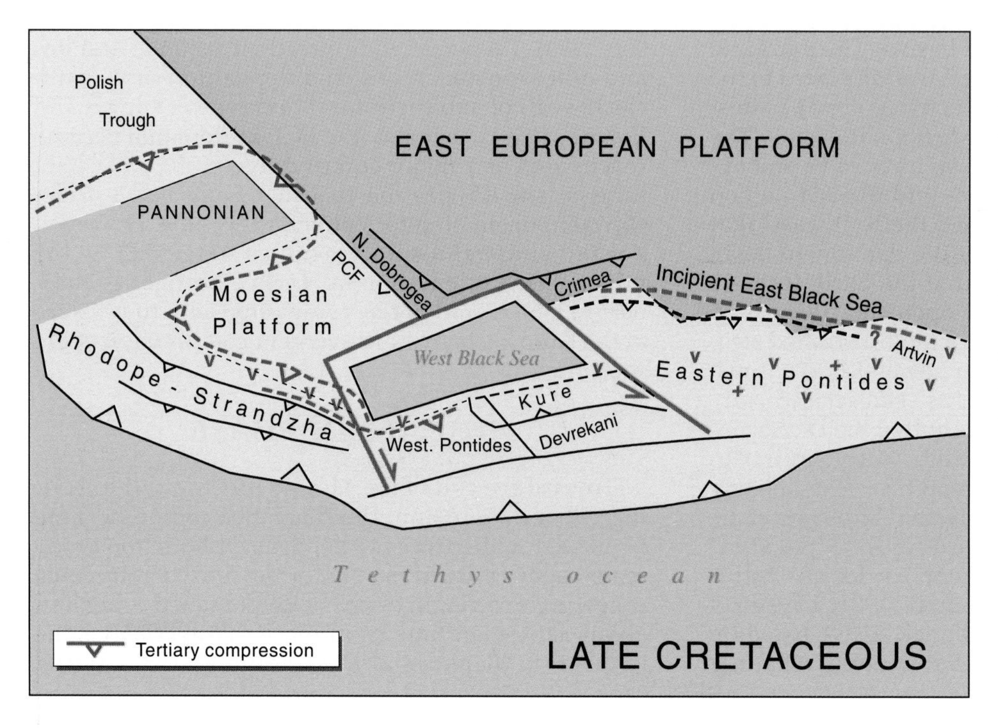

Figure 5. Late Cretaceous reconstruction. This map restores the Black Sea region to a time after opening of the Western Black Sea (green lines) but prior to the onset of Alpide compression (dashed red lines with thrust marks). This was a peak period for arc magmatism (v and +). The Eastern Black Sea is thought to have opened in the Paleocene–Eocene.

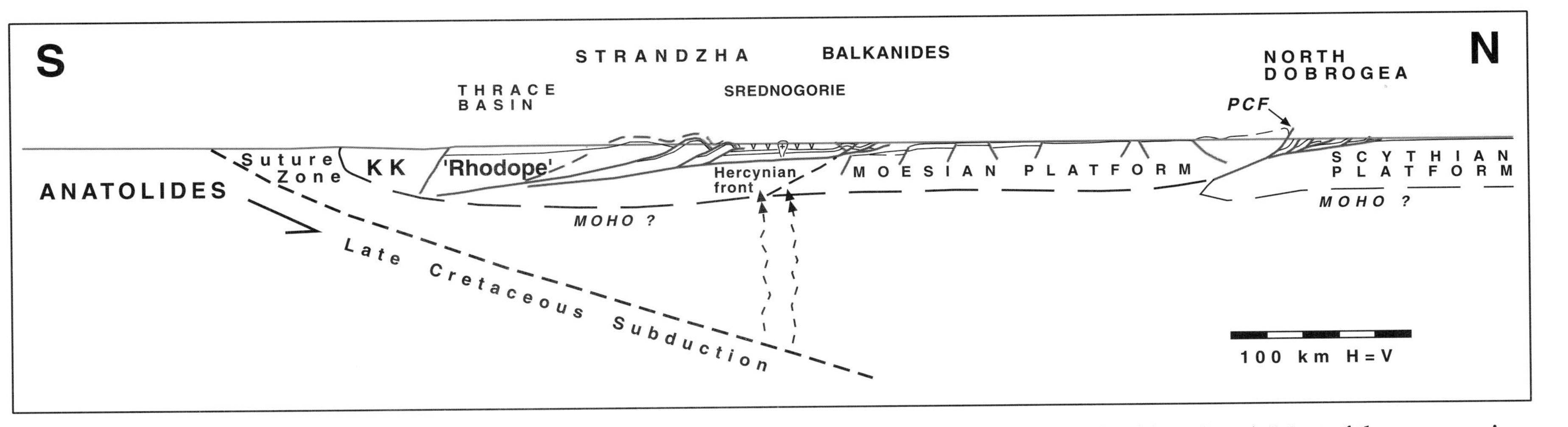

Figure 6. Structural cross section through northwest Turkey, Bulgaria, and Romania to Ukraine (after Banks, this volume). Most of the compressive structure (except Balkanides) is Jurassic (red lines). Extension near the southern margin of the Moesian Platform (blue lines) is related to the opening of the Western Black Sea.

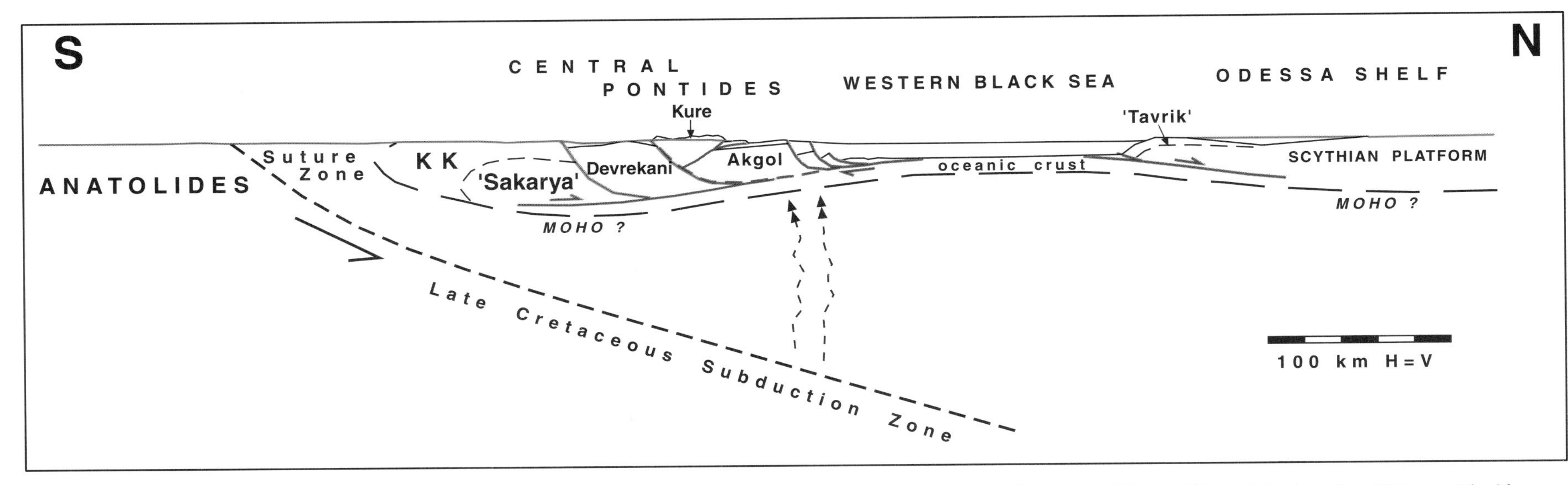

Figure 7. Structural cross section through the eastern part of the Western Black Sea from central Turkey (Central Pontides) to the Odessa Shelf. Cimmeride compressive structures are obscured by later events. The Western Black Sea is shown as the result of highly asymmetric extension above a crustal detachment. In the Pontides, Cretaceous extensional basins were inverted in the Tertiary. Both Figures 6 and 7 show the subducting Tethys Plate and related magmatism as it would have been in the Late Cretaceous, to identify fore-arc and back-arc regions.

and Achara-Trialet belt). Compression continued into the Miocene, but decreased thereafter as the convergence between Europe and the Arabian Plate became taken up by the westward escape of Anatolia by using the North Anatolian fault system. Compression had little direct impact on the Western Black Sea but appears to have completely closed the eastern end of the Eastern Black Sea (Banks et al., this volume). Extensional basin margin structures such as the Odessa Shelf, the Shatsky Ridge, and the Mid-Black Sea High retained their Cretaceous geometries (with local minor inversion) while being buried by the thick Tertiary sediments.

ACKNOWLEDGMENTS

We thank our former colleagues at BP, especially John Rudat, for numerous contributions to our studies of the Black Sea; Alastair Robertson (Edinburgh University), Timur Ustaömer (İstanbul University) and Okan Tüysüz (İstanbul Technical University), for useful ideas and discussions on Pontide geology; and Mircea Sandulescu and Eugen Gradinaru for introducing us to Dobrogea and the Peceneaga-Camena fault.

REFERENCES CITED

Banks, C.J., this volume, Basins and thrust belts of the Balkan coast of the Black Sea, *in* A. Robinson, ed., Regional and petroleum geology of the Black Sea and surrounding region: Memoir 68, p. 115–128.

Banks, C.J., A.G. Robinson, and M.P. Williams, this volume, Structure and regional tectonics of the Achara-Trialet thrust belt and the adjacent Rioni and Kartli foreland basins, Republic of Georgia, *in* A. Robinson, ed., Regional and petroleum geology of the Black Sea and surrounding region: Memoir 68, p. 331–346.

Catuneanu, O., 1992, The geology of the Black Sea Romanian shelf of Central Dobrogean type: Revue Roumaine de Geologie, v. 36, p. 73–81.

Chatalov, G., 1988, Recent developments in the geology of the Strandzha Zone in Bulgaria: İstanbul Technical University Bulletin, v. 41, p. 433–465.

Dachev, C., V. Stanev, and P. Bokov, 1988, Structure of the Bulgarian Black Sea area: Bolletino di Geofisica Teorica e Applicata, v. 30, no. 117-118, p. 79–107.

Dewey, J.F., W.C. Pitman III, W.B.F. Ryan, and J. Bonnin, 1973, Plate tectonics and the evolution of the Alpine system: Geological Society of America Bulletin, v. 84, p. 3137–3180.

Finetti, I., G. Bricchi, A. Del Ben, M. Pipan, and Z. Xuan, 1988, Geophysical study of the Black Sea area: Bolletino di Geofisica Teorica e Applicata, v. 30, no. 117-118, p. 197–324.

Görür, N., 1988, Timing of opening of the Black Sea Basin: Tectonophysics, v. 147, p. 247–262.

Gradinaru, E., 1984, Jurassic rocks of North Dobrogea. A depositional-tectonic approach: Revue Roumaine de Géologie, Géophysique et Géographie, v. 28, p. 61–72.

Gradinaru, E., 1988, Jurassic sedimentary rocks and bimodal volcanics of the Cirjelari-Camena outcrop belt: evidence for a transtensile regime of the Peceneaga-Camena Fault: Revue Roumaine de Géologie, Géophysique et Géographie, v. 32, p. 96–121.

Guterch, A., M. Grad, R. Materzok, and E. Perchuc, 1986, Deep structure of the Earth's crust in the contact zone of the Palaeozoic and Precambrian platforms in Poland (Tornquist-Teisseire Zone): Tectonophysics, v. 128, p. 251–279.

Letouzey, J., B. Biju-Duval, A. Dorkel, R. Gonnard, K. Kristchev, L. Montadert, and O. Sungurlu, 1977, The Black Sea: a marginal basin; geophysical and geological data, *in* B. Biju-Duval and L. Montadert, eds., International Symposium on the Structural History of the Mediterranean Basins: Editions Technip, Paris, p. 363–376.

Manetti, P., M. Boccaletti, and A. Peccerillo, 1988, The Black Sea: remnant of a marginal basin behind the Srednegorie–Pontides island arc system during the Upper Cretaceous–Eocene times: Bolletino di Geofisica Teorica e Applicata, v. 30, no. 117-118, p. 39–51.

Nachev, I.K., 1991, Hettangian–Bathonian paleogeodynamics of Bulgaria: Review of the Bulgarian Geological Society, v. LII/3, p. 30–38.

Okay, A.I., and H. Mostler, 1994, Carboniferous and Permian radiolarite blocks from the Karakaya Complex in northwest Turkey: Turkish Journal of Earth Sciences 3, p. 23–28.

Okay, A.I., A.M.C. Şengör, and N. Görür, 1994, Kinematic history of the opening of the Black Sea and its effect on the surrounding regions: Geology, v. 22, p. 267–270.

Pol'ster, L.A., et al., 1976, History of geological development of northern Bulgaria during the Paleozoic: International Geological Review, v. 19/6, p. 633–646.

Robinson, A.G., and E. Kerusov, this volume, Stratigraphic and structural development of the Gulf of Odessa, Ukrainian Black Sea: implications for petroleum exploration, *in* A. Robinson, ed., Regional and petroleum geology of the Black Sea and surrounding region: Memoir 68, p. 369–380.

Robinson, A.G., G. Spadini, S.A.P.L. Cloetingh, and J. Rudat, 1995a, Stratigraphic evolution of the Black Sea: inferences from basin modelling: Marine and Petroleum Geology, v. 12, p. 821–835.

Robinson, A.G., C.J. Banks, M.M. Rutherford, and J.P.P. Hirst, 1995b, Stratigraphic and structural development of the Eastern Pontides, Turkey: Journal of the Geological Society, v. 152, p. 861–872.

Robinson, A.G., J.H. Rudat, C.J. Banks, and R.L.F. Wiles, 1996, Petroleum geology of the Black Sea: Marine and Petroleum Geology, v. 13, p. 195–223.

Sandulescu, M., 1978, The Moesic Platform and the North Dobrogean orogen, *in* M. Lemoine, ed., Geological atlas of Alpine Europe and adjoining areas: Elsevier, Amsterdam, p. 427–460.

Sarıbudak, M., 1989, A palaeomagnetic approach to the origin of the Black Sea: Geophysical Journal International, v. 99, p. 247–251.

Şengör, A.M.C., and Y. Yılmaz, 1981, Tethyan evolution of Turkey: a plate tectonic approach: Tectonophysics, v. 75, p. 181–241.

Şengör, A.M.C., Y. Yılmaz, and I. Ketin, 1980, Remnants of a pre-Late Jurassic ocean in Northern Turkey: fragments of Permian–Triassic Palaeotethys: Geological Society of America Bulletin, v. 91, p. 599–609.

Şengör, A.M.C., Y. Yılmaz, and O. Sungurlu, 1984, Tectonics of the Mediterranean Cimmerides: nature and evolution of the western termination of Palaeotethys, *in* J.E. Dixon and A.H.F. Robertson, eds., The geological evolution of the Eastern Mediterranean: Geological Society Special Publication 17, p. 17–112.

Şengör, A.M.C., D. Altiner, A. Cin, T. Ustaömer, and K.J. Hsü, 1988, Origin and assembly of the Tethyside orogenic collage at the expense of Gondwanaland, *in* M.G. Audley-Charles and A. Hallam, eds., Gondwana and Tethys: Geological Society of London Special Publication 37, p. 119–181.

Tüysüz, O., A.A. Dellaloglu, and N. Terzioglu, 1995, A magmatic belt within the Neotethyan suture zone and its role in the tectonic evolution of northern Turkey: Tectonophysics, v. 243, p. 173–191.

Ustaömer, T., and A.H.F. Robertson, 1994, Palaeozoic marginal basin and subduction-accretion, the Palaeotethyan Küre Complex, Central Pontides, northern Turkey: Journal of the Geological Society of London, v. 151, p. 291–305.

Yılmaz, O., and D. Boztuğ, 1986, Kastamonu granitoid belt of northern Turkey: first arc plutonism product related to the subduction of the Paleotethys: Geology, v. 14, p. 179–183.

Ziegler, P.A., 1990, Geological atlas of Western and Central Europe: Shell International Petroleum Maatschappii and Geological Society, London.

Zonenshain, L.P., and X. Le Pichon, 1986, Deep basins of the Black Sea and Caspian Sea as remnants of Mesozoic back-arc basins: Tectonophysics, v. 123, p. 181–212.

Tari, G., O. Dicea, J. Faulkerson, G. Georgiev, S. Popov, M. Stefanescu, and G. Weir, 1997, Cimmerian and Alpine stratigraphy and structural evolution of the Moesian Platform (Romania/Bulgaria), *in* A.G. Robinson, ed., Regional and petroleum geology of the Black Sea and surrounding region: AAPG Memoir 68, p. 63–90.

Chapter 6

Cimmerian and Alpine Stratigraphy and Structural Evolution of the Moesian Platform (Romania/Bulgaria)

Gabor Tari
Amoco Production
Houston, Texas, U.S.A.

Oprea Dicea
Prospectiuni S.A.
Bucharest, Romania

Joe Faulkerson
Amoco Production
Houston, Texas, U.S.A.

Georgi Georgiev
St. Kliment Ohridski University
Sofia, Bulgaria

Svetlozar Popov
Geology and Geophysics Corporation
Sofia, Bulgaria

Mihai Stefanescu
Amoco-Romania
Bucharest, Romania

Gary Weir
Amoco Production
Houston, Texas, U.S.A.

ABSTRACT

The vast thickness (>10 km) of relatively undeformed Cambrian to Recent sedimentary cover of the Moesian Platform in Romania and Bulgaria offers an exceptional record of Cimmerian and Alpine tectonics in the surrounding Carpathian and Balkan thrust-fold belts.

Above the Hercynian unconformity, Permian to Middle Triassic continental to shallow marine sediments deposited in a facies succession are quite typical for the European passive margin. Widespread Anisian–Carnian volcanism indicates an aborted rifting period also marked by locally very thick

(>2000 m) evaporites. Based on systematic analysis of reflection seismic data and isopach maps, we interpret two large-scale subsurface features (Optasi-Peris uplift and North Bulgarian arch) as Middle Triassic rift flanks associated with two aborted, E-trending branches of the Paleotethys Basin. The striking appearance of the crystalline basement and the deeper levels of the Paleozoic succession (Cambrian-Silurian systems) in the subcrop of the overlying Jurassic can be understood in terms of rapid uplift and severe denudation of the rift shoulders.

The extensional period was replaced during the Norian–Rhaetian times by a compressional regime in the whole Moesian Platform. Although these Late Triassic Cimmerian folds were undoubtedly formed due to compression, detailed structural analysis permitted a more specific interpretation of the deformation in terms of fault-bend folding in a north-vergent, thin-skinned thrust-fold belt. Structural modeling of the anticlines suggests relatively minor shortening (9–18%). Whereas these structures are very characteristic for North Bulgaria, their structural significance is gradually diminishing to the north, in the Romanian part of the platform. In a wider paleotectonic scenario, the north-vergent anticlines beneath the Moesian Platform are interpreted as the frontal, foreland thrust-fold belt of the Mediterranean Cimmerides propagating into the foreland.

Above the Cimmerian unconformity, the sedimentary facies and thickness relations of Lower to Middle Jurassic carbonates clearly show the development of a south-facing passive margin. East-west–trending Jurassic troughs bounded by normal faults can be documented in the southern, Bulgarian side of the Moesian Platform. From the Early Cretaceous on, sedimentation was clearly influenced by successive compressional periods in the Balkans approaching the southern edge of the Moesian Platform. These consecutive Cretaceous through Eocene Alpine compressive periods, such as the Austrian, Mediterranean, Laramian, Illyrian, and Pyrenean, created the north-vergent thrust-fold belt of the Balkans separated from the platform sequence by a series of relatively narrow foredeeps. Whereas the final docking of the Balkans on the Moesian Platform margin occurred at the end of the Eocene, this did not happen on the northern edge until the late Miocene, when the Carpathians stopped moving onto the platform.

INTRODUCTION

The Black Sea is bordered on the west by the Scythian Platform of the Ukraine, the North Dobrudja Orogene of Romania, the Moesian Platform of Romania and Bulgaria, and the Balkanides s.l. of Bulgaria and Turkey (Figure 1). Whereas to date hydrocarbon exploration efforts have resulted in fairly modest discoveries in the Black Sea (Robinson et al., 1996), starting in the 1950s, the Moesian Platform turned out to be one of the most prolific petroleum provinces in Central/Eastern Europe.

The Moesian Platform is generally considered a mature basin from an exploration point of view (e.g., Georgiev and Atanasov, 1993; Ionescu, 1994; Nicolescu and Popescu, 1994; Vuchev et al., 1994; Popescu, 1995). Therefore, a large number of papers were published discussing the specifics of the area in Romania and in Bulgaria. However, with some exceptions, such as the work of Semenovich and Namestnikov (1981), the Moesian Platform has not been described in its entirety. In this chapter, we present a regional overview of the stratigraphy and tectonic evolution of the entire Moesian Platform. It is our goal to document that the Moesian Platform witnessed a much more complex structural history than previously thought. While this chapter should be regarded as a compilation of existing data and interpretations

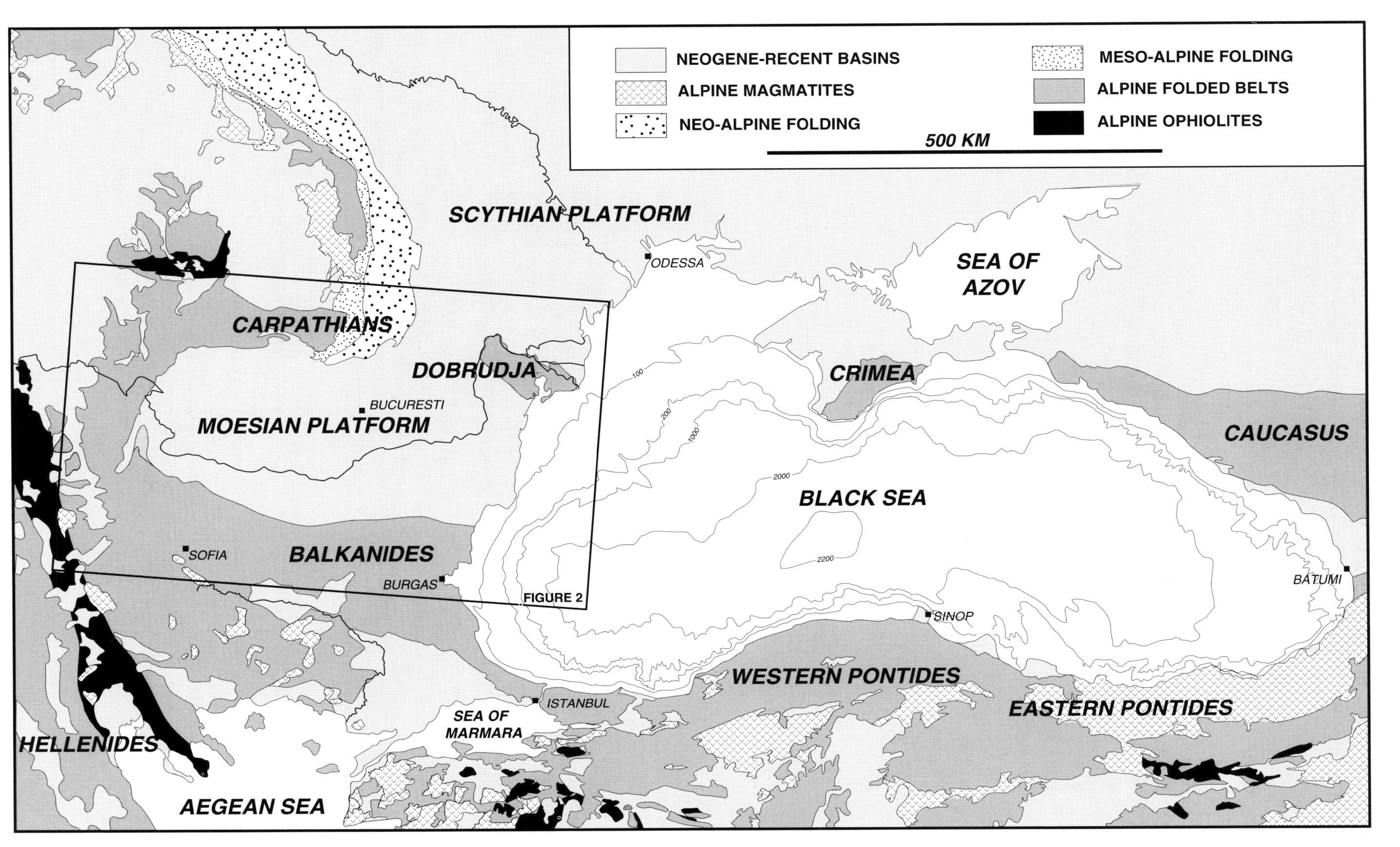

Figure 1. Geologic map of the Black Sea and surrounding regions. General setting of the Moesian Platform in relation to the Black Sea, compiled from maps by Sandulescu (1984) and Bocaletti et al. (1988). Inset shows the location of Figure 2a.

on the Alpine (i.e., Cretaceous–Recent) time period, a drastically new model is proposed here concerning the Cimmerian (i.e., Triassic–Jurassic) time period. Consequently, the Cimmeride orogenic events and their interpretation are discussed in more detail.

After the overview of the general geologic setting of the Moesian Platform, we begin with a brief description of the Phanerozoic stratigraphy. To illustrate the entire subsurface geology of the area, a few original reflection seismic data sections are reproduced from both the Romanian and the Bulgarian sides of the platform. We then consider further evidence for our new interpretation of the Cimmerian evolution of the Moesian Platform. The supporting data, such as isopach and subcrop maps, suggest a Middle Triassic rift shoulder and associated rift and hinterland basins in Northern Bulgaria, followed by a compressional regime in the Late Triassic. After the overview of the Alpine evolution of the area, the discussion returns to the regional implications of our new Cimmerian geodynamic scenario in the context of the geology of the Black Sea.

GEOLOGICAL SETTING

The Moesian Platform, as the promontory of the European Platform s.l. , is separated from the Scythian Platform by the North Dobrudja orogen on its northeastern side (Figure 1). The platform is bordered to the north and to the west by the South Carpathians, to the south by the Balkanides, and to the east by the Black Sea. In contrast to surrounding thrust-fold belts, the Moesian Platform has a flat topography, with typical elevations only up to 200 m above sea level. The geological boundary of the platform is well defined by the leading edge of the surrounding Alpine thrust belts (Figure 2a). However, toward the Black Sea, only a broad transitional zone can be outlined where the relatively undeformed platform succession has been downfaulted to the east during the Middle Cretaceous opening of the Western Black Sea Basin (Okay et al., 1994; Robinson et al., 1996; Banks, this volume).

The basement of the Moesian Platform is traditionally subdivided into a western, Wallachian, and an eastern, Dobrudjan block, separated by the Intra-Moesian fault (Figure 2b). This NW-trending fault was introduced based on the different development of the basement (Visarion et al., 1988). Whereas the western part is made up of epi- and mesometamorphic Precambrian rocks, the eastern unit is characterized by weakly metamorphosed, Upper Vendian–Early Cambrian flyschoid deposits ("greenschists"), unconformably overlying a middle Proterozoic metamorphic succession. The distinction between the Wallachian and Dobrudjan blocks is also supported by geophysical data, the crustal thickness being ~30–33 km in the west as opposed to ~40–45 km in the east (Mocanu et al., 1991). Geothermal data (Andreescu et al., 1989) also show a distinction between the two basement areas: The western area is significantly warmer (5–6°C/100 m) than the eastern one (1–2°C/100 m).

Other major NW-trending faults in the Romanian part of the platform, such as the Peceneaga-Camena fault (Figure 2b), have been defined based on variations in the tectonostratigraphic development of the very thick (>10 km) Phanerozoic succession. In general, the platform sequence tends to be thinner and has more stratigraphic gaps in it to the northeast, in the Dobrudja area. These changes are attributed to the inferred strike-slip character of the NW-trending faults as the result of distributed transcurrent deformation along the Tornquist-Teisseyre Zone (Sandulescu, 1984).

Further to the west, however, the influence of the NW-trending faults seem to diminish, and major basement highs, such as the Craiova-Optasi-Peris and Vidin-Strehaia uplifts (Paraschiv, 1979), are controlled by E- and NE-trending faults, respectively (Figure 2b). In the area of these uplifts, the crystalline basement or the deeper part of the Paleozoic was found below the Jurassic unconformity. Similarly, in the North Bulgarian uplift, rocks as old as Devonian subcrop below the Jurassic. Between these basement highs, a number of basins can be outlined where the cumulative thickness of the Paleozoic and Triassic succession can exceed 10 km. These apparently pre-Jurassic basins are the Lom-Bailesti, Alexandria, and Tutrakan-Calarasi basins (Figure 2b).

In a tectonostratigraphic sense, the Phanerozoic succession of the Moesian Platform can be subdivided into three major units, corresponding to (from bottom to top) the Hercynian, Cimmerian, and Alpine orogenic stages. The anchi- to epimetamorphic pre-Carboniferous Paleozoic succession of the Moesian Platform (Figure 3) was formed during the Hercynian orogeny. However, rocks younger than Devonian show no sign of metamorphism and are relatively undeformed. The overlying Permian–Lower Cretaceous rocks were formed during the Cimmerian orogeny (Şengör et al., 1984). The boundary between the Cimmerian and Alpine succession is not nearly as well defined as the Hercynian/Cimmerian one and should be placed, somewhat arbitrarily, close to the top of the Lower Cretaceous sequence in the area of the Moesian Platform. The apparent lack of a well-defined boundary (Figure 3) is due to the temporal and spatial overlap between the Cimmerian and Alpine orogenes (Şengör, 1984).

PHANEROZOIC STRATIGRAPHY OF THE MOESIAN PLATFORM

The thick (locally ≥10 km) Phanerozoic sedimentary fill overlying the crystalline basement is traditionally subdivided into four sedimentary megasequences (Paraschiv, 1979). These are the Middle Cambrian–Upper Carboniferous, Permian–Upper Triassic, Jurassic–Senonian, and Paleogene–Quaternary megasequences, separated by major unconformities (Figure 3). Note that this subdivision is somewhat different from the tectonostratigraphic scheme outlined above. The main lithologic characters of the major lithologic units are described below. Although the descriptions below do not enter the level of individual

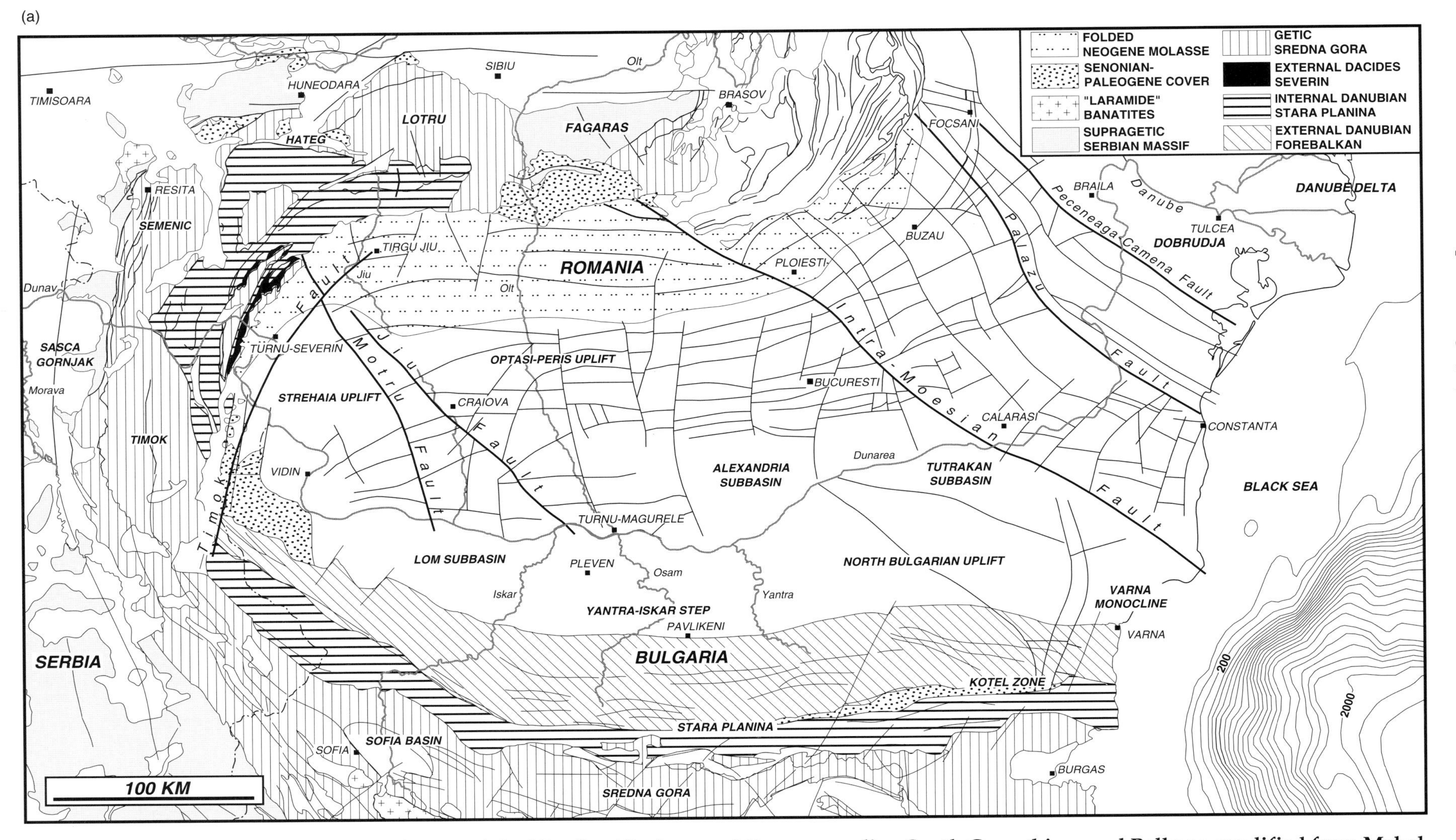

Figure 2. (a) Simplified geological sketch map of the Moesian Platform and the surrounding South Carpathians and Balkans, modified from Mahel (1974), Sandulescu (1984), and Visarion et al. (1988).

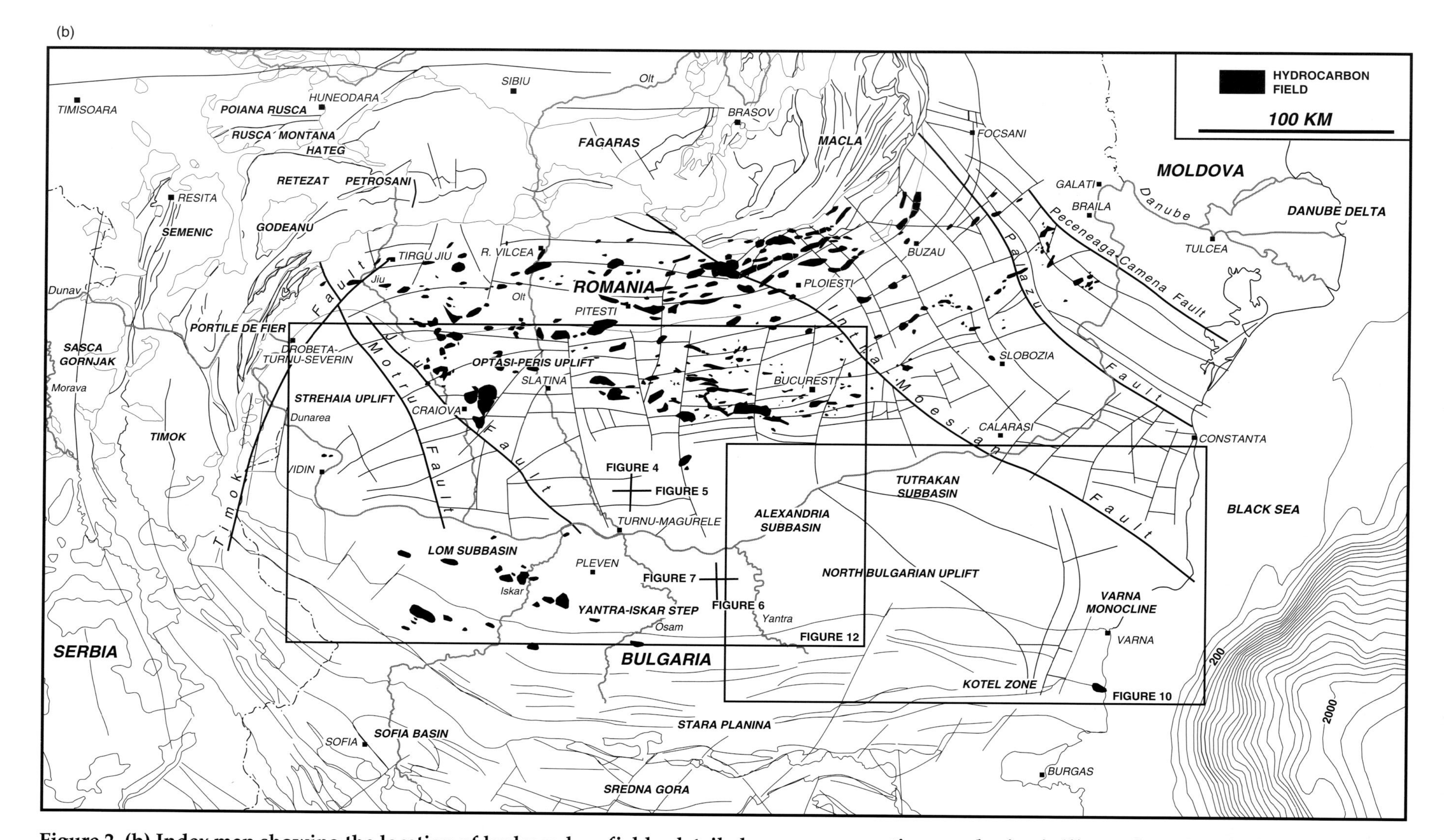

Figure 2. (b) Index map showing the location of hydrocarbon fields, detailed maps, cross sections, and seismic illustrations. For the location of the area shown relative to the Black Sea, see Figure 1.

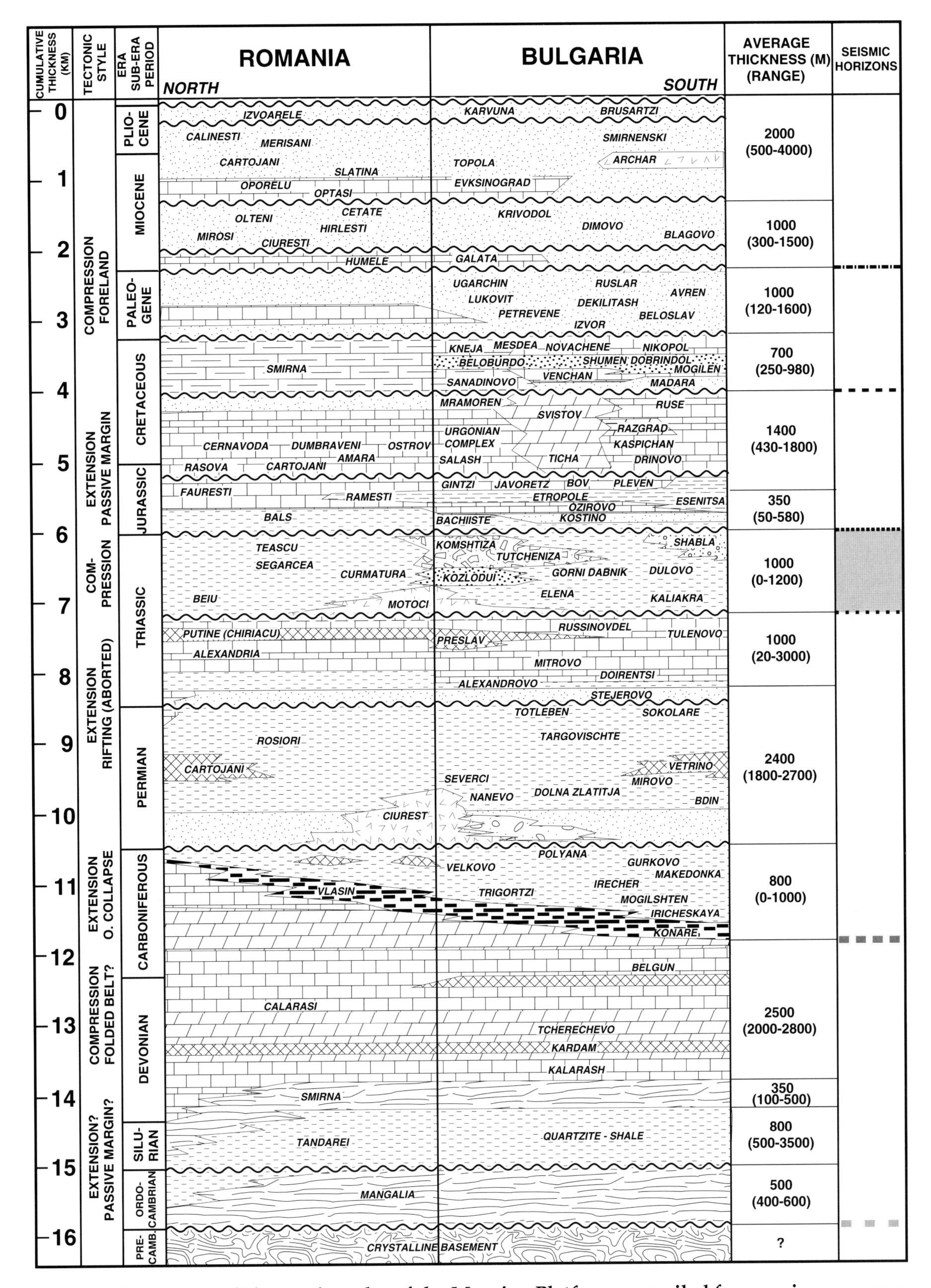

Figure 3. Phanerozoic lithostratigraphy of the Moesian Platform, compiled from various sources listed in the text.

formations, the lithostratigraphy of the Bulgarian side of the platform has been defined in much more detail (Figure 3).

The Middle Cambrian–Upper Carboniferous megasequence can be further subdivided into three lithological subunits, reaching 5500 m in total thickness:

1. The lower clastic group (Upper Cambrian–Middle Devonian) contains basal clastic formations made up of arkose-like and quartzitic sandstones with silt and shale intercalations. This sequence is overlain unconformably by Silurian graptolite-shales with an average thickness of 800 m. The lowermost part of the Devonian is represented by quartzitic sandstones with silts, limestones, and conglomerate interbeddings (average thickness of ~370 m).
2. The carbonate group (Middle Devonian–Carboniferous) is predominantly composed of massive limestones and dolomites, with bituminous limestones and evaporitic levels, reaching a total thickness up to 2800 m.
3. The upper clastic group (Middle–Upper Carboniferous) is represented by a characteristic coal succession overlain by silts, marls, and sandstones with a typical thickness of 700–800 m. These molasse-like clastics are missing in certain areas.

The Permian–Triassic megasequence is very different from the underlying sequence, having red-colored continental clastics, and evaporitic and carbonated rocks with maximum thickness (>6000 m) in the Alexandria basin (Figure 2b). Above major basement uplifts, such as in the area of the Craiova-Optasi-Peris uplift (Figure 2b), this megasequence may be partially or completely missing, primarily due to postdepositional erosion rather than nondeposition. Within the Permian–Triassic megasequence, three subunits can be distinguished:

1. The lower red clastic group (Permian–Lower Triassic) directly overlies the Hercynian unconformity and is composed of clay, silt, sand, quartzitic sandstone, calcareous sandstone, and conglomerate with interbeddings of dolomitic limestones, anhydrite, and salt. The total thickness of this subunit can reach 2700 m. Figure 3 shows an unconformity between the Permian and the Lower Triassic. According to Paraschiv (1982), this unconformity reflects not only a break in sedimentation, but it is the result of the latest Hercynian orogenetic event.
2. The carbonate group (Middle Triassic) averages ~1000 m in thickness, transitionally overlying the shallow-water clastics. This succession is predominantly composed of neritic limestone and dolomites with marl and anhydrite/salt intercalations.
3. The upper red clastic group (Upper Triassic) can have a maximum thickness of about 1200 m; however, this succession is only locally developed. This unit is made up of shales, marls, sands, sandstones, and conglomerates, deposited dominantly in continental environments. Anhydrites, gypsum, and, rarely, salt can also be found (Georgiev, 1981).

Magmatic activity was quite common during this megacycle, especially at the beginning of the Permian and around the boundary of the Middle–Upper Triassic. Effusive volcanic activity produced rocks of bimodal composition accompanied by large volumes of pyroclastites.

The Jurassic–Cretaceous megasequence (Lower Jurassic–Senonian) can reach a maximum thickness of ~3500 m, mostly in the southern, Bulgarian side of the platform. After the break of deposition at the end of the Triassic, sedimentation typically resumed in the Middle Jurassic and lasted, with a short break in the Aptian, until the Senonian. This megasequence is characterized by carbonate development.

1. The sedimentary column begins with continental to neritic clastics with a maximum thickness of ~600 m. Whereas sedimentation in the northern side of the platform did not commence until the Toarcian, it started at significantly earlier times in the southern side, locally as early as in the Cimmerian.
2. Starting with the Callovian, clastic sediments were replaced by massive carbonates with an average thickness of 1700 m, developed in both neritic and pelagic facies. Locally, reefal buildups can be found in Urgonian facies. Within this carbonate complex, a somewhat subdued unconformity may correspond to the Late Cimmerian orogenic phase. The carbonate succession has some siliciclastic intercalations in it formed during the Albian and Cenomanian.
3. Above a major unconformity, the Senonian is unevenly developed throughout the area, and it is mostly missing in the western part of the Romanian Moesian Platform. Its thickness is typically a few hundred meters and is mainly composed of neritic limestones.

The Paleogene–Neogene megasequence (Paleocene–Pleistocene) shows an asymmetry in space and time, reflecting the changing influence exerted by the Balkans and the Carpathians, respectively.

1. The Paleocene and Eocene sedimentation is thick (≤1600 m) in the southern part of the platform, whereas it is missing or very thin in the north. The lithology is characterized by marls and sandstones, and locally by carbonates. A major unconformity on top of the Paleogene succession marks an extended period of subaerial exposure and erosion during the late Oligocene and early Miocene.
2. The Neogene succession is very thick in front of the nonemergent leading edge of the Carpathians at the northern margin of the platform, with a thickness >5500 m. A relatively thin (20–200 m), middle Miocene shallow-water carbonate-dominated unit (locally with anhydrites) is overlain by upper Miocene deep-water clastics, marls, and sandstones. The unconformity separating them can be understood in terms of a foredeep unconformity in the sense of Bally (1989). Within the upper Miocene succession, another regional

unconformity may correspond to a large (~1500 m) sea level fall in the Black Sea (Robinson et al., 1995). This fall, as a dramatic base-level change in the drainage area of the Carpathian foredeep, might be responsible for the widespread subaerial erosion associated with this unconformity. The overlying carbonates and clastics were developed in a brackish environment, indicating increasing isolation from the sea.

3. The Quaternary formations are of various thicknesses (0–200 m), developed mainly at the margins of the platform where significant neotectonic uplift occurred since the Pliocene. Consequently, these deposits are composed of continental clastics, such as conglomerate, sand, clay, and loess.

REPRESENTATIVE REFLECTION SEISMIC SECTIONS

The reflection seismic illustrations come from the central part of the Moesian Platform (Figure 2b). In this area, the post-Triassic sequence is fairly thin, ~1200 m thick, and has an undeformed, platform-like character. The seismic sections, however, clearly show the folded character of the pre-Jurassic sequence beneath the pronounced Cimmerian unconformity. These seismic examples are regarded as fairly typical in the boundary zone between Romania and Bulgaria. For additional seismic data from the Moesian Platform, see Dicea et al. (1980) and Ionescu (1994) on Romania, and Atanasov (1980) and Atanasov and Bokov (1983) on Bulgaria.

On the N-S–oriented dip sections (sections B, D in Figures 4, 6), the Cimmerian folds are typically 10–20-km-wide anticlines. The apexes of these anticlines are usually erosionally truncated to variable stratigraphic levels (Middle Triassic–Permian). A closer look on the anticlines reveals their asymmetric nature; the dip of beds on the limbs suggests northerly vergence. Available well data give a good stratigraphic control on the uppermost part of the anticlines and the Upper Triassic clastic basin fill in between them. In fact, this 0–2000-m-thick clastic sequence, the Segarcea Formation in Romania (Paraschiv, 1981) or the Moesian Group in Bulgaria (Vaptsarova et al., 1984), is the result of the syndepositional growth of the Cimmerian structures. This sequence has been highlighted in the line drawing interpretations because of its significance in the understanding of the Late Triassic deformations (see below). Given the published average thickness relations within the Triassic–Paleozoic succession of the Moesian Platform (Paraschiv, 1982), we tentatively correlated several deeper (i.e., pre-Permian) stratigraphic horizons too. The E-W–oriented strike sections (sections A, C in Figures 5, 7) illustrate the good lateral correlatability of these stratigraphic levels.

STRUCTURAL MODELING OF A CIMMERIAN ANTICLINE

In order to better understand the nature of the Cimmerian folds, we have analyzed one of them in detail. This particular structure is the Cirligati anticline, shown on the southern side of seismic section A (Figure 4a, b). Based on the observed geometric patterns, this structure can be best understood in terms of fault-bend folding (Suppe, 1983). Cross-section balancing of three alternative structural interpretations of this fold (Figure 8), based on vertical slip or flexural slip, revealed shortening of ~2–4 km (or ~9–18%). Whereas the stratigraphic position of the upper decollement level seems to be close to the Permian–Carboniferous boundary, the lower detachment either runs within the Devonian or deeper, close to the top of the Silurian. All of these stratigraphic levels can be regarded as potential decollement levels. However, in the line-drawing interpretations of the sections, we opted for a deeper, lower detachment.

Independent evidence for the fault-bend folding origin of the Cirligati anticline was provided by the forward modeling of the internal geometry of the growth sequence (e.g., onlap on the forelimb and thinning and truncation on the backlimb, see Figure 4a, b). A few analyses of these numerical models as described by Hardy and Poblet (1995) reproduced the observed geometric patterns of this particular Cimmerian structure (Figure 8).

CIMMERIAN (TRIASSIC–JURASSIC) TECTONICS

In the Moesian Platform area, an aborted rifting period occurred during the Anisian–Carnian?, followed by a Norian–Rhaetian compressional period. Because of debatable paleontological evidence (Petrunova-Olova, 1992), the exact time of this transition remains obscure.

Middle Triassic Rift Tectonics

The existing literature (Paraschiv, 1978) describes Permian–Triassic magmatites drilled in numerous wells around Craiova (Figure 2b) in the Romanian Moesian Platform as the general result of a failed intracratonic rifting period. A more specific picture of Middle Triassic rifting was outlined by Georgiev (1994, 1996a, b) and Byrne et al. (1995), who considered an E-W–trending rift basin just to the south of the North Bulgarian uplift (Figure 2b). In this particular area, a surprisingly thick (i.e., >2500 m) Middle Triassic evaporite succession was interpreted as a typical rift-basin deposit (Georgiev, 1994, 1996a, b). It is to be noted, however, that the extreme thickness is partly due to remobilization of the salt during Cretaceous compression (Georgiev, 1981; Georgiev et al., 1984).

In this chapter, we further refine this rifting model, interpreting the North Bulgarian uplift as the rift flank of the Middle Triassic rift basin. Uplifted shoulders in the proximity of rift basins are quite common (Braun and Beaumont, 1989). They have a typical asymmetric morphology (Figure 9), with a steep slope facing the rift basin and a gentle slope on the other side toward a basin termed the hinterland basin (van der Beek et al., 1994). The rift flank separating these basins has a typical height of ~2–3 km and, due to the long-lasting

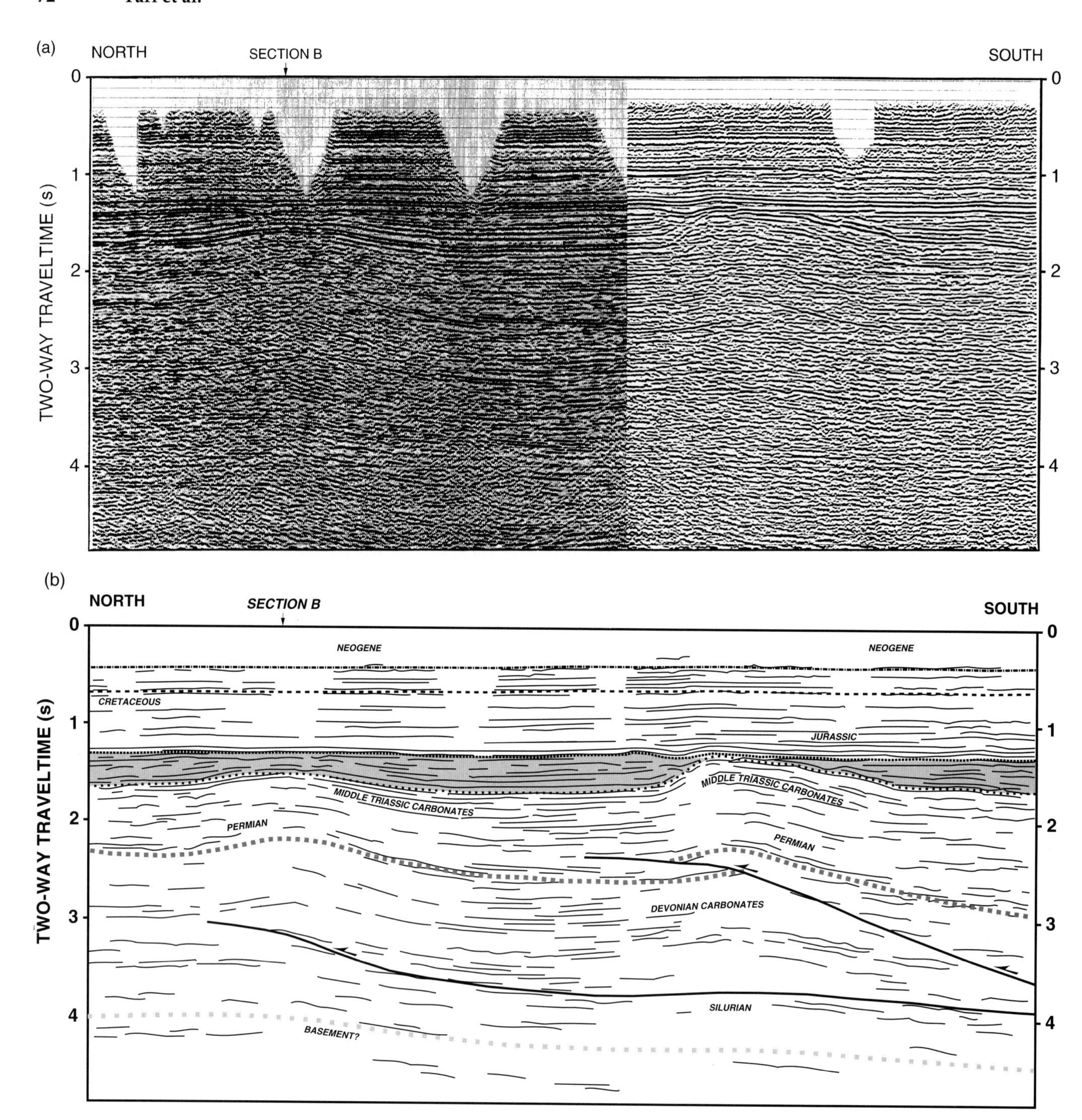

Figure 4. (a) Dip-oriented reflection seismic section A, from the Romanian side of the Moesian Platform. For location, see Figure 2c. (b) Line-drawing interpretation of reflection seismic section A. Legend of seismic horizons is shown in Figure 3.

erosion at its crest, basement rocks from 4–5 km depth can be exposed.

A series of published isopach and facies maps (Bokov and Chemberski, 1987; Figure 10) from NE Bulgaria (Figure 2b) illustrates the spatial and temporal evolution of the North Bulgarian rift shoulder. Figure 10a shows an Anisian carbonate platform with various lithofacies distributions, but with fairly uniform thickness. By the Ladinian (Figure 10b), a subaerially exposed, E-W–trending and elongated area emerged from this platform area. This incipient rift flank became even more pronounced by the Carnian and Norian?, when it clearly separated the evaporite rift basin to the south from the Tutrakan subbasin to the north (Figure 9c). This latter basin extends into Romania and is characterized by significantly thinner sedimentary Middle–Upper Triassic succession; therefore, it is interpreted as the hinterland basin of the North Bulgarian rift shoulder (Figure 9). By the Early Jurassic (Figure 10d), the whole

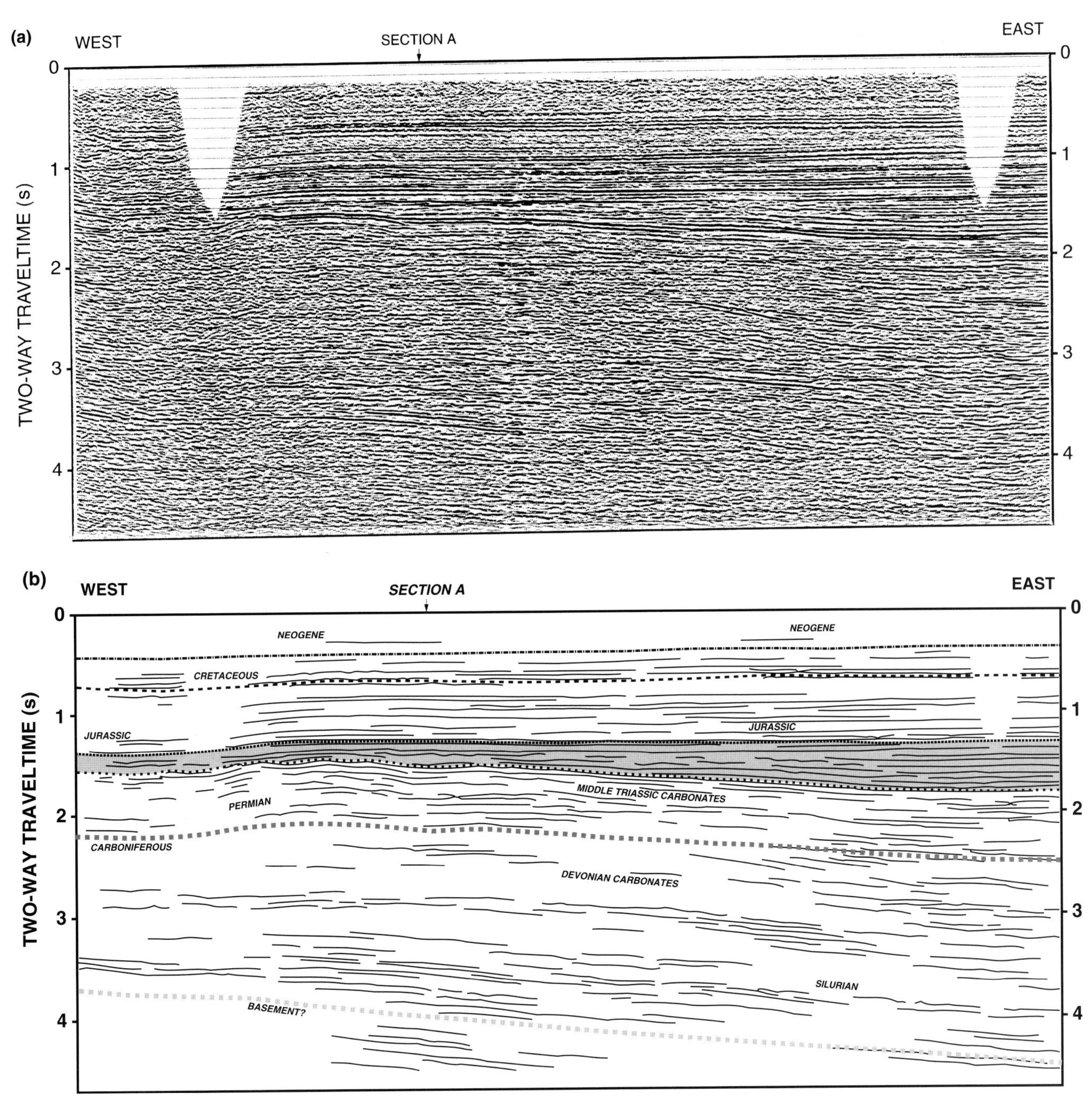

Figure 5. (a) Strike-oriented reflection seismic section B, from the Romanian side of the Moesian Platform. For location, see Figure 2b. (b) Line-drawing interpretation of reflection seismic section B. Legend of seismic horizons is shown in Figure 3.

region became subaerially exposed, except in the former rift basin where the topographic depression inherited from the Upper Triassic still served as a local depocenter.

The pre-Jurassic subcrop map (Figure 10e) illustrates the differential erosion removing from the crest of the rift shoulder ~1–4 km thick succession (Figure 3). The subcrop map also reveals the presence of a smaller extensional block between the rift flank and the rift basin, also striking E-W, between Veliko Tarnovo, Sumen, and Varna. Note the pronounced NW-SE–oriented Intra-Moesian fault and another fault with the same strike across the North Bulgarian uplift. These faults are shown as normal faults by Bokov and Chemberski (1987). However, since they appear to postdate the Upper Triassic (Figure 10e) and predate the Middle Jurassic (see numerous well formation tops in Figure 10d), they should be broadly coeval with the first compressional events in the Dobrudja Orogene (Sandulescu, 1984). Moreover, since the NW-SE strike is the same as in the Dobrudja area, ~100 km further to the northeast (Figure 1), we tentatively interpret these faults as steeply dipping, Lower Jurassic reverse faults.

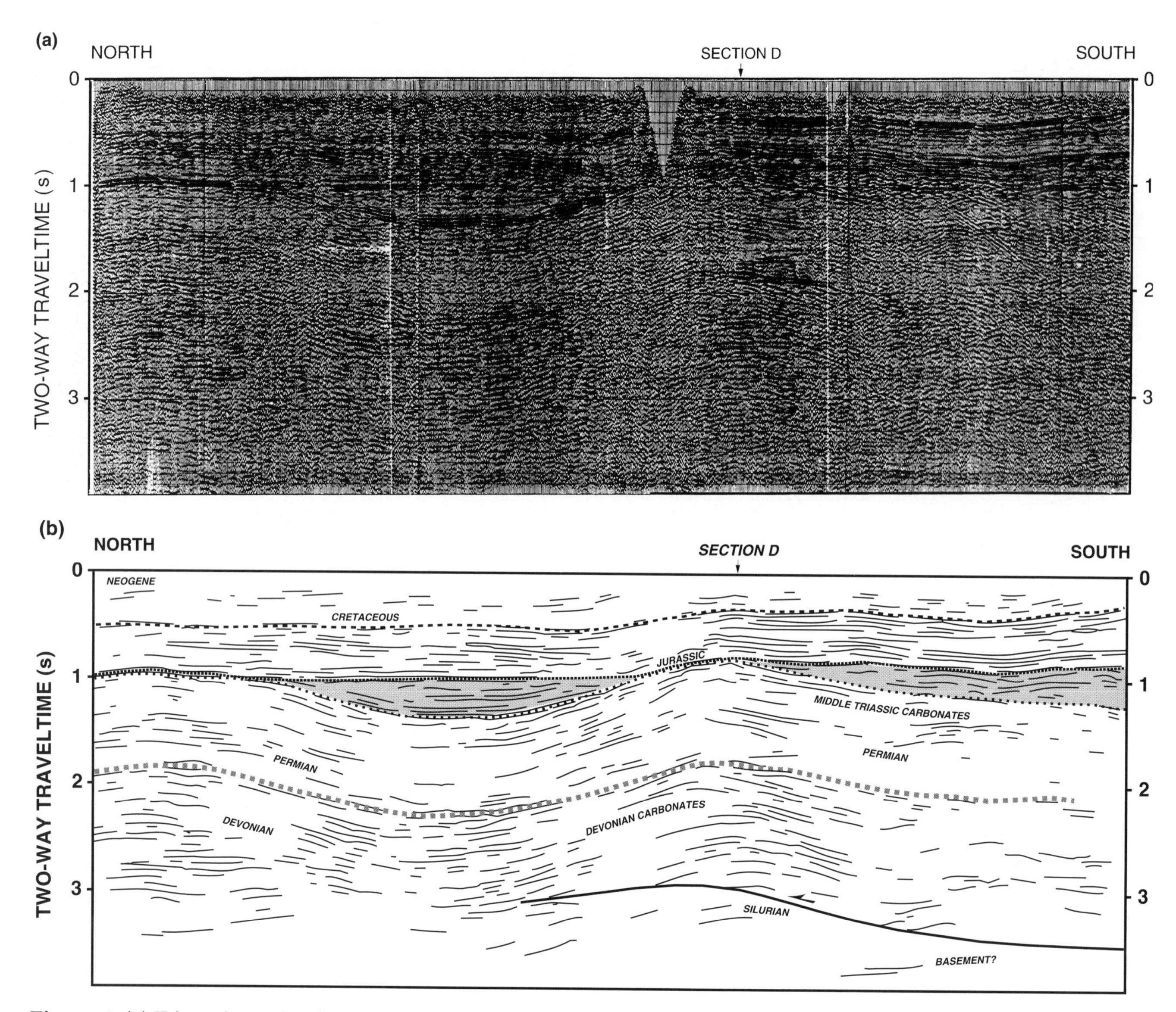

Figure 6. (a) Dip-oriented reflection seismic section C, from the Bulgarian side of the Moesian Platform. For location, see Figure 2c. (b) Line-drawing interpretation of reflection seismic section C. Legend of seismic horizons is shown in Figure 3.

Although there are no comparable published isopach and subcrop maps from the area of the Craiova-Optasi-Peris uplift in Romania (Figure 2b), several published cross sections, seismic profiles, and stratigraphic columns (Paraschiv, 1974, 1979, 1981; Vinogradov, 1988; Dicea et al., 1991; Ionescu, 1994) suggest a similar interpretation to that of the North Bulgarian uplift. An important difference is that in the case of the Craiova-Optasi-Peris uplift, even the crystalline basement subcrops the Jurassic along a narrow, E-W–trending elongated strip, suggesting ≤5 km of erosion removed the entire Paleozoic–Lower-Middle Triassic section (Figure 3). Thus, looking at the Moesian Platform as a whole (Figure 11), the North Bulgarian and Craiova-Optasi-Peris rift flanks may correspond to two separate rift basins, offset in an en-echelon manner. The Lom-Bailesti, Alexandria, and Tutrakan-Calarasi subbasins may represent depocenters in a larger hinterland basin (Figure 12) common to both rifts. Note that there is no evidence at present for a rift basin to the north of the Craiova-Optasi-Peris uplift, mostly because it is in considerable depth (5–10 km) underneath the leading edge of the Carpathians (Figure 13).

Late Triassic Compression

Widespread folding of the pre–Jurassic sequence underneath the Moesian Platform of Romania and Bulgaria is traditionally attributed to the Late Triassic Cimmerian phase (Georgiev and Atanasov, 1993). To the east, these folds can be traced to the Black Sea shelf (Dachev et al., 1988; S. Bottomley, 1995, personal communication).

As the selected seismic sections from the central part of the Moesian Platform demonstrated, the Cimmeride

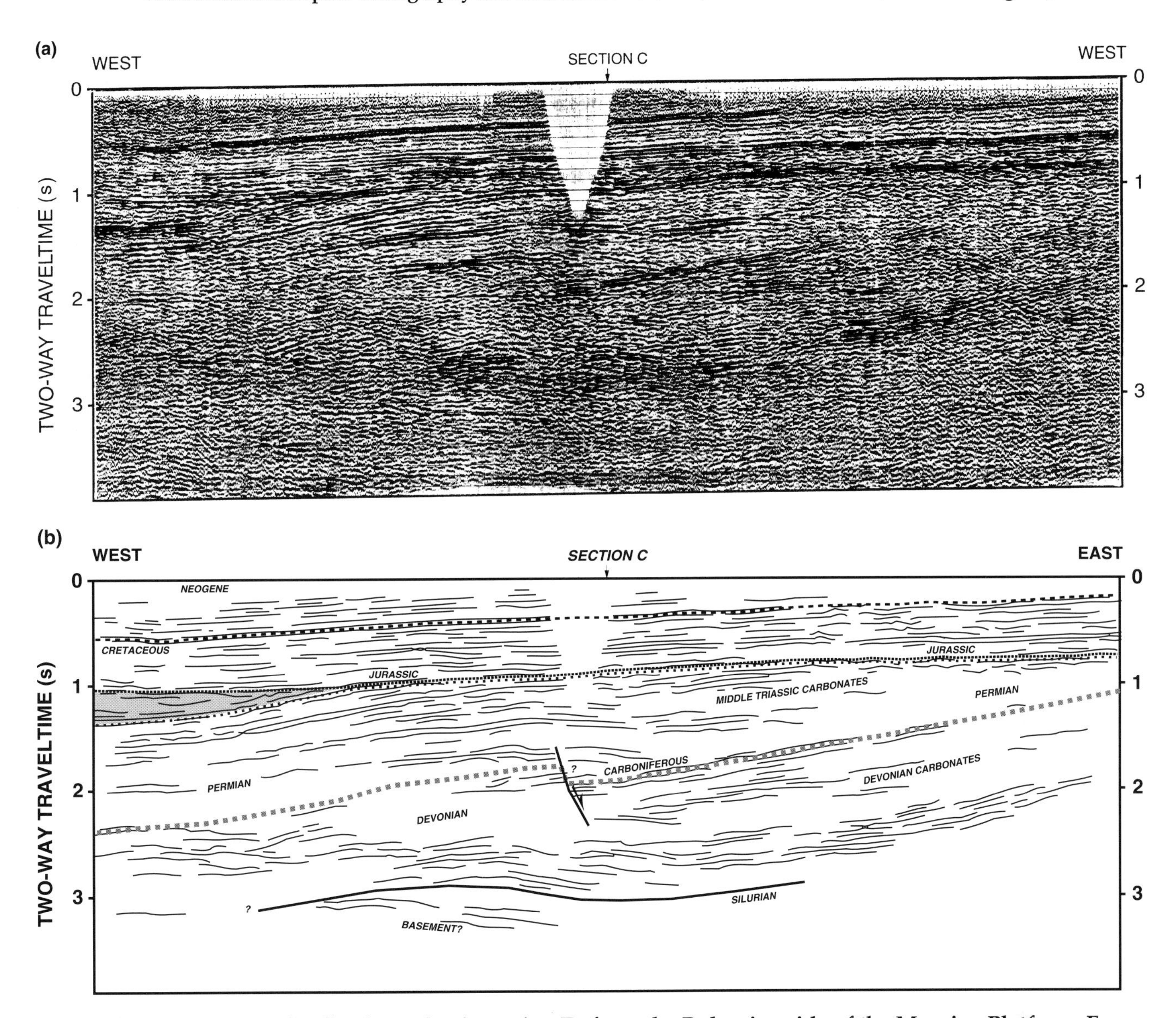

Figure 7. (a) Dip-oriented reflection seismic section D, from the Bulgarian side of the Moesian Platform. For location, see Figure 2c. (b) Line-drawing interpretation of reflection seismic section D. Legend of seismic horizons is shown in Figure 3.

folds are actually fault-bend folds eroded to highly variable stratigraphic levels. Between the anticlines, a 0–2000-m-thick Upper Triassic clastic sequence corresponds to the syntectonic growth of the structures. Therefore, even though the lower part of the Upper Triassic (Carnian?) corresponds to the rifting episode, it is this isopach map, based on the compilation of several published maps (Atanasov, 1980; Paraschiv, 1981; Atanasov and Bokov, 1983), that best shows the regional extent of the Cimmerian anticlines, diminishing gradually to the north of the Danube (Figure 12). Note that the short-wavelength, 10–30-km-wide "piggyback" basins are superimposed on the large-wavelength, E-W–trending, roughly 100-km-wide hinterland basin.

The detailed analysis of a particular anticline above indicated the top of the Carboniferous and the top of the Silurian as the most likely levels of detachment. However, based on the lithology of the pre-Jurassic succession, several potential decollement horizons can be outlined (Figure 3). Three anhydrite and/or salt levels can provide efficient decollements: the Middle Triassic, the Middle Permian, and the Middle Devonian. The dominantly shaly Upper Carboniferous and Silurian periods are also potential decoupling levels. Finally, the top of the Precambrian crystalline basement is also a good candidate for a regional decoupling level. Therefore, our conceptual transect through the whole Moesian Platform (Figure 13) shows the potential involvement of these other detachment levels in the Cimmerian fault-bend folding, too.

Since the observed Cimmerian fold geometry consistently shows a northerly vergence, the lower detachment may not be associated with an evaporite and/or salt horizon (Davis and Engelder, 1985).

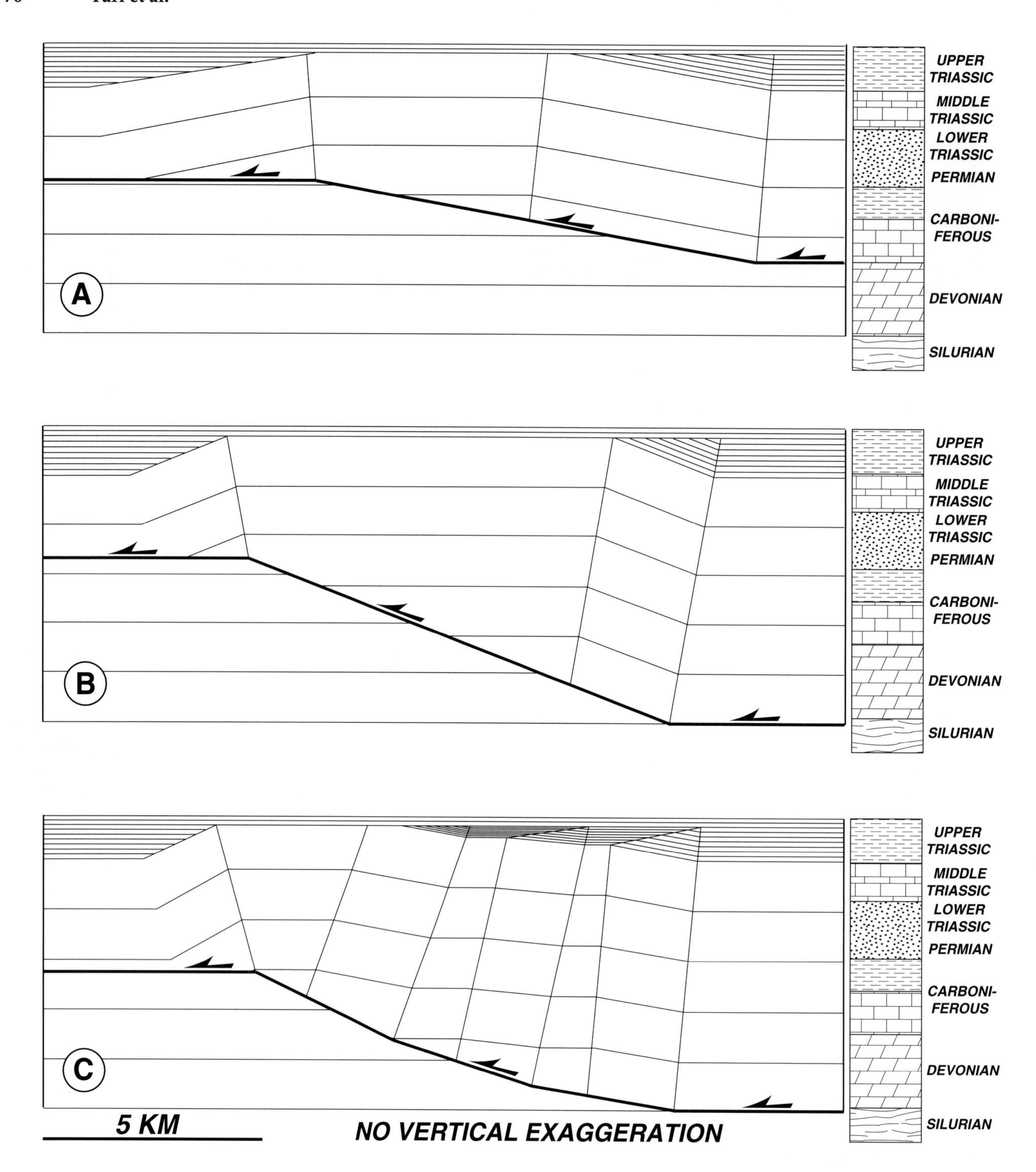

Figure 8. Forward modeling of the Upper Triassic growth strata geometry associated with the Cirligati anticline, Romania. These models were constrained by a reflection seismic data section located very close to section A shown in Figure 4a. These forward models were run by Josep Poblet (1995, personal communication) using the technique described by Hardy and Poblet (1995). The pregrowth strata show fault-bend folding geometry with the involvement of different upper and lower detachment levels: (A) top Carboniferous/top Devonian, (B) intra-Permian/top Silurian, and (C) top Carboniferous/top Silurian. The observed growth strata are approximately 800 m thick and encompass a time span of ~28 m.y.; therefore, an average sedimentation rate of 0.025 m/ka was used. The total run time of all the models is 36 m.y., with the actual growth occurring during the first 28 m.y. (displayed at intervals of 4 m.y.). All of these models were run assuming a background sedimentation rate of 0.025 m/ka and a diffusion coefficient of 1.0 m^2/a. From the three models shown, version C appears to approximate the best observed geometry of the Cirligati anticline (Figure 4a).

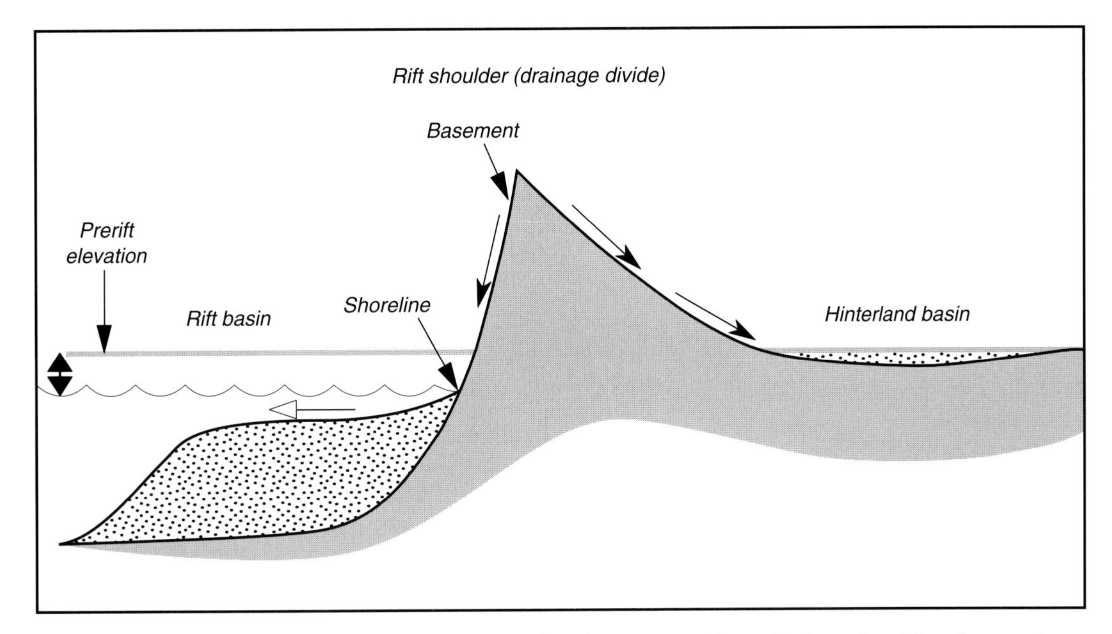

Figure 9. Diagram illustrating the relationship between rift and hinterland basins and the rift shoulder (flank) in between (van Balen, 1995).

Jurassic Passive Margin

Following a short-lived period of subaerial exposure, the Jurassic and lowermost Cretaceous saw gradual subsidence in a passive-margin setting (Emery and Georgiev, 1993). The overall thickening of the Jurassic to the south (Figure 13) suggests a south-facing passive margin. Especially at the southern, Bulgarian edge of the Moesian Platform, several normal faults formed, controlling a Jurassic horst-and-graben system (Tchoumatchenko and Sapunov, 1994). On the Romanian side of the platform, these half-grabens appear to be missing. However, Dicea et al. (1991) report Jurassic faulting from the western area shifting generally to the east by the Early Cretaceous.

ALPINE (CRETACEOUS/TERTIARY) TECTONICS

The Jurassic–Early Cretaceous extensional period was followed by multiphase compression along the perimeter of the platform. Within this overall extensional period, the Late Jurassic "New" Cimmerian phase produced only a subdued unconformity (Figure 3). This is in contrast with other areas of the Paleotethys, farther to the east, where this compressional phase seems to be far more significant (Şengör, 1984).

Cretaceous Compression

In the southern, Bulgarian margin of the Moesian Platform, the growth of the north-vergent Balkan thrust-fold belt commenced in the Early Cretaceous, continued during the Paleocene, and concluded during the Eocene (Emery and Georgiev, 1993). The development of the Cretaceous shows increasing influence from the south by the approaching Balkan folded belt. This is very clear looking at the drastic thickening of the Cretaceous to the south over the Moesian Platform (Figure 13). The extent of the allochthonous thrust sheets of the Balkans over the Moesian Platform is a much-debated problem (Bokov et al., 1993). Similarly, the evidence of consecutive compressional phases in the platform as foredeep unconformities has not been documented so far.

Note that, on the Romanian side of the Moesian Platform, there is no evidence for a Cretaceous foredeep basin, since the thin Cretaceous has a fairly uniform thickness (Figure 13).

Paleogene Compression

The sinistrally transpressive movements in the Balkans culminated in a well-defined foredeep basin (Kamchia Basin) by the end of the Eocene (Doglioni et al., 1996). Again, on the Romanian side of the platform there is no evidence for a comparable foredeep basin, and the Eocene succession is just locally developed, probably due to subsequent erosion (Leu et al., 1983).

The thrust-fold belt of the Balkanides became inactive by the end of the Eocene and the entire area of the Moesian Platform was subaerially exposed until the end of the early Miocene. During this period, a large river system developed in the area of the Moesian Platform, creating large paleovalleys (Paraschiv, 1979) somewhat resembling the present-day drainage system (Figure 2a). The important difference, however, is that this Oligocene?–Early Miocene river system was not draining into the Black Sea Basin, but was draining instead to the area of another basin to the north, at present occupied by the Carpathians.

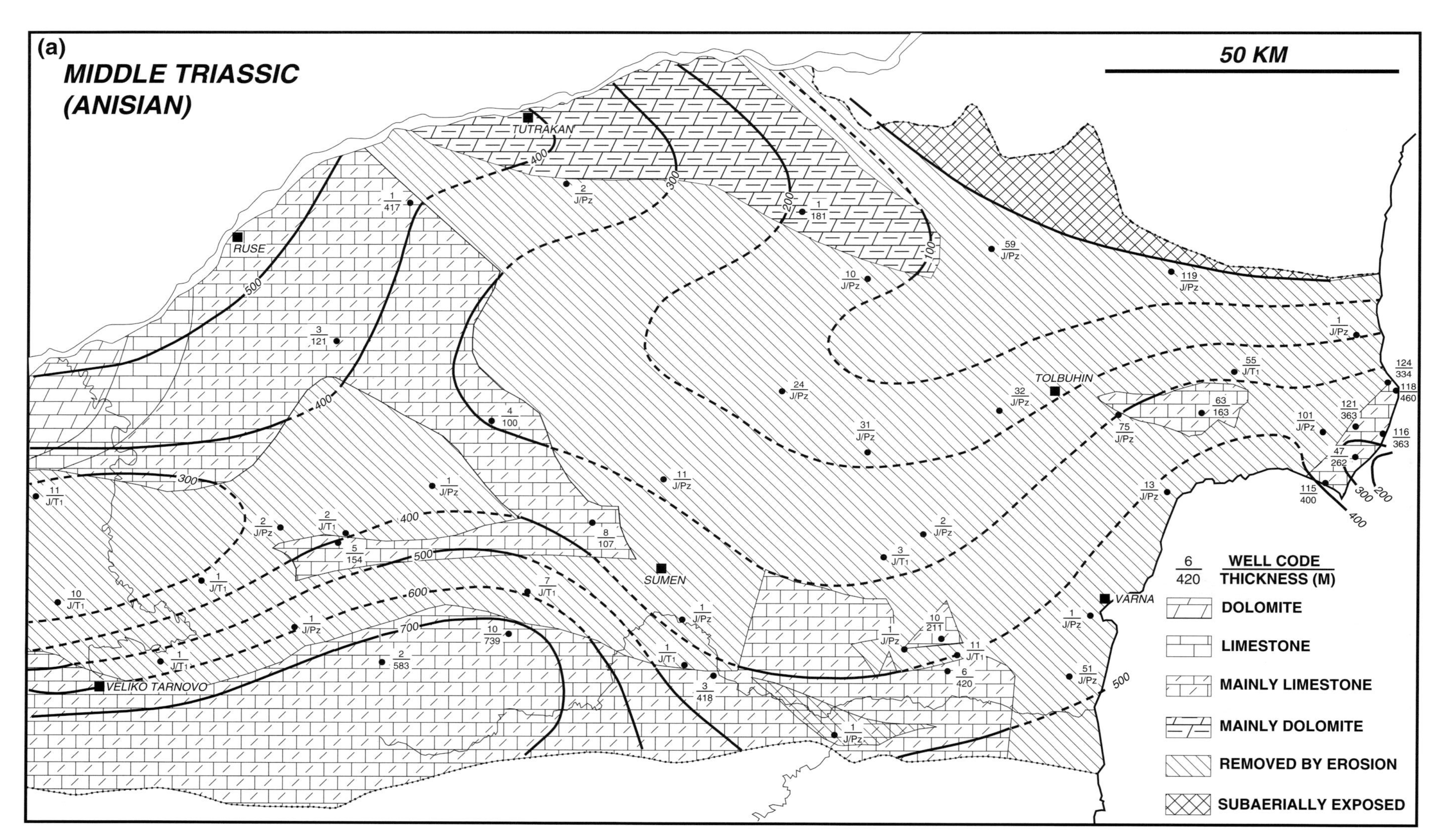

Figure 10. (a) Isopach map of the Anisian (Middle Triassic), North Bulgarian uplift. For location, see Figure 2b. Adapted from Bokov and Chemberski (1987).

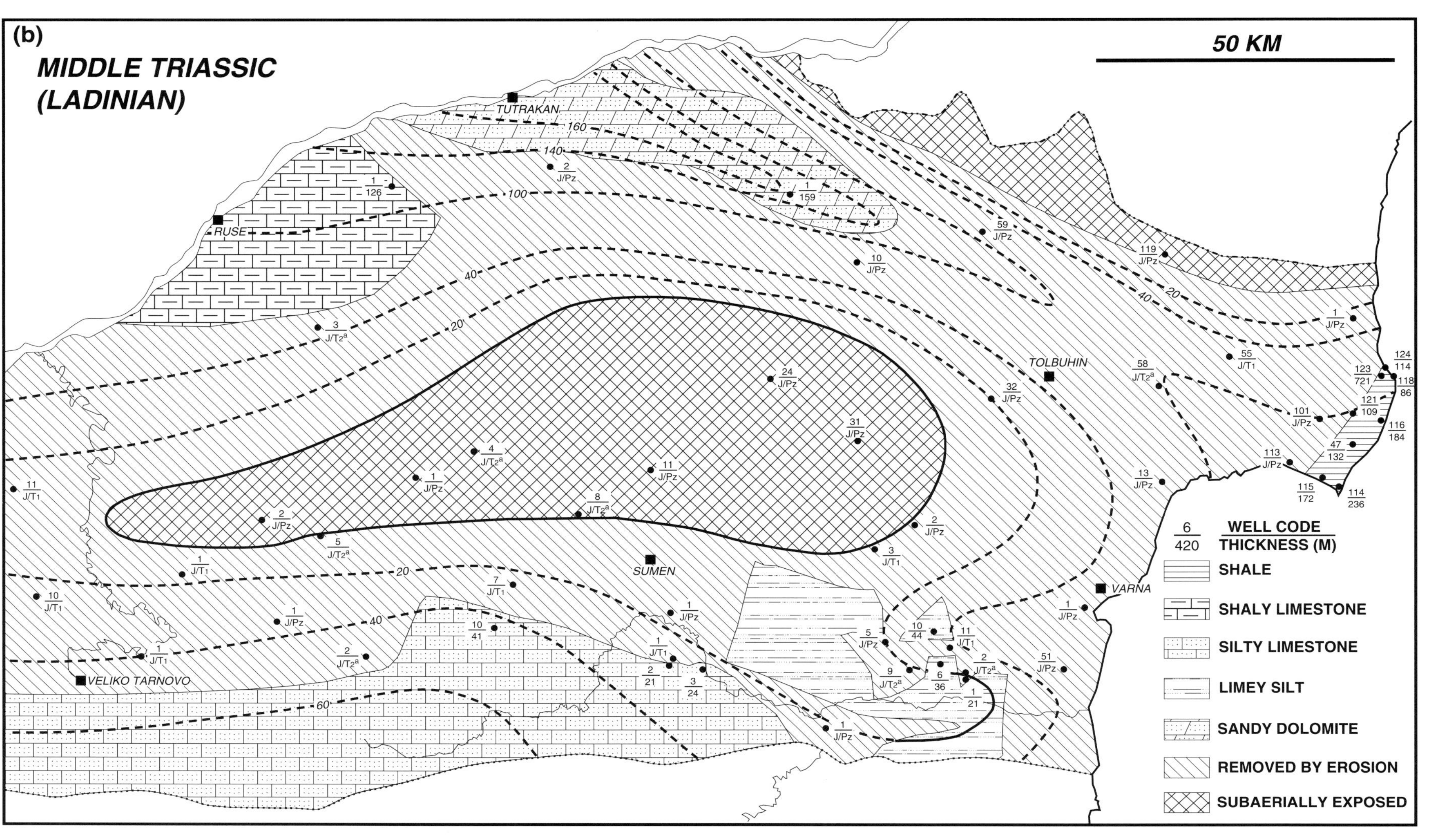

Figure 10. (b) Isopach map of the Ladinian (Middle Triassic), North Bulgarian uplift. For location, see Figure 2b. Adapted from Bokov and Chemberski (1987).

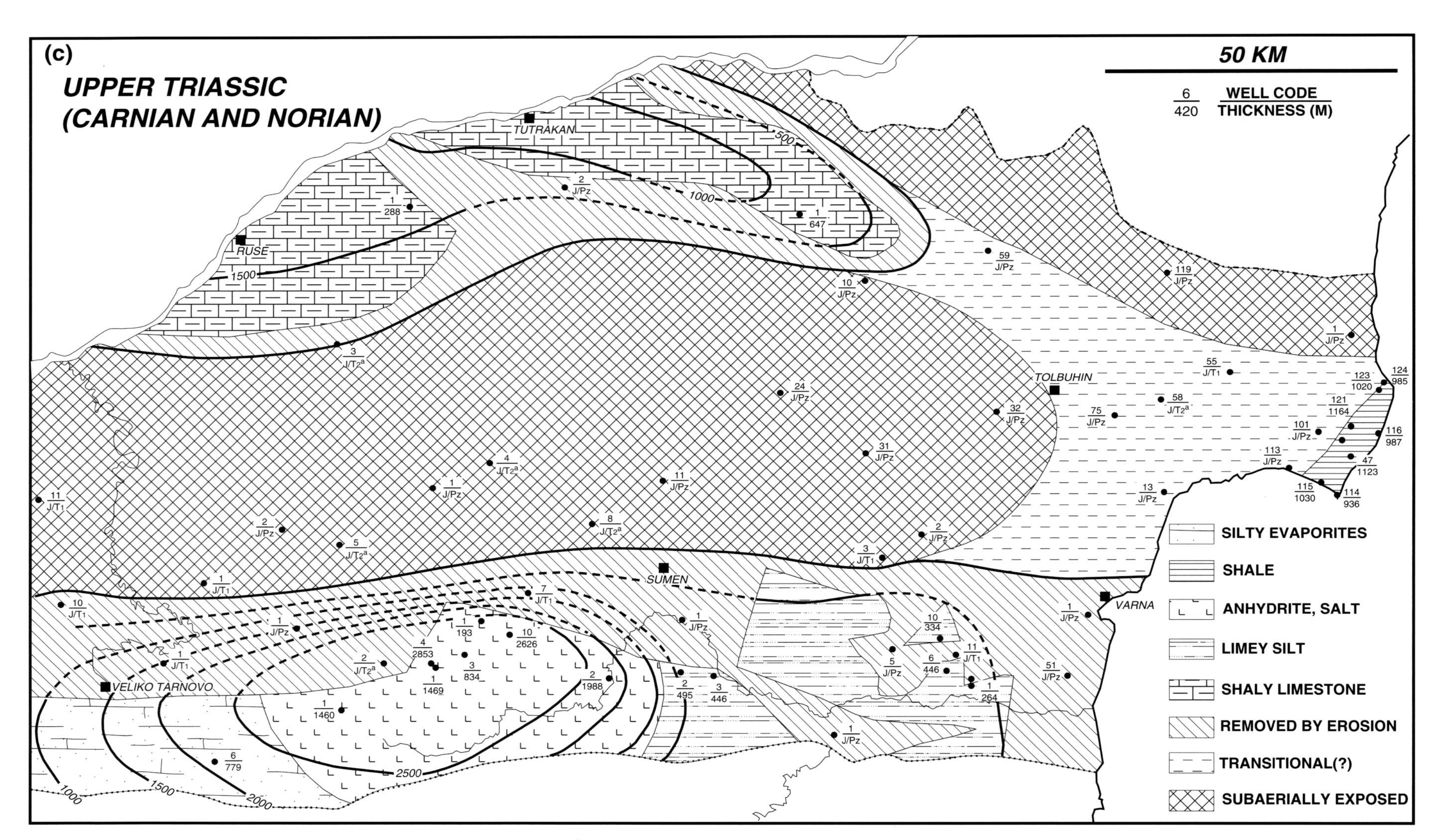

Figure 10. (c) Isopach map of the Carnian and Norian (Upper Triassic), North Bulgarian uplift. For location, see Figure 2b. Adapted from Bokov and Chemberski (1987).

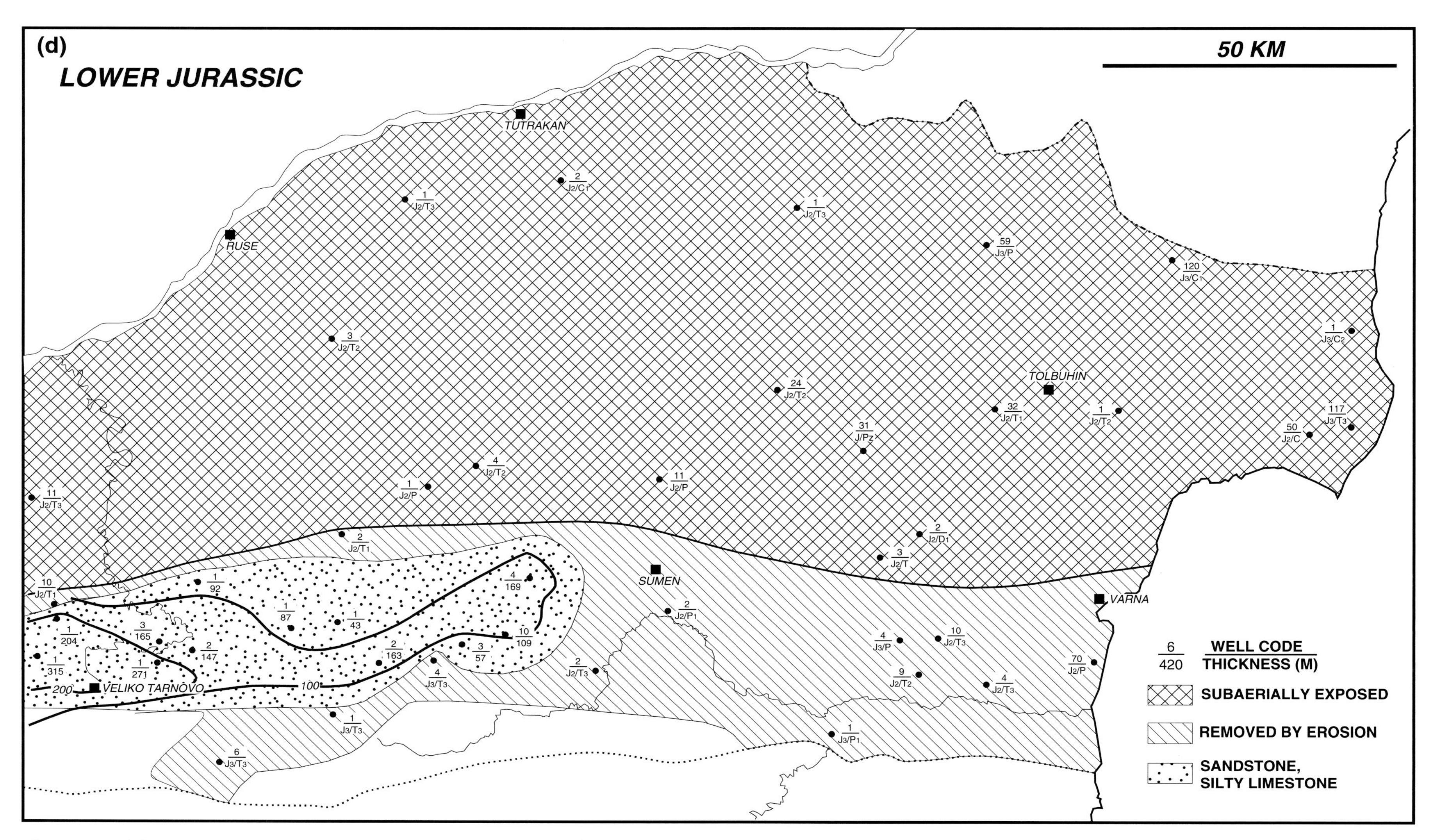

Figure 10. (d) Isopach map of the Lower Jurassic North Bulgarian uplift. For location, see Figure 2b. Adapted from Bokov and Chemberski (1987).

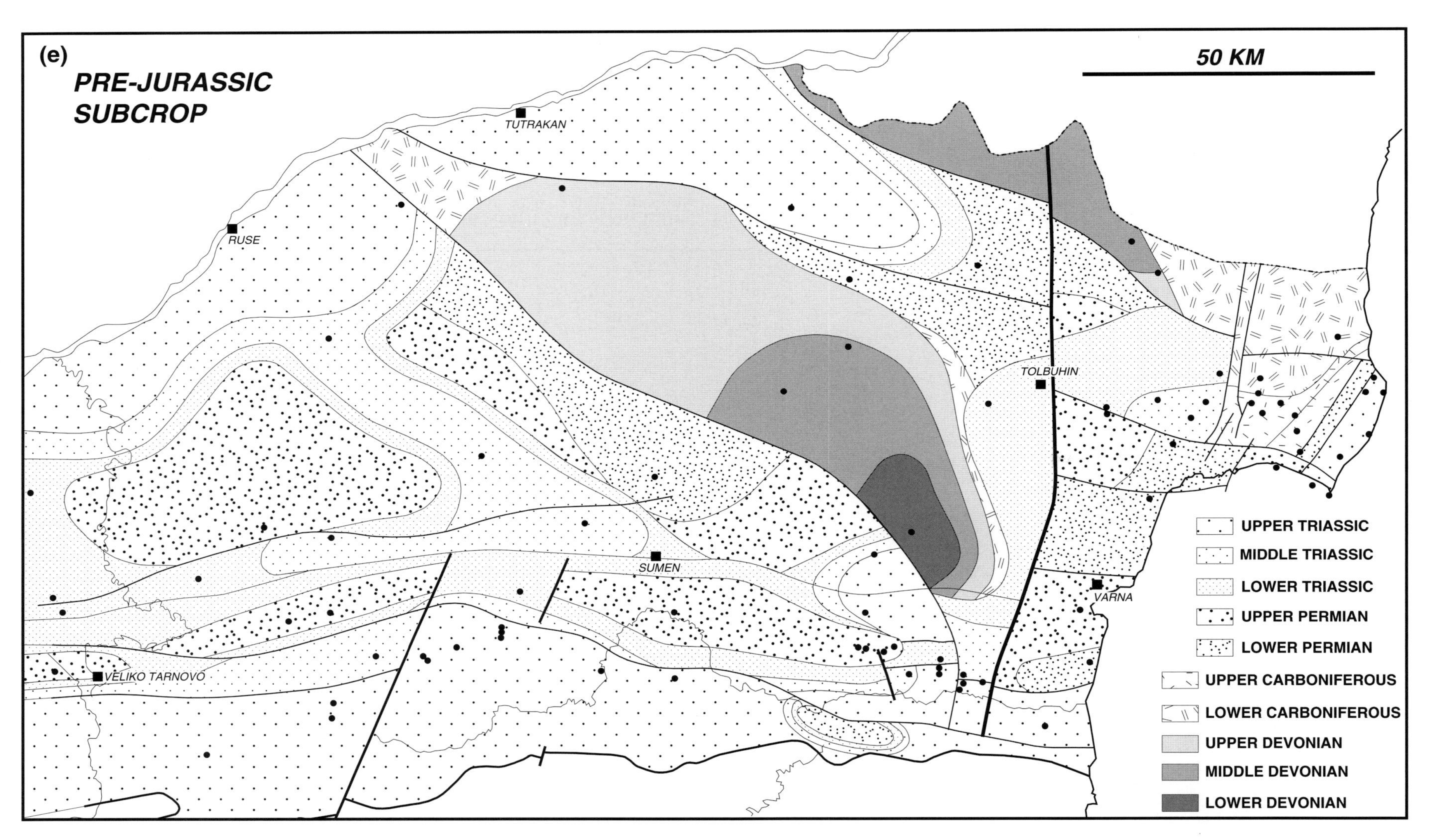

Figure 10. (e) Subcrop map of the Pre-Jurassic, North Bulgarian uplift. For location, see Figure 2b. Adapted from Bokov and Chemberski (1987).

Miocene Compression and Pliocene to Recent Extension

In contrast to the Balkans, at the northern, Romanian edge of the platform, orogeny continued until the late Miocene, creating the outermost belt of the Carpathians and an associated deep foredeep basin (Stefanescu and Polonic, 1993). The leading edge of this Neogene Carpathian thrust front is nonemergent (Figure 2a). During the Miocene, the thrust load of the Carpathian thrust-fold belt produced a very pronounced and deep foredeep basin along the northern margin of the platform. The overall compressional regime (with a component of dextral shear) (Linzer, 1996) created a large number of the E-W–trending normal faults by flexural extension in the platform sequence (Figure 2). These normal faults show repeated periods of reactivation until the end of the late Miocene (Dicea et al., 1991), when the final docking of the southern segment of the Carpathians took place.

Interestingly enough, the southern, Bulgarian side of the platform began to uplift during the Pliocene, this ongoing process is clearly expressed in the present-day topography. This differential uplift, which is also responsible for the formation of the Stara Planina Range (Figure 2a), is interpreted as the result of flexurally driven footwall uplift at the northern edge of the neotectonic Srednogorie rift system (Roy et al., 1996).

PETROLEUM GEOLOGY OF THE MOESIAN PLATFORM

The hydrocarbon fields of the Moesian Platform are distributed in a very asymmetric way: most of the reserves are concentrated in Romania (Figure 2b). Commercial hydrocarbon accumulations were encountered in reservoirs of various ages and lithologies: in Middle–Late Devonian to Early Carboniferous, Middle Triassic, Malm-Neocomian, and Turonian-Senonian carbonates; in Barremian and Albian calcarenites; in Early Sarmatian (late Miocene) limestones; in sandstones of the Permo–Triassic and Dogger; in Albian glauconitic sandstones; in poorly consolidated sands and sandstones of the Mio–Pliocene (Nicolescu and Popescu, 1994; Vuchev et al., 1994). There are also a great many potential source rock intervals in the Phanerozoic sequence (Baltes, 1983).

Fields producing from Paleozoic, Permo-Triassic, and Dogger are located in the western and southern parts, while those in the Cretaceous and Neogene series are found in the central and eastern parts of the platform (Paraschiv, 1979; Georgiev and Atanasov, 1993; Stefanescu and Popescu, 1993; Popescu, 1995). The majority of the fields in the Moesian Platform are oil-bearing. More than two-thirds of the oil and gas/condensate pools were found in the Mesozoic, equally distributed between the Cretaceous, Dogger, and the Permo-Triassic. To date, only a few oil accumulations have been discovered in the Paleozoic succession.

The origin of the numerous oil and gas fields in the Moesian Platform is much debated. According to Paraschiv (1984), hydrocarbons of the Moesian Platform have been formed in several consecutive stages since the Paleozoic. During these stages, the hydrocarbons were frequently remobilized and redistributed. The last, Neogene stage of hydrocarbon generation still appears to be the most prolific.

In contrast, Patrut et al. (1982) suggested that there was only one generation period, the Neogene, when all the formations with source rocks had reached their respective oil and/or gas windows due to the subsidence imposed by the Carpathian thrust-fold belt. In fact, simple one-dimensional modeling of subsidence for several deep wells from the Moesian Platform clearly shows that all the potential source rocks within the Silurian–Badenian interval have reached the oil window during the Late Badenian (Dicea et al., 1991). The Badenian and Sarmatian source rocks reached this maturity level only at their lowermost interval, below ~3500 m. The Paleozoic formations have rapidly crossed this interval and entered the gas window, also indicated by vitrinite reflectance values (Pene, 1996). An additional problem related to the deeper part of the Paleozoic (e.g., Silurian) is that these rocks might have already generated hydrocarbons once during the Hercynian orogeny.

The distribution of hydrocarbon fields is primarily controlled by the E-W–trending Neogene normal faults on the Romanian side of the Moesian Platform (Paraschiv, 1979; Figure 3c). Besides the dominantly structural traps (Figure 13), there are stratigraphic traps related to Triassic and Miocene incised-valley fills. On the Bulgarian side of the platform, most of the fields are structural/stratigraphic (Figure 13) and connected to the Cimmerian unconformity at the Triassic–Jurassic boundary (Georgiev and Atanasov, 1993). These fields were primarily generated by Triassic and Jurassic source rocks (Emery and Georgiev, 1993).

Note that most of the fields on the northern part of the Moesian Platform are located ~70 km to the south of the leading edge of the Carpathians (Figure 2). To explain this distribution, one has to consider exceptionally long lateral migration routes (Popescu, 1995) from the deep kitchen area in the foredeep out onto the platform (Figure 13). An alternative explanation is to infer the generation and vertical migration of hydrocarbons within the platform succession itself (Dicea et al., 1991). Indeed, a large number of fields in the central area of the platform to the southwest of Bucharest (Videle-Cartojani) seem to coincide with an area of relatively high geothermal gradients (5–6°C/100 m) (Paraschiv, 1979).

IMPLICATIONS FOR THE REGIONAL GEOLOGY OF THE BLACK SEA REGION

To the south of the Bulgarian Moesian Platform, in the Forebalkan Zone, widespread folding of the pre-Jurassic succession was documented by Monov (1991). Further to the south, within the Balkanides, the relics of the Cimmerian orogen were classified by Boyanov

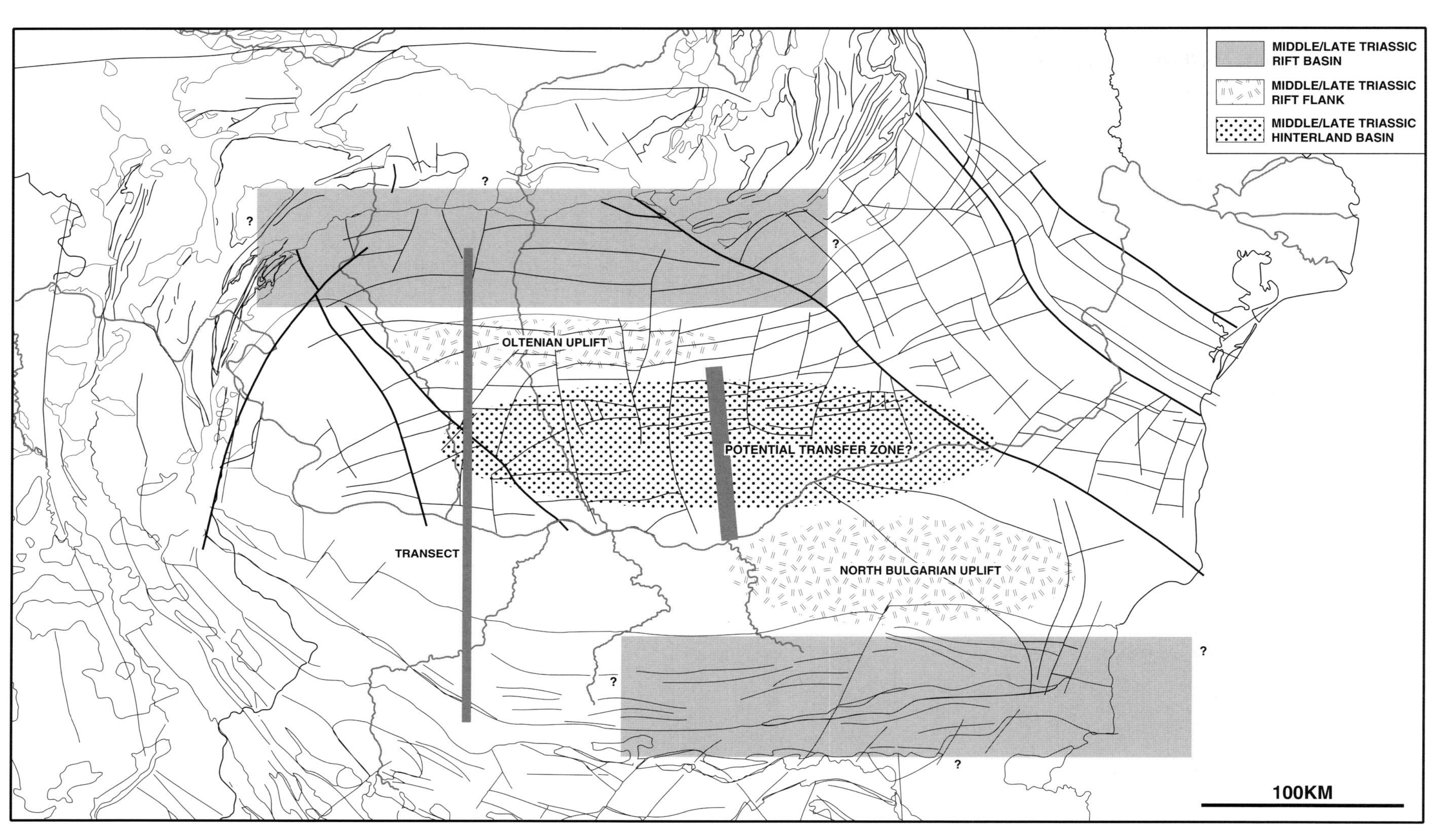

Figure 11. Sketch map showing the relative position of the North Bulgarian and Oltenian rift flanks in the Moesian Platform. The area shown is identical to that in Figure 2.

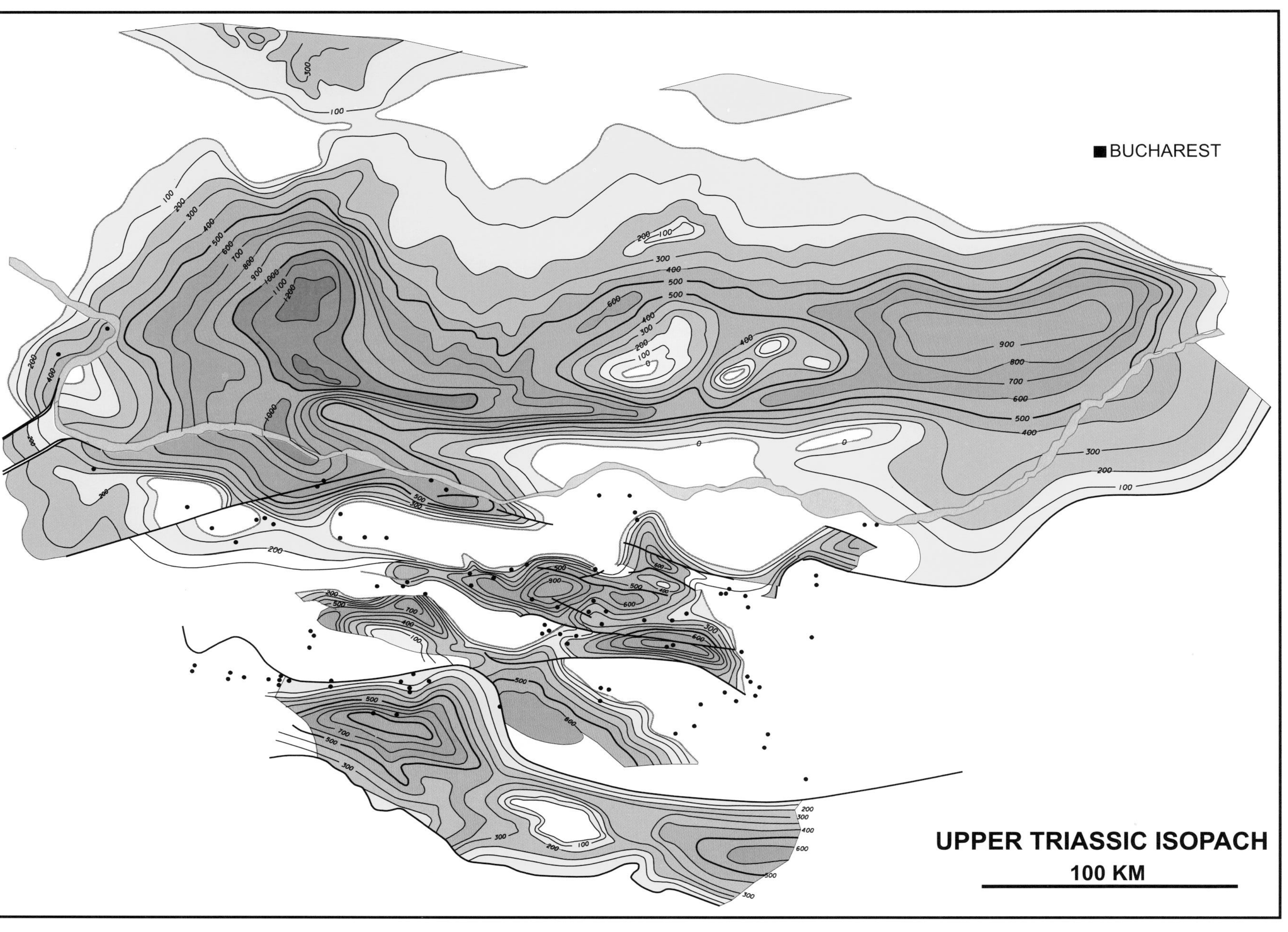

Figure 12. Isopach map of the Upper Triassic Segarcea (Romania) and Moesian Group (Bulgaria), compiled from Paraschiv (1981), Atanasov (1980), and Atanasov and Bokov (1983). For the location of the area shown, see Figures 2b, 11.

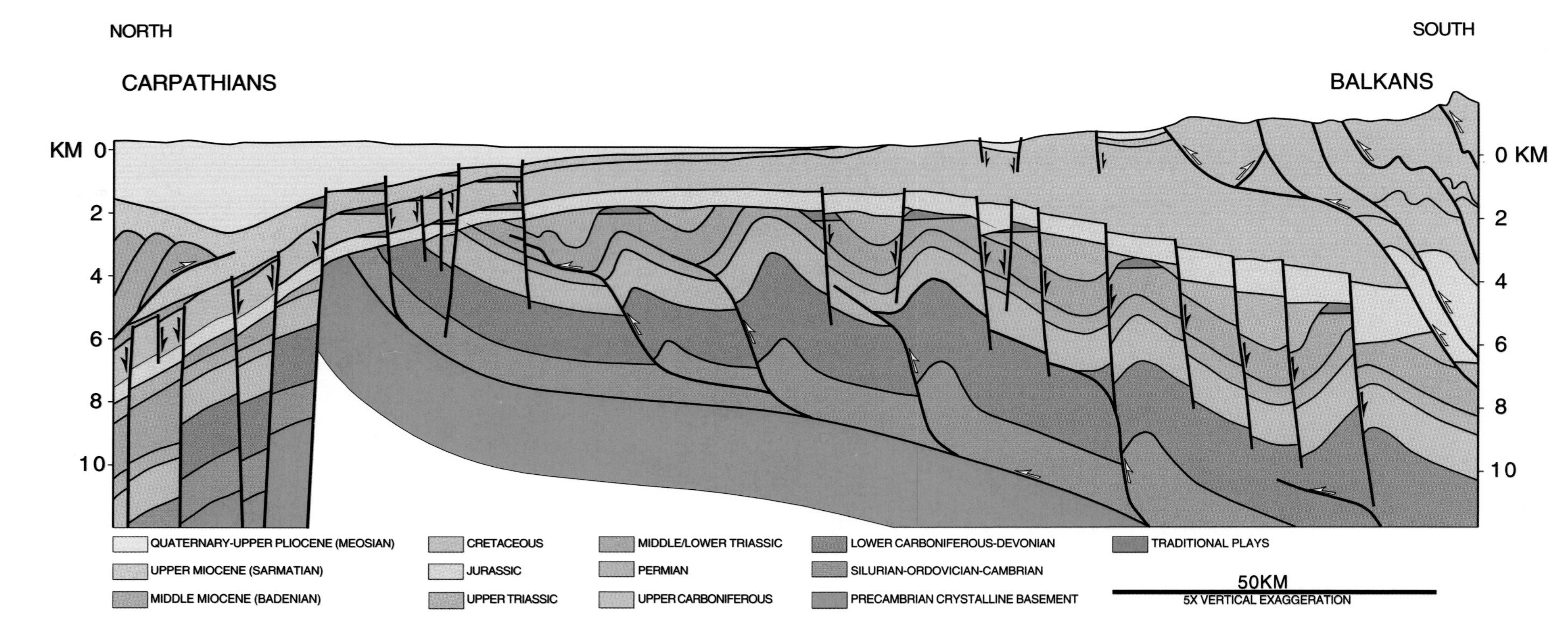

Figure 13. Conceptual cross section across the Moesian Platform of Romania and Bulgaria. For an approximate trace of the section, see Figure 10.

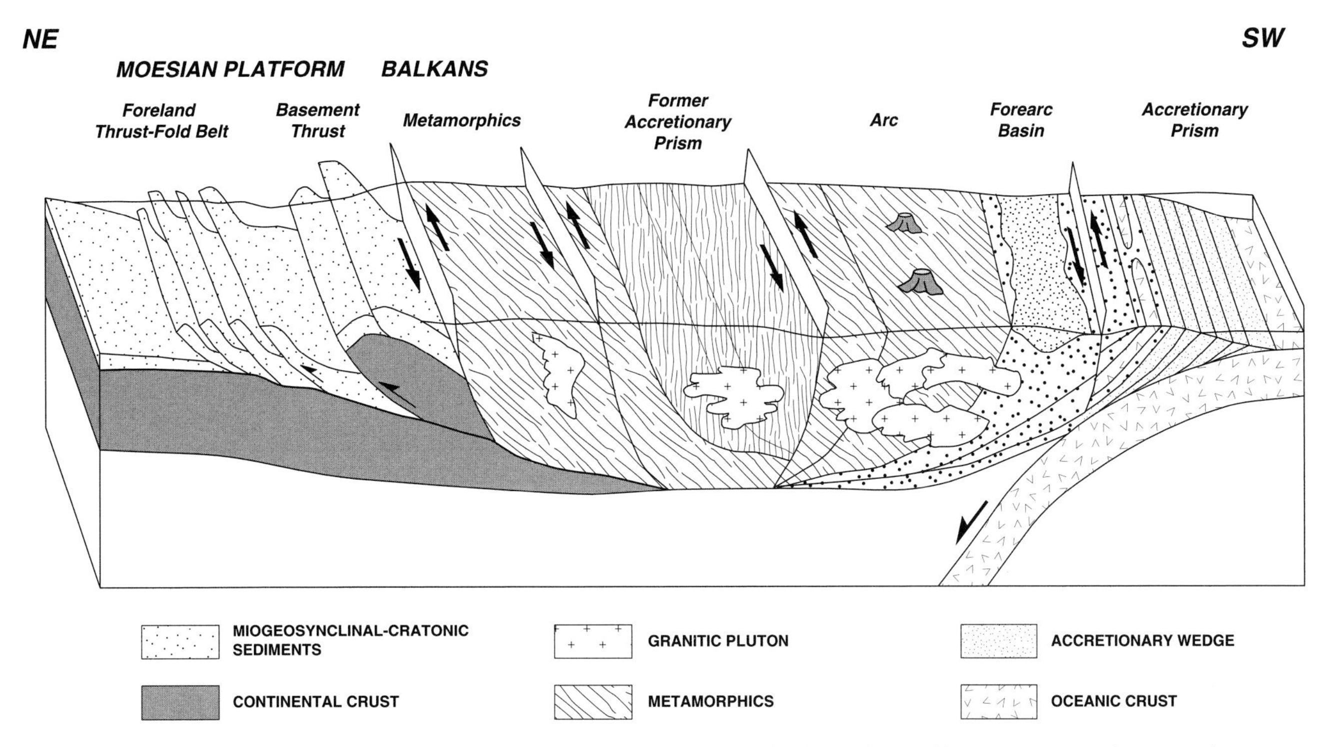

Figure 14. Reconstruction of the Cimmeride orogenic system in the broader Balkans region, adapting the orogenic float concept of Oldow et al. (1989).

et al. (1989) as "single folds," "fold chains," and "folds displaying the involvement of the basement." The spatial pattern of these Late Triassic deformational styles clearly indicates the gradual increase of shortening in a southerly direction. Indeed, the Cimmeride nappes in the Strandzha region (Chatalov, 1988; Gocev, 1991) represent the more internal part of the orogen. Thus, in a wider paleotectonic scenario, the north-vergent anticlines beneath the Moesian Platform are interpreted as the frontal, foreland thrust-fold belt of the Mediterranean Cimmerides (Figure 14).

The recognition of a Cimmerian foreland thrust-fold belt in the Moesian Platform area (Tari et al., 1995) has an important impact for the reconstruction of the western Paleotethys (Şengör, 1984; Kovács, 1992; Dercourt et al., 1993). Using the reconstruction of Kovács (1992), with two opposing Paleotethyan subduction zones combined with the concept of orogenic float (Oldow et al., 1989), we interpret the Moesian Cimmerides in terms of an A-subduction. This southerly vergent subduction was antithetic to the northerly vergent B-subduction in the Sicilian-Aegean branch of the Paleotethys. Note that probably the Moesian A-subduction laterally changed to the east into a B-subduction in the Pontides of Turkey. Based on the model of Kovács (1992), the Neotethyan oceanic basin opened up within the Mediterranean Cimmerides, south of the Late Triassic thrust-fold belt of the Balkan Peninsula.

As to the Black Sea Basin, our new model of the Cimmerian evolution of the Moesian Platform may have several important implications. One of them is the projection of the North Bulgarian Middle Triassic rift basin and the associated rift flank to the offshore area. The same holds for the Late Triassic foreland thrust-fold belt as it is indicated by several seismic data reflection profiles from the Bulgarian offshore (Dachev et al., 1988; S. Bottomley, 1995, personal communication). The strike of these offshore fault-bend folds, however, was strongly modified due to drag along a major dextral strike-fault during the Middle Cretaceous opening of the Western Black Sea Basin (Okay et al., 1994). Since the opening of this ocean resulted in the separation of the Moesian Platform from its eastward continuation, Cimmerian structures similar to those described can be expected to be present in the Western Pontides of Turkey (Yılmaz et al., this volume).

CONCLUSIONS

Based on new observations, the Cimmerian structures formed during the Middle–Late Triassic within the pre-Jurassic sequence of the Moesian Platform of Romania and Bulgaria are interpreted in terms of a rift flank and foreland fault-bend folds. All of these structures are traditionally attributed to the loosely defined Triassic "Old Cimmerian" phase.

We interpret two large-scale subsurface features, the Oltenian and North Bulgarian uplifts, as rift flanks of two separate, east-trending branches of the Paleotethys, based on isopach and pre-Jurassic subcrop maps. These uplifts were mainly formed during the Middle Triassic (Anisian–Ladinian) and perhaps during the early Late Triassic (Carnian–Norian?).

Numerous folds formed during the Late Triassic (Norian?–Rhaetian) in the Moesian Platform are interpreted as fault-bend folds involving various Paleozoic decollement levels. This north-vergent foreland thrust-fold belt is characterized by fault-bend folds displaying relatively small shortening (9–18%). In a wider paleotectonic scenario, this thrust-fold belt represents the frontal part of the Mediterranean Cimmerides propagating into the European foreland.

Both the Romanian and the Bulgarian sides of the Moesian Platform can be considered as mature exploration areas. Hydrocarbon exploration efforts, however, were focused on the Tertiary–Mesozoic succession. Therefore, a better understanding of the structure, stratigraphy, and evolution of the pre-Jurassic sequence may open up some new possibilities for exploration.

ACKNOWLEDGMENTS

We thank Bogdan Popescu and Randell Stephenson for helpful comments on an earlier version of this chapter, and Andrew Robinson for his editorial efforts. Discussions with Albert Bally, Eddy Blunt, Steven Bottomley, Andy Cunningham, Martin Emery, Celal Şengör, and Dian Vangelov are also acknowledged. Josep Poblet and Stuart Hardy kindly modified their forward-modeling program in order to simulate the growth of the Cirligati anticline. Thanks to Mousumi Roy, Giacomo Spadini, and Andrew Robinson for providing us a number of manuscripts prior to publication; and to Chingju Liu and Rosemary Tran for the drafting of some of the figures.

REFERENCES CITED

Andreescu, M., D. Burst, C. Demetrescu, M. Ene, and G. Polonic, 1989, On the geothermal regime of the Moesian Platform: Tectonophysics, v. 164, p. 281–286.

Atanasov, A., ed., 1980, Oil and gas in the Forebalkan (in Bulgarian): Sofia, Technika, 207 p.

Atanasov, A., and P. Bokov, eds., 1983, Geology and oil and gas perspectives of the Moesian Platform in Central North Bulgaria (in Bulgarian): Sofia, Technika, 287 p.

Bally, A.W., 1989, Phanerozoic basins of North America, *in* A.W. Bally and A.R. Palmer, eds., The geology of North America—an overview: Boulder, Geological Society of America, v. A, p. 397–446.

Baltes, N., 1983, Hydrocarbon source rocks in Romania: Annuaire de L'Institut de Géologie et de Géophysique, v. 60, p. 265–270.

Banks, C.J., this volume, Basins and thrust belts of the Balkan coast of the Black Sea, *in* A.G. Robinson, ed., Regional and petroleum geology of the Black Sea and surrounding regions: AAPG Memoir 68, p. 115–128.

Boccaletti, M., P. Dainelli, P. Manetti, and M.R. Mannori, 1988, Tectonic framework of the circum-Black Sea region: Bolletino di Geophisica Teoretica et Applicata, v. 30, p. 117–118.

Bokov, P., and H. Chemberski, 1987, Petroleum geology of Northeastern Bulgaria (in Bulgarian): Sofia, Technika, 332 p.

Bokov, P., P. Gocev, and R. Ognyakov, 1993, Tectonic position, hydrocarbon exploration and future potential of Bulgaria: Geologica Balcanica, v. 23, p. 3–34.

Boyanov, I., C. Dabovski, P. Gocev, A. Harkovska, V. Kostadinov, Tz. Tzankov and I. Zagorcev, 1989, A new view of the Alpine tectonic evolution of Bulgaria: Geologica Rhodopica, v. 1, p. 107–121.

Braun, J., and C. Beaumont, 1989, A physical explanation of the relation between flank uplifts and the breakup unconformity at rifted continental margins: Geology, v. 17, p. 760–764.

Byrne, P., G. Georgiev, I. Todorov, and E. Marinov, 1995, Structure, depositional setting and petroleum geology of eastern Balkanides, Bulgaria (abs.): EAEG Conference, Glasgow, v. 2, p. E021.

Chatalov, G.A., 1988, Recent developments in the geology of the Strandzha zone in Bulgaria: Bulletin of the Technical University of İstanbul, v. 41, p. 433–465.

Dachev, C., V. Stanev, and P. Bokov, 1988, Structure of the Bulgarian Black Sea: Bolletino di Geophisica Teoretica et Applicata, v. 30, p. 79–107.

Davis, D.M., and T. Engelder, 1985, The role of salt in fold-and-thrust belts: Tectonophysics, v. 119, p. 67–88.

Dercourt J., L.E. Ricou, and B. Vrielynck, eds., 1993, Atlas Tethys palaeoenvironmental maps: Paris, Gauthier-Villars, 307 p.

Dicea, O., N. Moldovenau, C. Vasilieva, and C. Cristescu, 1980, Zones of karst structogenesis detected by the seismic survey of the Mesozoic formations at Hirlesti (the Moesian Platform): Revue Roumanie de Géologie, Géophysique et Géographie, v. 24, p. 125–134.

Dicea, O., N. Ionescu, and D.C. Morariu, 1991, Geological framework of oil and gas accumulations in the main sedimentary basins of Romania: Paper presented at the AAPG Diamond Jubilee Convention, Dallas, April 1991.

Doglioni, C., C. Busatta, G. Bolis, L. Marianini, and M. Zanella, 1996, Structural evolution of the eastern Balkans (Bulgaria): Marine and Petroleum Geology, v. 13, p. 225–251.

Emery, M., and G. Georgiev, 1993, Tectonic evolution and hydrocarbon potential of the southern Moesian Platform and Balkan-Forebalkan regions of northern Bulgaria: AAPG Bulletin, v. 77, p. 1620–1621.

Georgiev, G., 1981, Occurrence of salt tectonics in the East Forebalkan and its oil-gas perspectives: Review of the Bulgarian Geological Society, v. 42, p. 67–78.

Georgiev, G., 1994, Development of the Triassic evaporite basin in the Eastern Balkan Forebalkan foldbelt (abs.): EAPG Conference, Vienna, p. P506.

Georgiev, G., 1996a, Development of the Triassic evaporite basin in the Eastern Balkan/Forebalkan foldbelt, *in* G. Wessely and W. Liebl, eds., Oil and gas in Alpidic thrustbelts and basins of Central and Eastern Europe: European Association of Petroleum Geologists Special Publication 5, p. 201–206.

Georgiev, G., 1996b, Overview of the oil and gas exploration and production of Bulgaria, *in* G. Wessely and W. Liebl, eds., Oil and gas in Alpidic thrustbelts and basins of Central and Eastern Europe: European Association of Petroleum Geologists Special Publication 5, p. 29–33.

Georgiev, G., and A. Atanasov, 1993, The importance of the Triassic–Jurassic unconformity to the hydrocarbon potential of Bulgaria: First Break, v. 11, p. 489–497.

Georgiev, G., P. Mandev, S. Valceva, T. Mincheva, and S. Zelev, 1984, Oil-gas potential of the Mesozoic sediments in the Provadia syncline and Gornociflik horst: Annuaire de l'Universite de Sofia, Faculte de Géologie et Géographie, v. 78, p. 150–170.

Gocev, P.M., 1991, Triassic paleogeography and Cimmerian orogeny in SE Bulgaria and on adjacent territories: Acta Geologica Hungarica, v. 34, p. 3–14.

Hardy, S., and J. Poblet, 1995, The velocity description of deformation, 2: sediment geometries associated with fault-bend and fault-propagation folds: Marine and Petroleum Geology, v. 12, p. 165–176.

Ionescu, N., 1994, Exploration history and hydrocarbon prospects in Romania, *in* B. Popescu, ed., Hydrocarbons of Eastern Central Europe: Berlin, Springer, p. 217–248.

Kovács, S., 1992, Tethys "western ends" during the Late Paleozoic and Triassic and their possible genetic relationships: Acta Geologica Hungarica, v. 35, p. 329–369.

Leu, M., S. Gartner, and I. Costea, 1983, The Paleocene–Eocene in the southwest of the Moesian Platform (Romania): Annuaire de l'Institut de Géologie et de Géophysique, v. 60, p. 213–219.

Linzer, H.G., 1996, Kinematics of retreating subduction along the Carpathian arc, Romania: Geology, v. 24, p. 167–170.

Mahel, M., ed., 1974, Tectonics of the Carpathian Balkan regions: Bratislava, Dionyz Stur Geological Institute, 455 p.

Mocanu, V., F. Radulescu, and C. Dinu, 1991, Lithospheric structure of Romania and recent crustal movements, geodynamic connections: Revue Roumanie de Géologie, Géophysique et Géographie, v. 35, p. 1–11.

Monov, B., 1991, Old Cimmerian structural plan in the Western Forebalkan: Geologica Balcanica, v. 21, p. 85–96.

Nicolescu, N., and B.M. Popescu, 1994, Romania, *in* H. Kulke, ed., Regional petroleum geology of the world: Stuttgart, Gebrüder Borntrager, p. 287–311.

Okay, A.I., A.M.C. Şengör, and N. Görür, 1994, Kinematic history of the opening of the Black Sea and its effect on the surrounding regions: Geology, v. 22, p. 267–270.

Oldow, J.S., A.W. Bally, H.G. Ave Lallemant, and W.P. Leeman, 1989, Phanerozoic evolution of the North American Cordillera. United States and Canada, *in* A.W. Bally and A.R. Palmer, eds., The geology of North America—an overview: Geological Society of America, v. A, p. 139–232.

Paraschiv, D., 1974, Stratigraphic study of the Devonian and Carboniferous to the west of the Arges River (in Romanian): St. Technice si Economice, Bucuresti, v. J/12, p. 165.

Paraschiv, D., 1978, Considerations of the stratigraphic position of Triassic magmatites in the Moesian Platform (in Romanian): Studii si Cercetari de Geologie, Geofizica, Geografie, Seria Geologie, v. 2, p. 291–298.

Paraschiv, D., 1979, Romanian oil and gas fields: Bucharest, Annuaire de l'Institut de Géologie et de Géophysique, 382 p.

Paraschiv, D., 1981, The Segarcea Formation (in Romanian): Mine, Petrol si Gaze, v. 32, p. 77–81.

Paraschiv, D., 1982, The principal lithostratigraphic units in the pre-Jurassic of the Moesian Platform (in Romanian): Mine, Petrol si Gaze, v. 33, p. 134–136.

Paraschiv, D., 1983, The evolution of the hydrocarbon field distribution in the Moesian Platform: Annuaire de l'Institut de Géologie et de Géophysique, v. 60, p. 205–213.

Patrut, I., A. Butac, and N. Baltes, 1983, Main stages of hydrocarbon generation and accumulation on the Romanian territory of the Moesian Platform: Annuaire de l'Institut de Géologie et de Géophysique, v. 60, p. 315–323.

Pene, C., 1996, Hydrocarbon generation modelling in the west of the Moesian Platform, Romania: Petroleum Geoscience, v. 2, p. 241–248.

Petrunova-Olova, L., 1992, Palynological evidence of the Early Carnian age of the Moesian Group in Northwest Bulgaria (abs): Geologica Balcanica, v. 22, p. 94.

Popescu, B.M., 1995, Romania's petroleum systems and their remaining potential: Petroleum Geoscience, v. 1, p. 337–350.

Robinson, A.G., G. Spadini, S. Cloetingh, and J.H. Rudat, 1995, Stratigraphic evolution of the Black Sea: inferences from basin modelling: Marine and Petroleum Geology, v. 12, p. 821–835.

Robinson, A.G., J.H. Rudat, C.J. Banks, and R.L.F. Wiles, 1996, Petroleum geology of the Black Sea: Marine and Petroleum Geology, v. 13, p. 195–223.

Roy, M., L.H. Royden, B.C. Burchfiel, Tz. Tzankov, and R. Nakov, 1996, Flexural uplift of the Stara Planina Range, Central Bulgaria: Basin Research, v. 8, p. 143–156.

Sandulescu, M., 1984, Geotectonics of Romania (in Romanian): Bucharest, Editura Technika Publishing House, 336 p.

Semenovich, V., and J. Namestnikov, 1981, Petroleum and gas-bearing basins of European socialist countries and Cuba (in Russian): Moscow, Comecon, 400 p.

Şengör, A.M.C., 1984, The Cimmeride orogenic system and the tectonics of Euroasia: Geological Society of America Special Paper 195, 82 p.

Şengör, A.M.C., Y. Yılmaz, and O. Sungurlu, 1984, Tectonics of the Mediterranean Cimmerides: nature and evolution of the western termination of Palaeotethys, *in* J.E. Dixon and A.H.F. Robertson, eds., The geological evolution of the eastern Mediterranean: Geological Society of London Special Publication 14, p. 117–152.

Stefanescu, M., and P. Polonic, 1993, Deep structure of Romania and the related hydrocarbon prospects: First Break, v. 2, p. 99–105.

Stefanescu, M., and B. Popescu, 1993, Romania's petroleum systems (abs): AAPG Bulletin, v. 77, p. 1668.

Suppe, J., 1983, Geometry and kinematics of fault-bend folding: American Journal of Science, v. 283, p. 684–721.

Tari, G., G. Georgiev, M. Stefanescu, and G. Weir, 1995, A Late Triassic thrust-fold belt beneath the Moesian Platform: implications for the Cimmeride orogenic system: AAPG Bulletin, v. 79, p. 1251–1252.

Tchoumatchenko, P., and I. Sapunov, 1994, Intraplate tectonics in the Bulgarian part of the Moesian Platform during the Jurassic: Geologica Balcanica, v. 24, p. 3–12.

van Balen, R., 1995, Tectonic control on the hydrodynamics and sedimentary record of extensional basins: Ph.D. thesis, Free University, Amsterdam, 202 p.

van der Beek, P.A., S. Cloetingh, and P. Andriessen, 1994, Mechanisms of extensional basin formation and vertical motions at rift flanks: constraints from tectonic modeling and fission track thermochronology: Earth and Planetary Science Letters, v. 121, p. 317–330.

Vaptsarova, A., H. Tchemberski, and G. Chatalov, 1984, Facies and evolution of sedimentary environments during the Triassic period in Bulgaria (in Bulgarian): Geologica Balcanica, v. 14, p. 57–76.

Vinogradov, C., 1988, Relationships between sedimentary facies and tectonics in the Moesian Platform (Romania): Revue Roumanie de Géologie, Géophysique et Géographie, v. 32, p. 55–65.

Visarion, M., M., Sandulescu, D. Stanica, and S. Veliciu, 1988, Contributions a la connaissance de la structure profonde de la plate-forme Moesienne en Roumanie: Studii de Technica, Economica, Geofizica, v. 15, p. 211–222.

Vuchev, V., P. Bokov, B. Monov, A. Atanasov, R. Ognyanov, and D. Tochkov, 1994, Geologic structure, petroleum exploration development and hydrocarbon potential of Bulgaria, *in* B. Popescu, ed., Hydrocarbons of Eastern Central Europe: Berlin, Springer-Verlag, p. 29–69.

Yılmaz, Y., O. Tüysüz, E. Yigibas, Ş. C. Genç, and A.M.C. Şengör, this volume, Geology and tectonic evolution of the Pontides, *in* A.G. Robinson, ed., Regional and petroleum geology of the Black Sea and surrounding regions: AAPG Memoir 68, p. 183–226.

Sinclair, H.D., S.G. Juranov, G. Georgiev, P. Byrne, and N.P. Mountney, 1997, The Balkan thrust wedge and foreland basin of Eastern Bulgaria: structural and stratigraphic development, *in* A.G. Robinson, ed., Regional and petroleum geology of the Black Sea and surrounding region: AAPG Memoir 68, p. 91–114.

Chapter 7

The Balkan Thrust Wedge and Foreland Basin of Eastern Bulgaria: Structural and Stratigraphic Development

H.D. Sinclair
The University of Birmingham
Edgbaston, Birmingham, United Kingdom

S.G. Juranov
G. Georgiev
Sofia University "St. Kliment Ohridski"
Sofia, Bulgaria

P. Byrne
British Gas Exploration and Production Limited
Reading, Berkshire, United Kingdom

N.P. Mountney
The University of Birmingham
Edgbaston, Birmingham, United Kingdom

ABSTRACT

The Balkan Mountains of Bulgaria run east-west and outcrop along the north-south–running Black Sea coastline. Immediately north of the Balkan thrust front is the Kamchia Depression, which has been interpreted to represent the North Balkan foreland basin. To the south is the Srednogorie Zone, comprising Cretaceous calc-alkaline volcanics representing a remnant volcanic arc. A north-south structural cross section can be generated by the integration of coastal exposures, with deeper level constraint from onshore and offshore seismic data. In this section, the Balkans comprise two large synclines bounded by major faults. This folding and thrusting detached at a horizon within the Jurassic succession at ~5 km depth. Section restoration across the Balkans from the remnants of the volcanic arc in the south to the Balkan thrust front in the north gives a minimum of 18 km of shortening.

Seismic stratigraphy indicates two periods of shortening across the Balkans. Initially, deep-seated normal faults that offset the Triassic were reactivated as reverse faults at the end of the Cretaceous. The sea-floor topography generated during this compression was subsequently draped by Paleocene and lower and middle Eocene strata. At end-middle Eocene times, thin-skinned thrusts propagated into the basin, initiating the main Balkan structures. The termination of shortening is recorded by the blanketing of thrust-related topography at end-Oligocene times. Therefore, the >18 km of shortening took place from early Paleocene to end-Oligocene times; this indicates a time-averaged rate of shortening of ~0.5 km/m.y.

The sedimentary fill of the Kamchia Depression is intimately linked to the growth of the Balkan Mountain belt. At end Cretaceous/early Tertiary times, it was characterized by emergence in the north linked to the deep-level fault reactivation, and deepening in the south to bathyal depths, where calci-turbidites accumulated. During the early Eocene times, siliciclastics were deposited in the south and center of the basin, and the northern margin experienced a marine transgression; this is thought to be related to the load-induced subsidence of the southern margin of the Moesian Platform by the Balkan Mountains. By the middle Eocene, immediately prior to thrust encroachment into the basin, the northern margin underwent mass wasting in the form of debris flows, slumps, and gravity glide sheets. At a similar time, micropaleontological indicators suggest reduced oceanic circulation, possibly linked to physical isolation of the Black Sea region by growing mountain belts to the south.

Subsidence analysis offshore indicates accelerated tectonic subsidence during middle and upper Eocene times, thus strengthening the proposed link between early thrusting and deepening of the basin. The structural, sedimentological, and subsidence history of this basin strongly supports its interpretation as the north Balkan retro-arc foreland basin. Rates of tectonic subsidence (>0.05 km/m.y.) and crustal shortening (≤0.5 km/m.y.) are slow compared to other thrust wedge/foreland basin settings.

INTRODUCTION

The Balkan Mountains represent one of the many small mountain belts that form the main Alpine–Himalayan system. They run east-west through Bulgaria, linking to the west and north with the Carpathians, and to the east terminating in the Black Sea (Figure 1). They developed from the convergence of two plate fragments, the Rhodopian and Moesian fragments, which themselves have been sandwiched between the main African and Eurasian plates (Burchfiel, 1980). North-eastward subduction began in the Late Jurassic in what is now central Greece along on oceanic suture called the Vardar Zone (Figure 1). Deformation continued, with the deformation front migrating southwestward to the present-day Hellenic trough (Figure 1). The Balkan mountain chain involves northward overthrusting onto the margin of the Moesian plate, and as such is opposite in its vergence to the deformation of the Hellenic trough to the south. This opposing vergence, combined with the history of extensive arc volcanism, has resulted in the Balkans being interpreted as a retro-arc thrust wedge (Boccaletti et al., 1974).

The Balkans are ~30 km wide at the coastline, and are bound to the south by the calc-alkaline volcanics of the Srednogorie Zone and to the north by the Kamchia Depression (Figure 2). This basin to the north has long been interpreted as a foredeep depression associated with the development of the Balkan mountain chain (Boncev, 1978). The aim of this chapter is to document the structure, stratigraphy, and sedimentology of the Balkan mountain chain, the onshore Kamchia basin, and its offshore extension into the Black Sea. Using this information, constraints will be placed on the timing of the onset and termination of deformation, and approximate values are given for the rates and total amounts of shortening. These data can then be compared to subsidence history from well data; hence, an overall picture of the structural and basinal development of the Balkan mountain chain/foreland basin system can be proposed.

The new data presented in this chapter come from three sources: (1) onshore structural mapping and sedimentological logging backed up with sample collection for micropaleontological analysis, (2) offshore and onshore seismic data, and (3) offshore well data. The new data are integrated within an existing biostratigraphic framework.

BALKAN STRUCTURE

Onshore Exposures

The Balkan Mountains are formed of thrusted and folded Cretaceous and Tertiary rocks in the east, and

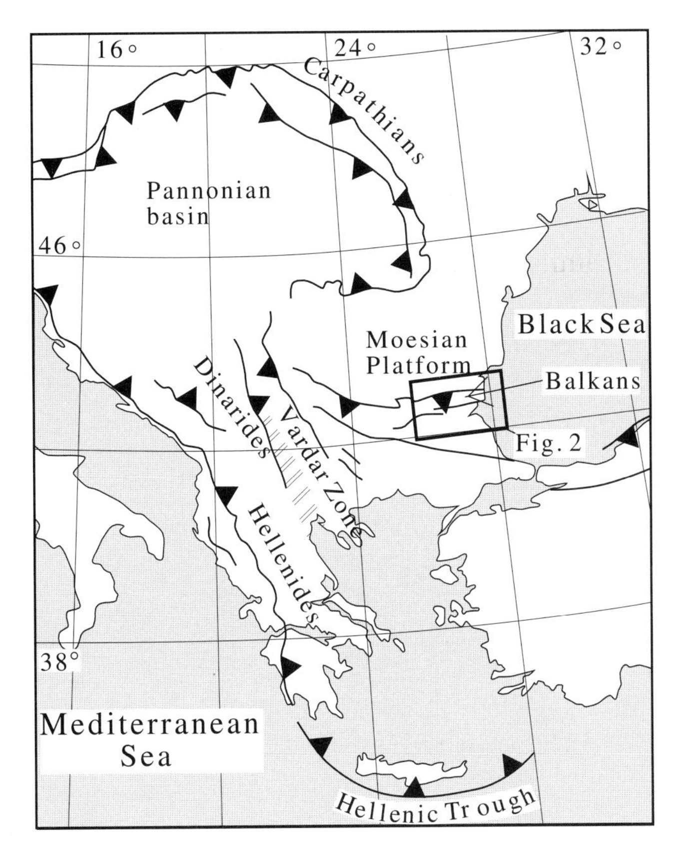

Figure 1. Tectonic setting of the Balkan Mountains, with study area located in the box.

incorporate Jurassic and Triassic rocks farther inland (Byrne et al., 1995; Banks, this volume). The Kamchia Depression is a Tertiary basin located to the north of the Balkan thrust front (Figure 2) in eastern Bulgaria, and continues offshore into the Black Sea. Tertiary sediments are preserved ≤70 km inland from the coast, with thicker and younger successions preserved eastward at the coastline and offshore. The coastline runs N-S, perpendicular to strike, and provides an opportunity to construct a structural cross section through the Balkans and the basin to the north (Figure 3).

The coastal exposures from Cape Emine in the south to Varna in the north can be divided into the folded and thrusted region from Cape Emine to a location 3 km north of Byala, which are the Balkans, and a gently folded zone northward to Varna, which is the Kamchia Depression; the frontal thrust to the Balkans separates these two regions. The Balkans along this transect are dominated by two synclines: the Irakli syncline (an open parallel upright fold with an 8 km half-wavelength) and the Obsor syncline [an overturned syncline with a moderately inclined axis (~40° SSW)], verging N-NE. The Obsor syncline has a significant variation in the thickness of strata in each limb. The northern limb comprises a thicker succession dominated by Eocene slumps and olistostromes, which are not present in the southern limb (see discussion of stratigraphy). The northern limb of the Obsor syncline also comprises intense 10-m-scale folds in the region south of Cape Atanas (Figure 3). There is no

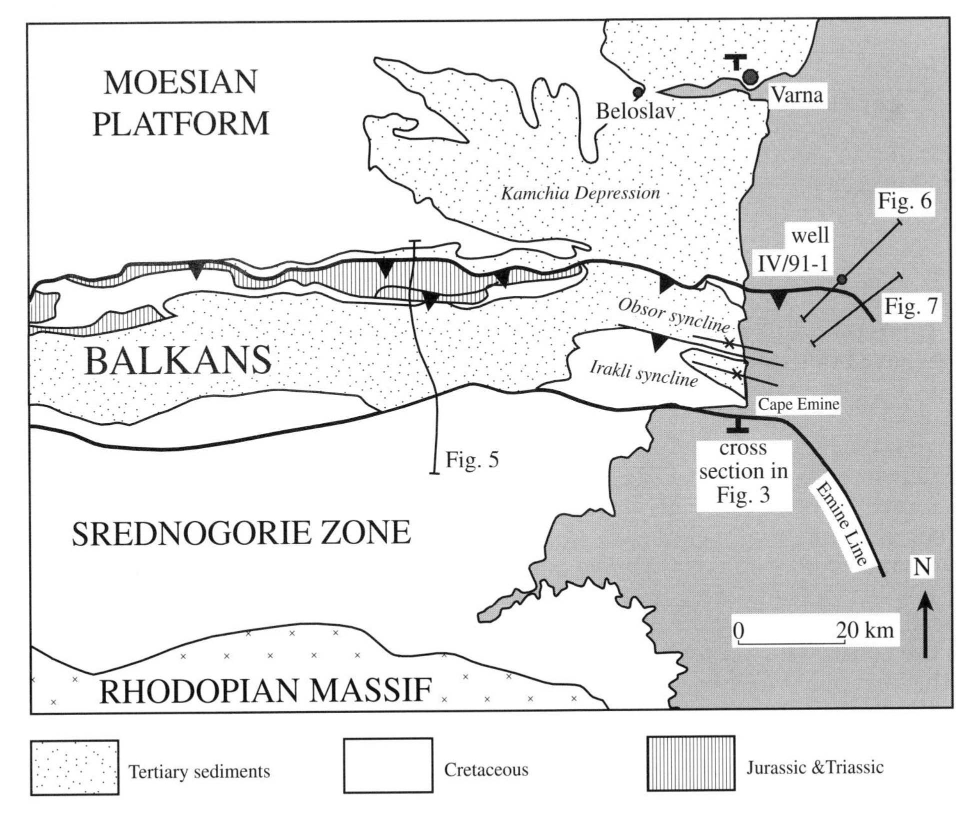

Figure 2. Detailed map of the Balkan Mountains of eastern Bulgaria, with the seismic lines and well located.

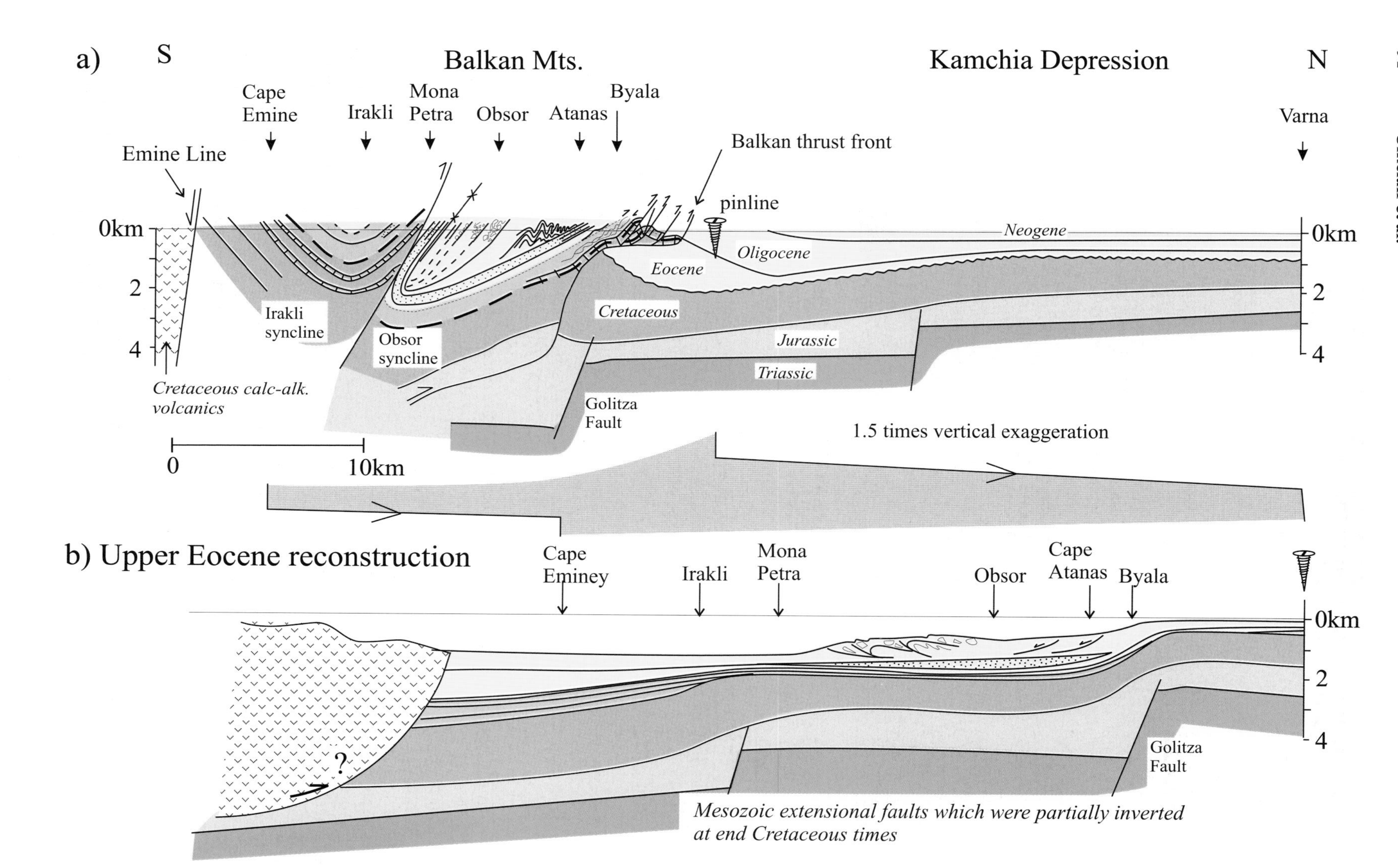

Figure 3. (a) Structural cross section from the coastal exposures between Cape Emine and Varna. (b) Structural reconstruction to the upper Eocene of the cross section using a line-length technique and using the Maastrichtian/Paleocene boundary to link parts of the section.

Figure 4. Intense cleavage development in sheared Paleocene marls along the Byala beach.

evidence of an axial planar cleavage associated with any of the large- or small-scale structures.

Bounding these two synclines are major thrust faults. The southern margin of the Irakli syncline and the Balkans is marked by a major fault boundary called the Emine Line, which records the boundary with the Cretaceous calc-alkaline volcanics of the Srednogorie Zone. The northern margin of the Irakli syncline is marked by a thrust dipping ~60° southward, which outcrops 200 m south of Cape Mona Petra (Figure 3). The northern margin of the Obsor syncline is characterized by the thrust imbrication of Upper Cretaceous and Paleocene strata over a 4-km zone north of Byala. The transition from the beds on the northern limb of the Obsor syncline and this zone of imbrication is marked by a 200–300-m-wide zone characterized by intense foliation dipping ~20° southward, with localized shear zones and associated calcite veining (Figure 4). North of the Byala imbricate zone is a gently dipping Oligo-Miocene succession, indicating that the Balkan thrust front is located ~3.5 km north of the town of Byala.

Structural information from the Kamchia Depression comes mainly from well and seismic surveys (Atanasov, 1961; Bokov and Ognyanov, 1978; Bokov et al., 1979; Bogatskaja and Chuparova, 1986). The depression comprises a broad, very open synclinal structure dominated by a thick Oligocene succession (Figure 3). The strata on the northern margin of the Kamchia Depression flatten out and continue horizontally northward onto the Moesian Platform of northern Bulgaria.

Seismic Sections

Extensive hydrocarbon exploration in the area has generated a dense coverage of onshore and offshore seismic and well data. The data presented here are from British Gas exploration in offshore Block IV and onshore Block 10. The lines shown are aligned perpendicular to strike, and chosen to illustrate a number of important structural and stratigraphic features. The onshore line 04 (Figure 5) illustrates a strong set of reflectors at 1.8–2.0 s TWT (two-way traveltime) in the north of the line and at 2.7–3.4 s TWT in the south of the line, which represent Triassic carbonates. Approximately 12 km from the northern edge of the section, the Triassic is downthrown to the south by 1.4 s TWT. Overlying this normal fault (the Golitza fault) is a succession of Jurassic, Cretaceous, and Tertiary rocks, constrained from surface mapping, which exhibit fold and thrust structures verging northward. The northernmost thrust represents the Balkan thrust front, and the broad syncline in the Tertiary toward the south of the section correlates along strike to the coastal section with the Obsor syncline. The deformation within the cover sequence is underlain by a thrust fault that ramps up 2.0–0.6 s TWT at a location overlying the Golitza fault in the underlying Triassic. The main structural features in this section can be linked to the structures exposed along the coast through a network of onshore seismic lines.

Offshore seismic data (Block IV) reveal the structure and stratigraphic character of the submarine Balkan thrust wedge. Line 12 (Figure 6) is constrained by well IV/91-1 (Figure 2), which intersects at shotpoint 538 and is tied to line 20 (Figure 7) by a strike-parallel line. The shallow-level deformation front can be located at approximately shotpoint 500 on line 12 and shotpoint 700 on line 20; this is where the frontal thrust propagates up to the top middle Eocene boundary and is draped by upper Eocene deep-water mudstones and

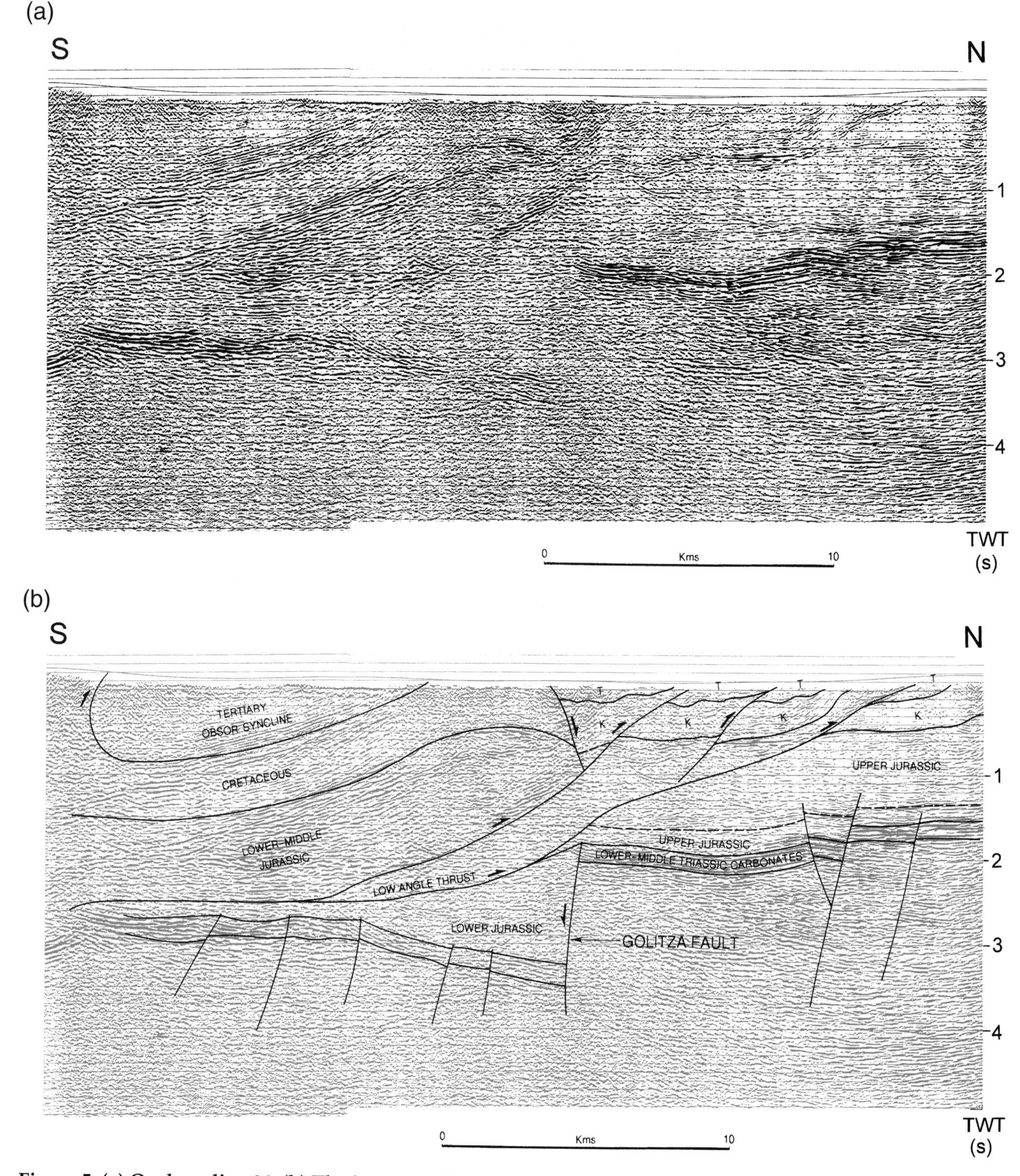

Figure 5. (a) Onshore line 04. (b) The interpreted section with a normal offset in the Triassic, and fold-and-thrust deformation in the overlying Jurassic to Tertiary succession.

sandstones. The unconformity that separates the thrust-truncated lower and middle Eocene from the overlying upper Eocene drape is locally termed the Illyrian unconformity. Depth conversion of the two lines indicates that the depth to detachment of these thrusts is ~5–6 km, with the thrust tip at 2–3 km depth (Figures 6b, 7b). The position of the thrust tip can be linked onshore to the Balkan thrust front, which is underlain by the footwall ramp of the Golitza fault. North of the thrust wedge, deeper level, high-angle reverse faults cut down into the sub-Triassic basement and terminate upward, gently folding the Cretaceous.

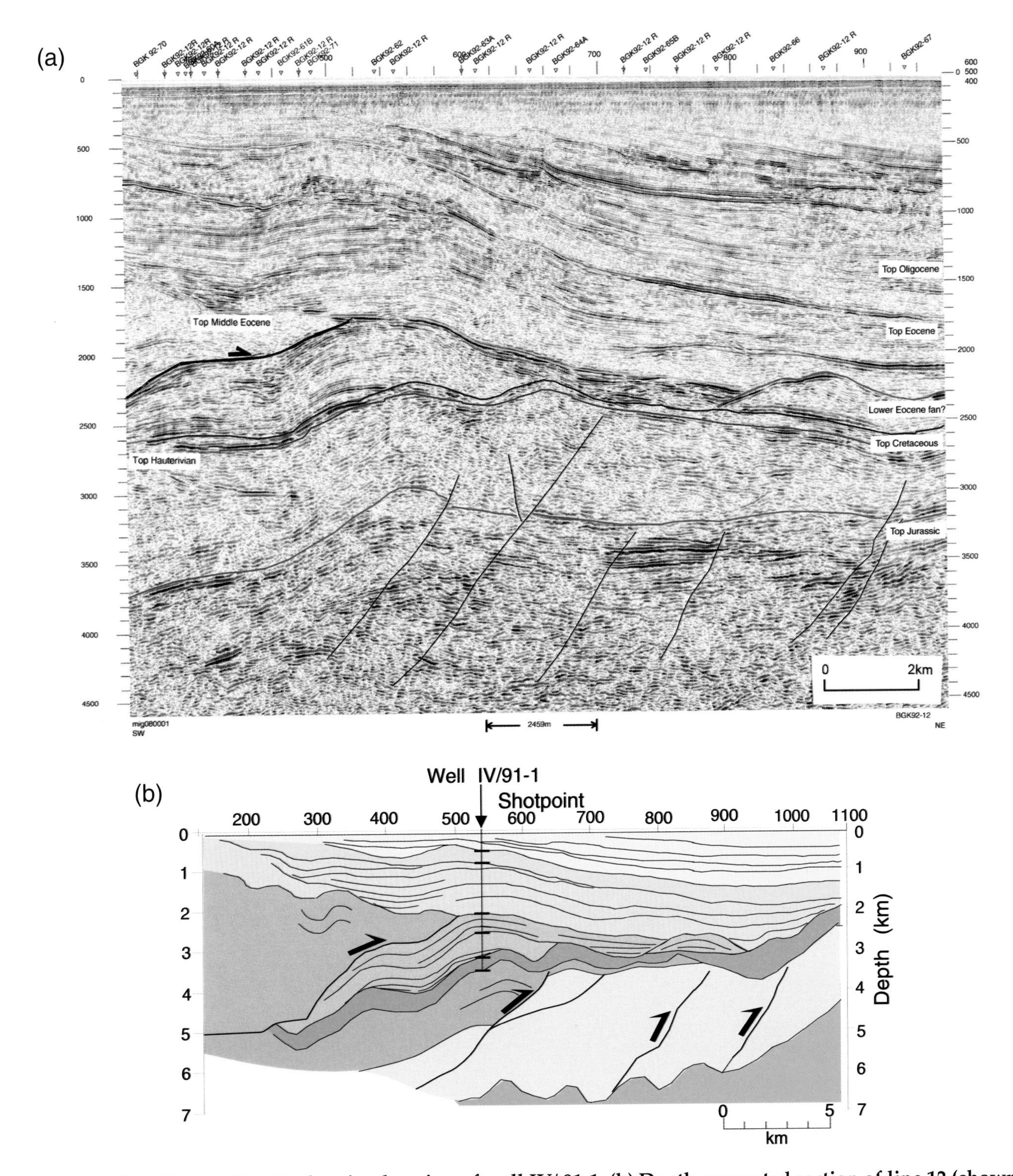

Figure 6. (a) Offshore line 12 showing location of well IV/ 91-1. (b) Depth-converted section of line 12 (shown at 1.8 vertical exaggeration).

Regional Cross Section

By mapping out the normal offset in the Triassic from offshore and onshore data, it is possible to project the depth and location of offset of the Triassic onto the coastal section (Figure 3). The projected cross section shows a complete section through the Balkan thrust wedge and Kamchia Depression. In the southern region, the calc-alkaline volcanic rocks of the Srednogorie Zone abut the southern limb of the Irakli syncline along the Emine Line. This contact has been interpreted as a transtensional fault from offshore seismic data (Doglioni et al., 1996). The Irakli and Obsor synclines are underlain by a thrust detachment located between 4–6 km depth, based on seismic velocity profiles from

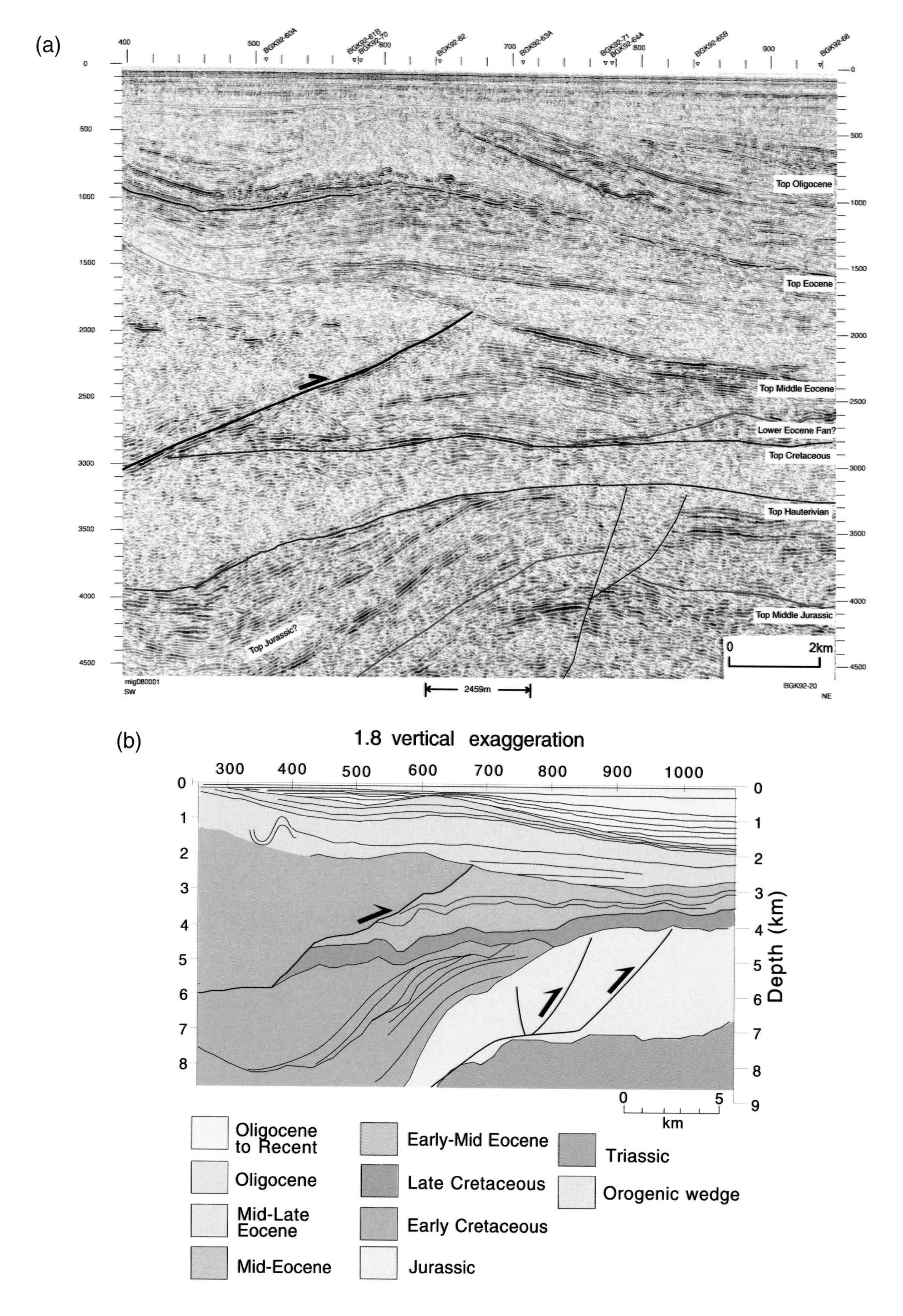

Figure 7. (a) Offshore line 20, which has been linked to line 12 by a tie line. (b) Depth-converted section of line 20.

the sections (Figures 6b, 7b). The fault ramp in the Triassic is projected onto the coastline near Cape Atanas. Overlying this point, the basal thrust detachment ramps up to a depth of <1 km in the region of Byala, where the Upper Cretaceous and lower Paleocene successions show complex fold and thrust imbrication structures (Figure 3). North of the Balkan thrust front, the deep structure is recorded from previous Bulgarian exploration in the area (1981–1984) and shows little deformation heading toward Varna.

A line-length restoration of this section was achieved using the Cretaceous–Tertiary boundary, with a pin line located just north of the thrust front (Figure 3b). The fold limbs of each of the synclines were projected downward until they intersect, with a subrounded fold-hinge geometry. The Maastrichtian–Paleocene boundary from the northern limb of the Irakli syncline was projected straight onto the fault separating the two synclines at Mona Petra. Restoration of the section indicates that a minimum 18 km of shortening has taken place across the Balkan Mountains; this represents 44% section shortening. The line length does not take into account internal strain within a succession. However, there is virtually no evidence of a pervasive cleavage in this section; therefore, internal strain is not thought to have played a significant role.

SEISMIC STRATIGRAPHY

Both offshore seismic lines illustrate the relationship between the frontal parts of the Balkan thrust wedge and the associated stratigraphy, which is constrained by the British Gas well LA IV/91-1 and Bulgarian well Samotino More. The lines are described chronostratigraphically.

Jurassic

The Jurassic of the region is thought to have been controlled by a series of E-W–running horst-and-graben structures that were infilled initially by shallow marine siliciclastics, followed by deeper water flysch deposits during the Late Jurassic (Tchoumatchenko and Sapunov, 1994). In the offshore lines, the Jurassic strata do not show significant lateral variations; however, based on facies variations, the Jurassic shelf edge can be located along the line of the Golitza fault, with deepening to the south (Bokov et al., 1981; Byrne et al., 1995).

Cretaceous

Offshore, the Cretaceous is divided in two by a mid-Cretaceous unconformity (Figure 6). In line 20 (Figure 7), the Hauterivian to Aptian succession below the unconformity thickens southward over the inverted Golitza fault, and comprises an aggradational to progradational seismic geometry, with truncation or offlap in the most southerly portion of the topset strata (Figure 7). The lowermost Hauterivian strata show a northward onlap and southward downlap relationship with the underlying Valanginian. In seismic stratigraphic terms, this package has the geometric characteristics of a shelf-margin wedge systems tract; however, the time period of development and thickness of this wedge are greater than the model third-order sequence cycles (Vail, 1987). In well LA IV/91-1 the Hauterivian to Aptian succession comprises siliciclastics with a mid-shelf microfaunal assemblage (Campion, 1993). The significance of the Lower Cretaceous paleogeography to the subsequent foreland basin succession is that it locates the shelf edge above the Golitza fault immediately prior to the development of the Balkan thrust wedge and foreland basin. The succession overlying the unconformity in the well comprises 91 m of Cenomanian to Maastrichtian strata (Mezdza, Novatchene, and Madaza formations), which show a uniform thickness across line 12, and comprises outer-shelf to upper-bathyal calcareous mudstones and siltstones.

Tertiary

The Paleocene is ≤50 m in the well and, therefore, below the resolution necessary to pick up seismic geometries. The lowermost Tertiary seismic feature is located in the northern part of line 12 where an ~5-km-wide, 0.3-km-high mound with bidirectional downlap overlies the Cretaceous succession; the seismic geometry of the mound suggests that it may be some form of localized basin-floor fan. The exact age of this mound is hard to pinpoint, but it is likely to be of either Paleocene or lowermost Eocene age; the latter age is preferred, based on the presence of a succession of massive amalgamated turbidite sandstones (Atanas sandstones) exposed onshore and dated as lower Eocene.

The lower to middle Eocene succession onlaps and downlaps onto an irregular surface at or near the Cretaceous–Tertiary boundary and onto the southern margin of the mound north of line 20 (Figures 6, 7). The irregularity of the underlying surface is associated with compressional reactivation of the Golitza normal fault, which offsets the Triassic. This reactivated fault zone ramps up through Jurassic and Cretaceous rocks, but is then blanketed by the base Tertiary succession. In Figure 6, a wedge of lower and middle Eocene strata (Obsor Conglomerate and Dvoijnitsca Formation) downlap toward the NE in the footwall to a thrust plane. Overlying this lower wedge, upper Eocene reflectors of the Avren Formation onlap to the SW onto the high generated by the thrust that truncates the underlying lower and middle Eocene succession. This thick succession of onlapping reflectors is then gently domed above the location of the underlying thrust. This doming is then onlapped by undeformed post-Oligocene sediments, recording the termination of compressional deformation.

These geometric relationships indicate that the initiation of shortening was by the reactivation of deep-level normal faults that occurred at or near the Cretaceous–Tertiary boundary. Thrust shortening continued until the middle to late Eocene boundary, with shallower level thrusting in more southerly locations relative to the deep-level reactivation; therefore, thrusting did not progress in a simple piggyback manner. The most recent evidence of shortening is recorded by the

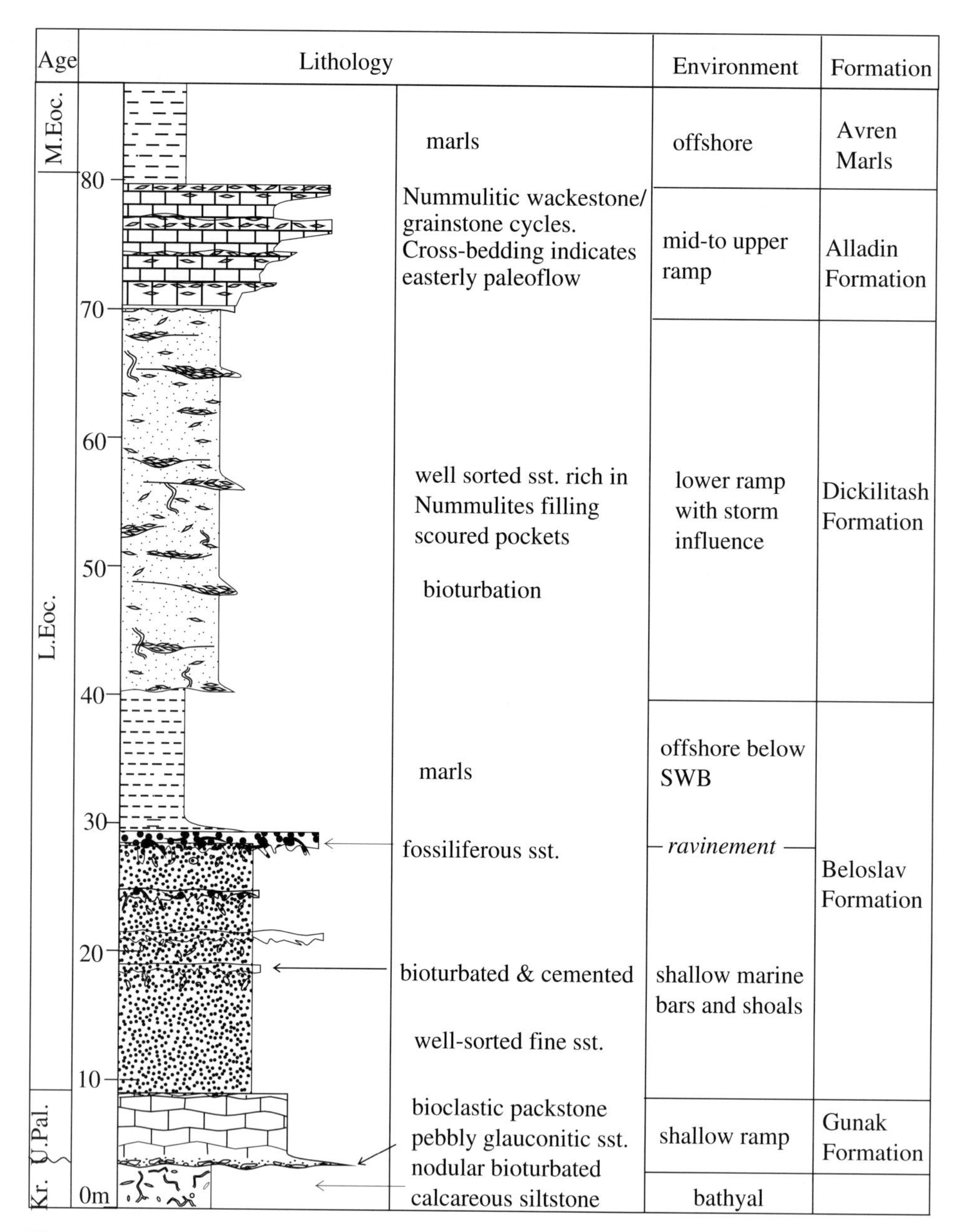

Figure 8. Sedimentary section from just west of the town of Beloslav (grid ref. 27°42′E, 43°11′N, ± 00°00.5′). sst. = sandstone, SWB = storm wave base.

doming of Oligocene strata over the thrust tips that truncate the lower Eocene, indicating deformation at end-Oligocene times. To summarize, the seismic stratigraphy indicates that the bulk of the shortening was by thin-skinned thrusting and folding that occurred from base Tertiary to middle Eocene times, with subsequent times doming overthrust tips in Oligocene times. Prior to this thin-skinned deformation, deep-level reactivation of normal faults had occurred on the edge of the Moesian Platform at or near the Cretaceous–Tertiary boundary.

SEDIMENTOLOGY

The seismic stratigraphy indicates that the onset of compressional deformation in the area took place near the Cretaceous–Tertiary boundary. The onshore exposures allow an analysis of the depositional environments that were present during the transition from a passively draped continental margin to an active compressional setting. The data also allow a comparison of time-equivalent processes and environments from areas proximal to the developing thrust wedge and areas more distal on the Moesian Platform.

The sedimentological data come primarily from three localities: the town of Beloslav, inland from Varna (Figure 2); the northern limb of the Obsor syncline; and the southern limb of the Irakli syncline. These sections are described and interpreted separately, and subsequently compared.

Beloslav Section

The Beloslav section (Figure 8) was measured in the cliffs immediately SW of the town of Beloslav (Figure 2). The succession exposed is ~100 m thick and is made up of six distinct stratigraphic units: the lowermost Maastrichtian, which does not have a formation name. This area is unconformably overlain by five formations ranging from upper Paleocene to middle Eocene in age (Aladjova-Hrisceva et al., 1983; Aladjova-Hrisceva, 1984) termed the Gunak, Beloslav, Dickilitash, Aladan, and Avren formations (Figure 8). The sedimentology and bounding surfaces of each of these units is described separately.

Maastrichtian

The lowermost outcrops in this region have been dated as Maastrichtian using benthic foraminifera, nannoplankton, and coccoliths (Aladjova-Hrisceva et al., 1983; Aladjova-Hrisceva, 1991). Lithologically, this unit comprises light-gray, calcareous siltstones/wackestones with a marked nodular appearance, which seem to form tubular shapes, suggesting that zones of cementation followed burrow traces; smaller (2–4 mm) burrows are evident. Fragments of flat bivalves ≤10 cm across are also present. The microfaunal assemblage indicates a bathyal setting for the accumulation of these sediments.

Gunak Formation

The unconformity between the Maastrichtian and the upper Paleocene Gunak Formation is planar and abrupt. Immediately above the contact is ~30 cm of greeny/gray fine glauconitic, bioclastic wackestone. At the contact are isolated small, rounded clasts of the underlying wackestone, with a green coating thought to be glauconite. Above the glauconitic wackestone is 6 m of roughly bedded, cream-colored, bioclastic grainstones rich in bryozoans, *Lithothamnium*, and nummulites. These deposits are interpreted to represent an initial transgression over the unconformity, followed by sedimentation in a shallow marine ramp setting above fair-weather wave base.

Beloslav Formation

The lower 20 m of this formation predominantly comprises poorly cemented, well-sorted fine quartz sandstones. Toward the top are four horizons, from 4–20 cm thick, of highly cemented, medium sandstones, which are intensely bioturbated. The burrows penetrate ≤40 cm down into the intervening fine sandstones. Within the lower two of the well-cemented horizons, approximately 10% of the lithology is composed of nummulites, small fish teeth, fragments of bryozoans, small bivalves with pecten-type ribbing, and large *Ostrea*. The uppermost of these horizons (29 m on Figure 8) contains approximately 90% shell material with, in addition to the above fauna, brachiopods, smooth-shelled turritellid gastropods, large flat bivalves, and many large *Ostrea*. These latter shells are ≤13 cm thick, with a 20 cm diameter, and may also be found isolated within the surrounding fine sandstones. Overlying the uppermost of these horizons, the sandstones fine upward over 0.5 m into laminated calcareous mudstones with few isolated nummulite tests. These mudstones are 10 m thick and mark the upper part of the Beloslav Formation.

The Beloslav Formation is interpreted to represent a transgressive succession. The clean sandstones are thought to record shallow marine shoal or bar sands, with episodes of deepening toward the top of the succession, producing thin condensation surfaces. The uppermost of these is interpreted as a ravinement surface recording the transition from nearshore sands to offshore mudstones accumulating below storm wave base.

Dickilitash Formation

The transition from the upper Beloslav to the Dickilitash Formation is not well exposed. The Dickilitash Formation comprises 30 m of very well sorted, light-gray fine sandstones with localized large burrow networks. Small scours from 0.2–1.0 m wide and ≤30 cm deep are common and are filled with nummulite tests forming localized bioclastic pockets and lenses. This formation is interpreted to record a sandy shelf setting, with episodic storm currents reworking nummulite tests from shallower water environments and filling scoured depressions on the seabed.

Aladan Formation

The Aladan Formation forms the prominent ridge around the top of the hills surrounding Beloslav. In this area, this formation is ~10 m thick, and comprises 1-m-scale alternations of nummulite-rich wackestone and packestone. These units form coarsening-upward cycles, with sharp, coarse bioturbated tops and localized *Ostrea* and other smaller bivalve shells scattered along the surface. Localized cross-bedding is present within the beds; the only measurement of the cross-bedding indicates an easterly flow (80°). The wackestone/packstone cycles thicken upward through the formation and, when looking from a distance, low-angle downlapping geometries can be identified. At the top of the Aladan Formation, the uppermost cycle is overlain by a thinly bedded siltstone, which marks the arrival of the Avren Formation.

The Aladan Formation represents a shallow marine, nummulitic ramp setting similar to many other ramps around the Tethyan margin during the Eocene (Allen et al., 1991). Water depths fluctuated from subfair-weather wave base (wackestone) to above-fair-weather wave base (packstone). The thickening-upward nature of the cycles and the downlapping geometry indicate that the ramp was prograding broadly eastward. The transition from the Aladan to the Avren formation indicates a subsequent drowning of the nummulite ramp at the lower to middle Eocene boundary.

Obsor Syncline

The northern limb of the Obsor syncline (Figure 9) exposes a 3000-m-thick, Maastrichtian to Eocene succession from the Byala imbricate zone in the north to Obsor beach in the south (Figure 3). The biostratigraphy in the lower part of this section has been completed

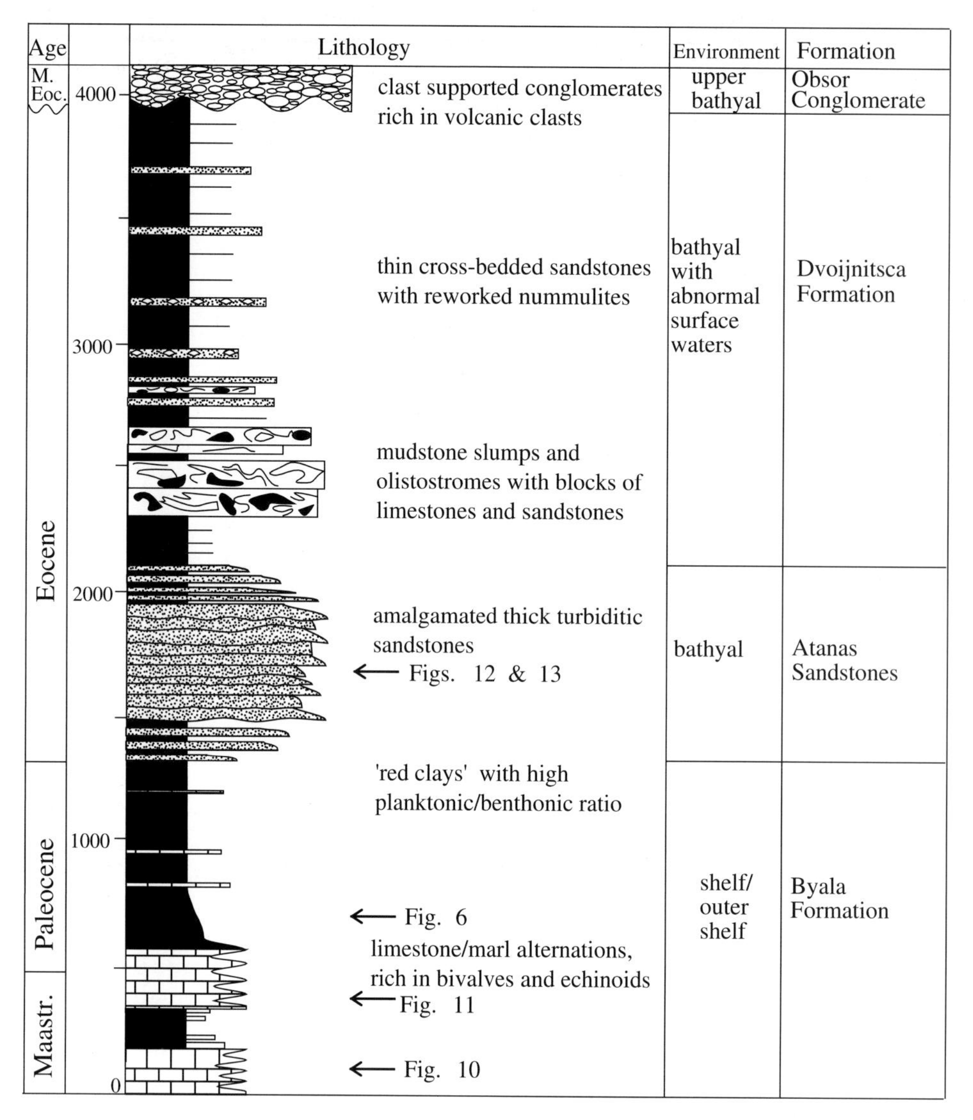

Figure 9. Log of northern limb of Obsor syncline from composite coastal sections.

by Juranov (1989). The succession is divided into three formations—Byala, Atanas Sandstones, and Dvoijnitsca—and the uppermost Obsor Conglomerate (Juranov, 1983; Juranov and Pimpirev, 1989).

Byala Formzation

This formation is best exposed immediately north of the Byala beach. Lithologically, the formation is characterized by three facies: cream-colored micrites (Figure 10), limestone/marl alternations (Figure 11), and cleaved marls. Locally, either the micrites or the marls may develop more massive units. The structural complexities have been interpreted (see above), and it is possible to identify a facies succession in the Byala Formation; however, exact thicknesses of the various facies are hard to quantify. The stratigraphically lower portions are exposed at the headland to the north of the beach and comprise light-cream-colored, well-indurated micrite (Figure 10). This facies shows 3–10-cm bedding and is bioturbated with a few echinoid fragments. Overlying this is a succession of limestone/marl alternations. This succession then becomes more marl rich for ~50 m, with a pervasive cleavage. Overlying the marls, there is a gradual return to limestone/marl alternations dominated by 0.5–0.8-m-thick, light-gray alternations of well-cemented micrite and more fissile marl (Figure 11). Within this facies, Stoykova and Ivanov (1992) documented the location and nature of the Cretaceous–Tertiary boundary using calcareous nannoplankton. Also present are a number of bivalves, including *Inoceramus* and other smaller species, and echinoid fragments identified as *Stegaster hebertii* Seunes, which is a typical shallow-burrowing echinoid of Maastrichtian age. A variety of trace fossils are present, the most predominant being an echinoid-grazing trace. Overlying this limestone/marl succession, the lithology becomes increasingly fissile and argillaceous, without any noticeable macrofauna; this unit is intensely cleaved and sheared in the region of the Byala beach (Figure 6).

Overall, the Byala Formation records deposition in a shelf/outer-shelf setting, with varying proportions of fine siliciclastics diluting the accumulation of micrite.

Figure 10. Cream-colored, thinly bedded micrite of the Byala Formation from the headland north of Byala. Camera for scale. For stratigraphic location, see Figure 9.

Figure 11. Limestone marl alternations of the Byala Formation, from coastline north of Byala. It is within this facies that Stoykova and Ivanov (1992) located the Cretaceous–Tertiary boundary. For stratigraphic location, see Figure 9.

Atanas Sandstones

The transition between the Byala Formation and the overlying Atanas Sandstones is located at the first occurrence of sandstones. This occurs ~500 m south of the Byala beach where light-gray marls with localized limestone beds are overlain by dark-gray mudstones with ≤50% fine sandstone forming thin (<10 cm), laterally persistent beds. The transition between the carbonates and the siliciclastics occurs in ~10 m of section. The mudstones in the lower parts of the Atanas Sandstones locally weather to a red color, leading to their being termed the "red clays" by local workers. These mudstones contain a lowermost Eocene planktonic assemblage, with a 99.9% plankton-to-benthon foraminiferal ratio (Juranov, 1983).

Up section of the Atanas Sandstones, the sandstone/mudstone ratio increases, and the sandstones become coarser. Mudstone samples contain a sparse foraminiferal assemblage, which combined with palynology indicate a late Paleocene–early Eocene age for this part of the succession (Campion, 1993). Approximately 100 m above the red clays are medium-to-thick bedded, poorly sorted, very coarse sandstone/mudstone alternations. The sandstone beds are sharp-based, locally erosive, and laterally persistent. Internally, they show normal grading from a structureless lower portion with localized mudstone clasts, up into planar-bedded medium/fine sandstones, and then overlain by a ripple cross-laminated unit that fines up into mudstones. The mudstones are sometimes calcareous, with

Figure 12. Amalgamated massive sandstones of the Atanas Sandstones at Cape Atanas. Variations in the weathering generate a nodular appearance, picking out more highly cemented lenses and layers. For stratigraphic location, see Figure 9. It is possible that these form the interpreted basin-floor fan in the north of Figure 6.

Figure 13. Close-up of amalgamation surface between two sandstone units in the Atanas Sandstones. The lower shows planar bedding in coarse to very coarse sandstones interpreted as inertia flows (Hiscott, 1994). For stratigraphic location, see Figure 9.

a light cream color and extensive *Chondrites* bioturbation and other larger burrows. Cross-bedding is locally developed within the sandstones, with ≤1-m-thick, planar cross-sets. Two measurements were possible of the foresets, and both indicated a S-SE paleoflow. This sandstone/mudstone facies succession within the Atanas Sandstones has been identified as a separate formation by Doglioni et al. (1996), who termed it the Gebesh Formation. Higher up the section, sandstones become more massive, with structureless coarse sandstones ≤4 m thick. The thickest and coarsest part of the succession is exposed at Cape Atanas, where the sandstones become fully amalgamated, with no fine intercalations for at least 100 m (Figure 12). Internally, the sandstones are normally graded and planar bedded, picked out by variations in grain size in 2–10 cm units (Figure 13). There are no clear grain-sized breaks in the planar bedding, so both normal and inverse grading are seen. Locally, these structures may develop low-angle (2–10°), large wavelength (1–10 m) undulations. The base of sandstone beds commonly truncates the underlying bedding with an irregular contact (Figure 13). Within sandstone beds, mudstone clasts are locally present and may be ≤0.5 m across.

The lower part of the Atanas Sandstones is interpreted to reflect turbidite processes transporting sands into a basinal setting, as recorded by the background mudstones. The mudstones contain a very restricted microfauna, which indicates bathyal or deeper water, with highly stressed bottom-water conditions (Campion, 1993). The upward increase in bed thickness and grain size reflects increased transport of sands into this portion of the basin, with high-concentration flows recording steadier flow conditions, with the development of thick, massive sandstones (Kneller and Branney, 1995). The planar bedding reflects the development of inertia layers recording fluctuating flow conditions under a sustained flow (Hiscott, 1994).

The occurrence offshore of a marked mound overlying the base Tertiary unconformity (Figure 6), which is interpreted as a possible basin-floor fan, suggests that these may represent the offshore equivalents of the Atanas Sandstones.

Dvoijnitsca Formation

Overlying the massive sandstone facies exposed at Cape Atanas is the Dvoijnitsca Formation, which is a succession of folded, thin-bedded siltstone/mudstone alternations that contain a microfauna indicating that they are no older than middle Eocene age (Campion, 1993). The mudstones are light-gray, calcareous, and micaceous, with scattered carbonaceous material and carbonate. The siltstone beds are ≤10 cm thick and show current ripples, which are commonly climbing. The ripple geometries indicate flow toward the southeast. Bioturbation is common on the upper and lower bedding surfaces.

North of the town of Obsor, at Camping Luna, the thin-bedded facies of the Dvoijnitsca Formation give way to thick, disorganized deposits (Figure 9); the contact between these two facies is not exposed. These upper deposits are ≤300 m thick, and commence in the north with structureless units comprising poorly sorted medium to coarse sandstones, with fine mud preserved within the matrix of the sandstones, and with large folded clasts of laminated mudstone, which can be several meters across, and pebbles floating in the sandstone ≤30 cm across. Farther up the section (Figure 9), these disorganized units become more bedded, with lenses of planar-bedded sandstone and massive conglomerates and breccias ≤0.5 m thick. The conglomerates and breccias contain clasts of predominantly gray mudstone, cream-colored calcareous mudstones, and rounded basic volcanics. Farther up the succession (near the union rest house, south of Obsor), mudstones dominate, with localized coarse, poorly sorted, quartz-rich sandstone beds. The mudstones are micaceous and moderately calcareous, and contain a foraminiferal assemblage yielding a probable earliest middle Eocene age within Zone P10 (Campion, 1993). The intercalated sandstones are cross-bedded and are rich in reworked nummulites tests that show flow-induced imbrication.

The thin-bedded, rippled siltstones of the lower Dvoijnitsca Formation indicate a change from high-density, large-volume sustained flows of the Atanas Sandstones to low-density, lower-volume surge-type turbidity currents. The disorganized beds, which overlie the siltstone/mudstone alternations, record downslope mass-flow processes.The large, folded blocks of mudstones suggest slumping, associated with debris flows lubricated by minor amounts of mud in the matrix, causing grains to flow past each other (Lowe, 1982); these processes develop the very poorly sorted units with no clear bedding. Up the succession, the more bedded sandstones and conglomerates record high-concentration turbidity currents with a very coarse sediment load. Farther up the succession, the sandstone/mudstone ratio decreases and the sandstones record more dilute turbidite events. The presence of reworked nummulites and the dominance of mature, well-sorted quartz sandstones suggest that these flows were derived from the shallower conditions to the north. A mudstone sample in these upper mudstones contains agglutinated benthonic foraminifera, which indicates a bathyal setting. There is a relative sparseness of plankton, which, associated with small specimen sizes, suggests abnormal surface water conditions. This could be caused by isolation from access to fully open oceanic circulation (Campion, 1993).

Obsor Conglomerate

Inland from the coastline, around the town of Obsor, are exposures of a conglomerate that must overlie the succession described above; however, the contact is not exposed. The exposures comprise cliff faces up to 20 m high, but the overal thickness of the formation is unknown. The lithology is a poorly sorted conglomerate, with clasts averaging 10–20 cm with a maximum of 40 cm across. The matrix is a dark-gray, poorly sorted, argillaceous medium sandstone. The texture is clast supported, with localized differentiation of clast sizes forming a vague bedding, which appears as a low-angle cross-bedding. The clasts show a rough b-axis imbrication, broadly indicating flow to the S-SE. Clasts are well- to subrounded, comprising mainly basic igneous material (similar to the calc-alkaline volcanics of the Srednogorie Zone), with a few cream-colored micrite clasts.

This lithology is hard to interpret in terms of depositional environments based on the limited exposures. However, the clast-supported nature, the low-angle cross-bedding, and the b-axis imbrication suggest transport as bed load under a sustained flow. These conglomerates are also recorded in the offshore well IV/91-1, intercalated with middle Eocene, upper bathyal mudstones. Given that these conglomerates are likely to have been derived from the emergent Srednogorie Zone to the south, it is likely that these represent some of the earliest evidence of thrust activity on the southern margins of the Moesian Platform.

Irakli Syncline (Emine Formation)

The Maastrictian and Paleocene succession exposed in the Irakli syncline is all within the Emine Formation (Juranov and Pimpirev, 1989; Juranov, 1994). The exposed succession in the southern limb of the syncline is ~2.5 km thick (Figure 14) and comprises a dominantly turbiditic succession (Pimpirev et al., 1985).

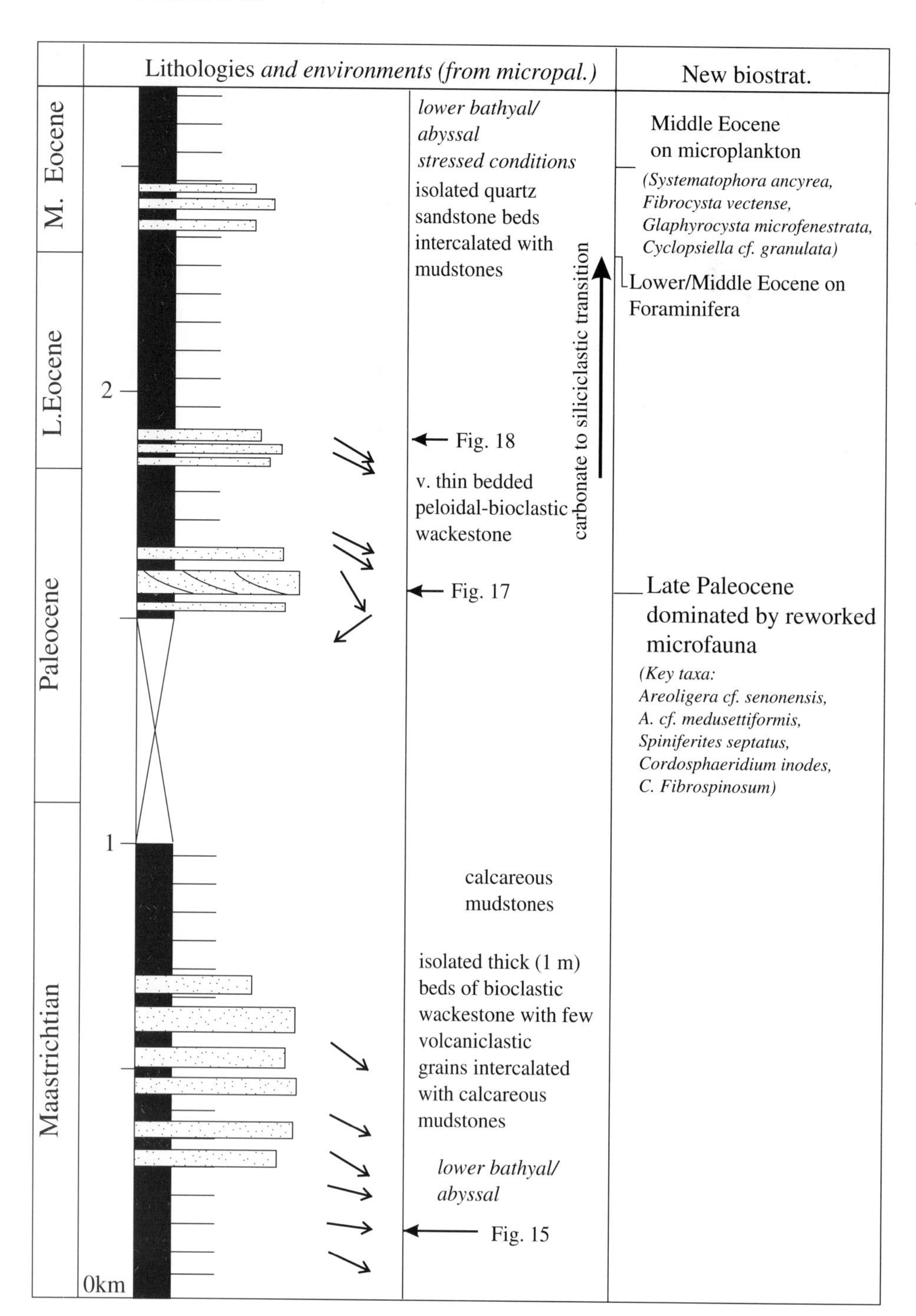

Figure 14. Composite sedimentary log constructed from numerous coastal sections within the Irakli syncline. Age ranges are from Juranov (1994), with new data in the right-hand column from Campion (1993).

The stratigraphically lowest part of the Emine Formation is exposed in the south along the shoreline of Cape Emine. The facies are dominated by cream- to light-gray colored, very fine- to medium-grained peloidal and bioclastic wackestone beds 2–20 cm thick intercalated with gray and cream micritic mudstones (Figure 15). The wackestones also contain variable amounts of quartz and isolated grains of glauconite. The beds are sharp based, and are ungraded to normally graded with planar, ripple, and convolute lamination. Flute and tool marks are common on the base of beds, yielding a dominantly south-easterly paleocurrent direction (Figure 16). Locally, coarser bioclastic wackestones form beds ≤1.5 m thick, and may comprise thick (≤1 m), cross-set stratification (Figure 17), convolute bedding, and/or thick units of planar-laminated sandstones with primary current lineation (Figure 18). Chondrites burrows are common; *Zoophycus* and other surface traces are also present.

Farther up the section, at approximately the Paleocene–Eocene boundary (Campion, 1993), the proportion of carbonate in the section diminishes; the section is dominated by gray sandstone/mudstone alternations. The sandstones are fine-grained, well-sorted quartz arenites, with minor glauconite and chlorite. This part of the succession is particularly well exposed

Figure 15. Fine calcareous sandstone/mudstone alternations of the Maastrichtian lower Emine Formation from the coastline near Cape Emine. Note that light-colored fine units are micrite bands.

in the cliffs to the north of Irakli (Figure 3). The dominant facies is thin-bedded, fine sandstone/mudstone alternations. Sandstone beds are sharp based and normally graded with planar and current ripple lamination, which indicates an E-SE paleoflow. The bioturbation in this part of the succession is much more variable, with chondrites, *Rhizocorallium*, *Zoophycus*, *Cruziana*, *Palaeodictyon*, and numerous other small traces. The burrows are sometimes lined with green glauconite grains.

The lower, more carbonate-rich part of the Emine Formation has a rich and diverse in-situ microplankton, which suggests a fully open marine setting (Campion, 1993). Other samples taken throughout the Emine flysch indicate lower bathyal to abyssal water depths. Samples taken from the uppermost, middle Eocene part of the formation contain a sparse foraminiferal assemblage of very small size, indicating highly stressed conditions, similar to the time-equivalent deposits in the Dvoijnitsca Formation. The facies in the Emine Formation indicate that this deep-water setting was fed by episodic turbidity currents that contained dominantly carbonate material lower in the formation, becoming increasingly siliciclastic at end-Paleocene. Variations in the sandstone/mudstone ratio through the succession suggest either the migration of lobe-type sand accumulations on the basin plain or variations in the flux of sandstone into the deeper part of the basin over time.

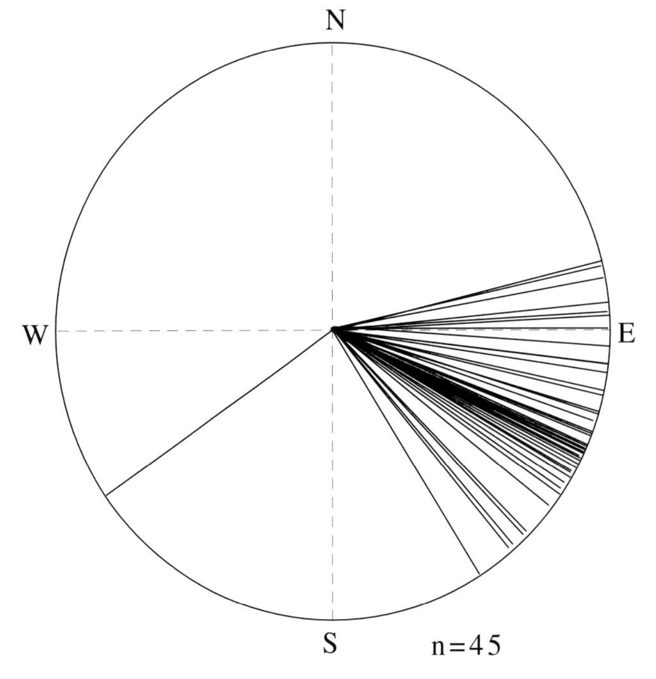

Figure 16. Paleocurrent data from the Emine Formation exposed in the Irakli syncline.

Overview of Sedimentation and Tectonics

The proposed depositional processes and environments for the three sections described above reveal significant variations in a north-south traverse across the basin during the Maastrichtian to middle Eocene (Figure 19). Time-averaged depositional settings were lower bathyal/abyssal in the south of the basin, outer shelf/upper bathyal in the center of the basin, and inner shelf/coastal in the north. During the Maastrichtian, carbonate-rich turbidites and mudstones were accumulating in the south, while outer-shelf limestone/marl alternations were being deposited in the center of the basin, and bioturbated shelf siltstones in the north. At the Maastrichtian–Paleocene boundary, similar processes continued in the south and in the center of the basin, while in the north, there was a depositional hiatus and/or the beginnings of erosion during the lower Paleocene. The Late Paleocene saw the onset of shallow marine sedimentation in the north

Figure 17. Thick, coarse sandstone bed from the middle Emine Formation exposed north of Irakli. This sandstone is intercalated with thin-bedded turbidites, and shows low-angle cross-bedding, which forms the complete thickness of the bed. The upper parts of the bed are convoluted and bioturbated.

Figure 18. Thick, ungraded coarse sandstone within very thin bedded siltstone/mudstone turbidites of the middle Emine Formation exposed north of Irakli. The unit comprises planar lamination covered by primary current lineation throughout.

of the basin, and continued deep-water carbonate accumulation in the center and southern portions. By early Eocene times, coarse, turbiditic sandstones started accumulating in the south and center of the basin, with continued deposition of shallow marine, nummulitic limestones in the north. Subsequently, during the early–middle Eocene, sedimentation in the south remained similar, whereas in the center of the basin, extensive mass flows, which are now preserved solely in the northern limb of the Obsor syncline, were shed from the north. At the same time, the northern margin of the basin started to deepen, accumulating the Avren Marls. Also during the middle Eocene, the micropaleontology indicates an increasingly stressed foraminiferal population, possibly linked to reduced circulation with the open oceans.

Throughout the development of the basin, each of the three portions of the basin had its own independent sedimentation patterns. Even when turbidite sedimentation was taking place in the central and southern parts of the basin during the early Eocene, the massive sandstones that are present at Cape Atanas and Cape Mona Petra did not develop in the southern sector. This sedimentological differentiation within the basin suggests that there may have been structural controls, which led to topographic confinement of the different parts of the basin at that time.

The drop in sea level during the early Paleocene, which generated the unconformity in the northern region of the basin, is not recorded sedimentologically in the central part of the basin in the sediments of the Obsor syncline. The seismic data (Figures 6, 7)

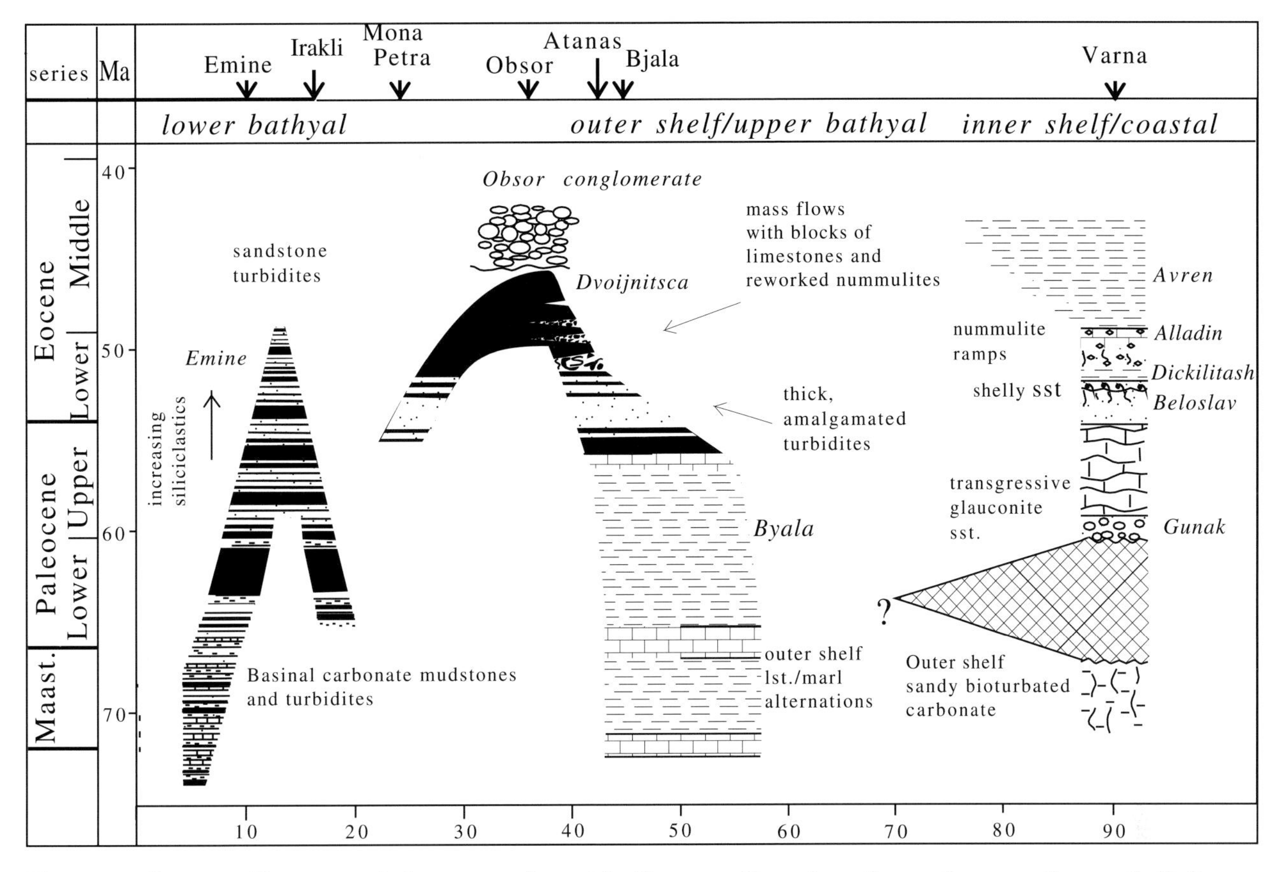

Figure 19. Structurally restored chronostratigraphic diagram aligned north-south across the north Balkan foreland basin. Also shown are the time-averaged depositional settings for each portion of the basin. lst = limestones; sst = sandstones; cross-hatching represents lacunae.

indicate the inversion of deep level normal faults at the end of the Cretaceous, which are subsequently onlapped at the onset of the Tertiary. It is proposed that the unconformity in the northern part of the basin underlying the Gunak Formation (Figure 8) was generated by the reactivation of deep-seated normal faults. The subsequent transgression of the Gunak Formation and final deepening, which deposited the Avren Marls (Figure 8), is interpreted as having been linked to the onset of foreland basin subsidence. A possible alternative interpretation for the generation of the unconformity is that it resulted from surface uplift in the forebulge region of the flexed Moesian plate. At this time, any possible thrust front must have been ≤80 km south of the area of erosion/hiatus that formed the unconformity. Depending upon the distribution of the thrust load over the plate and the flexural strength of the Moesian plate, it should be mechanically possible to develop forebulge uplift in this zone (Crampton and Allen, 1995); however, without more extensive knowledge of the system, this hypothesis remains speculative.

The middle Eocene Dvoijnitsca Formation of the central part of the basin comprises very coarse mass flows and slumps, which are thought to have derived from the unstable northern margin of the foreland basin during active thrusting in the south. At a similar time, the micropaleontology of the Emine and Dvoijnitsca formations indicates reduced oceanic circulation, which is possibly linked to the growth of the Balkan thrust wedge and geographic isolation of the Black Sea from the remnants of the Tethys Ocean to the south.

BASIN SUBSIDENCE

Insight into the subsidence history of the basin can be obtained from well IV 91-1, located on offshore line 12 (Figures 2, 7). The well penetrated 3.64 km into a thrust-related high in the Valanginian. The procedure followed for determining the tectonically induced subsidence from the well data is outlined in Appendix 1, and is based on that outlined by Allen and Allen (1990). Initially, to evaluate total subsidence: the section must be decompacted, and allowances must be made for paleobathymetry and eustacy. The tectonic subsidence is then obtained by removing the subsidence induced by the load of the sediment column.

The tectonic subsidence curve for well IV/91-1 shows two distinct pulses of subsidence: during the earliest Late Cretaceous and during the middle and late Eocene (Figure 20). The time-averaged tectonic-subsidence rate from the mid-Cretaceous to the present was at least 0.016 km/m.y., assuming Airy isostatic compensation of the sediment column. During the middle and late Eocene and the early Oligocene, rates were up to 0.05 km/m.y. The Moesian foreland plate is likely to have had a flexural rigidity during loading; therefore, Airy compensation of the sediment column

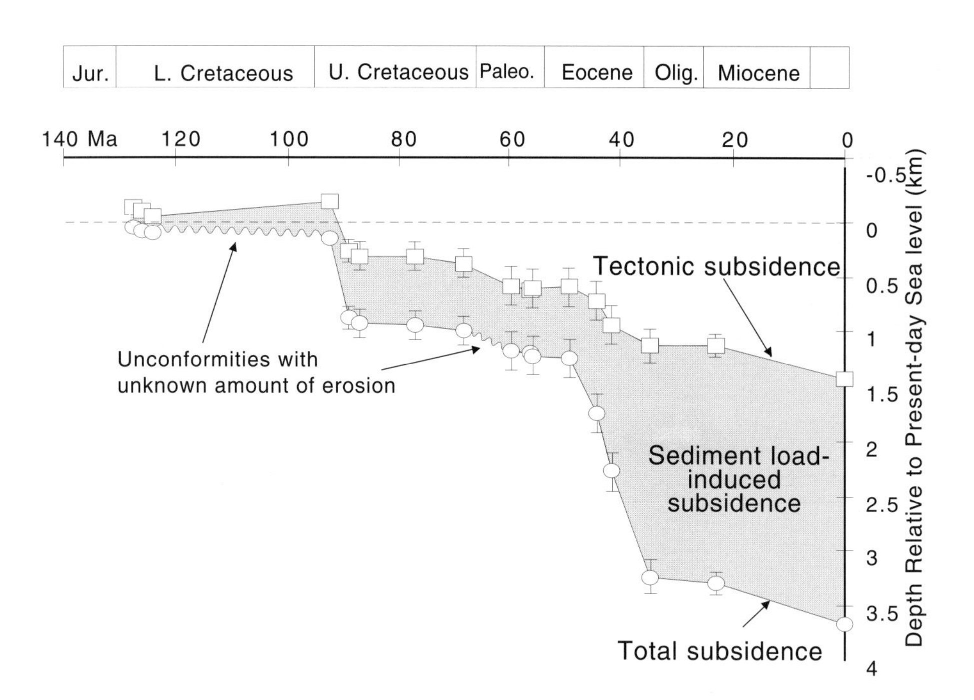

Figure 20. Subsidence curve for British Gas well IV 91-1, located on Figure 2. Error bars are for paleobathymetric uncertainties and are not cumulative.

is unlikely to be realistic, with increasing flexural rigidity of the plate so the sediment column is responsible for less of the total subsidence. For example, the tectonic-induced subsidence at the present day using the Airy case is ~1.4 km; if the plate had an equivalent elastic thickness of 50 km and the load had a wavelength of 400 km, the present-day tectonic subsidence would amount to 3.4 km. Without knowledge of the flexural rigidity of the Moesian Plate or the distribution of the load, the Airy case gives us a minimum value for tectonic subsidence.

TIMING AND RATES OF SHORTENING AND SUBSIDENCE

The timing of increased subsidence during the middle and late Eocene immediately postdates the development of the shallow-level thrusting at the present Balkan thrust front, as documented from the seismic data. It is proposed that these are linked, and that this pulse of subsidence was the result of crustal thickening and loading of the southern margin of the Moesian Platform by the Balkan thrust wedge. Hence, this stage in the development of the western margin of the Black Sea was linked to the growth of a foreland basin to the north of the Balkans in a retro-arc setting.

The 18 km (minimum value) of shortening in the section through the Balkan thrust wedge took place from the early Paleocene to end Oligocene—a time span of 41 m.y. (Haq et al., 1987). This gives a minimum time-averaged rate of shortening of ~0.5 km/m.y., which is less than half the rate of shortening of the early Cretaceous Idaho-Wyoming retro-arc thrust belt (1.8 km/m.y.) (Jordan, 1981), and is an order of magnitude slower than prothrust wedges such as the northern Alps of Switzerland (8–13 km/m.y.) or the Appalachians (19–33 km/m.y.) (Sinclair, 1997). While it is recognized that this is a minimum value for shortening, it is unlikely to have been significantly greater, because the structures are not complicated and there is virtually no indication of internal strain.

The time-averaged rate of tectonic subsidence of ≤0.05 km/m.y. for this foreland basin is also slow compared to the north Alpine foreland basin (0.1 km/m.y.) (Homewood et al., 1986) and the Cretaceous Sevier foreland basin infill (0.2 km/m.y.) (Cross, 1986), both of which also used an Airy plate model. Theoretically, the subsidence pattern within a foreland basin follows the cross-sectional profile of the flexed plate. The rate at which subsidence follows this profile is dependent on the rate of migration of the load and, hence, the rate of migration of the flexural profile across the foreland. Therefore, the rate of subsidence in a foreland basin setting is closely linked to the rate of shortening in the associated thrust wedge (Sinclair and Allen, 1992). In comparison to other thrust wedge/foreland basin systems in both retro- but particularly pro-arc settings, the Balkan system can be considered to have deformed and subsided slowly.

CONCLUSIONS

1. The Balkan thrust wedge along the Black Sea coast of Bulgaria is ~30 km wide, and comprises two large synclines, underlain by a deep-level detachment that ramps up to form the Balkan thrust front just north of Byala. The detachment geometry is controlled by the location of a normal fault in the underlying Triassic. Total shortening across the section is ≤18 km.
2. Offshore seismic stratigraphy indicates that the first evidence of shortening was the reactivation of deep-level normal faults at the end Cretaceous.

Shallow-level development of the Balkan thrust wedge took place from early Paleocene to end Oligocene times. The total of ≤18 km shortening over this time interval indicates a time-averaged rate of shortening for the Balkans of ≤0.5 km/m.y.

3. Upper Cretaceous and Lower Tertiary sedimentation in the basin immediately north of the developing Balkan thrust front records upper bathyal conditions in the south, shallowing to inner-shelf environments in the north, in the region of Varna. The shelf edge at this time was over the Golitza fault. The northern region was dominated by carbonate ramp deposits deepening into shelfal limestone/marl alternations. In the south, the system was characterized by calcturbidites, going up into more siliciclastic turbidites during early Eocene times. The transition from carbonate to siliciclastic sedimentation in the south is temporally coincident with deepening on the northern margin of the basin.
4. The initiation of shallow-level thrusting in the south of the basin was coincident with extensive mass-wasting off the shelf edge of the Moesian Platform, and reduced oceanic circulation linked to isolation from the Tethys Ocean.
5. Subsidence analysis of offshore well data indicates two pulses of subsidence, one in the mid-Cretaceous and another in middle and late Eocene times. The latter is coincident with the initiation of shallow-level Balkan deformation, and is therefore thought to be caused by thrust-load-induced flexural subsidence of the southern Moesian Platform to form the north Balkan retroarc foreland basin. Assuming Airy compensation of the sediment column, rates of subsidence were slow (0.05 km/m.y.) relative to other foreland basins. The slow rates of shortening and slow subsidence rates were mechanically linked through the process of thrust loading.

ACKNOWLEDGMENTS

This research was initiated while H. D. Sinclair was on a British Gas research fellowship at Durham University. A second field trip was supported by a Distinguished Geologists Memorial Trust fund coordinated by the Geological Society of London. Mick Oates (British Gas) is thanked for initial encouragement and support. Critical reviews of the manuscript by M. Whitehead (Enterprise Oil), C. Banks (RHBNC), and E. Blunt were appreciated. Editorial guidance by Andrew Robinson facilitated the revision procedure.

REFERENCES CITED

Aladjova-Hrisceva, K.I., 1984, Stratigraphy of the Eocene sediments near to Beloslav (in Bulgarian): Review of the Bulgarian Geological Society, v. 45, no. 1, p. 33–44.

Aladjova-Hrisceva, K.I., 1991, Stratigraphic subdivision and correlation of Paleogenic deposits in northeast Bulgaria (in Bulgarian): Geologica Balcanica, v. 21, no. 2, p. 12–38.

Aladjova-Hrisceva, K.I., N.G. Muzyilev, and S.G. Juranov, 1983, Micropaleontology of the Cretaceous and Palaeocene section near Beloslav, northeast Bulgaria (in Bulgarian): Comptes Rendus de l'Academie Bulgare des Sciences, v. 36, no. 7, p. 937–940.

Allen, P.A., and J.R. Allen, 1990, Basin analysis: principles and products: Oxford, Blackwell Scientific Press, 451 p.

Allen, P.A., S.L. Crampton, and H.D. Sinclair, 1991, The inception and early evolution of the North Alpine foreland basin, Switzerland: Basin Research, v. 3, p. 143–163.

Atanasov, A., 1961, Geology of the pre-Balkanides sea area and of the Kamchian foredeep: Trud. varhu geol. Bulgaria, Series on Stratigraphy and Tectonics no. 2, p. 154–178.

Athy, L.F., 1930, Density, porosity and compaction of sedimentary rocks: AAPG Bulletin, v. 14, p. 1–24.

Banks, C.J., this volume, Basins and thrust belts of the Balkan coast of the Black Sea, *in* A.G. Robinson, ed., Regional and petroleum geology of the Black Sea and surrounding areas: AAPG Memoir 68, p. 115–128.

Boccaletti, M., P. Manetti, and A. Peccerillo, 1974, The Balkanides as an instance of a back-arc thrust belt: possible relation with the Hellenides: Bulletin of the Geological Society of America, v. 85, p. 1077–1084.

Bogatskaja, G., and E. Chuparova, 1986, Depositional rhythmicity and correlation of Paleogene sediments in the Dolna-Kamchia Depression in relation to oil and gas content (in Bulgarian): Reports of the Bulgarian Academy of Sciences: Petroleum and Coal Geology, v. 24, p. 32–41.

Bokov, P., and R. Ognyanov, 1978, Relations between the upper Eocene and Oligocene sediments of the southern part of the Varna Depression in connection with their petroleum- and gas-bearing potential (in Bulgarian): Reports of the Bulgarian Academy of Sciences: Petroleum and Coal Geology, v. 8, p. 18–33.

Bokov, P., R. Ognyanov, and J. Shimanov, 1979, Relations between upper Eocene and Oligocene deposits in the Black Sea region (in Bulgarian): Geologica Balcanica, v. 9, no. 4, p. 3–34.

Bokov, P., G. Georgiev, and T. Nikolov, 1981, The southern slope of the Late Jurassic and Early Cretaceous paleoshelf in northeast Bulgaria (in Bulgarian): Geologica Balcanica, v. 11, no. 3, p. 67–94.

Boncev, E., 1978, The post-Lutetian turning point in the evolution of the Balkanide mobile area (in Bulgarian): Geologica Balcanica, v. 8, no. 3, p. 25–36.

Burchfiel, B.C., 1980, Eastern European Alpine system and the Carpathian orocline as an example of collision tectonics: Tectonophysics, v. 63, p. 31–61.

Byrne, P., G. Georgiev, I. Todozov, and E. Mazinov, 1995, Structure, depositional setting, and petroleum geology of eastern Balkanides, Bulgaria (extended abs.): 5th Conference of EAGE, Glasgow, v. 2, European Association of Petroleum Geologists (EAPG) Division, p. E-021.

Campion, K., 1993, Biostratigraphic analyses of selected field samples and core pieces from Bulgaria: Simon Petroleum Technology Limited Report for British Gas Exploration and Production Limited, no. 4803/Ia, 44 p.
Crampton, S.L., and P.A. Allen, 1995, Recognition of flexural forebulge unconformities associated with early-stage foreland basin development: example from the North Alpine foreland basin: AAPG Bulletin, v. 79, no. 10, p. 1495–1514.
Cross, T.A., 1986, Tectonic controls of foreland basin subsidence and Larimide-style deformation, western United States, *in* P.A. Allen and P. Homewood, eds., Foreland basins: International Association of Sedimentologists Special Publication 8, p. 15–39.
Doglioni, C., C. Busatta, G. Bolis, L. Marianini, and M. Zanella, 1996, Structural evolution of the eastern Balkans (Bulgaria): Marine and Petroleum Geology, v. 13, no. 2, p. 225–251.
Haq, B.U., J. Hardenbol, and P.R. Vail, 1987, Chronology of fluctuating sea-levels since the Triassic: Science, v. 235, p. 1153–1165.
Hiscott, R.N., 1994, Traction-carpet stratification in turbidites—fact or fiction?: Journal of Sedimentary Research, v. A64, no. 2, p. 204–208.
Homewood, P.W., P.A. Allen, and G.D. Williams, 1986, Dynamics of the Molasse basin in western Switzerland, *in* P.A. Allen and P. Homewood, eds., Foreland basins: International Association of Sedimentologists Special Publication 8, p. 119–217.
Ingle, J.C., Jr., 1980, Cenozoic paleobathymetry and depositional history of selected sequences within the southern California continental borderland: Cushman Foundation Special Publication 19, p. 163–195.
Jordan, T.E., 1981, Thrust loads and foreland basin evolution, Cretaceous, western United States: AAPG Bulletin, v. 65, no. 12, p. 2506–2520.
Juranov, S.G., 1983, Planktonic foraminiferal zonation of the Paleocene and the lower Eocene in part of east Balkan Mountains (in Bulgarian): Geologica Balcanica, v. 13, no. 2, p. 59–73.
Juranov, S.G., 1989, Geological data concerning the Byala area (East Stara Planina) (in Bulgarian): Annual of the Higher Institute of Mining and Geology, Sofia, v. 35, no. 1, p. 7–18.
Juranov, S.G., 1994, Paleocene planktonic foraminifera from the type region of the Emine flysch formation (eastern Balkan) (in Bulgarian): Palaeontology, Stratigraphy and Lithology, v. 30, p. 3–21.
Juranov, S.G., and H. Pimpirev, 1989, Lithostatigraphy of the Upper Cretaceous and the Paleogene in the coastal part of the East Stara Planina (in Bulgarian): Review of the Bulgarian Geological Society, v. L, no. 2, p. 1–17.
Kneller, B.C., and M.J. Branney, 1995, Sustained high density turbidity currents and the deposition of thick massive sands: Sedimentology, v. 42, no. 4, p. 607–616.
Lowe, D.R., 1982, Sediment gravity flows: II. Depositional models with specific reference to deposits of high density turbidity currents: Journal of Sedimentary Petrology, v. 52, p. 279–297.
Pimpirev, H.C., S.S. Stoikov, and D.A. Vangelov, 1985, Paleogeography of the Upper Cretaceous and Paleogene from the seashore parts of the east Balkan Mountains (in Bulgarian): Annual of the Faculty of Geology, University of Sofia 'St. Kliment Ohridski,' v. 79, no. 1, p. 14–18.
Sclater, J.G., and P.A.F. Christie, 1980, Continental stretching: an explanation of the post-Mid-Cretaceous subsidence of the central North Sea basin: Journal of Geophysical Research, v. 85, p. 3711–3739.
Sinclair, H.D., and P.A. Allen, 1992, Vertical versus horizontal motions in the Alpine orogenic wedge: stratigraphic response in the foreland basin: Basin Research, v. 4, p. 215–232.
Sinclair, H.D., 1997, Tectono-stratigraphic model for underfilled peripheral foreland basins: an Alpine perspective: Bulletin of the Geological Society of America, v. 109, no. 3, p. 324–346.
Stoykova, K.H., and M.I. Ivanov, 1992, An uninterrupted section across the Cretaceous/Tertiary boundary at the town of Byala, Black Sea Coast (Bulgaria): Comptes Rendus de l'Academie Bulgare des Sciences, v. 45, no. 7, p. 61–64.
Tchoumatchenko, P., and I. Sapunov, 1994, Intraplate tectonics in the Bulgarian part of the Moesian Platform during the Jurassic: Geologica Balcanica, v. 24, no. 3, p. 3–12.
Vail, P.R., 1987, Seismic stratigraphy interpretation procedure, *in* A.W. Bally, ed., Atlas of seismic stratigraphy: AAPG Studies in Geology, v. 27, no. 1, p. 1–10.

APPENDIX 1: SUBSIDENCE ANALYSIS OF WELL IV/91-1

Decompaction

Table 1 summarizes the stratigraphic units encountered in well IV/91-1, from which a decompacted subsidence plot has been constructed. The stratigraphic decompaction process assumes a commonly used exponential porosity–depth relationship (Athy, 1930) of the form

$$\phi = \phi_0 e^{-cy} \tag{1}$$

where ϕ is the porosity at depth y, ϕ_0 is the surface porosity, and c is the depth at which ϕ is e times the surface porosity. The overlying water column is assumed to have only a negligible effect on the compaction of the underlying sedimentary layers, and is therefore not considered in the decompaction exercise.

Successive backstripping enables the effects of compaction due to the overburden of younger horizons to be removed step by step. The decompacted thickness $(y'_2 - y'_1)$ of an individual layer presently located between the depth intervals y_1 and y_2 is given by

Table 1. British Gas Well IV/91-1 Subsidence Analysis Data.

Unit	Depth to Top (m)	Age Range	Assigned Age at Top (Ma)	Paleo-bathymetry	Water Depth at Top (m)	Eustacy at Top (m)	Surface Porosity	Compaction Coefficient	Sediment Density (kg.m^{-3})
16	0	Oligocene–Recent	0	mid–inner shelf	320	0	0.49	0.27	2650
R									
15	622	Oligocene	23.3	outer shelf–upper bathyal	125	150	0.56	0.30	2685
T-A									
14	811.5	mid–late Eocene	35.4	upper bathyal	237.5	200	0.56	0.30	2685
T-B									
13	2038	mid–Eocene	42.1	upper bathyal	325	180	0.52	0.34	2670
T-C									
12	2592	early–mid-Eocene	45	upper bathyal	325	220	0.56	0.39	2685
T-D									
11	3135	intra early Eocene	50	upper bathyal	325	220	0.49	0.27	2650
T-E									
10	3160	late Paleocene	56.5	upper bathyal	325	200	0.63	0.51	2720
T-F									
9	3195	Mid Paleocene	57	upper bathyal	325	190	0.7	0.71	2710
T-G									
8	3210	Maastrichtian–mid-Paleocene	60.5	?	325	200	?	?	?
U/C 1									
7	3210	Campanian–Maastrichtian	69.5	outer shelf–upper bathyal	150	220	0.7	0.71	2710
UK-A									
6	3240	Coniacian–Campanian	78.5	outer shelf–upper bathyal	150	240	0.66	0.61	2715
UK-B									
5	3260	Turonian	88.5	outer shelf–upper bathyal	150	230	0.66	0.61	2715
UK-C									
4	3280	mid-Late Cenomanian	90.4	outer shelf	125	250	0.63	0.51	2720
UK-D									
3	3625	Valanginian–Mid-Cenomanian	93.7	?	100	220	?	?	?
U/C 2									
2	3625	Berriasian–Early Valanginian	126	mid-shelf	50	90	0.7	0.71	2710
LK-A									
1	3630	Berriasian	128	mid-shelf	50	120	0.7	0.71	2710
LK-B									
0	3640	Early Berriasian	129.5	mid-shelf	50	130	?	?	?
"Basement"									

Table 2. Porosity–Depth Parameters for Various Lithologies.*

Lithology	Surface Porosity	Compaction Coefficient (km^{-1})	Sediment Grain Density ($kg.m^{-3}$)
Shale	0.63	0.51	2720
Sandstone	0.49	0.27	2650
Chalk	0.70	0.71	2710
Shaley sandstone	0.56	0.39	2680

*Based on North Sea Basin data of Sclater and Christie (1980).

$$y'_2 - y'_1 = y_2 - y_1 - \frac{\phi_0}{c}\left[exp(-cy_1) - exp(-cy_2)\right] + \frac{\phi_0}{c}\left[exp(-cy'_1) - exp(-cy'_2)\right] \quad (2)$$

The derivation is given by Allen and Allen (1990). The solution of equation 2 is by numerical iteration to isolate either y'_2 or y'_1, given the other.

Typical surface porosity, compaction constant, and sediment grain densities for sediments that are neither overpressured nor have undergone diagenesis are offered by Sclater and Christie (1980) (Table 2). In the absence of any porosity–depth data recovered from the well site, these values have been adopted.

Paleobathymetry

Paleobathymetry has been estimated according to the fauna recovered from the well. Water depths vary from a minimum of 32 m at the present day to upper bathyal depths (150–500 m) throughout the Eocene and Paleocene. Assigned values for paleowater depths are assumed to correspond to the middle of each paleobathymetric zone (Ingle, 1980). Associated error bars have been included to illustrate the likely possible range of depths. The paleobathymetric correction of the subsidence plots has been achieved simply by adding in estimates of paleowater depths.

Eustacy

Estimates of eustatic changes in sea level have been taken from the curve of Haq et al. (1987) and show an overall increase throughout the Cretaceous to a maximum of 250 m outside diameter, followed by a decrease throughout the Tertiary to the present. The eustacy data have been incorporated into the isostasy calculations in order to isolate the tectonic subsidence from the total subsidence.

Sediment Load

The isostatic effects of sediment loading must be accounted for in order to isolate the tectonic subsidence from the total subsidence. This has been achieved using a simple Airy isostatic model. The tectonically induced subsidence Y is given by

$$Y = S\left(\frac{\rho_m - \bar{\rho}_s}{\rho_m - \rho_w}\right) - \Delta SL\left(\frac{\rho_w}{\rho_m - \rho_w}\right) - (W_d - \Delta SL) \quad (3)$$

where S is the total thickness of the entire column corrected for compaction; $\bar{\rho}_s$ is the bulk density of a series of sedimentary columns; ρ_m and ρ_w are mean mantle and water densities, respectively; ΔSL is the paleosea level relative to the present; and W_d is the paleowater depth.

Banks, C.J., 1997, Basins and thrust belts of the Balkan Coast of the Black Sea, *in* A.G. Robinson, ed., Regional and petroleum geology of the Black Sea and surrounding region: AAPG Memoir 68, p. 115–128.

Chapter 8

Basins and Thrust Belts of the Balkan Coast of the Black Sea

Chris J. Banks
Royal Holloway University of London
Eghan, Surrey, United Kingdom

ABSTRACT

Three minor thrust belts are abruptly terminated at the Balkan coast of the Black Sea: the Strandzhides of Thrace and Bulgaria, the Balkanides of central Bulgaria, and the North Dobrogea belt of Romania.

The Strandzhides are the eastern external zones of the Rhodope Massif and were the site of a south-facing continental margin that started as a passive margin in the Triassic, but soon became active. The major compression was in the Late Jurassic, and the belt is made up of at least four large thrust nappes, with large displacements. The foreland basin, if it exists at all, is now buried by a Late Cretaceous magmatic arc. The Balkanides are a narrow thrust belt involving Mesozoic–Paleogene stratigraphy that is remarkably different from south to north of the belt. The area was affected by extension, mainly in the late Triassic and early-mid Cretaceous (when the Western Black Sea opened). It was not seriously compressed until the Eocene, at which time a narrow foreland basin formed due to thrust loading of the otherwise stable Moesian Platform. North Dobrogea is an enigmatic zone separating Moesia from the Eastern European Platform. It was highly extended during the Triassic, and then compressed, probably transpressively, in the Late Jurassic.

The Mesozoic–Paleogene tectonic history of the Balkans was controlled by the northward subduction of the Vardar oceanic plate (a branch of Tethys) from the Mid-Late Triassic until its closure in the Eocene. It is suggested that North Dobrogea marks a major crustal boundary at the northern limit of back-arc deformation, where the Moesian Platform was displaced SE by a distance of several hundred kilometers during the Late Triassic to Early Jurassic. The Strandzhides and Balkanides constituted a mobile active margin of the overriding Moesian–European Plate, which was alternately extended (Triassic and Cretaceous) and compressed (Jurassic/Cimmeride and Paleogene/Alpide), so that the area has become a mosaic of extensional and compressive structural elements.

INTRODUCTION

Three minor thrust belts abut the Balkan coast of the Black Sea: North Dobrogea in Romania; the Balkanides in Bulgaria; and the Strandzhides, straddling the Bulgaria–Turkey border (Figure 1). General accounts of the regional tectonics of this area (Hsü et al., 1977; Sandulescu, 1978; Şengör, 1984; Zonenshain and Le Pichon, 1986; Dercourt and Ricou, 1987; Nachev, 1991, 1992, 1993) give insufficient detail to reveal the significance of these structures satisfactorily. Although some detailed field and stratigraphic work has been done (Aydın, 1982; Gradinaru, 1988; Chatalov, 1990; Tchoumatchenko et al., 1992), none of the studies have received much attention outside their countries of origin, none of the interpretations have been subjected to modern methods of tectonic analysis, and the three zones have never been linked to derive an adequate synthesis. This chapter is an attempt to remedy these deficiencies.

The tectonic zones concerned are described in sequence from south to north, and are illustrated by three detailed cross sections (Figures 2, 4, and 5), originally drawn at 1:100,000 scale, crossing the three thrust belts. They have been tested for restorability, but this procedure could not be done with the full rigor of the balanced cross-section method because of the scanty nature of the data available—outcrop is far from perfect, there is little subsurface data, and accurate formation thicknesses were not available. The regional cross section (Figure 6) is necessarily more schematic, but it, too, is based on a cross section accurately drawn at 1:200,000 scale.

TECTONIC ZONES

Thrace Basin and Rhodope Massif

The Thrace Basin (Figure 1), at the southern end of the cross sections, is a Paleogene basin developed on the Rhodope and Strandzha zones, obscuring the contact between them. The Rhodope Massif is a sequence of igneous and sedimentary rocks regionally metamorphosed to amphibolite and locally granulite grade. Rhodope has traditionally been considered as an ancient stable continental fragment of Paleozoic or Proterozoic age, but studies in southern Bulgaria (Burg et al., 1990) suggest that some of the deformation and metamorphism is Cretaceous or even Paleogene, so it cannot be regarded as stable. However, basal Triassic rocks in medium grades of metamorphism can be recognized overlying metagranites and gneisses in several places, demonstrating that there was a major igneous, metamorphic, and erosional event of pre-Triassic, presumably Hercynian age. Rhodope is essentially the internal zone of the Strandzha thrust belt, and the history can be determined more easily from the external zone.

The basin is small and arcuate in shape, with a central deep zone with ≤9000 m of Tertiary sediment fill. Turgut et al. (1991) claim that it is a rift basin of Middle Eocene age, but this seems to be based on poor seismic data and wells that do not reach the bottom of the basin. The stratigraphy brought up by local compression in the Gelibolu (Gallipoli) Peninsula (off the map) includes clastics as old as late Paleocene overlying latest Cretaceous micritic limestones. However, Okay and Tansel (1992) believe that this is an Eocene olistostrome with olistoliths derived from the "Intra-Pontide" ocean, which closed in the Paleocene–Eocene. In this case, the basin may be a small intermontane basin resulting from compression from the south at this time. There is a second compressive event in the basin in the mid-late Miocene, related to transpressive splays off the North Anatolian fault, including the Gelibolu uplift.

The long-lived accretion complex (Karakaya Complex) related to northward subduction of the Tethys Ocean from the Triassic to the Eocene is located in mainland Turkey a short distance to the south (Okay and Mostler, 1994).

Strandzha Thrust Belt

The Strandzha thrust belt straddles the Turkish–Bulgarian border. Most previous work has dealt with one side or the other (Aydın, 1982; Gochev, 1985; Chatalov, 1990, 1992). It is a NE-vergent thrust belt of mainly Jurassic age, with at least four major thrust slices (nappes). These are described from structurally highest downward, which is generally considered to be in deformation sequence. The southernmost outcrops of Strandzha rocks are in the Çatalca area of the eastern Thracian Peninsula, separated a short distance from nonmetamorphosed Paleozoic–Triassic rocks of the Western Pontides. (The actual contact, presumed to be a major strike-slip fault, is concealed beneath flat-lying Eocene and younger sediments.) The Çatalca rocks are medium-grade metamorphosed flysch, thought to be of Triassic, and metagranitic basement, possibly correlating with the Kırklareli Nappe (Görür et al., 1992). However, the lithologies are not identical, and the connection is obscured by Eocene sediments of the Thrace Basin.

Zabernovo Nappe

The rocks in this zone lie in a synformal klippe preserved near the external margin of the thrust belt (Figure 2). They comprise a thick sequence of phyllites, clastic and calcareous flysch, marbles, and some volcanics, attributed to the Stoilovo and Gramatikovo formations, of Early-Middle Triassic age, according to their conodonts, and are overturned (Chatalov, 1990). The marine facies of the Lower Triassic rocks marks these as clearly different from rocks of the same age in the other nappes, implying that this is a far-traveled nappe originating to the SW of the zones on which it lies, but possibly comparable with the Çatalca Zone.

Kırklareli Nappe

This nappe forms the southernmost exposures on the cross section. It comprises mostly a sheared metagranitic basement, overlain to the north by a synclinal remnant of moderately metamorphosed rocks. The

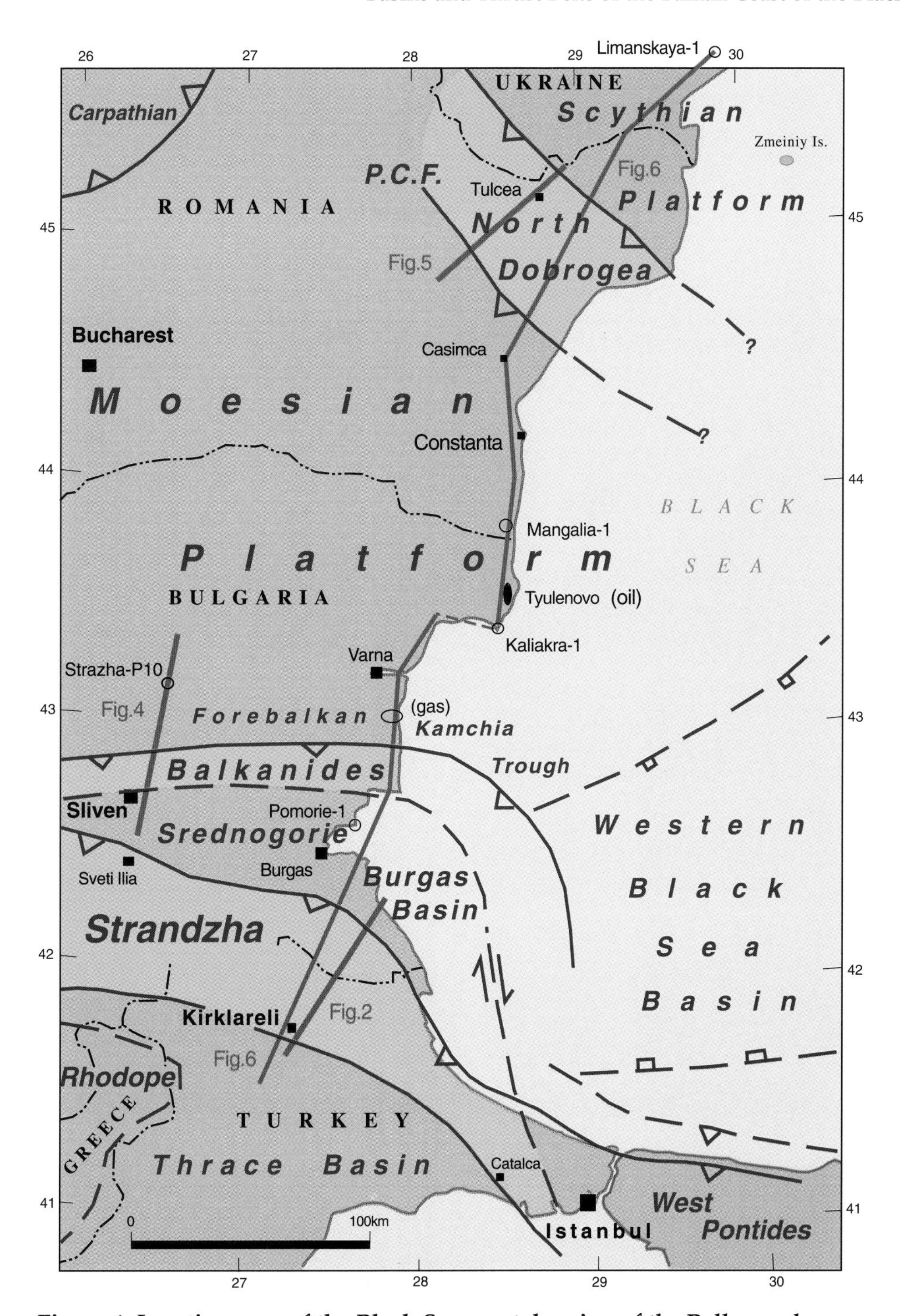

Figure 1. Location map of the Black Sea coastal region of the Balkans, showing structural zones and geological cross-section lines. Open circles are wells cited in the text; PCF = Peceneaga-Camena fault.

basal unit consists of conglomerate with granite clasts, followed by phyllites, quartzites, and finally marbles and dolomites. This section is considered to be Early to Middle Triassic in age by lithological correlation, although Aydın (1982) mistakenly puts the carbonates in the Jurassic. At the northern boundary of the nappe, the phyllites are in probable thrust contact with shales containing ferruginous nodules with fossils said to be of Jurassic age, representing the top of the underlying Zvezdets nappe. The latter is in a major regional antiform, bringing the Kırklareli nappe back to ground level to the north, before it disappears again below the Zabernovo nappe. Here it consists only of thick Middle Triassic limestones of the Malko Turnovo Formation. The nappe emerges yet again in the Kondolovo antiform, where the limestone becomes progressively thinner, and is overlain by Upper Triassic flysch of the Lipachka Formation.

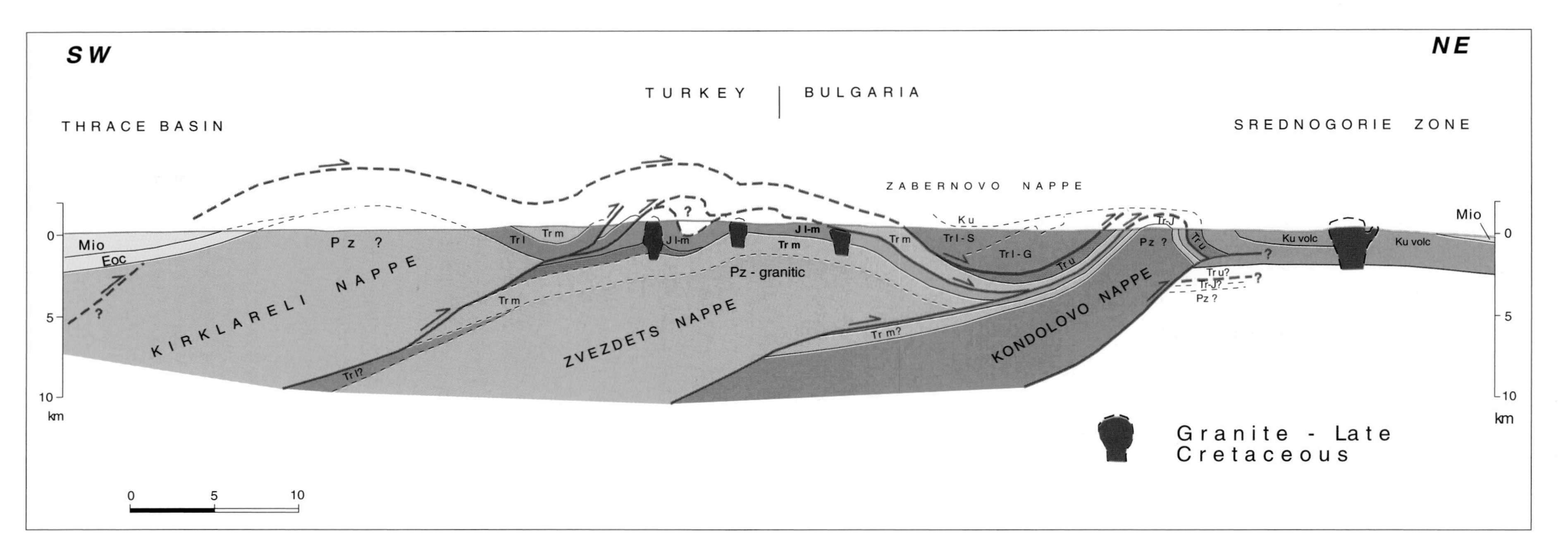

Figure 2. Strandzha cross section. Dashed lines for eroded geology, and where uncertain. Pz ? = Paleozoic and Precambian metamorphics, Tr l = Lower Triassic clastics, Tr lG and S = Gramatikovo and Stoilovo formations of Zabernovo nappe, Tr m = Middle-Upper Triassic carbonates, Tr u = Upper Triassic flysch, J l-m = Lower-Middle Jurassic marine facies, Ku = Upper Cretaceous flysch and volcanics. Depth and nature of pre-Upper Cretaceous basement of the Srednogorie Zone are not known; presumed similar to Kondolovo anticline.

The stratigraphic ranges of these occurrences of the Kırklareli nappe can be understood if it is recognized that the major thrusts that bound it both ramp progressively up-section in transport direction (Figures 2, 3).

Zvezdets Nappe

This nappe is exposed in a large antiform that runs down the national border. On the detailed cross section, only Lower to Middle Jurassic shales with some calciturbidites are seen, and they were intruded, after deformation, by Upper Cretaceous granites. A fuller sequence from basement metagranite through thin Lower Triassic clastics, Middle to Upper Triassic dolomites, and Lower to Middle Jurassic marine clastics occurs a short distance to the NW, near the village of Zvezdets.

The boundary between the Zvezdets and Kondolovo nappes is not seen, because it is overlain by the upper nappes. However, a NE-vergent thrust rising directly from basement to a flat at the top of the Jurassic is the simplest relationship.

Kondolovo Nappe

This nappe forms the core of the Kondolovo antiform, which is the frontal structure of the Strandzha Zone. It contains granitic basement overlain directly by a thin Triassic dolomite with a basal clastic bed, then a thin Middle Jurassic shale. The antiform also includes Upper Triassic Lipachka flysch of the Kırklareli nappe, thrust flat-on-flat over the Kondolovo nappe. On the north flank of the antiform, the Lipachka is unconformably overlain by Cenomanian–Turonian flysch, and then Santonian volcanics, with the same steep (60°–90°) dip. Cenomanian basal conglomerates also occur unconformably on the eroded top of the Zabernovo nappe, demonstrating pre-Cenomanian and post-Santonian phases of deformation of this structure. However, the poor outcrop in this area means that these relationships may be questionable. The Sveti Ilia antiform, located about 120 km to the W-NW, also shows evidence for two phases of deformation and is probably analogous if not continuous with the Kondolovo antiform.

Discussion of the Strandzha Zone

Some general conclusions about the Strandzha thrust belt can readily be drawn from the above information and the cross sections.

- The timing of the main phase of deformation is constrained by stratigraphy as post-Middle Jurassic and pre-Cenomanian, and this may be tied down more closely by radiometric datings of 144–150 m.y. (Tithonian) (Aydın, 1982) as the cooling age of metamorphism in the Zvezdets nappe. The second phase of deformation, in which the Kondolovo antiform was folded, is constrained as post-Santonian. It may be as young as Mid-Miocene, as in the Thrace Basin, but it is most probably late Eocene—the age of deformation in the Balkanides.
- Deformation is in the style of thin-skinned compression. Thrusts probably originate at a mid-crustal detachment, and cut up-section in the transport direction (NE), with ramps in competent formations and flats where they reach relatively incompetent formations such as the Lower Triassic clastics (at base of carbonates), the Upper Triassic flysch, and the top of the Middle Jurassic shales (synorogenic sea bed). Minimum total shortening is estimated at 150 km.
- There is a major unconformity that eroded unmetamorphosed Paleozoic rocks regionally before the Triasssic, presumably a Hercynian event. [Some Paleozoic stratigraphy is preserved farther west, in the Dervent Heights (Lakova et al., 1992)]. The early Mesozoic stratigraphy restores as a passive continental margin (Figure 3), with clastic sedimentation (conglomerates) starting in the earliest Triassic, followed by sandstones and shales, leading to the buildup of a major carbonate platform in the Middle Triassic (actually continuing until the Carnian, with a shale interval in the Ladinian). All formations thin, if not pinch-out, toward the NE, and the carbonate platform becomes a thin, sandy dolomite coastal deposit.
- The change to deep-water clastics (Lipachka flysch) in the Late Triassic (late Carnian/Norian) may signify the onset of active margin tectonics (subduction of the Tethys/Vardar Ocean). The Lipachka flysch may then be a foredeep basin fill following the earliest phase of deformation, which would have involved only the most internal zones in the Rhodope Massif (Şengör, 1992, personal communication). Alternatively, subsidence may have been due to the onset of back-arc extension. The basin-margin shelf clastics advanced into the area of the Zvezdets nappe in the Middle Jurassic.
- The exposed front of the Strandzha Zone is a Paleogene anticline deforming a sequence that contains a flat-on-flat thrust of Jurassic, carrying Lipachka flysch of the Kırklareli nappe—it is not known where this finally gets cut out.

Srednogorie Zone

The Srednogorie Zone is a low-lying area of outcropping Upper Cretaceous marine volcanics and volcaniclastics, with occasional hills marking the presence of granite intrusions. A minimum thickness of 3000 m of volcanics was proven in the Pomorie-1 borehole (Dachev et al., 1988). There is a transition in geochemistry of the lavas from calcalkaline in the south (Michurin Group) to potassic alkaline (Burgas Group) in the north, suggesting that both subduction and crustal extension were involved. Popov (1987) describes the zone as a rift, and extends it as far as the Apuseni Mountains in Romania. However, there seems to be no evidence for the presence of major extensional faults with the same trend as the zone of volcanism; the present southern boundary of the zone is certainly not extensional (Figure 2). There may have been major extension going on in the Mid–Late Cretaceous, but it is more likely to have been related to the western margin of the Western Black Sea, which opened at this time (Görür, 1988; Robinson et al.,

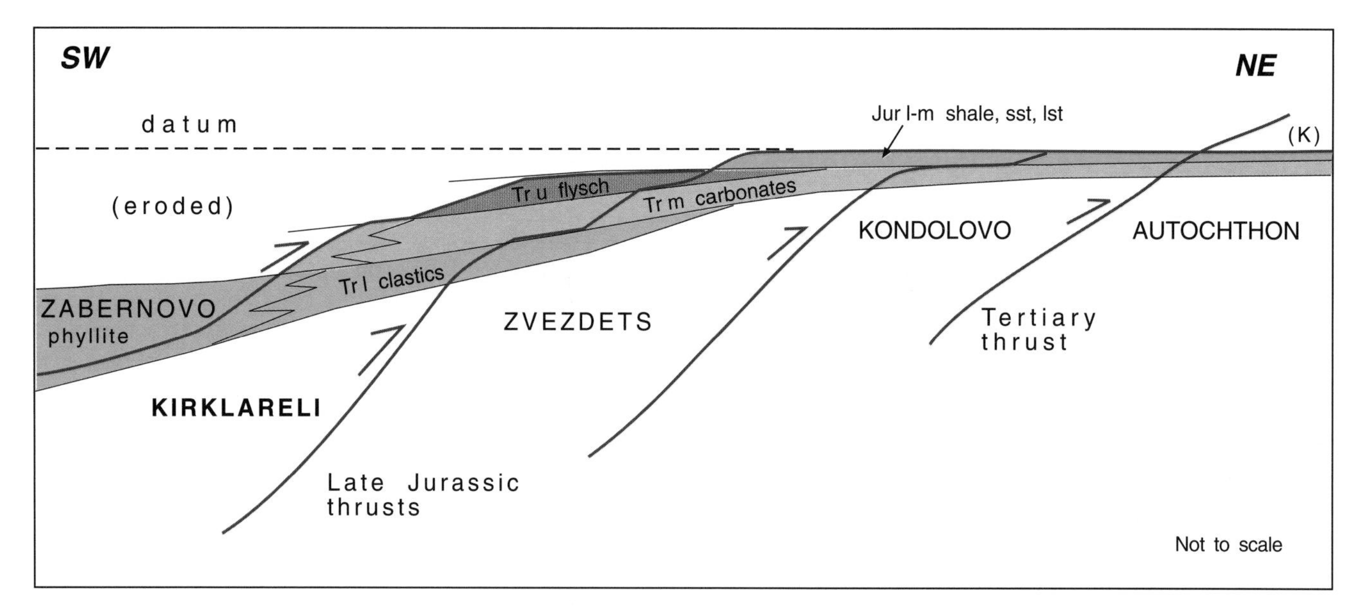

Figure 3. Schematic restoration of the Strandzha thrust belt, showing Triassic passive-margin geometry. Thick (red) lines are locations of incipient major nappe-boundary thrusts (all deformation phases), thinner (black) lines are stratigraphic boundaries. Ages indicated are approximate only. Jurl-m = Lower–Middle Jurassic marine facies.

1996). The E-W alignment of the Srednogorie volcanics suggests that it is primarily a subduction-related magmatic arc that can be linked (with an offset) to the Pontide magmatic arc, offshore of the Western Pontides. The subduction zone must have passed south of the Rhodope Massif; that is, it probably involved continuing subduction of the Vardar Ocean (Nachev, 1993).

It is possible that there may be some Jurassic or Lower Cretaceous sediments hidden in the depths of the basin, but the present form of the basin is defined by Tertiary compressive tectonics. Offshore, the Srednogorie Zone subsided further as an intermontane basin during the Late Paleogene to allow the accumulation of ~1500 m of postvolcanic sediment in the Burgas Basin (Dachev et al., 1988).

Balkanide Thrust Belt

The Balkanide range is a narrrow E-W–trending thrust belt of mainly Paleogene age. It continues to the west into Serbia, turning north to join the southern branch of the Carpathians. To the east, below the Black Sea, it turns sharply south toward the Bosporus, but it apparently dies out before linking with the Western Pontide thrusts (Dachev et al., 1988; Robinson et al., 1996). If displacement really does die out, this would imply that shortening across the Balkanides is very slight. The eastern part of the range, in the study area, comprises two strands of thrusted structures separated by the E-W–trending Luda Kamchia syncline; the whole belt is ~30 km south to north. The interpretation given here is based on limited data and should be regarded as provisional.

Sliven Structure and Luda Kamchia Syncline

The Mesozoic stratigraphy of the southern Balkanides is thin, and not very different from that of the Kondolovo nappe. A thin Triassic limestone rests directly on a gneissic basement or metamorphosed Paleozoic sediments (or on supposedly Permian quartz porphyry, as near Sliven). This is followed in places by basinal deposits of Late Triassic (Norian) age to Middle Jurassic shales, and then by Upper Cretaceous and Paleogene flysch.

The Sliven structure, on the cross section (Figure 4), is a north-vergent thrust structure bringing up the Permian and the Triassic limestone. A minor backthrust makes the whole structure a small pop-up. It is significant, however, because the Upper Cretaceous is volcanic to the south but flysch to the north. This suggests that either thrust displacement is fairly large or that there was a preexisting Late Cretaceous fault that controlled the northern extent of the volcanics. Antova et al. (1993) maintain that the north-vergent thrust, juxtaposing volcanics with Cretaceous to Eocene flysch, continues all the way to the coast. The Luda Kamchia syncline is an asymmetric syncline that probably started to form as a piggyback basin (Emine Trough) in the Campanian, in front of this active thrust. Near Sliven, the Campanian Vetrila Formation contains boulders of Triassic limestone from the overriding thrust sheet, and the Paleocene–Middle Eocene rocks consist of flysch with pebble/boulder beds on the steep-to-overturned southern flank of the basin. The deformed flysch is overlain unconformably by flat-lying late Eocene conglomerates and sandstones with coals, dating the end of deformation. On the north flank of the syncline, the Upper Cretaceous emerges as a thin unit of calcareous flysch, overlying Jurassic shales of the Stara Planina Zone.

Stara Planina Zone

This is a complex zone of thrust slices, involving Triassic to Lower Paleogene rocks only. Of the Triassic rocks, only Norian flysch is seen at outcrop, and then

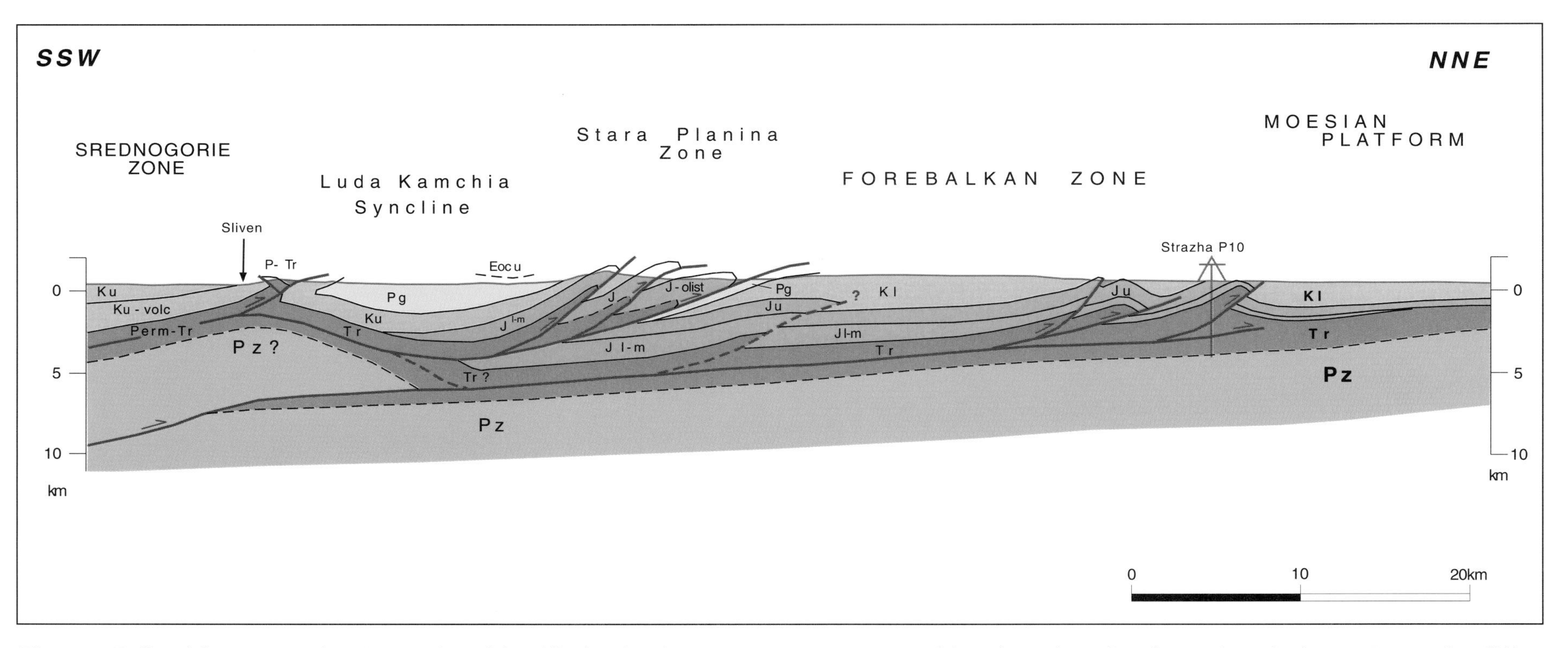

Figure 4. Balkanide cross section. Formations identified as in Figure 2. Pz = nonmetamorphic Paleozoic rocks of Moesian Platform. Note major differences in stratigraphy between the Stara Planina and the Forebalkan zones, making section as drawn unrestorable. Some buried extensional faulting must be inferred. See Figure 2 for legend.

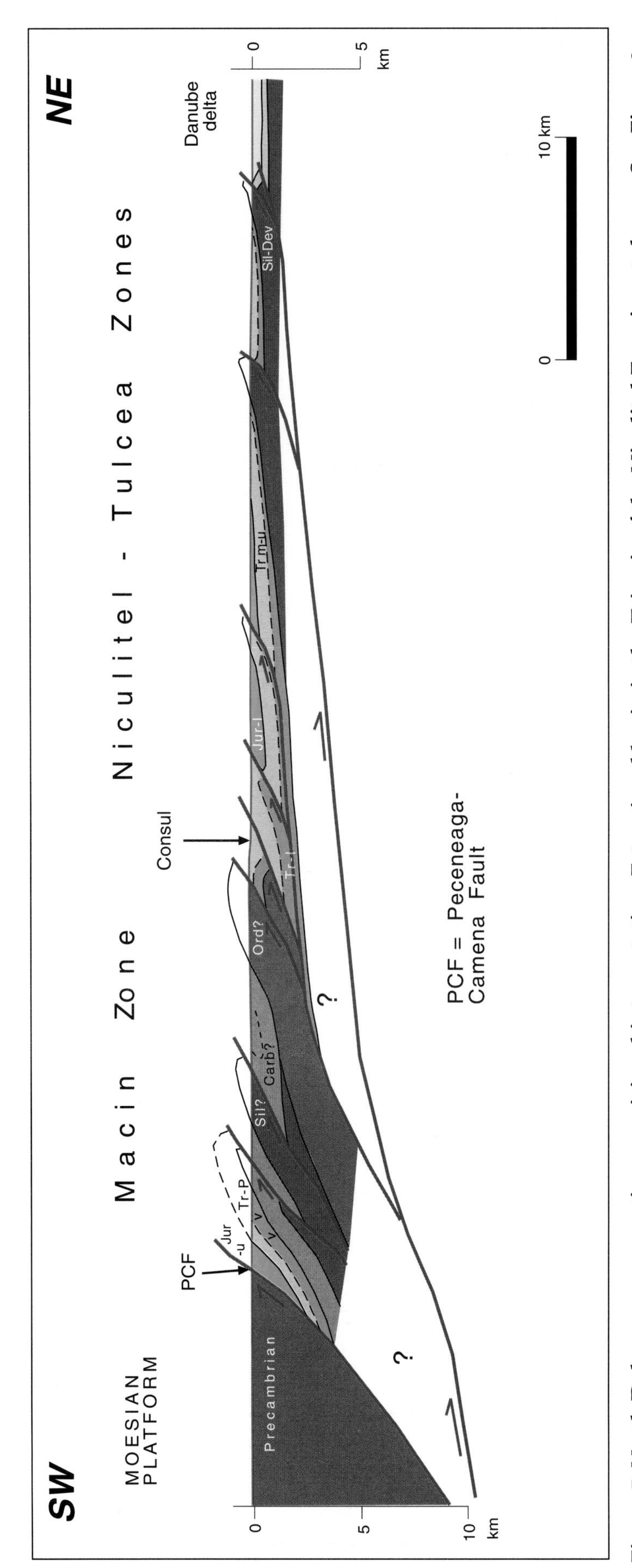

Figure 5. North Dobrogea cross section, provisional interpretation. Extensional basin in the Triassic of the Niculitel Zone is not shown. See Figure 2 for legend.

only in the southernmost thrust slice. The Lower to Middle Jurassic stratigraphy has been worked out in detail by Tchoumatchenko et al. (1992). The Pliensbachian to Aalenian rocks consist of flysch, with the greatest proportion of sand and pebbles in the middle unit. This is followed locally by the Kotel olistostrome, with matrix dated as Bajocian–Bathonian. The clasts are varied in size and lithology, and have been reconstructed into four provenance terranes, involving Sinemurian to Toarcian limestones of marine platform type (reddened, shelly, and nodular limestones) overlying karstified Triassic limestones. These formations are in most places directly overlain by Campanian flysch, as in the Luda Kamchia syncline. Tchoumatchenko et al. (1992) propose that the Late Triassic–Early Jurassic basinal rocks of the Stara Planina Zone were deposited in a Late Triassic oceanic basin that closed by southward subduction in the Middle Jurassic. However, there is no evidence for oceanic crust of Triassic or for significant Middle Jurassic compression in this area.

The structure of the Stara Planina Zone, as seen in the Kotel area (Figure 4) and in the Rish Pass (Paskalev, 1993), comprises two or three north-vergent thrust slices, presumably detaching in the Triassic flysch. The thrusts rise through the stratigraphy northward in a systematic way with ramps and flats, which indicates that the southern margin of this basin had simply layered sediments without major pre-Eocene fault deformation. Tracing this nappe structure to the west, it disappears, revealing a north-dipping monocline involving stratigraphy of Forebalkan type, passing downward into basement of Balkanide type (Geological Map, 1:500,000).

Kamchia Trough and Forebalkan Zone

The frontal thrust of the Stara Planina Zone places the Triassic to Upper Cretaceous rocks over a very different sequence in the Forebalkan Zone. This includes Upper Jurassic limestones (and locally coarse clastics); a thick unit of Lower Cretaceous marls, sandstones, and thin limestones; and then a thin Upper Cretaceous platform limestone (locally absent). The Paleocene to Middle Eocene rocks are thin, and lie directly below and parallel with the thrust. Upper Eocene and Oligocene rocks are discordant, present only in local basins and only gently folded by subsidiary thrusts. This post-tectonic unit thickens rapidly toward the coast and offshore, in the Kamchia Trough (foredeep basin). Gas has been discovered in this basin, so seismic data exist and many wells have been drilled onshore and offshore (Bokor et al., 1993).

The Upper Jurassic of the Forebalkan Zone lies with minor unconformity on thin Lower–Middle Jurassic clastics that pinch out northward, and a thick Triassic sequence proven at the Strazha P-10 well (with thrust repeats) lying on the nonmetamorphosed and only slightly deformed Paleozoic rocks of the Moesian Platform. The Triassic probably contains the basal detachment of the north-vergent thrusts in the eastern Forebalkan Zone, as shown on the cross section.

Discussion of the Balkanides

The interpretation shown in Figure 4 incorporates all of the points noted above, and is based on the assumption that the dominant process involved is north-vergent thin-skin thrust compression of continental crust. Autochthonous basement is projected south at a shallow dip under the thrust belt, in line with this assumption. The major detachment is probably in the Triassic, but its exact level is hard to determine. A basement culmination is shown below the Sliven structure, resulting from a thrust ramping from midcrust up to autochthonous Triassic level, causing north dip on its front limb below the Luda Kamchia syncline (and also propagating north, to cause the Forebalkan anticlines). This is probably the youngest thrust, and it accounts for only a small amount of shortening. The Stara Planina nappe is probably a duplex, with thrusts rising from Triassic to Paleogene level and emplacing the nappe onto the Paleogene of the Forebalkan Zone. Total shortening at top Jurassic (or top Triassic, where the Jurassic is absent) is 33 km as drawn. However, the cross section as presented is not restorable and not fully satisfactory, because it does not take full account of the major stratigraphic changes across the belt.

Although the interpretation suggests that all of the deformation is essentially a single event—middle Eocene—there is structural and stratigraphic evidence for at least minor deformation at several earlier dates. The basin shape of the Lower–Middle Jurassic suggests a possible postrift basin following Triassic extension. The presence of the Kotel olistostrome in this basin is evidence for erosion of a flank of this basin in the Middle Jurassic, but this seems to be too early to result from Strandzhide compression. The Upper Jurassic, with conglomerates in the southern Forebalkan Zone, is the right age to be a foreland basin related to compressive uplift (inversion?) of the Stara Planina Zone, where Upper Jurassic–Lower and Mid-Cretaceous formations are absent. There was another minor compressive event in the Campanian. The easterly plunge of the whole belt must be the result of postrift subsidence following Mid-Cretaceous extension in the Western Black Sea, while erosion of the Upper Cretaceous in the Forebalkan Zone may be due to flank uplift.

Moesian Platform

The Moesian Platform is the relatively stable foreland block of the Strandzhide–Balkanide thrust belts. It is affected only near its edges by the compressive and extensional events of the region. The NW and W margins are thrust-loaded and partially compressed by the Carpathians and Getics mountains, and the SW and S margins by the Balkanides (Forebalkan Zone and Kamchia Trough). The SE margin, offshore Bulgaria and Romania, is cut by the major extensional faulting of the Western Black Sea Basin (Figure 1) (Robinson et al., 1996), and the NE margin is the Peceneaga-Camena fault (PCF) in Dobrogea, Romania.

Basement consisting of Upper Proterozoic schists and graywackes (greenschist) is exposed to the north of the platform. To the south, Lower Paleozoic shales, Devonian clastics and limestones, and Carboniferous clastics with coals are seen in wells (Burchfiel, 1976; Pol'ster et al., 1976; Vinogradov, 1988). At the base of the Permo–Triassic layer is a late Hercynian unconformity, but there is little evidence for significant deformation or deep erosion at this time. The Permian is present in a local basin filled with clastics and evaporites, including halite (Yanev, 1993). The Triassic starts with red-bed clastics, followed by a limestone unit of approximately Middle Triassic (Trifonova and Vaptzarova, 1988), and Late Triassic marine clastics, only locally preserved (e.g., at Kaliakra-1) (Dachev et al., 1988). There is a regional unconformity of Early Jurassic age, with renewed sedimentation starting in the latest Early Jurassic, with deposition of ferruginous oolites (Vinogradov and Papiu, 1987). The platform was fully covered in the Bathonian to late Jurassic, with deposition of a layer of limestones (the reservoir at the Tyulenovo oil field).

During the Late Jurassic, probably Kimmeridgian (Gradinaru, 1984, 1988), there was a major compressive event, in which the PCF was active as a NE-vergent thrust, placing the NE edge of the Moesian Platform onto the SW edge of the Scythian Plate, crumpling its sedimentary cover into what is now North Dobrogea (Figure 1). Folding is also seen in the Casimca syncline on the Moesian Platform. In the Tithonian, evaporites were deposited in local basins around Constanta (Vinogradov, 1988). Offshore, the evaporites are found in an asymmetric basin controlled by a near-vertical fault, suggesting possible transtension (Robinson et al., 1996).

In the Early Cretaceous, prior to the Albian, a further phase of extensional faulting occurred, defining the present SE margin of the Moesian Platform by the rifting and opening of the Western Black Sea. Upper Cretaceous and Tertiary deposits are thin on the platform, but thicken sharply offshore.

North Dobrogea

The North Dobrogean thrust belt is composed of a series of mainly NE-vergent thrust nappes, making a wedge-shaped orogen thinning onto the Scythian Platform (Figure 5). North Dobrogea can be conveniently divided into two main zones (Burchfiel, 1976; Gradinaru, 1984, 1988; Geological Map, 1:200,000). Adjacent to the PCF is the Macin Zone, which has stratigraphy from Precambrian to Upper Jurassic involved in thrusting, and flat-lying Upper Cretaceous cover. The more external zone includes the Consul, Niculitel, and Tulcea units, where outcrops are mainly Triassic and Lower Jurassic.

Macin Zone

The Macin Zone occupies most of western Dobrogea, narrowing toward the SE. Precambrian amphibolite schists are exposed in the core of an antiform, but there is nothing equivalent to the graywackes unit on the Moesian Platform. There is an Ordovician? to Devonian sequence, overlain with some degree of unconformity by a red-bed clastic unit known as the Carapelit Formation and assumed to be Carboniferous–Permian. There are rhyolite lavas and large granite bodies, dated as Permian, associated with the Carapelit Formation. Middle Triassic limestones are locally present, followed after a significant regional unconformity by Middle to Upper Jurassic (Kimmeridgian) limestones and conglomerates, some of which contain clasts of Moesian graywackes. Şengör (1984) comments on the overall similarity of Dobrogean and Western Pontide stratigraphy, but there are some significant differences.

On the line of the cross section (Figure 5), there are believed to be three thrust sheets in the Macin Zone, the uppermost including occurrences Triassic to Jurassic in age, overlying Permian rhyolites and Silurian schists. These beds dip about 60° SW, approximately the same as the dip of the PCF. This means that the PCF was originally horizontal, with Moesian rocks placed over, and eroded into, the Upper Jurassic basin. The present steep attitude of the fault results from stacking of the thrust sheets in the Macin Zone beneath it. The actual plane of the PCF as it is today is not a strike-slip fault, as it is considered by some authors (Gradinaru, 1984; Visarion et al., 1990). The second thrust nappe includes clastic Permo–Carboniferous and Silurian–Devonian rocks, and the third has Permo–Carboniferous rocks lying unconformably on Cambro–Ordovician Boclugea Formation thrust over Triassic limestones of the Consul unit.

The substantial thickness of stratigraphy involved in this zone implies a deep detachment in the Precambrian rocks, at a depth >10 km below the PCF, as is also suggested by magnetotelluric studies (Visarion et al., 1990).

External Zones

The external zone of Dobrogea includes several thrust slices with a generally thin-skinned character, containing a well-developed Triassic to Lower Jurassic stratigraphy. The Consul nappe has a Scythian to Carnian sequence with rhyolites and limestones, resting on Boclugea Formation at depth. The Niculitel Zone has a Middle–Upper Triassic sequence including pelagic platform ("halstatt") facies with pink limestones, passing up into basinal flysch facies, both intermixed with large volumes of basaltic pillow lavas. The volcanics are of intraplate-stretched continental type (Savu, 1986) and do not represent oceanic crust. In the Tulcea Zone, the sequence passes up to Lower Jurassic, which consists of chevron-folded clastic flysch (Nalbant Formation) and locally Middle Jurassic. In the most external parts of the Tulcea Zone, anticlinal culminations bring Paleozoic schists and Devonian silicified marls to the surface, showing that there is a deeper detachment level than the Triassic detachment that is presumably responsible for the other small-scale structures in the rest of the external zone.

Unconformably resting on truncated rocks of both major units, especially in the south, is the Babadag Basin, containing near-flat-lying Upper Cretaceous (Cenomanian–Coniacian) sediments (omitted from Figure 5). These are considered to be postrift fill of the Western Black Sea. They show no sign of Tertiary compressive deformation. The only younger sediments are Danube delta fluvial sediments and widespread glacial loess, which blankets much of the region, so that the outcrops of pre-Cretaceous rocks are very patchy.

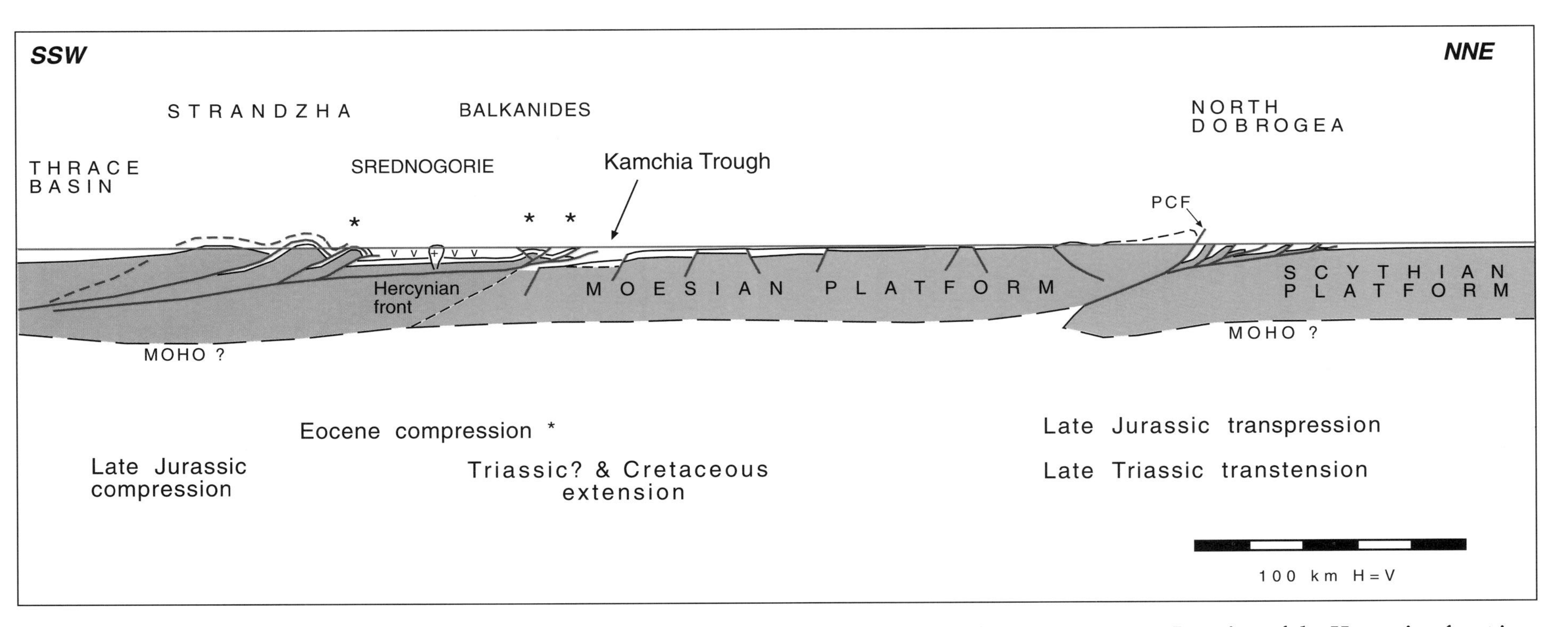

Figure 6. Regional crustal cross section from Thrace Basin to Scythian Platform, showing three basement terranes. Location of the Hercynian front is very uncertain. Ages of main deformation events are shown. Note that no data on Moho depth/structure were available for this study; dashed line shown is speculative.

Scythian/East European Platform

The Scythian Platform is the northern foreland of the Dobrogea thrust belt. Magnetotelluric data (Visarion et al., 1990) suggest that the dense Scythian basement (i.e., the base of unmetamorphosed Paleozoic and Late Proterozoic sediments) dips at ~5° to the south below the Tulcea Zone, ~5 km below surface at the thrust front. Unfortunately, we do not have well data from near the Dobrogea thrust front to confirm this. The regional cross section (Figure 6) stops at the Limanskaya-1 well, just north of the Danube delta in Ukraine. Here there are still about 3000 m of sediments, including a Mesozoic section ~1000 m thick, overlying the Devonian, Silurian, and Precambrian. A short distance offshore, at Zmeiniy Island, folded Paleozoic rocks outcrop. Immediately to the north of this (Morgunov et al., 1974), we reach the suture of the East European Platform, but why this should be considered a suture, and what it means, is unclear.

REGIONAL CHRONOLOGICAL SYNTHESIS

Hercynian compressive deformation affects the area from the Rhodope Massif to the Balkanides. In this area there is a major unconformity at the base of the Permo–Triassic, with high-grade metamorphic rocks or granites below. But on the Moesian Platform, Paleozoic rocks are present, generally more or less parallel with younger rocks, and not deformed to a significantly greater degree. It is notable that the Hercynian deformation coincides in location with more recent deformations. The exact position of the Hercynian deformation front cannot be placed with any accuracy, especially considering the wide band in which the pre-Triassic material is too deep for study, under the Forebalkan or the Balkanide thrusts (Figure 6).

Subsidence of the southern passive margin of Southeastern Europe began in the Early Triassic. While most of the area, including the Moesian Platform, was covered with red-bed clastics, southern Strandzha (Zabernovo nappe) was already a site of marine sedimentation in the Early Triassic. In the Middle Triassic, a regional south-facing carbonate platform was established in Strandzha, extending north onto the Moesian Platform to Dobrogea (and much of the rest of Eastern Europe). The transition to an active margin, with a subduction trench located south of Thrace and Rhodope, probably occurred before the end of the Early Triassic. The Vardar Ocean (an extension of Tethys) began to subduct to the north.

There is regionally widespread evidence for back-arc extension disrupting this platform in the Late Triassic and Early Jurassic, most notably in the Küre area in the Central Pontides, where there is an ophiolite of Late Triassic (Ustaömer and Robertson, 1994). These basins have been interpreted as evidence for a "Paleotethys" Ocean lying between the Pontides and the Eastern European continent (Şengör et al., 1980; Nachev, 1991). However, this interpretation is untenable, since the Western Pontides are clearly European, and evidence for ophiolites, such as at Küre, is very localized. A simpler interpretation, requiring only one subduction zone, is proposed (Banks and Robinson, this volume). We interpret the external zones of North Dobrogea and the Stara Planina Zone to be deep transtensional basins at this time, part of the back-arc basin system.

A major compressive episode, the Cimmeride orogeny, began in the Middle Jurassic (Aalenian, in Crimea). The hypothesis put forward by Şengör (1984) to explain its origin involved closure of his Paleotethys Ocean by collision of a "Cimmerian" continent, but we think that it was only the Triassic back-arc basins that closed (Banks and Robinson, this volume). Compression did not reach the Strandzhides until the Bathonian at the earliest, and then propagated northward at some deep crustal level without greatly affecting the Balkanides. In the Kimmeridgian, compression reached Dobrogea, as the edge of the Moesian Platform pushed NE onto the Scythian Platform margin (Figure 6). A new south-facing carbonate platform started to become established early in the Late Jurassic (before compression had ceased), but the Strandzha Zone had been too recently folded and uplifted for any sediments to be deposited. Clastic foredeep sediments from the Strandzha orogen, and possibly from inversion-uplift in the Balkanides, were deposited in the "Nis-Trojan" trough (Nachev, 1992) and in the Forebalkan Zone.

The Mid-Cretaceous opening of the Western Black Sea only affected the onshore area marginally, and this major event has been described more fully elsewhere (Finetti et al., 1988; Nachev, 1993; Robinson et al., 1996; Banks and Robinson, this volume). Briefly, the Western and Central Pontide microplate (with a forearc system presumably attached on its south side) broke away from the Moesian and Scythian platforms. It moved SE between transform faults, one (sinistral) located immediately to the SW of Crimea and the Mid-Black Sea High, and the other (dextral) now obscured by the offshore extension of the Balkanides, leaving the Western Black Sea as a back-arc basin behind it.

Again, back-arc extension was followed by regional compression, caused by the final closure of Tethys, with north-vergent compression reaching the Kondolovo anticline and the Balkanides in the late Eocene. This involved only minor shortening, as in the Western Pontides, to which they must be linked, through an oblique deformation zone. The structural history of the region from the Early Triassic until the Miocene is the result of northward subduction of Tethys at the Vardar-İzmir-Ankara suture.

ACKNOWLEDGMENTS

This chapter is based in part on a field trip held in April 1992, arranged jointly between BP and the İstanbul Technical University, involving the key experts in the areas visited. The interpretations presented here adopt many ideas that were discussed by the participants (notably G. Chatalov, N. Görür, E. Gradinaru, R.H. Graham, S. Hall, A. Okay, M. Sandulescu, A.M.C. Şengör, P. Tchoumatchenko, and I. Zagorchev), but the conclusions are solely those of the author. A. Robinson is thanked for wide-ranging discussions on the geology of the Black Sea area, and for reviewing and improving an early version of this manuscript.

I. Zagorchev is also thanked for help in obtaining Bulgarian literature.

REFERENCES CITED

Antova, N., G. Nikolov, and T. Rankova, 1993, The relationships between Burgas Group and Emine flysch formation from the town of Sliven to the Black Sea: Review of the Bulgarian Geological Socety v. 54, no. 2, p. 113–116.

Aydın, Y., 1982, Yildiz Dağlari (Istranca) Masifi'nin jeolojisi (in Turkish): Ph.D. thesis, İstanbul Technical University.

Banks, C. J., and A.G. Robinson, this volume, Tectonic evolution of the Western Black Sea region, *in* A.C. Robinson, ed., Regional and petroleum geology of the Black Sea and surrounding region: AAPG Memoir 68, p. 53–62.

Bokov, P., P. Gochev, and R. Ognyanov, 1993, Tectonic position, hydrocarbon exploration and future potential of Bulgaria: Geologica Balcanica, v. 23, no. 3, p. 3–34.

Burchfiel, B.C., 1976, Geology of Romania: Geological Society of America Special Paper 158, 82 p.

Burg, J-P., Z. Ivanov, L.-E. Ricou, D. Dimov, and L. Klain, 1990, Implications of shear-sense criteria for the tectonic evolution of the central Rhodope Massif, southern Bulgaria: Geology, v. 18, p. 451–454.

Chatalov, G., 1990, Geology of Strandzha Zone in Bulgaria (in Bulgarian, with English summary): Geologica Balcanica, Series Operum Singulorum No. 4, Bulgarian Academy of Sciences, Sofia, 263 p.

Chatalov, G., 1992, Notes on the geology of the Turkish part of Strandzha Mountains (in Bulgarian): Review of the Bulgarian Geological Society, v. 53, no. 1, p. 55–62.

Committees of Geology, Bulgaria and Romania: Sofia, Bucharest geological maps at 1:500,000 and 1:200,000 scale, respectively.

Dachev, C., V. Stanev, and P. Bokov, 1988, Structure of the Bulgarian Black Sea area: Bollettino di Geofisica Teorica ed Applicata, v. 30, p. 79–107.

Dercourt, J., and L. Ricou, 1987, Discussion sur la place de la Bulgarie au sein du système alpin: Review of the Bulgarian Geological Society, v. 48, no. 3, p. 1–14.

Finetti, I., G. Bricchi, A. Del Ben, M. Pipan, and Z. Xuan, 1988, Geophysical study of the Black Sea: Bollettino di Geofisica Teorica ed Applicata, v. 30, no. 117-118, p. 197–324.

Gochev, P., 1985, Strandzhides: Geotect., Tectonophyz. and Geodinam, v. 18, p. 28–52.

Görür, N., 1988, Timing of opening of the Black Sea Basin: Tectonophysics, v. 147, p. 247–262.

Görür, N., A.I. Okay, A.M.C. Şengör, and M.M. Özkaya, 1992, Guide book: Geology of the İstanbul Paleozoic–Triassic sequence and the Istranca Massif: İstanbul Technical University, unpublished.

Gradinaru, E., 1984, Jurassic rocks of North Dobrogea, a depositional-tectonic approach: Revue Roumanie de Géologie, v. 28, p. 61–72.

Gradinaru, E., 1988, Jurassic sedimentary rocks and bimodal volcanics of the Cirjelari-Camena outcrop belt: evidence for a transtensile regime of the Peceneaga-Camena fault: St. Cerc. Geol. Geofiz. Geogr., v. 33, p. 97–121.

Hsü, K.J., I.K. Nachev, and C.T. Vuchev, 1977, Geologic evolution of Bulgaria in light of plate tectonics: Tectonophysics, v. 40, p. 245–256.

Lakova, I., P. Gochev, and S. Yanev, 1992, Palynostratigraphy and geological setting of the Lower Paleozoic allochthon of the Dervent Heights, SE Bulgaria: Geologica Balcanica, v. 22, no. 6, p. 71–88.

Morgunov, Yu.G., V.P. Vorob'yev, P.N. Kuprin, A.V. Kalinin, V.V. Kalinin, and B.L. Pivovarov, 1975, New data on the geologic structure of the Danube-Dniester part of the Black Sea shelf (Translated from Russian): Doklady Akademii Nauk SSSR, v. 219, p. 47–49.

Nachev, I.K., 1991, Hettangian–Bathonian paleogeodynamics of Bulgaria (in Bulgarian): Review of the Bulgarian Geological Society, v. 52, no. 3.

Nachev, I.K., 1992, Callovian–Albian evolution of Bulgaria (in Bulgarian): Review of the Bulgarian Geological Society, v. 53, no. 3, p. 67–77.

Nachev, I.K., 1993, Late Cretaceous paleogeodynamics of Bulgaria: Geologica Balcanica, v. 23, no. 4, p. 3–23.

Okay, A.I., and H. Mostler, 1994, Carboniferous and Permian radiolarite blocks from the Karakaya complex of northwest Turkey: Turkish Journal of Earth Sciences, v. 3, p. 23–28.

Okay, A.I., and I. Tansel, 1992, New data on the upper age of the Intra-Pontide Ocean from north of Sarköy (Thrace): Ankara, Bulletin of Mineral Research and Exploration, no. 114, p. 23–26.

Paskalev, M., 1993, Structural investigations in the Kotel unit of the Rish Pass area (in Bulgarian): Review of the Bulgarian Geological Society, v. 54, no. 2, p. 13–18.

Pol'ster, L.A., et al., 1976, History of geological development of Northern Bulgaria during the Paleozoic: International Geology Review, v. 19, no. 6, p. 633–646.

Popov, P.N., 1987, Tectonics of the Banat-Srednogorie rift: Tectonophysics, v. 143, p. 209–216.

Robinson, A.G., J.H. Rudat, C.J. Banks, and R.L.F. Wiles, 1996, Petroleum geology of the Black Sea: Marine and Petroleum Geology, v. 13, no. 2, p. 195–223.

Sandulescu, M., 1978?, Structure and tectonic history of the northern margin of Tethys between the Alps and the Caucasus: IGCP Project 198, p. 3–16.

Savu, H., 1986, Triassic continental intra-plate volcanism in North Dobrogea: Revue Roumanie de Géologie, v. 30, p. 21–29.

Şengör, A.M.C., 1984, The Cimmeride orogenic system and the tectonics of Eurasia: Geological Society of America Special Paper 195.

Şengör, A.M.C., Y. Yılmaz, and I. Ketin, 1980, Remnants of a pre-Late Jurassic ocean in northern

Turkey: fragments of Permian–Triassic Paleotethys?: Geological Society of America Bulletin, v. 91, no. 1, p. 599–609.

Tchoumatchenko, P., B. Peybernès, S. Chernjavska, G. Lachkar, J. Surmont, J. Dercourt, Z. Ivanov, J. P. Rolando, I. Sapunov, and J. Thierry, 1992, Étude d'un domaine de transition Balkan-Moésie: évolutions paléogéographique et paléotectonique du sillon du flysch jurassique inférieur et moyen dans la Stara Planina orientale (Bulgarie orientale): Bulletin de la Societe Geologique de France, v. 1, p. 49–61.

Trifonova, E., and A. Vaptzarova, 1988, Paleoenvironments and foraminifera at the end of the Early Triassic and the beginning of the Middle Triassic epochs in Northern Bulgaria: Revue de Paléobiologie, Vol. Spec. 2, p. 161–166.

Turgut, S., M. Türkarslan, and D. Perinçek, 1991, Evolution of the Thrace sedimentary basin and its hydrocarbon prospectivity, *in* A.M. Spencer, ed., Generation, accumulation, and production of Europe's hydrocarbons: European Association of Petroleum Geoscientists Special Publication 1, p. 415–437.

Ustaömer, T., and A.H.F. Robertson, 1994, Palaeozoic marginal basin and subduction-accretion, the Palaeotethyan Küre Complex, Central Pontides, northern Turkey: Journal of the Geological Society of London, v. 151, p. 291–305.

Vinogradov, C., 1988, Relationships between sedimentary facies and tectonics in the Moesian Platform (Romania): Revue Roumanie de Géologie, v. 32, p. 55–65.

Vinogradov, C., and V.C. Papiu, 1987, Oolitic ironstones in the Upper Liassic–Middle Jurassic deposits of the Moesian Platform (Romania): Revue Roumanie de Géologie, v. 31, p. 87–93.

Visarion, M., M. Sandulescu, V. Rosca, D. Stanica, and L. Atanasiu, 1990, La Dobrogea dans le cadre de l'avant-pays Carpatique: Revue Roumanie de Géophysique, v. 34, p. 55–65.

Yanev, S.N., 1993, Permian in North Bulgaria II. Formal lithostratigraphy related to the Upper Permian: Geologica Balcanica, v. 23, no. 1, p. 3–24.

Zonenshain, L.P., and X. Le Pichon, 1986, Deep basins of the Black Sea and Caspian Sea as remnants of Mesozoic back-arc basins: Tectonophysics, v. 123, p. 181–211.

Harbury, N., and M. Cohen, 1997, Sedimentary history of the Late Jurassic–Paleogene of Northeast Bulgaria and the Bulgarian Black Sea, *in* A.G. Robinson, ed., Regional and petroleum geology of the Black Sea and surrounding region: AAPG Memoir 68, p. 129–168.

Chapter 9

Sedimentary History of the Late Jurassic–Paleogene of Northeast Bulgaria and the Bulgarian Black Sea

Neil Harbury
Geological & Geophysical Research School, Birkbeck College
London, United Kingdom

Martin Cohen
Enterprise Oil
London, United Kingdom

ABSTRACT

Callovian to Paleocene strata outcrop in the Varna region of northeast Bulgaria, and have also been recorded from several wells in both the Black Sea and onshore locations to the northeast and the south of Varna in the Kamchia Basin. Sedimentological data collected from the abundant core material recovered from these wells allow detailed facies schemes to be developed and regional paleofacies maps to be constructed.

During the Callovian to Valanginian, eastern Bulgaria and the Bulgarian Black Sea were divided into areas dominated by shallow-marine carbonate sedimentation and deeper water environments. The boundary between these facies belts is a broadly east-west line south of Shumen and Varna, and becomes more northeast-southwest in the Black Sea. Seismic data and well studies suggest the platform had a ramp morphology with a gradation of facies from shallow-marine through deeper ramp to basinal facies from north to south. Limited reworking of shelfal material into the basin is recognized, with some intraformational calcirudites and slumping, which suggest that the ramp may, in places, have been distally steepened. Local faulting of the ramp allowed carbonate breccias derived from a shallow-marine area to be reworked into the basin in places. Hauterivian and Barremian marls were deposited, and turbiditic sandstones are recognized in the more basinal areas.

The ramp morphology of the platform was lost by Aptian times. Aptian facies include sandstones, mixed carbonate/siliciclastic facies, and marls. These shallow-marine sedimentary rocks indicate that the Kamchia Basin had become filled by the Aptian. Sedimentary rocks of Albian age are not recorded in the subsurface nor in outcrops of the eastern Moesian Platform; possibly, the late Aptian was a period of erosion and/or nondeposition in eastern Bulgaria. The "mid" Cretaceous elevation of the region above sea level may be interpreted as rift-flank uplift, which was a local response to a Western Black Sea rift event. Basement uplift may also explain the continental basement clasts that provided an important siliciclastic source to the Aptian shallow-marine deposits in an otherwise carbonate-dominated basin.

Upper Cretaceous–Paleocene rocks are commonly exposed in the Varna region. Facies include a variety of carbonates and mixed siliciclastics/carbonates, in which pelagic, shallow-marine, and siliciclastic components were mixed by shallow-marine hydrodynamic processes and bioturbation. Deposition of laterally extensive lime mudstones during Campanian times suggests widespread flooding of the northern platform region. Intensely bioturbated intervals, abundant glauconite, and increased proportions of siliciclastic detritus in certain intervals imply periods of condensed sedimentation over a broad platform.

In late Paleocene times, shallow-marine coralline algal buildups developed in the Ravna Gora region and are correlatable with similar algal-rich deposits recorded in outcrop in northeast Bulgaria. Early Eocene facies include sandstones and packstones, often containing abundant nummulite foraminifera.

INTRODUCTION AND REGIONAL SETTING

Northeast Bulgaria lies on the Black Sea and is bounded to the north by Romania and to the south by a relatively narrow east-west mountain chain known as the Stara Planina or Balkans (Figure 1). Five broadly east-west aligned tectonic units are recognized by most workers in Bulgaria (Vuchev et al., 1994). These units are, from north to south, the Moesian Platform, the Forebalkans (or Transition Zone), the Balkans (or Stara Planina), the Srednogorie Zone, and the Rhodopian Massif. [Refer to Zonenshain and Le Pichon (1986), Görür (1988), Okay et al. (1994), and Robinson et al. (1995a, b) for reviews of the regional rifting events and subsidence history of the Black Sea Basin.]

The Balkan Mountains are a result of mainly Late Cretaceous and early Tertiary compression caused by the convergence of the Rhodopian and Moesian plate fragments (Burchfiel, 1980; Sinclair et al., this volume). The Balkans are bounded to the south by the calc-alkaline volcanics of the Srednogorie Zone.

In this chapter, we describe and evaluate the sedimentary history of the Upper Jurassic to Paleogene successions in outcrop and in selected wells. The wells were drilled by the Bulgarians and Russians in the 1970s and 1980s, and are located both onshore eastern Bulgaria and offshore in the Black Sea (Figure 2). Offshore wells examined are Elyzavetino R-1 and Nanevo R-1. Onshore wells examined are, from north to south: East Dobruja C-179A, Tiulenovo Field development wells, Ravna Gora R-76, Unak R-1, and Staro Oryahovo R-9. A small amount of field data has been collected from the outcrop area in the Varna region. The majority of the wells and outcrop examined during this study lie within the Moesian Platform zone. The strata in this region are arranged in fault-bounded plateaux (e.g., Varna or Avren Block) and are generally flat-lying or very gently dipping (Dachev et al., 1988). To the southeast, the area passes into the Kamchia Basin, which has a broad and very open synclinal structure (Dachev et al., 1988; Vuchev et al., 1994; Doglioni et al., 1996; Sinclair et al., this volume) and represents the foredeep to the Balkan thrustbelt. The junction between the Moesian Platform and the Kamchia Basin (or Kamchia Depression, Balkan foredeep) is marked by a long-lived fault/hinge line known as the Bliznatzi Flexure Zone, an east-west–trending feature ~20 km south of Varna (Vuchev et al., 1994).

The Bulgarian lithostratigraphy is shown in Figure 3. Several authors have outlined the chronostratigraphy of the onshore and offshore wells (Dachev et al., 1988; Marinov, 1994; Vuchev et al., 1994), although little sedimentological data was presented in these studies. This study has two objectives: (1) to describe the depositional environments of the Upper Jurassic to Paleogene carbonate and mixed carbonate/siliciclastic units and (2) to document the stratigraphic intervals present in each of the wells studied in order to develop a chronostratigraphy, construct paleofacies maps, and provide an overview of the sedimentary history of the region.

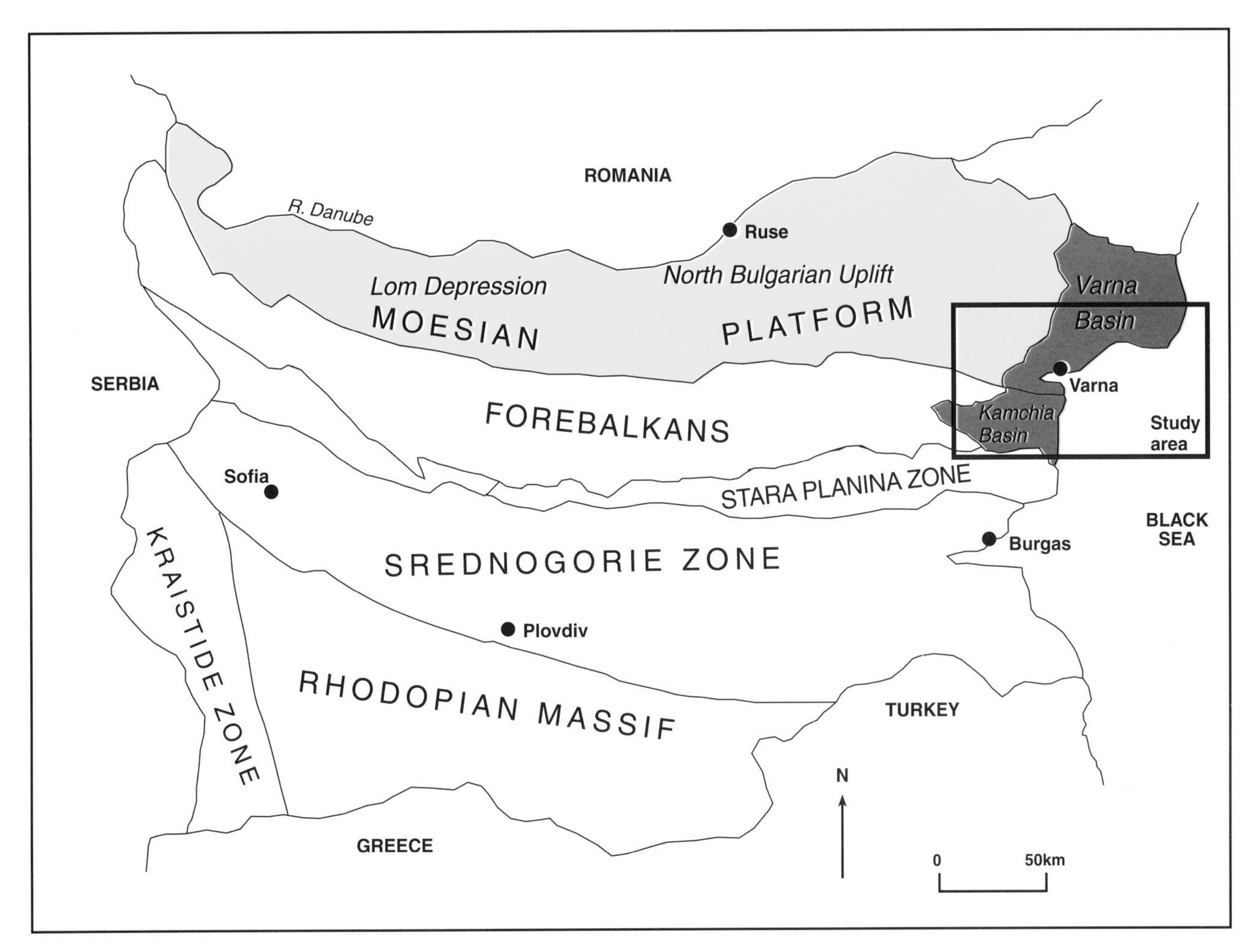

Figure 1. Geological setting of Bulgaria illustrating the major east-west–oriented tectonic units (after Vuchev et al., 1994).

METHODS AND FACIES ASSOCIATIONS

Cored intervals from four production wells from the Tiulenovo oil field and six exploration wells were examined in detail. Wells drilled by the Bulgarians often have considerable amounts of core, with generally good recoveries. For example, the East Dobruja C179A well was cored continuously from the surface through to the Carboniferous, and >2000 m of core was recovered. None of the cores in the wells are slabbed, and their state varies from excellent (e.g., Unak R-1, East Dobruja C179A) to poor (e.g., Staro Oryahovo R-9). Surfaces of the rock from some wells, particularly within carbonate intervals, may be heavily abraded by the coring process; this may hinder observation of facies and contacts between lithologies. Bulgarian composite logs of 1:1000 were available for many of the wells examined and enabled selection of appropriate core intervals for study. The composite logs include some electrical log information and proposed ages for the cored intervals.

The wide spatial distribution of the wells allows broad paleofacies maps to be constructed with reasonable confidence. In order to determine how sedimentation patterns changed with time and space, numerous samples were collected from each of the wells, and sedimentary logs were constructed. The majority of the cores were logged at 1:20 scale, although 1:100 logs were appropriate for monotonous intervals. More than 300 samples were collected, slabbed, and polished, and 180 thin sections were prepared.

Three localities where Cretaceous rocks outcropped were examined in the Devnia region to provide lateral control for the development of strata examined in the subsurface. Each locality lies within 1 km of the Varna-to-Devnia motorway (Figure 2).

Numerous biostratigraphic analyses of samples collected from the cored intervals have been undertaken (see Appendix 1). The samples were analyzed for nannofossils (90 samples), microfossils in thin section (60 samples), and palynological content (1 sample). Some ammonite fragments were also examined for age control. Index species are given where available. In some cases, the age determinations on the Bulgarian composite logs for the wells are the only information available on the age of the cored interval because the

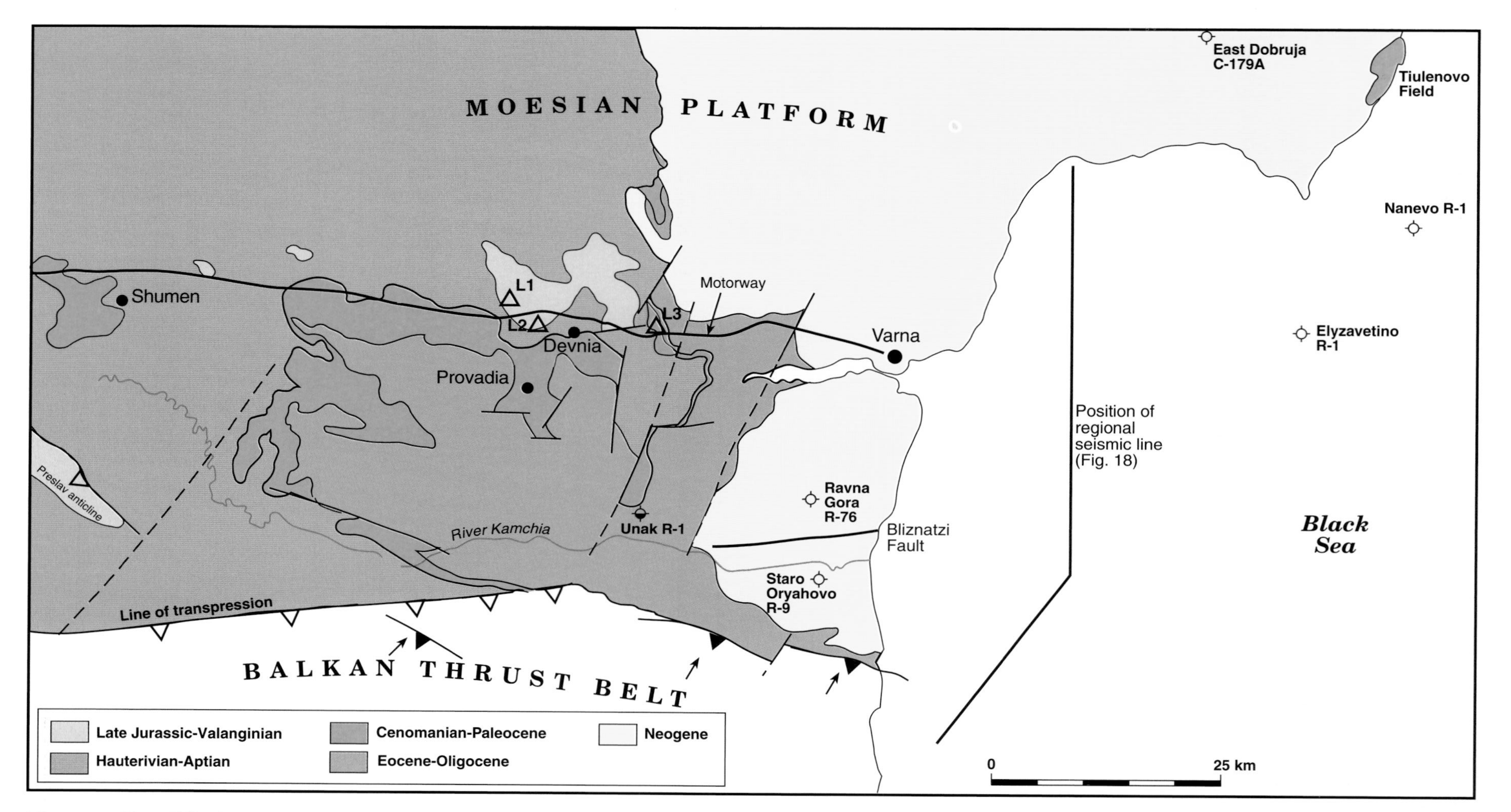

Figure 2. Simplified map of eastern Bulgaria (modified after Milanova and Cheshitev, 1989; Cheshitev et al., 1989). The Bliznatzi Flexure is documented in Vuchev et al. (1994). The seismic line illustrated in Figure 18 is located in the Black Sea.

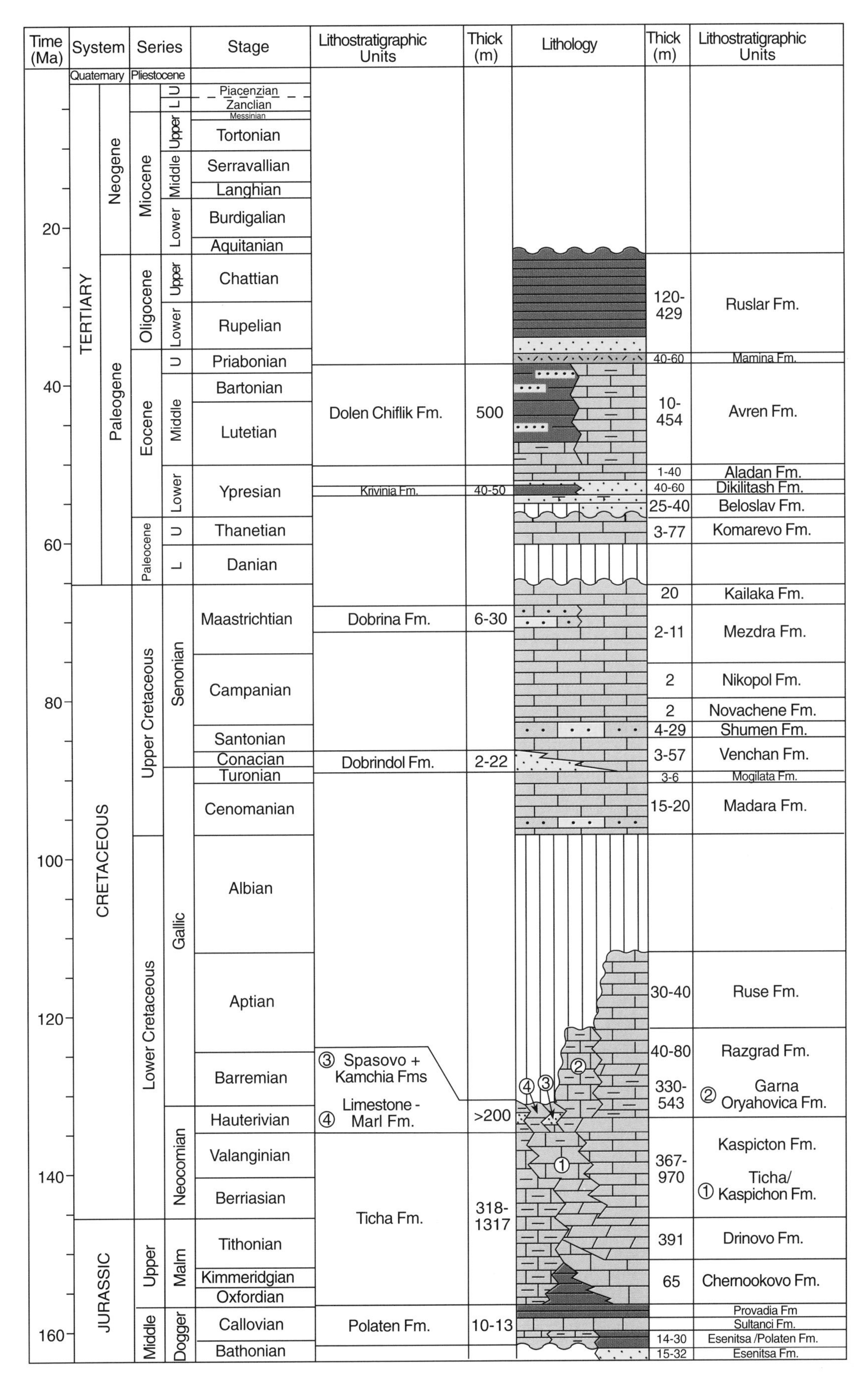

Figure 3. Summary stratigraphy of northeastern Bulgaria. Modified after Milanova and Cheshitev, 1989. Information from Juranov et al., 1993.

biostratigraphic analyses carried out in the U.K. did not yield age-diagnostic fauna. The biostratigraphic determinations of samples collected from the cores and at three outcrop locations have allowed constraints to be placed on the lateral variation of the sedimentary successions. These have enabled important conclusions to be drawn concerning the sedimentological evolution of the area.

The Callovian–Paleogene strata identified in the wells examined in NE Bulgaria and the Bulgarian Black Sea are divided into three groups differentiated by facies and corresponding sedimentary environment of deposition: (1) Callovian–Lower Cretaceous facies, (2) Aptian facies, and (3) Cenomanian–Paleogene facies.

CALLOVIAN–LOWER CRETACEOUS CARBONATE RAMP TO BASIN SEDIMENTATION

A number of lithofacies have been recognized and can be grouped into three facies associations: deep ramp and basinal, subtidal ramp, and peritidal ramp.

Deep Ramp and Basinal Facies Association

Seven lithofacies have been grouped in this facies association.

Bioturbated Lime Mudstone-Wackestone

Light-gray to light-brown homogeneous lime mudstone-wackestones are present in the Elyzavetino R-1, Nanevo R-1, Ravna Gora R-69, Unak R-1, and Staro Oryahovo R-9 wells (Figures 4–9).

The fossiliferous content of this facies varies from ~5% to ~15%. Skeletal fragments include comminuted shells, calcitized radiolaria, sponge spicules, and calpionellids; any of these skeletal components may dominate individual intervals. Rich assemblages of nannofossils have been recovered. Other relatively rare faunal detritus include echinoderm fragments (probably holothurian ossicles), small smooth ostracods, and fragments of perisphinctoid ammonites and poorly preserved benthic foraminifera including *Dentalina, Cornuspira, Spirillina, Protomarssonella*, and very small rotalines.

The facies may contain up to 5% silt-grade siliciclastic detritus. Bioturbation may be slight to intense, and some burrows may be filled with skeletal packstone. This facies may contain chert as incipient nodules or as silicified/dolomitized argillaceous stylolitic seams (Figure 9C); disseminated pyrite and fine-grained phosphatic fragments are rare to common. The matrix of this facies may be partially dolomitized, consisting of well-developed displacive dolomite rhombs. Calcite-cemented hairline fractures are common.

The fine-grained nature of the facies and skeletal components (radiolaria, sponge spicules, calpionellids, and nannofossils) indicate deposition below storm-wave base in a deep marine setting. This is supported by the relatively low-diversity benthic fauna and a lack of preserved current-generated sedimentary structures. The angular quartz grains may have been introduced by eolian processes. This facies, particularly when containing calpionellids, is a characteristic lithotype in the uppermost Jurassic and Lower Cretaceous pelagic facies of the Tethyan realm, often characterizing bathyal/abyssal depositional environments (Wilson, 1969; Cook and Enos, 1977).

Laminated Lime Mudstone-Wackestone

This horizontally laminated facies is seen in the uppermost part of the cored interval in the Nanevo R-1 well, between 550 and 560 m depth, in the interval between 341 and 343 m in the Elyzavetino R-1 well, and in Unak R-1. Rare low-amplitude ripple cross-lamination is observed in parts of the Nanevo R-1 core, although scour on the surface of much of the core prevents detailed observation of sedimentary structures. Horizontal laminae are defined by the proportion of bioclastic detritus and the alignment of elongate shelly material, although the abraded skeletal material is fine grained and unidentifiable. Microfossils identified include radiolaria, sponge spicules, calpionellids, and nannofossils. No macrofossils are recorded; rare echinoderm plates are observed in one sample. Slight bioturbation occurs in some intervals and low-amplitude, bedding-parallel stylolites are common. A small proportion of silt-grade siliciclastic detritus is observed in the samples, where it constitutes <5% of the lithology. Small, matrix-displacing dolomite rhombs are observed. Minor soft-sediment deformation occurs locally (e.g., Nanevo R-1, 553 m depth) as contorted to gently folded intervals ≤30 cm thick (Figure 10A). Truncation of laminae and low-angle bounding surfaces may be observed (Figure 9E).

Faunal components are similar to those observed in the bioturbated lime mudstone-wackestone facies; a deep-marine setting is also envisaged for this facies. Dysaerobic conditions may have limited burrowing in-fauna, thus preserving primary sedimentary structures. Minor reworking and sorting of fine-grained carbonate components may be a result of distal turbidites, generated updip on the slope, or contour currents. Small-scale slumping of fine-grained carbonate sediment was produced by incipient failure and downslope movement of semicohesive slope deposits.

Dolomite

Laminated to structureless medium-grained unimodal dolomite is observed in the Elyzavetino R-1 well between ~800 and 830 m. Laminae are defined by changes in dolomite crystal size and are emphasized by organic staining. Low-amplitude stylolites with dark hydrocarbon staining are common. A ghost lamination may be preserved within finer grained dolarenite, with subhedral unimodal dolomite crystals within individual laminae. Rare siliceous and phosphatic concretions are observed, and may form nodules ≤10 cm in diameter. The concretions may contain very poorly preserved phosphatized radiolaria and some displacive dolomite rhombs.

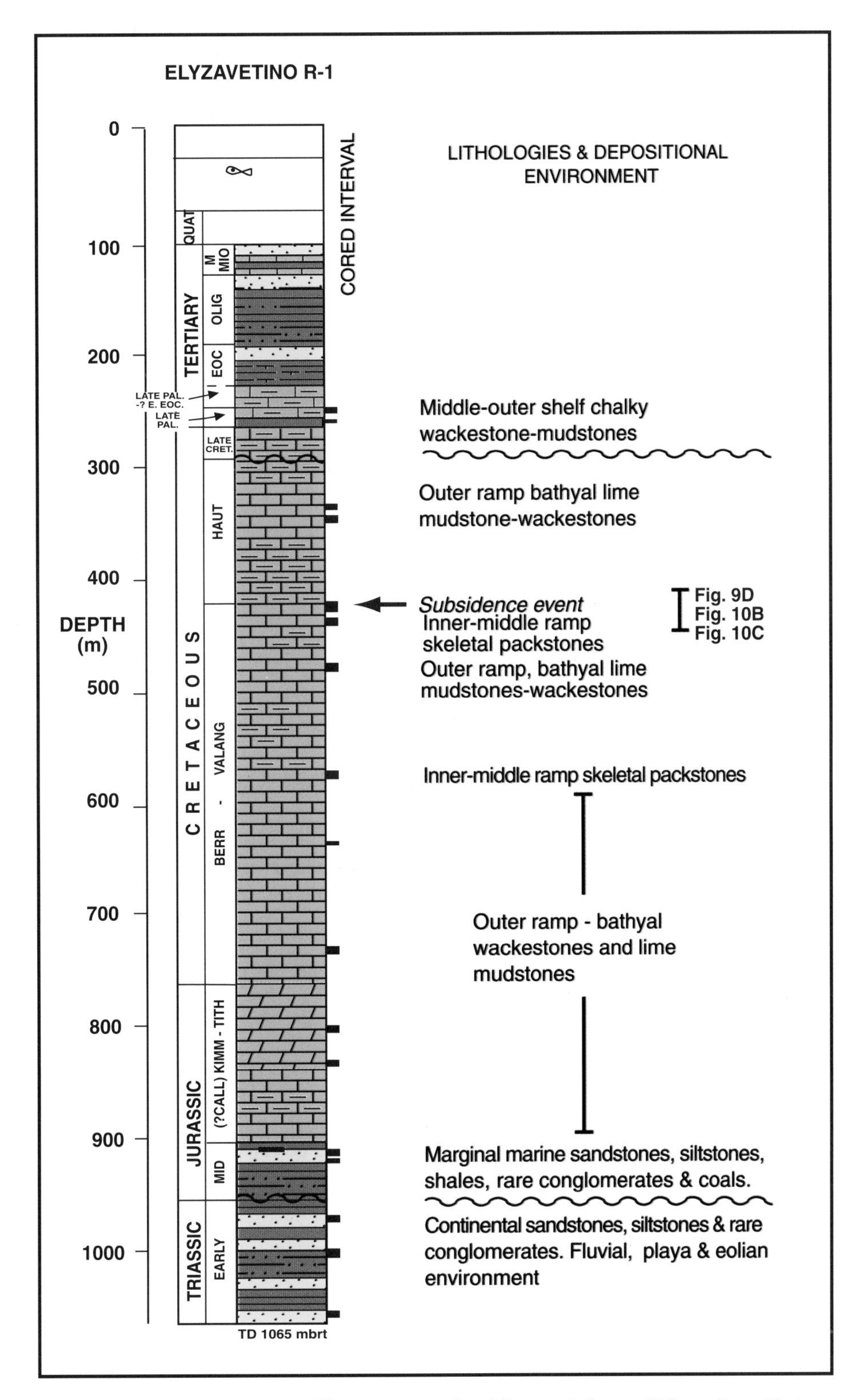

Figure 4. Elyzavetino-1 well summary. See Figure 2 for well location. Note location of core samples illustrated in Figures 9 and 10. mbrt = meters below rotary table.

Dolomitization of the original sediment precludes environmental interpretation of this lithofacies. However, association with bioturbated lime mudstones above and below the interval where these dolarenites occur suggests a bathyal/abyssal environment. The presence of chert nodules with poorly preserved radiolaria supports a deep-marine environment for the original sediment and suggests that the host sediment was a lime mudstone.

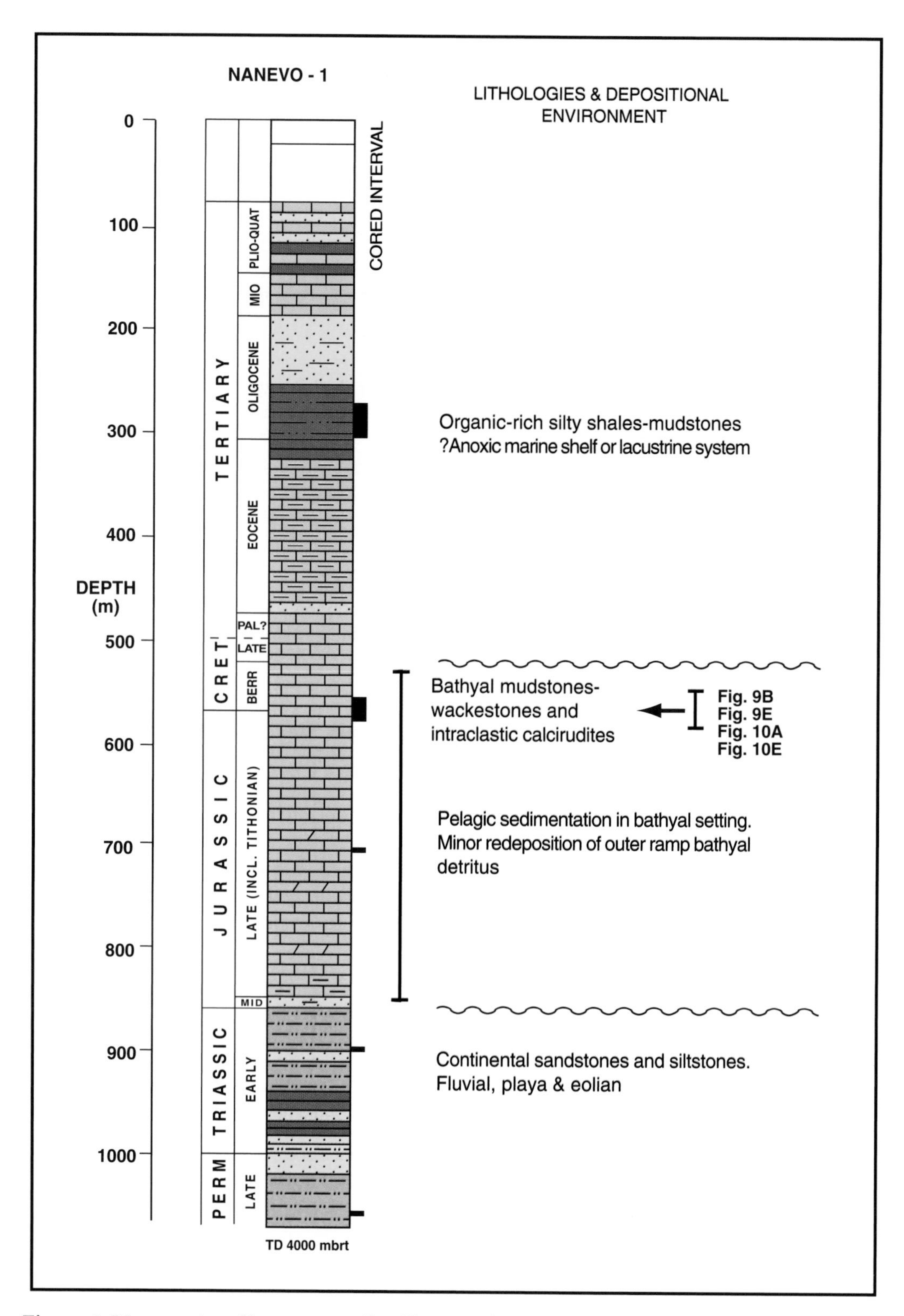

Figure 5. Nanevo-1 well summary. See Figure 2 for well location. Note location of core samples illustrated in Figures 9 and 10. mbrt = meters below rotary table.

Skeletal Packstone

This gray to brown calcarenitic packstone (and, rarely, wackestone) facies is observed in the Unak R-1 and Elyzavetino R-1 wells. The facies is observed at several intervals in Elyzavetino R-1, at 566 m and between 417.8 and 420 m, where beds, generally less than 1 m thick, rest within lime mudstone-wackestones, although no grading is observed (Figure 10B). In well Unak R-1, the bases of the beds, where preserved, may be erosive. Much of the facies is homogeneous, although the limestone breccia facies may grade up into the skeletal packstone in places.

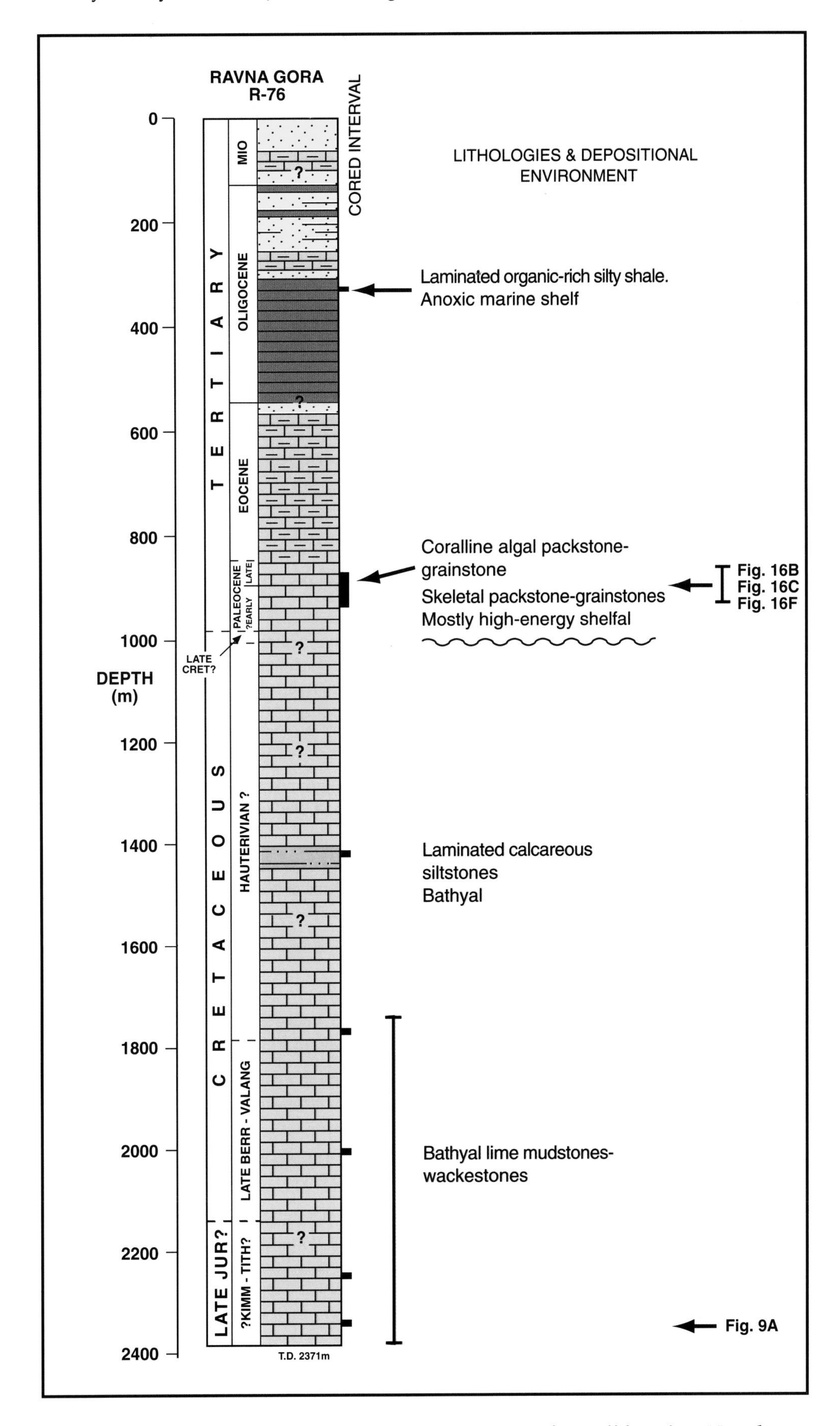

Figure 6. Ravna Gora R-76 well summary. See Figure 2 for well location. Note location of core samples illustrated in Figures 9 and 16.

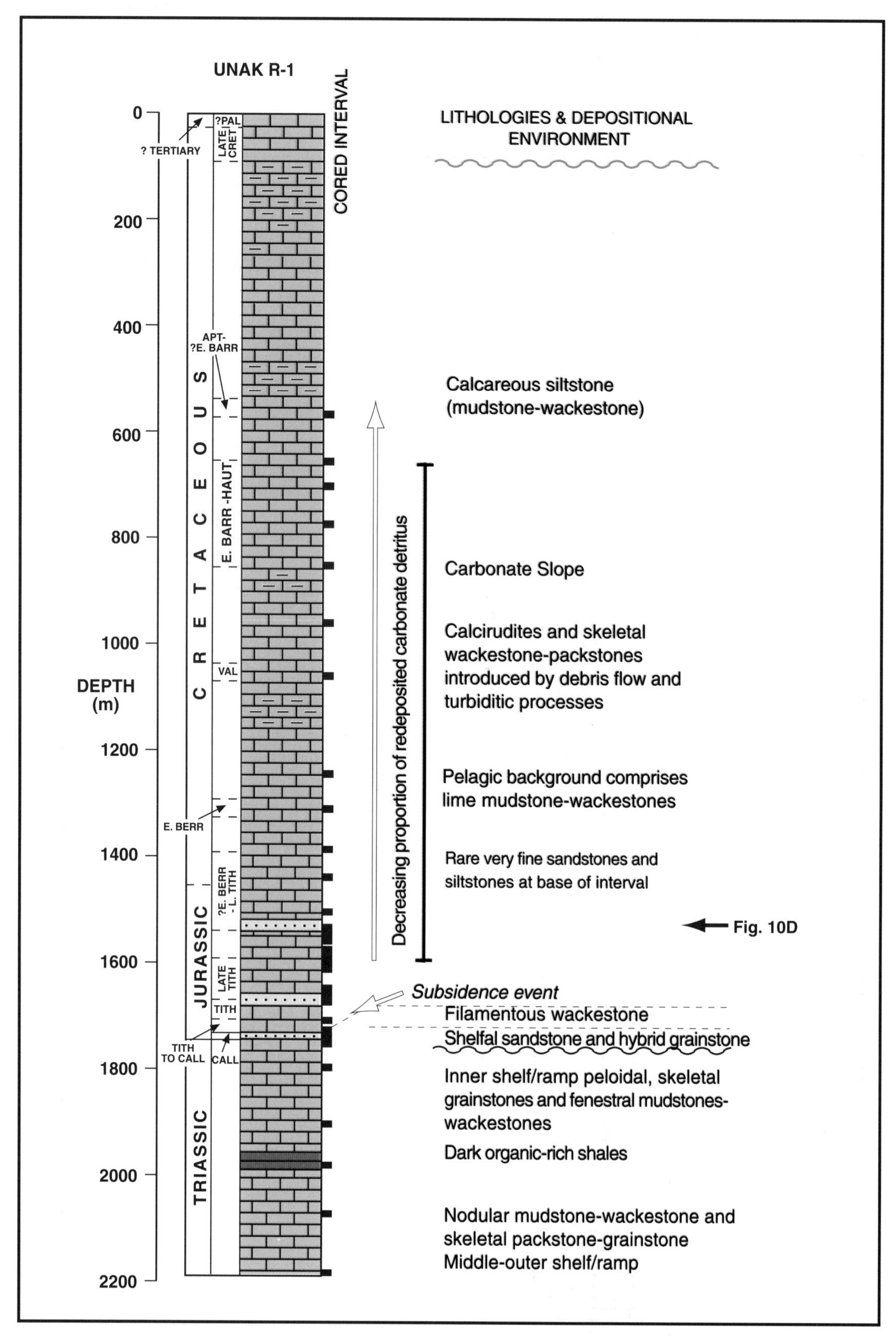

Figure 7. Unak R-1 well summary. See Figure 2 for well location. Note location of core sample illustrated in Figure 10.

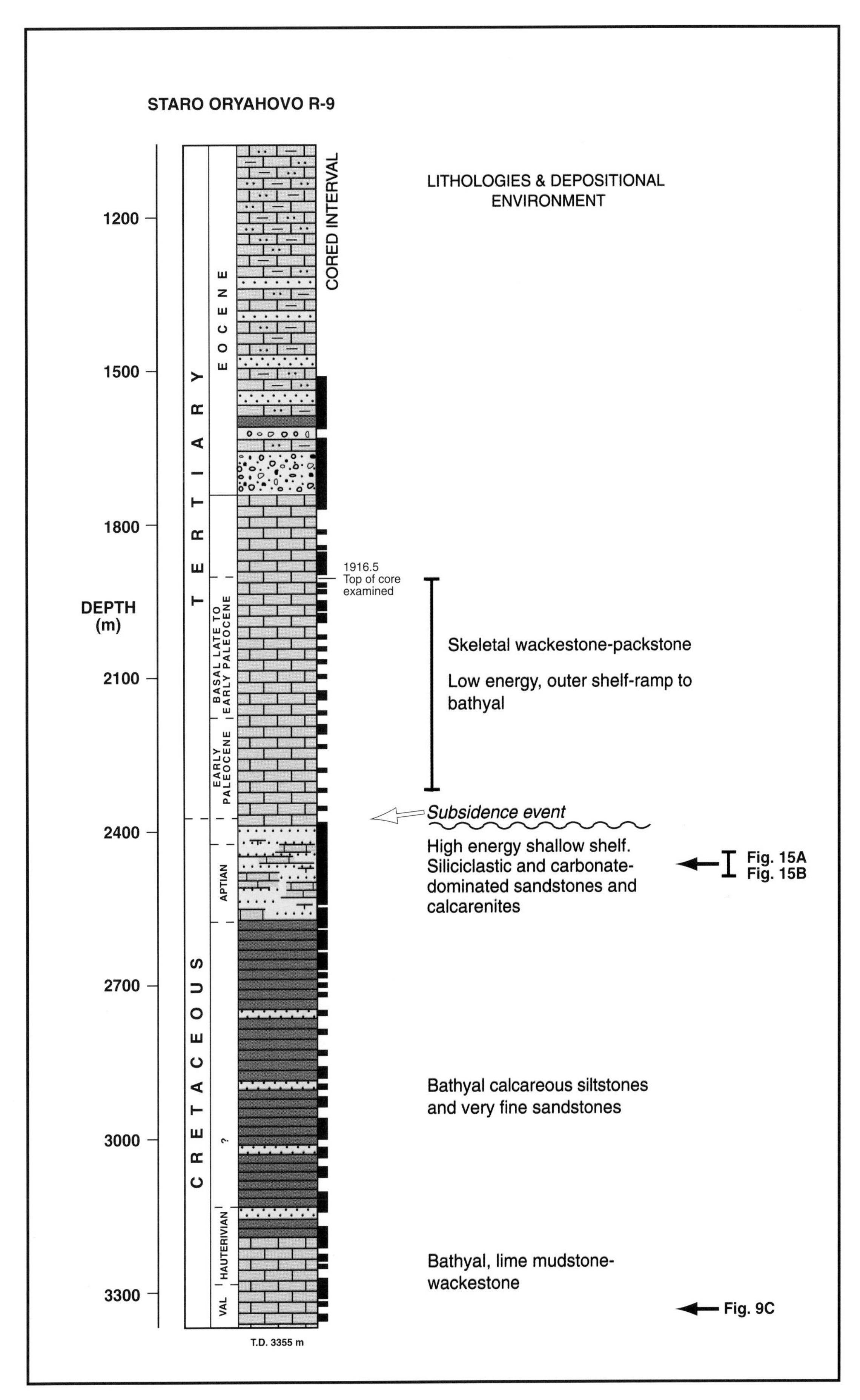

Figure 8. Staro Orayhovo R-9 well summary. See Figure 2 for well location. Note location of core samples illustrated in Figures 9 and 15.

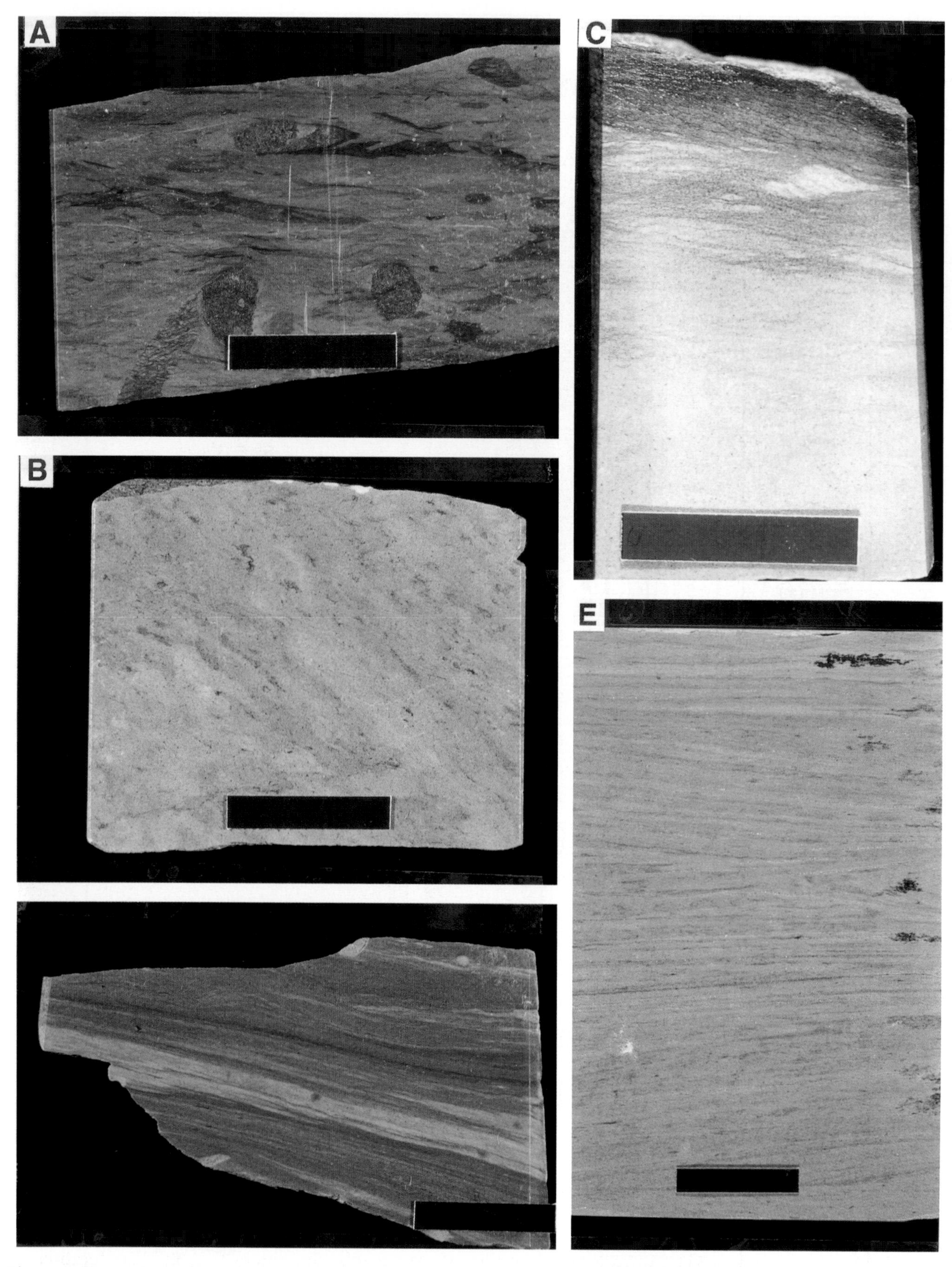

Figure 9. Upper Jurassic–Valanginian deep ramp to basinal lithofacies. (A) Bioturbated lime mudstone-wackestone: Well Ravna Gora R-76, 2345.8 m. (B) Bioturbated lime mudstone-wackestone: Well Nanevo R-1, 550.2 m. (C) Lime mudstone with flattened burrow; note wispy stylolites that pass up into dark stylolitic seam: Well Staro Oryahovo R-9, 3346 m. (D) Laminated lime mudstone-wackestone: Well Elyzavetino R-1, 426 m. (E) Laminated lime mudstone-wackestone with low-angle bounding surfaces and truncation of laminae: Well Nanevo R-1, 550.5 m. Scale bar is 2 cm on all photographs. See Figures 4, 5, 6, and 8 for location of core samples illustrated.

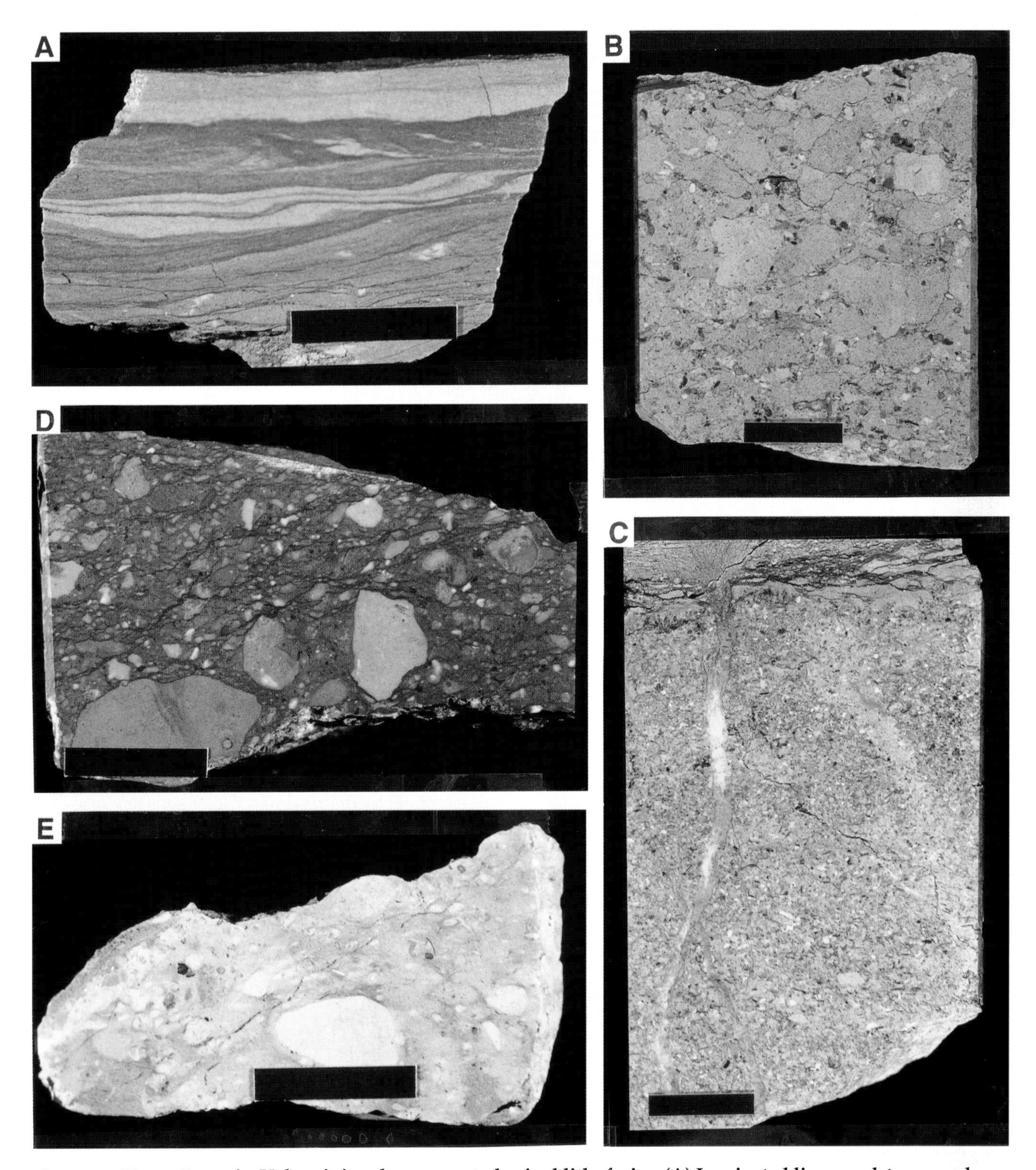

Figure 10. Upper Jurassic–Valanginian deep ramp to basinal lithofacies. (A) Laminated lime mudstone-wackestone with slight contortion of laminae: Well Nanevo R-1, 557 m. (B) Skeletal packstone with stylobreccia fabric: Well Elyzavetino R-1, 419.2 m. (C) Skeletal packstone of Valanginian overlain by stylolitized Hauterivian marly limestone: Well Elyzavetino R-1, 417.8 m. (D) Limestone breccia: Well Unak R-1, 1584.5 m. (E) Intraclastic calcirudite: Well Nanevo R-1, 562.2 m. Scale bar is 2 cm on all photographs. See Figures 4, 5, and 7 for location of core samples illustrated.

The facies contains fragmented skeletal detritus, including echinoderm, sponge spicule, coral, bryozoans and benthic foraminifera, and other, largely mollusk, shell debris. Many of the bioclastic components have micritic envelopes; some allochems have thick micritic coatings; and some bioclasts are partially silicified or more rarely pyritized. Rare, poorly preserved ostracods and "filaments" are observed. Benthic foraminifera include *Trocholina elongata, Favusella washitensis, Nautiloculina, Bolivinopsis, Textulariopsis, Verneuilinopsis, Arenobulimima,* and miliolids. Other allochems may include lime-mudstone intraclasts, peloids, and rare ooids. Echinoderm detritus may constitute ≤30% of the rock. Glauconite may be preserved within chambers of bryozoan and benthic foraminifera. Some samples may contain ≤2% silt to fine arenite-sized angular quartz grains. Euhedral dolomite rhombs have grown displacively in the sediment, and are more prominent in both intergranular areas and within the micritic matrix. Moderate bioturbation is observed in some intervals. Thin, low-amplitude stylolites with hydrocarbon? staining cut across the sample and are subparallel to bedding.

The skeletal packstone facies is closely associated with the limestone breccia facies in Unak R-1; both facies are interpreted in that well as deposits resulting from deposition by turbidity currents on a carbonate slope. The components in these calc-turbidites were derived from both a shallow-water carbonate platform and a carbonate slope area.

No grading was observed in this facies in the Elyzavetino R-1 well; the skeletal components suggest deposition in an outer-ramp setting with limited reworking by traction currents. The interval between 417.8 and 420 m is characterized by a varied fauna dominated by echinoderm fragments, some with micritic coatings, suggesting this interval was deposited in a shallow-marine environment (middle? to inner-shelf/ramp). However, since much of the skeletal detritus is fragmented and abraded, this interval may have been reworked into a deeper ramp setting by turbidity currents. This interpretation is supported by the association of deeper marine lime mudstone-wackestone facies in adjacent intervals in the core.

Limestone Breccia

This facies is common between 1495 and 1702 m depth in the Unak R-1 well (Figure 7). The beds range from 30 cm to >8 m in thickness and are light to dark gray. The beds are generally poorly sorted, often have sharp bases, and may grade up into calcarenitic skeletal packstones. Some slumped bedding is also observed in parts of the core. Clast-supported fabrics are the most common, although in some instances the proportion of micrite gives a matrix-supported appearance to the facies (Figure 10D). Stylolites are also common, and in some instances individual breccia clasts are rimmed by stylolites and have sutured boundaries. A large variety of clast types, ranging from subrounded to angular, are identified, including (1) peloidal grainstone/packstone, sometimes with a crudely developed lamination and containing abraded skeletal material including bivalve, coral, and bryozoan fragments; (2) lime mudstone, which may be either homogeneous or contain calcitized radiolaria, filaments, and bivalve fragments; (3) crudely laminated oncoids; and (4) individual skeletal fragments, including recrystallized coral, echinoderm, and bivalve fragments. All of these clast types may be partially silicified.

The sharp bases to many of the beds and their graded nature suggest some of these breccias originated by turbidite flows; other matrix-supported beds resulted from debris flow processes. Background sedimentation is represented by the fine-grained mudstone-wackestones between these coarse deposits. The carbonate clasts include a variety of low- and high-energy carbonate lithofacies, suggesting derivation from both a mature carbonate platform and the carbonate slope itself. Coral fragments may indicate the presence of reefal buildups in the shallow area. The clasts of lime mudstone containing calcitized radiolaria and filaments suggest some incorporation of slope material as the redeposited facies traveled downslope. The overall interpretation of this facies is therefore that of a slope environment, where juxtaposition of gravity-driven deposits and slope muds occurred.

Intraclastic Calcirudite

This facies is only identified in the Nanevo R-1 well, at 562 m depth, where it forms a bed 40 cm thick within laminated lime mudstone-wackestones. The facies consists of rounded micritic clasts embedded in a micritic matrix (Figure 10E). Clast types are dominated by rounded lime mudstones, some of which contain skeletal fragments (largely echinoderm and mollusks), poorly preserved benthic foraminifera, and clasts containing calcitized radiolaria and sponge spicules. Silt-grade siliciclastic detritus is distributed through the facies, where it constitutes <5% of the lithology.

That these rocks containing lime mudstone intraclasts were deposited in a deep bathyal environment is strongly supported by their close association with the lime mudstone-wackestone facies. The carbonate clasts were introduced into the outer-ramp–basinal environment by debris flows. Clasts such as those containing calcitized radiolaria and sponge spicules suggest derivation of at least part of the component from a deep-marine setting. The absence of detritus reworked from a shallow-marine environment differentiates this facies from the limestone breccias described above.

Calcareous Siltstone/Sandstone/Marl

This facies consists of light to dark brown and gray, generally homogeneous calcareous siltstones, with less common fine-grained sandstone, calcareous mudstones, and cream-colored marls. Beds are generally very thin to medium thickness, and range from thoroughly bioturbated and burrow mottled to laminated, with the laminae defined by the proportion of silt-grade quartz and white mica. The siliciclastic component comprises angular to subangular quartz and white mica laths with a phyllosilicate matrix. The small proportion (<5%) of skeletal material in the rock consists of very small, unidentifiable shell fragments, poorly preserved benthic foraminifera, calcitized radiolaria; and sponge spicules.

Calcareous siltstones and fine sandstones are observed in cored intervals from the Unak R-1 and Staro Oryahovo R-9 wells. In other wells (Elyzavetino R-1 and Nanevo R-1), this facies is superficially similar to the lime mudstone-wackestones described above: fine-grained siliciclastic detritus comprises small proportions, generally 2–10%, of that facies. Marly limestones are observed in the Hauterivian interval in the Elyzavetino R-1 well. The proportion of siliciclastic detritus in this facies increases during the Hauterivian (Figure 10C). The marls examined in outcrop in Locality 2 are generally easily weathered and poorly cemented. Some mottling is present, caused by the presence of randomly oriented burrows on a millimeter to centimeter scale, and chert nodules are also irregularly developed.

The fine-grained calcareous siltstone/sandstone facies was deposited in bathyal basin-floor and deep ramp settings. Deposition probably occurred in oxygenated to dysaerobic? conditions below the photic zone. Internal laminae may represent distal, low-density siliciclastic turbidites and/or limited reworking by contour currents. The absence of synsedimentary deformation features suggests that deposition occurred in parts of the basin with little topographic relief or slope gradients.

Subtidal Ramp Facies Association

Five lithofacies have been grouped in this facies association.

Lime Mudstone–Wackestone

This facies, identified in both East Dobruja C179A and the Tiulenovo wells (Figures 11, 12), consists of beige to cream-colored calcilutites, which may have an indistinct lamination. Where present, laminae are defined by very slight changes in grain size and oriented thin shell fragments; in other examples, minor burrow mottling is observed. The presence of small quantities of micropeloids indicates this lithofacies is transitional with the peloidal wackestone-packstone facies. Former shell fragments may be leached though some rare bivalve shells, and prismatic structures are recorded. Moderately rich nannofossil assemblages are observed. Both low- and high-amplitude stylolites are developed in a bedding-parallel orientation.

A moderately low-energy, subtidal marine environment is suggested by the fine-grained nature of this facies and the presence of nannofossils. The association with other facies including peloidal wackestone-packstones suggests deposition in an inner to middle ramp.

Peloidal Wackestone-Packstone

Brown to cream-colored, moderately sorted, peloidal wackestone-packstones are observed in both the East Dobruja C179A and Tiulenovo wells. These lithologies tend to be relatively homogeneous (Figure 13A). Allochems are dominated by dense micritic peloids, occasionally with a very faint concentric structure suggesting they originated as ooids; some micritized intraclasts are also observed. Stylolites and stylolitic seams are relatively common, as are calcite-filled hairline fractures; bioturbation is common in some cores (Figure 13B). Small chert nodules are irregularly distributed throughout the facies (Figure 13A); rare idiotopic dolomite rhombs have grown displacively in the matrix. Fauna tend not to be abundant in this facies, but where present include bivalve and echinoderm fragments, and ostracods; one sample contains moderate numbers of poorly preserved ammonites (Figure 13B). Poor to moderately rich nannofossil assemblages are also recorded in places.

This peloid-dominated facies was deposited in a low-to-moderate energy, subtidal shelf environment. The general absence of fauna and bioturbation in much of the facies may suggest some restriction of the environment, although no features have been observed that can be related to supratidal conditions. A subtidal environment of deposition is supported by the bioturbated ammonite- and nannofossil-rich horizons, which represent deposition within an open setting in which circulation of marine waters allowed accumulation of nektonic and pelagic organisms. Other samples with little fauna may represent deposition in a low intertidal environment where these organisms were not encouraged. Associated facies include lime mudstone-wackestones and coral framestone-floatstones.

Coral Framestone-Floatstone

These sedimentary rocks are observed in the East Dobruja C179A well and in the Tiulenovo development wells. They are generally poorly sorted and fossiliferous, with skeletal debris dominated by coral fragments (Figure 14A). The coral framestone facies consists of "sheets" of coral that commonly exceed the width of the core. The thicknesses of the coral-rich beds are usually between 50 cm and 5 m, although there are occasional thicker intervals of 10–15 m massive beds. Preservation of the cellular structure of the corals varies according to the degree of recrystallization and dolomitization, although the coral structure has in many instances been partially preserved by being partly-filled by micrite. The matrix between the coral clasts either is micritic or is heavily dolomitized. Other large clasts include mollusk shell fragments, which may be totally embedded within dolomite. Stylolites and stylolitic seams are relatively common, and small chert nodules are irregularly distributed throughout the facies (Figure 14A). Secondary porosity is common; dissolution of coral fragments resulted in vug development, although many vugs have been subsequently occluded by coarse spar.

The coral floatstones are poorly sorted fossiliferous sediments with skeletal debris dominated by tabular or subrounded coral fragments reaching ≤5 cm in diameter. Coral clasts are often abraded, with a thin micritic coating and/or fringe of encrusting foraminifera. As in the framestone facies, the coralline structure is largely recrystallized. Some of the larger chambers and/or borings in the shell structure are partially filled with micrite and micropeloidal sediment. Other skeletal components include echinoderm fragments and gastropods. The matrix is a skeletal-peloidal wackestone-packstone.

This coral-dominated facies was deposited in an open-marine, shallow-water environment where sheet-like biostromes developed. The high proportion of micrite in the facies collected during periods of relatively low energy, and growth of sheets of coral protected this fine-grained detritus from being winnowed. The location of these biostromes in an inner-ramp

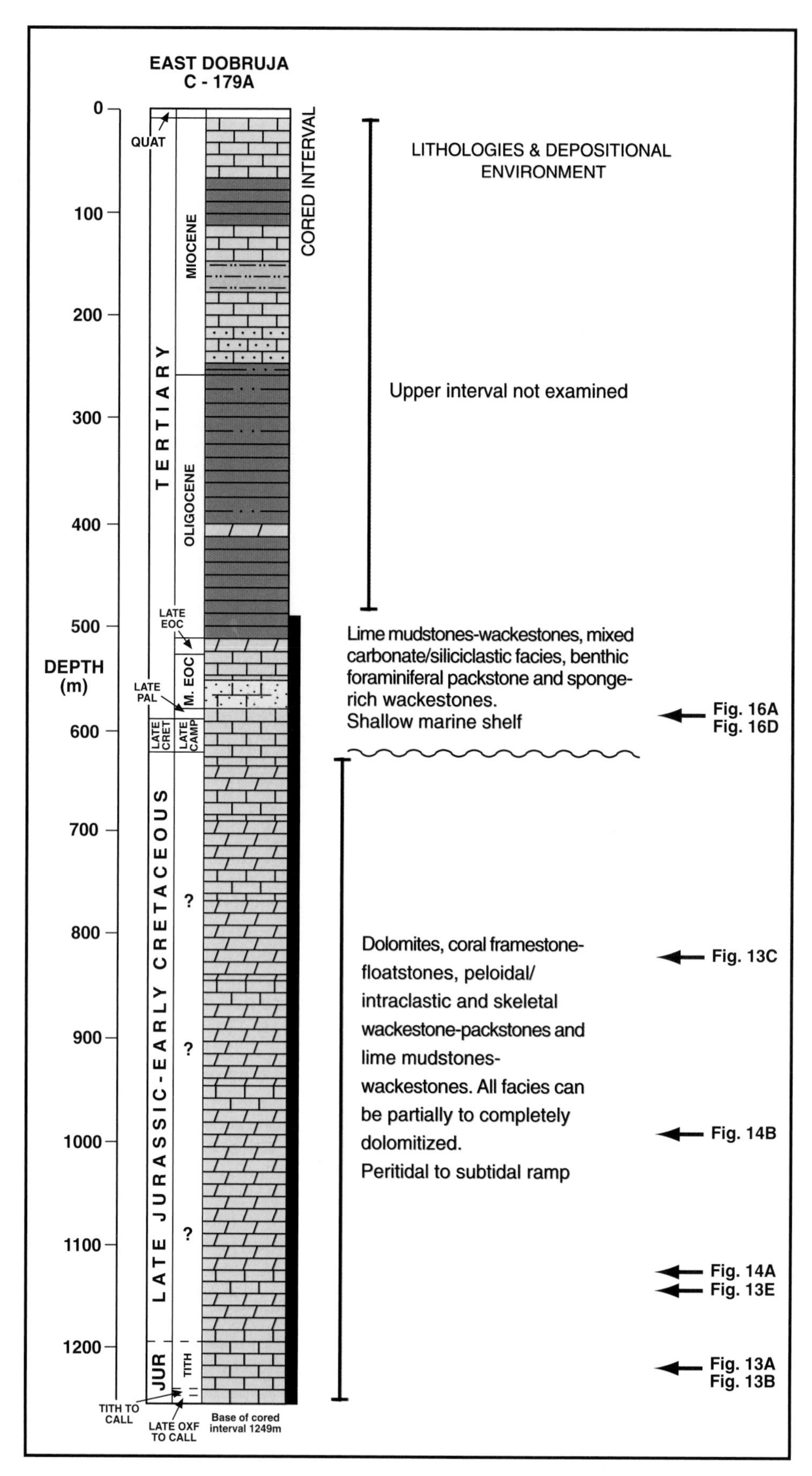

Figure 11. East Dobruja C-179A well summary. See Figure 2 for well location. Note location of core samples illustrated in Figures 13, 14, and 16. Core recovery was generally excellent; however, some intervals are missing.

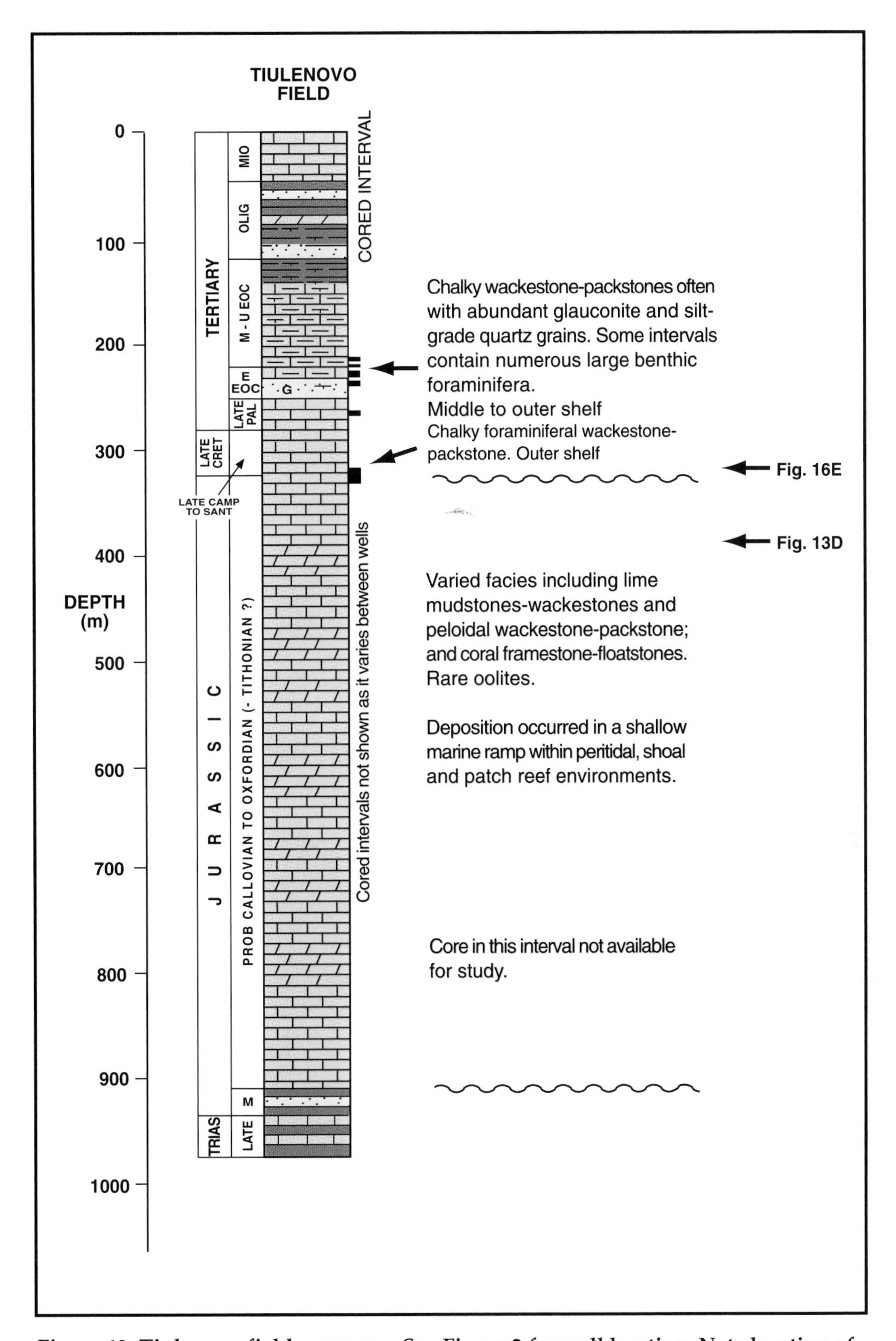

Figure 12. Tiulenovo field summary. See Figure 2 for well location. Note location of core samples illustrated in Figures 13 and 16. This log was constructed from core data from wells E445, E448, E454, and E457.

setting is suggested by their association with skeletal-peloidal wackestones and packstones. The absence of marine-phreatic cementation suggests these biostromes may have developed in an environment where there was little active circulation of marine waters, in a relatively protected part of the platform. The floatstones were reworked from coralline buildups, with the tabular clasts generated from the sheetlike framestones.

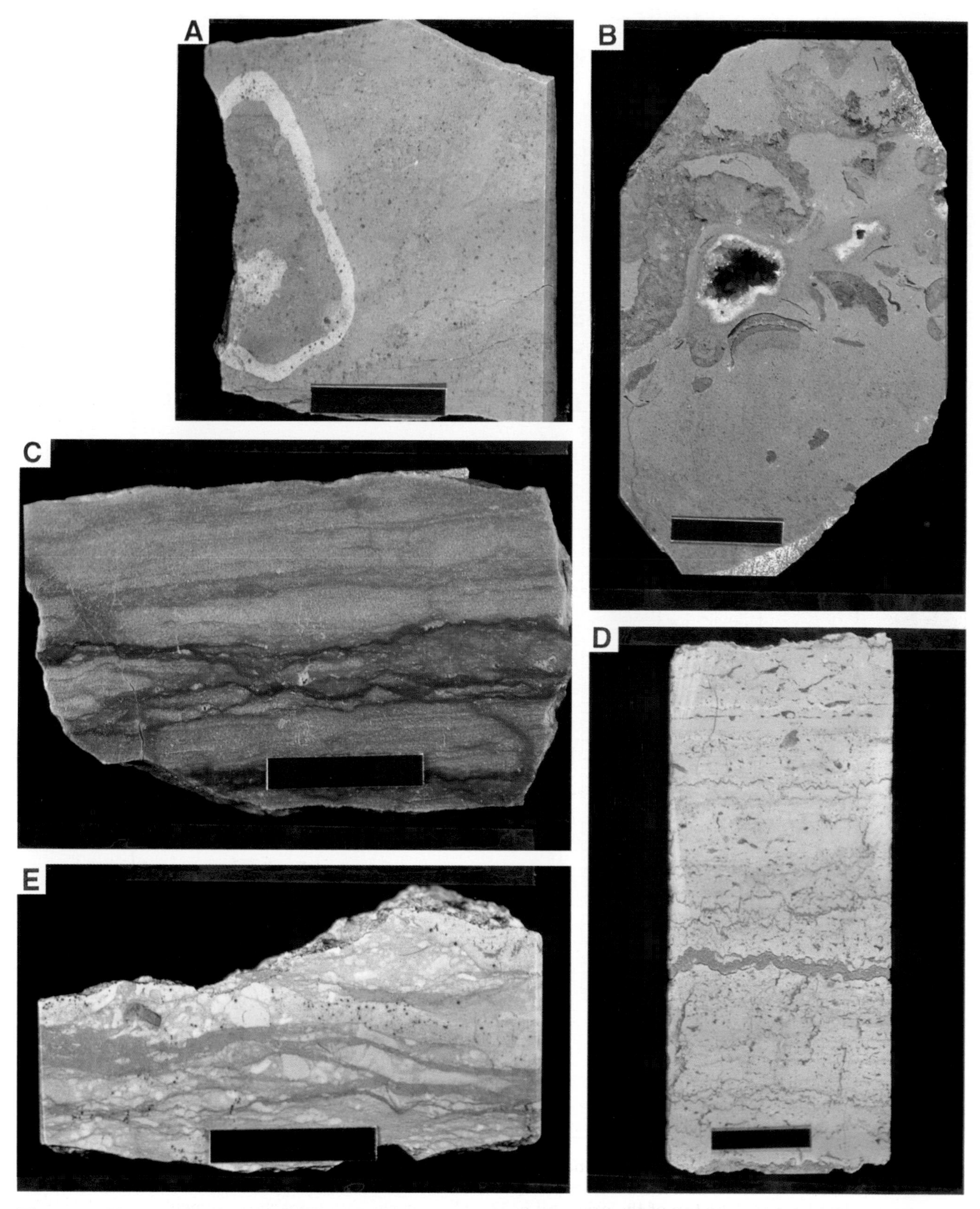

Figure 13. Upper Jurassic–Valanginian shallow-ramp lithofacies. (A) Peloidal wackestone-packstone with chert nodule: Well East Dobruja C179A, 1215 m. (B) Peloidal wackestone-packstone with ammonites and burrows: Well East Dobruja C179A, 1244 m. (C) Dolarenite with laminated fabric and numerous stylolites: Well East Dobruja C179A, 805 m. (D) Fenestral limestone: Well Tiulenovo E457, 394 m. (E) Intraclastic packstone with stylolites and stylolitic seams: Well East Dobruja C179A, 1147 m. Scale bar is 2 cm on all photographs. See Figures 11 and 12 for location of core samples illustrated.

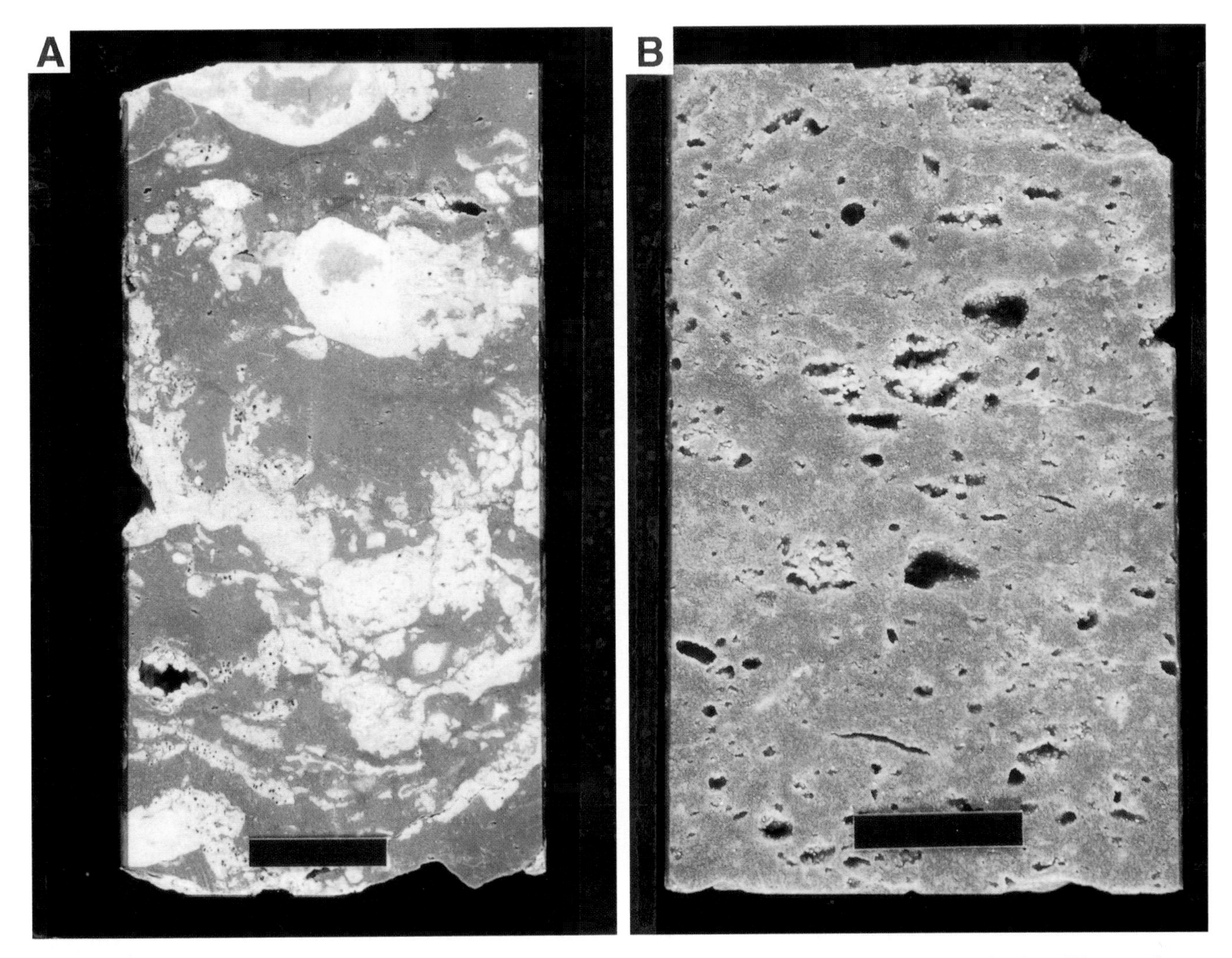

Figure 14. Upper Jurassic–Valanginian shallow-ramp lithofacies. (A) Coral framestone with sheetlike corals and silicified nodules: Well East Dobruja C179A, 1120 m. (B) Dolomitized skeletal-peloidal packstones-grainstones with biomoldic porosity: Well East Dobruja C179A, 989 m. Scale bar is 2 cm on both photographs.

Other framework clasts were rounded and became coated with micrite and/or encrusting foraminifera.

Skeletal-Peloidal Packstones-Grainstones

This facies is observed in outcrop north of Devnia, where it is extensively quarried; is also observed in the Tiulenovo E445 well; and is particularly common in the East Dobruja C179A well in the interval between 955 and 1085 m, where the facies is largely dolomitized. The rocks in this facies are cream to light brown, generally homogeneous and well–cemented carbonates (Figure 14B).

A coarsening-upward trend is recorded in the quarry at Locality 1, and there is a corresponding decrease in bed thickness upward. Occasional cross-beds with heights >2 m are observed. Vertical burrows are relatively common in all the beds, bedding planes are generally stylolitic, and intrabed stylolites are common. In Locality 2, the top of the grainstone-packstone interval is marked by a hardground with iron mineralization, which is then overlain by Hauterivian marls.

Lithologies range from moderately well sorted skeletal and peloidal grainstones to poorly sorted skeletal packstones. Skeletal detritus is varied and includes bivalve fragments, echinoderms, gastropods, corals, bryozoans, and numerous benthic foraminifera (including agglutinating forms, *Trocholina* spp., miliolids, and indeterminate valvulinids). Many of these organic components are abraded, with coatings of micrite; rare superficial ooids are observed. Some beds contain numerous rounded intraclasts. The facies generally contains very little siliciclastic detritus; however, some samples contain ~5–10% fine arenite to silt-grade quartzose detritus. This siliciclastic component includes subrounded to subangular monocrystalline quartz with undulose extinction and polycrystalline quartz. There is a tendency for the siliciclastic content to increase upward at Locality 2. Many of the grainstone samples have a two-stage cementation history: (1) an early, thin isopachous cement coating many of the allochems and (2) a secondary, coarse, pore-filling sparry calcite. Many of the echinoderm fragments have syntaxial overgrowth cements.

In well C179A, the facies is represented by sucrosic replacive dolomite with biomoldic and vuggy porosity (Figure 14B). The texture tends to be either an idiotopic or a hypidiotopic mosaic, and many of the dolomite rhombs are zoned. The shapes of the molds suggest the skeletal fragments were largely bivalves or brachiopods.

This facies was deposited in a moderate- to high-energy, wave-agitated, skeletal shoal on an extensive shallow-marine ramp. Skeletal detritus is abraded and often coated with micrite, emphasizing the continual reworking of carbonate detritus. This neritic setting is confirmed by the absence of well-preserved nannofossils in the samples. The siliciclastic fraction, where present, was derived from a metamorphosed basement. The coarsening- and thinning-upward trend in Locality 1 is interpreted to be part of a shallowing-upward sequence. The dolomitization in East Dobruja C179A hinders detailed environmental interpretation of these cores. However, the skeletal content of the lithology and its association with other open-marine facies (e.g., coral floatstone-framestone) suggest the facies was deposited in a moderate-energy, shallow-marine environment.

Dolarenite

The dolarenite facies is common in the East Dobruja C179A well between 710 and 1200 m depth. The dolomitic fabric is replacive in origin, and few preexisting structures are preserved in the rock. The facies ranges from homogeneous sucrosic dolomite to laminated, and stylolaminated, fine-grained dolomite (Figure 13C). Petrographic textures range from pseudo-intraclastic with stylolites to fine-grained homogeneous idiotopic dolomite, to examples with subhedral to anhedral hypidiotopic dolomitic mosaics.

The dolomitized nature of this facies hinders detailed environmental interpretation. However, the association of these lithologies with other open-marine facies in the core suggests the facies was originally a mudstone-packstone, deposited in a subtidal marine environment.

Peritidal Ramp Facies Association

Two lithofacies have been grouped in this facies association.

Fenestral Mudstone-Wackestone-Packstone

A laminated light-gray fenestral facies with a 1 cm alternation of mudstone and wackestone/packstone layers is relatively common in the Tiulenovo field wells (Figure 13D). Peloids, micritized skeletal fragments, and coated grains are the primary grain constituents within the facies. The minor skeletal material consists largely of bivalves, although some rare coral clasts are also observed. Some cryptalgal fabrics are observed with crinkly to irregular millimeter-scale laminations that may wrap around fenestral mudstone intraclasts. The fenestra are elongate and are partially geopetally filled with a vadose silt. Rare halite pseudomorphs are developed in the lime mudstone laminae, and euhedral dolomite rhombs have also grown displacively in the micritic material. The facies contains numerous prominent low- to high-amplitude bedding-parallel stylolites and stylolitic seams that are filled with idiotopic dolomite and minor pyrite.

A supratidal and high intertidal setting in an arid to semi-arid climate is envisaged for this facies (Kinsman, 1964; Kendall and Skipworth, 1969; Purser, 1973; Logan et al., 1974). Alternation of peloidal packstone and cryptalgally laminated lime mudstone suggests deposition in a moderately protected tidal flat where few organisms could tolerate the exposure and the increased salinities. Evaporitic conditions prevented burrowing organisms from destroying mechanical and algal laminations, and halite crystal growth was promoted. Storms intermittently deposited thin sheets of peloidal-rich sediment, and rare coral and bivalve clasts were reworked from subtidal environments during these events. The fenestra may have a synsedimentary or early diagenetic origin, and probably formed by either shrinkage or the formation of gas in the sediment. This lithofacies probably experienced minor subaerial exposure after shallow burial, during which the fenestra became partially filled with a micritic vadose silt washed in by waters flushed or percolating through the freshwater-vadose diagenetic zone.

Intraclastic Packstone

The intraclastic packstone facies is commonly distributed in the East Dobruja C179A core, where it is extensively dolomitized. This lithology commonly consists of subrounded-subangular micritic clasts resting in a dolomitized matrix. The intraclasts tend to be arranged in subparallel beds with sharp contacts with other fenestral limestone facies. Stylolitic seams and stylolites are common (Figure 13E). Few fauna have been recognized in this facies, although this may be due in part to dolomitization; rare faunal fragments include micritized echinoderms and recrystallized coral clasts. Idiotopic dolomite rhombs replace former micritic matrix, and are also commonly associated with stylolite development.

This facies was deposited in a restricted peritidal environment where increased salinities and possible subaerial exposure prevented colonization by organisms. Storm activity resulted in reworking of micritic clasts from adjacent tidal flats, and introduced skeletal material from subtidal environments nearby (cf. Purser, 1973; Tucker and Wright, 1990).

Summary of Callovian to Lower Cretaceous Carbonate Ramp to Basin Sedimentation

The distribution of facies outlined above suggests that during the Callovian to Barremian, eastern Bulgaria and the Bulgarian Black Sea were dominated by shallow-marine carbonate sedimentation in the north, which passed into an area of deep-marine character toward the south and southeast. The boundary between these facies belts is a broadly east-west line south of Shumen-Varna, becoming more northeast-southwest in the Black Sea area.

The Nanevo R-1, Staro Oryahovo R-9, and Ravna Gora R-76 wells are dominated by homogeneous micrite-rich lithologies containing largely pelagic organisms, implying deposition in a low-energy, deeper marine setting. Intraformational calcirudites observed in the Late Tithonian–Early Berriasian interval of the Nanevo R-1 well were introduced into the area by debris flows derived from an upper-slope environment, because there are no clasts, which suggest reworking of the detritus from a shallow-marine area. Minor reworking and sorting of fine-grained carbonate components by low-concentration turbidites or contour currents is observed in this deeper water setting; minor slumping confirms the presence of intrabasinal gradients. A lower (distal?) carbonate slope environment, therefore, existed in the Nanevo area.

The heterolithic facies deposited in the Unak R-1 region in the Tithonian to Barremian suggest deposition in a deep-marine slope environment. The thick succession consists of alternating pelagic/hemipelagic lime mudstone-wackestone facies, containing numerous pelagic organisms, with redeposited facies including limestone breccias and calcarenitic skeletal packstones. The redeposited facies were emplaced by a suite of processes including debris flows and both low- and high-concentration turbidity currents. Rare, thin, fine-grained sandstones-siltstones were derived from a different source region. The carbonate clasts in the redeposited beds contain clasts reworked both from an upper-slope setting and from a shallow-marine carbonate platform, in contrast to the calcirudites in the Nanevo R-1 well. Prompt delivery of the eroded carbonate material to the slope environment after erosion is suggested by the angularity of many of the clasts. This suggests that the detritus may have originated from a fault scarp. The limited well control in this region does not allow the orientation of this fault to be constrained; the absence of chaotic rock-fall deposits and the organized nature of these redeposited facies suggest the Unak R-1 well was located some distance from the fault, allowing some hydrodynamic organization of the clasts and incorporation of slope material prior to deposition into the deep-marine environment.

The Tithonian to Hauterivian interval in the Elyzavetino R-1 well is transitional between the shallow-marine ramp of the northern region and the deeper marine setting of the south. Lime mudstone-wackestones are dominated by pelagic organisms (calpionellids, radiolaria, sponge spicules, and holothurian echinoderm ossicles), suggesting bathyal to abyssal environments; skeletal packstones contain biota derived from a shallow-marine setting, including echinoderm, bryozoan, and coral fragments and shallow-water allochems such as ooids and algal oncoids. The packstones are barren of nannoflora, or contain very poor assemblages of nannofossils; there are no faunal fragments derived from a deep-marine setting in this facies. A neritic origin for the packstones is confirmed by the absence of grading and current-sorted fabric of these rocks; although some reworking of detritus may have occurred, there is little material of deeper water origin in this facies. The packstones may have developed as basinward-prograding clinoforms, which advanced during relative highstands of sea level from the shallow-marine ramp southward into deeper water. An alternative interpretation is that these rocks may have been deposited when shallow-ramp sedimentation was shifted to the former outer ramp during relative lowstands of sea level. The former hypothesis is preferred because of the sharp erosive contact, which may represent a sequence boundary, between the shallow-marine carbonates (highstand) and the deeper marine facies (lowstand).

Farther to the west and south, a full Late Jurassic to Valanginian sequence is preserved, overlain by Hauterivian to Aptian sediments. At outcrop localities 1 and 2 (Figure 2), massive Valanginian calcarenites are overlain by Hauterivian marls, with the contact marked by a hardground. In the Elyzavetino R-1 well, Valanginian skeletal packstones are also overlain sharply by Hauterivian marly limestones (Figure 10C). Subsidence was accompanied by an increase in detrital material into the basin and a corresponding facies change, although lime mudstone-wackestone facies were still deposited in the region of the Elyzavetino R-1 well.

The majority of siliciclastic material introduced into the northern region was fine-grained argillaceous or silty detrital material. Fine-grained sandstones are recorded in the Unak R-1 and Staro Oryahovo R-9 wells. In outcrops south of the Preslav anticline, medium- to coarse-grained sandstones with eastward-flowing paleocurrents are sandwiched in a marly succession (P. Dachev, 1995, personal communication). The distribution of siliciclastic detritus suggests this siliciclastic source lay to the west or south.

The platform in the north was characterized by shallow-marine sedimentation; details of the facies deposited in this area were determined by examination of core from the East Dobruja C179A and Tiulenovo wells. Carbonate facies include those deposited in a subtidal ramp and within a peritidal environment. The subtidal facies include lime mudstone-wackestone, peloidal wackestone-packstone, skeletal-peloidal packstone-grainstone, and coral floatstone-framestone, which were deposited in a moderately high energy setting with open circulation and normal marine salinities. The peritidal facies include intraclastic packstones and rocks with fenestral fabrics, with some evidence of hypersaline conditions. The facies are variably dolomitized, which can preclude recognition of original components and depositional fabrics. Organic buildups were relatively common, as shown by the coral framestones in well C179A. Lateral control is not sufficient to determine whether these are biostromes or bioherms, although the relatively thin nature of the facies (maximum thickness 15 m) suggests they are either biostromes or patch reefs. Coral floatstones are a relatively common facies, indicating breakup of organic frameworks and reworking to other locations on the platform. The reef-derived material may be rounded and coated with micrite, suggesting abrasion during reworking. The juxtaposition of coral-rich facies with skeletal and peloidal packstone/grainstone over tens of centimeters in several wells indicates the rapid juxtaposition of contrasting lithologies within this shallow-marine setting.

APTIAN SHALLOW-MARINE SEDIMENTATION

The Aptian interval is the most heterogeneous of the four intervals recognized in the Staro Oryahovo R-9 well (Figure 8). Five samples were selected from the interval between 2416 and 2575 m in the well, and three lithofacies are identified. The facies include sandstones, sometimes with abundant glauconite; skeletal grainstone hybrids, and microconglomerates with *Orbitolina* and corals; marls are seen in outcrop.

Sandstone

The sandstone lithofacies is characterized by gray to green, fine to medium sandstones, moderately sorted, with a burrow-mottled appearance. Poor core recovery does not allow identification of stratal surfaces or the nature of the bedding contacts. The sandstones classify as subfeldspathic arenites and are generally calcite cemented, even though some micritic matrix is occasionally present, and this yielded nannoflora assemblages. The grains are composed of angular to subangular, monocrystalline and polycrystalline quartz; plagioclase and orthoclase feldspar, which are often degraded and sericitized; and rare lithic siltstone grains. One of the samples examined from 2416 m consists of ~25% glauconite grains; it is this component that is responsible for the green color of the facies. Carbonate detritus consists of a small proportion of skeletal fragments that are largely unidentifiable, with the exception of rare echinoderm debris.

A shelfal marine environment of deposition for this facies is confirmed by the presence of minor echinoderm skeletal debris, glauconite, and nannoflora assemblages. A siliciclastic source fed both quartzose and feldspathic detritus, and this became mixed with minor carbonate material with subsequent reworking.

Mixed Carbonate/Siliciclastic Facies

The mixed carbonate/siliciclastic facies contains poorly sorted polymict microconglomerates, and moderately sorted, medium- to coarse-grained sandstones with a mixture of both carbonate and siliciclastic components (Figure 15A). The sandstones can be laminated, with laminae defined by elongate shell fragments. The siliciclastic component (45–60%) includes subrounded polycrystalline and monocrystalline quartz, vein quartz, and chert grains up to 6 mm in diameter. The carbonate component (40–55%) consists of skeletal material, including *Orbitolina* benthic foraminifera, corals, bivalves, echinoderms, and recrystallized carbonate clasts and some micritic matrix (Figure 15B). All the carbonate clasts may be rounded, have micritic coatings, and may be partially to largely recrystallized.

These hybrid facies were deposited in a shallow-marine setting. This environmental determination is suggested by the faunal content (corals, *Orbitolina*, and echinoderms). *Orbitolina* agglutinating foraminifera are useful biostratigraphic indicators in the Cretaceous and are normally found in considerable numbers in middle to outer ramp environments in areas of open-marine circulation and salinity (Wilson, 1975). The siliciclastic material was derived from a varied basement containing both igneous and metamorphic rocks. The rounded nature of the detrital component suggests considerable reworking in a fluvial or shoreface setting before being transported into a shallow-marine environment.

Marl

Cream-colored silty marls were examined in outcrop in Locality 3, where they are weathered and poorly cemented. Some fissility is observed in the facies, although the majority of the outcrop is structureless. The facies contains a rich nannofossil assemblage. The marls may be burrow-mottled, caused by the presence of randomly oriented burrows on a millimeter to centimeter scale.

In the absence of other sedimentary features, it is not possible to be precise about the depositional environment of this facies. The rocks contain a rich pelagic biota, confirming a low-energy setting, where accumulation was occurring largely from suspension. Deposition occurred in a subwave-base setting, where homogenization of the sediment occurred in oxygenated conditions.

Summary of Aptian Sedimentation

The Aptian facies observed in the Staro Oryahovo R-9 well were deposited in a shallow-marine environment and this interval therefore indicates a progressive shallowing from the Hauterivian–Barremian rocks below. The Aptian section in Staro Oryahovo R-9 indicates that siliciclastic and carbonate components were thoroughly mixed in a high-energy setting. Furthermore, the roundness of the detrital material, the variety of the carbonate components, and the provenance of the siliciclastic material suggest there was a relatively extensive shallow-marine area, possibly with continental basement exposed and eroded in subaerial environments in the region of the Staro Oryahovo well at this time. The absence of shallow-marine bedforms and faunal/floral composition of the marls suggest deposition in a quiet shelf environment.

CENOMANIAN TO PALEOGENE SHALLOW-MARINE SEDIMENTATION

Upper Cretaceous rocks are commonly exposed on the Moesian Platform, and many areas in the Varna region have a complete succession; the total thicknesses range from tens to hundreds of meters (Jolkicev, 1988). Twenty-one formal lithostratigraphic units are defined in the Upper Cretaceous in Northern Bulgaria (Jolkicev, 1989; Juranov et al., 1993), and Aladjova-Hrisceva (1991) has presented a comprehensive

Figure 15. Aptian mixed carbonate/siliciclastic lithofacies. (A) Well-sorted microconglomerate with clasts and little matrix: Well Staro Oryahovo R-9, 2451.5 m. (B) Moderately sorted hybrid facies with skeletal fragments and rounded siliciclastic clasts in a micritic matrix: Well Staro Oryahovo R-9, 2435 m. Scale bar is 2 cm on both photographs. See Figure 8 for location of core samples illustrated.

study of the Paleogene in northeast Bulgaria. All stages can be recognized in outcrop, and age determinations have largely been constrained by both macrofossils and microfossils. We recognize six lithofacies in this interval.

Lime Mudstone-Wackestone

This Upper Cretaceous chalky facies is seen in cored intervals from the East Dobruja C179A and Tiulenovo E454 and E457 wells, and comprises white to cream-colored fine-grained calcilutites-calcisiltites (Figure 16A). Similar facies are observed in the late Paleocene/early Eocene of the Elyzavetino R-1 well. Planktonic foraminifera and nannoflora form an important constituent of the facies, with rich assemblages generally very well preserved. Other skeletal components include echinoderm and bivalve shell fragments, gastropods, rare small ostracods, and *Inoceramus* fragments. Burrow mottling is present in places, the burrows being filled with a variety of material: peloids, silt- to fine-sand–grade quartz, and varying amounts of green to brown glauconite pellets. Common low-medium–amplitude stylolites are distributed throughout the core, and rare dolomite rhombs have grown displacively in the matrix.

A variation on this facies is a laminated to bioturbated spicular wackestone-packstone of late Paleocene in well C179A. This facies consists of moderately preserved sponge spicules, calcitized radiolaria, and poorly preserved planktonic foraminifera in a dense micritic matrix. Silt-grade quartz comprises <5% of the total rock. Lamination is present in parts of the core; other parts are bioturbated.

The well-preserved planktonic foraminifera and rich nannofossil assemblages suggest these sedimentary rocks were deposited in an open-marine middle- to outer-shelf setting. This is supported by the presence of the nektonic mollusk *Inoceramus*. Abundant bioturbation and pelagic settling of planktonic foraminifera and nannoflora occurred. The presence of glauconite and a small proportion of siliciclastic material concentrated in burrow fills suggest the bioturbation may have occurred during a change to relatively slow rates of sedimentation, in an open-marine environment. The upper Paleocene laminated spicular wackestone-packstone facies observed in the East Dobruja C179A well may have been deposited in a period of dysaerobic conditions on the shelf, when only limited bioturbation occurred.

Skeletal Packstone-Grainstone

Skeletal packstones and grainstones are a common Paleocene facies in the Ravna Gora R-76 well. The rocks have a massive appearance in the core, although numerous stylolites and stylolitic seams are observed. The grains consist of abundant skeletal detritus and micritic intraclasts in a micritic matrix. The skeletal component is dominated by echinoderm debris (Figure 16B), which may form ≤40% of the total rock; intact echinoderm plates ≤1 cm in diameter are quite common. Relatively rare nannofossils were recovered toward the base of the cored interval. Some intensely micritized benthic foraminifera are present; rare phosphatic ooids are also recorded. Some examples of the facies are dominated by peloids; in these examples, the shell fragments and benthic foraminifera have micritic envelopes and are largely micritized. Angular to subangular quartz grains are observed in some samples, where they constitute approximately 5–10% of the rock.

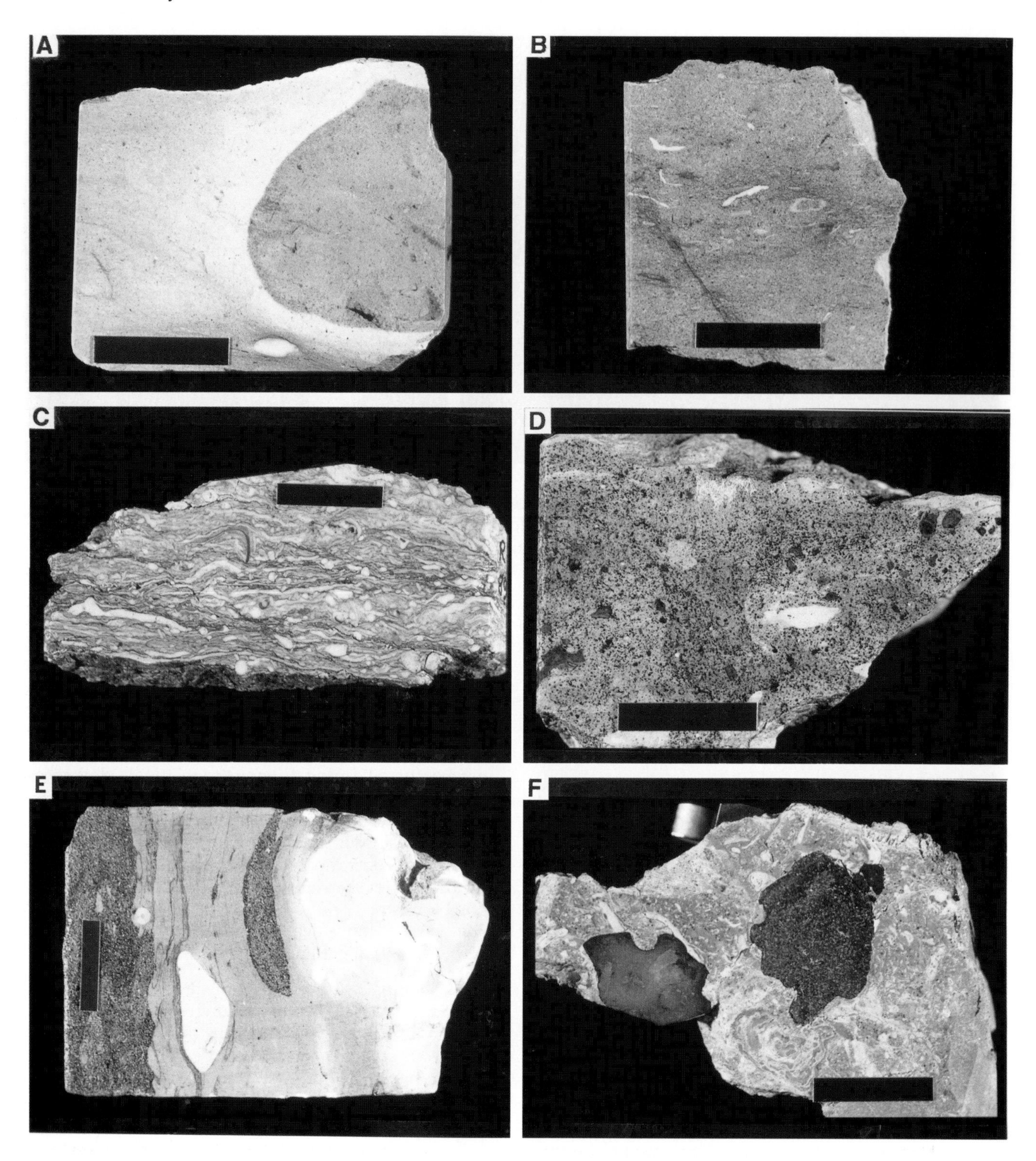

Figure 16. Cenomanian to middle Eocene lithofacies. (A) Lime mudstone-wackestone: Well East Dobruja C179A, 577.6 m. (B) Skeletal packstone-grainstone. White clasts are large echinoderm fragments: Well Ravna Gora R-76, 919.5 m. (C) Coralline algal packstone-grainstone. "Bindstone" subfacies with a prominent laminar fabric produced by elongate tabular clasts of coralline algae and emphasized by numerous stylolites: Well Ravna Gora R-76, 890.7 m. (D) Mixed carbonate/siliciclastic facies with abundant glauconite: Well East Dobruja C179A, 585.6 m. (E) Mixed carbonate/siliciclastic facies. Marly limestone contains white chalky rip-up clasts and intervals and burrow fills containing abundant glauconite: Well Tiulenovo E448, 315 m. (F) Coralline algal rhodoliths and large clasts of mixed glauconite-rich carbonate/siliciclastic sandstone and phosphatic pebbles: Well Ravna Gora R-76, 896.6 m. Scale bar is 2 cm on all photographs. See Figures 6, 11, and 12 for location of core samples illustrated.

Many examples of this facies have been subjected to partial dolomitization. The dolomite takes the form of small, generally silt- to fine-sand–grade rhombs, which may be isolated or be abundant enough to form a "framework," having replaced micritic matrix and/or cement. Thin, syntaxial overgrowths are developed on some echinoid grains.

This facies was deposited in a shallow-marine environment of deposition with relatively high energy and open water circulation, confirmed by the presence of abundant echinoderm skeletal debris and the paucity of calcareous nannofossils. Moderate sorting of the sediment must have occurred in this neritic setting, limiting the accumulation of calcareous mud. A significant input of siliciclastic detritus is recorded in the facies; considerable reworking of the detritus above wave base resulted in a thorough mixing of quartzose and carbonate detritus. Provisional data suggest the proportion of siliciclastic detritus increases upward within the facies. The rare phosphatic clasts imply possible sedimentation rates associated with condensed sedimentation and hardground/firmground development.

Coralline Algal Packstone-Grainstone

This facies occurs abundantly in the Ravna Gora R-76 well, where it lies on the skeletal packstone-grainstones. Samples from depths of 890.7 m and 874.5 m yielded nannoflora of late Paleocene age. The facies is dominated by coralline algal fragments, which have a white color in hand specimen (Figure 16C). Bedding is planar, with numerous stylolites and stylolitic seams. No sedimentary structures were observed. Two subfacies can be differentiated on the basis of grain composition and fabric: (1) a "bindstone" subfacies with a prominent laminar fabric, produced by elongate tabular clasts of coralline algae, and a bedding-parallel fabric emphasized by the stylolites; and (2) a more massive algal grainstone-packstone, with numerous rounded coralline algal clasts.

Algal coatings are also observed on other skeletal fragments, forming rhodoliths ≤2 cm in diameter. The other skeletal components include bryozoans, echinoderm fragments, benthic foraminifera (including encrusting species and *Discocyclina* types). Nannofossils were recovered from the facies, and some tests of planktonic foraminifera are moderately well preserved. Siliciclastic detritus, consisting of angular to subangular quartz grains, always constitutes <5% of the total rock, generally 1–2%. Early diagenetic fibrous cement is observed in some samples.

The fauna preserved in this facies consists of robust fossils such as coralline algae, large and small benthic foraminifera, and echinoderms, indicating this facies was deposited in a shallow-marine, relatively high energy environment. open-marine circulation is indicated by the foraminifera and nannoflora biota present. The coralline algae indicate deposition within the photic zone; their often-fragmented and abraded nature supports a high-energy setting, possibly within a shoal environment. The algal "bindstone" subfacies are shoal facies, where the elongate algal fragments have accumulated, in some cases with the near exclusion of other components. A shallow neritic environment is supported by the presence of *Discocyclina*-type benthic foraminifera and the fibrous early marine phreatic cement observed in some samples.

Mixed Carbonate/Siliciclastic Facies

Under this heading are grouped a number of lithologies seen in the Tertiary sections of the East Dobruja C179A and Tiulenovo wells. Components in these "hybrid" sedimentary rocks typically include both fine-grained quartz and skeletal detritus, generally with a micritic matrix. These rocks are generally packstones texturally, although in many instances the carbonate content can constitute <10% of the rock. Glauconite, generally developed as rounded grains, is often an important component and may in some cases reach 50% (Figure 16D, E). Other allochems include coralline algae, broken *Operculina* and *Discocyclina*-type benthic foraminifera, poorly preserved planktic foraminifera, echinoderm fragments, and miscellaneous mollusk fragments. Phosphatic grains and both lime mudstone and mixed carbonate/siliciclastic lithoclasts are observed at some horizons.

One interval at ~897 m depth in the Ravna Gora R-76 well contains abundant coralline algal rhodoliths and large clasts of hybrid sandstone and phosphatic pebbles ≤3 cm in diameter (Figure 16F). The phosphatic pebbles are bored, and the borings are filled with hybrid sandstone with abundant skeletal detritus, benthic foraminifera, and glauconite grains.

Another lithology assigned to this facies from a depth of 545 m in the East Dobruja well consists of moderately to well sorted, homogeneous, medium- to fine-grained quartz-rich sandstone, also containing minor rounded glauconite grains, with a micritic matrix (packstone fabric). The subangular to subrounded quartz fraction comprises ~85% of the total rock.

Eocene rocks of this facies group containing nummulite benthic foraminifera are common in the C179A well. The nummulites are moderately well preserved and either may be randomly scattered throughout the rock or define a crude lamination.

These lithologies are interpreted as having formed in moderate-energy, normal marine environments. The abundance of shallow-water bioclasts within many of the lithologies assigned to this broad facies group, including coralline algae and nummulites, suggests deposition within the photic zone. The presence of planktonic foraminifera and interbedding of some of these lithologies with lime mudstone-wackestones rich in planktonic foraminifera suggest an open oceanic influence. The formation of glauconite is restricted to the marine environment, and the abundance of rounded grains suggests that they probably result from the alteration and reworking of fecal pellets that have become concentrated by reworking. Lithologies containing phosphatic pebbles and lithic clasts, composed of both siliciclastic and carbonate components with abundant glauconite, suggest that these subfacies represent horizons of slow deposition.

The hybrid sandstones-packstones were deposited in a moderately high energy environment with a significant siliciclastic input. Nummulites flourished in adjacent areas on this shallow-marine platform and were washed into the region.

Benthic Foraminiferal Packstone

This facies occurs in the East Dobruja C179A well between 565 and 574 m, where microfossil studies suggest an early Eocene. It passes gradationally downward into mixed carbonate/siliciclastic sandstones with large benthic foraminifera. Nummulite- and *Discocyclina*-type foraminifera are the major constituent particles, comprising ≤80% of the facies by volume. Many of the foraminifera skeletons are fragmented and can be bored. Silt-grade quartz detritus forms ≤5% of the rock, and rounded glauconite clasts are common. The matrix is composed of fragmented fossils and microcrystalline calcite.

The abundance of large perforate foraminifera indicates this facies was deposited in normal marine conditions. Recent nummulitids occupy a wide range of shallow-marine environments within the photic zone, with small, stout forms occurring in relatively high energy settings and large, flat forms adapted for deeper, low-energy settings (Ghose, 1977). The fragmentation and abrasion of tests indicate high-energy reworking within a turbulent environment. This facies was developed after the mixed carbonate/siliciclastic facies and documents a gradational decrease in siliciclastic detrital input onto this part of the shelf.

Sponge Wackestone

Sponge wackestones are a relatively rare facies that has only been observed between 583.5 and 582.5 m depth in the East Dobruja C179A well, where it is developed in an interval less than 1 m thick. Nannoflora indicate a late Paleocene age. The delicate sponge fragments are moderately well preserved in a dense micritic matrix. Silica-rich nodules are common throughout this facies, and partial silicification of the calcilutite matrix has occurred.

Interpretation

A moderately low energy shelfal environment of deposition within the photic zone is suggested for this facies. The close association of this facies with lime mudstone-wackestone facies confirms a low-energy platform environment. Silica-rich nodules were developed during diagenesis, with silica derived from siliceous sponges and associated spicule-rich facies.

Summary of Upper Cretaceous to Paleogene Sedimentation

Upper Cretaceous to Paleocene rocks are commonly exposed on the Moesian Platform in the area south and west of Varna, where they typically form extensive escarpments above the softer Hauterivian and Barremian marls. Much of the Cenomanian to Paleogene facies examined in this study was deposited in a shallow-marine shelfal setting; the typical outcrop thickness of the northern Moesian Platform region is <100 m. Similar thicknesses are recorded in offshore wells (e.g., Nanevo R-1 and Elyzavetino R-1). Pelagic components (planktonic foraminifera, radiolaria, and nannofossils), shallow-marine components (largely mollusk and echinoderm shell fragments), and siliciclastic detritus were mixed by shallow-marine hydrodynamic processes and bioturbation. Intensely bioturbated intervals and glauconite-rich rocks suggest periods of reduced sedimentation.

MESOZOIC AND CENOZOIC BASIN HISTORY

Integration of the lithofacies described above with the biostratigraphic data, outcrop relationships, and offshore seismic data has allowed the definition of four tectonostratigraphic phases in the Upper Jurassic–middle Eocene of the NE Bulgarian Moesian Platform and adjacent Kamchia Basin (Figure 17).

1. Callovian–early Aptian differential subsidence on a passive margin
2. Late Aptian–Albian tilting, nondeposition, and erosion
3. Cenomanian–Paleocene differential subsidence
4. Early–middle Eocene foreland basin

The regional structure is illustrated by a composite north-south seismic line across the offshore Moesian Platform, Kamchia Basin, and frontal Balkan foldbelt (Figure 18).

Callovian to Early Aptian Differential Subsidence on a Passive Margin

An angular unconformity separates Jurassic strata from more heavily structured Triassic and Paleozoic rocks over the Moesian Platform (Dachev et al., 1988). This unconformity (the Cimmerian unconformity) is clearly seen on marine seismic data and lies just below the Base Late Cretaceous carbonate seismic horizon (Figure 18). The overlying Lower and Middle Jurassic strata are generally thin (50–70 m) and consist of shallow-marine sandstones and limestones with numerous belemnites and ammonites (Sapunov and Tchoumatchenko, 1987). Late Jurassic to early Cretaceous rifting of the Moesian carbonate province differentiated the area into platforms and basins (Emery and Georgiev, 1993). This Late Jurassic to early Cretaceous history can be divided into a Callovian to early Hauterivian phase and a late Hauterivian to early Aptian phase.

Oxfordian to Early Hauterivian Phase

Biota indicating a Callovian age is recorded from carbonates in both the Unak R-1 well and the Tiulenovo field (see Appendix 1). The subsequent Oxfordian to Valanginian section is dominated by carbonates, several hundreds of meters thick (Figure 19). This interval lies between the Base Upper Jurassic carbonates and the Top Valanginian seismic reflectors (Figure 18). During

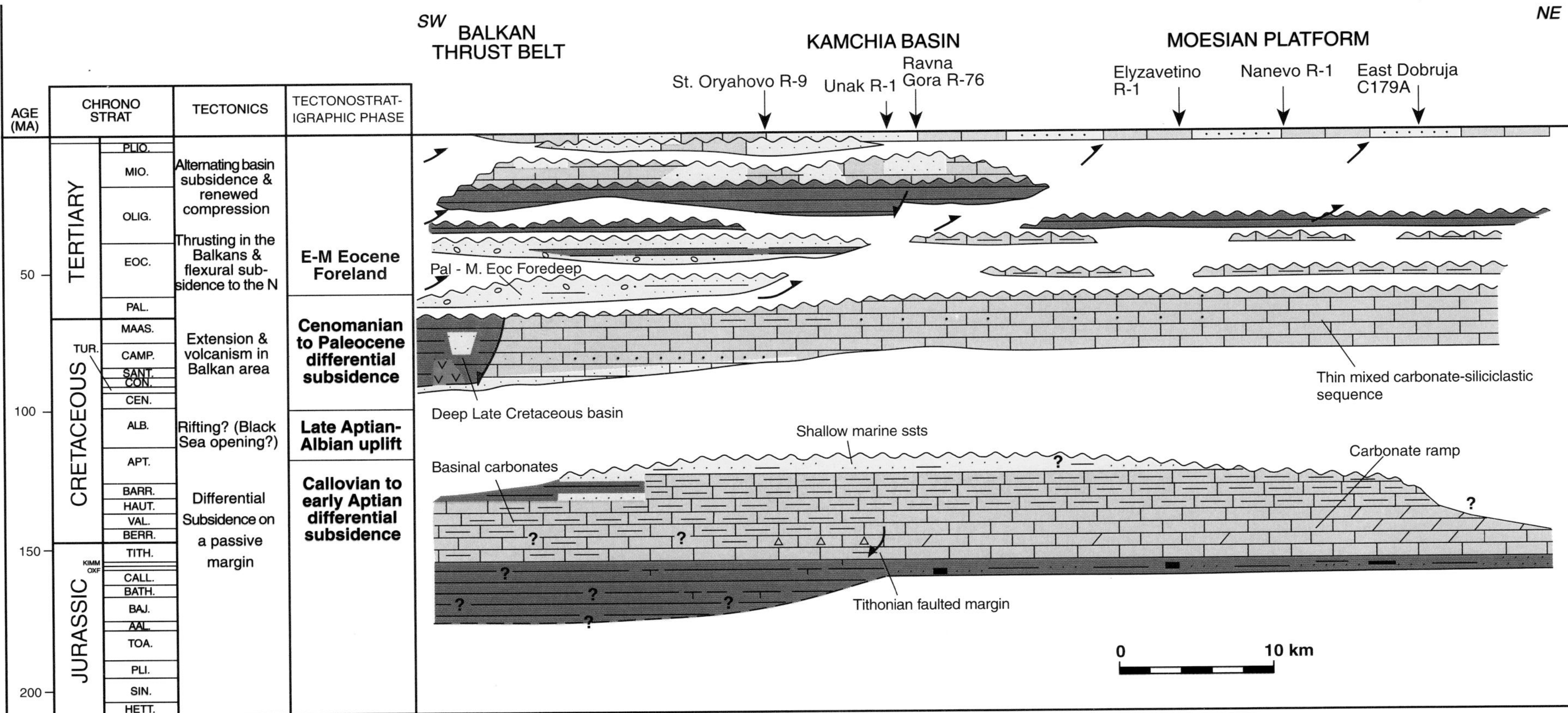

Figure 17. Chronostratigraphy of the Balkan thrust belt and Moesian Platform in eastern Bulgaria.

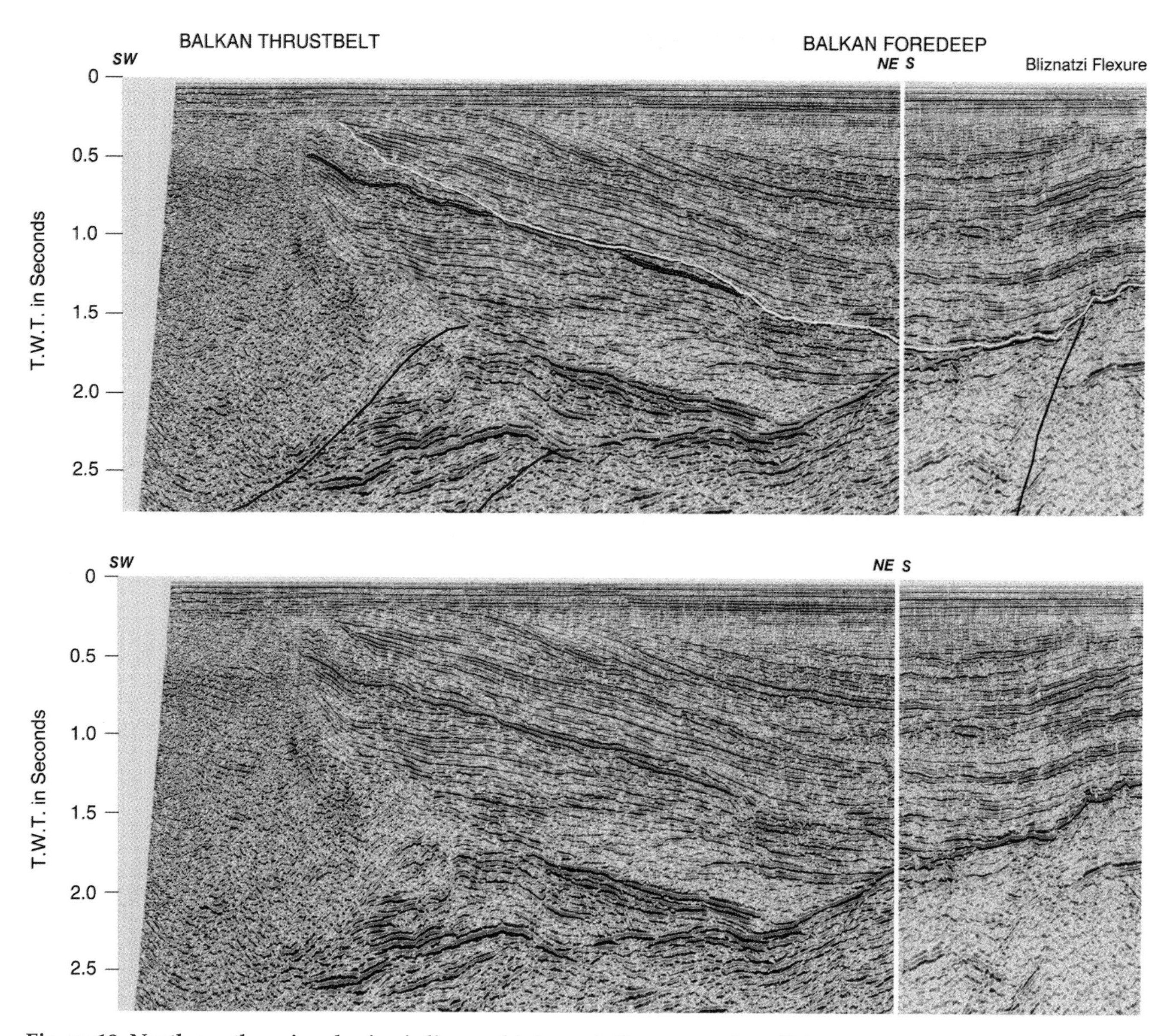

Figure 18. North-south regional seismic line and interpretation across the offshore Moesian Platform and Balkan foredeep, Bulgarian Black Sea. See Figure 2 for location. T.W.T. = two-way traveltime.

this period, eastern Bulgaria was divided into a region dominated by shallow-marine carbonate sedimentation in the north and areas of deeper water sedimentation to the south and southeast (Figure 20A). The northern region is characterized by a number of lithofacies representative of subtidal ramp and peritidal environments, as described above. Farther south, the Nanevo R-1, Staro Oryahovo R-9, and Ravna Gora R-76 wells are dominated by homogeneous micrite-rich lithologies containing largely pelagic organisms. These facies were deposited in a low-energy, deeper marine setting, and contain associated debris flows derived from an upper-slope environment (Figure 20A). The limestone breccia facies deposited in the Unak R-1 region suggests deposition in a deep-marine slope environment, influenced by faulting.

The lithofacies, with the offshore seismic data (Figure 18), suggest that, over most of the area, the platform had a ramp morphology; a transition is recorded from shallow-marine facies through to deeper ramp and basinal facies from north to south. The overall thickening of the Jurassic to the south is consistent with that of a south-facing passive margin (Tari et al., this volume; Robinson and Kerusov, this volume).

Late Hauterivian to Early Aptian Phase

There is little published data on the mid-Cretaceous in eastern Bulgaria. Although rocks of this age cover a considerable area on the geological map, they often consist of marly lithologies, and exposures are rare (Cheshitev et al., 1989; Milanova and Cheshitev, 1989). Similarly, the mid-Cretaceous is rarely encountered in the subsurface; there is little data on this interval in the wells examined in eastern Bulgaria as part of this study.

In the central study area (e.g., at outcrop localities 1 and 2; Figure 2), Late Jurassic to Valanginian shallow-water limestones are overlain by Hauterivian marls,

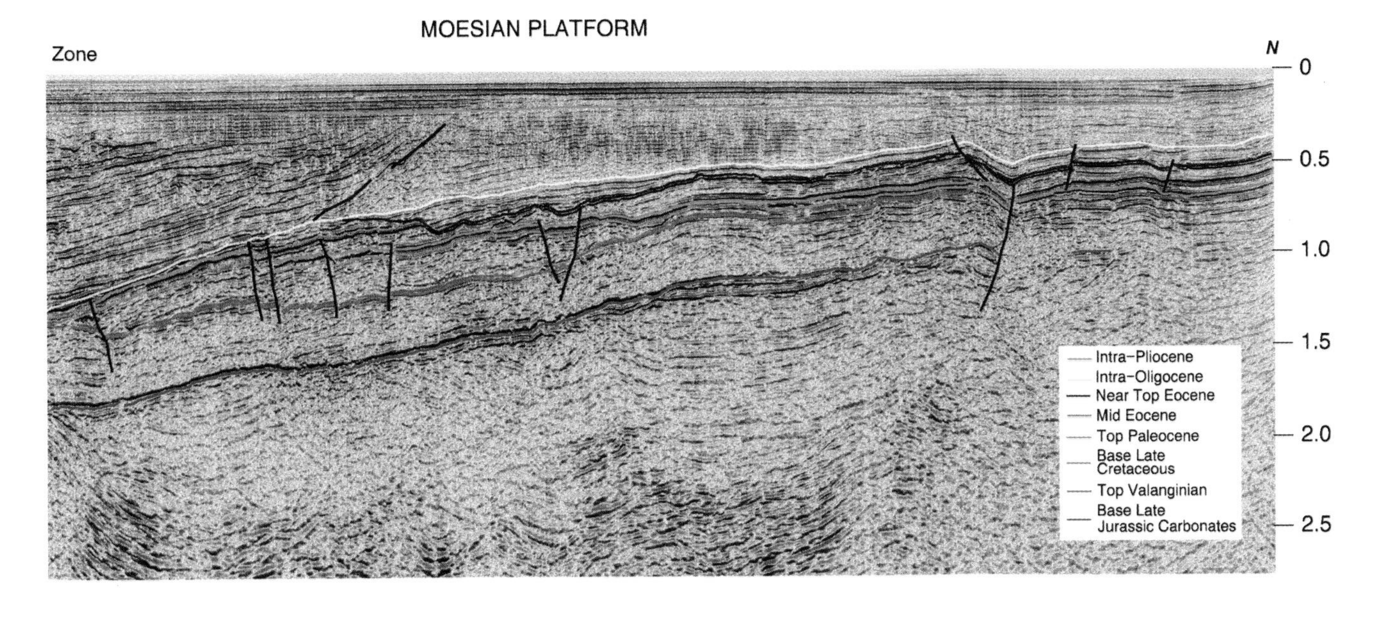

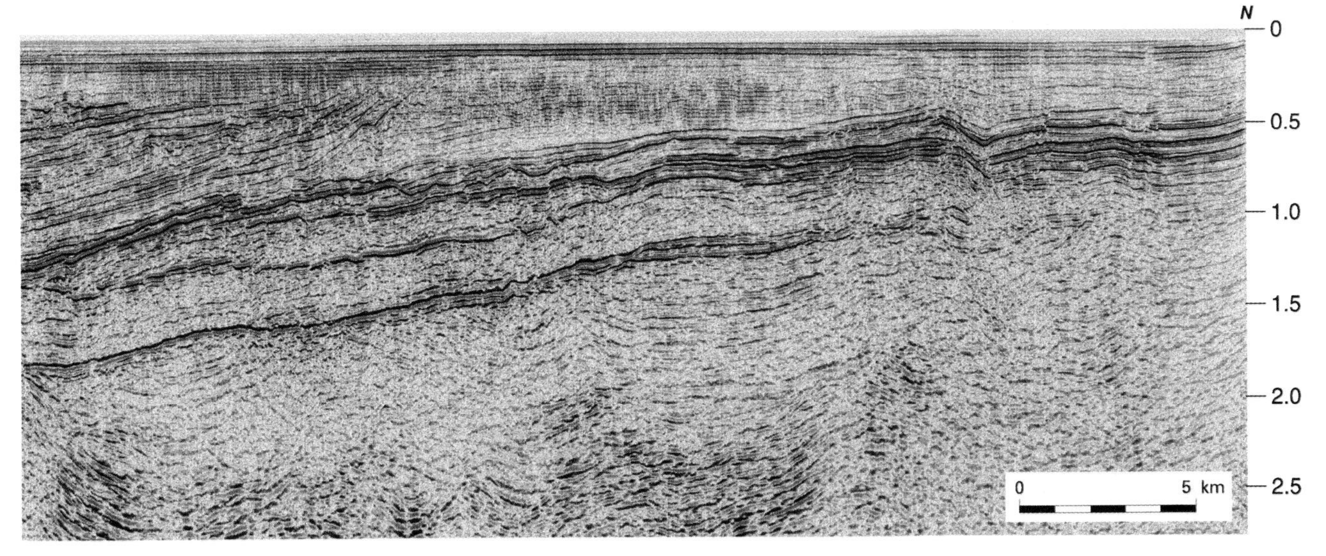

implying a flooding event (Figure 20B). Offshore, the top Valanginian horizon is marked by a prominent seismic event (Figure 18). Farther south, in the more basinal areas, there is little lithological change across this boundary, with fine-grained limestones characterizing both the Valanginian and Hauterivian sections.

The Aptian facies observed in the Staro Oryahovo R-9 well were deposited in a shallow-marine environment; this interval, therefore, indicates a shallowing from the Hauterivian rocks below (Figure 21A). The shallow-marine sedimentary succession recorded in this central part of the Kamchia Basin suggests that the basin was filling by Aptian times. However, the marls deposited in the area north of Devnia suggest that not all the area was subjected to neritic sedimentation. In the absence of other evidence that could be used to determine the paleobathymetry of these deposits, these marls are interpreted to have been deposited in a shallow shelfal area with open-marine circulation (Figure 21A). Stoikova (1983) recorded rich ammonite fauna from other Aptian successions in the area. A shallow-marine platform interpretation is consistent with that of Nachev (1992), who suggests the region was an epicontinental sea during the Aptian.

Late Aptian–Albian Tilting, Nondeposition, and Erosion

Outcrops of Albian age have not been recorded in the subsurface in the Kamchia Basin (Dachev et al., 1988; Marinov, 1994) or on the eastern Moesian Platform (Cheshitev et al., 1989; Milanova and Cheshitev, 1989). Bokov and Ognyanov (1991) indicate the late Aptian and Albian stages to be a period of erosion and/or nondeposition; they also suggest eastern Bulgaria was subaerially exposed in the Albian, even

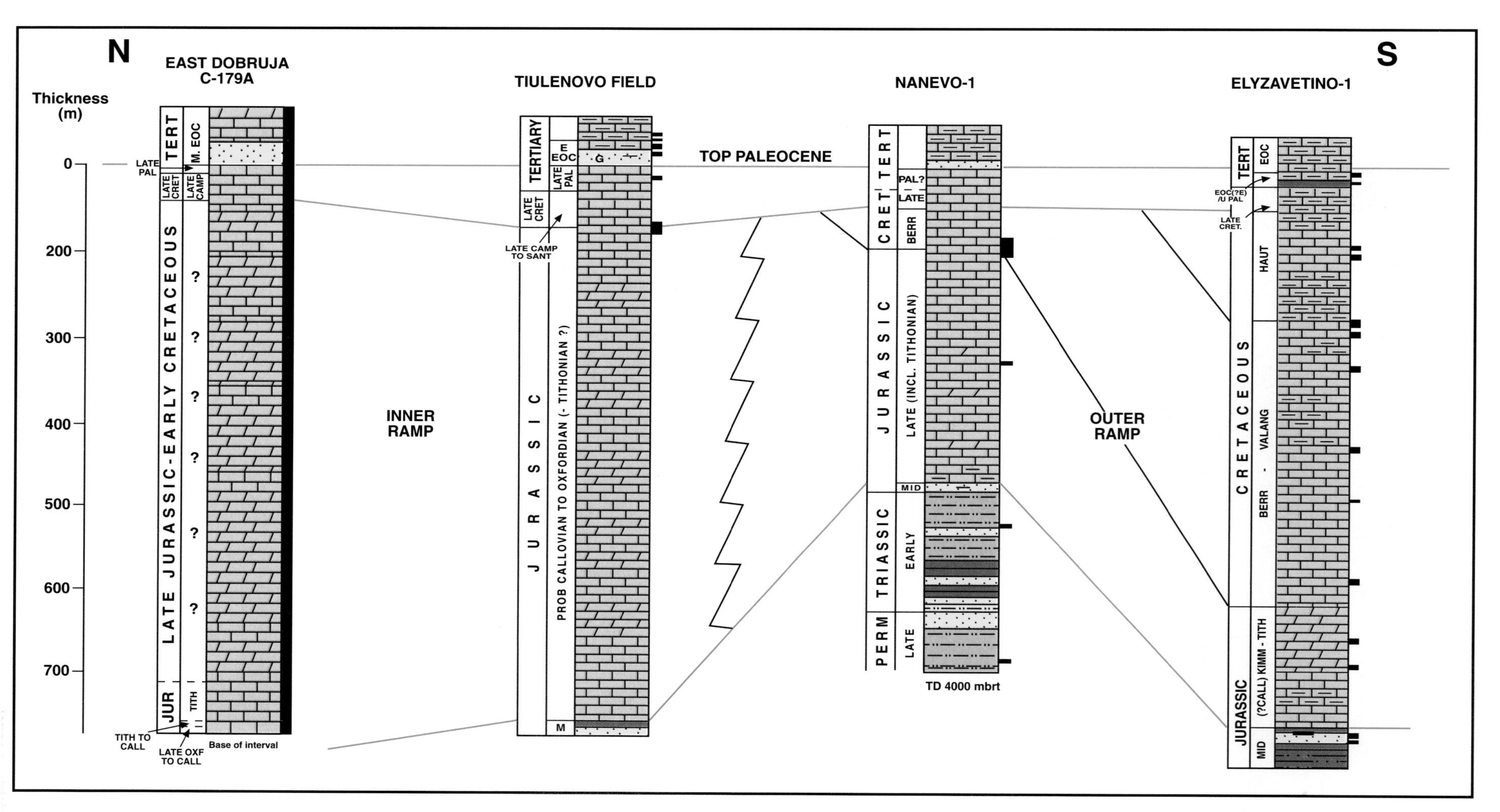

Figure 19. Correlation between East Dobruja C-179A, Tiulenovo field, Nanevo-1, and Elyzavetino-1.

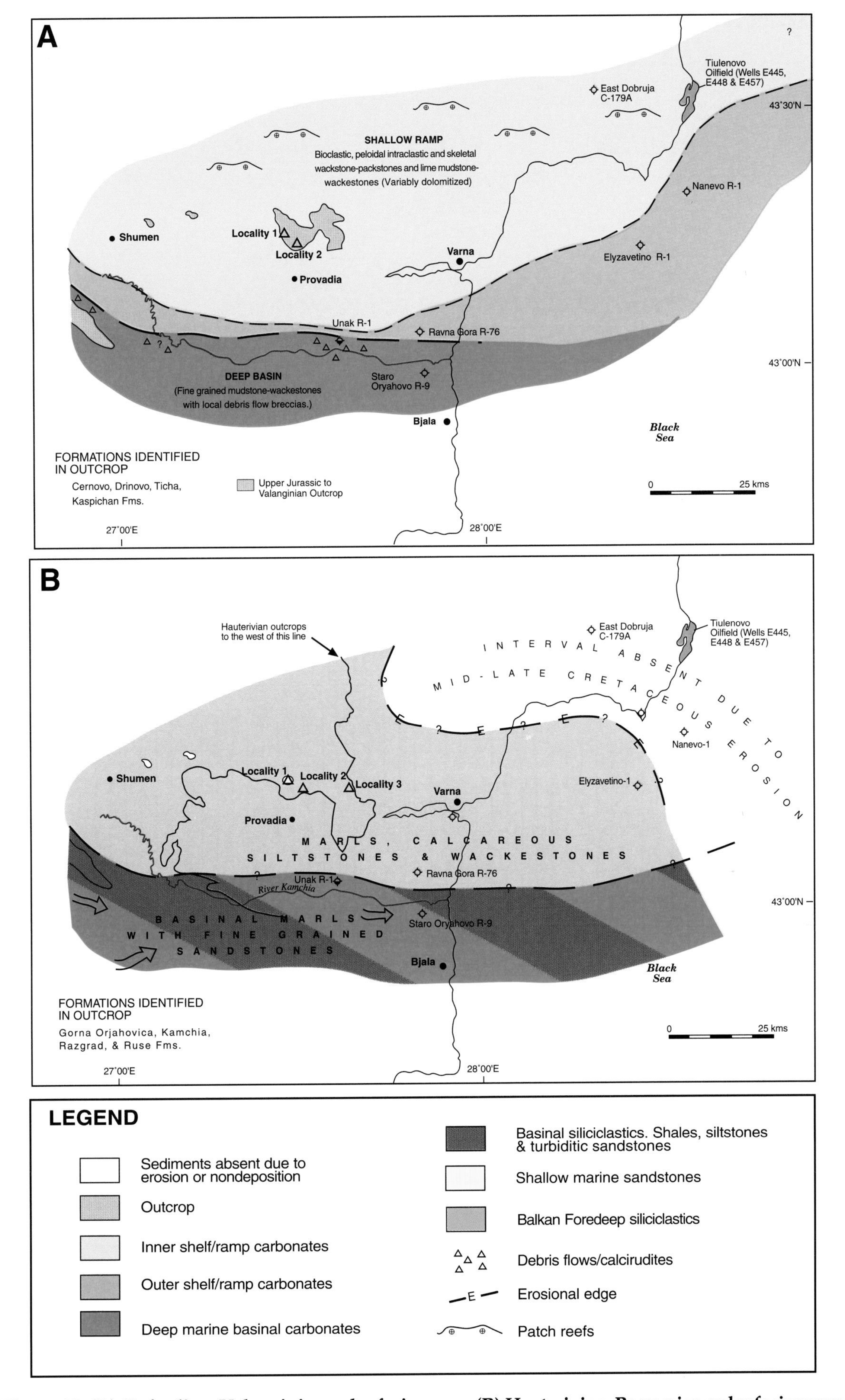

Figure 20. (A) Oxfordian–Valanginian paleofacies map. (B) Hauterivian–Barremian paleofacies map.

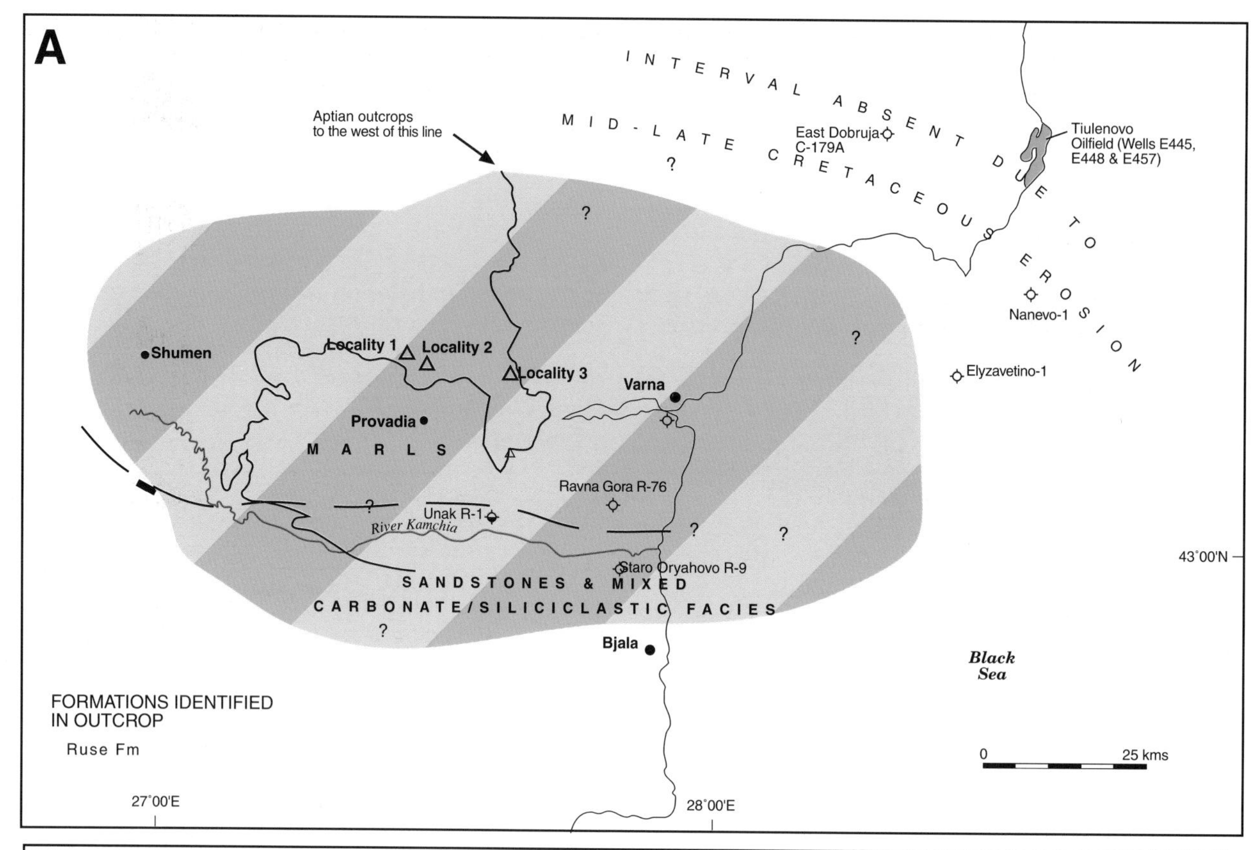

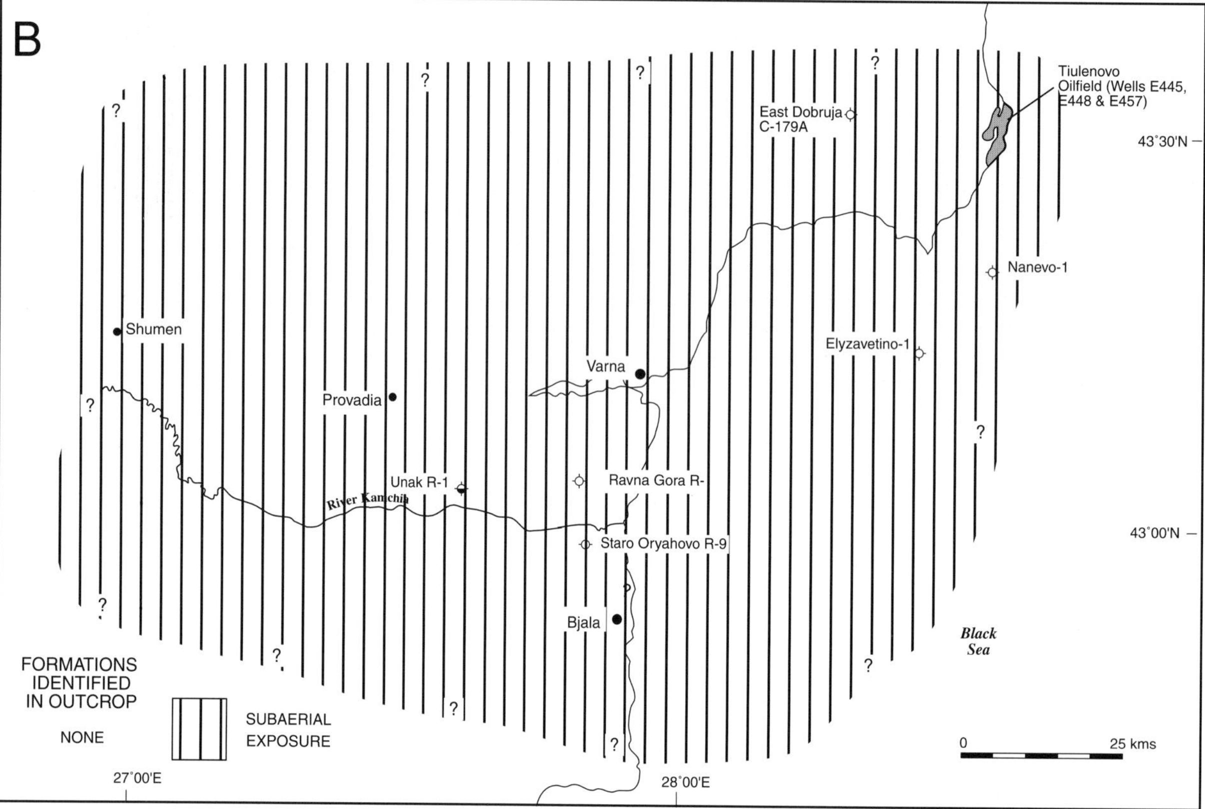

Figure 21. (A) Early Aptian paleofacies map. (B) Late Aptian–Albian paleofacies map. See Figure 20 for legend.

though siliciclastic deposition was occurring in the Lom Depression 250 km to the west (Vuchev et al., 1991).

Our own outcrop studies, together with offshore seismic data, confirm a period of uplift, tilting, and erosion in northeast Bulgaria and the adjacent Black Sea during the late? Aptian to Albian (Figures 18, 21B). This led to a regional unconformity and increased magnitude of erosion to the east-northeast, which we speculate may be due to uplift on the shoulders of a rift as the Western Black Sea began to open. As a result, Upper Jurassic–mid-Cretaceous strata subcrop the Upper Cretaceous progressively to the east across northeast Bulgaria and into the Black Sea. In particular, the Callovian–Oxfordian to Valanginian carbonates were progressively eroded to the northeast, and were subsequently onlapped by the regional Late Cretaceous transgression. Hence, carbonates of Valanginian are absent in the East Dobruja C179A, Tiulenovo, and Nanevo-1 wells, where only Callovian–Oxfordian carbonates subcrop Campanian limestones. Farther to the west and south, a full Upper Jurassic to Valanginian sequence is preserved, overlain by Hauterivian to Aptian sediments (e.g., at outcrop locality 3); even here, however, Albian sedimentary rocks are missing.

Sedimentary rocks of Aptian to Albian, interpreted as syn- to early postrift units, have been described from the Western and Central Pontides (Görür, 1988; Robinson et al., 1996; Görür et al., this volume) and the Gulf of Odessa and Crimea (Robinson and Kerusov, this volume). In both regions, Aptian to Albian shallow-marine and deep-marine sedimentary rocks show rapid thickness and facies changes approaching originally extensional faults, which are interpreted as synrift assemblages. Data collected from eastern Bulgaria and the Bulgarian Black Sea suggest that during the Albian, and possibly during the late Aptian, this region became subaerially exposed. The mid-Cretaceous elevation of the region above sea level may be interpreted as rift-flank uplift, which was a local response to a Western Black Sea rift event. Rift flanks may have a height of 2–3 km, and prolonged erosion at the crest of the uplifted shoulder provides a mechanism to expose basement rocks ≤5 km depth (e.g., Braun and Beaumont, 1989; van der Beek et al., 1994). This may explain the continental basement clasts that provided an important siliciclastic source to Aptian shallow-marine deposits in an otherwise carbonate-dominated basin.

Regional uplift of eastern Bulgaria led to exposure and erosion of the Callovian–Oxfordian to Valanginian ramp carbonates. Karstification and associated development of secondary porosity related to this period of exposure were important controls on the development of reservoirs in the Tiulenovo field on the northeast coast of Bulgaria (Vuchev et al., 1994).

Cenomanian to Paleocene Differential Subsidence and shallow-marine Sedimentation

There is good evidence for differential subsidence during the Late Cretaceous to Paleogene. The successions in the northern part of the study area form relatively thin, shallow-marine and glauconite-rich successions. Upper Cretaceous to Paleocene rocks of the Moesian Platform dip gently east beneath Eocene and younger sediments. To the south, however, beneath the Kamchia Basin, the section can reach several hundred meters in thickness (e.g., in Staro Oryahovo R-9); this may represent differential subsidence and infill of the southern part of the Moesian Platform developing during Late Cretaceous to Paleocene structuring. This interval lies between the Base Late Cretaceous and Top Paleocene seismic events on regional seismic data (Figure 18).

A transgressive relationship between Cenomanian deposits and those of the Lower Cretaceous is documented by Jolkicev (1989), who describes coarse sandstones and conglomerates of Cenomanian in eastern Bulgaria. Jolkicev interprets these often coarse siliciclastic-rich rocks to represent flooding after Albian subaerial exposure. A marine transgression is supported by the shallow-marine mixed siliciclastic/carbonate facies tentatively assigned a Cenomanian from the Staro Oryahovo R-9 well (Figure 22A). The Cenomanian transgression is also recorded from southeast Bulgaria in the Balkan Mountains and the Rhodope Massif, where Upper Cretaceous sedimentary rocks consist of nonmarine to marginal-marine conglomerates, sandstones, shales, and coals (Nachev and Dimitrova, 1996). The coarse clastic content compared with the Moesian Platform succession suggests a sediment source from the south, most likely the Rhodope Massif itself.

Turonian calcisiltite-calcarenitic sediments were identified in Locality 3 and are characterized by both carbonate and siliciclastic components deposited in shallow-marine outer-shelf environments. Jolkicev (1989) describes Turonian sequences in eastern Bulgaria as comprising "sandy, slightly silty and chalk-like limestones." Similar sedimentary rocks are recorded by Jolkicev (1989) in the Coniacian and Santonian, although glauconite becomes an increasingly important component in the facies. To the south of the study area during this time, in the Srednogorie Zone and in the area now occupied by the Balkan Mountains, thick sequences of marginal basin turbidites and volcanics were being emplaced (Figure 17).

The lack of Cenomanian to Santonian sediments in the northeastern part of the area, particularly the offshore, may be due to intra-Late Cretaceous erosion, but may also reflect continuing exposure of this region after the Albian uplift and tilting. During the Campanian, deposition extended onto this area (Figure 22B) and is recorded in the Tiulenovo and East Dobruja C-179A wells. The high proportion of planktonic foraminifera and rich nannofossil assemblages in Campanian strata confirm a flooding of the former platform, with widespread deposition of lime mudstone-wackestones in a subwave-base setting. At this time, the Balkan fold belt was beginning to develop to the south, and the thin succession on the Moesian Platform passed southward in southeast Bulgaria into a thick deep-water clastic succession, the Emine flysch, deposited in the early Balkan foredeep (Figure 22B).

Facies distributions in the Moesian Platform suggest the region had a shelf morphology for much of the late Cretaceous and Paleocene. Lithofacies changes

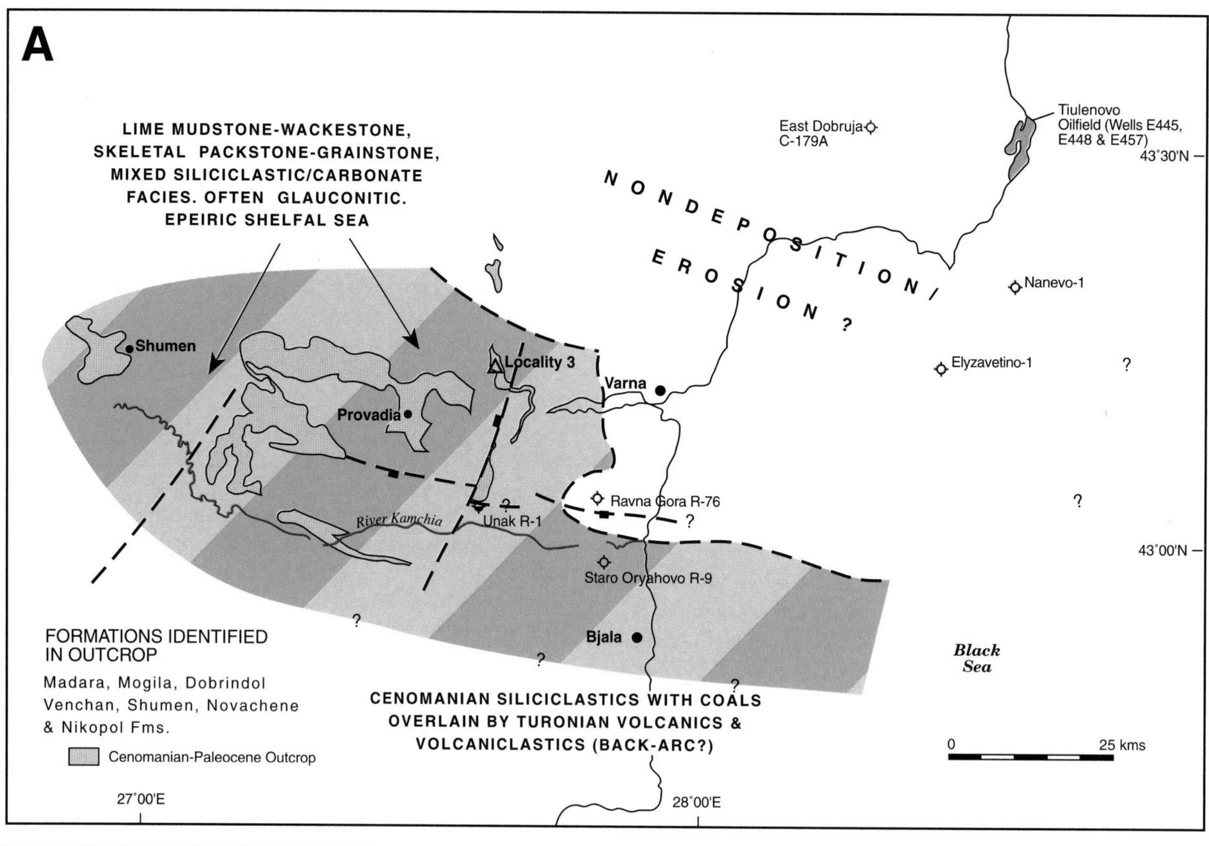

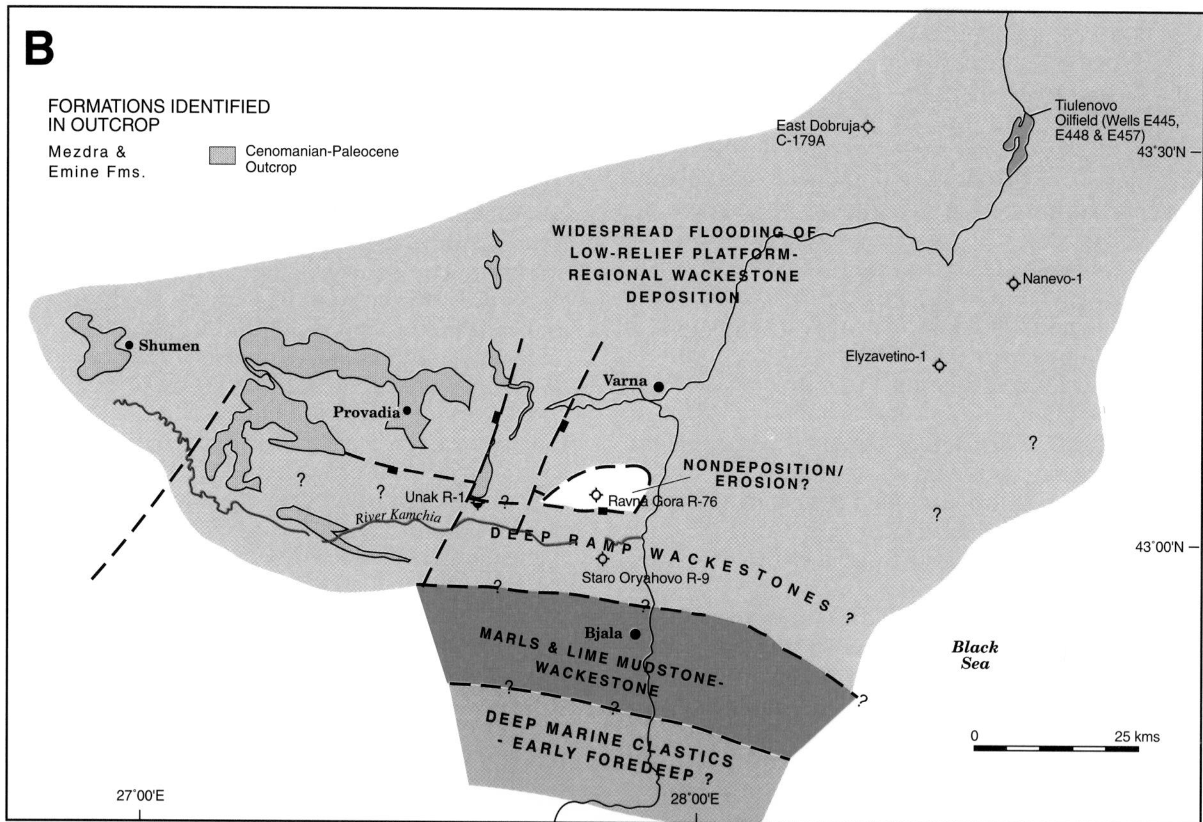

Figure 22. (A) Cenomanian–early Campanian paleofacies map. (B) Late Campanian paleofacies map. See Figure 20 for legend.

reflect deposition on a platform, with local carbonate buildups dominated by shallow-marine skeletal packstone-grainstones with variable amounts of siliciclastic detritus, which pass laterally into lime mudstone-wackestones deposited in subwave-base settings. This pattern suggests deposition occurred on an essentially flat-topped shelf. Shallow-water calcarenites were deposited as far south as the Ravna Gora R-76 well; this indicates that the southern margin of the shelf, at least in the Paleocene, was marked by skeletal packstones-grainstones in this area. Lime mudstones, observed in the Staro Oryahovo R-9 well, were deposited to the south of this region, where they accumulated in deeper water off the shelf edge in the Kamchia Basin. The shelfal pattern was inherited from Hauterivian to early Aptian infilling of the basin and the subsequent loss of the southward-dipping ramp.

Nannofossil assemblages in the Campanian platform succession have affinity with colder water, high-latitude (boreal) groups (K. Cooper, 1995, personal communication). A moderately temperate marine system in northeast Bulgaria in the Late Cretaceous to Paleocene is supported by the general paucity of coral material and increase in echinoderm/coralline algae detritus in the facies. Ooids and pellets—which tend to form in areas where the mean temperatures exceed 18°C, evaporation rates exceed precipitation, and seawater salinity is slightly raised (Lees and Buller, 1972 ; Lees, 1975)—are generally absent. The temperate nature of the waters also explains the general absence of corals in the Late Cretaceous succession.

The shallow-marine environment that developed on the Moesian Platform during the Late Cretaceous persisted into the Paleocene, with skeletal packstones and grainstones deposited on structural highs, such as the Ravna Gora area, while lime mudstone-wackestones continued to be deposited in areas below wave base. In the late Paleocene, shallow-marine coralline algal buildups developed in places; for example, in well Ravna Gora R-76 (Figure 23A). Similar algal-rich deposits are recorded in outcrop in northeast Bulgaria (Komarevo or Gunak Formation) by Aladjova-Hrisceva (1991) and Sinclair et al. (this volume).

Early to Middle Eocene Foreland

Eocene sediments rest with varying degrees of unconformity on Paleocene rocks. Regional seismic data suggest this hiatus may reflect foreland uplift of the Moesian Platform ahead of the Balkan foldbelt (Figure 18). Subsequently, thick Eocene clastic sediments were deposited to the south in the Balkan foredeep, while a thinner, condensed sequence was deposited on the platform.

To the west of Varna, the platformal Eocene consists of lower Eocene sediments of the Beloslav, Dikilitash, and Aladan formations (Aladjova-Hrisceva, 1990, 1991), consisting of sandstones with nummulitic foraminifera and nummulitic foraminiferal packstones deposited on a shallow-marine platform (Figure 23B). These rocks have also been described by Sinclair et al. (this volume), who present offshore data from the Black Sea that they interpret as indicating accelerated tectonic subsidence during the middle and late Eocene. A low-energy subwave-base environment is suggested by the presence of Eocene marls in the Nanevo R-1 well (Dachev et al., 1988), and Sinclair et al. (this volume) suggest the deposition of the middle Eocene Avren Marls is linked to the onset of flexural subsidence associated with thrust-loading to the south. To the northeast, the Paleocene–lower Eocene present in the Tiulenovo field cores record a transition from a basal sandy, glauconitic limestone, through nummulitic packstones, into lime mudstones and wackestones with a high content of planktonic foraminifera. Some facies contain abundant glauconite, and this component, coupled with the increased proportions of siliciclastic detritus in specific intervals, implies periods of condensed sedimentation over a broad platform area. These rocks are overlain by middle Eocene marls, which suggest regional subsidence of the southern part of the eastern Moesian Platform at this time.

CONCLUSIONS

During the late Jurassic to Valanginian, eastern Bulgaria and the Bulgarian Black Sea can be divided into areas dominated by shallow-marine carbonate sedimentation and regions where sedimentation was of deep-marine character. The boundary between these facies belts is a broadly east-west line south of Shumen-Varna, and becomes more northeast-southwest offshore in the Black Sea. Seismic studies suggest the platform had a ramp morphology and a gradational transition of facies from shallow-marine facies, although deeper ramp to basinal facies are recorded. The interval in the Elyzavetino R-1 well is transitional between the shallow-marine ramp of the northern region and the deeper marine setting of the south. Limited reworking of shelfal material into the basin is recognized in the region, even though some intraformational calcirudites and slumping suggest that the ramp may have been distally steepened in places. Local faulting of the ramp allowed carbonate breccias derived from a shallow-marine area to be reworked into the basin, but limited exposure and well control do not constrain the orientation of these faults.

There was a regional input of generally fine grained siliciclastic detritus during the Hauterivian phase, resulting in deposition of marls and calcareous siltstones, with gravity-flow sandstones in the more basinal areas. Limited data suggest this siliciclastic material was introduced from the west or south. The ramp morphology of the Upper Jurassic–Hauterivian was lost by the mid-Cretaceous, culminating in the Aptian with deposition of sandstones and marls deposited in a shallow epicontinental sea.

Upper Cretaceous–Paleocene facies include a variety of carbonates and mixed siliciclastic/carbonates. Pelagic, shallow-marine, and siliciclastic components were mixed by shallow-marine hydrodynamic processes and bioturbation. Deposition of laterally extensive lime mudstones during the Campanian

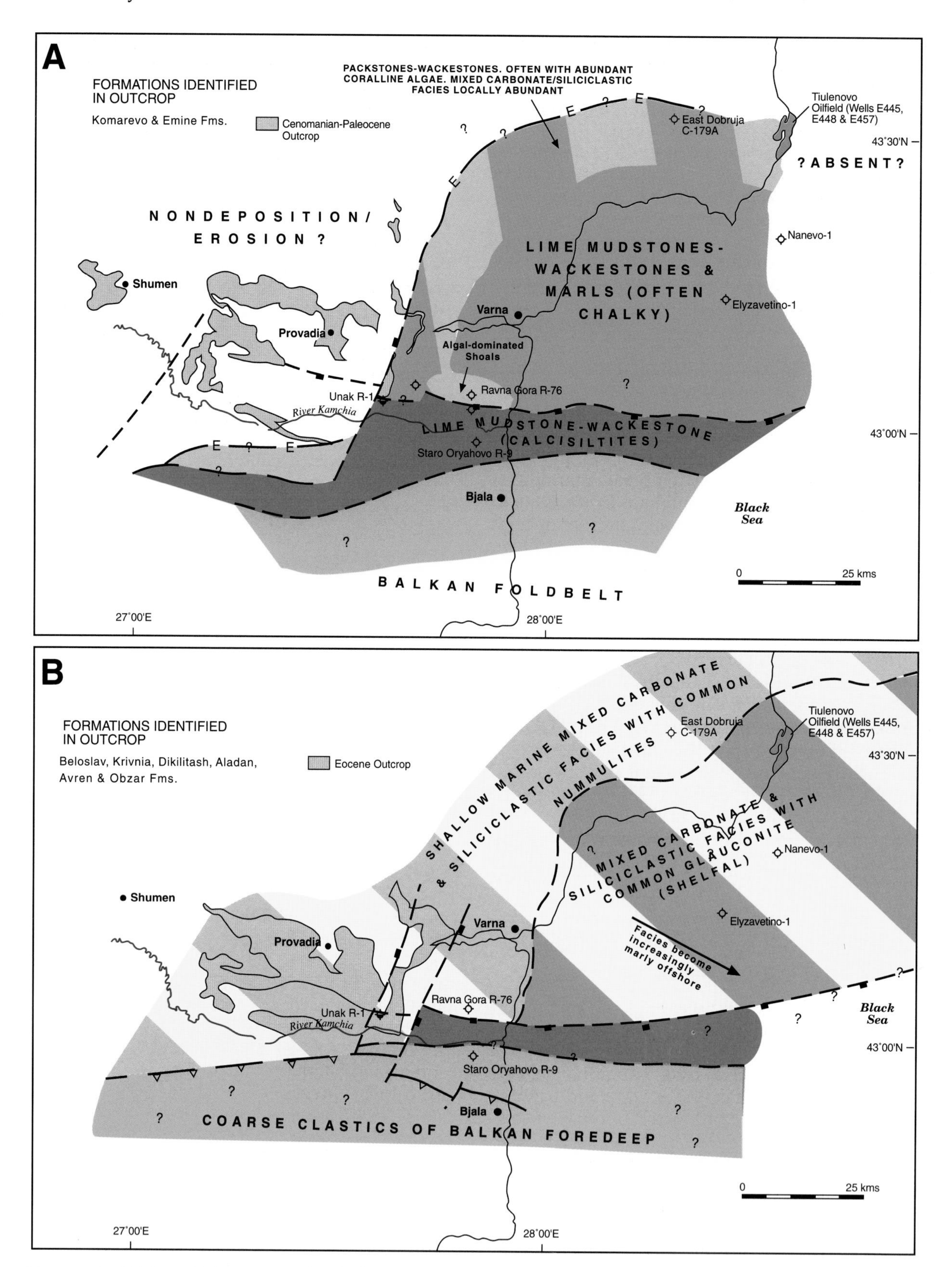

Figure 23. (A) Late Paleocene paleofacies map. (B) Eocene paleofacies map. See Figure 20 for legend.

suggests widespread flooding of the northern platform region. Intensely bioturbated intervals, abundant glauconite, and increased proportions of siliciclastic detritus in specific intervals imply periods of condensed sedimentation over a broad, flat-topped platform area. The paucity of corals and domination by echinoderm and calcareous red algae detritus probably results from deposition within a temperate marine basin. This is supported by Campanian nannofossil assemblages, which have affinity with high-latitude, boreal groups. In the Paleocene, shallow-marine packstone-grainstones accumulated in the Ravna Gora region; this facies marked the shelf edge, to the south of which lime mudstones-wackestones accumulated in the Kamchia Basin. These calcarenites were succeeded in late Paleocene time by shallow-marine coralline algal buildups, which are correlatable with similar algal-rich deposits recorded in outcrop in northeast Bulgaria. Early Eocene facies include sandstones and packstones, often containing abundant nummulitic foraminifera.

ACKNOWLEDGMENTS

We thank Enterprise Oil Plc, Texaco Exploration Offshore Bulgaria Ltd., OMV Aktiengesellschaft, and the Committee of Geology and Mineral Resources of the Republic of Bulgaria for giving their permission to publish this paper. The views expressed in this work are those of the authors. Kevin Cooper (TimeTrax Ltd.) and Jackie Burnett (University College, London) are thanked for the nannofossil biostratigraphy; Fred Banner and Marcelle Fadel for their microfossil identification; Alit Ascaria (Birkbeck College, London) and Ivan Terziev (Petroleum Geologist, Geological Prospecting & Planning, Varna) for their help in the core store at Preselci and Balchik. Angie Harbury and Rebecca Buckley improved the manuscript at an early stage. We are grateful to Andrew Robinson and Hugh Sinclair for their helpful and thorough reviews.

REFERENCES CITED

Aladjova-Hrisceva, K.I., 1990, Stratigraphy of the lower Eocene sediments in part of the plateaus in northeast Bulgaria: Review of the Bulgarian Geological Society, v. LI, part 1, p. 21–31.

Aladjova-Hrisceva, K.I., 1991, Stratigraphic subdivision and correlation of Palaeogenic deposits in northeast Bulgaria: Geologica Balcanica, v. 21, no. 2, p. 12–38.

Bokov, P., and R. Ognyanov, 1991, Hydrocarbon prospects in Bulgaria, *in* Hydrocarbon prospects in Eastern Europe and USSR: Occasional Publications, University of South Carolina, Earth Sciences and Resources Institute (ESRI): New Series, v. 7, no. 1, p. 33–51.

Braun, J., and C. Beaumont, 1989, A physical explanation of the relation between flank uplifts and the breakup unconformity at rifted continental margins: Geology, v. 17, p. 760–764.

Burchfiel, B.C., 1980, Eastern European Alpine system and the Carpathian orocline as an example of collision tectonics: Tectonophysics, v. 63, p. 31–61.

Cheshitev, G., V. Milanova, N. Popov, and E. Kojumdgieva, 1989, Varna sheet, geological maps of Bulgaria: Sofia, Committee of Geology, scale 1:100,000.

Cook, H.E., and P. Enos, 1977, Deep-water carbonate environments: SEPM Special Publication 25, 336 p.

Dachev, C., V. Stanev, and P. Bokov, 1988, Structure of the Bulgarian Black Sea area: Bollettino di Geofisica Teorica ed Applicata, no. 117–118, p. 79–107.

Doglioni, C., C. Busatta, G. Bolis, L. Mariaini, and M. Zanells, 1996, Structural evolution of the eastern Balkans (Bulgaria): Marine and Petroleum Geology, v. 13, no. 2, p. 225–251.

Emery, M., and G. Georgiev, 1993, Tectonic evolution and hydrocarbon potential of the southern Moesian Platform and Balkan-Forebalkan regions of northern Bulgaria: AAPG Bulletin, v. 77, p. 1620–1621.

Ghose, B.K. 1977, Paleoecology of the Cenozoic reefal foraminifers and algae—a brief review: Palaeogeography, Palaeoclimatology, Palaeoecology, v. 22, p. 234–256.

Görür, N., 1988, Timing of opening of the Black Sea Basin: Tectonophysics, v. 147, p. 247–262.

Görür, N., this volume, Cretaceous syn- to postrift sedimentation of the southern continental margin of the Western Black Sea Basin, *in* A.G. Robinson, ed., Regional and petroleum geology of the Black Sea and surrounding regions: AAPG Memoir 68, p. 227–240.

Jolkicev, N.A., 1988, Lithostratigraphical units, related to Upper Cretaceous in the eastern parts of the Moesian Plate: Review of the Bulgarian Geological Society, v. 49, no. 1, p. 11–25.

Jolkicev, N.A., 1989, Stratigraphy of the epicontinental type Upper Cretaceous in Bulgaria: Sofia University, "St. Kliment Ohridski" Press, 184 p.

Juranov, S., et al., 1993, Glossary of the formal lithostratigraphic units in Bulgaria (1882–1992), *in* Y. Tenchov, ed.: Sofia, Bulgarian Academy of Sciences, 397 p.

Kendall, C.G.St.C., and P.A.D.E. Skipworth, 1969, Holocene shallow-water carbonate and evaporite sediments of Khor al Bazam, Abu Dhabi, southwest Persian Gulf: AAPG Bulletin, v. 53, p. 841–869.

Kinsman, D.J.J., 1964, The recent carbonate sediments near Halat el Bahrani, Trucial Coast, Persian Gulf, *in* Deltaic and shallow marine deposits—developments in sedimentology: New York, Elsevier, v. 1, p. 185–192.

Lees, A., 1975, Possible influences of salinity and temperature on modern shelf carbonate sedimentation: Marine Geology, v. 19, p. 159–198.

Lees, A., and A.T. Buller, 1972, Modern temperate water and warm water shelf carbonates contrasted: Marine Geology, v. 13, p. 1767–1773.

Logan, B.W., P. Hoffman, and C.D. Gebelein, 1974, Algal structures, cryptalgal fabrics, and structures, Hamblin Pool, Western Australia, *in* B.W. Logan, J.F. Read, G.M. Hagen, P. Hoffman, R.G. Brown, P.J. Woods, and C.D. Gebelein, eds., Evolution and diagenesis of Quaternary carbonate sequences, Shark Bay, Western Australia: AAPG Memoir 22, p. 140–194.

Marinov, E.G., 1994, Geology and hydrocarbon potential of zones with thrust-fault structure: An example of the southern board of Lower Kamchia foredeep: Unpublished Ph.D. thesis, Sofia University, "St. Kliment Ohridski."

Milanova, V., and G. Cheshitev, 1989, Provadia sheet, geological maps of Bulgaria: Sofia, Committee of Geology, scale 1:100,000.

Nachev, I., 1992, Callovian–Albian palaeodynamics of Bulgaria: Review of the Bulgarian Geological Society, v. LIII, part 3, p. 67–77.
Nachev, I., and E. Dimitrova, 1996, Upper Cretaceous stratigraphy of the eastern Balkan Mountains: Geologica Balcanica, v. 25, p. 43–74.
Okay, A.I., A.M.C. Şengör, and N. Görür, 1994, Kinematic history of the opening of the Black Sea and its effect on the surrounding regions: Geology, v. 22, p. 267–270.
Purser, B.H., 1973, The Persian Gulf—Holocene carbonate sedimentation and diagenesis in a shallow-water epicontinental sea: Berlin, Springer-Verlag, 471 p.
Robinson, A.G., G. Spadini, S. Cloetingh, and J. Rudat, 1995a, Stratigraphic evolution of the Black Sea: inferences from basin modelling: Marine and Petroleum Geology, v. 12, no. 8, p. 821–835.
Robinson, A.G., C.J. Banks, M.M. Rutherford, and J.P.P. Hirst, 1995b, Stratigraphic and structural development of the Eastern Pontides, Turkey: Journal of the Geological Society, London, v. 152, p. 861–872.
Robinson, A.G., J.H. Rudat, C.J. Banks, and R.L.F. Wiles, 1996, Petroleum geology of the Black Sea: Marine and Petroleum Geology, v. 13, no. 2, p. 195–223.
Robinson, A.G., and E. Kerusov, this volume, Stratigraphic and structural development of the Gulf of Odessa, Ukrainian Black Sea: implications for petroleum exploration, *in* A.G. Robinson, ed., Regional and petroleum geology of the Black Sea and surrounding regions: AAPG Memoir 68, p. 369–380.
Sapunov, I., and P. Tchoumatchenko, 1987, Geological development of north-east Bulgaria during the Jurassic: Paleontology, Stratigraphy, and Lithology, v. 24, p. 3–56.
Sinclair, H.D., S.G. Juranov, G. Georgiev, N.P. Mountney, and P. Byrne, this volume, Timing and rates of Balkan shortening and basin subsidence: the sedimentological and stratigraphic record of events, *in* A.G. Robinson, ed., Regional and petroleum geology of the Black Sea and surrounding regions: AAPG Memoir 68, p. 91–114.
Stoikova, K., 1983, Ammonites from the Aptian stage in northeast Bulgaria: Review of the Bulgarian Geological Society, v. XLIV, part 1, p. 77–90.
Tari, G., O. Dicea, J. Faulkerson, G. Georgiev, S. Popov, M. Stefanescu, and G. Weir, this volume, Cimmerian and Alpine stratigraphy and structural evolution of the Moesian Platform (Romania/Bulgaria), *in* A.G. Robinson, ed., Regional and petroleum geology of the Black Sea and surrounding regions: AAPG Memoir 68, p. 63–90.
Tucker, M.E., and V.P. Wright, 1990, Carbonate sedimentology: Oxford, Blackwell, 482 p.
van der Beek, P.A., S. Cloetingh, and P. Andriessen, 1994, Mechanisms of extensional basin formation and vertical motions at rift flanks: constraints from tectonic modeling and fission track thermochronology: Earth and Planetary Science Letters, v. 121, p. 317–330.
Vuchev, V., P. Bokov, B. Monov, A. Atanasov, R. Ognyanov, and D. Tochkov, 1994, Geologic structure, petroleum exploration development and hydrocarbon potential of Bulgaria, *in* B. Popescu, ed., Hydrocarbons of Eastern Central Europe: Berlin, Springer-Verlag, p. 29–69.
Wilson, J.L., 1969, Microfacies ad sedimentary structures in "deeper water" lime mudstones: SEPM Special Publication 14, p. 4–19.
Wilson, J.L., 1975, Carbonate facies in geological history: New York, Springer-Verlag, 471 p.
Zonenshain, L.P., and X. Le Pichon, 1986, Deep basins of the Black Sea and Caspian Sea as remnants of Mesozoic back-arc basins: Tectonophysics, v. 123, p. 181–211.

APPENDIX 1: BIOSTRATIGRAPHIC AGE DETERMINATIONS

Upper Jurassic to Lower Cretaceous

The oldest basinal facies we have examined in the region contain the nannofossils *Ansulasphera helvetica* and *Stephanolithion bigotti bigotti*, indicating a Callovian age. This age is assigned to a wackestone from 1736 m depth in the Unak R-1 well. The deepest facies examined in the Staro Oryahovo R-9 well are from 3351 m depth and contain *Calcicalathina oblongata*, which has a stratigraphic range of Valanginian to early Barremian. A Hauterivian age is confirmed by the co-occurrence of *Conusphara mexicana mexicana* and *Nannoconus bucheri* in a sample from 3142.0 m, and an Aptian age is recorded for a sample from 2575 m depth by *Eprolithus floralis*, *Diazomatolithus lehmanii*, and *Nannoconus truitti*. Late Tithonian to early Berriasian ages are recorded from the Nanevo R-1 well. The late Tithonian age is suggested by the presence of the nannofossils *Nannoconus compressus*, *N. broennimannii*, *N. quadratus*, *Umbria granulosa*, and *Haquis ellipticus*. The early Berriasian age is confirmed by the occurrence of *Hexalithus noeliae*, *Polycostella senaria*, *Micrantholithus obtusus*, and *Rhagodiscus nebulosus* in samples from 562–550 m deep. An early Berriasian age is assigned to a sample from 728 m depth from the Elyzavetino R-1 well on the basis of a similar nannofossil assemblage. The lower age of the Tithonian to Hauterivian interval is, however, poorly defined in Elyzavetino R-1 as a result of dolomitization. This passes up in the Elyzavetino R-1 well into a thick Berriasian to late Hauterivian interval indicated by *Conusphara mexicana mexicana*, *Crusiellipsis cuvillieri*, *Zeugrhabdotus cooperi*, *Nannoconus broennimannii*, and *Calcicalathina oblongata*. Calpionellids are common in the interval from 728 to 733 m depth and include *Tintinnopsella* cf. *carpathica* and *Calpionellites darderi*, supporting a Tithonian to Valanginian age. Similar assemblages from samples obtained from the lower part of Ravna Gora R-76 (2011–2051 m) indicate a late Berriasian to Valanginian age.

A Valanginian age is assigned to the skeletal packstone-grainstone examined in field localities north of Devnia (Figure 2). The samples were examined for nannofossils and had very poor recovery of long-ranging species. This facies is dated by its stratigraphic position beneath Hauterivian marls, with rich nannofossil assemblages at Locality 2. The marls are assigned a Hauterivian age, probably early Hauterivian on the concurrent ranges of *Conusphaera rothii, Litharaphidites alatus magnus, Nannoconus bucheri,* and *Nannoconus cornuta*. A Valanginian age for these facies is also indicated by the Bulgarian geological map for the region (Milanova and Cheshitev, 1989).

The platform facies are less well constrained by biostratigraphic data, although samples from Tiulenovo wells E448 and E457 and East Dobruja C179A well confirm a Callovian to Tithonian age for depths between 341 and 395 m (Tiulenovo) and 1198 and 1246 m (C179A). Vuchev et al. (1994) assign a Berriasian to Valanginian age to the lower interval in the Tiulenovo well, and Bokov and Ognyanov (1991) suggest a Valanginian age for the limestones and dolomites in the Tiulenovo wells. Dolomitization hindered age determination of the interval between 620 and 1197 m in the C179A well, even though the upper boundary with upper Campanian wackestones is clearly observed by a facies change in the core. The lowest sample examined in the C179A well is from 1245 m depth and contains *Stephanolithion bigotii bigotii, Lotharingius crucicentralis,* and *Faviconus multicolumnatus,* indicating a Callovian to Late Oxfordian age. This stratal age is confirmed by the observation of the microfossils *Cladocoropsis mirabilis* and *Nautiloculina oolithica* in samples from the Tiulenovo wells E457 and E448. The strata between 1198 and 1234 m depth in the C179A well are assigned a Tithonian age on the basis of the nannoflora assemblage *Cyclagelosphaera tubulata* and the co-occurrence of *Faviconus multicolumnatus* and *Conusphaera mexicana minor.*

Aptian

The mixed carbonate and siliciclastic strata in the Staro Oryahovo R-9 well contain common *Orbitolina* spp., which range from the Barremian to Cenomanian, although some of the species may indicate an Aptian–Albian age (D. Bayliss, 1995, personal communication). An Aptian age is supported by the nannoflora obtained from a fine sandstone from 2575 m depth that contains *Eprolithus floralis, Diazomatolithus lehmanii,* and *Nannoconus tuittii*. Marinov (1994) and Dachev et al. (1988) describe a Lower Cretaceous interval in the Staro Oryahovo R-9 well overlain by Cenomanian strata, even though no detailed biostratigraphy is presented in either of these studies.

One sample from Locality 3, NE of Devnia, yielded a relatively rich nannofossil assemblage that either have their extinction or inception in, or are restricted to, the Aptian (K. Cooper, 1995, personal communication). Some of the age-significant taxa include *Assipetra infracretacea, Braarudosphaera africana, Conusphaera rothii, Diazomatolithus lehmanii,* and *Lithraphidites alatus magnus.*

Cenomanian to Middle Eocene

Despite abundant sampling of cored intervals during this study, biostratigraphic analyses of samples have only yielded nannofossils of late Campanian and Paleocene age. A Cenomanian age is tentatively recorded by the presence of the foraminifera *Multispirina iranensis* and *Orbitolina* species in a sample from 2435 m depth from the Staro Oryahovo R-9 well (M. Fadel, 1996, personal communication). Nannofossil assemblages from Tiulenovo E445 and E457 wells yielded *Calculites obscurus, Reinhardtites anthophorous, Eiffellithus eximius, Lithastrinus grillii,* and *Broinsonia parca,* indicating a Campanian age. Samples from the East Dobruja C179A well (587, 596, and 608 m depths) yielded the nannoflora *Reinhardtites anthophorous, R. levis, Eiffellithus eximius, Lithastrinus grillii,* and *Broinsonia parca,* which indicate a late Campanian age. This is supported by the foraminifera assemblage *Stensioina* cf. *exsculpta, Pseudovalvulineria* cf. *clementiana, G. coronata, G. linneiana, Globotruncana cretacea (d'Orb),* and *Spiroplecta, Contusotruncana* cf. *fornicata* s.l., *Globotruncana* cf. *cretacea (d'Orb)* praehedbergellids, hedbergellids, globotruncanids, *Globorotalites micheliniana, Eouvigerina aculeata, Pseudovalvulineria* cf. *lorneiana,* and *Stensioina* cf. *exsculpta.*

Paleocene deposits are recorded in the Ravna Gora R-69, Staro Oryahovo R-9, Elyzavetino R-1, East Dobruja, and Tiulenovo E448 wells. The interval between 874.5 and 944.5 m in the Ravna Gora R-69 well is assigned a Paleocene age. Limestones between 898.6 and 944.5 m depth contain *Coccolithus pelagicus* and *Ericsonia subpertusa* nannofossils, which indicate an age no older than Paleocene. A late Paleocene age is confirmed by the presence of *Heliolithus kleinpellii* and *Toweius eminens* in samples from 874.5 m and 890.7 m depth. Previous workers have suggested the interval between ~1846 and 2604 m depth is of Late Cretaceous age (Dachev et al., 1988; Marinov, 1994). However, nannofossils recovered from samples from 1916.5 m and 2379 m depth contain poor assemblages of the nannofossil species *Prinsius dimorphosus* and *Coccolithus pelagicus,* suggesting this interval is Paleocene in age. A late Paleocene age is recorded for a sample from 264 m depth in the Elyzavetino R-1 well on the basis of a nannofossil assemblage containing *Zygodiscus herlynii, Neochiastozygus distentus, Heliolithus kleinpellii, Bomolithus elegans,* and *Fasciculithus tympaniformis.* Similar assemblages are recorded from samples from 577.6 m and 582.5 m depth from the East Dobruja C179A well, although *Heliolithus riedelii* has also been identified from this well. Only one of the three wells examined from the Tiulenovo field has yielded nannofossils indicating a Tertiary age. A sample from 315.8 m depth in the E448 well yielded *Heliolithus riedelii, Dicoaster mohleri,* and *Zygodiscus herlynii,* indicating a late Paleocene age.

Eocene ages have been determined from the East Dobruja C179A and the Tiulenovo E448 wells. Samples between 308.40 and 314.80 m in the Tiulenovo E448 well yielded *Globigerina, Catapsydrax, Discocyclina* spp., *Planostegina, Operculina, Vlerkina, Operculinella, Ranikothalia, Heterostegina, Somalina, Amphistegina,* globigerines, and rotalines foraminifera (F. Banner, 1994, personal communication).

Georgescu, M.D., 1997, Upper Jurassic–Cretaceous planktonic biofacies succession and the evolution of the Western Black Sea Basin, *in* A.G. Robinson, ed., Regional and petroleum geology of the Black Sea and surrounding region: AAPG Memoir 68, p. 169–182.

Chapter 10

Upper Jurassic–Cretaceous Planktonic Biofacies Succession and the Evolution of the Western Black Sea Basin

Marius Dan Georgescu
PETROMAR
Constanta, Romania

ABSTRACT

Three planktonic biofacies successions are recognized in the Upper Jurassic and Cretaceous in the Western Black Sea, offshore Romania. Biofacies A (Oxfordian–Valanginian) contains rare *Globuligerina* tests in punctual occurrences. The planktonic foraminifera are recorded in carbonate inner-shelf deposits in the Upper Jurassic, and mixed (detrital, clayey, marly) shelf deposits in the Berriasian–Valanginian. The first records of the Western Black Sea opening are dated as Valanginian. Biofacies B largely corresponds to the turbiditic interval of the late Albian–Cenomanian. The planktonic foraminiferal assemblages consist of both primitive (globular chambered) and morphologically advanced taxa (keeled *Rotalipora* and *Praeglobotruncana*). The planktonic record is discontinuous, but some claystone levels accumulated under calmer water environments (very low terrigenous input) show remarkable consistency. Biofacies C is peculiar to the outer-shelf deposits of Cenomanian through Maastrichtian age. A gradual increase of the recorded taxa and group diversity is evident. Planktonics are ubiquitous.

INTRODUCTION

Recent studies concerning the planktonic foraminifera distribution within the water mass revealed that there is a close connection between the test architecture (e.g., test shape, peripheral structures, umbilical system, ornamentation, and presence or absence of particular features such as clavate chambers and tubulospines), depths between which different species develop their life cycles, evolutionary trends, diversity, and abundance.

The first planktonic foraminiferal occurrence in the Romanian Black Sea offshore is dated Upper Jurassic (i.e., deposits close to the Kimmeridgian–Tithonian boundary and Tithonian phase). Representatives of the group have also been encountered in various amounts within most of the Cretaceous lithostratigraphical units. It is possible to identify a succession of three planktonic foraminiferal biofacies, each of them specific for a certain environment, which may be recorded only once during the Western Black Sea evolution. By correlation with other data coming from different fossil groups (e.g., characeans, benthonic foraminifera, ostracoda), as well as tectonics and sedimentology, the three above-mentioned biofacies were proven to be relevant in identifying the evolutionary stages of the Western Black Sea Basin.

In this chapter, the planktonic foraminiferal taxa of generic level are considered based on Loeblich and

Tappan (1987). The taxa of specific rank are referred in Robaszynski et al. (1979, parts I and II), Robaszynski et al. (1984), Caron (1985), and Ellis and Messina (1940).

PLANKTONIC FORAMINIFERS AS BATHYMETRY INDICATORS—A HISTORY OF CONCEPTS

Grimsdale and van Morkhoven (1955) divided the large group of foraminifera into planktonic and benthonic types. In his work concerning the ecology and distribution of modern foraminifera, Phleger (1960) regarded the possibility of using planktonic forms as bathymetry indicators. The transportation of the planktonic tests by sea currents over the continental shelves was considered, at that time, an insurmountable difficulty. Later, Stehli and Creath (1964) took this model into account and, by using the planktonic/benthonic foraminifer ratio in basinal studies, introduced the planktonic foraminiferal amount as a major variable within their studies.

Douglas and Rankin (1969), Eicher (1969), and Eicher and Worstell (1970) postulated the restriction of the keeled planktonic foraminiferal species within the deeper waters and the dominance of the small, globular chambered species onto the shelf areas during the transgressive periods. Olsson (1977) suggested that such genera as *Archaeoglobigerina* and *Rugoglobigerina* were shallow-water dwellers, as they occur in shallow-water sediments. Hart (1980) accomplished a depth stratification model for the evolution of the planktonic foraminifers (Jurassic–Neogene). Within it, the heterohelicids, partly the planispirally enrolled *Globigerinelloides* and the trochospiral *Plummerita* and partly *Rotalipora* and *Ticinella,* are regarded as shallow-water inhabitants, while *Planomalina, Praeglobotruncana, Dicarinella, Marginotruncana* and partly *Globotruncana, Ticinella,* and *Rotalipora* (among others) are deep-water inhabitants. An intermediate zone was recognized, as was the transition between the upper and lower sea-water layers.

Vincent and Berger (1981) postulated the correspondence between eustatic cycles and the rhythm of evolution of the planktonic foraminifera. Caron and Homewood (1983) demonstrated that the following morphological series, recorded by Bé (1977), of modern planktonics with increasing depth may be also recognized in the Upper Cretaceous forms: globular>flattened>keeled biconvex>keeled planoconvex. They showed that during periods with high environmental stress (oligotaxic periods), the primitive morphotype (r-strategists) tendency is to colonize the oceanic water surface (trophy level); the oligotaxic periods are characterized by lower sea level and low diversity of the planktonics. The periods with high sea level (polytaxic periods) present planktonics with great diversity and, consequently, more complex assemblages; during these periods, the shallow-water primitive morphotypes colonized the deeper waters (sexual reproduction level).

Leckie (1987), working on the mid-Cretaceous planktonics, proposed three faunal groups. The epicontinental sea fauna is characterized by species of *Guembelitria* and *Heterohelix.* Shallow-water fauna is dominated by *Hedbergella* and *Globigerinelloides.* Deep-water fauna consists mainly of species of the keeled genera *Planomalina, Rotalipora,* and *Praeglobotruncana.* Premoli Silva and Sliter (1994) distinguished three groups of taxa based on gross test morphology and ornamentation patterns. The r-strategists comprise the representatives of the serial genera *Heterohelix* and *Laeviheterohelix,* and globular hedbergellids. The intermediate forms enhance the advanced heterohelicids (e.g., *Pseudoguembelina, Pseudotextularia, Planoglobulina, Gublerina,* and *Racemiguembelina*), globular morphotypes bearing aligned pustules and costellae (e.g., *Costellagerina, Whiteinella, Archaeoglobigerina, Rugoglobigerina, Kuglerina, Plummerita,* and *Trinitella*), planispirally coiled tests (*Globigerinelloides*), complex morphotypes lacking true peripheral keels (e.g., *Praeglobotruncana, Globotruncanella*), and tests having hemispherical chambers with more or less developed peripheral keel(s), such as *Dicarinella, Helvetoglobotruncana, Gansserina,* and *Rugotruncana.* The complex morphotypes (k-strategists) include all the keeled forms with acute and truncated margins (e.g., *Rotalipora, Marginotruncana, Globotruncanita, Abathomphalus, Radotruncana, Falsotruncana,* and *Planomalina*).

BIOFACIES PARAMETERS

The use of the benthonic foraminiferal biofacies in bathymetrical studies is well known from the works of Olsson and Nyong (1984) and Olsson (1988).

The planktonic foraminiferal biofacies consist of different taxa, within a certain time period, particular for an environment. Each biofacies is characterized by four parameters: taxa, stratigraphic occurrences, diversity, and consistency.

The taxa that may be present within a biofacies are highly influenced by the accumulation area of the planktonic foraminiferal-bearing deposits. As far as certain environments are involved, it was necessary to group the taxa upon their bathymetrical preferences. For the present study, the r-strategy (intermediate form) and k-strategy groups proved suitable as defined by Premoli Silva and Sliter (1994). Notable changes are usually observed within a biofacies. Their amplitude is reduced during the Upper Jurassic and lowermost Cretaceous, when only species of *Globuligerina* and *Conoglobigerina* may be encountered. During the Upper Cretaceous, when the group evolved rapidly, the changes affect not only species but also genera.

The stratigraphic occurrences are intimately related to the environment under which the deposits accumulated. Three types of occurrences have been recorded in the Romanian Black Sea offshore: punctual, discontinuous, and continuous. The diversity increases due to the group evolution and optimization of the environments to be colonized by the planktonic foraminifers. The consistency is the effect of the development of planktonic foraminiferal taxa within an ecologic niche, as well as the fossilization process.

PLANKTONIC FORAMINIFERAL BIOFACIES SUCCESSION

The lithostratigraphic and biostratigraphic formations of the Cretaceous deposits recorded in the Western Black Sea offshore are given in Figure 1.

Biofacies A: Epicontinental and Shallow-Water Upper Jurassic (Late Oxfordian–Tithonian) Throughout Early Neocomian (Berriasian–Valanginian) Fauna

Based on the recorded sediments, two intervals have been distinguished within this period.

During the Upper Jurassic (late Oxfordian–Tithonian), a wide carbonate platform extended over the entire Romanian Black Sea offshore area. Two planktonic foraminiferal occurrences have been encountered: (1) broken tests and single chambers of *Globuligerina* spp. in the beds adjacent to the Kimmeridgian–Tithonian boundary and (2) complete tests of *Globuligerina* spp. coming from Tithonian deposits. These occurrences are characterized by a reduced number of specimens, regardless of the method of sampling (detached fauna for the former and thin sections for the latter). The water depth estimations (Figure 2) indicate accumulation under inner-shelf conditions. Benthonic foraminifers consist mainly of miliolids and larger imperforate agglutinant taxa. The characean debris have constant occurrences within the entire Upper Jurassic sequence; they are regarded as indicative of supertidal conditions.

Above the Jurassic–Cretaceous boundary, the sedimentary regime suffers a dramatic change. The Upper Jurassic carbonates are completely replaced by clayey and detrital deposits all over the Romanian Black Sea offshore area. The sedimentary environments indicated a wider spectrum generated by the opening of the Western Black Sea Basin (Figure 3A). The tectonic movements implied by such a process increased the terrigenous input, and this affected the carbonate sedimentation. The planktonic foraminifers consist of *Globuligerina* spp. Few specimens have been recorded onto the northern block, in the Heraclea West well, within polychromic claystones, in a marine and brackish-water organism debris mixture.

The earliest planktonic foraminifers (i.e., *Globuligerina* and *Conoglobigerina*) were shallow-water inhabitants, and they were replaced toward the open ocean by other planktonic groups (e.g., radiolarians). Most of the opinions are convergent in this respect Colom, 1955; Caron and Homewood, 1983; Leckie, 1987; Riegraf, 1987.

Accordingly, biofacies A characterizes a period in the Western Black Sea evolution when deposits accumulated under shallow-water environments (deposits for which estimated sedimentation depth is about –120 to –150 m are also known, but they are devoid of calcareous tests). The index taxa consist of species of *Globuligerina*. They show numerically reduced "populations" and low diversity, since this was the initial attempt of the group to colonize the open ocean, and the rate of evolution was very low.

Biofacies B: Outer-Shelf–Slope Late Albian–(Partly) Cenomanian

After a gap comprising the Hauterivian–Barremian, sedimentation restarted during the Aptian. Continental deposits of this age are spread onto the intermediate and northern blocks, as shown in Figure 3B.

The Late Albian is characterized by turbidite accumulation in the Western Black Sea offshore area, particularly in the Sinoe-Portita–Lebada West–Lebada East oil fields area (Figure 3C). The Cenomanian sedimentary setting (Figure 3D) indicates the restriction of the area where upper-slope turbidites accumulated at the Lebada West–Lebada East oil fields. Adjacent to the slope turbidites, outer-shelf deposits have been recorded. They consist of siliciclastic sediments of Late Albian and dark-gray marls and claystones assigned to the Cenomanian. Two lithostratigraphical units have been recognized by Georgescu (1993) for the Late Albian–Cenomanian deposits. The Lebada Formation comprises the dominant detrital sediments (Late Albian–Cenomanian turbidites and Late Albian siliciclastic shelf deposits), while the marly and clayey deposits have been separated within the Tomis Formation.

The planktonic foraminiferal biofacies B has been recognized in the Lebada Formation.

Few assemblages are present within the thin claystone interbeds of the detrital sequence. However, the planktonic foraminifera are also encountered within the fine sandstones of the Lebada Formation, but they are absent in the coarse sandstone and microconglomerate beds. The high water energy strongly affected the plankton during periods with high terrigenous input from the adjacent emerged areas. During periods with calmer waters, the planktonics spread and flourished over the entire area.

As a whole, the planktonic foraminifera are more numerous when compared with those of biofacies A (Figure 4). Their occurrences are also more numerous, but the distribution within the Lebada Formation still shows the discontinuous pattern. In contrast, the occurrences of planktonic foraminifera within the deposits characterized by biofacies A are isolated.

The hedbergellid taxa (e.g., *Hedbergella* and *Whiteinella*) dominate the planktonic assemblage in the shelf area; in the turbidite accumulation zone, the keeled species belonging to the genera *Rotalipora* and *Praeglobotruncana* are most numerous.

It is worth noting that, in the turbidite sediments species with palno-convex tests [e.g., *Rotalipora reicheli* (Mornod), *R. deeckei* (Franke)], typical deeper water inhabitants are present in a various number of

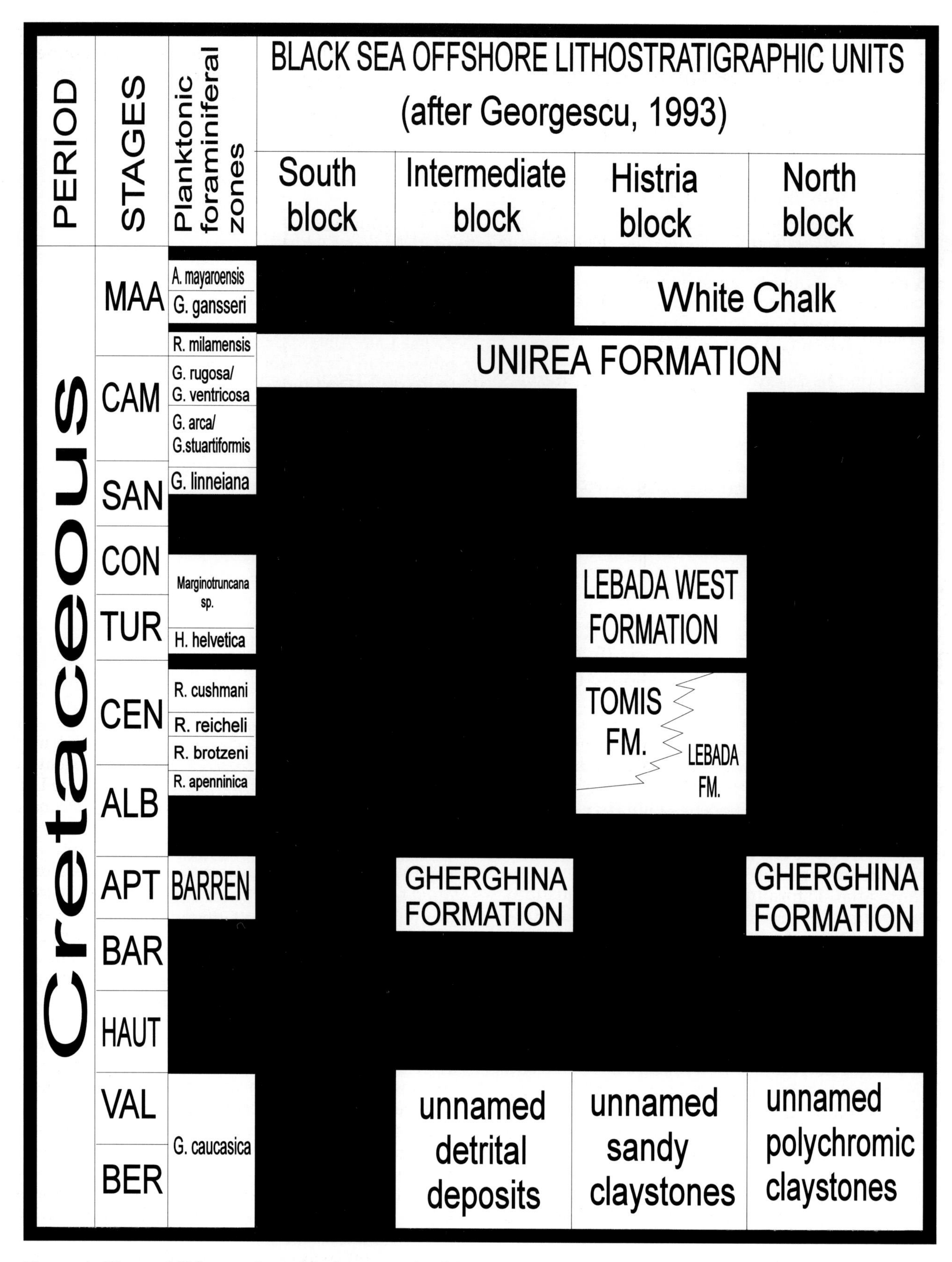

Figure 1. Bio- and lithostratigraphic framework of Cretaceous deposits in the Western Black Sea, offshore Romania. The tectonic blocks correspond to the offshore extensions of the following inland structural units: South block (SB) = South Dobrogean sector of the Moesian Platform, Intermediate block (IB) = Central Dobrogea, Histria block (HB) = Babadag basin, and North block (NB) = Scythian Platform.

Stratigraphic interval	Sediment accumulation area & basin evolutionary stage	Sediment general features	Estimated water depths	Planktonic foraminifers	Benthonic foraminifer assemblage features
Maastrichtian partly (*) Cenomanian	shelf, marine OUTER SHELF SEDIMENTATION	chalk carbonates marlstones	-75 to -150 meters	Abundant In situ	Abundant
partly (*) Cenomanian Late Albian	distal shelf and slope FILLING PHASE	siliciclastic shelf and turbidite sediments	-150 to -400 meters	Rare specimens In situ	Rare specimens
Mid Albian Early Albian	Hiatus	No sediments	No estimation	No record	No record
Aptian	Continental	conglomerates with clayey matrix	No estimation	Barren	Barren
Barremian Hauterivian	Hiatus	No sediments	No estimation	No record	No record
Valanginian Berriasian	inner to outer shelf OPENING INITIATION	clayey-detrital	+3 to -150 meters	Scarce taxa & individuals Allochtonous	Dominant agglutinant taxa
Tithonian Oxfordian	Inner shelf CARBONATE SEDIMENTATION	various carbonates	+3 to -10 meters	Scarce taxa & individuals Allochtonous	Dominant miliolids & larger imperforate taxa

Figure 2. General features of Western Black Sea sedimentation during the Upper Jurassic and Cretaceous.

individuals, but always as minor assemblage constituents. Starting with the middle Cenomanian (*R. reicheli* zone), representatives of the genus *Whiteinella* constantly increase in number of specimens and in species. No serial tests have been recorded in deposits accumulated under high-energy environments.

The benthonic foraminiferal assemblages usually consist of reduced numbers of specimens, and so do the ostracod shells. A great amount of reworked organic debris came from deposits accumulated onto carbonate platforms of the Triassic, Upper Jurassic, and Lower Cretaceous around the study area.

Biofacies C: Outer-Shelf Cenomanian (Partly) Throughout Maastrichtian Fauna

The Upper Cretaceous sediments in the Romanian offshore accumulated on a shelf, and consist of a sharply defined sequence on the seismic lines. Four lithostratigraphic units have been recognized by Georgescu (1993). The Tomis Formation (Cenomanian) includes marls and claystones, dark in color, and was penetrated by the wells drilled in the northwestern and southern parts of the Histria block. During the Turonian, and probably a part of the Coniacian, argillaceous limestones accumulated on the Histria block (Lebada West Formation). The Late Santonian–early Maastrichtian time interval corresponds to the accumulation of the deposits separated as the Unirea Formation; they include white-yellowish limestones with dark marl interbeds. The Late Campanian–early Maastrichtian interval points out the highest sea level during the Late Cretaceous. Middle-late Maastrichtian deposits consist of white chalk, and are recorded as patches north of the offshore extension of the Peceneaga-Camena fault.

The planktonic foraminifera of biofacies C occur in various amounts in all of the above-listed lithostratigraphic units. They are ubiquitous through the sediment column, in contrast with the planktonic foraminiferal record of biofacies A and B. The number of collected specimens gradually increases from the Cenomanian throughout Maastrichtian deposits.

The diversity presents the same trend, due to the group evolution and also the tendency for more and more of the morphologically complex forms to gradually colonize the shelf area, replacing the globular chambered, primitive morphotypes.

The planktonic foraminiferal assemblages consist of three groups of morphotypes; shallow-water, transition zone, and deeper water inhabitants (Premoli Silva and Sliter, 1994). The three categories occur in various amounts, with significant changes being recorded through time.

The r-strategists show a gradual decrease in number of species and individuals. This conservative group is mostly represented within the Tomis and Lebada West formations, mainly by species of the genera *Hedbergella* and *Whiteinella*. From the Unirea

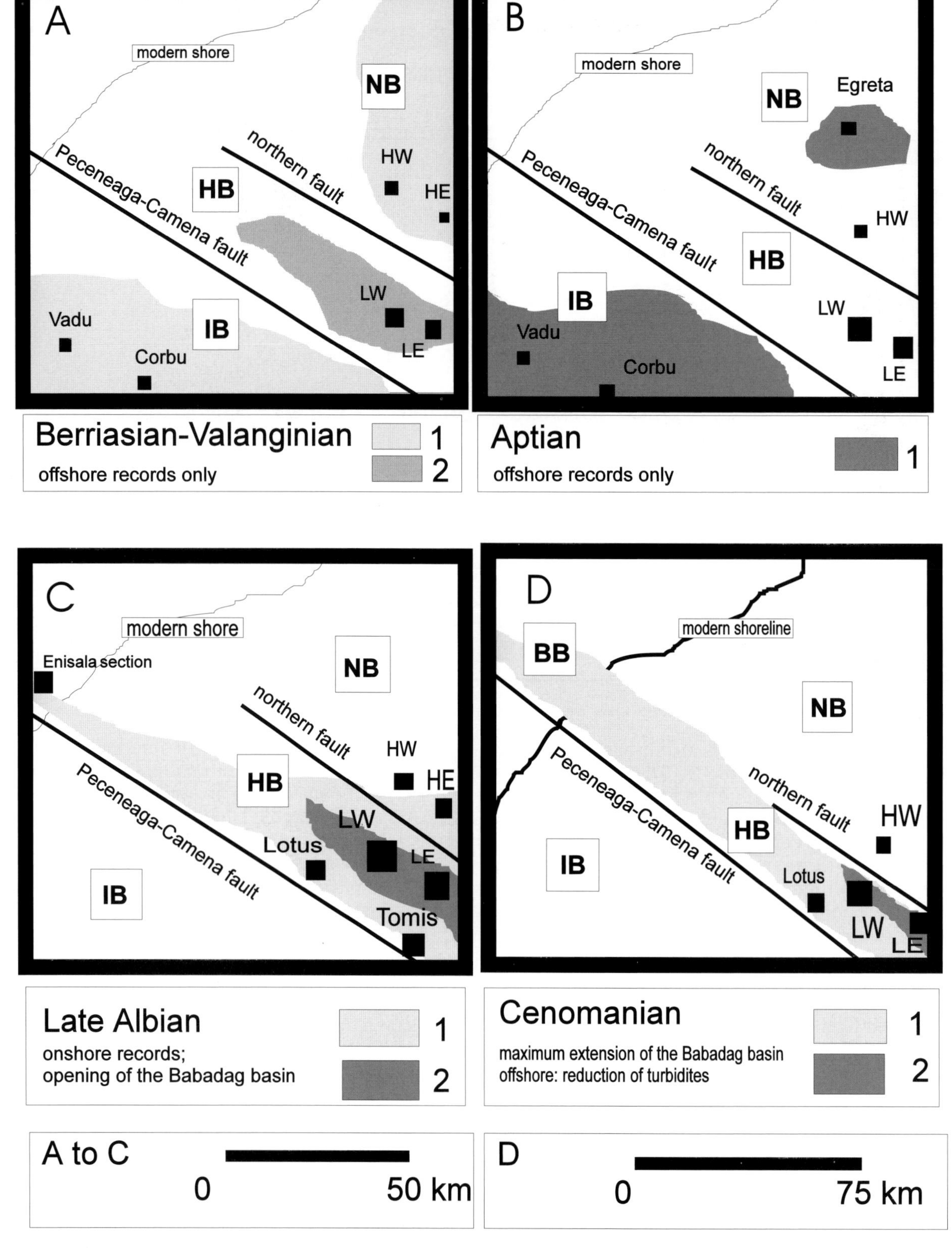

Figure 3. Berriasian to Cenomanian deposits recorded in the Romanian Black Sea offshore, in order to illustrate the Western Black Sea opening records. A = brackish-water (1) and marine (2) deposits; B = continental deposits (1); C = siliciclastic outer-shelf (1) and slope-turbidite (2) deposits; D = outer-shelf (1) and turbidite (2) deposits. HE = Heraclea East borehole, HW = Heraclea West borehole, LW = Lebada West oil field, LE = Lebada East oil field. The structural units (capitals in squares) are labeled as indicated in the caption for Figure 1.

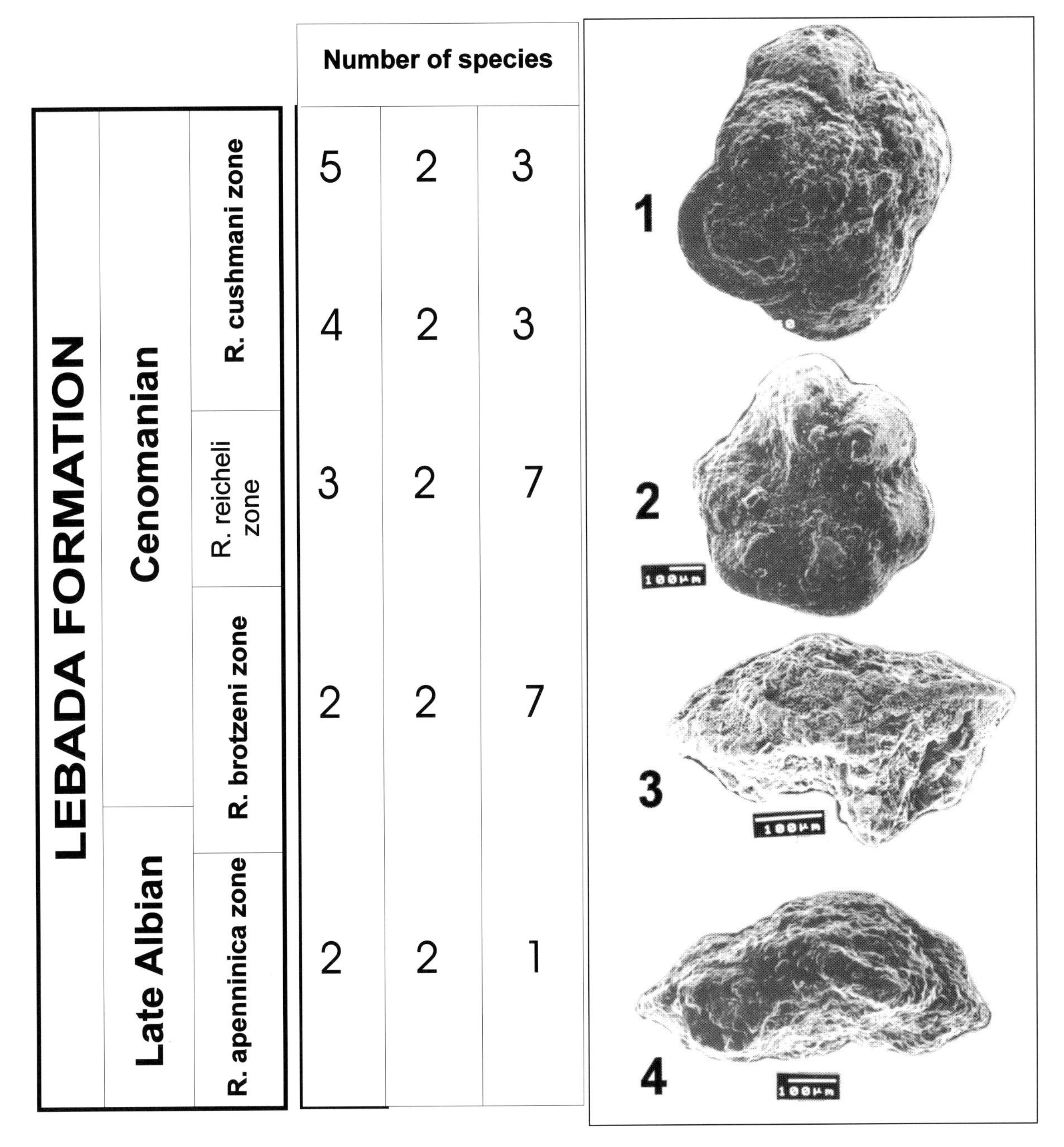

Figure 4. The constituents of biofacies B. Illustrated specimens belong only to the k-strategy group: 1 = *Rotalipora cushmani* (Morrow), 2 = *R. reicheli* (Mornod), 3 = *R. brotzeni* Sigal, 4 = *R. apenninica* (Renz). The r-strategy species are given in the left column, k-strategists in the right column, and intermediate forms in the middle.

Formation and white chalk, the species *Hedbergella flandrini* Porthault and *H. holmdelensis* Olsson are recorded, but their ranges do not overlap. The serial taxa belong to the genera *Heterohelix* and *Laeviheterohelix* (Figure 5).

The transitional zone inhabitants (Figure 6) are always present, but they are never abundant. The Tomis Formation contains the genus *Praeglobotruncana*. This genus persists within the Lebada West Formation, and *Helvetoglobotruncana* is added to it. Within the Unirea Formation, *Rugoglobigerina* has its last downhole occurrence. The Western Black Sea recordings indicate that both groups of species, those with low trochospires [e.g., *Rugoglobigerina hexacamerata* Brönnimann, *R. rugosa* (Plummer)] and high trochospire (*R. milamensis* Smith and Pessagno, and *R. pennyi* Brönnimann) are present. To them, other rugoglobigerinid genera are added: *Archaeoglobigerina* and *Kuglerina*. According to Georgescu (1995), the following serial genera are to be added: *Planoglobulina* and *Pseudoplanoglobulina*.

The most abundant are, surprisingly, the keeled taxa (Figures 7, 8) and what were previously described as typical deeper water dwellers. *Rotalipora*

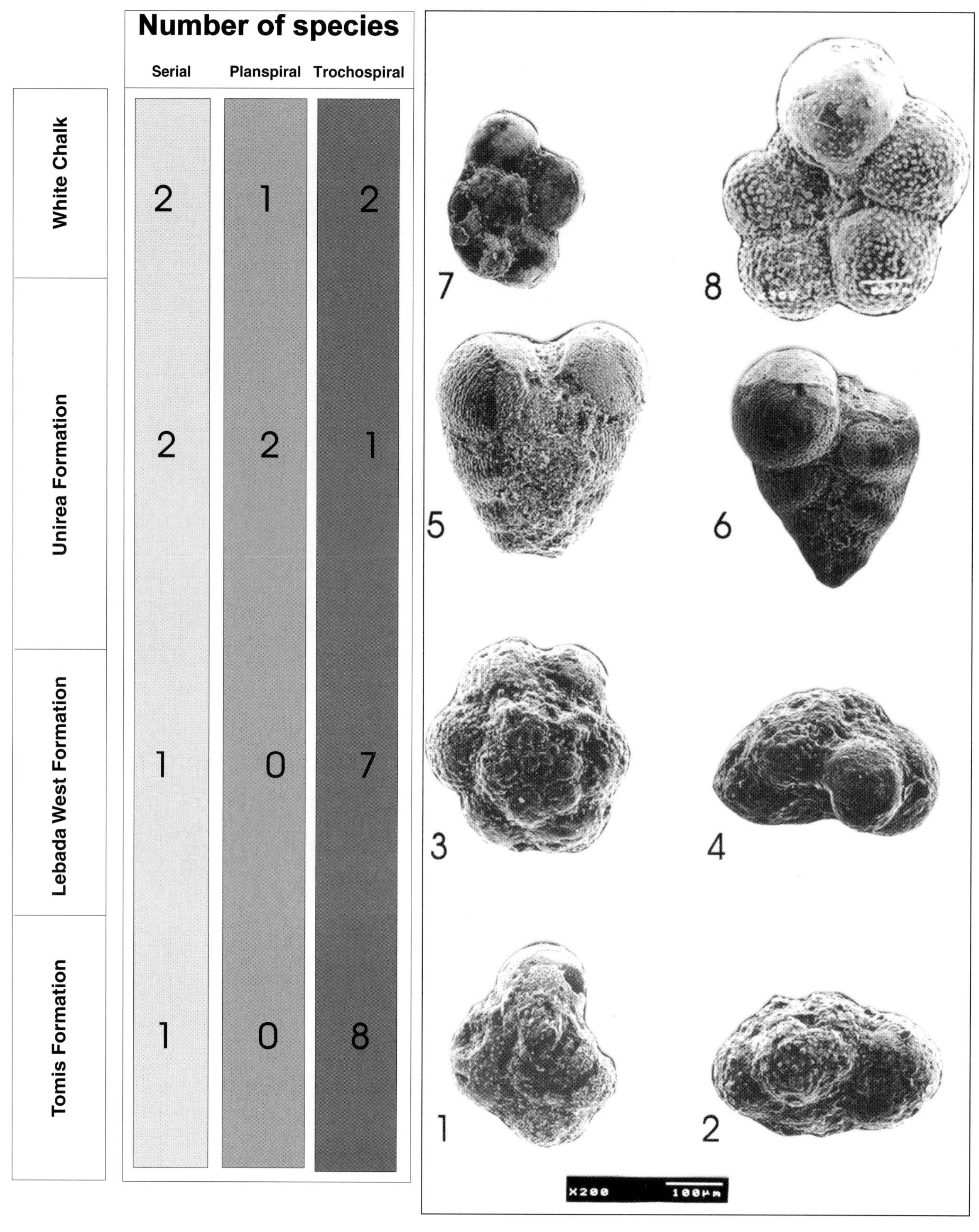

Figure 5. The r-strategists recorded within biofacies C. Illustrated specimens: 1 = *Hedbergella amabilis* Loeblich and Tappan, 2 = *Whiteinella brittonensis* (Loeblich and Tappan), 3–4 = *W. paradubia* (Sigal), 5 = *Heterohelix reussi* (Cushman), 6 = *H. globulosa* (Ehrenberg), 7 = *Hedbergella holmdelensis* Olsson, 8 = *Globigerinelloides prairiehillensis* Pessagno. The scale bar refers to all plates, except plate 8.

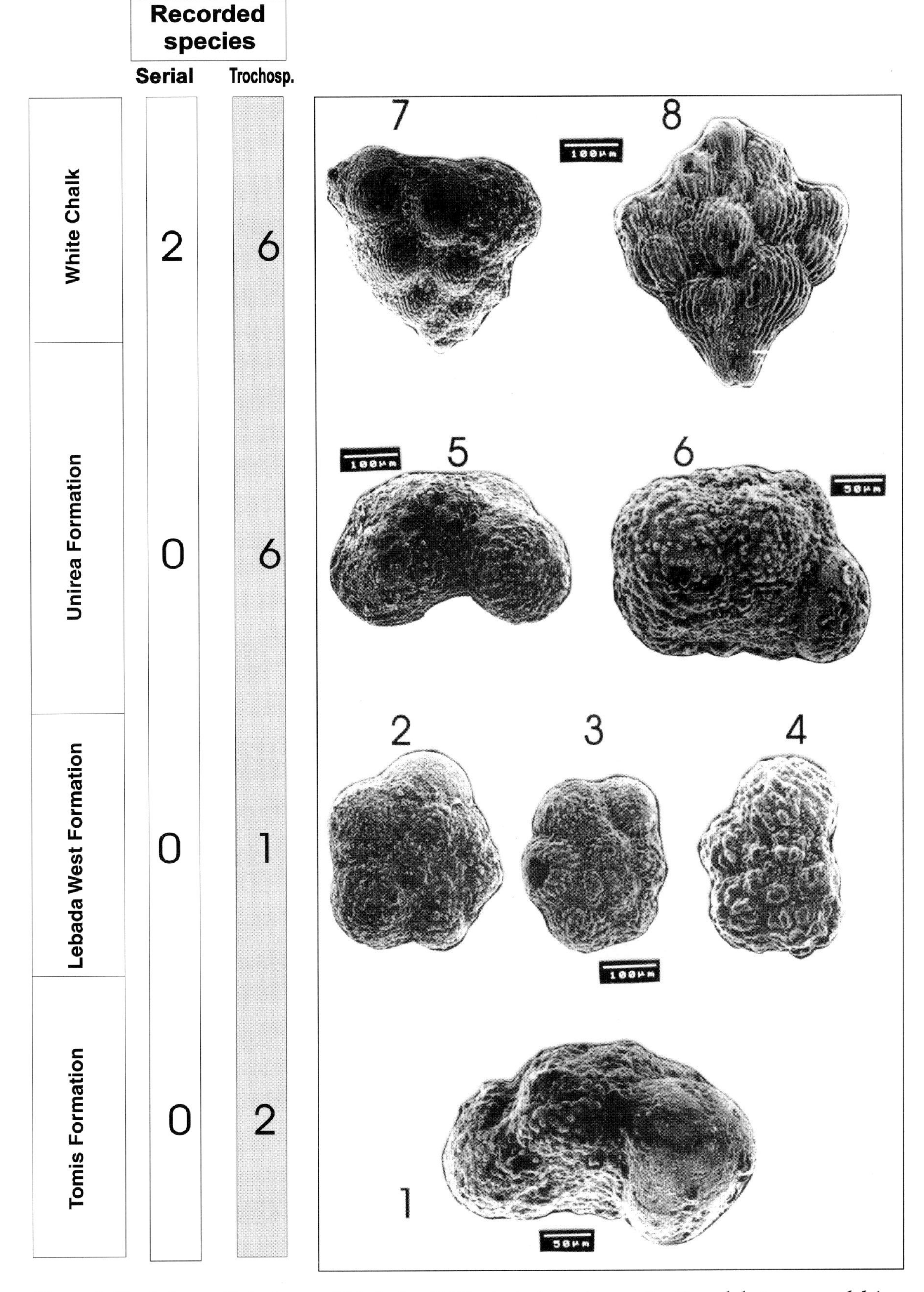

Figure 6. The intermediate forms of biofacies C. Illustrated specimens: 1 = *Praeglobotruncana delrioensis* (Plummer), 2 = *Archaeoglobigerina cretacea* (d'Orbigny), 3 = *Rugoglobigerina hexacamerata* Brönnimann, 4 = *R. rugosa* (Plummer), 5 = *R. milamensis* Smith and Pessagno, 6 = *R. pennyi* Brönnimann, 7 = *Pseudoplanoglobulina carseyae* (Plummer), 8 = *Planoglobulina acervulinoides* (Egger).

dominates within the Tomis Formation, while the double-keeled *Dicarinella* n.sp. is scarce. The Lebada West Formation yielded abundant *Marginotruncana* and *Dicarinella*. The Unirea Formation comprises a wider stratigraphical interval. In the Upper Santonian, the *Marginotruncana* and *Dicarinella* fauna are dominant, but the first *Globotruncana* [e.g., *G. arca* (Cushman), *G. bulloides* Vogler] and *Globotruncanita* [e.g., *G. stuartiformis* (Dalbiez)] have also been recorded. At the Santonian–Campanian boundary, the genera *Globotruncana*, *Globotruncanita*, and *Contusotruncana* are abundant. Only two *Marginotruncana* species pass this limit, namely, *M. coronata* (Bolli) and *M. pseudolinneiana* Pessagno. The only serial taxa are *Gublerina* sp.

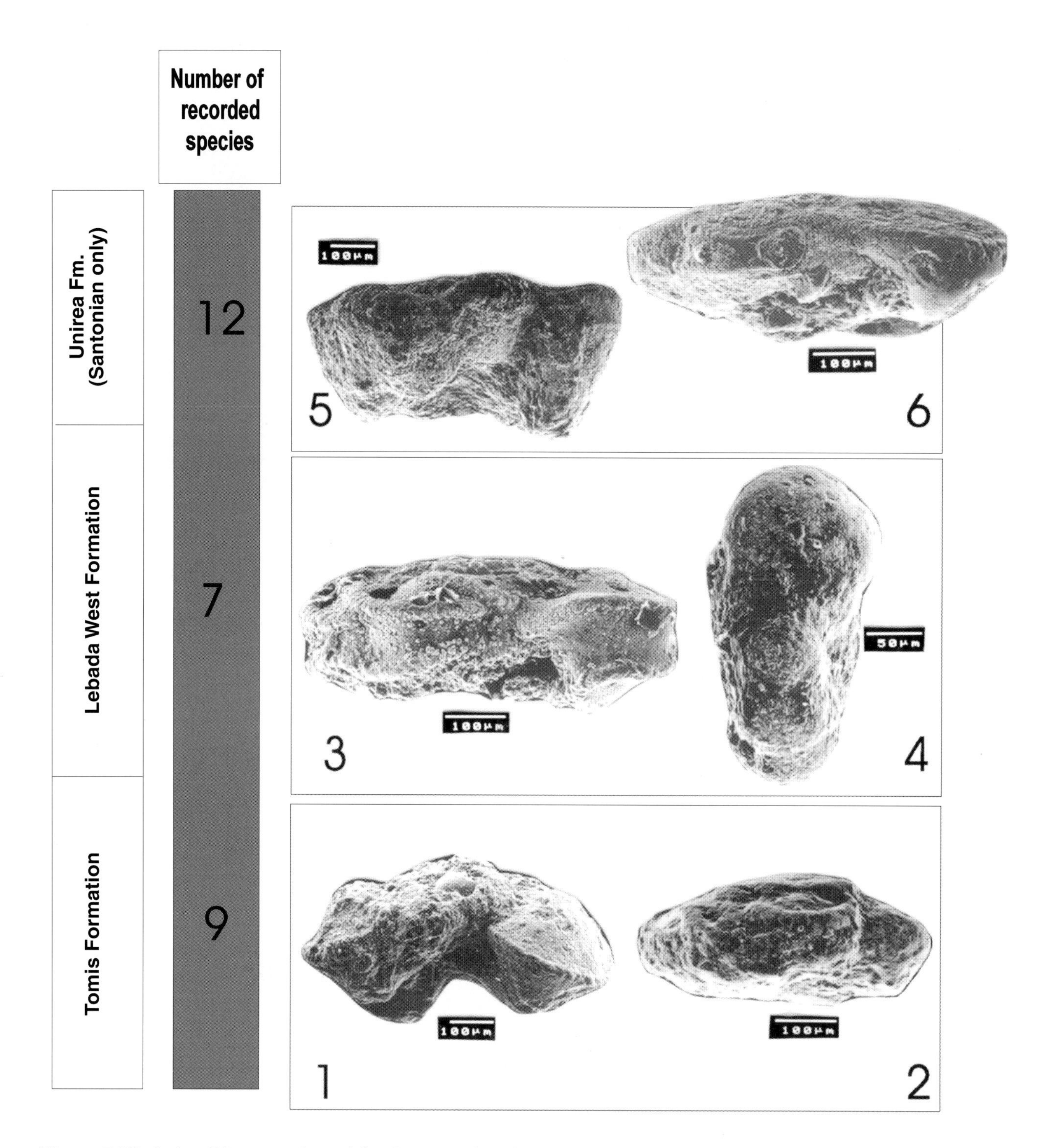

Figure 7. Biofacies C k-strategists of the Cenomanian–Santonian interval. 1 = *Rotalipora montsalvensis* (Mornod), 2 = *Dicarinella* n.sp., 3 = *Marginotruncana pseudolinneiana* Pessagno, 4 = *Helvetoglobotruncana helvetica* (Bolli), 5 = *Dicarinella asymetrica* (Sigal), 6 = *Marginotruncana paraconcavata* Porthault. Notice the plano-convex tests in plates 4–6.

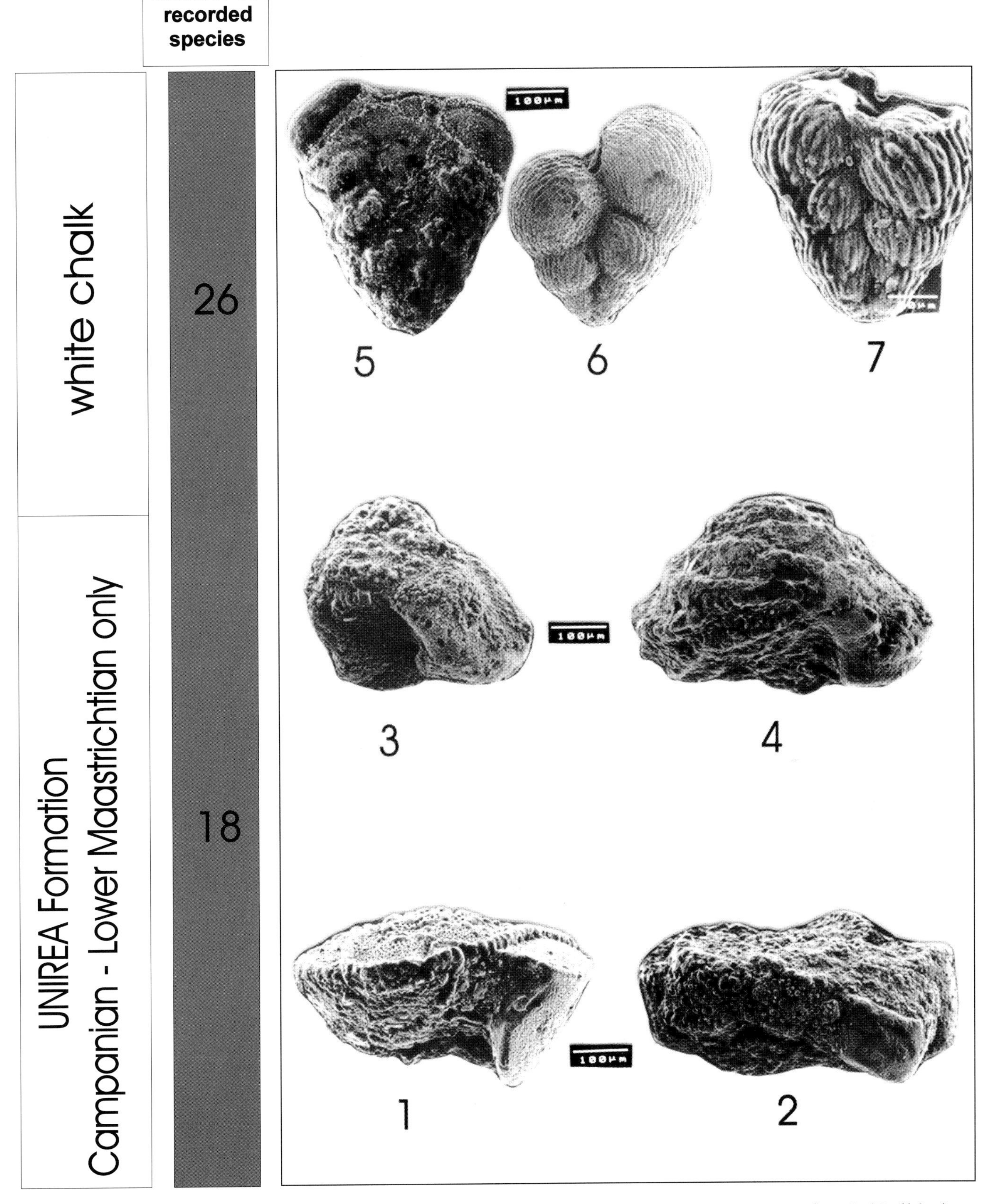

Figure 8. Campanian–Maastrichtian k-strategists of biofacies C. 1 = *Globotruncanita stuartiformis* (Dalbiez), 2 = *Globotruncana obliqua* Herm, 3 = *Contusotruncana plicata* (White), 4 = *C.* cf. *contusa* (Cushman), 5 = *Gublerina* sp., 6 = *Striatella striata* (Ehrenberg), 7 = *Pseudoguembelina costulata* (Cushman).

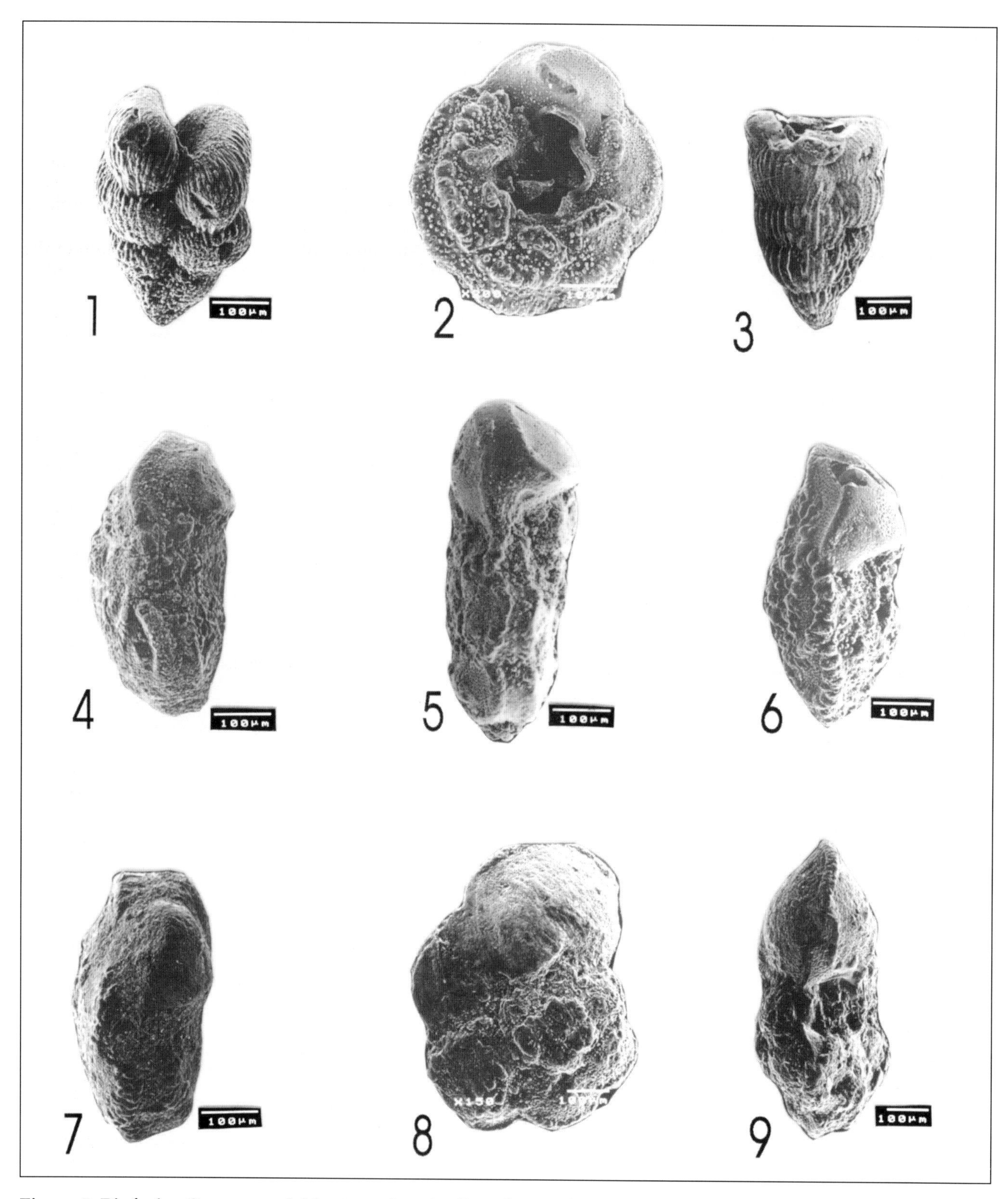

Figure 9. Biofacies C—successful k-strategists. 1 = *Pseudotextularia elegans* Rzehak, 2 = *Globotruncana arca* (Cushman), 3 = *Racemiguembelina fructicosa* Egger, 4 = *Contusotruncana fornicata* (Plummer), 5 = *G. bulloides* Vogler, 6 = *G. orientalis* El Naggar, 7 = *G. linneiana* (d'Orbigny), 8–9 = *Rotalipora cushmani* (Morrow).

and *Pseudoguembelina excolata* (Cushman), but these are known only as isolated, single specimens at the top of the Unirea Formation. The white chalk planktonic foraminiferal assemblages indicate that some high-spired *Contusotruncana* [e.g., *C. contusa* (Cushman) and *C. plicata* (White)] are minor taxa. The species *Globotruncana obliqua* Herm is enigimatic, and, as the Black Sea Middle Campanian–Lower Maastrichtian occurrences suggest, is a deeper water inhabitant; its strongly imbricated chambers seem to be a deeper water adaptation.

Such taxa as the serial *Pseudotextularia* and *Racemiguembelina* among *Heterohelicacea*, certain *Globotruncana* [e.g., *G. arca* (Cushman), *G. bulloides* Vogler, *G. mariei* Banner and Blow, *G. orientalis* El Naggar], *Marginotruncana* (e.g., *M. pseudolinneiana* Pessagno), *Contusotruncana* [e.g., *C. fornicata* (Plummer) and *C. plummerae* (Gandolfi)], and many others give abundant assemblages in the Black Sea offshore Upper Cretaceous shelf (Figure 9). They are regarded as successful k-strategists, suggesting shelf area recolonization by the morphologically advanced taxa.

CONCLUSIONS

Three planktonic foraminifera biofacies are now recognized in the Romanian Black Sea offshore.

Biofacies A characterizes the Late Jurassic–earliest Cretaceous time interval. During the Late Jurassic (late Oxfordian–Tithonian), a wide carbonate platform dominated the Romanian Black Sea offshore. The planktonic foraminifera are rare and allochthonous. The sedimentary regime suffered a major change in the earliest Cretaceous (Berriasian–Valanginian), when detrital and clayey sediments accumulated over the entire area, due to the initiation of the Western Black Sea rifting. Marine deposits accumulated under restrictive conditions in proximity to the offshore extension of the Peceneaga-Camena fault.

Starting in the late Albian, turbiditic deposits accumulated offshore. They contain scarce planktonic foraminifera, but some claystone intercalations yield richer assemblages. The planktonic foraminifera biofacies B shows more numerous planktonic foraminifers than the previous one, with discontinuous occurrences. Biofacies B is characteristic of deposits accumulated during the filling phase of the basin.

As the Black Sea Basin filled, outer-shelf deposits accumulated on more extended areas, yielding abundant planktonics, with continuous occurrences. Biofacies C is characteristic of the Cenomanian (outer-shelf sediments) throughout the Maastrichtian in the Romanian Black Sea offshore.

ACKNOWLEDGMENTS

A. Maftei (Enterprise Oil Romania) is acknowledged for the critical review in an earlier preparation stage of the manuscript. The author is indebted to Dr. A. Robinson (JKX Oil and Gas, London, UK) and two anonymous reviewers; their criticisms and recommendations improved the manuscript. Computer facilities from D. Ursulica (Chamber of Commerce, Constanta, Romania) are greatly appreciated. Dana Georgescu, by her permanent and enthusiastic support, made the present paper possible.

REFERENCES CITED

Bé, A.W.H., 1977, An ecological, zoogeographic and taxonomic review of Recent planktonic foraminifera, *in* A.T.S. Ramsay, ed., Ocean micropaleontology: London, Academic Press v. 1, p. 1–100.

Caron, M., 1985, Cretaceous planktic foraminifera, *in* H.M. Bolli, J.B. Saunders, and K. Perch Nielsen, eds., Plankton stratigraphy: Cambridge, Cambridge University Press, p. 17–86.

Caron, M., and P. Homewood, 1983, Evolution of the early planktic foraminifers: Marine Micropaleontology, v. 7, p. 453–462.

Colom, G., 1955, Jurassic–Cretaceous pelagic sediments of the western Mediterranean zone of the Atlantic: Micropaleontology, v. 1, p. 109–124.

Douglas, R.G., and C. Rankin, 1969, Cretaceous planktonic foraminifera from Bornholm and their zoogeographic significance: Lethaia, v. 2, p. 185–217.

Eicher, D.L., 1969, Cenomanian and Turonian planktonic foraminifera from the western interior of the United States, *in* E.J. Brill Leiden, ed., Proceedings of the First International Planktonic Conference on Planktonic Microfossils, Geneva, 1967, p. 163–174.

Eicher, D.L., and P. Worstell, 1970, Cenomanian and Turonian foraminifera from the Great Plains, United States: Micropaleontology, v. 13, p. 269–324.

Ellis, B.R., and A. Messina, 1940, Catalogue of foraminifera: New York, American Museum of Natural History, post-1940 supplements.

Georgescu, M.D., 1993, Albian through Maastrichtian lithostratigraphy in the Romanian Black Sea offshore: Bucharest, Analele Universitatii Bucuresti, v. 42, p. 85–88.

Georgescu, M.D., 1995, Paleobathymetry and evolution of the Mesozoic heterohelicids, Tethyan and boreal Cretaceous (abs.): Annual Meeting IGCP 362-Maastricht, September 21–23, Programme and Abstracts, p. 39–40.

Grimsdale, T.F., and F.P.C.M. van Morkhoven, 1955, The ratio between pelagic and benthonic foraminifera as a means of estimating depths of deposition of sedimentary rocks: Proceedings of the 4th World Petroleum Congress, section 1/D, p. 473–491.

Hart, M.B., 1980, A water depth model for the evolution of the planktonic foraminifera: Nature, v. 286, p. 252–254.

Leckie, R.M., 1987, Paleoecology of mid-Cretaceous planktonic foraminifera: a comparison of open ocean and epicontinental sea assemblages: Micropaleontology, v. 33, p. 164–176.

Loeblich, A.R. Jr., and H. Tappan, 1987, Foraminiferal genera and their classification: New York, Van Nostrand Reinhold Company, 970 p.

Olsson, R.K., 1977, Mesozoic foraminifera—Western Atlantic, *in* F.M. Swain, ed., Stratigraphic micropaleontology of Atlantic basin and borderlands: Amsterdam, Elsevier, p. 205–230.

Olsson, R.K., 1988, Foraminiferal modeling of sea-level change in the Late Cretaceous, *in* C.K. Wilgus et al., eds., Sea level changes—an integrated approach: SEPM Special Publication 42 p. 289–297.

Olsson, R.K., and E.E. Nyong, 1984, A paleoslope model for Campanian–lower Maastrichtian foraminifera of New Jersey and Delaware: Journal of Foraminiferal Research, v. 14, p. 50–68.

Phleger, F.B., 1960, Ecology and distribution of Modern foraminifera: Baltimore, Johns Hopkins Press, 235 p.

Premoli Silva, I., and W.V. Sliter, 1994, Cretaceous planktonic foraminiferal biostratigraphy and evolutionary trends from the Bottaccione section, Gubbio, Italy: Palaeontographia Italica, v. 82, p. 1–89.

Riegraf, W., 1987, Planktonic foraminifers (*Globuligerinidae*) from the Callovian (Middle Jurassic) of Southeast Germany: Journal of Foraminiferal Research, v. 17, p. 190–211.

Robaszynski, F., M. Caron, and the European Working Group on Planktonic Foraminifera, 1979, Atlas of mid-Cretaceous planktonic foraminifera: Cahiers de Micropaléontologie, v. 1–2, p. 1–185 (part I) and 1–181 (part II).

Robaszynski, F., M. Caron, J.M. Gonzalez Donoso, A.H. Wonders, and the European Working Group on Planktonic Foraminifera, 1984, Atlas of Late Cretaceous globotruncanids: Revue de Micropaléontologie, v. 26, p. 145–305.

Stehli, F.G., and W.B. Creath, 1964, Foraminiferal ratios and regional environments: AAPG Bulletin, v. 48, p. 1810–1827.

Vincent, E., and W.H. Berger, 1981, Planktonic foraminifera and their use in paleoceanography, *in* C. Emiliani, ed., The oceanic lithosphere: The Sea, v. 7, p. 1025–1119.

Yılmaz, Y., O. Tüysüz, E.Yiğitbaş, Ş. Can Genç, and A.M.C. Şengör, 1997, Geology and tectonic evolution of the Pontides, *in* A.G. Robinson, ed., Regional and petroleum geology of the Black Sea and surrounding region: AAPG Memoir 68, p. 183–226.

Chapter 11

Geology and Tectonic Evolution of the Pontides

Yücel Yılmaz
Okan Tüysüz
Erdinç Yiğitbaş
Ş. Can Genç
A.M.C. Şengör
İstanbul Technical University (İ.T.Ü.)
Maslak, İstanbul, Turkey

ABSTRACT

This chapter describes the internal divisions and the orogenic evolution of the Pontides, the northernmost tectonic division of Turkey.

The Pontides are an east-west–trending orogenic belt, representing an amalgamated tectonic entity in which three tectonostratigraphically different sectors can be distinguished: the Western Pontides, the Central Pontides, and the Eastern Pontides. The Western Pontides consist of the İstranca Massif, the İstanbul-Zonguldak Zone, the Armutlu-Almacık Zone, and the Sakarya continent. The Eastern Pontides are represented by the following east-west–trending tectonic zones: a magmatic belt, a fore-arc basin fill, a belt of metamorphic massif, an ophiolitic suture zone, and a remnant basin fill. The Central Pontides represent a tectonic knot where the eastern Pontide units and the western Pontide units have been tectonically juxtaposed.

The Pontides represent segments of the Tethyside system that carry the record of Cimmeride and Alpide orogenic events. The Cimmeride orogeny resulted from the elimination of Paleotethys and her dependencies such as the Karakaya marginal basin, which existed during the Triassic. The Paleotethyan Ocean was located to the north of the Cimmerian continent, parts of which form the basement of the Pontides. During the closure of the Paleotethys, an Andean-type magmatic belt was developed on the Cimmerian continent due to the southward subduction of the Paleotethyan Ocean floor. During this period, the Neotethys began to open, possibly as a back-arc basin, behind the Cimmerian continent. In the Dogger assemblage, while the collision between the Scythian platform of Laurasia and Cimmerian continent took place in the north and eliminated most of the Paleotethys Ocean floor, the Neotethys continued to grow in the south.

The late Cretaceous witnessed the elimination of the Neotethys due to its northward subduction under the Pontides. This created a new active continental margin arc. The closure of the Neotethys resulted in the collision between the Pontides arc and the Tauride-Anatolide Platform. Its effects continued until the middle Eocene. The present mountain regions began to elevate as a giant horst block during the late Miocene.

INTRODUCTION

The Turkish orogenic collage, of which the Pontides (Ketin, 1966) is a prominent part, forms a segment of the Tethyside superorogenic system, which itself consisted of two superimposed orogens, the Cimmerides and the Alpides (Şengör, 1987). Of all the Turkish blocks, the Pontides alone preserve a nearly complete record of the evolution of the Tethysides. The present tectonic framework of Turkey has formed mainly as a result of closure of the multibranched Neotethyan Ocean during the late Mesozoic and Cenozoic (Şengör and Yılmaz, 1981) (Figure 1). Figure 1 is a tectonic map showing the first-order tectonic units; that is, independently functioning plate tectonic elements that participated in the Neotethyan evolution of Turkey. These are, from north to south, the İstanbul-Zonguldak Zone [the İstanbul-Balkan fragment of Şengör (1987)] and the Sakarya continent [which together constitute Ketin's (1966) Pontides], the Kırşehir block, the Menderes-Taurus platform (Görür et al., 1984), and the Arabian platform. These blocks are separated by Neotethyan sutures, including the East Anatolian accretionary complex, which is characterized as a suture knot. Okay's (1989) descriptive unit names, İstanbul and Sakarya zones, correspond with our genetically named units. In this framework, the Pontides represent the northernmost tectonic zone that was formed as a consequence of the Neotethyan evolution. However, these units include a complex array of plate boundary systems that formed during the Neotethyan, as well as the pre-Neotethyan evolution (Şengör et al., 1980, 1984; Şengör and Yılmaz, 1981). The record of these activities is found in various places and in various states of preservation. The first step in reconstructing the past configurations is to identify different tectonic entities; that is, sutures, magmatic arcs, transform faults, and fragments of continental and oceanic crust. The approach in this chapter is to introduce different tectonic entities and to document their order of amalgamation in order to reconstruct the evolution of the Pontides.

The Pontides extend as a morphological entity from the Bulgarian Rhodope Mountains in the west to the Caucasus in the east (Figure 1). This mountain range was elevated to its present height rather late, as a consequence of late Miocene shortening. The geological boundaries of the Pontides do not exactly follow the limits of the present morphological entities. In many places, they extend far beyond the limits of this mountainous terrane. The northern boundary of the Pontides is hidden under the waters of the Black Sea. The southern boundary is the Erzincan-Ankara suture zone in the east. From Ankara westward it splays into two branches. The northern branch is known as the Intra-Pontide suture, and the southern branch is referred to as the İzmir-Ankara suture (Figure 1). The continental fragment between the Intra-Pontide suture and the İzmir-Ankara suture is known as the Sakarya continent (Şengör and Yılmaz, 1981); this continental lithospheric fragment shares many geological features with the Pontides.

The Pontides can be divided tectonically into three sectors; the Western Pontides, the Central Pontides, and the Eastern Pontides (Figure 1). The Western Pontides extend from the Bulgarian Rhodope Massif to the Kargı Massif. The Eastern Pontides are the westward extension of the Caucasus and are co-extensive with it. They comprise mountain ranges of Northeast Anatolia, north of the Ankara-Erzincan suture, and east of the Kargı Massif. The Kargı Massif and the surrounding areas constitute the Central Pontides. Each of these sectors represents an amalgamated tectonic mosaic that consists of different tectonic entities. These are displayed in Figures 1 to 13 and are described in the following paragraphs.

THE WESTERN PONTIDES

The Western Pontides are composed of the following tectonic entities (Figure 1): the İstranca Massif, the İstanbul-Zonguldak Zone, the Armutlu-Almacık Zone, and the Sakarya continent (Figures 1, 4). Each of these tectonic zones is separated from the others by major structural elements such as suture zones or transform faults, and records a different geological history from the surrounding tectonic zones.

The İstranca Massif

The İstranca Massif is a metamorphic complex that is located in the Southwestern Black Sea (Figures 1, 2), where it occupies a large area (~24,000 km^2) in the Thrace region and eastern Bulgaria. The northern boundary of the İstranca Massif is an east-west–trending flysch-volcanic zone (the Sredna Gora Zone) that is situated between the Moesian Platform and the İstranca Massif (Figure 2). Deep sea sediments, a flysch–wild flysch, and mafic and intermediate volcanic rocks of late Cretaceous age crop out in this zone (Gocev, 1970; Boccaletti et al., 1974, 1988a; Sandulescu, 1978; Burchfiel, 1980).

The southern boundary of the İstranca Massif is a fault zone (Figure 2) separating it from the Thrace Basin, which began to form during the Oligocene. This fault zone played a critical role in the development

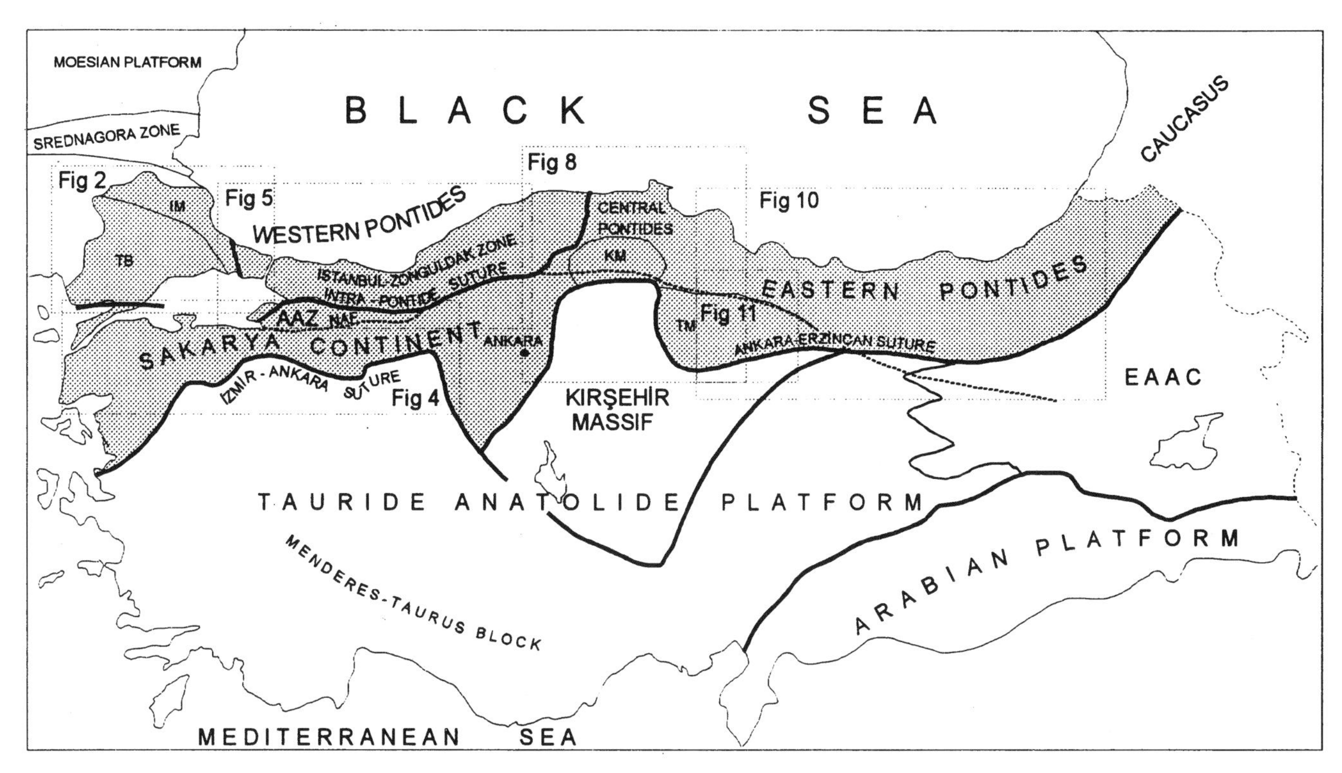

Figure 1. The Turkish orogenic collage with major tectonic divisions of the Pontides (the shaded region). IM = İstranca Massif, TB = Thrace Basin, AAZ = Armutlu-Almacık Zone, KM = Kargı Massif, NAF = North Anatolian transform fault zone, EEAC = eastern Anatolian accretionary complex. Insets show the locations of the maps displayed in the corresponding figures.

of the Thrace Basin. According to seismic and drilling data (Perinçek, 1991), the sediment fill of the Thrace Basin, which is Oligo–Miocene in age (Figure 2), is underlain by metamorphic rocks of the İstranca Massif (Alaygut, 1995). This indicates that the massif occupied much larger areas in the south than its present outcrop pattern suggests. The southern contact of the İstranca Massif with the Sakarya continent is controversial. According to Şengör and Yılmaz (1981), the Intra-Pontide suture forms the boundary (Figure 1) that extends in an east-west direction under the waters of the Marmara Sea between the scattered outcrops of ophiolitic melange that are observed in the Geyve–Armutlu area in the east and around the Gulf of Saros and Şarköy in the west (Figure 4). Kalkan (1993) suggests, based on seismic data, that the Intra-Pontide suture runs approximately north-south between the İstanbul and Çatalca areas (Figures 1, 2, 5). He also claims (Kalkan, 1995, personal communication) based on recent seismic reflection data obtained from the offshore Western Black Sea, that the suture zone runs westward toward Sredna Gora.

A generalized stratigraphic column of the İstranca Massif constructed from Turkish and Bulgarian studies is illustrated in Figure 3 (Aydın, 1974; Chatalov, 1988, 1991; Çăğlayan et al., 1988; Gocev, 1991; Okay et al., 1995). The İstranca Massif is composed of an autochthonous succession overlain tectonically by a northerly transported allochthon (Chatalov, 1988; Dabovski and Savov, 1988; Gocev, 1991). In the Turkish sector, mainly the autochthonous (parautochthon?) units crop out and consist essentially of the two major parts regarded as a core and a cover (Figure 3). The core is composed mainly of high metamorphic grade gneisses, schists, migmatitic granite, and amphibolites. They have undergone polyphase metamorphism and were later cut by granitic dykes and veins. In the core is a mylonitic granite body known as the Kırklareli metagranite displaying intrusive contact relations with the metamorphic assemblage. The Kırklareli granite is dated isotopically at 244 ±5 m.y. (Aydın, 1974).

The high-grade metamorphic rocks of the core and the mylonitic granites are overlain disconformably by phyllites, slates, and recrystallized limestones representing the cover assemblage. These have suffered low-grade regional, dynamothermal metamorphism. This enveloping succession begins at the base with a transgressive unit consisting originally of basal, polygenetic conglomerates and sandstones (Çağlayan et al., 1988; Okay et al., 1995). They pass upward into fine-grained clastics interbedded with limestones. The basal clastics show wide lateral and vertical variations and abrupt transitions. The basal unit is Lower Triassic in age (Chatalov, 1988). There is another Triassic facies in the massif (Okay et al., 1995) in which the core rocks are overlain by quartzitic sandstones (~250 m) followed by a metashale-limestone transition (~500 m). On top of these is a thick, now metamorphic, neritic limestone succession, which in turn is followed by a

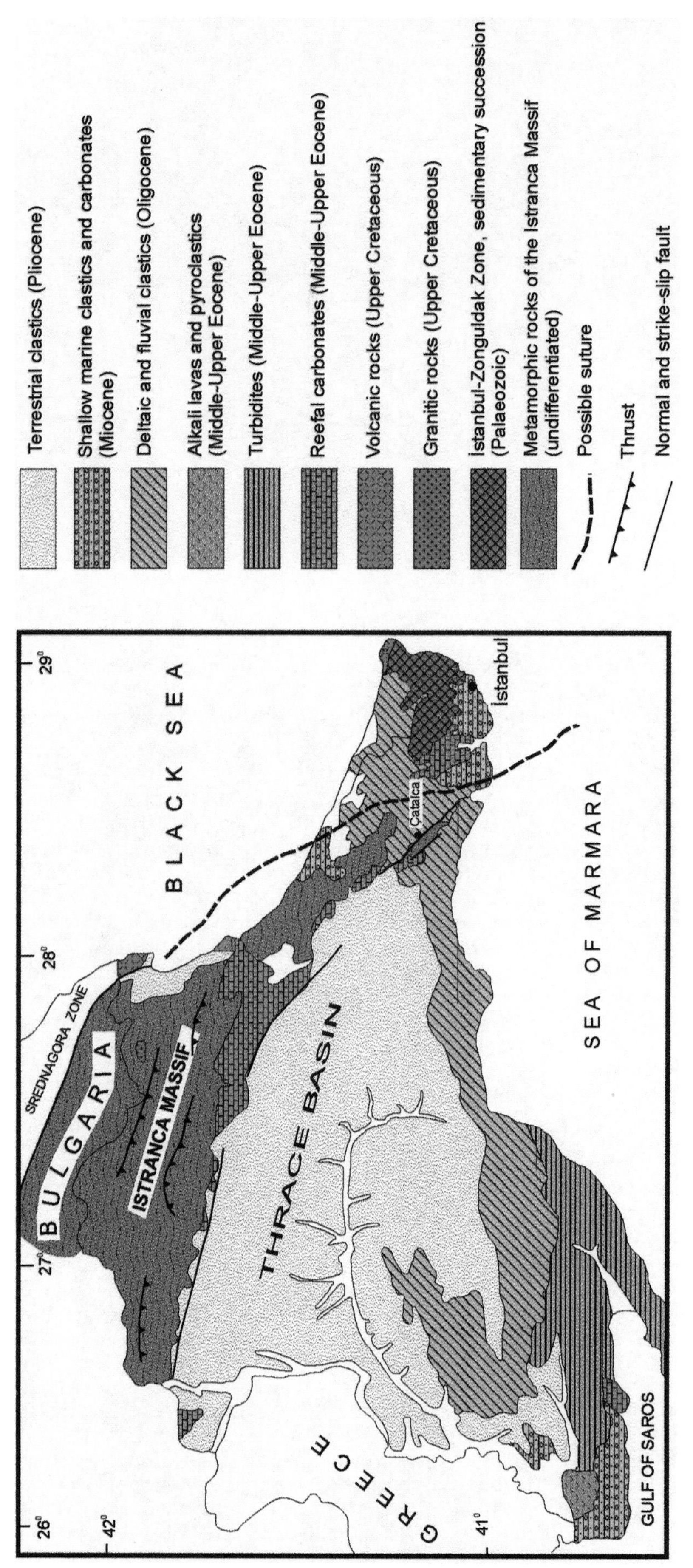

Figure 2. Geological map of the Thrace region, northwestern Turkey.

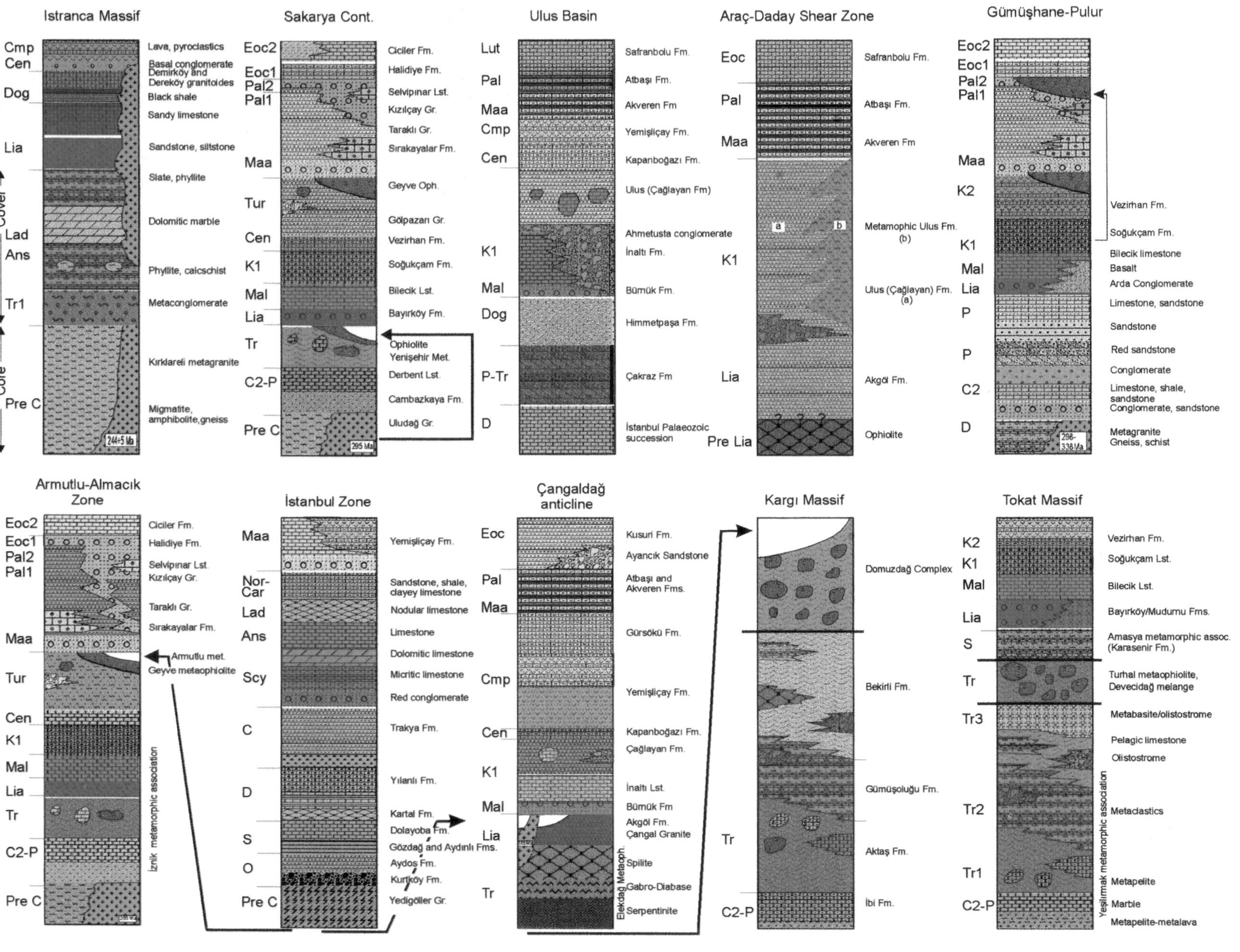

Figure 3. Representative stratigraphic sections from the major tectonic zones of the Pontides.

metasiltstone-shale-limestone alternation. The quartzitic basal unit and overlying neritic limestones are regarded as Early Triassic in age. The following fine-grained clastics and the limestones are Late Triassic in age, as indicated by a similar succession encountered across the border in Bulgaria (Chatalov, 1988).

In the eastern part of the Bulgarian İstranca Massif, the upper layers of the succession are overlain by the products of a new transgression. It begins at the base with coarse to fine detrital deposits of quartzitic metasandstones and conglomerates of Pliensbachian age. Locally, the oolitic, ferruginous, recrystallized limestones give way to Bathonian metasiltstone and metashale. These are followed by neritic limestones of Jurassic age (Chatalov, 1988).

The enveloping metamorphic rocks of the İstranca Massif are cut and intruded by a great variety of igneous rocks in the form of dykes, sills, stocks and plutons [the Dereköy and Demirköy plutons (Aykol and Tokel, 1991)] (Figures 2, 3). These are mainly granodiorite, quartz diorite, and adamellite in composition. The weakly metamorphosed cover succession is overlain by Upper Cretaceous sedimentary rocks and associated volcanic rocks, which are the oldest nonmetamorphic cover (Figure 2).

The rocks of the İstranca Massif display north-vergent thrust tectonics (Figure 2). With this, the different rocks of the massif were imbricated (Üşümezsoy, 1982; Çağlayan et al., 1988; Okay et al., 1995). The thrusting postdates regional metamorphism, and possibly occurred before or during the development of the Upper Cretaceous cover rocks.

The first uplift of the massif occurred before deposition of the Upper Cretaceous rocks. Possibly during this phase, the massif suffered a severe mylonitic deformation along south-verging ductile shear zones where schistose textures of the granitic and metamorphic rocks are observed. Some of the mylonitic orthogneisses, which are previously regarded as the ancient rocks of the İstranca Massif (Pamir and Baykal, 1947; Akartuna, 1953), were possibly formed during this period. One example of the orthogneiss is the syntectonically deformed granitic stock that crops out around the Üsküp village. South-verging stretching lineations were developed as a result of this deformation. These granitic bodies may therefore be considered as sills that were intruded into the metamorphic massif during this phase of extension and accompanying faulting.

The present relative elevation of the İstranca Massif took place mostly since the middle Miocene, judging from the warping and uplift of Neogene erosion surfaces (Erol, 1992), and has been a result of the overall extensional regime affecting the Balkans.

The Sakarya Continent

The Sakarya continent is delimited in the south by the İzmir-Ankara suture (Figure 1), and in the north by the Armutlu-Almacık Zone. The southern branch of the North Anatolian transform fault forms a tectonic boundary between the Sakarya continent and the Armutlu-Almacık Zone (Figures 1, 4, and 5).

In the Sakarya continent, there are two different types of metamorphic assemblages—the Uludağ Group and the Yenişehir Group—that form basement to the nonmetamorphic successions (Figures 3, 4). The Uludağ Group is composed of high-grade schists, gneisses, amphibolites, migmatites, and an intruding granitic pluton [the Söğüt granite (Yılmaz, 1977)] of Carboniferous age [dated isotopically 295 ±5 m.y. (Çoğulu et al., 1965)]. This is the oldest rock group of the region and is unconformably overlain by arkoses (Canbazkaya formation), which pass into richly fossiliferous neritic Permian limestones (Derbent limestone) (Altınlı, 1973; Saner, 1977; Genç, 1987). The autochthonous Permian and Carboniferous sedimentary successions are rare in the region. A few scattered outcrops displaying in-situ Carboniferous and Permian successions are observed along the Göksu Gorge and in the Sakarya River valley near Osmaneli. These rocks commonly outcrop as blocks and debris flow deposits enclosed by Upper Permian–Lower Triassic rocks (Bingöl et al., 1973; Yılmaz, 1981; Yılmaz et al., 1981; Okay et al., 1991). The Triassic successions show fast vertical and lateral transitions. Despite the rapid facies changes, two major rock groups are differentiated: (1) a lower, basal detrital unit and (2) an upper, fine-grained detrital and limestone sequence. The lower and upper units are early and late Triassic in age, respectively (Kaya, 1991; Okay et al., 1991; Genç and Yılmaz, 1995a). Granitic and quartzo-feldspathic metamorphic rocks are the provenance for the lower sequence. The lower clastic rocks pass vertically into a flysch sequence that alternates with volcanic rocks. Within this detrital-dominated host there are some Lower Triassic limestone layers and lenses. Upward in the succession, these rocks give way to a Middle–Upper Jurassic deep-sea sedimentary and volcanic association including red mudstones, shales, and micritic limestones (Genç, 1987; Önder and Göncüoğlu, 1989; Kaya and Möstler, 1992; Genç and Yılmaz, 1995a).

The Yenişehir Group that is known as the lower association with respect to the Uludağ Group [the upper association of Genç (1993) and Genç and Yılmaz (1995a)] consists of two tectonostratigraphic units: a metaophiolite, and a metamorphosed volcanic and sedimentary unit (Figure 3). This unit has undergone glaucophane-bearing greenschist facies metamorphism (Yılmaz, 1977, 1981; Okay et al., 1991; Genç, 1993; Genç and Yılmaz, 1995a). The metaophiolite is a tectonic slice, wedged into the metasedimentary and volcanic rocks of possibly Triassic age. The age inference is based on the lithological correlation of these rocks with the surrounding nonmetamorphic Triassic succession in the Uludağ Group (Genç, 1987; Yılmaz et al., 1990; Genç and Yılmaz, 1995a). This assumption is supported further by the radiometric age data (A. Okay, 1995, personal communication) and fossils from these rocks (Önder and Göncüoğlu, 1989; Kaya, 1991; Kaya and Möstler, 1992; Genç, 1993). In addition to the ophiolitic tectonic wedge, a thin tectonic eclogite sliver is seen within the group, near Bandırma (Okay et al., 1991).

The contact between the Uludağ Group and the Yenişehir Group is a thrust. This primary tectonic

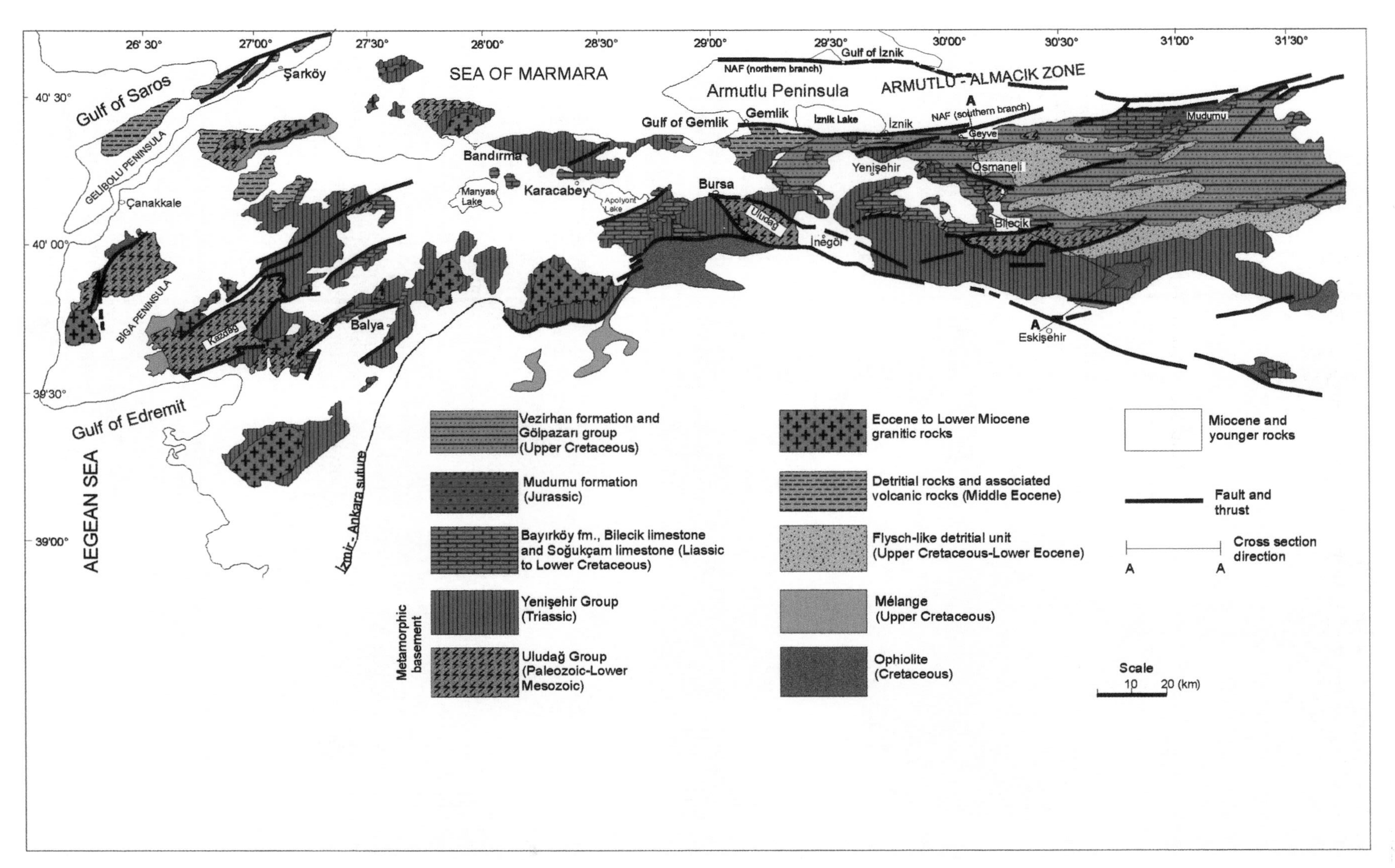

Figure 4. Geological map of the Sakarya continent. NAF = North Anatolian transform fault zone. AA′ is the direction of the cross section shown in Figure 6.

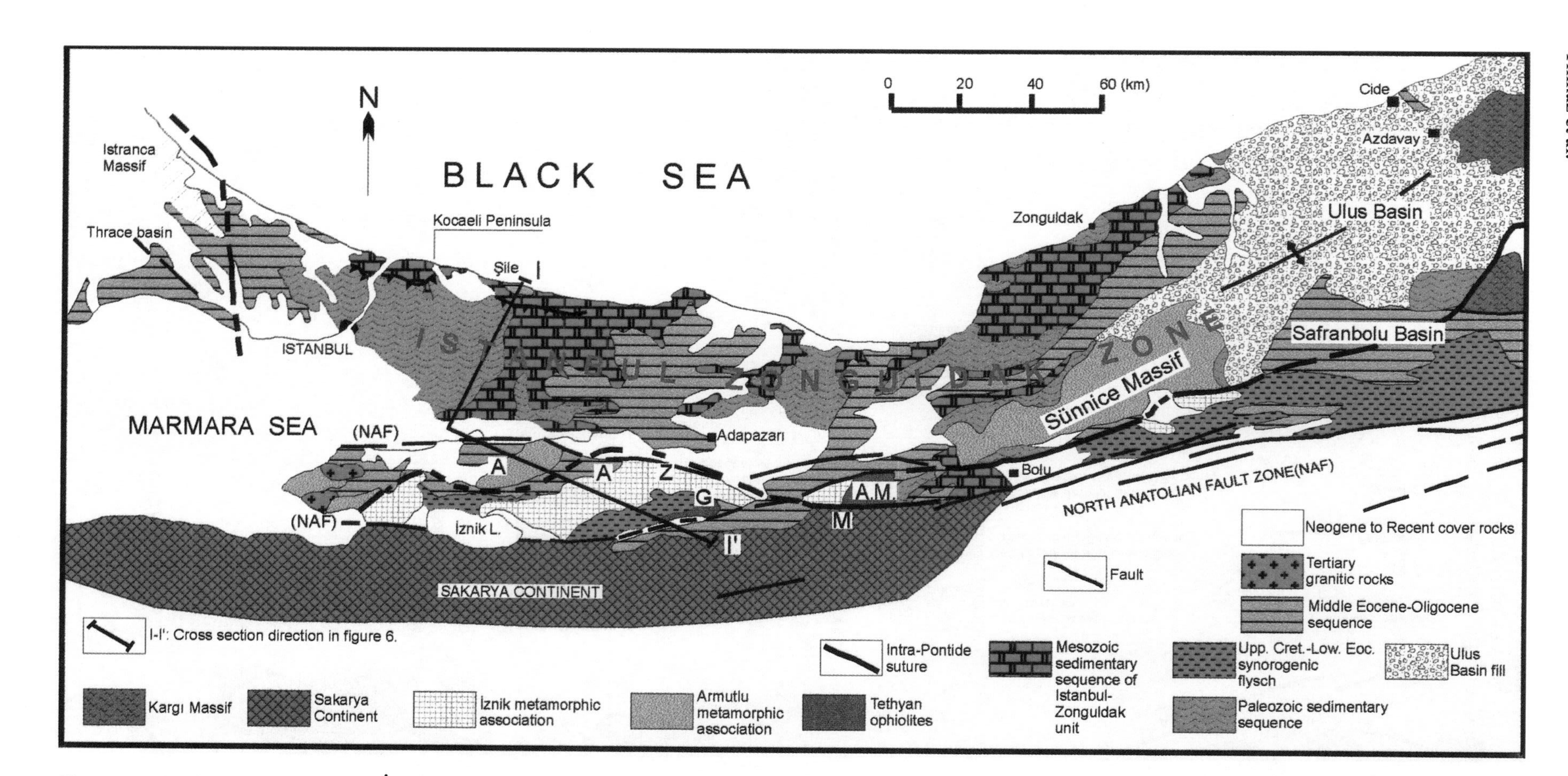

Figure 5. Geological map of the İstanbul-Zonguldak Zone and the Armutlu-Almacık Zone of the Western Pontides. AM = Almacık Mountain, AAZ = the Armutlu-Almacık zone, NAF = North Anatolian transform fault zone, G = Geyve, M = Mudurnu, L = Lake. II′ is direction of the cross section shown in Figure 6.

boundary is rarely observed in the outcrop because it is commonly hidden by younger rocks or offset by faults. The metamorphic rock units and their tectonic contacts are overlain by a transgressive sedimentary sequence that begins with basal sandstones of Liassic age (Bayırköy formation) (Figures 3, 4). These basal detrital rocks are overlain by a thick neritic limestone succession; beginning at the base with oolitic and ferruginous limestones passing upward into micritic limestones of Late Jurassic age [Bilecik limestone (Granit and Tintant, 1960; Altınlı, 1973; Koçyiğit et al., 1992)]. This pink limestone is gradually replaced by thinly bedded white limestone of Early Cretaceous age [Soğukçam limestone (Altınlı, 1973)], which in turn passes upward into a red pelagic limestone-mudstone unit of Cenomanian–Turonian age [Vezirhan formation (Altınlı, 1973)].

In the succession, there is a time gap corresponding to a Coniacian–Santonian interval, recorded as uplift, erosion, and severe deformation (Yılmaz et al., 1995). There is a sequence of late Campanian–Maastrichtian age, resting on the older units with a sharp angular unconformity (Figure 3) (Altınlı, 1973; Saner, 1977; Yılmaz, 1981; Yılmaz et al., 1981, 1995). At the base is a basal sandstone-conglomerate unit, followed by flysch. There are abundant blocks, olistoliths, and fragments of older units, comprising debris flows within the flysch. There are also ophiolitic blocks in the flysch succession. Following the incorporation of the blocks and olistostromes, the flysch is replaced gradually by shallow marine sandstones and reefal limestones (Selvipınar formation) (Altınlı, 1973), and then by continental red beds (Kızılçay Group) that formed during the Maastrichtian–Paleocene transition (Yılmaz, 1981; Yılmaz et al., 1995).

The Mesozoic and early Tertiary successions of the Sakarya continent are overlain unconformably by basal clastic rocks of a new transgression that occurred during the middle Eocene (Figure 3). In this marine environment were deposited shallow marine detrital rocks including sandy limestones, sandstones, and fine-grained clastic rocks (Ciciler Formation) alternating with widespread calc-alkaline, intermediate lavas, and pyroclastic rocks (Yılmaz et al., 1990, 1995; Bozcu, 1992). The volcanic products are not restricted to any belt and cover the entire region from the Black Sea to the central Anatolia. This new phase of deposition continued till the late Eocene and then was replaced by continental red beds during the Oligocene (Yılmaz et al., 1990).

The direct relationship between the Sakarya continent and the central Pontide range is hidden under the thick, Neogene volcanic blanket of the Galatean magmatic complex (Figure 8).

The Armutlu-Almacık Zone

The Armutlu-Almacık Zone is situated in the Armutlu Peninsula and its easterly continuation in the Almacık and Sünnice mountains (Figures 4, 5). This zone is made up of distinctly different metamorphic rock associations. They were amalgamated prior to the deposition of the Upper Campanian–Maastrichtian successions, which are the first nonmetamorphic common cover (Figure 3) (Yılmaz et al., 1995).

The northern boundary of the Armutlu-Almacık Zone is with the İstanbul-Zonguldak Zone, and is represented by the northern branch of the North Anatolian transform fault zone (Figures 1, 4, and 5). Within the North Anatolian transform fault zone between the Geyve Gorge in the west and the Bolu area in the east, there are a few scattered outcrops of an ophiolitic melange association of Late Cretaceous age (Figure 5). These ophiolites are considered to be remnants of the Intra-Pontide suture (Yılmaz et al., 1981, 1995).

In the Armutlu-Almacık Zone, three metamorphic assemblages are distinguished (Figures 3, 5). These are (1) a weakly and cataclastically metamorphosed Paleozoic succession (Armutlu metamorphic association), (2) a regional metamorphic association (İznik metamorphic association), and (3) a metamorphosed ophiolite association, the Geyve metaophiolite (Yılmaz et al., 1995).

Sequence of the Armutlu metamorphic association is shown in Figure 3, and is described in detail by Akartuna (1968), Göncüoğlu et al. (1987), and Yılmaz et al. (1990, 1995). This unit crops out in the western tip of the Armutlu Peninsula and in the central part of the Almacık Mountains and the Sünnice Mountains (Figure 5).

The basement rocks of the Armutlu metamorphic unit consist of amphibolite-grade micaschists, amphibolites, metagabbro, and an intrusive granite displaying pervasive ductile deformation (Yedigöller Group). The high-grade metamorphic assemblage is overlain nonconformably by a distinctly low-grade metamorphic succession (Yılmaz et al., 1990, 1995). At the base, there are slightly metamorphosed, mostly subareal felsic pyroclastic rocks including metaignimbrites. The metavolcanic rocks intercalate upward with thick quartzites and arkoses. These units gradually give way to thick and dark, graptolite-bearing slates that contain recrystallized limestone lenses. These rocks are regarded as Ordovician in age (Kaya, 1977; Yılmaz et al., 1981, 1990, 1995). The dark slates pass upward into a massive, dark gray, locally fossiliferous, recrystallized limestone and dolomite unit of Devonian age (Abdüsselamoğlu, 1959). This is followed by metaflysch containing blocks of the underlying units. The flysch is regarded as Carboniferous in age (Yılmaz et al., 1981).

The Armutlu metamorphic unit has undergone semibrittle, mylonitic deformation, which produced pervasive foliation. The metamorphic grade rarely exceeds the lower limit of the greenschist facies; therefore, the rocks still preserve most of their primary sedimentary features and yield fossils. The Armutlu metamorphic unit closely resembles the basement rocks and the overlying Paleozoic succession of the İstanbul-Zonguldak Zone (see Figure 3) (Abdüsselamoğlu, 1959; Kaya, 1977; Yılmaz et al., 1981, 1995). In the light of this, the Armutlu metamorphic unit may be regarded as the slightly metamorphosed equivalent of the Paleozoic and older rocks of the İstanbul-Zonguldak Zone.

The oldest nonmetamorphic cover rocks that overlie the Armutlu metamorphic assemblage begin with a basal conglomerate and sandstone unit (Figure 7). This gives way to the volcanogenic flysch succession of the Upper Crecateous (Campanian?–Maastrichtian) (Yılmaz et al., 1990, 1995; Bozcu, 1992).

Young strike-slip faults separate the Armutlu metamorphic association from a group of high-grade metamorphic rocks, the İznik metamorphic association (Figures 3, 5). The İznik metamorphic association crops out extensively in the central parts of the Armutlu peninsula and the Almacık Mountains (Figure 5). Despite the development of pervasive penetrative foliations and the attendant regional dynamothermal metamorphism from middle to higher greenschist facies in this unit, it was possible to recognize in detail the original stratigraphic sequence (Figure 3) (Yılmaz et al., 1990, 1995). That sequence comprises a thick (>3 km) Paleozoic and Mesozoic succession including the Upper Cretaceous rocks.

There is a close similarity between the İznik metamorphic sequence and coeval units of the Sakarya continent (Figure 3), suggesting that the İznik metamorphic assemblage represents the northern part of the Sakarya continent that has undergone regional metamorphism (Yılmaz et al., 1995). The uppermost rocks of the İznik metamorphic sequence consist of a slightly metamorphosed pelagic red limestone-mudstone sequence of Late Cretaceous age, interbedded with volcanic rocks. This passes into a slightly metamorphosed flysch succession. The flysch contains abundant blocks of recrystallized limestone and ophiolitic rocks. These units are very similar to the Cenomanian–Turonian rocks of the Sakarya continent.

The oldest nonmetamorphic unit that overlies the İznik metamorphic assemblage is a basal unit of a new transgression that occurred during the late Campanian–Maastrichtian (Figures 3, 7). This suggests that the metamorphism occurred during the Late Cretaceous, possibly pre-Campanian–post-Turonian, interval.

The İznik metamorphic succession may also be compared closely with the İstranca Massif (Figure 3). The lithologies, their ages, and the sequences are similar. The main difference between the two formations is the absence of the Upper Jurassic to Upper Cretaceous succession in the İstranca Massif. This absence may be attributed to the lack of data and/or to role of erosion in later phases, which might have completely obliterated the upper part of the succession.

There is a metamorphosed ophiolite association that outcrops along the Geyve Gorge and the Mudurnu River valley (Figures 5, 6) (Yılmaz et al., 1990, 1995; Bozcu, 1992). The Geyve metaophiolite represents an ophiolite slab that has undergone polyphase metamorphism. The ophiolite slab consists of two major tectonic slices (Figure 6). The lower slice is composed of layers of an intact ophiolitic stratigraphy from ultramafic rocks at the base to basalt lavas and interbedded pelagic rocks at the top. The upper slice consists of a diabase and basalt layer that rests on different layers of the ophiolite, over a thrust surface (Bozcu, 1992). The granitic veins and dykes, formed anatectically from the ophiolite, were injected into the ophiolite association across the thrust surface just mentioned (Yılmaz et al., 1990).

The Geyve metaophiolite was thrust onto the upper units of the İznik metamorphic association (Figures 3, 5, and 6). The Geyve metaophiolite, together with the İznik metamorphic association, is separated from the Armutlu metamorphic association by the branches of the North Anatolian transform fault (Figure 5); we assume that the Armutlu metamorphic association was thrust initially onto the Geyve ophiolite, and then the thrust contact has been cut and offset by the transform fault (Figure 6) (Yılmaz et al., 1995).

The oldest unit deposited on the Geyve metaophiolite is a thick (>500 m) conglomerate and sandstone unit of Campanian?–Maastrichtian age (Figure 5). This unit is commonly represented by a coarse fluvial sequence interfingering with reefal limestones and beach sandstones (Yılmaz et al., 1990, 1995; Bozcu, 1992). These are interpreted as having been deposited in an active tectonic environment, with various components forming a thick clastic wedge and showing rapid lateral and vertical variations. These units were primarily deposited in fault-bounded basins (Yılmaz et al., 1995). The ages of the units lying above and below the Geyve metaophiolite (Figure 3) restrict the time of emplacement of the ophiolite nappe to the Late Cretaceous (the post-Turonian–pre-Late-Campanian interval). The shallow marine sediments are gradually replaced by a flysch sequence (Gölpazari Group); the same flysch that extends from the Sakarya continent (Figures 3, 6) (Yılmaz et al., 1995).

The İstanbul-Zonguldak Zone

The İstanbul-Zonguldak Zone represents the northernmost part of the Western Pontides (Figures 1, 5). This zone was originally defined as the İstanbul nappe by Şengör et al. (1984), a now widely disputed interpretation (Okay et al., 1994) (Figure 3). Although its original tectonic setting is now discredited, its structural position has not yet been seriously challenged.

The stratigraphic section of the İstanbul-Zonguldak Zone is shown in Figure 3: there is a high-grade metamorphic assemblage at the base of the zone. Rare outcrops of this basement are exposed in the Sünnice Mountains and along the Karadere Stream valley in the Safranbolu area (Figure 5). This assemblage consists of metagabbro, metadiabase, dolerite dykes, migmatitic gneiss, schist, and an intrusive granite (Yılmaz and Tüysüz, 1984; Yiğitbaş et al., 1995). This crystalline basement is regarded as Precambrian in age, because the metamorphic rocks are overlain stratigraphically by a thick, lower Paleozoic sedimentary sequence (Dean et al., 1993) (Figure 3), which outcrops extensively in the Kocaeli Peninsula and in the Zonguldak area (Figure 5).

The lowermost unit lying above the metamorphic basement association is a red arkosic conglomerate, sandstone, and mudstone unit of Early Ordovician age (Kurtköy formation) (Dean et al., 1993). Quartzites (Aydos Formation) underlie dark-colored siltstones,

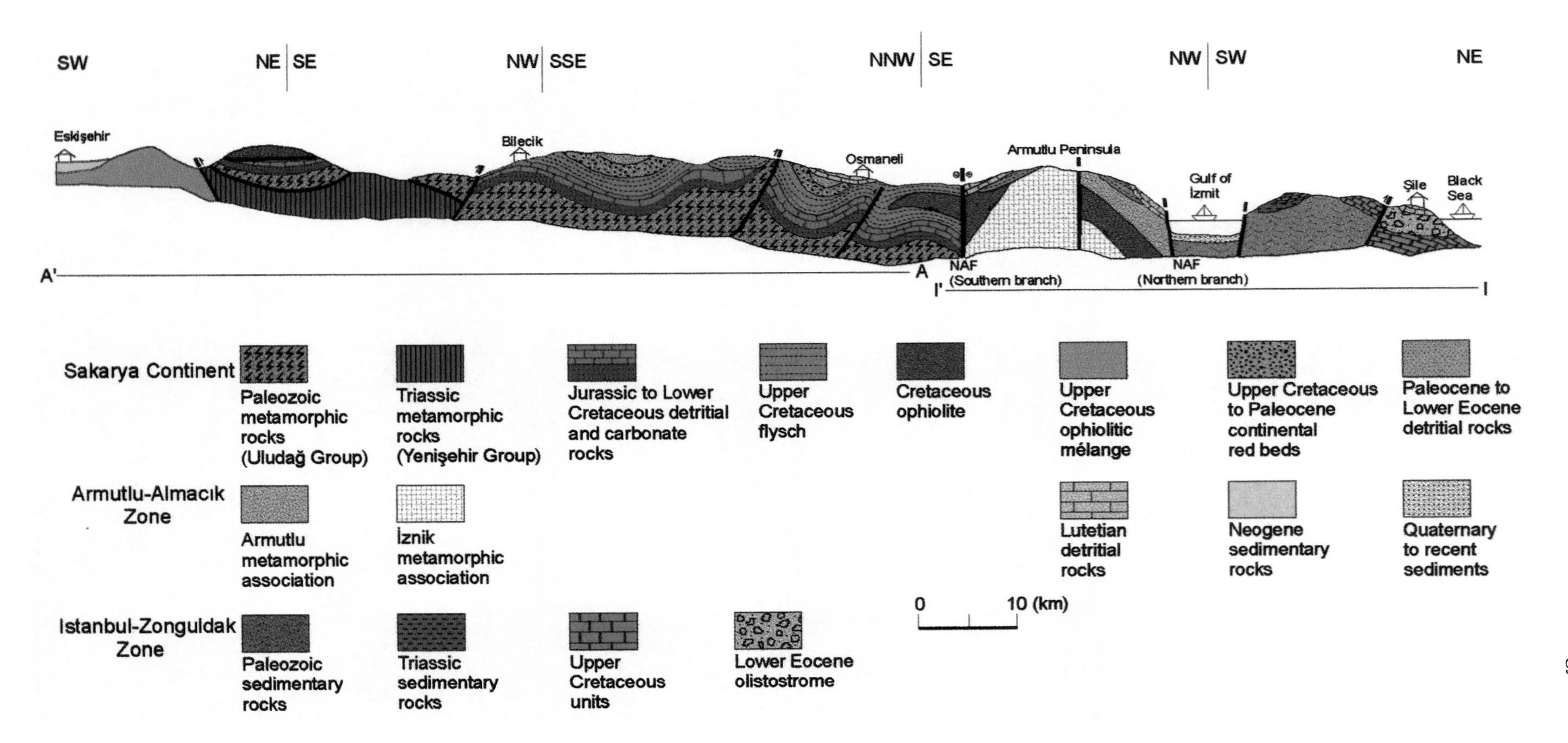

Figure 6. Geological composite cross section across the Western Pontides. Figures 4 and 5 show the cross section direction (II′ and AA′). NAF = Northern Anatolian transform fault zone. Horizontal distance is ~240 km. ⊗; ⊗ symbols indicate relative displacement along the fault.

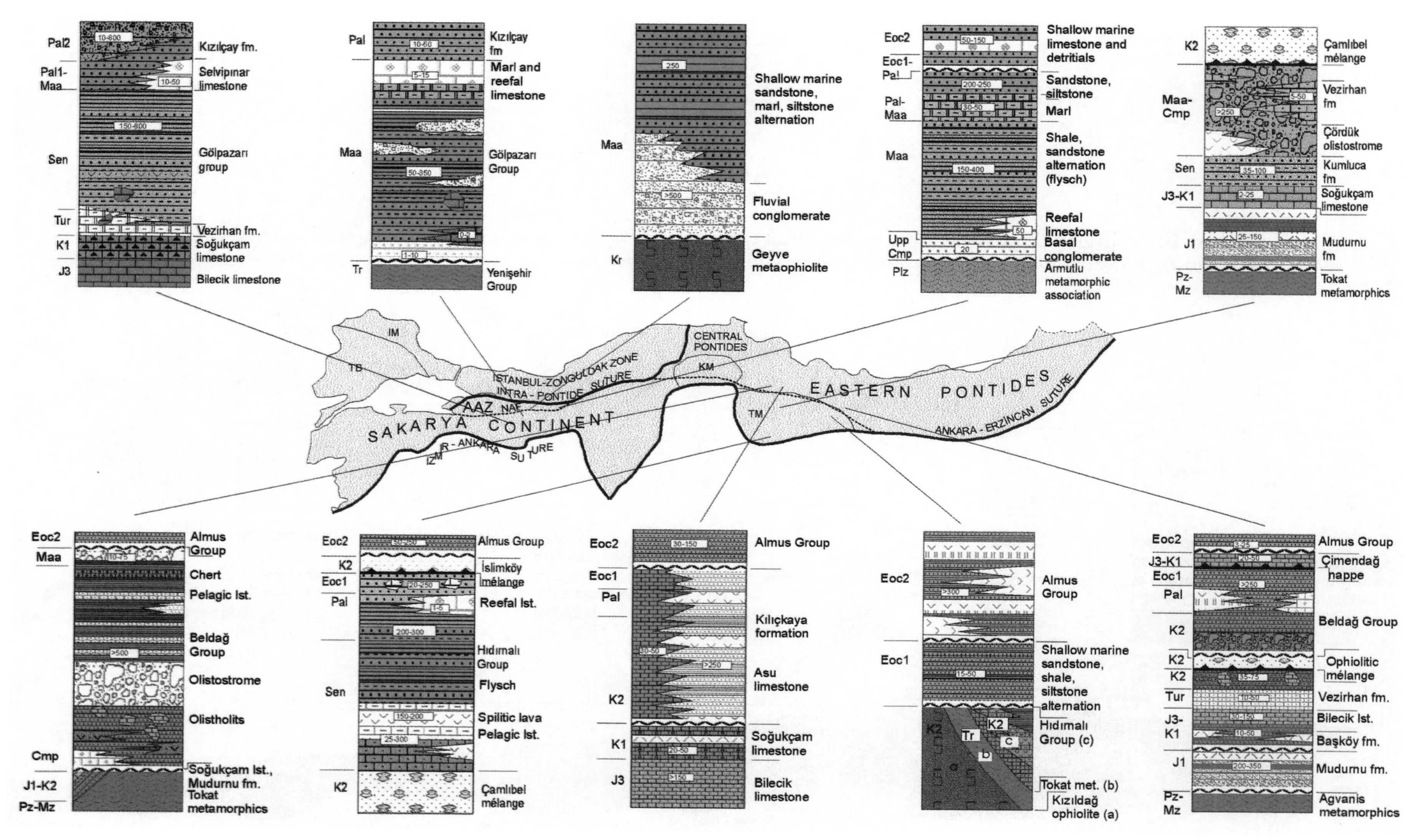

Figure 7. Representative stratigraphic sections from the different parts of the Pontides displaying upper Cretaceous–Eocene successions. Numbers indicate thickness of the rock units.

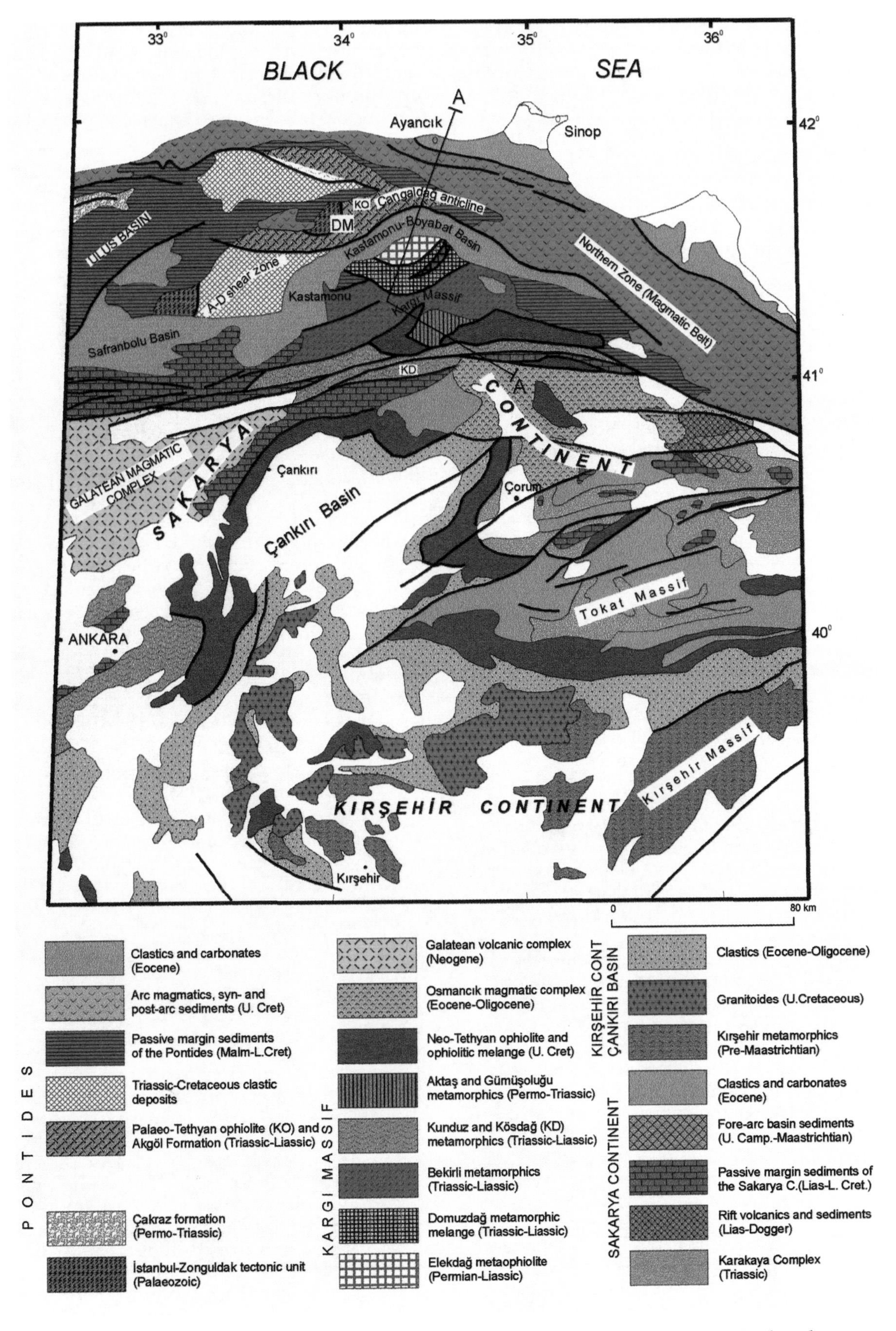

Figure 8. Geological map of the Central Pontide regions. A.D. shear zone = Araç-Daday shear zone, DM = Devrekani massif, KO = Küre ophiolite. AA′ is the direction of the cross section shown in Figure 9.

graywackes, and chamositic shales (Gözdağ Formation). These grade into thin upper quartzitic layers, which in turn are overlain by gray graptolitic mudstone and limestone units of Middle Silurian age (Aydınlı Formation) (Dean et al., 1993). These sandy limestones grade into coralline limestones and bituminous alternating limestones and marls of Silurian age (Dolayoba Formation). According to Dean et al. (1993), the Upper Silurian is missing in the Zonguldak region. The Devonian begins with quartzitic layers passing into limestones, which grade laterally into interbedded shales and siltstones (Kartal Formation). In the İstanbul area, on the other hand, Silurian and Devonian units are transitional (Ketin, 1983). Upward in the section, siltstones and then an alternating sandstone-shale-limestone unit become dominant. These are Late Devonian in age. They are gradually replaced by thinly bedded limestones and cherty limestones with chert and phospate nodules (Yılanlı Formation), which are followed by turbiditic sandstones and shales of Carboniferous age (Trakya Formation).

The flysch unit lying at the top of the succession in the western sector is absent in the Zonguldak area, where the Carboniferous sequence is represented by a succession deposited in shallow marine to continental transitional environments (Kerey, 1984). The dolomitic limestone of the Lower Carboniferous underlies sandstones, siltstones, and claystones, which are followed by coal-bearing sandstones, claystones, and conglomerates.

The Paleozoic sequence is severely deformed by asymmetrical folding and west-vergent thrusting in the İstanbul area (Ketin, 1983, 1992). On top of the deformed Paleozoic sequence, patchy outcrops of Mesozoic and Tertiary rocks are observed in the Kocaeli Peninsula, where the Paleozoic sedimentary sequence is overlain unconformably by a thick, red, fluvial, coarse clastic unit, alternating with alkaline lavas. The continental red beds that outcrop in the İstanbul area and the Çakraz area in the east (Figure 8) are overlain by Scythian oolitic limestones, sandstones, and shales. These pass into marly and micritic limestones, which underlie a nodular limestone of Ladinian age. This sequence gives way to halobia-bearing flysch of Carnian age (Özdemir et al., 1973).

Jurassic and Lower Cretaceous rocks outcrop only east of Zonguldak, where there is a thick Mesozoic sedimentary sequence that is observed in a northeast-southwest–trending syncline of the Ülüs basin (Figures 3, 5). At the base of the succession, there are two different sequences, a wild flysch–flysch unit of Late Jurassic age [Ahmetusta conglomerate (Aydın et al., 1995)] and a partly coeval neritic limestone unit (İnaltı Formation). Both of these are overlain by Middle Cretaceous turbiditic flysch deposits that contain blocks of the underlying Jurassic units (Baykal, 1954; Saner, 1980; Yergök et al., 1989; Derman, 1990).

Along the northern margin of the Pontide Mountains near Azdavay, the succession unconformably overlies the Permo–Triassic red beds of the Çakraz Formation with the ammonite-bearing Middle Jurassic sandstone-mudstone-shale alternation (Himmetpaşa formation) (Sayılı and Derman, 1992). This is overlain by the red basal conglomerate-sandstone, mudstone units (Bürnük Formation of the Late Jurassic). This succession indicates a fault-controlled environment of deposition, followed by a transgression. In this active tectonic environment, coarse clastic wedges passed through to fine detrital rocks (Ulus and Çağlayan formations) and into reefal limestone lenses (İnaltı Formation) during the Late Jurassic to Late Cretaceous (Derman, 1990). These are overlain unconformably by a new sequence in which a very thin clastic unit is followed by a pelagic red limestone unit (Kapanboğazı Formation). Volcanoclastic sediments and pyroclastic rocks are interbedded with the clastic rocks (Yemişliçay Formation), which give way to a turbiditic flysch of Campanian–Maastrichtian age (Blumenthal, 1940; Ketin and Gümüş, 1963; Akyol, 1974; Gedik and Korkmaz, 1984). The flysch passes upward into neritic and pelagic limestones overlain by shales [the Akveren Formation of the Maastrichtian–Paleocene (Ketin and Gümüş, 1963)]. This unit transits to the red-marl-marly limestone unit of the Paleocene (the Atbaşı Formation).

The Upper Cretaceous is also widespread around the beginning of the İstanbul region. It is represented by two different rock groups. Along the Black Sea coast, andesitic lavas, pyroclastic rocks, and volcanogenic sedimentary rocks crop out (Yemişliçay Formation). Along the coast of the Marmara Sea, thinly bedded, clayey, white limestones dominate and are followed by a flysch (Gürsökü Formation). The Lutetian clastic units (the Kilimlı Formation) unconformably overlie the older rocks.

THE CENTRAL PONTIDES

The Central Pontides are made up of approximately east-west–trending tectonic zones (Figure 8). From the north to the south these are; (1) the northern zone (the Çangaldağ high), (2) the Araç-Daday shear zone, (3) the Kastamonu-Boyabat Basin fill, (4) the Kargı Massif, and (5) the ophiolite belt. Figure 9 displays a north-south geological cross section across the Central Pontides that shows the tectonic positions of the constituent tectonostratigraphic units.

The Northern Zone

The northern zone represents a magmatic belt. The generalized stratigraphic section of this zone is displayed in Figures 3 and 9 and may be characterized as a metamorphic basement complex and an overlying volcanic Mesozoic and Cenozoic sequence. There is a big anticline of Tertiary age in the northern zone, extending approximately east-west along the Çangaldağ high (Figures 8, 9). At the core of the anticline, there are two rock groups that form the basement (Figure 9). The first rock group is a metamorphosed, ordered ophiolite (Küre ophiolite) and overlying deep-sea cover sedimentary rocks (Akgöl Formation) (Ketin and Gümüş, 1963; Yılmaz and Tüysüz, 1984). The epiophiolitic sedimentary rocks were dated as Carboniferous to Liassic in age (Yılmaz and Şengör,

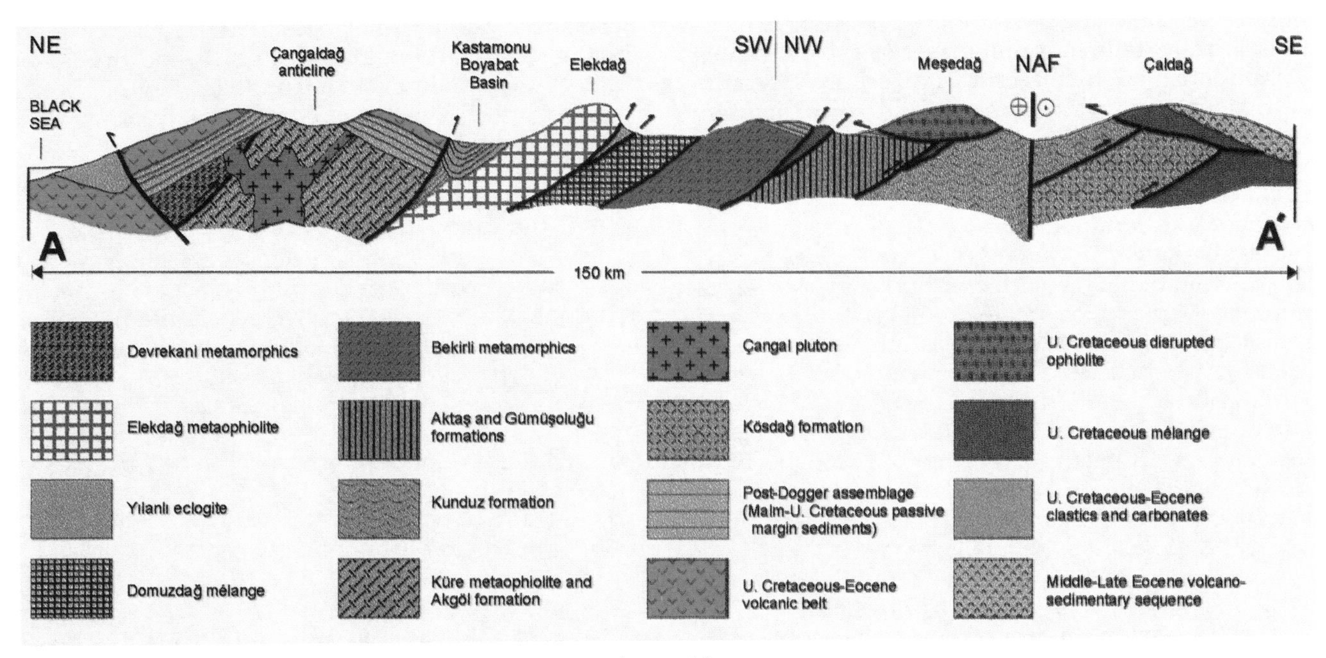

Figure 9. Geological cross section across the Central Pontides.

1985; Aydın et al., 1986; Önder et al., 1987), based on spores and palynomorphs. This ophiolite is regarded as the remnant of the Paleotethys Ocean; its geological significance is discussed by Şengör (1979a), Şengör et al. (1984), Yılmaz and Şengör (1985), Şengör (1990), and Ustaömer and Robertson (1993, 1994) and will not be repeated here. The second rock group is a dynamothermally metamorphosed, pelitic association that is referred to as the Devrekani Massif (Figures 8, 9) (Yılmaz and Tüysüz, 1984; Yılmaz, 1990; Tüysüz, 1990, 1993). The Devrekani Massif is represented by high-grade gneisses, amphibolites, quartzo-feldspathic schists, marbles, and overlying slates and phyllites. This sequence is considered to be basement of the İstanbul-Zonguldak Zone of the Western Pontides (Yılmaz and Tüysüz, 1984; Tüysüz, 1990; Ustaömer and Robertson, 1993). Tüysüz (1990) describes a transition between the Devrekani Massif and the İstanbul-Zonguldak Zone in the Karadere-Araç area. The Devrekani Massif rests tectonically on the pelagic sedimentary rocks of the Küre-Elekdağ ophiolites (Figures 8, 9). A posttectonic, intrusive granite (the Çangal granite) intruded into the Küre ophiolite and the Devrekani Massif, and cut the thrust contact that separates them (Figure 9). The granite is dated 165 ±5 m.y. by K/Ar data (Yılmaz, 1979; Bonhomme and Yılmaz, 1984; Yılmaz and Boztuğ, 1986).

A thick Mesozoic and Tertiary succession overlies this metamorphic and granitic basement. The early to middle Mesozoic units of the Central Pontides are of two types: the Sakarya type and the Pontide type (Tüysüz and Dellaloğlu, 1992). The Sakarya type begins with clastic units of Liassic age on the metamorphic basement rocks (Yılmaz, 1980; Yılmaz et al., 1995). These are followed by buff-colored, thickly bedded, clayey limestones (Bilecik limestone) of the Late Jurassic–Early Cretaceous age, which grade into pelagic limestone units (the Soğukçam limestone and Vezirhan Formation) of Early and Late Cretaceous age.

The Pontide-type sequence begins with a coarse clastic unit of Malm age, the Bürnük Formation (Yılmaz and Tüysüz, 1984; Aydın et al., 1986), resting on a mosaic of metamorphosed ophiolite sequence (Yılmaz and Boztuğ, 1986) (Figure 9). The coarse, clastic units pass laterally into a gray, neritic Malm–Barremian carbonate unit (İnaltı limestone) of Barremian–Callovian age (Yılmaz and Tüysüz, 1984; Aydın et al., 1986; Tüysüz, 1990). Across a surface of locally developed unconformity, these are followed by black shales and a turbiditic sandstone-siltstone-shale alternation (Çağlayan Formation) that contains neritic limestone lenses at the base, and blocks and fragments of the same carbonate rocks at the top of the succession. This clastic sediment deposition was in part coeval with the İnaltı sedimentation and reached from the Malm to the Albian (Yılmaz and Tüysüz, 1984; Tüysüz, 1990). The Pontide-type sequence may be regarded as the eastward extension of the succession encountered in the Ülüs Basin of the Western Pontide range (Figures 3, 5, 8, and 9).

The Araç-Daday Shear Zone

Between the Pontide-type sequence and the Sakarya-type sequence, there is a zone known as the Araç-Daday shear zone (Figure 8). This zone is parallel to the Ülüs Basin and lies in front of the main Dogger nappe system (Figure 8). In the Araç-Daday shear zone, there is an uninterrupted Mesozoic sequence (Figure 3) (Deveciler et al., 1989; Şengün, 1993; Aydın et al., 1995) that presumably developed above an ophiolitic foundation. In this sequence, the Middle to Late Cretaceous is represented by debris flows and olistostromes derived from a westerly source. This is evidenced by fragments of the basement rocks of the İstanbul-Zonguldak Zone that were incorporated into this internally chaotic sedimentary unit. The olistostromes pass laterally into a deep-sea flysch unit that crops out in the east and the southeast into the flysch tectonic wedges of the basement rocks of the İstanbul-Zonguldak Zone; an ophiolitic melange association of Late Cretaceous age was incorporated. Vergence of these tectonic wedges is commonly toward the east and the southeast. All of these units have undergone penetrative, cataclastic deformation and metamorphism to greenschist facies. In the Ballıdağ area, east of Safranbolu, for example, a gradual transition from phyllites and phyllonites to Upper Cretaceous flysch of Coniacian–Turonian age (Figures 3, 8) is observed.

The Pontide-type and the Sakarya-type Mesozoic successions are overlain by basal clastic rocks of the Late Cretaceous.

The Kastamonu-Boyabat Basin Fill

The Kastamonu-Boyabat Basin fill is located between the northern zone and the Kargı Massif (Figures 8, 9). Along the Gökirmak River valley, the Kastamonu–Boyabat Basin contains a sequence continuous from the Upper Cretaceous to the Oligocene. At the bottom of the sequence, there is a condensed limestone unit of late Cenomanian–Turonian age [Kapanboğazı Formation (Ketin and Gümüş, 1963)]. This is followed by volcanoclastic rocks interbedded with basalt lavas of Campanian age [Yemişliçay Formation (Ketin and Gümüş, 1963)]. These are overlain by a flysch sequence replaced by marls and marly limestones of Maastrichtian age [Gürsökü and Akveren formations (Yılmaz and Tüysüz, 1984; Aydın et al., 1986)]. These are followed by micritic limestones and mudstones (Atbaşı Formation), followed by the Eocene flysch (Kusuri Formation). These pass upward into upper Eocene–Oligocene fluvial sediments (Gedik and Korkmaz, 1984; Yılmaz and Tüysüz, 1984). The regressive units forming the top of the succession suggest that the basin was filled by coarse clastics before the early Miocene.

The present Gökirmak River valley corresponds with a continental ramp basin formed due to the elevation of the northern (the Çangaldağ high) and the southern (the Elekdağ high) shoulders (Figures 8, 9) during the Neogene (Yılmaz and Tüysüz, 1984, 1991), showing the postcollisional shortening within the Pontides.

The Kargı Massif

The Kargı Massif is a tectonic mosaic that is composed of various accreted tectonostratigraphic units (Figures 3, 8, and 9). In the massif, the pre-Dogger and post-Dogger assemblages can be distinguished. The pre-Dogger assemblage is composed mainly of the Elekdağ metaophiolite; the Domuzdağ melange; the Kunduz metamorphic association; the Kösdağ metamorphic assemblage; the Gümüşoluğu, Aktaş, and Bekirli metamorphic associations, and the İbı Formation. The post-Dogger assemblage consists of the Upper Cretaceous ophiolite (the Kızılırmak ophiolite) and the Malm–Upper Cretaceous units.

The pre-Dogger tectonostratigraphic units were assembled during the Dogger (Yılmaz and Tüysüz, 1984; Tüysüz et al., 1989; Tüysüz, 1990; Yılmaz, 1990) and were collectively covered by the Malm–Lower Cretaceous sediments (Figure 9).

The different tectonic units of the Kargı Massif are observed as south-vergent imbricates (Figure 9). Within this nappe pile, each tectonostratigraphic unit has distinctly different geological characteristics. The Elekdağ metaophiolite consists of a thick slab of an ordered ophiolite with ultramafic rocks at the base to pillow lavas and an interbedded pelagic cover succession. These have undergone greenschist facies metamorphism during the post-Liassic–pre-Malm interval (Yılmaz and Tüysüz, 1984; Tüysüz, 1990; Yılmaz, 1990). The Elekdağ metaophiolite is regarded as similar to the Küre ophiolite (Yılmaz and Tüysüz, 1984) and thus represents the remnant of the Paleotethyan Ocean (Şengör et al., 1984; Yılmaz and Şengör, 1985; Ustaömer and Robertson, 1993, 1994). There is a thin ultramafic sliver (the Yılanlı ophiolite) underneath the Elekdağ nappe (Figure 9) that displays eclogite facies metamorphism (Milch, 1907; Eren, 1979).

The Yılanlı and Elekdağ ophiolitic slabs rest tectonically on a metamorphosed melange association, the Domuzdağ melange (Figure 9), a subduction-accretion complex (Yılmaz and Tüysüz, 1984; Tüysüz, 1985). The melange has a matrix of mafic lavas and metatuffs, and a variety of blocks, embedded in this matrix. The blocks consist of cherts, limestones, and ophiolitic and volcanic rocks of Paleozoic and Triassic age. The melange underwent high P/low T (blueschist) metamorphism (Milch, 1907; Eren, 1979; Yılmaz and Tüysüz, 1984; Tüysüz, 1985).

The epiophiolitic deep-sea sedimentary rocks (Akgöl Formation) of the Elekdağ and the Küre metaophiolites cover a time span from Permian? to Liassic (Fratschner, 1953; Ketin, 1962; Kutluk and Bozdoğan, 1981; Aydın et al., 1986).

The Kunduz metamorphic association is a metamorphosed mafic lava–sediment alternation. The lavas are dominant in the succession. Within this group there are ophiolite and marble blocks. Geochemically, the Kunduz metalavas are alkaline and tholeiitic, and show affinity to the rift and active continental margin volcanic rocks (Doğan, 1990).

The Aktaş metamorphic association is a regional, dynamothermal metamorphic unit (Yılmaz and Tüysüz, 1984; Tüysüz, 1985). The metamorphic grade ranges from the greenschist facies to the epidote amphibolite facies. Upper Carboniferous and Permian fossils were found from the marbles at the base of the succession; the İbı Formation represents the platform carbonates. The Aktaş metamorphic association represents what was originally a transgressive section partly similar to the Gümüşoluğu metamorphic rocks.

The Gümüşoluğu metamorphic association (Figure 3) is mainly a metapelite–metavolcanic succession (Yılmaz and Tüysüz, 1984; Tüysüz, 1985, 1990). At the base of this unit, there are marbles and schists. They are followed by phyllites with marble lenses, which pass upward into a phyllite–recrystallized limestone alternation. Upper layers of the sequence consist of lavas and tuffs alternating with the phyllites. The top of the unit is made of pelagic mudstones and limestones containing ophiolite and marble blocks. The Gümüşoluğu metamorphics pass up into the Bekirli metamorphic rocks, which consist of metashales and a metaflysch (Figure 3). From the Aktaş Formation to the Bekirli Formation, the succession indicates a transgressive Triassic sequence developed above the continental basement.

This sequence represents continental rifting and rupture of the Permo-Carboniferous continental platform, and then the rift evolved into a deep basin. The Aktaş and Gümüşoluğu metamorphic association closely resembles the Karakaya complex of the Sakarya continent (Yılmaz and Tüysüz, 1984; Tüysüz et al., 1989; Tüysüz, 1990; Doğan, 1990).

The Kösdağ unit is a sequence consisting of metafelsic volcanic rocks and interlayering metapelitic rocks. Geochemically, this unit may be considered an active continental margin volcanic association (Doğan, 1990).

The geological cross section in Figure 9 shows that the oceanic assemblages (the Küre and Elekdağ ophiolites and Domuzdağ melange) were tectonically emplaced onto the continental margin units (the Aktaş, Gümüşoluğu, and Bekirli formations), possibly during Dogger resemblage, because these units contain rocks including the Liassic and are overlain stratigraphically by the Malm conglomerates (Figure 9).

On top of the Kargı Massif rests tectonically an ophiolitic nappe pile (Figure 9). This is composed of serpentinized ultramafic rocks, gabbros, diabases, spilitic basalt lavas, and deep-sea sediments of the Late Cretaceous (Yılmaz and Tüysüz, 1984; Tüysüz, 1990, 1993; Yiğitbaş et al., 1990). The nappe consists of thin, south-dipping tectonic slices. Within the slices, the ophiolite stratigraphy is preserved.

The Ophiolite Belt

Immediately south of the Kargı Massif, there are dismembered ophiolites (Kızılırmak ophiolite) and an ophiolitic melange association (Kirazbaşı melange) that is in tectonic contact with the metamorphic rocks. The melange association also occurs as thin thrust slices imbricated with the Kargı Massif (Figure 9). The melange is composed mainly of blocks of red micritic limestones, black shales, ophiolitic fragments, and metamorphic rocks derived from the Kargı Massif. Wherever exposed, there is an internally ordered pelagic sedimentary succession (i.e., pelagic limestone and shale) at the base of each of the melange slices. They yield a Campanian age (Yılmaz and Tüysüz, 1984, 1988; Tüysüz, 1990; Yiğitbaş et al., 1990). The thrust planes appear to have preferentially followed this lithological boundary. The ophiolitic detritus increases toward the top of each of the thrust slices. The amount of the ophiolitic materials and thickness of the melange slices within the imbricated pile show an apparent increase toward the south. This evidence suggests that tectonic disruption began in a pelagic environment in the south and advanced to the north.

According to the stratigraphic data, time of generation of the melange is Campanian (Yiğitbaş et al., 1990), and the emplacement of the melange is broadly constrained as the latest Campanian, since the matrix of the melange contains Campanian rocks, and the overlying sequence is a syntectonic flysch of Campanian age.

The disrupted ophiolite rests tectonically on the Kargı Massif and the overlying Mesozoic cover rocks (Figure 9). This ophiolite overlies all the layers of an ordered ophiolite from peridotite to pillow lavas. Although data are scarce, emplacement of the Kızılırmak ophiolite is assumed to be Eocene in age, according to the correlation with the ophiolites along the extension in the Eastern Pontides.

The Çankırı Basin is a young peripheral molasse basin that surrounds the amalgamated tectonic mosaic of the Pontides and the Kırşehir Massif (Figure 8). The basin fill rests on a variety of older rocks including the upper Eocene units, and begins with very thick (3000 m), red-colored continental clastic deposits. This passes into a thick evaporitic unit. The lower and upper units are Oligocene and upper Miocene in age, respectively (Tüysüz and Dellaloğlu, 1992).

THE EASTERN PONTIDES

The Eastern Pontides comprise the following east-west–trending tectonic zones (Figure 10): the magmatic belt, the Beldağ Basin fill (the Beldağ Group), the ophiolite belt, and the Yıldızeli Basin fill (the Hıdırnalı Group). The magmatic belt is the easterly extension of the northern zone of the Central Pontides. The Beldağ Basin fill represents a thick sequence of Upper Cretaceous rocks that crop out along a narrow, east-west–trending zone. The Tokat Massif is a metamorphic complex, located south of the Eastern Pontides range. The ophiolite belt represents the eastern part of the Ankara-Erzincan suture zone (Figure 1). The Yildizeli Basin fill is a sedimentary succession that outcrops between the Tokat Massif and the southerly situated metamorphic complex (the Kırşehir Massif), which belongs to the Tauride-Anatolide platform (Figure 1). We begin the description of the geology of the Eastern Pontides with the Tokat Massif, because it contains the oldest rocks in the tectonic entity, and thus allows a chronological sequence to be outlined.

The Tokat Massif

The Tokat Massif is an amalgamated tectonic mosaic that is composed of three distinctly different tectonostratigraphic units (Figures 3, 10, and 11). These are (1) the Yeşılırmak metamorphic association; (2) a metamorphosed ophiolitic slab, the Turhal metaophiolite, and an ophiolitic melange association (the Devecidağ melange); and (3) the Amasya metamorphic unit.

The Yeşılırmak metamorphic assemblage is the dominant tectonostratigraphic unit of the Tokat Massif, which outcrops extensively from Çorum in the

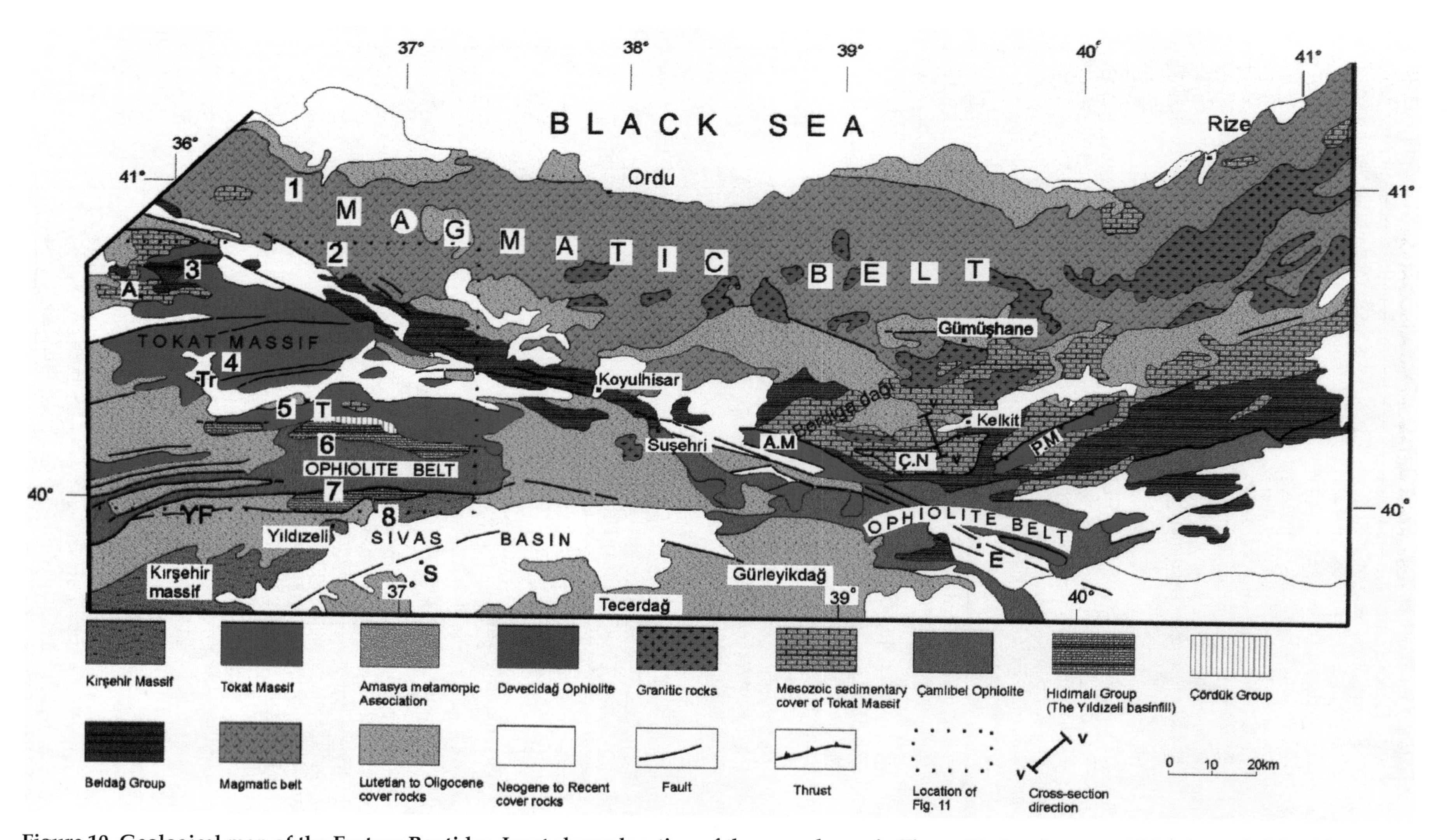

Figure 10. Geological map of the Eastern Pontides. Inset shows location of the map shown in Figure 11. A = Amasya, AM = Agvanis Massif, E = Erzincan, PM = Pulur Massif, S = Sıvaş, T = Tokat, Tr = Turhal, ÇN = Çimendağ nappe, YF = Yildizeli fault. VV′ is the cross section shown in Figure 13. Numbers 1 to 8 indicate locations of the stratigraphic columns displayed in Figure 12.

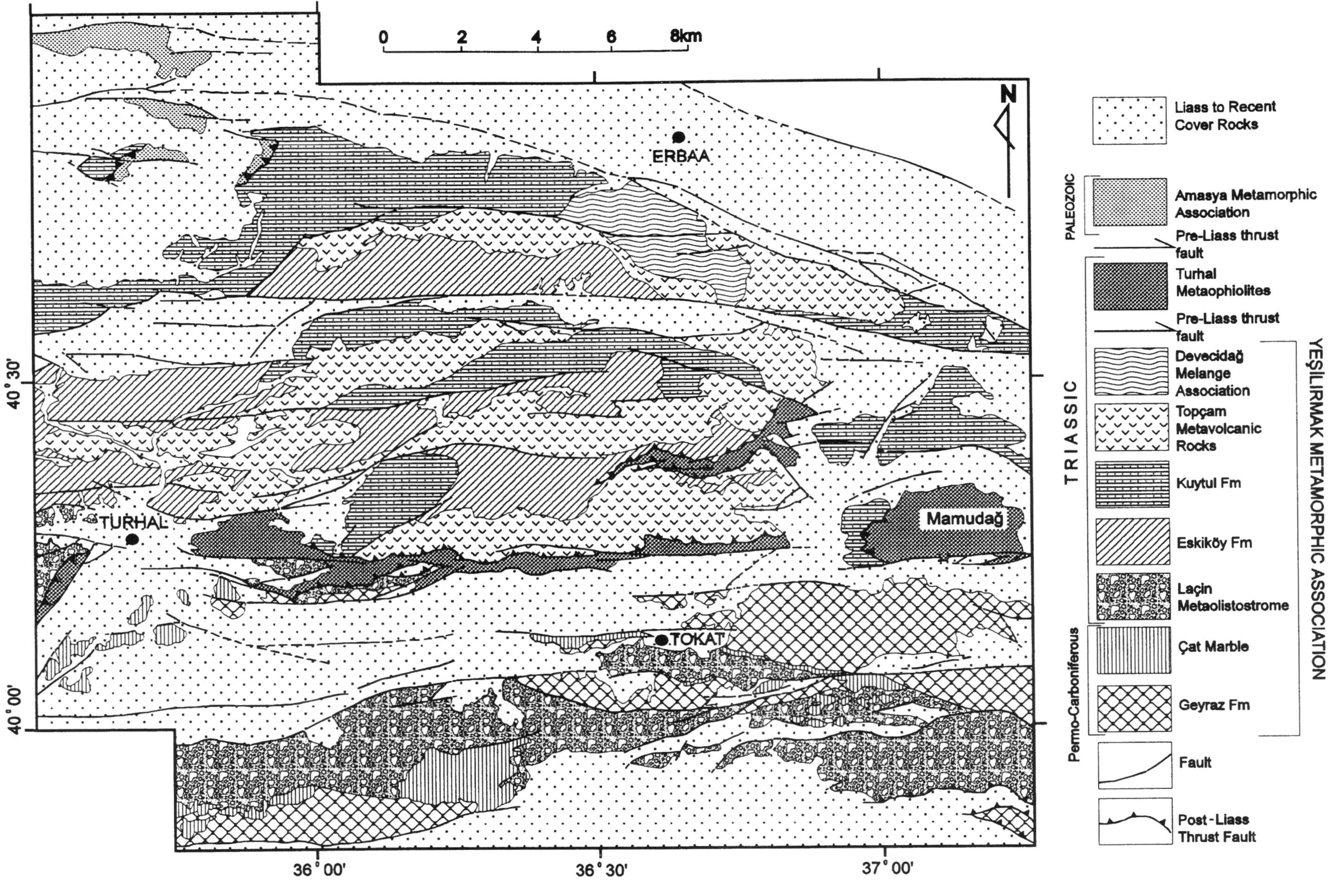

Figure 11. Geological map of the Tokat Massif and the surrounding regions.

west to Suşehri in the east (Figure 10). This represents a continental assemblage consisting of a Paleozoic metamorphic basement and enveloping metamorphosed Triassic rocks (Figure 3). The Liassic units are the oldest sediments deposited on the massif (Yılmaz, 1980; Yılmaz et al., 1993). They are seen to have undergone locally developed cataclastic metamorphism, particularly in the areas south of Tokat (Yılmaz et al., 1993). The Turhal metaophiolite is a disrupted ophiolite containing most of the layers of an ordered ophiolite. Together with the Turhal metaophiolite, there is also a metamorphosed ophiolitic melange association. The Amasya metamorphic unit is a slightly metamorphosed, lower Paleozoic sedimentary succession.

The stratigraphy of the Yeşılırmak metamorphic assemblage is displayed in Figure 3. At the base of the sequence, there is a polyphase deformed metapelite–metalava succession. This passes upward into marbles, which are fossiliferous, yielding Late Permian ages (Yılmaz et al., 1993). This is followed by an internally disordered unit that contains blocks of the underlying marbles, embedded in a matrix of metavolcanic and metapelitic rocks. Within the metapelitic rocks, there are some limestone lenses that contain Lower Triassic fossils (Yılmaz et al., 1993). This passes upward into an alternating metasiltstone– metasandstone sequence. This vertically and laterally grades into a metalava unit with locally well developed pillow structures; this in turn gives way to a metamorphosed pelagic rock unit consisting of red micritic limestones, mudstones, shales, and alternated mafic lavas. On top of the sequence, there is an olistostrome (Yılmaz, 1980; Yılmaz et al., 1993) in which the matrix is made up of pelagic sedimentary rocks enclosing blocks of serpentinite, gabbro, diabase, and marble. The Permo–Triassic succession of the Yeşılırmak metamorphic assemblage closely resembles the Karakaya complex of northwest Anatolia.

The Turhal metaophiolite outcrops in Turhal, north of the Tokat and Almus areas, as thin thrust slices often imbricated with the Yeşılırmak metamorphic assemblage (Figure 11). The Devecidağ melange is spatially and temporally associated with the Turhal metaophiolite and is composed of an olistostrome and a tectonic melange. The olistostrome contains a variety of pelagic rocks including manganiferous cherts, red mudstones, radiolarites, and spilitic basalts. The tectonic melange has a matrix of metashales and metagraywackes surrounding the ophiolitic blocks. The olistostrome and the tectonic melange are tectonically mixed.

The Amasya metamorphic unit (Figures 3, 10, and 11), also known as the Karasenir Formation (Alp, 1972), outcrops in the Karasenir and Eryatağı areas near Amasya and further east around the Doğyadağı. This unit occurs as a nappe that rests tectonically on the upper units of the Tokat metamorphic assemblage (Figures 3, 10). This is represented by a slightly metamorphosed sedimentary succession, preserving its original sequence, which displays widespread cataclasis and locally developed, pervasive foliation. The degree of metamorphism varies between zeolite facies and lower greenschist facies. There is a conglomerate and sandstone unit at the base of the Amasya metamorphic sequence. This passes into dark shales and graywackes, which contain thin, dark-colored limestone lenses that are fossiliferous and yield Silurian ages (Alp, 1972).

The above summary of the constituent tectonic unit of the Tokat Massif indicates that this mosaic is made up of an ophiolitic unit that is squeezed and sandwiched between the two different continental assemblages (Figures 3, 11). This "sandwich" has the following structure: the Amasya metamorphic rocks rest tectonically on the younger and higher-grade metamorphic rocks of the Yeşılırmak metamorphic assemblage and on the epiophiolitic rocks. This tectonic assemblage was formed before the Liassic, possibly during the latest Triassic.

In the Eastern Pontides, in addition to the Tokat Massif, there are a number of smaller metamorphic inliers (Figure 10). From the west to the east these are: the Agvanis Massif, the Gümüşhane-Bayburt metamorphics, the Pulur Massif, and the Yusufeli-Artvin metamorphics. The Agvanis Massif, the Pulur Massif, and the Gümüşhane-Bayburt metamorphics display broadly similar geological features and share a common stratigraphic sequence with the Tokat Massif. Therefore, these may be regarded as belonging to the same tectonostratigraphic entity, forming the basement to the post-Triassic rocks. In the Gümüşhane-Bayburt metamorphics, and in the Agvanis Massif, the lowermost lithostratigraphic units are exposed (Yılmaz et al., 1993). These are amphibolite-grade schists, gneisses and migmatites (Zankl, 1961; Schultze-Westrum, 1961, 1962; Maucher, 1962; Yılmaz et al., 1993), and an intrusive granite of Carboniferous age, the Gümüşhane granite (Yılmaz, 1972), dated to be 298–338 m.y. by the whole-rock Pb isotope method (Çoğulu, 1975; Okay, 1984). Similar granitic intrusions are observed in the other metamorphic associations of the Eastern Pontides, but they are much smaller. The metamorphic massifs and the granites are overlain by the basal units of the Liassic transgression (Figures 3, 12). This transgressive sequence begins with a basal conglomerate that passes upward into a beach facies characterized by well-sorted quartzites. These are followed by a red mudstone and limestone unit containing abundant ammonites (Yılmaz, 1972). Interbedded siltstones and graywackes containing coal horizons and numerous volcanic interlayers were laid down next. To the south, a fault-bounded sequence of conglomerate interlayered with tholeiitic basalts (Schultze-Westrum, 1961; Zankl, 1961; Yılmaz, 1972) and some alkaline trachytes (Bergougnan, 1987) were formed, indicating the beginning of an extensional regime (Şengör et al., 1980). Sedimentation was interrupted after the Early Jurassic, but there are places where the sequence passes uninterruptedly into upper Jurassic rocks (i.e., south of Tokat, the Borabay Lake, and the Şiran-Kelkit and Ispir areas) (Wedding, 1963; Ağraly et al., 1966; Koçyiğit et al., 1988; Yılmaz et al., 1993). In these localities, there is a thick volcanogenic flysch of Liassic–Dogger age (Mudurnu Formation) (Figures 3, 12).

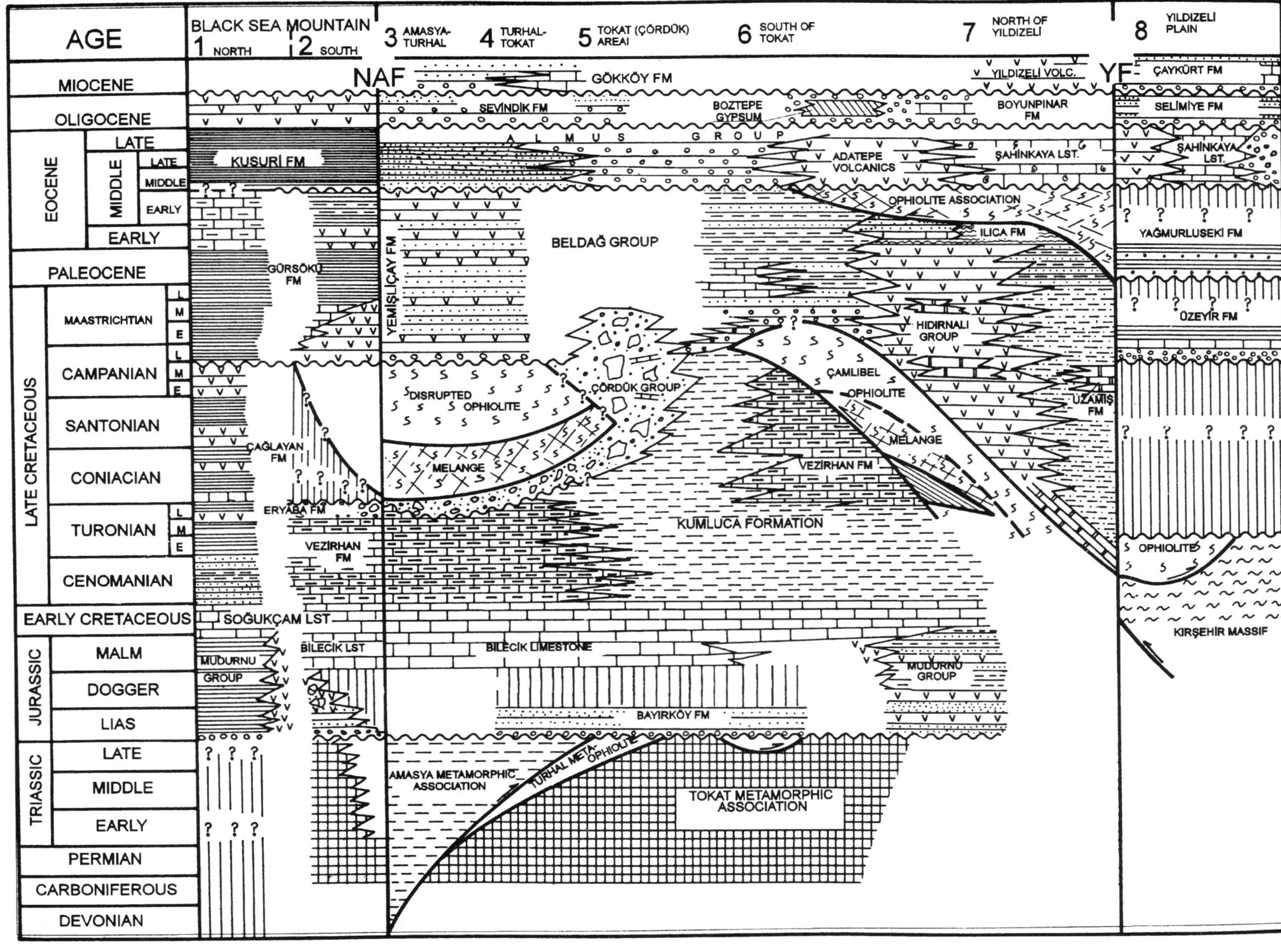

Figure 12. Stratigraphic correlation chart showing the typical successions encountered across the Eastern Pontides. The section locations are located on Figure 10. FM = Formation, LST = Limestone, NAF = North Anatolian transform fault zone, YF = Yildizeli fault.

In addition to the metamorphic basement complexes we have discussed, there is another metamorphic entity in the Eastern Pontides range that is distinctly different from the rest of the metamorphic associations. This is a metamorphosed ophiolite exposed along the deep gorge of the Çoruh River, near the present Turkish-Georgian border (Figure 1). From the base to the top, gabbros, amphibolites, and mafic volcanics interlayered with slates characterize this association (Şengör et al., 1980; Yılmaz and Şengör, 1985). The Yusufeli-Artvin ophiolite is undoubtedly oceanic in origin, and has been affected by regional metamorphism. This metaophiolite is similar to the Küre ophiolite or the Elekdağ ophiolite of the Central Pontides, and is regarded as representing the remnant of the Paleotethys (Şengör et al., 1980, 1984).

The Yusufeli-Artvin metaophiolite, like the Küre and Elekdağ ophiolites, survived in the oceanic environment until the Dogger. This is evidenced by the epiophiolitic sediments in stratigraphic contact with the pillow lavas: the shales, ribbon cherts, and fine-grained siltstones-sandstones that contain Early Jurassic fossils (MTA, 1977; Ertunç, 1980). The metaophiolite was emplaced in its present tectonic position during the Dogger, and was overlain stratigraphically by Late Jurassic sediments over a sharp angular unconformity. At the base is a conglomerate containing clasts of the underlying oceanic assemblage; above this basal unit is a sequence of alternating limestones and sandstones. This sequence passes up concordantly into the Lower Cretaceous, represented by a cherty limestone unit. Locally, around the Kelkit areas, tholeiitic basalts injected into and intercalated with the Lower Cretaceous limestones (Figure 3). The limestones laterally grade into the carbonate flysch in the southern part of the region (Yılmaz et al., 1993) (Figure 12).

The Ophiolite Belt

The ophiolitic belt (the Çamlıbel ophiolite) represents a subduction-accretion complex. Within this belt, different ophiolitic tectonostratigraphic units may be distinguished; some of these units are internally chaotic, while others are represented by dismembered and ordered ophiolite slices (Yılmaz, 1980; Norman, 1988; Yılmaz et al., 1993). The matrix of the tectonic melange is Upper Cretaceous pelagic sediments. The blocks are made of a variety of ophiolitic rocks and other Mesozoic sedimentary rocks. The ophiolitic tectonic units were emplaced into their present tectonostratigraphic positions during two periods, Late Cretaceous and Eocene (Figure 12). During the Late Cretaceous, an ophiolitic tectonic melange association was emplaced onto the Pontides from the south (Figure 12). During this period, the Pontides were deformed by south-vergent thrusts (Yılmaz et al., 1993). As a result of this, ophiolite slivers were imbricated with the basement metamorphic rocks (see the Kargı Massif) (Yılmaz et al., 1993). The imbricated zone outcrops extensively in the Çorum-Doğyadağı, Amasya, Turhal, Çamlıbel, and Erzincan areas (Figure 10). There are glaucophane-lawsonite facies metamorphic rocks incorporated tectonically into ophiolitic melange association outcropping in the north of the town of Yildizeli (Tatar, 1971).

The second phase of ophiolite emplacement occurred during the early Eocene–middle Eocene transition (Figure 12). Age of this emplacement is tightly constrained by the stratigraphic data. The autochthonous sedimentary succession that was tectonically underlain by the ophiolite nappe includes the lower Eocene rocks; the ophiolite nappe is stratigraphically overlain by the Lutetian basal conglomerates (Yılmaz et al., 1993).

This Eocene ophiolite nappe package is composed mainly of thick and dismembered ophiolitic slices (Yılmaz et al., 1993). The subduction-accretion melange units in this nappe are only subsidiary. The nappe was thrust onto a pelagic and hemipelagic succession (the Hıdırnalı Group) of the Yildizeli Basin (Figure 12), and was emplaced tectonically onto a variety of older rock units. The asymmetrical folds, thrusts, and duplex structures indicate that nappe transport was from south to north (Figure 13) (Yılmaz et al., 1993).

The Eocene ophiolite nappe package (>500 m) consists mainly of serpentinized peridotites that locally contain podiform chromites. The primary igneous features of the rocks are only rarely observed; the peridotites belong mostly to the ultramafic cumulates layer in which intrusive dunite pockets and associated chromites may be identified. Upper layers of the ophiolite are commonly missing. Under the ophiolite nappe, there are locally preserved, thin tectonic slivers of the ophiolitic melange. These are interpreted to be the tectonic slices dragged along with the nappe.

The Magmatic Belt

At the begining of the Late Cretaceous, different facies series began to develop in the Eastern Pontides across and along the mountain belt (Figures 7, 8) (Yılmaz et al., 1993). In the northern areas, a volcanic chain, accompanied by clastic units, formed between the Turonian and the Campanian. The magmatic rocks are represented commonly by calc-alkaline basalt, basaltic andesite, andesite, and associated pyroclastic rocks. South of the volcanic belt, a volcanogenic flysch was deposited during the Turonian. Farther south, in the Amasya-Turhal area, the flysch was laterally transitional to red, pelagic limestones (the Vezirhan formation). South of Tokat, a wild flysch was deposited containing abundant blocks of underlying limestones and fragments of an ophiolite (Çördük olistostrome). To the south of this zone, in the Yildizeli plain, a subduction-accretion melange outcrops. This was emplaced during the Late Cretaceous. The calc-alkaline magmatic activity began during the Turonian and continued intermittently till the end of Paleocene. During the same period, granitic intrusions rose into the shallow levels of the crust and formed the first components of a composite pluton called the Rize granite (Figure 10) (Çoğulu, 1975; Taner, 1977). The pluton extends from Ordu in the west to the Armenian border in the east (Figure 10). Emplacement of the pluton

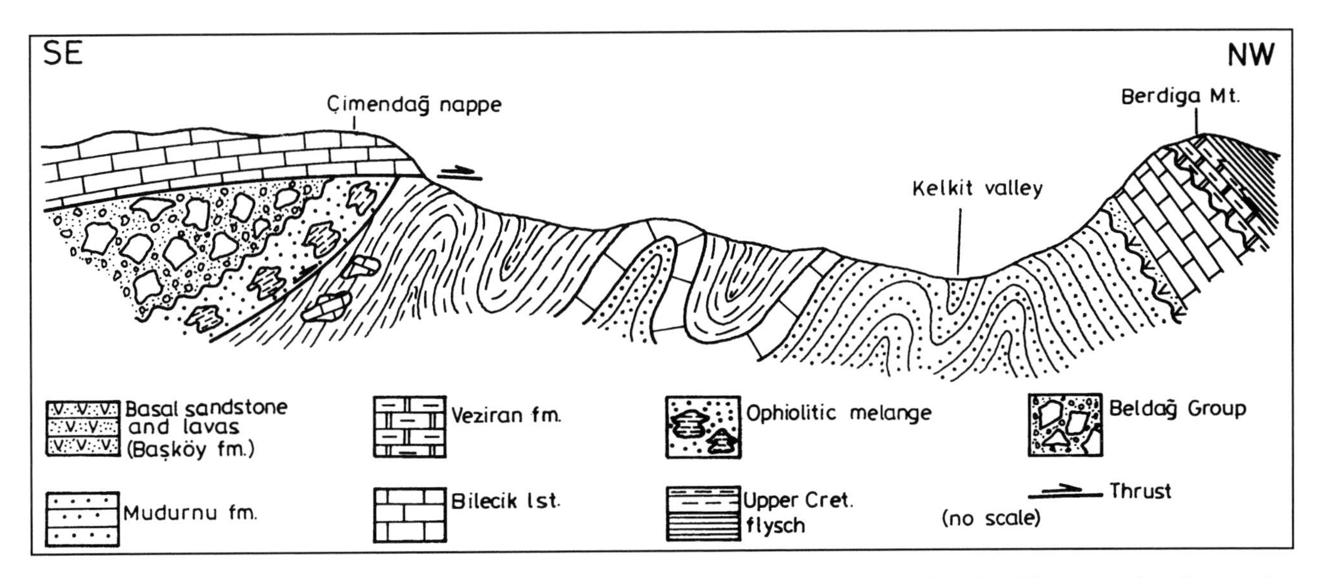

Figure 13. Schematic cross section across the Çimendağ nappe, Eastern Pontides. See Figure 10 for the section direction. Horizontal distance is ~15 km.

occurred in pulses and lasted into the late Eocene. Taner (1977) obtained K/Ar mineral age dates from 80 to 40 m.y.

From stratigraphic sections measured along the Eastern Pontides, there is a marked angular unconformity corresponding to Coniacian–Santonian erosion (Figures 7, 12). An exception to this is seen in the extreme south along the Sıvaş-Yildizeli areas and in the extreme north (presently the northern flank of the Pontides range), where the Upper Cretaceous successions are conformable (Figure 12).

The Coniacian–Santonian unconformity surface is overlain by the basal units of a new transgression that began during the Campanian (Figure 12). The Upper Campanian–Maastrichtian successions are widespread and display abrupt north to south lateral transitions. The volcanic belt appears to have migrated southward in this period. The areas occupied previously by the arc volcanics are now occupied by the flysch successions (Figure 12). In turn, the volcanic belt overlies the previous flysch-carbonate belt of Turonian age.

The Beldağ and Yildizeli Basin Fills

South of the Turonian magmatic belt, there is a thick sequence outcropping east to west, known as the Beldağ Group (Figures 10, 12). This begins as an internally chaotic unit, deposited over a variety of older rocks, and represents a transgressive unit that gives way to debris flow deposits. The olistoliths are derived mainly from the Mesozoic limestones. They were accompanied by alkaline mafic lavas and pyroclastic rocks. This internally chaotic unit gives way to a more orderly flysch succession, showing rapid lateral variations and slump structures. The blocks as well as the enclosing sedimentary rocks underwent synsedimentary cataclastic deformation. Diabase dykes were injected into these sediments. Toward the top, the flysch is replaced by a marl-sandstone-conglomerate alternation of Paleocene–lower Eocene age. During this period, the basin continued to be filled with coarse clastic rocks (Yılmaz et al., 1993).

Between the Tokat and Kırşehir massifs, there is a thick succession, referred to as the Yildizeli Basin fill (Figures 10, 12). This consists of a continuous marine sequence from the Upper Cretaceous to the lower Eocene (Hıdırnalı Group, Figure 12) (Tekeli et al., 1991; Yılmaz et al., 1993). This group was deposited on the subduction-accretion melange and is tectonically overlain by the Eocene nappes. The basin fill indicates that the depositional environment gradually changed from deep to shallow marine (Figure 12) (Tekeli et al., 1991; Yılmaz et al., 1993).

In the Eastern Pontides, the early Eocene–middle Eocene transition is an unconformity (Figure 12). The middle Eocene rocks rest on the older rocks with a marked angular unconformity. This suggests that the whole region was deformed and elevated above the sea at the end of the early Eocene. The Lutetian basal clastic units are accompanied by a thick pile of calc-alkaline volcanic rocks ranging in composition from basalt to dacite. The volcanic activity waned gradually, showing a decrease from the middle Eocene into the late Eocene.

The marine sedimentary rocks are replaced by the continental deposits during the Oligocene, indicating that the region was uplifted once again at the beginning of the Oligocene (Figure 12).

The Neogene succession is widespread in the Pontides (Figure 10). The lower Miocene units are represented by shallow marine and lacustrine environments (Figure 12) (Seymen, 1975; Yılmaz et al., 1993). However, during this period, continental sediment deposition occurred in the Pontides; the sea retreated from the Pontides during the middle Miocene (Seymen, 1975).

The Sıvas Basin is a young trough that is situated between the Tokat Massif and the adjacent elevations in the north and the Gürleyik-Tecer Mountains in the south (Figure 10). The development of the basin is genetically related to the final collision of the Pontides with the Kırşehir block (Figure 15E, F). There is thus a major molasse basin related to this collision (Şengör and Yılmaz, 1981; Yılmaz et al., 1993). The basin fill was deposited over a variety of rock groups up to and including the Eocene sedimentary units (Cater et al., 1991). The succession (Figure 12) begins at the base with continental red beds. They give way to the lacustrine, green siltstone-marl alternations. These basal units are Oligocene in age (Aktimur et al., 1990; Cater et al., 1991; Temiz et al., 1992; Poisson et al., 1995). This sequence is followed by lower Miocene marls, claystones, sandstones, and limestones deposited in a shallow marine environment (Dellaloğlu and Meşhur, 1980; Cater et al., 1991). Over a surface of angular unconformity, this is followed by a thick evaporite horizon that passes laterally and vertically into continental deposits consisting of sandstones, limestones, marls, and claystones of possibly lower to middle Miocene ages (Aktimur et al., 1990; Poisson et al., 1995). They are followed by lacustrine limestones of possibly Pliocene age (Dellaloğlu and Meşhur, 1980; Aktimur et al., 1990).

DISCUSSION AND GEOLOGICAL EVOLUTION

In this section, the tectonic evolution of the Pontides is outlined in terms of seven time intervals. The intervals have been selected to show the major changes during the tectonic evolution.

Permo-Triassic Events

During the Permian, the present Pontides region, with the exception of the İstanbul-Zonguldak Zone, possibly constituted a part of the northern margin of Gondwana Land, facing Paleotethys (Figure 15A) (Şengör et al., 1984; Robertson and Dixon, 1984; Şengör, 1990). This geological view is supported further by the paleomagnetic data (Lauer, 1981; Orbay et al., 1981; Westphal et al., 1986) that indicate that the Pontides show a better fit with African paleolatitudes. The İstanbul-Zonguldak Zone, on the other hand, consisting of a pre-Cambrian metamorphic basement overlain by a transgressive sedimentary sequence extending from the Ordovician to the Carboniferous, represents a south-facing, passive continental margin of Laurasia (Haas, 1968; Şengör and Yılmaz, 1981; Ustaömer and Robertson, 1993; Okay et al., 1994). This geological evidence is in agreement with the existing paleomagnetic data (Gregor and Zijderveld, 1964; Sarıbudak et al., 1989; Evans et al., 1991). The above summary on the origin and the initial tectonic positions of the major zones of the Pontides is compatible with the Permian paleogeographic reconstruction of the world, which shows a large oceanic realm in the region (Scotese et al., 1979; Smith et al., 1981) and is known as Paleotethys (Şengör, 1979a).

During the Triassic, the Gondwanan Platform ruptured to produce extensional basins in two areas at two different times (Figure 15B) (Şengör and Yılmaz, 1981). The Taurides of southern Turkey provides evidence for a Ladinian–Norian rifting event, which rifted Turkey away from Gondwana Land (Friedman et al., 1971; Şengör and Yılmaz, 1981; Yılmaz, 1993). This event marks the opening of Neotethys. The northern strip that was separated from Gondwana Land is referred to as the Cimmerian continent (Şengör, 1979a). This eastern Mediterranean Sea (the Vardar Ocean) is beyond the scope of this chapter. The other rifting event is documented along a line extending from the Biga Peninsula of the Sakarya continent through Bilecik and Ankara to the Tokat Massif of the Eastern Pontides range (Şengör and Yılmaz, 1981). This basin fill is known as the Karakaya Formation, or the Karakaya complex (the Sakarya continent). The Karakaya rifting began during the Late Permian–Triassic (Yılmaz, 1981; Okay et al., 1991). A metamorphosed Triassic succession similar to the Karakaya Formation is encountered in the İstranca Massif (Figure 3). The similarity between the İstranca and the Pontide Triassic assemblages was noted by Chatalov (1991). In addition to this, Gocev (1991) and Chatalov (1991) emphasized the north-vergent thrusting within the İstranca Massif, which is observed in the Sakarya continent (Yılmaz et al., 1990; Genç and Yılmaz, 1995a).

In the Sakarya continent, the basement metamorphic assemblage is overlain unconformably by Permian and Triassic units. The Triassic stratigraphic successions display rapid vertical and lateral transitions (Genç and Yılmaz, 1995a). Despite the rapid transitions, two major rock groups can be distinguished, a lower, shallow marine sequence and an upper deep-sea sequence (Figure 3). The complete Triassic section can be regarded as a transgressive sequence beginning with shallow marine deposits, which gives way to increasingly deeper marine deposits, the ocean floor assemblages (Yılmaz, 1981; Yılmaz et al., 1990; Okay et al., 1991; Genç and Yılmaz, 1995a). The Karakaya Basin was short lived, and closed during the latest Triassic (Figure 15C) (Bingöl et al., 1973; Yılmaz, 1980; Okay et al., 1991; Genç and Yılmaz, 1995a). During this closing stage, the leading edge of the continent was deformed with a north-directed tectonic transport and underwent polyphase greenschist to glaucophone-bearing greenschist metamorphism (Genç and Yılmaz, 1995a). After the metamorphism, the upper association was thrust onto the metamorphic rocks of the lower association. These tectonically juxtaposed Triassic assemblages were overlain by the Liassic transgressive sandstones (Figure 3) (Altınlı, 1973; Saner, 1977; Yılmaz, 1981; Yılmaz et al., 1995). The succession in İstranca (Figure 3) also indicates the development of a short-lived Triassic basin. This basin closed before the Early Jurassic.

Among the tectonostratigraphic units of the Kargı Massif, in the Central Pontides, the Aktaş, Gümüsoluğu, and Bekirli metamorphic associations (Figure 3) resemble closely the Paleozoic metamorphic rocks and the overlying Triassic continental margin units of the Sakarya continent. This succession represents a north-facing continental margin that is tectonically overlain by the Küre and Elekdağ ophiolites of the Paleotethys Ocean (Figures 3, 9) (Tüysüz, 1990; Yılmaz, 1990).

The data above indicate that the Pontides region and oceanic realm already existed before the opening of the Karakaya marginal basin because the Paleotethys is documented to have survived from the Paleozoic until the Dogger (Aydın et al., 1986; Chatalov, 1991; Ustaömer and Robertson, 1993). With the development of the Karakaya Basin, two partly penecontemporaneous basins, the Karakaya Basin and the Paleotethys Ocean, survived in the region (Şengör and Yılmaz, 1981; Yılmaz and Tüysüz, 1984; Tüysüz, 1990). The Paleotethys was located to the north of the Cimmerian continent (Figures 9, 14). This is shown in the two sets of data: (1) the palinspastic reconstruction of the nappes and (2) the vorticity indicators such as the asymmetrical folds, the thrusts, and the small-scale structures that collectively suggest a south-directed tectonic transport (Yılmaz and Tüysüz, 1984; Tüysüz, 1985).

In the Kargı Massif, the Paleotethyan assemblages and the Karakaya sequence are in direct contact (Figure 9), suggesting that the Karakaya marginal basin and the Paleotethys Ocean were probably connected with one another (Figures 14, 15B) (Yılmaz and Tüysüz, 1984; Tüysüz et al., 1989; Tüysüz, 1990), with the Karakaya marginal basin possibly being a subsidiary branch of the Paleotethys.

The calc-alkaline felsic volcanic rocks of Permian age in the Bayburt area (Ketin, 1951) (the Eastern Pontides), the post-tectonic shallow level granitic pluton of Carboniferous age in the Gümüşhane area (the Gümüşhane granite), and the Kösdağ felsic calc-alkaline metavolcanic rocks of possible Triassic age in the Kargı Massif (Figure 15A) all display subduction-related magma affinities; therefore, they may be interpreted as the products of a south-dipping subduction of Paleotethys under the Cimmerian continent.

Early Jurassic Events

The data documented on the previous pages indicate that the Küre and Elekdağ ophiolites were generated in the Paleotethyan oceanic realm. According to Ustaömer and Robertson (1994), the Küre ophiolite represents a suprasubduction ophiolite. The palinspastic reconstruction of the Elekdağ ophiolite, the underlying Domuzdağ melange, the continental margin units such as the Aktaş, Gümüsoluğu, and Bekirli metamorphics, and the Kösdağ continental margin volcanics suggest collectively that the Paleotethyan Ocean floor was consumed by the southward subduction (Figure 14). This view is supported further by the north-vergent structures within the Küre ophiolite and the associated epiophiolitic sedimentary rocks noted by Ustaömer and Robertson (1994), corroborating the original view proposed by Şengör and Yılmaz (1981) and Şengör et al. (1984). The southward subduction initially generated the Karakaya marginal basin behind the volcanic arc during the Triassic. After the closure of the Karakaya Basin in the latest Triassic, the continuing subduction possibly opened Neotethys (the İzmir-Ankara Ocean) as a new basin during the Liassic (Figure 15B, C). This rifting ruptured the Karakaya suture zone (Figure 15C).

The evidence for development of the Liassic rifting event is discussed in detail by Yılmaz (1972), Brinkmann (1972), Seymen (1975), Şengör and Yılmaz (1981), Yılmaz (1981), Görür et al. (1983), and Dercourt et al. (1986). In the Pontides, the basal units are thick, coarse-clastic rocks, accompanied by alkaline and tholeiitic basalt lavas. They are overlain by the typical shelf deposits of the Middle–Late Jurassic (the Bilecik limestone; Altınlı, 1973). This is followed by the pelagization of the platform (the Soğukçam limestone and the Vezirhan Formation) (Figure 3). The data summarized above collectively indicate the establishment of a south-facing Atlantic-type continental margin (Seymen, 1975; Yılmaz, 1979, 1981; Şengör and Yılmaz, 1981; Bergougnan, 1987; Koçyiğit et al., 1992). The opening of this new arm of Neotethys greatly reduced the width of the Cimmerian continent in this region and separated the Eastern-Central Pontides and the Sakarya continent from the Tauride-Anatolide (the Menderes-Taurus) Platform (Figure 15C) (Şengör and Yılmaz, 1981). This marks the beginning of a faunal differentiation between the Pontides and the rest of Turkey (Bassoullet et al., 1975).

As a result of the gradual demise of the Paleotethys, its oceanic units, a suprasubduction ophiolite (the Küre ophiolite), and a subduction melange (the Domuzdağ melange) were assembled and then were emplaced collectively onto the continental margin units (the Aktaş, Gümüsoluğu, and Bekirli formations) as a giant nappe package during the Dogger (Figure 9). The Devrekani Massif of the İstanbul-Zonguldak Zone (Figure 9) was thrust from the north onto this amalgamated ophiolitic association. The oceanic assemblages sandwiched between the two continental fragments are interpreted as the products of the closure of Paleotethys, which resulted in the collision of the Scythian Platform and the Cimmerian continent (Figure 15C).

The collision gave rise to south-vergent structures, thrusts in the Elekdağ (Yılmaz and Tüysüz, 1984; Tüysüz, 1985), and asymmetrical folds in the underlying rocks. The underlying units were penetratively deformed and cataclastically metamorphosed to the greenschist facies (Yılmaz, 1990; Tüysüz, 1990; Yılmaz et al., 1995). Due to the shortening deformation, the crust is assumed to have gradually elevated; consequently, sedimentation was interrupted in most of the Pontides regions during the Dogger (Figure 3) (Yılmaz, 1972; Yılmaz and Tüysüz, 1984). The few exceptions to the cessation of the sediment deposition are seen in the following areas: to the north of Tokat and to the northeast of Suşehri, where fluvial and shallow sea sediments were continually deposited in locally preserved, fault-bounded basins during the Dogger (Wedding, 1963; Pelin, 1977; Yılmaz et al., 1993).

During the Dogger, a bimodal magmatism began on the collided assemblage of the Central Pontides (Figure 3). The Çangaldağ intrusive complex was injected into this tectonic mosaic and cut the mutual contacts (Figure 9). Some of the stocks reached the surface and produced subareal felsic extrusives (Yılmaz and Tüysüz, 1984; Yılmaz et al., 1990). For

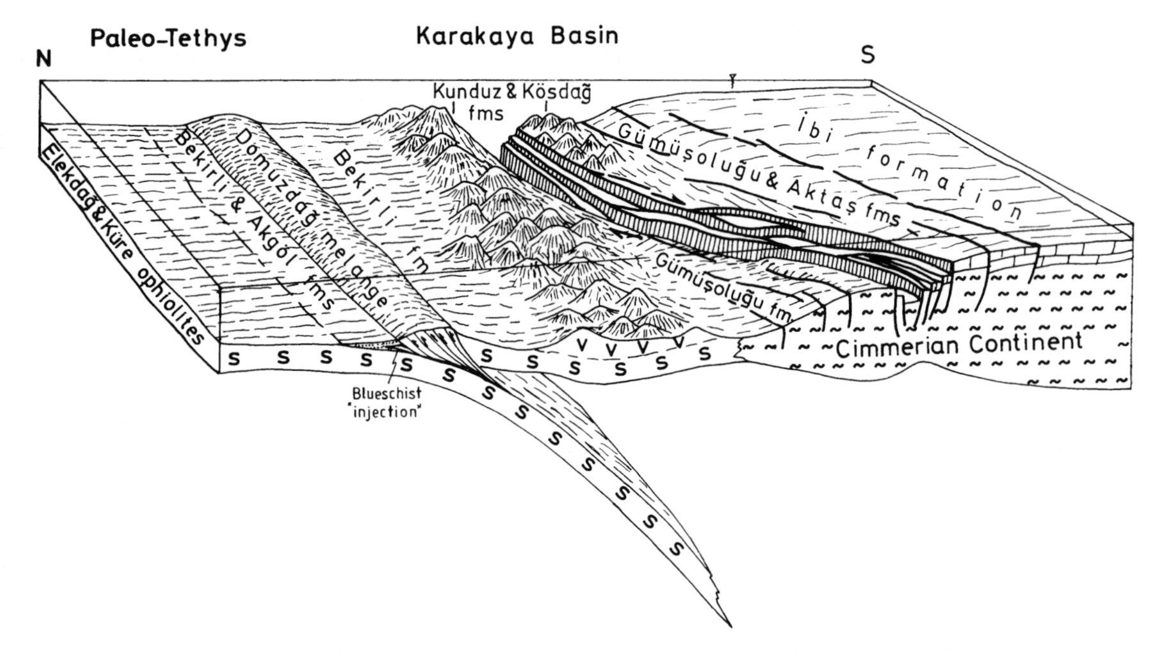

Figure 14. Interpretative block diagram showing the tectonic setting of the rock units of the Central Pontides during the Triassic (modified after Tüysüz and Yiğitbaş, 1994).

this reason, the calc-alkaline magmatism may be regarded as Tibetan type and formed because of the mixing of the mantle-derived magmas and crustal components (Yılmaz and Boztuğ, 1986). This magmatic activity continued into the Late Jurassic. Its later products are observed in the central and Eastern Pontides; that is, the Çangaldağ area and the Oltu region.

Despite the collision that is recorded in the Kargı Massif and the surrounding areas, the field evidence, obtained from the region lying to the west of Kastamonu, indicates that sediment deposition, possibly on an oceanic foundation, continued uninterruptedly during the Middle–Late Mesozoic (Figure 3) (Deveciler et al., 1989; Şengün, 1993; Aydın et al., 1995). This suggests that while the collision was going on in the Kargı Massif, an oceanic realm in the west, away from the converging jaws of the colliding continents, remained unclosed (Figure 15C). This region appears to have formed an eastward-narrowing triangular gap and extended along the trend of the present Intra-Pontide suture. The sedimentary fill of this remnant basin is observed within the Araç-Daday shear zone (Figure 3).

Malm–Early Cretaceous Events

During the Malm–Early Cretaceous, a new extensional regime began and affected the entire central and the Eastern Pontides regions. This is shown by rapid lateral facies changes of the Malm basal units (Yılmaz et al., 1990). In places, these units are delimited by basin-bounding faults, with abrupt thickness variations across the faults indicating the presence of horsts, grabens, and progressively rotated, uplifted, and subsided regions next to one another (Yılmaz and Tüysüz, 1984, 1988; Tüysüz et al., 1990). The rapid lateral lithological transitions vanish upward in the succession (Figures 3, 12). The basal clastic deposits (the Bürnük Formation) are followed by platform carbonates, the İnaltı Formation, and the Bilecik limestone. The Lower Cretaceous sediments are accompanied by tholeiitic basaltic lavas to the west of the Eastern Pontides between Giresun and Suşehri (Figures 7, 12) (Zankl, 1961; Yılmaz et al., 1993). The Black Sea might have opened in the Aptian–Albian time during the ongoing extensional system, when neritic limestones were replaced by syntectonic clastic deposits (the Çağlayan Formation) (Görür, 1988). During this period, the İstanbul-Zonguldak Zone of the Western Pontides possibly represented a structural high, because the Lower Cretaceous units are absent in this zone (Figure 3), and the contacts of Lower–Middle Jurassic clastic rocks that surround the İstanbul-Zonguldak Zone in the eastern sector to the north of Safranbolu display a westerly located source area and trend approximately in a north-south direction (Figure 5). This trend butts against the major Late Cretaceous and Tertiary structural trends that are mainly east-west.

The carbonate platform began to subside during the Early Cretaceous. This is evidenced by the replacement of the Bilecik limestone and the İnaltı Formation by the deep-sea cherty limestones (the Soğukçam limestone) (Figure 3).

Late Cretaceous–Early Eocene Events

The Late Cretaceous and Paleocene age rocks in the Pontides and the Sakarya continent are intimately connected genetically. In some areas, this genetic union extends into the early Eocene; therefore, we treat them together in this chapter.

In the Sakarya continent and in the Pontides, the lower Cretaceous micritic white limestones are followed

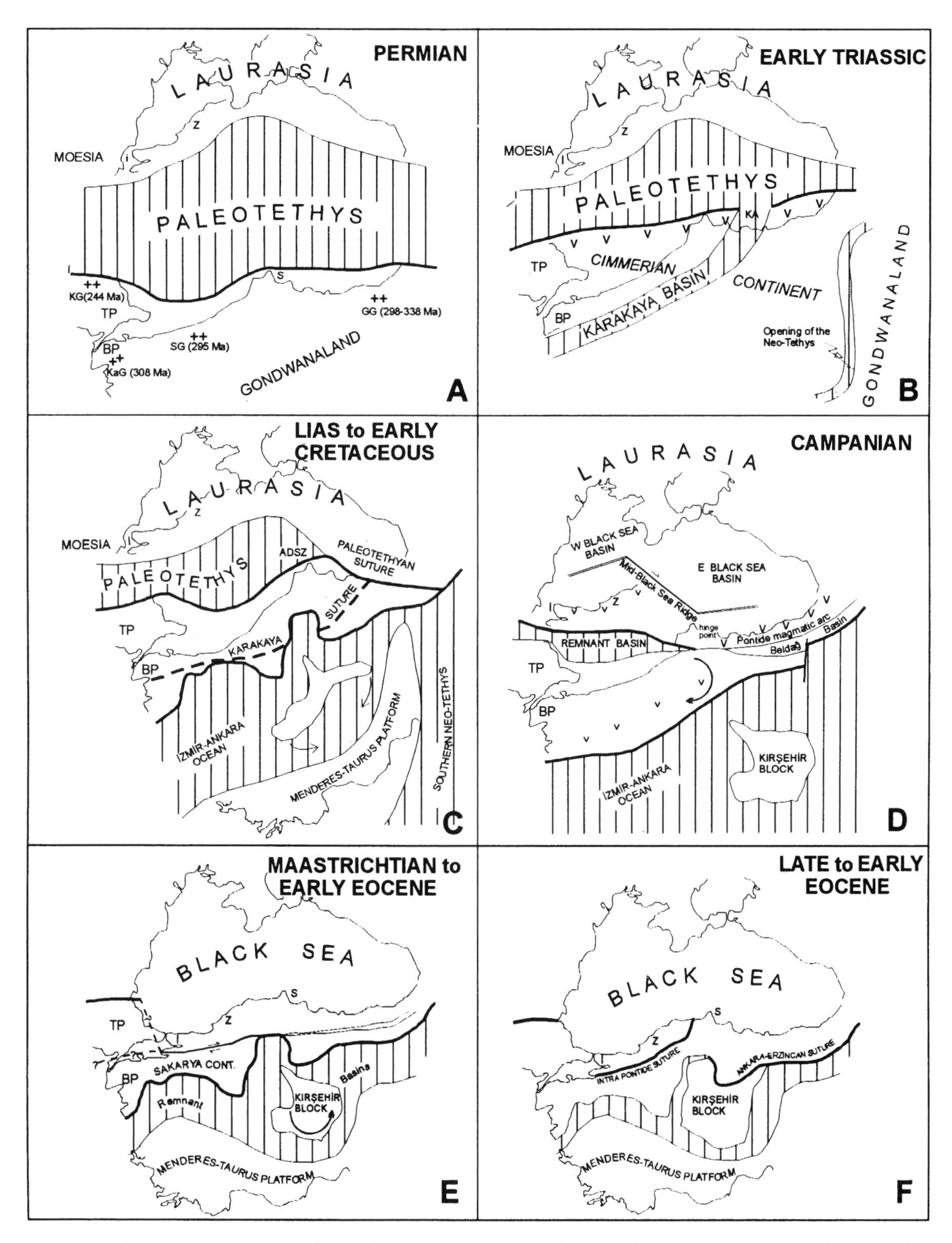

Figure 15. Paleotectonic maps depicting the tectonic evolution of the Pontides from the Permian to the Eocene. In the paleotectonic maps, the present shapes of the coastlines are dotted for reference purposes. ++ = arc plutonics, vv = arc volcanics. Heavy lines with black triangles = subduction zones, lines with half arrows = transform faults. Thin lines = Atlantic-type continental margins. ADSZ = Araç-Daday shear zone, BP = Biga Peninsula, GG = Gümüşhane granite, KaG = Kazdağ granite, KA = Kargı area, K.G. = Kırklareli granite, S = Sinop, SG = Söğüt granite, TP = Thrace Peninsula, I = İstanbul, Z = Zonguldak.

by pelagic rocks (the Vezirhan Formation). This regionwide pelagization occurred during the Cenomanian–Turonian (Figure 3). Following the steady subsidence of the carbonate platforms, flysch deposition began during the Turonian (Figures 3, 12). It is believed, therefore, that a passive margin with well-defined carbonate platform, slope (the carbonate flysch and flysch) (Figure 3), and abyssal plain was developed facing southward where the Neotethyan Ocean floor is believed to have formed (Figure 15C, D). The evidence for the ocean floor is obtained from the ophiolite and epiophiolitic pelagic sedimentary units that were emplaced onto the continental margin from the south in a later period during the Late Cretaceous.

In the northern part of the Eastern Pontides and the Sakarya continent, the flysch deposition is accompanied by volcanic rocks during the Turonian (Figures 12, 15C, 16A). The volcanism was severe in the Pontides range, but relatively mild in the Sakarya continent, involving mostly a few pyroclastic horizons and lava layers (Altınlı, 1973; Yılmaz, 1981). The lavas range in composition from basalt to dacite, showing tholeiitic (Moore et al., 1980; Akıncı et al., 1991), calc-alkaline (Tokel, 1977; Manetti et al., 1981; Yılmaz, 1981; Ercan and Gedik, 1983; Boccaletti et al., 1988a), and shoshonitic (Manetti et al., 1981, 1983) affinities and compare favorably with subduction-related magmas (Peccerillo and Taylor, 1975; Tokel, 1977; Eğin and Hirst, 1979; Moore et al., 1980; Yılmaz, 1981; Akıncı et al., 1991). Therefore, the volcanic products forming active continental margin magmatism were developed directly on top of the sedimentary prism of the previous passive margin (Figure 16A) (Yılmaz, 1980). Arc magmatism was generated, possibly due to the northward subduction of the Neotethyan Ocean floor under the Pontides (Figure 16A). Evidence for this is seen by the development of an subduction-accretion melange that formed in front of the leading edge of the continental platform in the south (Figures 8, 10, 16A, B). The blueschists are seen to be associated with the melange; that is, in the Yildizeli area (Tatar, 1971).

Around the volcanic belt, a volcanogenic flysch, the Yemişliçay Formation, was developed extensively (Figures 3, 7, 11, and 12) (Aydın et al., 1986; Tüysüz et al., 1990). During the same period, a narrow fore-arc basin was formed in front of the volcanic arc in the Pontides and was filled with the arc-derived debris and volcanic fragments (the Eryaba and Çördük olistostromes and the Beldağ group) (Figures 3, 7, 12, and 16C). The subduction-accretion complex was uplifted as the melange wedge continued to grow (Figure 16B). This corresponds to the beginning of a new north-south compressional deformation, which produced thrusts, asymmetrical folds, and uplifts in the fore-arc region (Figures 11, 16B). The tectonism occurred during the Coniacian–Santonian and is recorded as a regionwide stratigraphic gap in the entire Pontides region (Figures 3, 7, and 12), with the exceptions of the back-arc region (presently the northern flank of the Pontides) where the flysch deposition continued (the Kapanboğazı Formation; Ketin and Gümüs, 1963; Yiğitbaş et al., 1990), and the oceanic realm where the Hıdırnalı Group was deposited continually (Tekeli et al., 1991). As a result of this severe deformation, the melange and fore-arc units were imbricated (Figure 9), and the elevated regions were deeply eroded. At the same time, the ophiolitic melange was overthrust onto the previously deformed fore-arc terrains (Figure 16B) (Yılmaz, 1979; Norman, 1988; Koçyigit, 1991; Yılmaz et al., 1993). The magnitude of the thrusting is small. The thrusting of the melange was formed possibly with a retrocharriage mechanism as a consequence of the progressive growth, elevation, and overthrusting of the melange prism (Karig, 1974).

The shortening deformation is followed by a new extensional regime during the late Campanian. This is evidenced by the basal units of a new regionwide transgression on the older units with a marked angular unconformity (Figures 3, 7, and 12). This occurred simultaneously with the southward migration of the volcanic front (Figures 12, 16B). The region that was occupied previously by the arc-volcanic rocks during the Turonian, and left in the back-arc setting during the Campanian–Maastrichtian, began to collapse rapidly. This is evidenced by the fast transition from flysch to pelagic limestone, mudstone, and radiolarite units (the Akveren Formation; Figure 3). This event may be regarded as the main opening phase of the Black Sea Basin (Figure 16B). There is an agreement on the opening of the Black Sea during the Late Cretaceous (Neprechov et al., 1975; Bulandje, 1976; Siderenko, 1978; Zonenshain and Le Pichon, 1986) as a mini-ocean (Brinkmann, 1972; Dewey et al., 1973; Şengör and Yılmaz, 1981; Robertson and Dixon, 1984; Boccaletti, 1988a; Görür et al., 1993). In the southern edge of the Pontides, the elevated melange prism formed a nonvolcanic outer arc—a barrier between the fore-arc region and the ocean—and delimited the southward extension of the fore-arc basin(s) (Figure 16B). In the Çördük area, for example, to the south of Tokat (Figure 12), the fore-arc basin was bounded by two elevations (the volcanic arc in the north and the volcanic outer arc in the south) and was filled rapidly by debris flow deposits (the "Çördük olistostrome," Koçyiğit, 1979) derived from both source regions: the volcanic pile and the melange prisms (Yılmaz et al., 1993) (Figure 16B).

The southward-migrating magmatic front swept through the Pontides range. The new volcanic products blanketed the previous fore-arc region, the subduction-accretion melange wedge, and the hemipelagic rock units that were deposited on the melange association (Figure 12). In this period, the Neotethyan Ocean floor was possibly completely eliminated. However, a remnant basin underlain by the melange foundation survived (Figure 16C). This is evidenced by the continual deep-sea sediment deposition throughout the Late Cretaceous. The pelagic sediments are the red micritic limestone-marl-shale alternation (the Hıdırnalı Group), intercalated with calc-alkaline lavas and pyroclastic units (Figure 12). The remnant basin (the Yildizeli Basin) was situated between the forebulge (the back stop) and the Kırşehir Massif. The sediment deposition in the remnant basin continued uninterruptedly till the

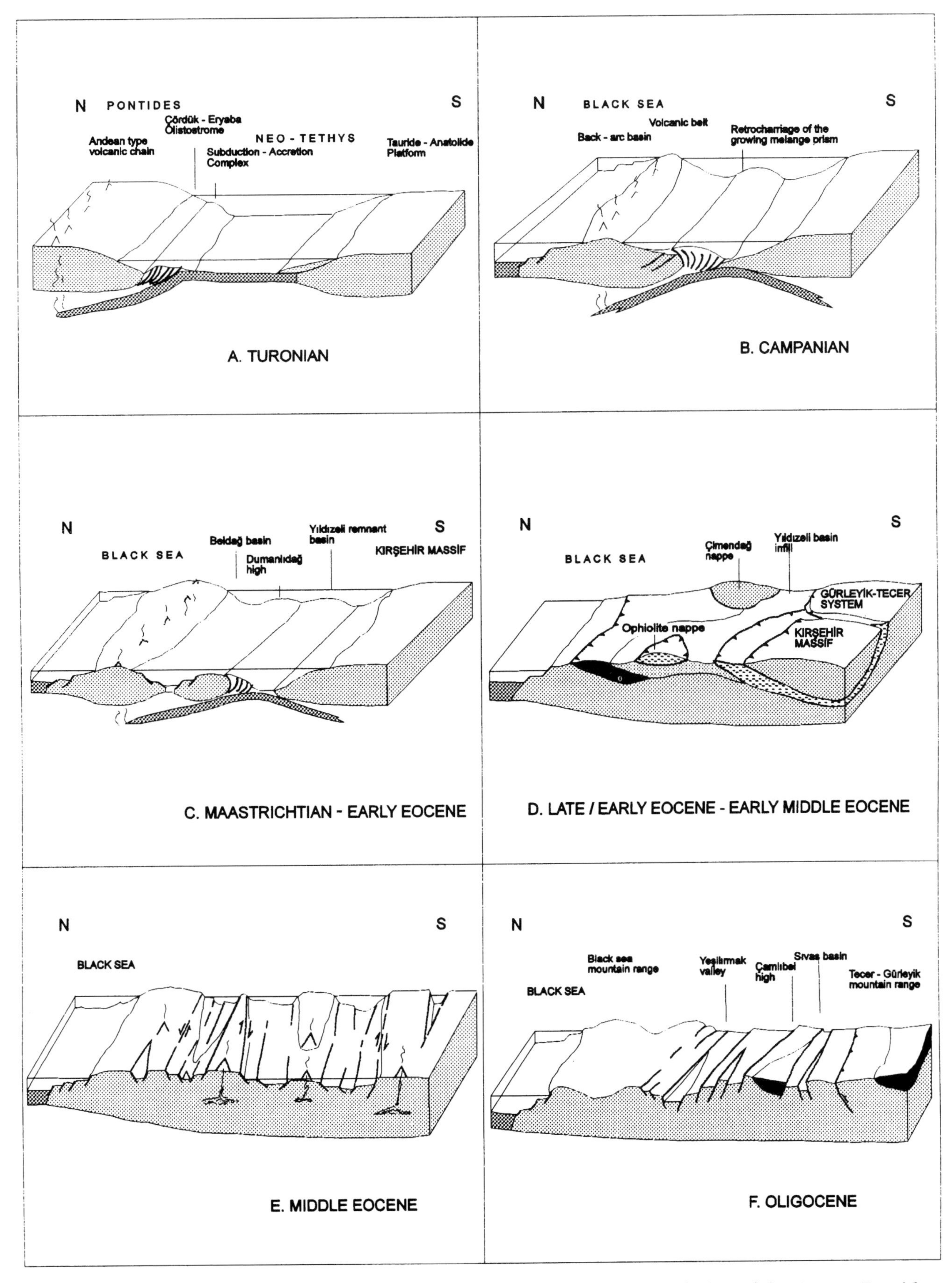

Figure 16. Block diagrams showing the subsequent stages of the orogenic evolution of the Eastern Pontides during the Late Cretaceous–Oligocene.

end of early Eocene, in a progressively shallowing marine environment. This is evidenced by the gradual replacement of the deep-sea sediments by the shallow marine units during the Paleocene–early Eocene (Figure 12).

A similar evolution to that of the Central and Eastern Pontides regions occurred along the southern regions of the Sakarya continent during the Late Cretaceous, where the ophiolitic melange association overlain by a peridotite nappe was backthrust onto the south-facing continental margin units (Figure 6), and high P/low T metamorphic rocks occur within the subduction melange units: the Sarıcakaya and Sivrihisar areas (Çoğulu, 1967) (Figures 3, 6). On top of the Sakarya continent platform, shallow water sediments in a regressive facies were developed during the Maastrichtian to early Eocene (Figure 3).

While the southern part of the Sakarya continent was evolving in this way, its northern regions underwent a slightly different development. Pelagic sediment deposition was interrupted during the Coniacian–Santonian (Figures 3, 7); part of the northern areas was elevated and eroded. The materials eroded from the high regions were transported to, and were laid down in, the neighboring flysch basin as turbidites and debris flow deposits (Saner, 1977; Yılmaz, 1981; Yılmaz et al., 1995). With the beginning of the late Campanian, a new transgression, depositing basal clastic rocks, occurred (Figures 3, 7). These rapid and abrupt changes from continuous to discontinuous successions, with the north-vergent thrusts and folds that are recorded in the succession (Figure 6) (Bargu, 1982; Genç, 1993; Yılmaz et al., 1995), indicate clearly that the region suffered a severe north-south compressional deformation during the Coniacian–Santonian interval. The post-erosion flysch yields late Campanian?–Maastrichtian ages (Figures 3, 7). The rock fragments within the flysch include ophiolitic and blueschist metamorphic debris (Yılmaz, 1981), which increases in size and proportion to the north, suggesting the presence of an elevated melange association nearby in the north; the ophiolitic debris may have been shed from the Geyve ophiolitic slab topping the melange and was advancing southward.

The data summarized above suggest that an ophiolitic slab was detached from the oceanic lithosphere, possibly during the Turonian, and advanced toward the northern margin of the Sakarya continent. In fact, in the Geyve-Tarakli area (the northernmost part of the Sakarya continent), a severely deformed, sheared serpentinite crops out (Figure 5), resting on Upper Cretaceous flysch (Figure 3). The ophiolite is overlain by the Maastrichtian marine sedimentary rocks (Figures 3, 7). This branch of the ocean was separating the Sakarya continent from the İstanbul-Zonguldak Zone (Figure 15C, D) (Şengör and Yılmaz, 1981; Şengör et al., 1984; Okay et al., 1994). Corresponding with this interval, a forebulge formed on the continental platform, possibly in front of the advancing nappe. Evidence for this is displayed in the Coniacian–Santonian shoaling of the northern edge of the continental platform and in the consequent subareal erosion of the sedimentary cover (Figures 3, 7). Depositional equivalents of this erosion are seen in the form of debris flow deposits that were shed onto the continental slope. The continuing advance of the ophiolite nappe rapidly depressed the formerly uplifted and eroded edge of the continental platform. As a result, a new marine transgression began in the region, starting with shallow marine sediments passing rapidly into deep-sea deposits, such as the pelagic sedimentary rocks that interfinger with the flysch (the Gölpazari Group; Altınlı, 1973) (Figures 3, 7). Following the incorporation of the olistostromes and blocks, the depositional environment on the platform area changed from deep to shallow marine, as evidenced by the gradual replacement of the flysch initially by shallow marine sediments and then by continental red beds (Figures 3, 7). This occurred during the Maastrichtian–Paleocene transition (Altınlı, 1973; Saner, 1977; Yılmaz, 1981; Yılmaz et al., 1995).

Farther north, the North Anatolian transform fault zone separates the Sakarya continent from the metamorphic rocks of the Armutlu-Almacık Zone, which contains the İznik metamorphic unit (Figure 5). This unit is closely similar to the coeval rocks of the Sakarya continent (Figure 3), suggesting that the İznik metamorphic sequence represents the northern edge of the Sakarya continent that underwent metamorphism. The metamorphism occurred during the post-Turonian–pre-late Campanian interval and corresponds to the period of severe deformation recorded in the northern part of the Sakarya continent. It also coincides with the emplacement of the ophiolite slab onto the continent (Figure 3). These coeval events suggest a genetic link between ophiolite obduction, regional deformation, and metamorphism that occurred during the severe phase of deformation between the late Turonian and the late Campanian. The northern edge of the Sakarya continent is estimated to have been buried to a depth of ~12 km, and underwent metamorphism at 350–500°C and 3.5–4 kb (Bozcu, 1992; Yılmaz, 1992; Yılmaz et al., 1995). After the metamorphism, the metamorphic association was rapidly uplifted before the late Campanian transgression (Figures 3, 7).

Following the uplift, the metamorphosed and nonmetamorphosed parts of the northern edge of the Sakarya continent, an overlying metamorphosed ophiolite slab, and the İstanbul-Zonguldak Zone of the Western Pontides were inundated for the first time. This is the area where a wide range of coeval sedimentary rocks were deposited during the late Campanian–Maastrichtian. From the İstanbul region in the north to the Sakarya continent in the south, transition from a shallow sea passing rapidly into a deep-sea environment is recorded in the upper Campanian–Maastrichtian successions (Figures 3, 7).

The initial collision between the İstanbul-Zonguldak Zone and the Sakarya continent possibly occurred during the Coniacian–Santonian, as evidenced by the following data: (1) the İznik metamorphic assemblage representing the northern edge of the Sakarya continent is composed of units up to and including Turonian age (Figures 3, 7); (2) a metamorphosed ophiolite slab (the Almacık-Geyve ophiolite), possibly representing the remnant of the ocean separating the two continents rests tectonically on the uppermost unit of the İznik metamorphic assemblage (Figures 3, 6) [the ophiolite, in turn, is tectonically overlain by the İstanbul-Zonguldak tectonic unit (Figures 3, 6)]; (3) these amalgamated tectonic units are stratigraphically covered by the Upper Campanian–Maastrichtian sedimentary rocks (Figures 3, 7).

The Coniacian–Santonian interval corresponds to the burial and subsequent metamorphism of the Armutlu-Almacık Zone and the regional uplift and erosion of the Sakarya continent (Figures 3, 7). The coeval uplift and deep burial in the neighboring regions may be due to progressive stacking of the nappes during the southerly transportation of the allochthons. This possibly created a heavy burden on the northern edge of the Sakarya continent and the consequent collapse. The collapsed edge subsided steadily and has undergone regional metamorphism. The contact between the equivalent metamorphic and nonmetamorphic units is sharp everywhere and is deformed by a high-angle fault that corresponds presently to the southern branch of the North Anatolian transform fault zone (Figures 5, 6). This evidence suggests that this fault zone also divided the two continents during the Late Cretaceous, and has been rejuvenated during the development of the North Anatolian transform fault system in the Late Miocene–Pliocene (Yılmaz et al., 1995).

Following the regional metamorphism, the İstanbul-Zonguldak Zone, the Armutlu-Almacık metamorphic pile, and the Sakarya continent acted collectively as a basement for the late Campanian–Maastrichtian basin (Figure 15D). These successions, when followed from the north to the south across the suture zone (Figure 7), indicate that sediment deposition during this period continued in a remnant flysch basin that was trapped between the two continents. The northern edge of the basin resided on the İstanbul-Zonguldak Zone, while the southern edge was located on the Sakarya continent (Figures 7, 15D). The lithological nature of the sediments along the northern side (the İstanbul area, for example) and the southern side (the Geyve-Tarakli area) was located on two tectonically controlled highs, where the thick succession of coarse clastic wedges was deposited initially (Figure 7) (Bozcu, 1992; Yılmaz et al., 1995). The structural highs possibly correspond to fault-induced elevations, which may have obliterated most of the Mesozoic continental margin successions, mainly from the İstanbul Zone (Figures 3, 7), which structurally represent the highest tectonic unit (Figure 6).

The flysch basin was filled with material while being gradually elevated; this process formed a thick wild-flysch deposit (Figures 3, 7) due to the continuous convergence between the opposite continents. The flysch basin turned gradually into shallow sea realms, as evidenced by the upward-shallowing sediment deposition during the Maastrichtian (Figures 3, 7). As a result of the convergence, the suture zone and the immediate surroundings rose above sea level, while the shallow marine environment remained in both of the continental interiors until the end of the Early Eocene (Figures 3, 7).

The collision between the İstanbul-Zonguldak Zone and the Sakarya continent appears to have resulted from the consumption and total demise of the eastward-narrowing triangular oceanic gap, which remained unclosed after the initial collision between the İstanbul-Zonguldak Zone and the Central Pontides region during the Dogger (Figure 15D). This oceanic realm, although referred to previously as the northern branch of the Neotethys (Şengör and Yılmaz, 1981), appears to be the remainder of the Paleotethys (Figure 15A–D). The data in favor of the survival of the Paleotethyan Ocean are derived from the Araç-Daday shear zone (Figures 8, 15C), where the deep-sea sedimentary succession is continuous from the Jurassic to the upper Cretaceous (Figure 3) (Deveciler et al., 1989; Şengün, 1993; Aydın et al., 1995).

The triangular oceanic gap that began to be consumed by the subduction under the İstanbul-Zonguldak Zone during the Late Cretaceous produced a subduction-accretion melange in front of the Western Pontides. The remnants of this melange are preserved along the North Anatolian transform fault zone (Figure 5) (Yılmaz et al., 1981, 1995). The same process generated a volcanic arc along the present Black Sea coast (Figure 15D). During the closure of this oceanic realm, the Sakarya continent, which was assumed to have been attached to the Eastern Pontides range, began to be rifted off the Pontides and moved away from it, while rotating clockwise (Fig 15D). This is shown by the following observations:

(1) The paleomagnetic data support the independent motions of the two regions. According to Evans et al. (1982), the upper Jurassic limestone unit of the Bilecik area (the Sakarya continent) has undergone an ~90° clockwise rotation. On the other hand, the Jurassic to Late Cretaceous rocks of the Eastern Pontides range display an ~40–45° counterclockwise rotation (van der Voo, 1968; Orbay and Bayburdi, 1979; Lauer, 1981; Channel et al., 1995). Distribution of the inclinations suggests that the Sakarya continent and the Eastern Pontides were situated around the +50 paleolatitude during the Jurassic and Cretaceous. Furthermore, the data displayed by Evans et al. (1982) demonstrate clearly that the clockwise rotations of the Sakarya continent occurred sometime between the post-Late Jurassic and the Paleocene. The paleomagnetic data demonstrate further that this rotation cannot be attributed to the motions along the North Anatolian transform fault zone (Evans et al., 1982, 1990).

(2) The facies boundaries of the Mesozoic continental platform and the slope units of the Sakarya continent trend approximately north-south (Saner, 1977). This is an apparent contradiction to the east-west elongation of the Sakarya continent and the surrounding suture zones, but is in favor of a clockwise rotation.

(3) A fault-bounded, east-west–trending basin began to form in the Eastern Pontides during the Campanian–Maastrichtian, along the belt occupied presently by the branches of the North Anatolian transform fault zone. This basin fill is referred to as Beldağ Group (Figures 12, 15D, and 16C). This unit extends all along the belt, from Amasya in the west to the north of Erzincan in the east (Figure 10). The Beldağ basin is regarded as having developed under a transtensional regime, because the faults that delimited the basin and controlled the sediment deposition display strike-slip and dip-slip components (Yılmaz et al., 1993).

This clockwise rotation of the Sakarya continent resulted in its approach toward the İstanbul-Zonguldak Zone (Figure 15C, D). This motion began to be accommodated, possibly by an oblique subduction in front of the İstanbul-Zonguldak Zone, which progressively eliminated the remaining ocean. As a result, the ocean floor is assumed to have been destroyed by a mechanism similar to the westward-closing blades of a pair of the scissors; the initial collision began to be taken up by thrusting (Figure 3). In later phases, the nappes were truncated and offset by the right-lateral strike-slip faults that deformed the Intra-Pontide suture zone (Figures 5, 6, and 15E) (the present North Anatolian transform fault zone) as documented above. The right-lateral offset along the fault zone explains the peculiar distribution pattern of some Jurassic rocks; the Mudurnu Group, for example (Figures 4, 12), has long remained a problem. This unit crops out solely in the Mudurnu area in the Sakarya continent, adjacent to the North Anatolian transform fault zone (Figure 4). The nearest identical unit that outcrops widely to the north of the North Anatolian transform fault zone in the Central Pontides is ~400 km to the east of the Mudurnu area. Only a small fraction of the present offset may be attributed to the motions along the present North Anatolian transform fault zone, since the cumulative right-lateral offset due to the post-Miocene fault system is assumed to be ~90 km at the most (Şengör, 1979b; Şengör and Canıtez, 1982; Barka, 1992).

The successions and the metamorphic histories encountered in the Armutlu-Almacık Zone and the İstranca Massif are similar (Figure 3); therefore, these two tectonic zones may be viewed as parts of the same tectonic unit. The Armutlu-Almacık Zone is regarded here continuing westward into the İstranca Massif. If this interpretation is correct, then the previous assumption that the Intra-Pontide suture runs in east-westerly direction under the water of the Marmara Sea and thus separates the Thrace region from the Sakarya continent (Şengör and Yılmaz, 1981) must be revised. The Intra-Pontide suture is thus given a sharp bend from a predominantly east-west orientation to an almost north-south orientation at the western end of the Armutlu Peninsula (Figure 5). This sharp bend may correspond with a strike-slip fault that offsets the suture northward and coincides with the southern tip of a large transform fault zone proposed by Okay et al. (1994). Kalkan (1993) places the Intra-Pontide suture along the covered contact of the İstanbul-Zonguldak Zone with the İstranca Massif (Figures 5, 15E). It is assumed that the suture extends westward toward the Sredna Gora Zone in Bulgaria (Figure 1), which is a pelagic unit of Late Cretaceous age, consisting of radiolarite, pelagic limestone, turbidite, and submarine basic to intermediate volcanic rocks intercalated with the sediments (Gocev, 1970; Boccaletti et al., 1974; Sandulescu, 1978). This unit is interpreted as representing a zone where an oceanic basin has disappeared (Dewey et al., 1973; Hsü et al., 1977; Burchfiel, 1980). However, this interpretation still leaves a few scattered Mesozoic ophiolitic outcrops in the Sakarya continent problematic; there are some serpentinite bodies and exotic melange units of Late Cretaceous age outcropping along the North Anatolian transform fault zone in the Saros area and in the Ezine areas of the Biga Peninsula (Figure 4). These may be evaluated as the remnants of the new rifting (the Şarköy basin) that ruptured the northern edge of the Sakarya continent (Figure 15E).

In conclusion, the westerly course of the Paleotethyan suture is problematic, largely because the geology of the blocks it is supposed to separate, is so similar, at least with respect to the data gathered at the present reconnaissance stage. One possibility is to place it between the Armutlu and the İstranca metamorphics. This accounts for the Liassic rift/continental margin facies that developed above the Armutlu basement by connecting the former with the Neotethyan rift assemblages farther east. To test this hypothesis, one would have to check the similarly aged rocks in Turkish İstranca; unfortunately, no rocks younger than the Anisian have been preserved in Turkish İstranca, except for a Moesian tectonic window around Demirciköy.

The problem with this interpretation is the great similarity between the İstranca and the Armutlu basements. An alternative interpretation is to take the suture north of the Turkish İstranca, thus separating it from the Moesian Platform. As Moesian stratigraphy is very similar to that of the İstanbul-Zonguldak Zone and very dissimilar to that of the Turkish İstranca, this is at first sight a comfortable solution. But this interpretation leaves unexplained the deep-sea deposits, now phyllites, near Çatalca, which have been likened to, and considered the root zone for, the İstranca nappes in Bulgaria (G.A. Chatalov, 1988, personal communication). It also leaves unexplained why sedimentation ceased in the Anisian in Turkish İstranca, just before the İstranca nappes began moving northward. Finally, there is no Mesozoic magmatism in Turkish İstranca to account for southerly subduction of the Paleotethyan Ocean.

Until more detailed structural study and age dating are undertaken in the Armutlu and the İstranca basements, it is impossible to reach a decision. Most of the authors of this chapter prefer to put the main Paleotethyan suture to the north of Turkish İstranca; Şengör opts for Gocev's (1979) solution in contrast to his previous opinion based on Aydın's (1974) now largely discredited data.

Late/Early Eocene to Early Middle Eocene Events

The early Eocene–Middle Eocene transition corresponds to the final stage of the collision between the Pontide arc and the Menderes-Taurus Platform and the Kırşehir block (Figures 15F, 16D). Therefore, this period witnessed a compressional regime everywhere, and was particularly characterized by thrusting and nappe emplacement. During this phase of deformation, the remnant basin fill in the Yildizeli region, which remained after the total consumption of the Neotethyan Ocean floor, was severely deformed and partly destroyed. A coeval large-scale internal deformation then began within the Pontides. The remnant basin, which was filled with turbiditic flysch and coarse clastic sediments during the Paleocene and early Eocene (Figure 12) (Dellaloğlu and Meşhur, 1980; Tekeli et al., 1991; Yılmaz et al., 1993), was later tectonically overriden by the ophiolitic nappe package that consists mainly of melange and an overlying disrupted ophiolite slab (Figures 12, 16D).

The nappes were thrust from the south to the north, as indicated clearly by the north-vergent structures such as overturned folds and thrusts in the underlying sedimentary rocks (Yılmaz et al., 1993) (Figure 13). A coeval north-vergent thrusting also occurred along the southern margin of the remnant basin, as exemplified by the northern boundaries of the Akdağ Massif (the Kırşehir Massif) and the Gürleyik-Tecer Mountains in the south of Sıvas (Figure 10) (Dellaloğlu and Meşhur, 1980; Cater et al., 1991). The geological data obtained from the southern part of the basin suggest that the northward nappe transport continued throughout the Latest Cretaceous–Early Eocene. As a result, the remnant basin was filled with the material shed from the northerly advancing nappes. Evidence for this is the progressive northward shoaling of the southern shelf edge (Cater et al., 1991; Tekeli et al., 1991; Yılmaz et al., 1993). This is indicated by the subareal erosion and accompanying northward prograding of the flysch and debris flow deposits, which gradually replaced the pelagic limestones and radiolarites (Figure 12). At the final stage, the Kırşehir Massif was thrust onto the remnant basin fill and the overlying ophiolite nappes (Figures 12, 16D) (Yılmaz et al., 1993). Because of the presence of the nappe blanket, the remnant basin fill may be observed in areas where the younger faults cut and displace the succession, or around tectonic windows (Figures 10, 16D).

The region to the south of the North Anatolian transform fault zone between Koyulhisar and Suşehri widely exposes the peridotite nappes. The nappes were imbricated with the basement metamorphic assemblage and its cover succession. The timing of this thick-skinned deformation is tightly constrained as Early–Middle Eocene transition because (1) the metamorphic basement rocks and its in-situ cover succession including the lower Eocene rocks were tectonically overlain by the peridotite nappe and (2) these imbricated units were stratigraphically covered by the Lutetian basal conglomerates and sandstones (Figure 7) (Yılmaz et al., 1993).

Evidence for the north-directed compressional deformation is also observed clearly in the northern regions (the Kelkit and Çimendağ areas), where the Pulur metamorphic massif moved tectonically onto the Mesozoic succession along a high-angle reverse fault (Figure 10). In turn, the Mesozoic limestone succession, lying in front of the massif, was detached from the basement and transported northward over a decollement surface, and was thrust onto the thick sedimentary sequence comprising the Paleocene (Yılmaz, 1982; Bergougnan, 1987) and possibly the lower Eocene units (Yılmaz et al., 1993). Along the tectonic contact, a few-hundred-meter-thick zone of cataclasis was developed, and the rocks were involved in penetrative deformation and metamorphism (Yılmaz et al., 1993).

A contemporaneous compressional deformation also occurred in the Central Pontides, where the thrust transport was south-directed in the southern areas and north-directed in the northern areas (Tüysüz and Dellaloğlu, 1992). An outstanding example of this is in the Sinop area, where the geological and geophysical data in the hinterland of the Türkeli-Ayancık area, south of Sinop, show that a Berriasian–Eocene succession lying above the Çağlayan shales of the Upper Cretaceous was detached from the underlying strata and transported northward with inconsistent vergence. The resultant structures are dominated by the thrust and the associated overturned folds (Şengör, 1995).

Changes of the thrust transport direction, from mainly northward in the Eastern Pontides to the north and the south in the Central Pontides, may in part be attributed to the counterclockwise rotation of the Kırşehir Massif (Figure 15E, F) (Sanver and Ponat, 1981).

In the interior of the Sakarya continent, the north-south compression produced folds of large wavelength. Along the southern edge of the continent, a thick-skinned deformation occurred in which the basement metamorphic rocks were imbricated with the cover rocks (Figure 6) (Yılmaz, 1977, 1981). The continental margin succession was thrust onto the Upper Cretaceous melange and the overlying Paleocene terrigeneous units (Altınlı, 1973; Yılmaz, 1981; Yılmaz et al., 1981). A wide zone of severe cataclasis was developed as a result (Yılmaz, 1977, 1981).

In the Western Pontides range, Eocene thrusting is observed along the Black Sea coast, north of İstanbul (Parejas and Baykal, 1937; Y. Ketin, 1990, personal communication) (Figure 5), where the basement Paleozoic and overlying units were thrust onto the lower Eocene debris flow deposits that were shed from the northerly advancing nappe into the Eocene basin lying in front of it (Baykal and Önalan, 1979).

Middle Eocene–Oligocene Events

The middle Eocene series is characterized by a transtensional regime, which followed the north-south–directed compressional deformation. During this period, a marine invasion began over the previously deformed, uplifted, and eroded land (Figures 3, 12). The basal conglomerates and sandstones of this transgression were deposited above a variety of older rocks, with a marked angular unconformity. These detrital units show rapid lateral facies changes from thick fluvial conglomerates (i.e., the Almus area) to shallow marine clastics and locally developed reefal limestone lenses (Figure 12). These units are regarded as having been formed in a tectonically active environment that produced a horst-graben system (Figure 16E) (Yılmaz et al., 1993).

The sedimentation was accompanied by active volcanism that produced large quantities of volcanic rocks ranging in composition from basalt to andesite, which show calc-alkaline affinity (Tokel, 1977; Yılmaz, 1981; Ercan and Gedik, 1983). These lavas were previously considered to be arc related (Yılmaz, 1981; Ercan and Gedik, 1983). However, the geological characteristics of the volcanic rocks differ significantly from the arc-derived Upper Cretaceous magmatic rocks of the region (Moore et al., 1980; Manetti et al., 1983); therefore, we think that the Eocene volcanics owe their origin not to the subduction, but to the ongoing extension, because the subduction had long ended in this period (Genç and Yılmaz, 1995b). The Eocene magmas were possibly generated from the source area in the mantle, which was previously enriched by the subduction components, possibly during the Late Mesozoic subduction event, with a mechanism similar to that of the basin and range province (Hamilton, 1989) or to western Anatolia (McKenzie and Yılmaz, 1991). This view is supported further by the evidence that Middle Eocene volcanic activity developed throughout northern and Central Anatolia, regardless of the plate boundaries.

The middle Eocene basal clastic units were followed by flysch deposition (Figures 3, 12). The flysch continued to be deposited until the Late Eocene and was replaced by the progressively shallowing marine sediments. The turbidites were succeeded by shallow marine clastic rocks and occasional tuffs (Figure 12) (Yılmaz et al., 1993). This suggests that the volcanic activity survived, but waned gradually. A number of channels were cut into the shallow marine sediments; these channels increase in size and amount upward in the succession (Yılmaz et al., 1993). This may indicate a variety of submarine environments ranging from marine turbidites, submarine slope deposits, and shelf deposits, to submarine fans. The fan development is occasionally arrested abruptly, probably by structural east-west–trending barriers (Figure 16E). The sediment deposition indicates the presence of actively rising source regions. The narrow contemporaneous carbonate shelves dominated by the reef bodies were locally developed in this period (Yılmaz et al., 1993). The succeeding sediments display an upward-shoaling succession through shallow marine sediments to the deltaic and fluvial sequences in the Oligocene (Yılmaz et al., 1993).

Evidence for synsedimentary fault development in the region is obtained from Late Eocene successions that crop out extensively along the Doğansar-Suşehri-Amasya areas, where steeply dipping wrench faults and fault-bounded clastic wedges are observed (Yılmaz et al., 1993). The faults trend approximately east-west and divide the region into subparallel and narrow structural highs and lows (Gökçen and Kelling, 1985; Yılmaz et al., 1993). Under the transpressional system, the Eastern and Central Pontides as well as the Sakarya continent were gradually elevated above the sea (Figure 16F). As a result, the upper Eocene marine sediments were replaced by evaporites and then continental red beds during the Oligocene (Figure 12) (Dellaloğlu and Meşhur, 1980; Gökçen and Kelling, 1985; Cater et al., 1991).

A right-lateral strike-slip fault zone also began to develop in the Thrace region during the Oligocene. This fault system probably initiated the development of the Thrace Basin. The fault zone delimited the northern boundary of the basin against the İstranca Massif (Figure 2). It also controlled the consequent sediment deposition in the basin. The wrench-related structures are concentrated along narrow zones, and the thick clastic succession was deposited in this rapidly subsided basin (Perinçek, 1991).

During this period, a group of peripheral basins began to develop, surrounding the collided plate mosaic of northern Anatolia (Figures 1, 8). The basins extend from the Sıvas region in the east to the Eskişehir area in the west, and appear to have been connected with one another. The largest of these basins is the Sıvas Basin (Figure 10), which was formed as a ramp basin due to the elevation of the northern (the Tokat Massif) and the southern (the Gürleyik-Tecer Mountains) shoulders by wrench faults (Figure 16F).

The Pontides and the immediate surroundings were eroded, in places deeply, during the Oligocene (Figure 12). As a result, the morphological irregularities were mostly obliterated, and a regionwide peneplain developed. This is shown by lower Miocene units that are deposited on a smooth topography over large regions and are characterized by continental sediments deposited mostly in a low-energy environment (Dellaloğlu and Meşhur, 1980; Cater et al., 1991; Yılmaz et al., 1993).

Miocene and Younger Events

The early Miocene was the time of a new episode of extension in the Pontides and the Sakarya continent. The extension in the Thrace Basin continued uninterruptedly in this period.

As a result of north-south extensional regime, the Late Oligocene peneplain was dissected, and two basins, one in the north and the other in the south, began to form in the Eastern Pontides region (Figure 10). The northern basin was small and situated around the Almus-Koyulhisar area. The southeast basin was much larger and situated in the Sıvas area; this formed the Sıvas Basin. An incursion of the sea took place in the same interval into these continental basins from the north where the Paratethys (Lac Mer) was situated (Rögl and Steininger, 1984); shallow-water marine and lacustrine sediments began to be deposited in the fault-bounded structural lows (Dellaloğlu and Meşhur, 1980; Cater et al., 1991; Yılmaz et al., 1993). The tectonic control on the deposition continued during the Middle Miocene, but the sea retreated from the region before the Late Miocene. The basins continued to be filled with continental clastic deposits (Figure 12).

The western part of the Sakarya continent was occupied by interconnected lakes and associated fluvial systems developed over a gentle topography (Benda et al., 1977). The continental sediment deposition was accompanied by calc-alkaline magmatic activity, producing granitic intrusions and varieties of intermediate and felsic lavas and pyroclastic rocks (Yılmaz, 1988). During the Late Miocene, the north-south extensional system was initiated in western Anatolia, creating east-west–trending rifts and grabens (Şengör et al., 1985; Görür et al., 1995).

During the late Miocene–Pliocene transition, the North Anatolian transform fault zone began to develop (Saroğlu and Yılmaz, 1991). This fault system, although it follows the older lineaments and zones of weaknesses, does not define the southern boundary of the Pontides, contrary to the suggestion of Boccaletti et al. (1988b). Along the North Anatolian transform fault zone, a 50-km right-lateral offset is measured between Suşehri and Erzincan on the basis of the displacement of the Eocene nappe fronts that were mapped on both sides of the fault (Yılmaz et al., 1993).

The present elevation of the Pontides began during the Late Miocene and continued in the Quaternary. As a result, the Pontides turned into an east-west–trending giant horst block separated from subsident margins to the north and to the south by step faults. This fault-dominated structural character of the mountain ranges has been emphasized by a number of workers, including Oswald (1912), Zankl (1961), Schultze-Westrum (1962), and Kronenberg (1970), who likened the Pontides to a Germano-type broken mass.

SUMMARY

The Pontides as an orogen may be divided into three main sectors: the Eastern Pontides, the Central Pontides, and the Western Pontides (Figure 1). Each of these represents an amalgamated tectonic mosaic consisting of remnants of oceanic, continental, and island-arc segments. The mountain ranges display evidence of progressive consumption and demise of the Paleotethys and Neotethys oceans, and collisions of the associated active continental margin arcs with the continents that surrounded the Tethyan oceans.

The Eastern and Western Pontides tectonostratigraphic units meet in the Central Pontides region, where they structurally mixed and formed a tectonic knot. In this tectonic mosaic, there are Cimmerian continental fragments and Paleotethyan oceanic assemblages. The units representing the Cimmerian continents are the Aktaş and Gümüsoluğu metamorphic assemblages. Their equivalent tectonostratigraphic units in the Western and the Eastern Pontides regions are the Uludağ Group (the Upper association) and the Tokat-Gümüşhane-Bayburt basement metamorphic association, respectively. The remnants of the Paleotethyan Ocean are the Küre, Elekdağ, and Artvin ophiolites. Their epiophiolitic, pelagic sedimentary units range in age from Carboniferous to Liassic, suggesting that the Paleotethyan Ocean existed from the Paleozoic till the Dogger.

The Paleotethyan Ocean began to be consumed mainly by the southward subduction under the Cimmerian continent. This generated active continental margin magmatism from the Carboniferous onward. The initial products of this subduction are the Gümüşhane, Söğüt, and Uludağ granites and the Bayburt volcanic association (Figure 15A). The arc magmatism continued during the Triassic with the Kösdağ felsic volcanics. At the beginning of the Triassic, rifting began behind the Cimmerian continent. This rifting led to the opening of a back-arc basin known as the Karakaya marginal basin (Figure 15A), which evolved into an ocean. This basin was connected directly with the Paleotethys Ocean (Figure 15B). The Karakaya Basin was short-lived and closed by the end of the Triassic (Figure 15C). During the closing stage, the continental margin units (the Uludağ Group) were thrust northward onto the leading edge of the continent and the adjacent oceanic units. This tectonic assemblage was penetratively deformed and underwent glaucophane-bearing greenschist facies metamorphism (the Yenişehir Group).

The southward consumption of the Paleotethyan Ocean under the Cimmerian continent generated a subduction-accretion melange displaying high P/low T metamorphism (the Domuzdağ metamorphic melange). During the Liassic, a new basin began to develop. This opening marked the birth of the Neotethys behind the Cimmerian continent (Figure 15B, C). During the opening phase, the Cimmerian continent, representing a long, narrow continental fragment, was surrounded on the north and south by the two partly coeval oceanic realms, the Paleotethys and the Neotethys, respectively (Figure 15C). The Dogger witnessed the demise of the Paleotethys. As a result, the Scythian Platform of Laurasia, representing the northern continent (the İstanbul-Zonguldak Zone), collided with the Cimmerian continent (Figure 15C). During the collision, the Paleotethyan oceanic units were assembled to form a nappe package, which was thrust onto the continental margin. Within this nappe package, a suprasubduction ophiolite association (the Küre ophiolite) and a peridotite slab (the Yılanlı ophiolite) underwent eclogite facies metamorphism. These oceanic assemblages were squeezed and sandwiched between the two continental fragments. In this amalgamated nappe package, the İstanbul nappe represents the highest standing nappe. As a consequence of the convergence of the two continents, the Pontides were gradually elevated above sea level.

The collided tectonic assemblage was intruded by post-tectonic plutons (the Çangal granite). Despite the continental collision, an eastward-narrowing triangular oceanic realm remained open between the Cimmerian continent and the İstanbul-Zonguldak Zone, where deep-sea sediment deposition continued without interruption until the Late Cretaceous. This is represented by the Mesozoic sediments of the Araç-Daday shear zone (Figure 15C).

The collision-related convergent regime was followed by north-south extension during the Malm, which continued until the Early Cretaceous. During this period, the region was dominated by horsts and grabens, which controlled marine invasions and the subsequent sediment deposition. The Pontides subsided steadily during the Early Cretaceous, and a well-developed passive continental margin facing the Neotethys Ocean was formed (Figure 15C). The Neotethyan Ocean floor began to be consumed by the northward subduction under the Pontides at the beginning of the Late Cretaceous. This generated a subduction melange at the leading edge of the continent; during the Turonian, it formed east-west–trending active continental margin volcanism along the northern part of the present Pontides mountain ranges. These volcanic rocks form northern magmatic zones of the Central and Eastern Pontides (Figure 16A). The melange prism was back-thrust (southward verging) onto the continental foreland during the Late Cretaceous (Figure 16B). During this period, the foreland was severely deformed by the south-vergent thrusts. Beneath the thick pile of thrust sheets, the lowermost cover rocks were penetratively deformed and cataclastically metamorphosed. Regional erosion also took place in the Pontides during this period.

Despite the consumption of the Neotethys Ocean floor, a remnant basin survived south of the Pontides. In this basin, pelagic units (the Hıdırnalı Group) were deposited above the melange foundation throughout the Late Cretaceous (Figures 15E, 16C).

The volcanic-arc front migrated to the south during the Campanian–Maastrichtian (Figure 16B). This was accompanied by a regional transgression. The southward migration of the volcanic arc generated an extensional system in the back-arc region. As a consequence, the region collapsed rapidly to open the Black Sea Basin (Figure 16B). The southerly migrated volcanic arc was nested within the previous fore-arc region, which was severely deformed and deeply eroded prior to the accumulation of the new volcanic pile.

During the Campanian–Maastrichtian, a basin began to develop in the fore-arc region (the Beldağ Group) (Figure 16C). This opening phase began to divide the region into two sectors. The southern sector gradually drifted away from the northern one, in a clockwise rotation (Figure 15D). This motion led to the closure of the existing part of the Paleotethyan Ocean, which remained open in the west (Figure 15D). This closure led to the development of the Araç-Daday shear zone and the Intra-Pontide suture.

The westerly transported continental fragment, which is surrounded by the two suture zones, the Intra-Pontide suture and the Neotethyan suture, is known as the Sakarya continent (Figure 15E). The convergence between the continental fragments initially eliminated the remaining ocean floor. At this point, convergence became oblique, due to the clockwise rotation of the Sakarya region. Oblique convergence was taken up by the westward escape of the Sakarya continent following the development of a transform fault, located approximately along the present North Anatolian transform fault zone (Figure 15E). As a result of the development of the transform fault zone, the Sakarya continent drifted westward away from the Eastern Pontides during the same period.

The remnant basin to the south of the Eastern Pontides began to be filled with materials derived from the surrounding structural highs. In this progressively shallowing marine environment, sedimentation continued from the Late Cretaceous to the end of the early Eocene (Figure 16C). A new phase of north-south compression began during the early Eocene–middle Eocene transition. The compressional regime affected all of northern Turkey. As a result, the northerly transported nappes moved onto the remnant basin fill (Figure 16D). Because of the north-south shortening, the Mesozoic carbonate platform succession of the Pontides was detached from its basement and moved northward as a decollement.

The compression gave way to north-south extension at the beginning of the middle Eocene (Figure 16E). A new marine invasion covered the previously elevated and eroded region during the Lutetian. The middle Eocene sediment deposition was delimited by fault-bounded and approximately east-west–trending transtensional basins (Figure 16E). The Lutetian sediment deposition was accompanied by intense volcanic activity, which produced mostly calc-alkaline intermediate and felsic lavas and pyroclastic rocks. The volcanic rocks blanketed the entire Pontides, the Anatolides, and the sutures that separate them. The sediment deposition and the volcanism continued until the end of the Late Eocene.

During the latest Eocene–Oligocene transition, a transpressional tectonic regime was initiated. A set of strike-slip faults developed as a result (Figure 16F). Under the transpressional system, the Pontides began to be uplifted. Consequently, the sea that previously existed in the region began to retreat, as evidenced by the gradual replacement of marine sediments with continental red beds. The Sıvas Basin was formed during this period in front of the Pontides as a ramp basin. The Sıvas Basin (Figure 16F) is the easternmost of a group of interconnected peripheral basins that surround the Kırşehir-Pontides tectonic collage. These peripheral basins extend westward to the Eskisehir area. At the same time, the Thrace Basin began to form in the west. The basin was delimited to the north by an east-west–trending wrench-fault zone, which lifted the İstranca Massif.

At the end of the Oligocene, the Pontides and its immediate surroundings were eroded extensively. As a result, a regionwide peneplain surface developed. Continental sediments were laid down over this surface. The peneplain surface was later cut by a set of east-west–trending faults, which were generated possibly due to north-south extension during the Early Miocene. A marine invasion began into these fault-bounded depressions. The surrounding flatlands were occupied by interconnected lacustrine and associated fluvial sediments. The sea invasion was followed by a regional regression during the latest Early Miocene or the Middle Miocene. This was followed by the uplift of the Pontides mountain belt.

The present tectonic mosaic of the Pontides is the result of the geological evolution summarized above. Its main components may be documented as follows: in the Western Pontides, four tectonic zones and two sutures may be distinguished (Figure 1) (the İstanbul-Zonguldak Zone, the Sakarya continent, the Armutlu-Almacık Zone, the İstranca Massif, the Intra-Pontide suture, and the İzmir-Ankara suture).

- The İstanbul-Zonguldak Zone belongs originally to the Scythian platform of Laurasia.
- The Sakarya continent represents a continental lithospheric fragment that was rifted from the Eastern Pontides during the Late Cretaceous. These are considered to have been originally part of the Cimmerian continent, which was rifted off Gondwana Land during the Triassic (Figure 15B). The basement metamorphic assemblage of the Sakarya continent records the following history: the Cimmerian continent was ruptured during the Triassic to form a short-lived basin, probably due to the southward consumption of the Paleotethyan Ocean. This basin, known as the Karakaya marginal basin, closed by the end of the Triassic.
- The Armutlu-Almacık Zone is interpreted as the metamorphic equivalent of the northern edge of the Sakarya continent, which underwent metamorphism during the collision between the Sakarya continent and the İstanbul-Zonguldak Zone (Figure 15D).
- The İstranca Massif may be interpreted as the western extension of the Armutlu-Almacık Zone (Figure 1).
- The Intra-Pontide suture is viewed as a remnant of the Paleotethyan Ocean floor, which survived until the Late Cretaceous (Figure 15C, D).
- The İzmir-Ankara suture is a remnant of the Neotethyan Ocean floor that was consumed between the Sakarya continent and the Tauride-Anatolide Platform (Figure 15D, E).

The Central Pontides consist of the following main components: the northern zone (the magmatic belt), the Kastamonu-Boyabat Basin fill, the Araç-Daday shear zone, the Kargı Massif, the ophiolite belt, and the Çankırı Basin.

- The northern zone is interpreted as an Andean-type magmatic belt that formed above the passive continental margin succession during the Late Cretaceous (Figure 15C, A).
- The Kastamonu-Boyabat Basin fill was deposited within a fore-arc basin formed in association with the volcanic belt.
- The Araç-Daday shear zone is interpreted as a highly tectonized basin fill that was deposited in the easterly narrowing oceanic remains of the Paleotethys (Figure 15C).
- The Kargı Massif is a tectonic mosaic that is composed of southerly transported oceanic assemblages that were sandwiched between two continental fragments. The different tectonostratigraphic units of the Kargı Massif record a continent-continent collision between the İstanbul-Zonguldak Zone and the Cimmerian continent that occurred during the Dogger. This nappe pile consists, from top to bottom, of the following units: (1) the Devrekani Massif, interpreted as the eastward extension of the İstanbul-Zonguldak Zone, which itself represents the Scythian Platform; (2) the Paleotethyan oceanic assemblages (the Küre ophiolite and associated rock units); and (3) the Cimmerian continental margin assemblages (the Gümüsoluğu and Aktaş metamorphic associations).
- The ophiolite belt is characterized by the disrupted ophiolite and the upper Cretaceous ophiolitic melange association, which were developed as a result of northward subduction and progressive consumption of the Neotethyan Ocean floor.

The Eastern Pontides is an extension of the Central Pontides, and therefore displays geology similar to that of the Central Pontides. One exception is the Kargı Massif of the Central Pontides, in which the closure of the Paleotethyan evolution is recorded. The Eastern Pontides consists of four main components: the magmatic belt, the Tokat Massif, the Beldağ Group, and the Yildizeli basin fill.

- The magmatic belt corresponds to an Andean-type magmatic belt, formed as a consequence of the northward consumption of the Neotethyan Ocean floor.
- The Tokat Massif represents the metamorphic basement of the Eastern Pontides and records the Karakaya marginal basin evolution.
- The Beldağ Group represents the infill of the fore-arc basin formed during the Late Cretaceous.
- The Yildizeli Basin fill is viewed as a remnant basin succession of Late Cretaceous to Eocene age that was deposited on the subduction-accretion melange. This melange is a result of the progressive consumption and total demise of the Neotethyan Ocean floor.

The Sıvas Basin is a peripheral basin that formed following the final tectonic rearrangement of the orogenic belts during the Oligo–Miocene.

ACKNOWLEDGMENTS

This tectonic synthesis is based on more than two decades of field studies and geological mapping conducted on the Pontides by Y. Yılmaz and his students (O. Tüysüz, E. Yiğitbaş, Ş.C. Genç, A. Elmas, and Ö.F. Gürer). The works were supported initially by MTA (the Mineral Research Exploration Institute of Turkey) and then by TPAO (Turkish Petroleum Company). As a result, more than 100 sheets of maps of 1:25,000 scale have been produced in different parts of the Pontides, representing every major segment from the eastern end of the Pontides to its western tip. We are indebted to these institutes for their enthusiastic support throughout the research. During the preparation of this paper, we discussed many problems of the Pontides with a number of our collegues in Turkey and abroad. Their contributions are greatly acknowledged. We also thank the Glo-Tek research unit TUBA and the Laurasia Institute for their support.

REFERENCES CITED

Abdüsselamoğlu, M.S., 1959, Almacıkdaği ile Mudurnu ve Göynük Civarının jeolojisi: İstanbul Üniversitesi Fen Fakültesi Monografileri (Tabii Ilimler Kismi), v. 14, 94 p.

Ağralı, B., E. Akyol, and Y. Konyali, 1966, Kelkit-Bayburt Jurassiğinde üç kömür damarının palinolojik etüdü: Türkiye Jeoloji Kurumu Bülteni, v. 10, p. 155–158.

Akartuna, M., 1953, Çatalca-Karacaköy bölgesinin jeolojisi: İstanbul Üniversitesi Fen Fakültesi Monografileri, v. 13, 88 p.

Akartuna, M., 1968, Armutlu yarimadasinin jeolojisi: İstanbul Üniversitesi Fen Fakültesi Monografileri (Tabii Ilimler Kismi), v. 20, 105 p.

Akıncı, O., M. Berbieri, G. Calderoni, V. Ferrini, U. Masi, M. Nicoletti, C. Petruciani, and L. Tolomeo, 1991, The geochemistry of hydrothermally altered lavas of the lower volcanic cycle from the Eastern Pontides (Trabzon, NE Turkey): Chem. Erde, v. 51, p. 173–186.

Aktimur, H.T., M.E. Tekirli, and M.E. Yurdakol, 1990, Sıvas, Erzincan Tersiyer havzasinin jeolojisi: Maden Tetkik Arama Enstitüsü Dergisi, v. 111, p. 25–36.

Akyol, E., 1974, Etude palynologiques des veines du Namurian et du Westphalian A, recoupées par les ailes sud et est l'une galerie de Cote-50a Asma, Üzülmez-Zonguldak: Mineral Research Exploration Institute Bulletin, v. 83, p. 50–104.

Alaygut, D., 1995, The petrographic investigation of the Turkish Strandja under the Thrace sedimentary basin, NW Turkey (abs.): International Earth Sciences Colloquium on the Aegean Region, 1995, IESCA-İzmir, Güllük, Turkey, p. 1.

Alp, D., 1972, Amasya yöresinin jeolojisi: İstanbul Üniversitesi Fen Fakültesi Monografileri (Tabii Ilimler Kismi), v. 22, 101 p.

Altınlı, I.E., 1973, Orta Sakarya jeolojisi, Cumhuriyetin 50. Yili Yerbilimleri Kongresi, Tebliğler: Maden Tetkik Arama Enstitüsü, p. 159–191.

Aydın, Y., 1974, Etude petrographique et geochimique de la partie centrale du Massif d'Istranca (Turquie): Ph.D. thesis, University of Nancy, 131 p.

Aydın, M., O. Demir, Y. Özçelik, N. Terzioğlu, and M. Satyr, 1995, Geological revision of Inebolu-Devrekani, Ağlı, and Küre areas: new observations in PaleoTethys-NeoTethys sedimentary successions: Proceedings of International Symposium on the Black Sea Region, Chamber of Geological Engineers of Turkey, p. 33–38.

Aydın, M., Ö. Şahintürk, H.S. Serdar, Y. Özçelik, I. Akarsu, A. Üngör, R. Çokuğras, and S. Kasar, 1986, Ballıdağ-Çangaldaği (Kastamonu) arasindaki bölgenin jeolojisi: Türkiye Jeoloji Kurumu Bülteni, v. 29, no. 2, p. 1–16.

Aykol, A., and S. Tokel, 1991, The geochemistry and tectonic setting of the Demirköy pluton of the Srednogora-Istranca granitoid chain, NW Turkey: Mineralogical Magazine, v. 55, p. 249–256.

Bargu, S., 1982, The geology of the İznik-Yenişehir (Bursa), Osmaneli (Bilecik) area: İstanbul Yerbilimleri, v. 3, no. 1–2, p. 191–234.

Barka, A., 1992, The North Anatolian fault zone: Annales Tectonicae Special Issue, Supplement to Volume VI, p. 164–195.

Bassoullet, J.P., H. Bergougnan, and R. Enay, 1975, Répartition des faunes et faciés Jurassique dans l'est de la Turquie région du Haut-Euphrate: Comptes Rendus de Academie de Science Paris, v. 280, p. 583–586.

Baykal, F., 1954, Eflani ile Ulus (NE-Anadolu) arasindaki Kretase-Tersiyer arazisi ve yabanci bloklar: İstanbul Üniversitesi Fen Fakültesi Mecmuasi, Series B, v. 19, no. 3, p. 191–201.

Baykal, F., and M. Önalan, 1979, Sile sedimenter karisiği (sile olistostromu), Altınlı Sempozyumu: Türkiye Jeoloji Kurumu, Ankara, p. 15–25.

Benda, L., J.E. Maulenkamp, S.P. Steffen, and J. Zachariasse, 1977, Biostratigraphic correlations in the eastern Mediterranean Neogene. 2. Correlation between sporomorph associations and marine microfossils from the upper Oligocene–lower Miocene of Turkey: Newsletter Stratigraphy, v. 6, no. 1, p. 1–22.

Bergougnan, H., 1987, Etudes geologiques dans l'est Anatolien: Memoires des Sciences de la Terre, Academi de Paris Université Pierre et Marie Curie, 606 p.

Bingöl, E., B. Akyürek, and B. Korkmazer, 1973, Biga yarimadasinin jeolojisi ve Karakaya Formasyonunun bazi özellikleri. Cumhuriyetin 50. Yili Yerbilimleri Kongresi, Tebliğler, Maden Tetkik Arama, Ankara, p. 70–77.

Blumental, M.M., 1940, Geologie des chaines Pontiques entre la vallée du Gökırmak et la Mer Noire (Boyabat-Sinop): Maden Tetkik Arama Enstitüsü, Rapor No. 1067 (unpublished report).

Boccaletti, M., R. Cassinis, P. Danielli, C.M. Marino, A. Tibaldi, and A. Zanchi, 1988b, Landsat features in the Black Sea area: their tectonic significance: Bolletino di Geofisica Teorica ed Applicata "Monograph on the Black Sea," Trieste, v. 30, no. 117–118, p. 17–37.

Boccaletti, M., P. Dainelli, P. Manetti, and M.R. Mannori, 1988a, Tectonic framework of the circum-Black Sea region: Bolletino di Geofisica Teorica ed Applicata "Monograph on the Black Sea," Trieste, v. 30, no. 117–118, p. 5–8.

Boccaletti, M., P. Gocev, and P. Manetti, 1974, Mesozoic isopic zones in the Black Sea region: Bull. Soc. Geol. Italia, v. 93, p. 547–565.

Bonhomme, M.G., and O. Yılmaz, 1984, First K/Ar data from the Daday-Devrekani and Ilgaz massifs and the Kastamonu granitoid belt, Northern Turkey: Terra Cognita, v. 4, no. 2, p. 199–200.

Bozcu, M., 1992, Geyve (Adapazariili)-Sapanca dolayinin jeolojik ve petrolojik incelenmesi: Ph.D. thesis, İstanbul Üniversitesi, 247 p.

Brinkmann, R., 1972, Mesozoic troughs and crustal structure in Anatolia: Geological Society of America Bulletin, v. 83, p. 819–826.

Bulandje, Y.D., ed., 1976, Kompleksnoye Isseleddovaniye Chernomorksky Vpadini: Akad. Nauk SSR, Moscow, 98 p.

Burchfiel, B.C., 1980, East European Alpide system and the Carpathian orocline as an example of collision tectonics: Tectonophysics, v. 63, p. 31–66.

Çağlayan, A.M., M. Şengün, and A. Yurtsever, 1988, Main fault systems shaping the İstranca Massif, Turkey: Middle East Technical University, Journal of Pure and Applied Sciences, Series A 'Geosciences,' Tokay v. 21, p. 145–154.

Cater, J.M.L., S.S. Hanna, A.M. Ries, and P. Turner, 1991, Tertiary evolution of the Sıvas Basin, central Turkey: Tectonophysics, v. 195, p. 29–46.

Channel, J.E.T., O. Tüysüz, O. Bektaş, and A.M.C. Şengör, 1995, Jurassic–Cretaceous paleomagnetism and paleogeography of the Pontides (Turkey): Tectonics, v. 15, no. 1, p. 201–212.

Chatalov, G.A., 1988, Recent developments in the geology of the Stranzha Zone in Bulgaria: Bulletin of the Technical University of İstanbul, v. 41, no. 3, p. 433–465.

Chatalov, A.G., 1991, Triassic in Bulgaria—a review, *in* J.F. Dewey, ed., Special issue on tectonics: Bulletin of the Technical University of İstanbul, v. 44, no. 1–2, p. 103–135.

Çoğulu, H.E., 1967, Etude petrographique de la région de Mihaliccik (Turquie): Bull. Suisse, Min. Pet., v. 47, p. 683–824.

Çoğulu, H.E., 1975, Gümüşhane ve Rize bölgelerinde petrolojik ve jeokronolojik araştirmalar: İstanbul Teknik Üniversitesi Yayini, v. 1034, 112 p.

Çoğulu, H.E., M. Delaloye, R. Chessex, 1965, Sur l'age de quelques roches plutoniques acides dans la région d'Eskisehir-Turquie: Arch. Sci. Geneve, v. 18, p. 692–699.

Dabovski, C., and S. Savov, 1988, Structural studies in the nappes of southeast Strandza: Geologica Balcanica, v. 18, p. 18–36.

Dean, W.T., F. Matin, and O. Monod, 1993, Report on field program with Turkish Petroleum Co. in northern and southern Turkey (1990–1992): Turkish Petroleum Co. (TPAO) Arch., Ankara, 64 p. (unpublished report).

Dellaloğlu, A.A., and M. Meşhur, 1980, Sıvas baseni jeolojisi ve hidrokarbon olanaklari: Türkiye Petrolleri Anonim Ortakliği (TPAO), Rapor No. 1530, 28 p.

Dercourt, J., et al., 1986, Geological evolution of the Tethys belt from the Atlantic to the Pamirs since the Liass: Tectonophysics, v. 123, p. 241–315.

Derman, A.S., 1990, Bati Karadeniz bölgesinin geç Jura ve erken Kretasedeki jeolojik evrimi: Türkiye 8 Petrol Kongresi, Bildiriler, Jeoloji, p. 328–339.

Deveciler, E., et al., 1989, Çatalzeytin (Kastamonu) dolayinin jeolojisi; Maden Tetkik Arama Enstitüsü, Rapor No. 8617 (unpublished report).

Dewey, J.F., W.C. Pitman III, W.B.F. Ryan, and J. Bonnin, 1973, Plate tectonics and the evolution of the Alpine system: Geological Society of America Bulletin, v. 84, p. 3137–3180.

Doğan, M.M., 1990, Pontid kuşaği Paleotetis ofiyolitlerının jeokimyasal verilerle petrolojik, magmatik ve tektonik modellemesi: Ph.D. thesis, İstanbul Universitesi Fen Bilimleri Enstitüsü, 201 p.

Eğin, D., and M.D. Hirst, 1979, Tectonic and magmatic evolution of volcanic rocks from the northern Harşit River area, NE Turkey, in Geocome-I: First Geological Congress of the Middle East, Mineral Research and Exploration Institute (MTA), Ankara, p. 56–93.

Ercan, T., and A. Gedik, 1983, Pontid'lerdeki volkanizma: Jeoloji Mühendisliği, v. 18, p. 3–22.

Eren, R.H., 1979, Kastamonu-Taşköprü bölgesi metamorfitlerının jeolojik ve petrografik etüdü: Ph.D. thesis, İstanbul Teknik Üniversitesi, Mihendisi-Mimarlik Facultesi (M.M.F.) Yayinlari, 143 p.

Erol, O., 1992, Çanakkale yöresinin jeomorfolojik ve neotektonik evrimi: Türkiye Petrol Jeologlari Derneği Bülteni, v. 4, no. 1, p. 147–165.

Ertunç, A., 1980, Çoruh havzasi olasi baraj yerleri, göl alanlarive tünel güzergahlarının mühendislik jeolojisi incelemesi: Docentus thesis, İstanbul Üniversitesi, 139 p.

Evans, I., S.A Hall, and M.F. Carman, 1990, Paleomagnetic constraints on the tectonic evolution of the Sakarya continent, northwestern Anatolia: Tectonophysics, v. 182, p. 357–372.

Evans, I., S.A. Hall, M.F. Carman, M. Senalp, and S. Coskun, 1982, A paleomagnetic study of the Bilecik limestone (Jurassic), northwest Anatolia: Earth and Planetary Science Letters, v. 61, p. 199–208.

Evans, I., S.A. Hall, M. Sarıbudak, and A. Aykol, 1991, Preliminary paleomagnetic results from Paleozoic rocks of the İstanbul-Zonguldak region, NW Turkey: Bulletin of the Technical University of İstanbul, v. 44, p. 165–190.

Fratschner, W. Th., 1953, Kurucaşile-Eflani-Cide bölgesindeki saha etüdü hakkinda ilk not: Maden Tetkik Arama, Rapor No. 2061 (unpublished report), 32 p.

Friedman, G.M., A. Barsel, and B. Derin, 1971, Paleoenvironments of the Jurassic in the coastal belt of northern and central Israel and their significance in the search for petroleum reservoirs: Geol. Surv. Israel, Report No. OD/1/71, 71 p.

Gedik, A, and S. Korkmaz, 1984, Sinop Havzasinin jeolojisi ve petrol olanaklari: Jeoloji Mühendisliği, v. 19, p. 53–80.

Genç, Ş., 1987, Geology of the region between Uludağ and İznik Lake, guidebook for the field excursion along Western Anatolia, Turkey: Mineral Research and Exploration Institute (MTA), Ankara, p. 19–25.

Genç, Ş.C., 1993, İznik-Inegöl (Bursa) arasindaki tektonik birliklerin jeolojik ve petrolojik incelenmesi: Ph.D. thesis, İstanbul Teknik Üniversitesi, Fen Bilimleri Enstitüsü, 522 p.

Genç, Ş. C., and Y. Yılmaz, 1995a, Evolution of the Triassic continental margin, NW Anatolia: Tectonophysics, v. 243, p. 193–207.

Genç, Ş. C., and Y. Yılmaz, 1995b, Postcollisional Eocene magmatic activity of NW Anatolia: EUG VII, Strasbourg, Terra Abstracts, Terra Nova, v. 7, p. 181.

Gocev, P.M., 1970, The Senonian complex in the Srednogorie Zone: Acad. Sc. Bulgaria Comp. Red., v. 23, p. 975–978.

Gocev, P.M., 1979, The place of Strandza in the alpine structure of the Balkan peninsula: Rew. Bulgarian, Geol. Soc., v. 40, no. 1, p. 27–44.

Gocev, P.M., 1991, Some problems of the nappe tectonics of the Strandzhides in Bulgaria and Turkey: Bulletin of the Technical University of İstanbul, v. 44, p. 137–164.

Gökçen, S.L., and G. Kelling, 1985, Oligocene deposits of the Zara-Hafik region, Sıvas (Central Turkey). Evolution from storm-influenced shelf to evaporitic basin: Geologische Rundschau, v. 74, no. 1, p. 139–153.

Göncüoğlu, M.C., M. Erendil, O. Tekeli, A. Aksay, I. Kusçu, and B.M. Ürgün, 1987, Geology of the Armutlu peninsula, guidebook for the field excursion along western Anatolia, Turkey: Mineral Research and Exploration Institute (MTA), Ankara, p. 1–19.

Görür, N., 1988, Timing of opening of the Black Sea Basin: Tectonophysics, v. 147, p. 247–262.

Görür, N., F.Y. Oktay, I. Seymen, and A.M.C. Şengör, 1984, Palaeotectonic evolution of the Tuzgölü basin complex, Central Turkey: Sedimentary record of a Neotethyan closure, *in* J.E. Dixon and A.H.F. Robertson, eds., The geological evolution of the eastern Mediterranean: Geological Society of London Special Publication 17, p. 467–482.

Görür, N., A.M.C. Şengör, R. Akkök, and Y. Yılmaz, 1983, Pontidlerde Neotetisin kuzey kolunun açilmasina ilişkin sedimentolojik veriler: Türkiye Jeoloji Kurumu Bülteni, v. 26, no. 1, p. 11–20.

Görür, N., O. Tüysüz, A. Aykol, M. Sakynç, E. Yiğitbaş, and R. Akkök, 1993, Cretaceous red pelagic carbonates of northern Turkey: their place in the opening history of the Black Sea: Eclogae Geologica Helvetia, v. 86, no. 3, p. 819–838.

Görür, N., et al., 1995, Rift formation in the Gökova region, southwest Anatolia: implications for the opening of the Aegean Sea: Geol. Magazine, v. 132, no. 6, p. 637–650.

Granit, Y., and H. Tintant, 1960, Observation preliminaires sur le Jurassic de la région de Bilecik (Turquie): Comptes Rendus Acad. Science, Paris, v. 251, p. 1801–1803.

Gregor, C.B., and J.D.A. Zijderweld, 1964, The magnetism of some Permian red sandstones from NW Turkey: Tectonophysics, v. 1, no. 4, p. 289–306.

Haas, W., 1968, Das AH-Palaozoikum von Bithynien (Northwest Turkei): Neuses Jahrbuch für Geologie and Paleaontologie, Abshandlungen, v. 131, p. 178–242.

Hamilton, W.B., 1989, Crustal geological processes of the United States: Geological Society of America Memoir 172, p. 743–780.

Hsü, K.J., I.K. Nachev, and V.T. Yuchev, 1977, Geologic evolution of Bulgaria in light of plate tectonics: Tectonophysics, v. 40, p. 245–256.

Kalkan, F.E., 1993, The structure and stratigraphy of the Marmara Sea basin and its environs offshore, Turkey: Ph.D. thesis, Texas A&M University, 127 p.

Karig, D.E., 1974, Evolution of arc system in the Western Pacific: Ann. Rev. Earth Planet. Sci., v. 2, p. 51–75.

Kaya, O., 1977, Gemlik-Orhangazi alaninin Paleozoyik temel yapisina yaklasim: Yerbilimleri, Hacettepe Üniversitesi, v. 3, no. 1–2, p. 115–118.

Kaya, O., 1991, Stratigraphy of the Pre-Jurassic sedimentary rocks of the western parts of Turkey: type area study and tectonic considerations: Newsletter for Stratigraphy, v. 23, no. 3, p. 123-140.

Kaya, O., and H. Möstler, 1992, A Middle Triassic age for low-grade greenschist facies metamorphic sequence in Bergama (İzmir), western Turkey: The first paleontologic age assignment and structural-stratigraphic implications: Newsletter for Stratigraphy, v. 26, p. 1–17.

Kerey, E., 1984, Facies and tectonic setting of the Upper Carboniferous rocks of Northwestern Turkey, *in* J.E Dixon and A.H.F. Robertson, eds., The geological evolution of the Eastern Mediterranean: Geological Society of London Special Publication 17, p. 123–128.

Ketin, I., 1951, Über die Geologie der Gegend von Bayburt in Nordost Anatolien: Fac. Sci. of Univ. İstanbul Rev., ser. B, v. 16, p. 113–127.

Ketin, I., 1962, 1:500.000 ölçekli Türkiye Jeoloji Haritasi izahnamesi (Sinop): Maden Tetkik Arama Enstitüsü Yayini, Ankara, 111 p.

Ketin, I., 1966, Anadolunun tektonik birlikleri (tectonic units of Anatolian Asia Minor): Maden Tetkik Arama Enstitüsü Yayini, Ankara, v. 66, p. 20–34.

Ketin, I., 1983, Türkiye jeolojisine genel bir bakiş: İstanbul Teknik Üniversitesi Kütüphanesi, Sayi: 1250, 591 p.

Ketin, I., 1992, İstanbul ve dolayinin jeoloji haritasi, ISKI: the Greater İstanbul municipality (unpublished geology map of İstanbul).

Ketin, I., and A. Gümüş, 1963, Sinop-Ayancik arasinda III. Bölgeye dahil sahalarin jeolojisi: hakkinda rapor, Turkish Petroleum Co. Arch., Report No. 288, 33 p. (unpublished report).

Koçyiğit, A., 1979, Çördük olistostromlari: Türkiye Jeoloji Kurumu Bülteni, v. 22, p. 59–68.

Koçyiğit, A., 1991, An example of an accretionary forearc basin from northern Central Anatolia and its implications for the history of subduction of Neotethys in Turkey: Geological Society of America Bulletin, v. 103, p. 22–36.

Koçyiğit, A., D. Altiner, A. Farinacci, N. Umberto, and M.A. Conti, 1992, Late Triassic–Aptian evolution of the Sakarya divergent margin: implications for the opening history of the northern Neotethys in Northwest Anatolia, Turkey: Geologica Romana, v. 27, p. 81–99.

Koçyiğit, A., S. Özkan, and B.F. Rojay, 1988, Examples for the fore-arc basin remnants at the active margin of northern Neotethys development and emplacement ages of the Anatolian nappe, Turkey: METU Journal of Pure and Applied Sciences, Series A "Geosciences I," v. 21, no. 1–3, p. 183–210.

Kronenberg, P., 1970, Doğu Karadeniz Dağlarının (kuzeydoğu Türkiye) tektoniği üzerinde fotojeolojik veriler: Maden Tetkik Arama Enstitüsü Bülteni, v. 74, p. 57–66.

Kutluk, H., and N. Bozdoğan, 1981, IV. Bölge Üst Paleozoyik-Alt Mesozoyik çökelleri palinoloji ön raporu: Türkiye Petrolleri Anonim Ortakliği (TPAO), Rapor No. 1545 (unpublished report), 8 p.

Lauer, J.P., 1981, L'evolution geodynamique de la Turquie et de Chypre deduite de l'etude paleomagnetique: Ph.D thése, L'Institut de Physique du Globe de L'Universite, Louis Pasteur de Strasbourg, 299 p.

Manetti, P., A. Peccerillo, F. Corsini, and G. Poli, 1981, Geodynamic significance of Cretaceous–Eocene volcanism of the Eastern Pontides: Rend. Soc. Geol. Italia, v. 4, p. 250–260.

Manetti, P., A. Peccerillo, G. Poli, and F. Corsini, 1983, Petrochemical constraints on the models of Cretaceous–Eocene tectonic evolution of the Eastern Pontide chain (Turkey): Cretaceous Research, v. 4, p. 159–172.

Maucher, A., 1962, Geologisch-Lagerstötten kundliche untersuchunges im Ostpontichen gebirge. Einfuhrung, problemsteliung und ubersicht über die ergebnisse abhandl: Bayerische Akad. Wiss, N.F.H., v. 109, p. 5–23.

McKenzie, D., and Y. Yılmaz, 1991, Deformation and volcanism in Western Turkey and the Aegean: Bulletin of the Technical University of İstanbul, v. 44, no. 1–2, p. 345–373.

Milch, L., 1907, Über glaukophan und glaukophangesteine von Elek-Dagh (nördlisches Kleinasien) mit beitragen zur kenntnis der chemischen bezienungen basischer galukophan-gesteine: Neu Jahr für Mineral. Geol. Palaeont., p. 348–396.

Moore, W.J., E. McKee, and O. Akıncı, 1980, Chemistry and geochronology of plutonic rocks in the Pontide Mountains, Northern Turkey: European Copper Deposits, Belgrade, p. 209–216.

MTA, 1977, Geological map of the Tortum G47a quadrangle: Geol. Map of Turkey, scale 1:500.000, Mineral Research and Exploration Institute, Ankara.

Neprechnov, Y.P., Y.P. Malovitsky, V.S. Belokurov, and I.A. Garkalenko, 1975, Profilnie sechenia koripo dannim gze, *in* Y.D. Boulandje, M.V. Muratov, S.I. Subbotin, and B.K. Balavadze, eds., Zemnaya kara I istoriye razvitiya Chernomorskoy vpadiny, Moscow, p. 284–288.

Norman, T., 1988, Hafik (Sıvas) kuzeyindeki melanjin yapisi: Türkiye Petrolleri Anonim Ortakliği (TPAO), Rapor No. 2571 (unpublished report), 56 p.

Okay, A.I., 1984, The geology of the Agvanis metamorphic rocks and neighboring formations: Mineral Research and Exploration Institute Bulletin, v. 99/100, p. 191–256.

Okay, A.I., 1989, Tectonic units and sutures in the Pontides, Northern Turkey, *in* A.M.C. Şengör, ed., Tectonic evolution of the Tethyan region: NATO ASI Series C, v. 259, p. 109–116.

Okay, A.I., A.M.C. Şengör, and N. Görür, 1994, Kinematic history of the opening of the Black Sea and its effect on the surrounding regions: Geology, v. 22, p. 267–270.

Okay, A.Y., M. Siyako, and K.A. Bürkan, 1991, Geology and tectonic evolution of the Biga Peninsula, Northwest Turkey: Bulletin of the Technical University of İstanbul, Special Issue on Tectonics, v. 44, p. 191–256.

Okay, A.I., O. Tüysüz, and S. Akyüz, 1995, İstranca masifinin bati kesiminin jeolojisi ve tektoniği: Turkish Petroleum Co. Report No. 3521, 107 p. (unpublished report).

Önder, F., D. Boztuğ, and O. Yılmaz, 1987, Bati Pontidlerdeki Göynükdaği-Kastamonu yöresi Alt Mesozoyik kayaçlarinda yeni paleontolojik (konodont) Bulgular, Bati Pontidler, Türkiye: Melih Tokay Jeoloji Sempozyumu, Bildiri Özleri, p. 127–128.

Önder, F., and M.C. Göncüoğlu, 1989, Armutlu yarimadasinda (Bati Pontidler) Üst Triyas konodontlari: Maden Tetkik Arama Enstitüsü, Dergisi, v. 109, p. 147–152.

Orbay, N., and A. Bayburdi, 1979, Paleomagnetism of dykes and tuffs from the Mesudiye region and rotation of Turkey: Geophys. J. R. Astr. Soc., v. 59, p. 437–444.

Orbay, N., I. Özdoğan, A.M. Işikara, 1981, Türkiye ve yakin çevresinden elde edilen palomagnetik sonuçlar ve levha hareketleri: Yerbilimleri, İstanbul Üniversitesi, v. 3–4, p. 187–191.

Oswald, F., 1912, Armenien: Handbuch der regionalien geologie, Karlwinters Universitat Bucahandlung, H 10, Heidelberg, 40 p.

Özdemir, Ü., G. Talay, and A. Yurtsever, 1973, Kocaeli Triyasi Projesi 'Kocaeli Triyasinin Biyostratigrafik Etüdü' (biostratigraphy of the Triassic rocks from the Kocaeli Peninsula): Cumhurietin 50. Y. L. Yerbilimleri Kongresi, 1973, Maden Tetkik ve Arama Enstitusü (MTA), p. 115–130.

Pamir, H.N., and F. Baykal, 1947, İstranca masifinin jeolojik yapisi: Türkiye Jeoloji Kurumu Bülteni, v. 1, no. 1, p. 7–43.

Parejas, E., and F. Baykal, 1937, Une lame de charriage a sile: Rev. de la Fac. Des Sc. D. L'Univ. d'İstanbul, III, Fasc. 1.

Pecerillo A., and S.R. Taylor, 1975, Geochemistry of Upper Cretaceous volcanic rocks from the Pontic chain, Northern Turkey: Bulletin Volcanologique, v. 39, p. 1–13.

Pelin, S., 1977, Alucra (Giresun) güneydoğu yöresinin petrol olanaklari bakimindan jeolojik incelenmesi: Karadeniz Teknik Üniversitesi, Yayin No. 13, 103 p.

Perinçek, D., 1991, Possible strand of the North Anatolian Fault in the Thrace basin, Turkey—an interpretation: AAPG Bulletin, v. 75, no. 2, p. 241–257.

Poisson, A.M., J.C. Guezou, H. Temiz, H. Gürsoy, S. Inan, A. Öztürk, K. Kavak, and S. Özden, 1995, The central Anatolian basins, general evolution, the Sıvas Basin, as an example (abs.): International Earth Sciences Colloquium on the Aegean Region (IESCA-1995), Program and Abstract, p. 44.

Robertson, A.H.F., and J.E. Dixon, 1984, Introduction: aspects of the geology of the Eastern Mediterranean, *in* J.E. Dixon and A.H.F. Robertson, eds., The geological evolution of the Eastern Mediterranean: Geological Society of London Special Publication 17, p. 1–74.

Rögl, F., and F.F. Steininger, 1984, Neogene Agvatexliys, Mediterranean and Indo-Pacific seaways, *in* P.J. Brenchley, ed., Fossils and climate: Chichester, New York, Brisbane, Toronto, John Wiley & Sons, p. 171–200.

Sandulescu, M., 1978, The Moesic platform and the North Dobrogean orogene, *in* M. Lemoine, ed., Geological atlas of Alpine Europe and adjoining Alpine areas: Elsevier, Amsterdam, p. 427–442.

Saner, S., 1977, Geyve-Osmaneli-Gölpazari-Tarakli alaninin jeolojisi, eski çökelme ortamlari ve çökelmenin evrimi: Ph.D. thesis, İstanbul Üniversitesi Fen Fakültesi, 314 p.

Saner, S., 1980, Baty Pontidlerin ve komsu havzalaryn olusumlarının levha tektoniği kavramiila açiklanmasi, Kuzeybati Türkiye: Maden Tetkik Arama Enstitüsü Dergisi, v. 93/94, p. 1–19.

Sanver, M., and E. Ponat, 1981, Kırşehir ve dolaylarina ilişkin paleomanyetik Bulgular: Kırşehir masifinin rotasyonu: İstanbul Yerbilimleri, v. 2, no. 3–4, p. 231–238.

Saroğlu, F., and Y. Yılmaz, 1991, Geology of the Karliova region: intersection of the North Anatolian and East Anatolian transform faults: Bulletin of the Technical University of İstanbul, v. 44, no. 3, p. 475–493.

Sarıbudak, M., M. Sanver, and E. Ponat, 1989, Location of Western Pontides, NW Turkey, during Triassic time, preliminary paleomagnetic results: Geophysical Journal, v. 96, p. 43–50.

Sayılı, A., and A.S. Derman, 1992, Sedimentology and diagenesis of the Upper Jurassic İnaltı formation in the Western Black Sea region: 9th Turkish Petroleum Congress Proceedings, p. 151–160.

Schultze-Westrum, H.H., 1961, Das geologische profil des Aksudere bei Giresun: Mineral Research and Exploration Institute Bulletin, v. 57, p. 65–74.

Schultze-Westrum, H.H., 1962, Geologisch-lager statten kundliche untersuchungen im Ost Pontischen Gebirge: Bevar. Akad. Wiss. Methnat. K1., Abh. N.F. 109, Munchen.

Scotese, C.R., R.K. Bambach, C. Barton, R. van der Voo, and A.M. Ziegler, 1979, Paleozoic base maps: Journal of Geology, v. 87, p. 217–277.

Şengör, A.M.C., 1979a, Mid-Mesozoic closure of Permo-Triassic Tethys and its implications: Nature, v. 279, p. 590–593.

Şengör, A.M.C, 1979b, The North Anatolian fault: its age, offset, and tectonic significance: Journal of the Geological Society of London, v. 136, p. 268–282.

Şengör, A.M.C., 1987, Tectonics of the Tethysides: orogenic collage development in a collisional setting: Ann. Rev. Earth Planetary Sciences, v. 15, p. 213–44.

Şengör, A.M.C., 1990, A new model for the late Paleozoic–Mesozoic tectonic evolution in Iran and implications for Oman: Geological Society of London Special Publication 49, p. 799–833.

Şengör, A.M.C., 1995, The larger tectonic framework of the Zonguldak coal basin in Northern Turkey: an outsider's view, *in* M.N. Yalçyn and G. Gürdal, eds., Zonguldak Basin research wells-1, Kozlu-K20/G: Special Publication of Turkiye Bilimsel ve Teknik Arastirma Kurumu, Marmara Araştirma Merkezi (TUBITAK-MAM) p. 1–26.

Şengör, A.M.C., and N. Canıtez, 1982, The North Anatolian fault, *in* Alpine Mediterranean Geodynamics: Geodynamic Series, v. 7, p. 205–216.

Şengör, A.M.C., N. Görür, and F. Saroğlu, 1985, Strike-slip faulting and related basin formation in zones of tectonic escape: Turkey as a case study: SEPM Special Publication 37, p. 227–264.

Şengör, A.M.C., and Y. Yılmaz, 1981, Tethyan evolution of Turkey: A plate tectonic approach: Tectonophysics, v. 75, p. 181–241.

Şengör, A.M.C., Y. Yılmaz, and O. Sungurlu, 1984, Tectonics of the Mediterranean Cimmerids: nature and evolution of the western termination of Palaeotethys, *in* J.E. Dixon and A.H.F. Robertson, eds., The geological evolution of the Eastern Mediterranean: Geological Society of London Special Publication 17, p. 77–112.

Şengör, A.M.C., Y. Yılmaz, and I. Ketin, 1980, Remnants of a pre-Late Jurassic ocean in northern Turkey: fragments of Permian–Triassic Palaeotethys?: Geological Society of America Bulletin, v. 91, no. 1, p. 599–609.

Şengün, M., 1993, Geologic evolution of the Anatolian segment of the Tethyan belt: Geological Bulletin of Turkey, v. 36, p. 81–98.

Seymen, I., 1975, Kelkit vadisi kesiminde Kuzey Anadolu fay zonunun tektonik özelliği: İstanbul Teknik Üniversitesi Maden Fakültesi Yayini, 198 p.

Siderenko, A.V., 1978, Karta razlomov teritorii SSSR I sopredelnich stran, 1:25,000: Akad. Nauka, SSSR, Moscow.

Smith, A.G., A.M. Hurley, and J.C. Brides, 1981, Phanerozoic paleocontinental world maps: Cambridge, Cambridge University Press, 102 p.

Taner, M.F., 1977, Etude geologique et petrographique de la region de Güneyce, Ikizdere, située au sud de Rize (Pontides orientales, Turquie): Ph. D. these no. 1788, Geneve, 180 p.

Tatar, Y., 1971, Ofiyolitli Çamlıbel (Sıvas-Yildizeli kuzeyi) dolaylarinda jeolojik ve petrografik araştirmalar: Docentus thesis, İstanbul Teknik Üniversitesi, Maden Fakültesi, 156 p.

Tekeli, O., E. Göktan, and A. Yurtsever, 1991, Karaçayir masifi ve Akdağ masifinin, doğu kesiminin jeolojisi (Yildizeli-Sıvas-Hafik arasi): Türkiye Petrolleri Anonim Ortakliği, Rapor No. 3001 (unpublished report), 86 p.

Temiz, H., T.C Guezou, A. Poisson, and S.Z. Tutkun, 1992, Sıvas havzasi doğusunun tektonostratigrafisi ve kinematiği (Kemah-Erzincan): Cumhuriyet Üniversitesi Dergisi, Seri A,Yerbilimleri, v. 9 no. 1–81, p. 27–34.

Tokel, S., 1977, Doğu Karadeniz bölgesinde Eosen yasli kalk-alkalen andezitler ve jeotektonizma: Türkiye Jeoloji Kurumu Bülteni, v. 20, p. 49–54.

Tüysüz, O., 1985, Kargı masifi ve dolayindaki tektonik birliklerin ayirdy ve araştirilmasi (Petrolojik inceleme): Ph.D. thesis, İstanbul Üniversitesi Fen Bilimleri Enstitüsü, 431 p.

Tüysüz, O., 1990, Tectonic evolution of a part of the Tethyside orogenic collage: the Kargı Massif, Northern Turkey: Tectonics, v. 9, no. 1, p. 141–160.
Tüysüz, O., 1993, Karadeniz'den Orta Anadolu'ya bir Jeotravers: Kuzey Neo-Tetisin tektonik evrimi: Türkiye Petrol Jeolojisi Bülteni, v. 5, no. 1, p. 1–33.
Tüysüz, O., and A.A. Dellaloğlu, 1992, Çankırı havzasinin tektonik birlikleri ve havzanin tektonik evrimi: Türkiye 9 Petrol Kongresi, Bildiriler, p. 333–349.
Tüysüz, O., and E. Yiğitbaş, 1994, The Karakaya basin: a Paleotethyan marginal basin and its age of opening: Acta Geologica Hungarica, v. 37, no. 3-4, p. 327–350.
Tüysüz, O., E. Yiğitbaş, and H.S. Serdar, 1989, Orta Pontidlerin güney kesiminin jeolojisi: Türkiye Petrolleri A.O., Rapor no. 2596, 291 p.
Tüysüz, O., Y. Yılmaz, E. Yiğitbaş, and H.S. Serdar, 1990, Orta Pontidlerde Üst Jura-Alt Kretase stratigrafisi ve tektonik anlami: Türkiye 8 Petrol Kongresi Bildiriler, p. 340–351.
Ustaömer, T., and A.H.F. Robertson, 1993, A Late Palaeozoic–Early Mesozoic marginal basin along the active southern continental margin of Eurasia: evidence from the Central Pontides (Turkey) and adjacent regions: Geological Journal, v. 28, p. 219–238.
Ustaömer, T., and A.H.F. Robertson, 1994, Late Paleozoic marginal basin and subduction-accretion: the Paleotethyan Küre complex, Central Pontides, northern Turkey: Journal of the Geological Society of London, v. 151, p. 291–305.
Üşümezsoy, S., 1982, Igneous and metamorphic petrology and mineralization of the İstranca region: İstanbul Yerbilimleri, v. 3, p. 277–294.
van der Voo, R., 1968, Paleomagnetism and the Alpine tectonics of Eurasia, Part 4, Jurassic, Cretaceous, and Eocene pole positions from NE Turkey: Tectonophysics, v. 6, p. 251–269.
Wedding, H., 1963, Beitrage zur geologie der Kelkitline und zur stratigraphie des Jura im gebiet Kelkit-Bayburt (Gümüşhane): Mineral Research and Exploration Institute Bulletin, v. 61, p. 30–37.
Westphal, M., M.L. Barhenov, J.P. Lauer, and J.C. Silbuet, 1986, Paleomagnetic implications on the evolution of the Tethys belt from the Atlantic Ocean to the Pamirs since the Triassic: Tectonophysics, v. 123, p. 37–82.
Yergök, A.F., et al., 1989, Bati Karadeniz bölgesinin jeolojisi (II): Maden Tetkik Arama Enstitüsü Rapor No. 8848 (unpublished report), 68 p.
Yiğitbaş E., O. Tüysüz, and H.S. Serdar, 1990, Orta Pontidlerde Üst Kretase yasli aktif kita kenarının jeolojik özellikleri: Türkiye 8 Petrol Kongresi, Bildiriler, Jeoloji, p. 141–151.
Yiğitbaş, E., Y. Yılmaz, and A.M.C. Şengör, 1995, Transcurrent plate boundary along the Rhodop–Pontide fragment: Northwestern Turkey (abs.): Terra Abstracts, Abs. Suppl. No. 1 to Terra Nova, EUG 8, Strasbourg, v. 7, p. 176.
Yılmaz, A., 1980, Tokat ile Sıvas arasindaki bölgede ofiyolitlerin kökeni, iç yapisi ve diğer birimlerle iliskisi: Ph.D. thesis, Ankara Üniversitesi Fen Fakültesi, 97 p.
Yılmaz, A., 1981, Tokat ile Sıvas arasindaki bölgede bazi volkanitlerin petro-kimyasal özellikleri: Türkiye Jeoloji Kurumu Bülteni, v. 24, no. 2, p. 51–58.
Yılmaz, A., 1982, Tokat (Dumanlidağ) ile Sıvas (Çeltekdağy) dolaylaryinin temel jeolojik özellikleri ve ofiyolitli karmasiğin konumu: Maden Tetkik Arama Enstitüsü, Dergisi, v. 99–100, p. 1–18.
Yılmaz, K., 1992, Mekece (Adapazari)-Bahçecik (Kocaeli) dolayinin jeolojik ve petrolojik incelenmesi: Ph.D. thesis, İstanbul Üniversitesi Fenbilimleri Enstitüsü, 260 p.
Yılmaz, O., 1979, Daday-Devrekani masifi kuzeydoğu kesimi metamorfik petrolojisi: Docentus thesis, Hacettepe Üniversitesi Yerbilimleri Enstitüsü, 176 p.
Yılmaz, O., and D. Boztuğ, 1986, Kastamonu granitoid belt of northern Turkey: First arc plutonism product related to the subduction of Paleotethys: Geology, v. 14, p. 179–183.
Yılmaz, Y., 1972, Structure and petrology of the Gümüşhane granite and surrounding rocks: Ph.D. thesis, University of London, 284 p.
Yılmaz, Y., 1977, Bilecik-Söğüt dolayindaki "Eski temel karmasiği" nin petrojenetik evrimi: Docentus thesis, İstanbul Üniversitesi Fen Fakültesi, 169 p.
Yılmaz, Y., 1981, Sakarya kitasi güney kenarının tektonik evrimi: İstanbul Yerbilimleri, v. 1, no. 1–2, p. 33–52.
Yılmaz, Y., 1988, An approach to the origin of the Aegean volcanism, *in* A.M.C. Şengör, ed., Tectonic evolution of the Tethyan region: NATO ASI, 259, p. 177–201.
Yılmaz, Y., 1990, Allochthonous terranes in the Tethyan Middle East: Anatolia and the surrounding regions: Philosophical Transactions of Royal Society of London, A 331, p. 611–624.
Yılmaz, Y., 1993, New evidence and model on the evolution of the Southeast Anatolian orogen: Geological Society of America Bulletin, v. 105, p. 251–271.
Yılmaz, Y., and A.M.C. Şengör, 1985, Paleotethyan ophiolites in northern Turkey, petrology and tectonic setting: Ofioliti 10, no. 2–3, p. 485–504.
Yılmaz, Y., and O. Tüysüz, 1984, Kastamonu-Boyabat-Vezirköprü-Tosya arasindaki bölgenin jeolojisi (Ilgaz-Kargı masiflerının etüdü): Maden Tetkik Arama Enstitüsü Rapor No. 275, 275 p. (unpublished report).
Yılmaz, Y., and O. Tüysüz, 1988, Kargı masifi ve dolaylarinda Mesozoyik tektonik birliklerının düzenlenmeleri sorununa bir yaklaşim: Türkiye Petrol Jeologlari Derneği Bülteni, v. 1, no. 1, p. 73–86.
Yılmaz, Y., and O. Tüysüz, 1991, Anatomy of an imbricated zone: geology of the Kargı massif, Central Pontides: Bulletin of the Technical University of İstanbul, v. 44, no. 1–2, p. 279–299.
Yılmaz, Y., A.M. Gözübol, and O. Tüysüz, 1981, Geology of an area in and around the Northern Anatolian transform fault zone between Bolu and Akyazi, *in* A.M. Isikara and A. Vogel, eds., Multidisciplinary approach to earthquake prediction: Earthquake Prediction Research, Friedr. Vieweg and Sohn, Braunschweig/Wiesbaden, v. 2, p. 45–66.

Yılmaz, Y., O. Gürpinar, Ş.C. Genç, M. Bozcu, K. Yılmaz, H. Şeker, E. Yiğitbas, and M. Keskin, 1990, Armutlu yarimadasi ve dolayinin jeolojisi: Türkiye Petrolleri Anonim Ortakliği Rapor No. 2796, 210 p.

Yılmaz, Y., Ş. C. Genç, E. Yiğitbaş, M. Bozcu, and K. Yılmaz, 1995, Geological evolution of the Late Mesozoic continental margin of northwestern Anatolia: Tectonophysics, v. 243, p. 155–171.

Yılmaz, Y., O. Gurpinar, E. Yiğitbaş, M. Yildirim, Ş. C. Genç, Ö.F. Gürör, A. Elmas, M. Bozcu, B.A. Galiskan, and H.S. Şerdar, 1993, Tokat masifi ve yakyn çevresinin jeolojisi: Türkiye Petrolleri Anonim Ortaklyğy Rapor No. 3390, 429 p.

Zankl, H., 1961, Magmatismus und Bauplan des Ost Pontischen Gebirges im quer profil des Harsit-tales, NE Anatolien: Geologische Rundschau, v. 51, p. 218–240.

Zonenshain, L., and X. Le Pichon, 1986, Deep basins of the Black Sea and Caspian Sea as remnants of Mesozoic back-arc basins: Tectonophysics, v. 123, p. 181–211.

Görür, N., 1997, Cretaceous syn- to postrift sedimentation on the southern continental margin of the Western Black Sea Basin, *in* A.G. Robinson, ed., Regional and petroleum geology of the Black Sea and surrounding region: AAPG Memoir 68, p. 227–240.

Chapter 12

Cretaceous Syn- to Postrift Sedimentation on the Southern Continental Margin of the Western Black Sea Basin

Naci Görür
İstanbul Technical University (İ.T.Ü.)
Ayazağa, İstanbul, Turkey

ABSTRACT

The Western Black Sea Basin began opening as a back-arc basin by the rifting of a juvenile continental margin magmatic arc during the Aptian. Its southern continental margin succession is well exposed in the Western Pontides, Northwest Turkey. This succession consists predominantly of volcanogenic coarse clastic rocks, shales, and carbonates with a deepening-upward character. The volcanogenic clastic rocks are mostly turbidites and mass-flow deposits in places with huge exotic blocks. The volume and nature of this clastic material were controlled by both relief of nearby sediment sources and arc volcanism, whereas the carbonates depended on ocean circulation and surface organic productivity. The Aptian to lower Cenomanian part of the succession formed during the synrift stage, whereas the rest accumulated during the postrift stage. The synbreakup stage is marked by the upper Cenomanian to Campanian sedimentary facies.

The synrift sediments commence locally with Aptian lagoonal black shales, rich in organic matter. They pass laterally and upward into an Albian unit, comprising marginal marine glauconitic sandstones succeeded by siliciclastic turbidites, marls, sandy limestones, and blue to black shales with abundant glauconite. This unit includes several levels of mass-flow deposits, comprising mostly conglomerates and olistoliths of various sizes, ranging from a few centimeters to hundreds of meters in diameter. The synrift sediments end with a Cenomanian succession of blue to black shales and clayey limestones, in part with exotic blocks derived from the underlying rocks.

The postrift sediments at the base of upper Cenomanian to Campanian consist of pelagic red micrites and marls followed by mainly volcanogenic (both andesitic and basaltic) terrigeneous and carbonate turbidites and deep-water sediments, ranging from Turonian to lower Eocene. The basal pelagic carbonates rest with a slightly angular unconformity on the synrift deposits and represent the breakup facies.

Facies analyses of the rift succession indicate that the Western Black Sea Basin was isolated during its synrift stage from free interchange with the

Intra-Pontide Ocean to the south, and therefore was euxinic. During the rift-drift transition in the late Cenomanian, the euxinic conditions largely disappeared, and the water column above the arc margin of this basin became well mixed. The volcanic activity in the arc also increased in intensity soon after this transition, and largely controlled the postrift sedimentation.

INTRODUCTION

Cretaceous rocks of the Pontides represent two continental margins of different tectonic setting. Those that are exposed in the inner Pontides along the Neotethyan sutures belong to the northern continental margin of the Neotethys Ocean, whereas those cropping out along the Black Sea coast belong to the southern continental margin of the Black Sea. This chapter describes in detail only the Western Black Sea succession in order to reconstruct the early geological history of this oceanic basin (Bulandje, 1976; Letouzey et al., 1977; Sidorenko, 1978; Zonenshain and Le Pichon, 1986; Görür, 1988). Unraveling this history is important, because it may lead to more general conclusions on both the origin of this mini-ocean and the tectonic development of the Anatolian Tethysides as a whole. The conclusions reached in this study support the idea that the Western Black Sea Basin was created by rifting during the Aptian to Cenomanian behind the Pontide magmatic arc of Cretaceous to Eocene age (Hsü et al., 1977; Letouzey et al., 1977; Hsü, 1988; Görür, 1988, 1989; Görür et al., 1993; Okay et al., 1994) (Figure 1). These conclusions may prove useful in interpreting the depositional and tectonic evolution of other back-arc basins elsewhere in the stratigraphic record.

REGIONAL TECTONICS AND THE DEVELOPMENT OF THE WESTERN BLACK SEA BASIN

The Western Black Sea Basin is delimited to the south by the İstanbul Zone (Okay, 1989), one of the main paleotectonic units of the Pontides (Figure 1). This zone is characterized mainly by a nonmetamorphic sedimentary succession, ranging in age from Ordovician to Carboniferous. It is exotic with respect to the surrounding tectonic units (Şengör, 1984; Okay et al., 1994). In the west, it is bordered by the Strandja Massif, and in both the south and the east by the Sakarya Zone and the intervening Intra-Pontide suture (Şengör and Yılmaz, 1981). The Sakarya Zone is formed mainly from strongly deformed and locally metamorphosed Permo-Triassic active margin units, with a thick Jurassic to Cretaceous sedimentary cover (Okay et al., 1991; Robinson et al., 1995). The Intra-Pontide suture consists of a mixture of serpentinite, blueschist, basic volcanic rock, and Upper Cretaceous to Paleocene pelagic limestone, indicating that the İstanbul and the Sakarya zones were juxtaposed after the middle Paleocene (Şengör and Yılmaz, 1981; Okay and Tansel, 1994). According to Okay (1989) and Okay et al. (1994), during the late Early Cretaceous, the Intra-Pontide Ocean was a narrow Gulf of California–type basin with active western and northern margins (Figure 2a). The western margin was represented by the Strandja Zone and the Moesian Platform, whereas the northern margin was formed by the İstanbul Zone (Okay et al., 1994). Its eastern margin was passive and defined by the Eastern Black Sea block, comprising the Sakarya Zone in the south. Between the Aptian and the Cenomanian, the İstanbul Zone was rifted from Laurasia along the juvenile Pontide magmatic arc that had been developing since the Aptian as a result of the northward subduction of the Intra-Pontide Ocean (Şengör and Yılmaz, 1981; Aydın et al., 1982; Görür, 1988; Okay et al., 1994). The movement of this Hercynian continental fragment was realized along two transform faults and resulted in the back-arc opening of the Western Black Sea Basin (Figure 2b). The continuing southward drift of the İstanbul Zone during the early Eocene led to a collision with the Sakarya Zone in the south. This arc-continent collision obliterated the eastern part of the Intra-Pontide Ocean (Okay and Görür, 1995), ended the extension in the Western Black Sea Basin, and deactivated the transform faults, railroading the İstanbul Zone to the south (Okay et al., 1994). These transform faults can be inferred from seismic sections in the present Black Sea off both the Bulgarian (Dachev et al., 1988, their figure 7) and the west Crimean shelves (Finetti et al., 1988, their figure 51). For more details of this back-arc opening, refer to Görür (1988), Görür et al. (1993), and Okay et al. (1994).

STRATIGRAPHY OF THE SOUTHERN CONTINENTAL MARGIN OF THE WESTERN BLACK SEA BASIN

Basement

The stratigraphic basement for the continental margin succession of the Western Black Sea Basin is represented mostly by the pre-Aptian rocks of the İstanbul Zone. This zone is characterized mainly by an Ordovician to Carboniferous nonmetamorphic succession, corresponding with a typical Atlantic-type continental margin facies (Abdüsselamoğlu, 1977). The succession starts at the base with thick continental conglomerates and arkosic sandstones of Ordovician age, passing upward into Silurian marginal marine quartz arenites and shales. These clastic rocks are conformably overlain

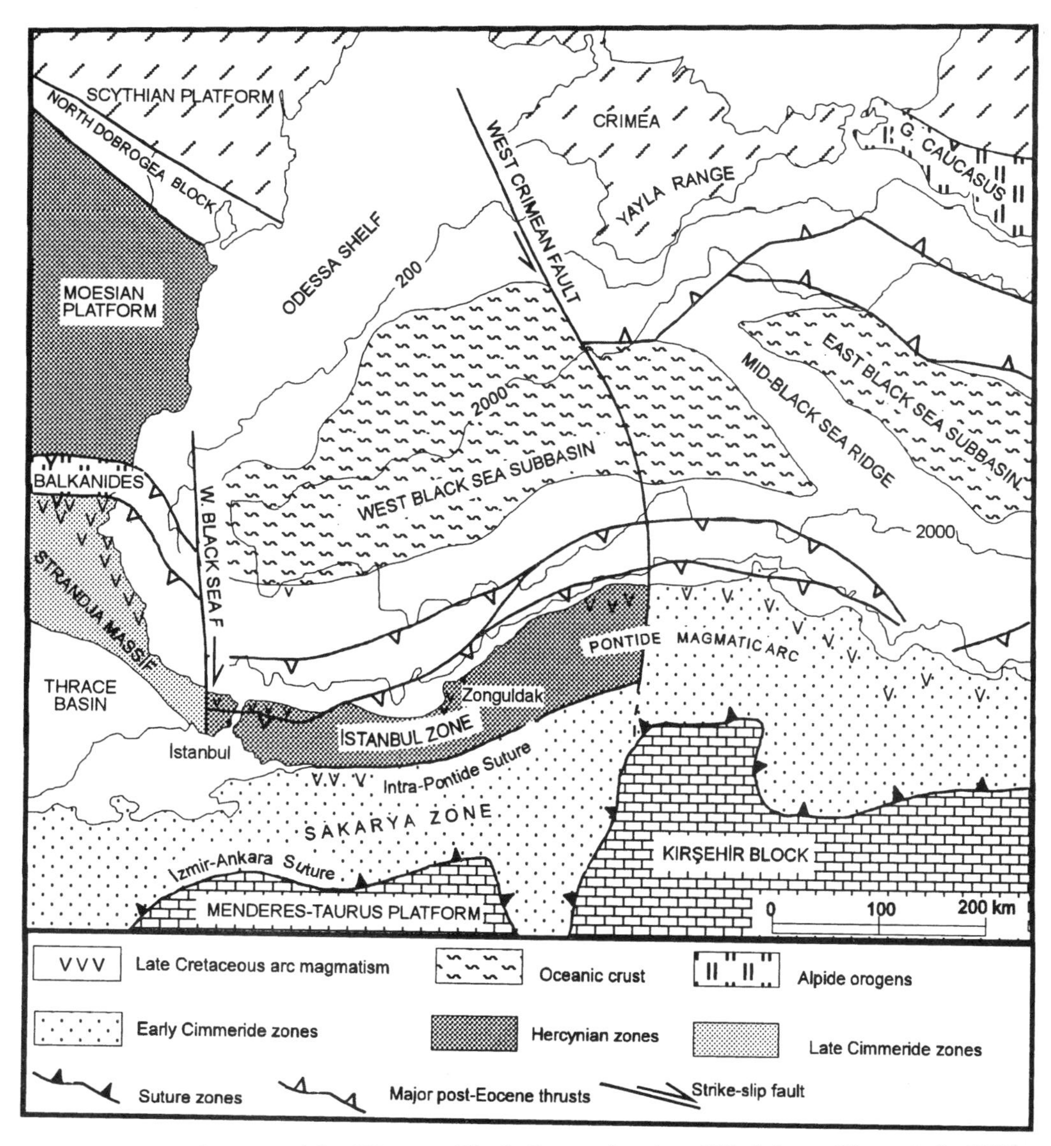

Figure 1. Tectonic map of the Western Black Sea region (modified from Okay et al., 1994). Reproduced with changes with the permission of the Geological Society of America, Inc.

by a deepening-upward carbonate assemblage of Devonian age. From base to top, the assemblage consists of bioclastic to reefal limestones, calciturbidites, and deep-water cherty and nodular limestones (Görür, 1982). This assemblage grades upward into Lower Carboniferous radiolarites and siliciclastic turbidites. On the contrary, the Devonian facies in the eastern part of the İstanbul Zone (around the Zonguldak region) are represented by shallow-water limestones and intercalated shales succeeded by the Carboniferous deltaic sediments and coal measures (Görür et al., 1995). The Paleozoic succession of the İstanbul Zone, which is very similar to European Hercynian sections (e.g., the Carnic Alps and the Pyrenees), ends with unconformable Triassic deposits cropping out extensively in the Kocaeli Peninsula (east of İstanbul). Here, the Triassic deposits commence with basal red beds and local basaltic andesites followed by shallow- to deep-water carbonates and siliciclastic turbidites (Erguvanli, 1949; Özdemir et al., 1973; Abdüsselamoğlu, 1977; Ketin, 1983). They are unconformably overlain by Upper Cretaceous rocks of the Western Black Sea Basin, with no intervening Jurassic and Lower Cretaceous sediments. These sediments are widespread in the Zonguldak-İnebolu region (Görür et al., 1993) (Figure 3).

Rift Succession

Extensive outcrops of the rift sediments of the Western Black Sea Basin occur in the eastern part of the İstanbul Zone. These sediments show great changes in both facies and thickness. As a result, they are divided in many areas into a number of formations with different local names. This causes great confusion among geologists who want to make regional correlations and to generate a simplified stratigraphic scheme of the region.

The best exposures of the Western Black Sea rift sediments are seen in two regions separated by a basement

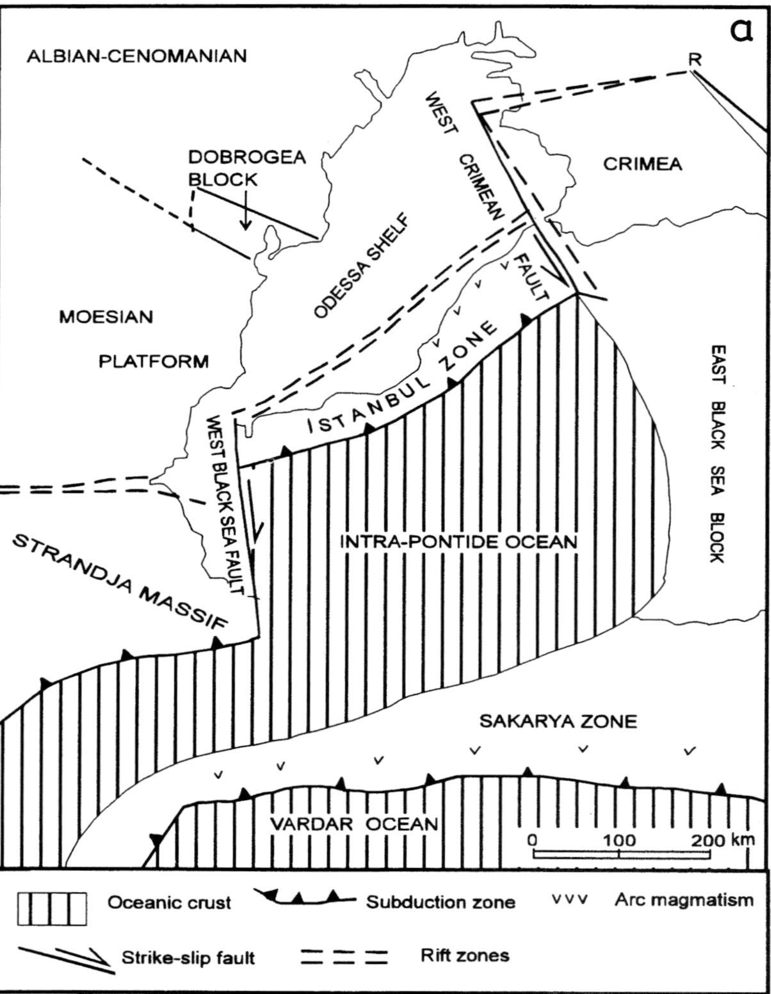

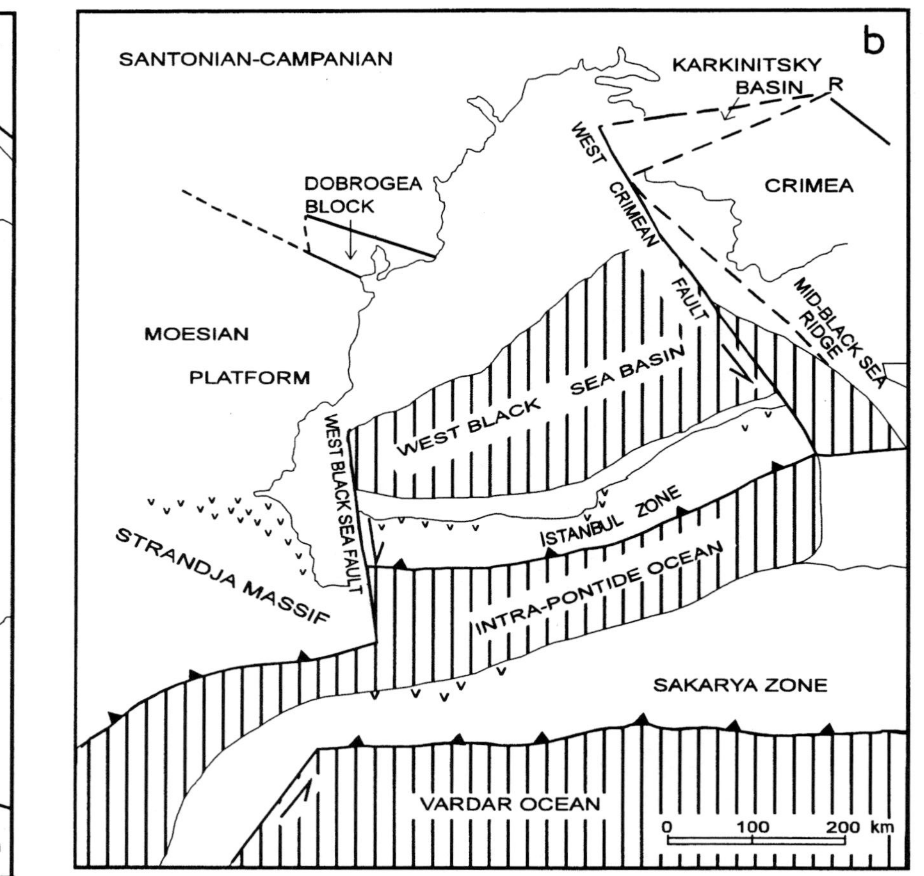

Figure 2. Albian to Cenomanian (a) and late Cretaceous (b) palinspastic paleogeographic maps of the Western Black Sea region (modified from Okay et al., 1994). R = rotation pole of East Black Sea block. Reproduced with changes with the permission of the Geological Society of America, Inc.

high. One is the coastal region between Zonguldak and İnebolu, and the other is the Ülüs Basin between Safranbolu and Ülüs (Figure 3). In the Zonguldak-İnebolu region, the rift succession permits subdivision into synrift, postrift, and synbreakup successions; in the Ülüs Basin, such a distinction is not possible, probably because this more-southerly basin was only an off-axis subsidiary graben that disrupted the main rift shoulder. The entire Lower Cretaceous succession in this basin is collected under the Ülüs Formation. This formation consists of a series of conglomerates overlain by thick turbiditic sandstones and shales. Similar Cretaceous rocks are observed in the Sinop region located in the adjacent Sakarya Zone (Gedik and Korkmaz, 1984) (Figures 1, 3). This observation casts doubt on Okay et al.'s (1994) tectonic model for the origin of the Black Sea Basin, in which the İstanbul and the Sakarya zones throughout the Cretaceous constituted two different margins of the Intra-Pontide Ocean. However, this similarity has not yet been documented by means of detailed mapping and facies analysis; whether these two successions developed in physical continuity with each other is a matter of debate. In this study, the rift succession of the Western Black Sea Basin will be described from the Zonguldak region, where it is best developed (Figure 4).

Synrift Succession

Synrift sediments are represented by the Çağlayan Formation (Tokay, 1952; Ketin and Gümüs, 1963). This formation is of Aptian to Cenomanian age (Aydın et al., 1986) and is divided by the Turkish Petroleum Company geologists (Aydın et al., 1987) into four members. These are, in stratigraphic order, the Kilimli Shale Member, the Velibey Sandstone Member, the Sapça Sandstone Member, and the Tasmaca Shale Member. They are exposed side by side in a narrow belt along the Black Sea Coast, younging in a landward direction (Figure 4). Since all the members are mappable units, they are regarded in this study as formations and named as the Kilimli, Velibey, Sapça, and the Tasmaca formations. Consequently, a group rank is assigned to what was previously the Çağlayan Formation. The thickness of the Çağlayan Group shows great changes, ranging from 200 m to 1300 m (Görür et al., 1993).

Kilimli Formation

This unit (Charles, 1930) developed locally at the base of the Velibey Formation (Tokay, 1952; Kaya et al., 1983) (Figure 5). It crops out along the Black Sea coast in Zonguldak, Kilimli, and Amasra (Figure 4); its distribution elsewhere is uncertain. It consists mainly of 0–200-m-thick, locally well-bioturbated and organic-rich gray to black shales and marls, in part with glauconite and iron nodules. It is poor in fossils, although fragments of ammonites, gastropods, and brachiopods are locally found [in the Amasra area (Akman, 1992)]. Besides these macrofossil fragments, some nannoplankton, including *Predicosphaera cretacea* (Arkhangelsky), *Chiastozygus litterarius* (Gorka), *Cribrosphaerella ehrenbergi* (Arkhangelsky), *Wautznaueria barnasae* (Black), *Microstaurus chiastius* (Worsley), *Rhaqodiscusa asper* Stradner, *Nannoconus* cf. *grandis* Deres and Acheriteguy, *Micrantholithus obtusus* Stradner, and *Zygodiscus diplogrammus* (Deflandre) are present (Akman, 1992). On the basis of these fossils and their stratigraphic position, an Aptian age is attributed to the Kilimli Formation (Tokay, 1952; Yergök et al., 1987; Akman, 1992). This formation rests on the Upper Jurassic to Lower Cretaceous İnaltı Formation (Figure 6) (Ketin and Gümüs, 1963) with a depositional contact, ranging in nature from gradational to disconformity. Where the contact is a disconformity, the Kilimli shales and the overlying sediments commonly include limestone blocks of the İnaltı Formation, marking the local disintegration of the carbonate platform represented by this formation (Tokay, 1952). The Kilimli Formation also overlies the older basement rocks in the Amasra region (Akman, 1992).

Velibey Formation

This formation (Tokay, 1952) consists mainly of a yellowish-gray, medium to thickly bedded and planar cross-bedded quartz arenite, in part with conglomerate and sandy limestone interbeds (Figure 7). The arenite is a medium- to coarse-grained sandstone with well-rounded to angular grains, consisting of ≤95% quartz with small amounts of feldspars (altered orthoclase), mica, glauconite, and lithic grains. Interstitial minerals include minor quantities of authigenic quartz, chlorite, and siderite. Cement is represented predominantly by silica, although local carbonate cements are also recorded in the basal part of the formation. Toward the top of this unit, lithic grains (including fragments of igneous, metamorphic, and sedimentary rocks derived from the basement) increase in abundance; consequently, the quartz arenite becomes a quartzose litharenite with common glauconite. The conglomerates in this formation form thick beds or units, in part with local channeling and cross-bedding. Their clasts are composed predominantly of quartz with subordinate pebbles of the İnaltı limestone (Derman, 1990a). The limestone interbeds are mostly found in the upper parts of the formation and are formed mainly from bioclastic limestones, rich in rudists and *Orbitolina* (Tokay, 1952; Ketin, 1955; Derman, 1990a). On the basis of some rudist types, an upper Albian age is assigned to the limestone interbeds (Özer, 1986). No fossils have been recovered from the quartz arenite below, but the ages of the Kilimli Formation beneath and the limestone interbeds above bracket its age as Lower Albian.

The Velibey Formation unconformably overlies the İnaltı Formation or the Paleozoic rocks where the Kilimli Formation is absent (Figure 5). Like the Kilimli Formation, it displays a great variation in thickness. It ranges in thickness from 50 to 160 m at outcrop in Ereğli, and is about 250 m in the Zonguldak region (Tokay, 1952; Görür et al., 1993) (Figure 3). It thins and becomes shaley toward the east, passing both laterally and vertically into the Sapça Formation (Ketin and Gümüs, 1963).

Sapça Formation

This formation comprises alternations of thinly to thickly bedded turbiditic sandstones, marls, sandy

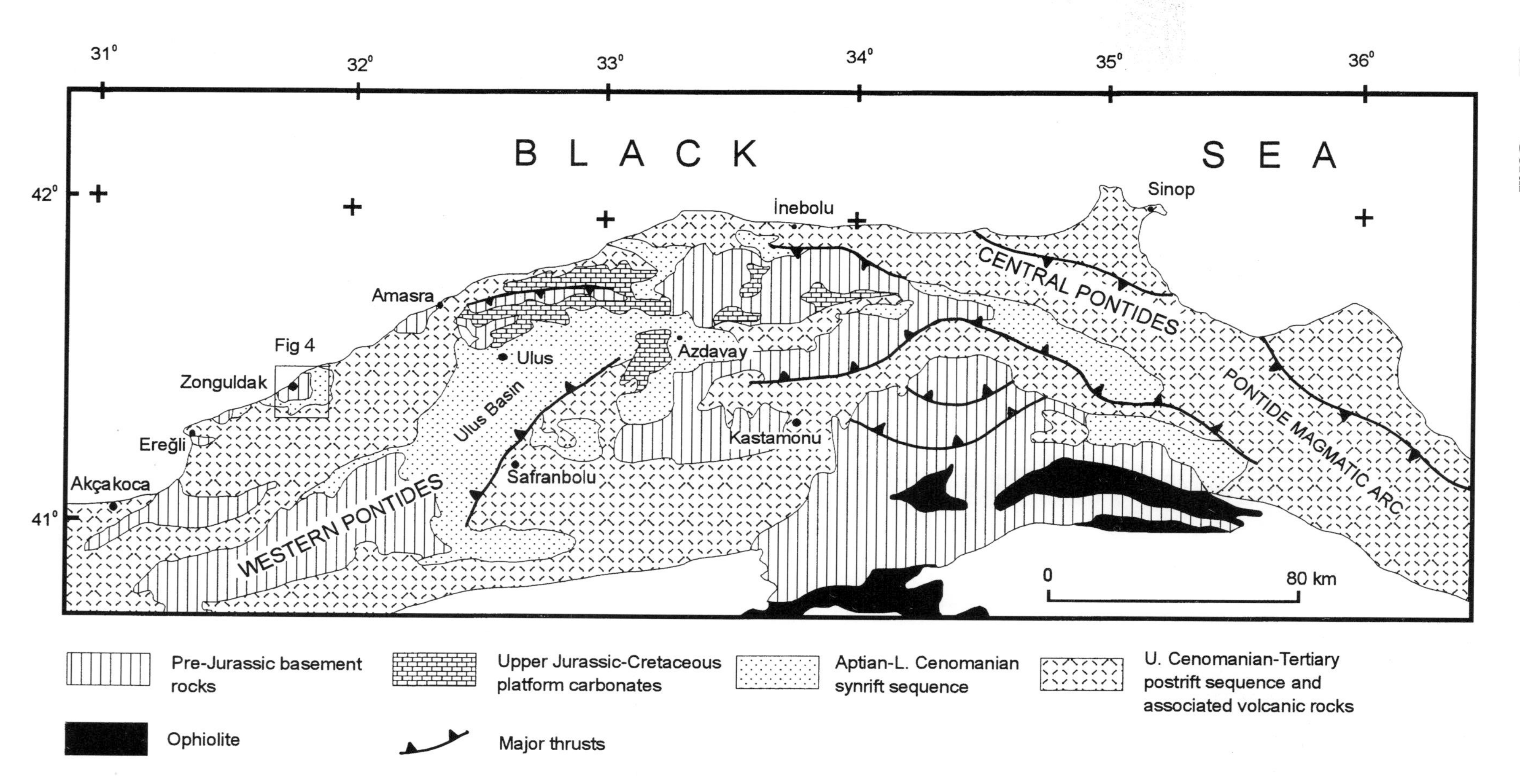

Figure 3. Simplified geological map of the Zonguldak-Sinop region. The framed area is shown in detail in Figure 4. The İstanbul and Sakarya zones are not differentiated.

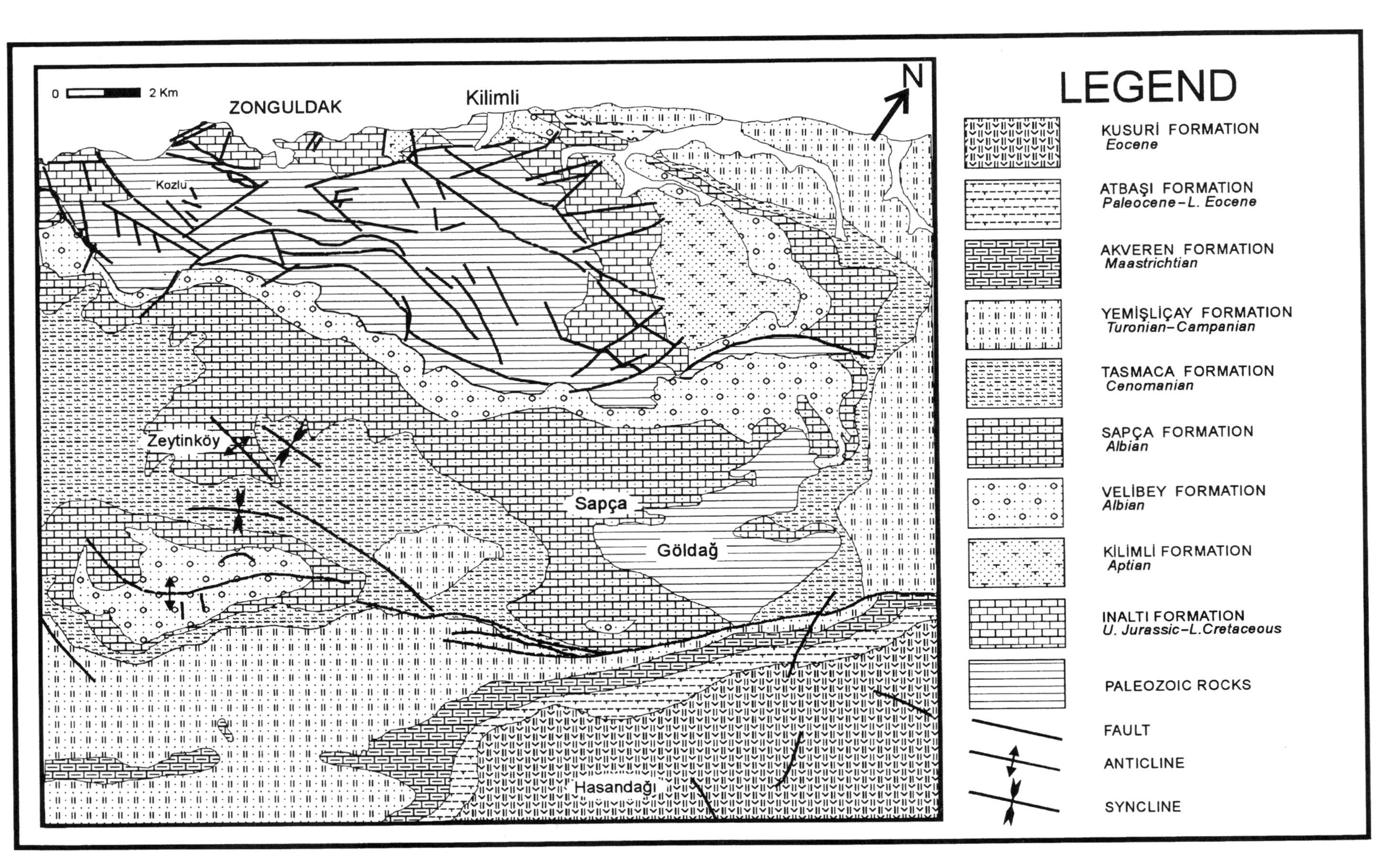

Figure 4. Geological map of the Zonguldak region (after Canca, 1994).

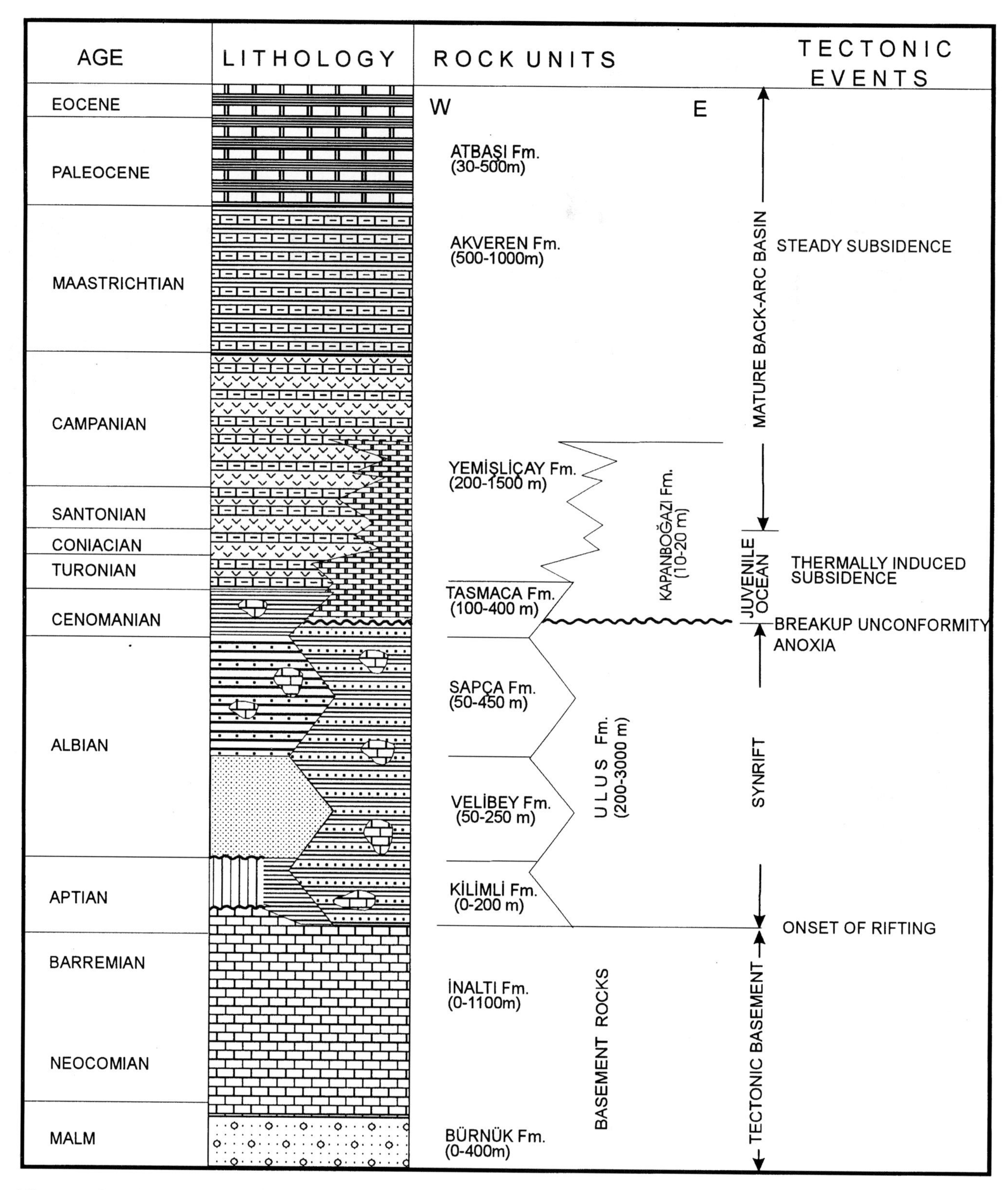

Figure 5. Stratigraphy and major tectonic events of the southern continental margin of the Western Black Sea Basin.

limestones, and blue to black shales with abundant glauconite (Siyako et al., 1981) (Figures 5, 8). The sandstones are fine- to medium-grained and generally poorly sorted feldspathic litharenite or arkose with angular to subrounded quartz, feldspar, and rock fragments. The latter include igneous, metamorphic, and sedimentary rocks derived from the basement. The sandstones are laterally continuous and display Ta-c Bouma units, in part with well-developed sole marks, including flute cast, groove cast, load cast, and tool marks (Görür et al., 1993). The alternating blue to black shales are in part rich in organic matter and increase in abundance toward the top of the

Figure 6. Well-bedded oolitic and bioclastic limestones of the Upper Jurassic to Lower Cretaceous İnalti Formation in the town of Zonguldak.

Figure 7. Medium- to thickly bedded quartz arenite of the Lower Albian Velibey Formation, around the Sapça tunnel, near Zonguldak.

formation. Between Zonguldak and Ereğli (Figure 3), this formation includes local boulder beds, slumps, and debris flows (Tokay, 1952). Clasts of these coarse sediments range in size from pebbles to huge blocks measured in tens of meters. They are mostly derived from the İnaltı Limestone, although those of older rocks are also common (Derman, 1990b; Tüysüz et al., 1990; Tüysüz, 1993). The following fauna have been identified from various sediments of the Sapça Formation (Tokay, 1952; Aydın et al., 1987): *Prohysteroceras (Goodhalites) goodhalli* (Sowerby), *Kossmatella* cf. *chabaudi* Fallot, *Leymeriella tardefurcata* Leymerie, *Leymeriella* aff. *regularis* (Bruguiere), *Hoplites dentatus* Sowerby, *Douvilleiceras mammilatum* Schlumberger, *Natica gaultiana* d'Orbigny, *Lenticulina* sp., Textularidae, and bryozoans. This fauna indicates an Albian age (Tokay, 1952; Aydın et al., 1987). Like the other formations of the Çağlayan Group, this formation shows a great variation in thickness and ranges from 50 to 450 m (Tokay, 1952; Aydın et al., 1987; Görür et al., 1993).

Tasmaca Formation

This formation consists of a 100- to 400-m-thick uniform succession of poorly bedded and locally laminated blue to black shales and clayey limestones, in part with abundant slumps and exotic blocks (Siyako et al., 1981) (Figures 5, 8). The shales are organic rich and in part sandy and micaceous with a distinct Cenomanian ammonite fauna, including *Schloenbachia inflata* Sowerby, *Hoplites auritas* Sowerby, and *Scaphites hugardianum* d'Orbigny (Tokay, 1952). The limestone interbeds are generally thinly to medium bedded and contain clayey to sandy micrites. The exotic blocks mostly occur in the upper part of the formation as boulder beds, deeply cut channel fills, or individual blocks, ranging in size from a few centimeters to tens of meters in diameter. They were derived not only

Figure 8. The turbiditic sandstone facies of the Albian Sapça Formation (the brown area in the lower-right corner) passes within a short distance into the gray shales and the clayey limestones of the Cenomanian Tasmaca Formation along the Zonguldak-Ereğli road, near Zonguldak.

from the basement rocks, but also from the synrift Velibey Formation (Tokay, 1952).

Synbreakup Succession

The synbreakup succession of the Western Black Sea Basin is represented by the typically red Kapanboğazı Formation (Ketin and Gümüs, 1963) (Figures 5, 9). This formation crops out to the east of Amasra (Figure 3) and comprises thinly to medium bedded biomicrites, in part with marl, sand, and volcanic interbeds. The biomicrites are locally cherty and rich in planktonic foraminifera, with subordinate radiolaria and echinoderm fragments. The planktonic foraminifera include *Praeglobotruncana delrioensis* (Plummer), *Dicarinella imbricata* (Mornod), *Globotruncana lapparenti* Brotzen, *G. linneiana* (d'Orbigny), *G. bulloides* Vogler, *G. ventricosa* White, *Helvetoglobotruncana helvetica* (Bolli), *Globotruncanita calcarata* (Cushman), *Marginotruncana coronata* (Bolli), *M. pseudolinneiana* Pessagno, *Heterohelix globulosa* (Ehrenberg), and *Rugoglobigerina* sp. (Görür et al., 1993). These fossils indicate ages ranging from upper Cenomanian to Campanian. The marl interbeds alternate with the biomicrites, with or without a regular interval. The thickness of each marl unit ranges from a few centimeters to 1 m. Both the limestones and the marls commonly show horizontal laminae, in part with burrows and mottling. Instrumental analyses show that these sediments contain a certain amount of hematite, which is probably responsible for their red color (Görür et al., 1993). The volcanic interbeds commonly occur in the upper part of the formation and are formed from andesitic and basaltic volcanic and volcanogenic material. Between Amasra and İnebolu (Figure 3), the Kapanboğazı Formation overlies the synrift sediments with a slightly angular unconformity (Figures 5, 9). Toward Zonguldak, it passes laterally into the Tasmaca and the Yemişliçay formations. The Kapanboğazı Formation seems to have a fairly uniform thickness (about 10–20 m) throughout the area studied.

Postrift Succession

This succession comprises all the postbreakup sediments (the Kapanboğazı Formation is excluded) and the associated magmatic rocks formed between the late Cenomanian and the present. In this study, only the Cretaceous formations are described (Figure 5).

Yemişliçay Formation

This formation rests conformably on the Kapanboğazı Formation and is characterized by a thick (≤1500 m) series of volcanic rocks, volcaniclastic sediments, shales, marls, and pelagic limestones (Ketin and Gümüs, 1963) (Figures 5, 10). The volcanic and volcaniclastic rocks consist mainly of andesites, basalts, lithic tuffs, tuffites, pyroclastic sandstones, and agglomerates. Most of the volcaniclastic beds show many characteristic features of turbidites, including graded bedding, sole marks, channeling, and Tb-c Bouma units (Görür et al., 1993). They locally contain large blocks of both the basement rocks and the older rift facies in the lowermost part of the formation. The interbedded marls and the pelagic limestones are generally red in color and look like the carbonates of the underlying Kapanboğazı Formation. They contain abundant planktonic foraminifera and nannoplankton. The following planktonic foraminifera, which suggest a Turonian to Campanian age, have been identified throughout these sediments (Aydın et al., 1986; Tüysüz, 1990; Görür et al., 1993): *Dicarinella concavata* (Brotzen), *Marginotruncana coronata* (Bolli),

Figure 9. The Upper Cenomanian to Campanian Kapanboğazı Formation, which comprises yellow sandstones, marls, and red pelagic limestones, rests on the dark gray shales of the Çağlayan Group above a slightly angular unconformity, east of Amasra.

Globotruncana arca (Cushman), *Marginotruncana renzi* (Gandolfi), *Globotruncana lapparenti* Brotzen, and *Hedbergella* sp.

Akveren Formation

The Akveren Formation consists of ≤1000-m-thick interbedded limestones, marls, and shales (Ketin and Gümüs, 1962). The limestones are characterized mainly by medium-bedded, cherty, and clayey to sandy calciturbidites with well-developed grading and sole marks. The grading is distinct from calcirudite to calcarenite within single beds. The sole marks include mostly flute casts and tool marks on bed bases. Up the section, the shaley and the marly interbeds become red in color and form a key horizon throughout the area studied. It is reported that this unit passes laterally into reefal limestones toward the Central Pontides; that is, in the Devrekani region (Tüysüz, 1985; Aydın et al., 1986).

The Akveren Formation conformably overlies the Yemişliçay Formation; its upper boundary passes transitionally into the 30- to 500-m-thick Paleocene to lower Eocene Atbaşi Formation, comprising red marls, shales, and sandstones (Figure 5). On the basis of the following fauna, a Maastrichtian age is attributed to the Akveren Formation: *Globotruncana lapparenti* Brotzen, *G. arca* (Cushman), *G. stuarti* (de Lapparent), *Globotruncanita stuartiformis* (Dalbiez), *Rosita fornicata* (Plummer), *Globotruncanita conica* (White), *Globotruncana bulloides* Vogler, *G. calciformis* Vogler, *Morozovella pseudobulloides* (Plummer), *Morozovella* cf. *trinidadensis* (Bolli), *Globorotalia ehrenbergi* Bolli, *Planorotalites pseudomenardii* (Bolli), *P. compressa* (Plummer), *Orbitoides medius* (d'Archiac), *Heterohelix* sp., and Nodosaridae (Kaya et al., 1983; Aydın et al., 1987).

CONCLUSIONS: GEOLOGICAL HISTORY OF THE RIFTED SOUTHERN CONTINENTAL MARGIN OF THE WESTERN BLACK SEA BASIN

During the Early Cretaceous, before the rifting of the Western Black Sea Basin started, the İstanbul Zone constituted the south-facing Atlantic-type continental margin of Laurasia (Şengör and Yılmaz, 1981; Görür, 1988; Okay et al., 1994). In large part, it was underlain by a carbonate platform, passing into lowlands in the west. In the Aptian–Albian, a north-dipping subduction zone was generated all along the southern periphery of the İstanbul Zone; thus, the Laurasian margin was converted here from a passive continental margin into an active one (Aydın et al., 1982; Görür, 1988, 1991) (Figure 2a). Subsequently, from the Aptian-Albian onward, a continental margin magmatic arc, with back-arc extension in its early stages, developed in this region. This subduction-related extension led to the disintegration of the carbonate shelf by pervasive normal faulting. Evidence for the syndepositional normal faulting includes rapid facies changes, great thickness variations, and the presence of huge exotic blocks in the various formations of the Çağlayan Group. On the subsided fault blocks, the deepening-upward synrift sediments of this group accumulated during the Aptian to Cenomanian period. These sediments are dominated by turbidites with exotic blocks derived mostly from the underlying İnaltı carbonates and the older rocks, although the blocks from the basal part of the synrift succession itself are also locally present. These coarse exotic components were derived from the neighboring upstanding fault blocks. They were probably transported by either submarine slumping and sliding on steep slopes adjoining actively rising fault blocks or by the catastrophic collapse of the newly formed fault escarpments (Görür et al., 1993). The Aptian to Cenomanian block-faulting and the contemporaneous relatively deep-water sedimentation in the İstanbul Zone are interpreted by Görür (1988) as a rifting event that separated this zone from the Laurasian continental margin along a juvenile magmatic arc, developing here in response to the northward subduction of the

Figure 10. Well-developed turbidites of the Turonian to Campanian Yemişliçay Formation, near Ereğli.

Neotethys Ocean (Şengör and Yılmaz, 1981; Okay et al., 1994). The rifting reached its climax in the late Albian to early Cenomanian. During this time, no oceanic crust was generated, but the sedimentation in the rift basin lagged behind fault-controlled subsidence. This resulted in both deepening of the basin and a small rate of detrital sedimentation during nonturbiditic depositional intervals, as indicated by the presence of glauconite-bearing shales and carbonates of this age. These sediments are also rich in organic matter, suggesting a silled depocenter for the Western Black Sea rift. Restricted water circulation probably led to the development of anoxic conditions in the water column, favorable for the accumulation of these sediments (Dickinson, 1974; Schlanger and Jenkyns, 1976; Demaison and Moore, 1980; Jenkyns, 1980; Tucker and Wright, 1990; Görür, 1991; Görür et al., 1993). Recent research suggests that high primary organic production also plays an important role in the accumulation of such deposits (Pedersen and Calvert, 1990).

The Western Black Sea rift evolved between the late Cenomanian and the Campanian into a protoocean when the İstanbul Zone was separated from Laurasia, creating new oceanic crust (Figure 2b). This interpretation is supported by the drastic change in the sedimentation during the late Cenomanian. The sedimentation switched from the accumulation of the dark-colored and organic-rich siliciclastic sediments of the synrift phase to the red pelagic carbonate deposition of the synbreakup phase. This marked change in the sedimentary regime may imply cessation of normal faulting, rapid widening of the rift to end the anoxia, and a widespread subsidence on the major part of the southern margin to allow deposition of the pelagic carbonates (Görür et al., 1993). All these events are expected to be seen when a rift passes from the initial rifting phase to a period of seafloor spreading (Bond et al., 1995). The subsidence probably took place as a result of both cooling of the lithosphere and increasing sediment load. It caused development of a slight angular unconformity between the syn- and postrift successions (Falvey, 1974; Pitman, 1978; Currey, 1980; Einsele, 1992; Bond et al., 1995; Ingersoll and Busby, 1995; Marsaglia, 1995). The presence of the andesitic and basaltic interbeds in the upper part of the pelagic carbonates suggests that the arc magmatism, which initiated on the İstanbul Zone in Aptian–Albian time, intensified during the deposition of these sediments (Görür et al., 1993).

Following the formation of the new oceanic crust in the late Cenomanian, the Western Black Sea protoocean continued widening throughout the rest of the Cretaceous (Figure 2b) and Paleocene. Common volcanogenic deposits of this stage indicate that during this period, the magmatic arc largely controlled the sedimentation on the Southern Black Sea margin. It provided large quantities of volcanic and volcaniclastic material, which were mostly transported by slumps, debris flows, and turbidity currents.

Enlargement of the Western Black Sea back-arc basin ended during the early Eocene, when the İstanbul and the Sakarya zones collided along the Intra-Pontide suture (Okay et al., 1994). This arc-continent collision deformed the southern margin of this basin and trapped it behind the Pontides as a relict back-arc structure (Hsü et al., 1977; Hsü, 1988).

ACKNOWLEDGMENTS

This study was supported by a Türkiye Bilimsel ve Teknik *AraStirma Kurumu (TÜBITAK)*-Glo Tek grant.

I thank the following AAPG reviewers for their constructive comments and suggestions, all of whom improved this manuscript: M.E. Tucker, A.J. Tankard, and A.G. Robinson.

REFERENCES CITED

Abdüsselamoğlu, S., 1977, The Palaeozoic and Mesozoic in the Gebze region: explanatory text and excursion guidebook, 4th Colloquium on Geology of the Aegean Region, Excursion 4: Western Anatolia and Thrace, 16 p.

Akman, A.Ü., 1992, Amasra-Arit arasyinin jeolojisi: Ph.D. thesis, Ankara University, 209 p.

Aydın, M., Ö. Sahintürk, H.S. Serdar, Y. Özçelik, I. Akarsu, A. Üngör, R. Çokuğras, and S. Kasar, 1986, Ballıdağ-Çangaldağ (Kastamonu) arasindaki bölgenin jeolojisi: Türkiye Jeoloji Kurumu Bülteni, v. 29, p. 1–16.

Aydın, M., H.S. Serdar, Ö. Sahintürk, M. Yazman, R. Çokuğras, O. Demir, and Y. Özçelik, 1987, Çamdağ (Sakarya) Sünnicedağ (Bolu) yöresinin jeolojisi: Türkiye Jeoloji Kurumu Bülteni, v. 30, p. 1–14.

Bond, G.C., M.A. Kominz, and R.E. Sheridan, 1995, Continental terraces and rises, *in* C.J. Busby and R.V. Ingersoll, eds., Tectonics of sedimentary basins: Cambridge, Massachusetts, Blackwell Science, 579 p.

Canca, N., 1994, 1:100.000 ölçekli Türkiye Bati Karadeniz taskömürü havzasi jeoloji haritalari: Ankara, Maden Tetkik ve Arama Genel Müdürlüğü, 10 p.

Charles, F., 1930, Contribution à l'étude des terrains crétacés du Nord de l'Anatolie (Asie Mineure): Comptes Rendus et Sommaires de la Société Géologique de France, 191 p.

Currey, J.R., 1980, The International Programme for Ocean Drilling (IPOD) programme on passive continental margins: Philosophical Transactions of the Royal Society of London, A 294, p. 17–33.

Dachev, C., V. Stanev, and P. Bokov, 1988, Structure of the Bulgarian Black Sea: Bollettino di Geofisica Teorica ed Applicata, v. 30, p. 79–107.

Demaison, G.J., and G.E. Moore, 1980, Anoxic environments and oil source bed genesis: AAPG Bulletin, v. 64, p. 1179–1209.

Derman, S., 1990a, Bati Karadeniz Bölgesinin geç Jura ve erken Kretase'deki jeolojik evrimi: Türkiye. 8 Petrol Kongresi, Bildiriler, p. 328–339.

Derman, S., 1990b, Fayli basen kenarindaki sedimentasyon. Bati Karadeniz'de Kretase'den bir örnek: Türkiye 8. Petrol Kongresi Bildiriler, p. 314–321.

Dickinson, W.R., 1974, Plate tectonics and sedimentation, *in* W.R. Dickinson, ed., Tectonics and sedimentation: SEPM Special Publication 22, p. 1–27.

Einsele, G., 1992, Sedimentary basins: Berlin, Springer-Verlag, 628 p.

Erguvanli, K., 1949, Hereke pudingleri ile Gebze taslarinin insaat bakimindan etüdü ve Civarının jeolojisi: Ph.D. thesis, İstanbul Teknik Üniversitesi, 89 p.

Falvey, D.A., 1974, The development of continental margins in plate tectonic theory: Australian Petroleum Exploration Association Journal, v. 14, p. 95–106.

Finetti, I., G. Bricchi, A. Del Ben, M. Pipan, and Z. Xuan, 1988, Geophysical study of the Black Sea: Bollettino di Geofisica Teorica ed Applicata, v. 30, p. 197–324.

Gedik, A., and S. Korkmaz, 1984, Sinop Havzasinin jeolojisi ve petrol olanaklari: Jeoloji Mühendisliği, v. 19, p. 53–79.

Görür, N., 1982, Kocaeli Yarimadasinda Silüriyen-Alt Devoniyen yasli "Gebze Kireçtasinin" sedimentolojisi (abs.): Türkiye Jeoloji Kurultayi, Bildiriler, p. 69–70.

Görür, N., 1988, Timing of opening of the Black Sea Basin: Tectonophysics, v. 147, p. 247–262.

Görür, N., 1989, Timing of opening of the Black Sea: sedimentological evidence from the Rhodope-Pontide Fragment, *in* A.M.C. Şengör, ed., Tectonic evolution of the Tethyan region: Dordrecht, Kluwer Academic Publishers, 698 p.

Görür, N., 1991, Aptian–Albian palaeogeography of Neotethyan domain: Palaeogeography, Palaeoclimatology, Palaeoecology, v. 87, p. 267–288.

Görür, N., A.I. Okay, O. Tüysüz, E. Yiğitbaş, and R. Akkök, 1995, İstanbul-Zonguldak Paleozoyik istifinin paleocoğrafik ve tektonik konumu, *in* M.N. Yalçin and G. Gürdal, eds., Zonguldak Havzasi arastirma kuyulari-1: Kozlu-K20/G: TÜBITAK, MAM, Özel Yayini, 217 p.

Görür, N., O. Tüysüz, A. Aykol, M. Sakinç, E. Yiğitbaş, and R. Akkök, 1993, Cretaceous red pelagic carbonates of northern Turkey: their place in the opening history of the Black Sea: Eclogae Geologica Helvetica, v. 86, p. 819–838.

Hsü, K.J., 1988, Relict back-arc basins: Principles of recognition and possible new examples from China, *in* K.L. Kleinspehn and C. Paola, eds., New perspectives in basin analysis: New York, Springer-Verlag, 453 p.

Hsü, K.J., I.K. Nacev, and V.T. Vucev, 1977, Geologic evolution of Bulgaria in the light of plate tectonics: Tectonophysics, v. 40, p. 245–256.

Ingersoll, R.V., and C.J. Busby, 1995, Tectonics of sedimentary basins, *in* C.J. Busby and R.V. Ingersoll, eds., Tectonics of sedimentary basins: Cambridge, Massachusetts, Blackwell Science, 579 p.

Jenkyns, H.C., 1980, Cretaceous anoxic events: from continents to oceans: Journal of the Geological Society of London, v. 137, p. 171–188.

Kaya, O., A. Dizer, I. Tansel, and E. Meriç, 1983, Stratigraphy of the Cretaceous in the Ereğli area, Zonguldak: Bulletin of Mineral Research and Exploration Institute of Turkey, v. 99/100, p. 1–16.

Ketin, I., 1955, Über die Geologie der Gegend von Ovacuma östlich Zonguldak: Revue de la Faculté des Sciences de l'Université d'İstanbul, v. B-20, p. 147–154.

Ketin, Y., 1983, Türkiye jeolojisine genel bir bakis: İstanbul, İstanbul Teknik Üniversitesi Vakfi, 595 p.

Ketin, I., and Ö. Gümüs, 1963, Sinop-Ayancik arasindaki III. bölgeye dahil sahalarin jeolojisi hakkinda rapor, 2. Kisim, Jura ve Kretase Formasyonlarinin etüdü: Türkiye Petrolleri Arama Grubu Arsivi (unpublished report) no. 213-288, 118 p.

Letouzey, J., B. Biju-Duval, A. Dorkel, R. Gonnard, K. Kristchev, L. Montadert, and O. Sungurlu, 1977, The Black Sea: a marginal basin: geophysical and geological data, *in* B. Biju-Duval and L. Montadert, eds., International symposium on the structural history of the Mediterranean basins: Paris, Editions Technip, p. 363–376.

Marsaglia, K.M., 1995, Interarc and backarc basins, *in* C.J. Busby and R.V. Ingersoll, eds., Tectonics of sedimentary basins: Cambridge, Massachusetts, Blackwell Science, 579 p.

Okay, A.I., 1989, Tectonic units and sutures in the Pontides, northern Turkey, *in* A.M.C. Şengör, ed., Tectonic evolution of the Tethyan region: NATO Advanced Science Institute (ASI) Series, C 259, p. 109–116.

Okay, A.I., and N. Görür, 1995, Baty Karadeniz ve Trakya Havzalarinin kökenleri arasinda zaman ve mekan iliskisi: Trakya Havzasi Jeolojisi Simpozyumu, Bildiri özleri, Türkiye Petrolleri Anonim Ortakliği-Ozan Sungurlu Bilim, Eğitim ve Yardim Vakfi, Abstract, p. 9–10.

Okay, A.I., A.M.C. Şengör, and N. Görür, 1994, Kinematic history of the opening of the Black Sea and its effect on the surrounding regions: Geology, v. 22, p. 267–270.

Okay, A.I., M. Siyako, and K.A. Bürkan, 1991, Geology and tectonic evolution of the Biga Peninsula, Northwest Turkey: Bulletin of the Technical University of İstanbul, v. 44, p. 191–256.

Okay, A.I., and I. Tansel, 1994, New data on the upper age of the Intra-Pontide Ocean from north of Darköy (Thrace): Bulletin of Mineral Reasearch and Exploration Institute of Turkey, v. 114, p. 23–26.

Özdemir, Ü., G. Talay, and A. Yurtsever, 1973, Kocaeli Triyasi projesi "Kocaeli Triyasinin biyostratigrafik etüdü": Cumhuriyetin 50. yili Yerbilimleri Kongresi, Tebliğler, Maden Tetkik ve Arama Enstitüsü, p. 112–127.

Özer, S., 1986, Bati Karadeniz Alt Kretase Rudist faunasi ve paleoekoloji: Türkiye Petrolleri Arama Grubu Arsivi (unpublished report #1813), 67 p.

Pedersen, T.F., and S.E. Calvert, 1990, Anoxia vs. productivity: what controls the formation of organic-rich sediments and sedimentary rocks?: AAPG Bulletin, v. 74, p. 454–466.

Pitman, III, W.C., 1978, Relationship between eustasy and stratigraphic sequences of passive margins: Geological Society of America Bulletin, v. 89, p. 1389–1403.

Robinson, A.G., C.J. Banks, M.M. Rutherford, and J.P.P. Hirst, 1995, Stratigraphic and structural development of the Eastern Pontides, Turkey: Journal of the Geological Society, London, v. 152, p. 861–872.

Schlanger, S.O., and H.C. Jenkyns, 1976, Cretaceous oceanic anoxic events: causes and consequences: Geologie Mijnbouw, v. 55, p. 179–184.

Şengör, A.M.C., 1984, The Cimmeride orogenic system and the tectonics of Eurasia: Geological Society of America Special Publication 195, 82 p.

Şengör, A.M.C., and Y. Yılmaz, 1981, Tethyan evolution of Turkey: a plate tectonic approach: Tectonophysics, v. 75, p. 181–241.

Siyako, M., Z. Aksoy, K.A. Bürkan, and O. Demir, 1981, Zonguldak dolayinin jeolojisi ve hidrokarbon olanaklari: Türkiye Petrolleri Arama Grubu Arsivi (unpublished report), no. 1536, 72 p.

Tokay, M., 1952, Contribution à l'étude géologique de la région comprise entre Ereğli, Alapli, Kiziltepe, et Alacaağzi: Maden Tetkik ve Arama Enstitüsü Mecmuasi, Sayi 42–43, p. 37–78.

Tucker, M.E., and V.P. Wright, 1990, Carbonate sedimentology: Oxford, Blackwell Scientific, 482 p.

Tüysüz, O., 1985, Kargı Masifi ve dolayyndaki tektonik birliklerin ayirdi ve arastirilmasi (petrolojik inceleme): Ph.D. thesis, İstanbul University, 431 p.

Tüysüz, O., 1990, Tectonic evolution of a part of the Tethyside orogenic collage: the Kargı Massif, Northern Turkey: Tectonics, v. 9, p. 141–160.

Tüysüz, O., 1993, Karadeniz' den Orta Anadolu' ya bir jeotravers: Kuzey Neo-Tetisin tektonik evrimi: Türkiye Petrol Jeologlari Derneği Bülteni, v. 5, p. 1–33.

Tüysüz, O., E. Yiğitbaş, and H.S. Serdar, 1990, Orta Pontidlerde Üst Jura-Alt Kretase stratigrafisi ve tektonik anlami: Türkiye 8 Petrol Kongresi, Bildiriler, p. 340–350.

Yergök, A.F., et al., 1987, Bati Karadeniz Bölgesinin jeolojisi: Maden Tetkik ve Arama Enstitüsü, Derleme Raporu (unpublished report), no. 8273, 65 p.

Görür, N., and O, Tüysüz, 1997, Petroleum geology of the southern continental margin of the Black Sea, *in* A.G. Robinson, ed., Regional and petroleum geology of the Black Sea and surrounding region: AAPG Memoir 68, p. 241–254.

Chapter 13

Petroleum Geology of the Southern Continental Margin of the Black Sea

Naci Görür
Okan Tüysüz
İstanbul Technical University (İ.T.Ü)
Ayazağa, İstanbul, Turkey

ABSTRACT

The southern continental margin of the Black Sea back-arc basin is represented predominantly by a thick clastic sequence of Aptian to Recent age. Potential source, reservoir, and cap rocks are common in various stratigraphic levels of this sequence. The most prospective source and reservoir rocks appear to have been deposited in the synrift stage of the basin. During this stage, the rift trough was probably relatively shallow and restricted from free interchange with the Neotethys Ocean in the south. During the postrift stage, a thick sequence of volcaniclastic turbidites and subordinate pelagic limestones, with limited source and reservoir potential, accumulated. This accumulation was interrupted at the end of the early Eocene by compressional tectonics, which resulted from the closure of the Neotethys. The postrift sedimentation probably carried the earlier source rocks into the hydrocarbon generation window, while the Eocene compressional tectonics generated the main prospective traps.

INTRODUCTION

In the southern margin of the Black Sea Basin, the Aptian to lower Cenomanian synrift sequence (Figure 1) is associated with a series of horsts, grabens, and rotated fault blocks buried beneath the upper Cenomanian to Tertiary volcanogenic turbidites of the postrift sequence. This geological character makes the margin attractive for hydrocarbon exploration, because the petroleum potential of such areas is generally high (Smith and Landis, 1995). Such regions may contain widespread structural and stratigraphic traps formed by fault blocks, fault-tilted structures, rollover anticlines, and facies changes. Source rocks accumulate mostly during the synrift stage of these margins (Dow, 1977; Weissert et al., 1979; Görür, 1991). Moreover, high heat flow and steep geothermal gradients are the other determinants of high hydrocarbon potential of these arc margin basins (Schlanger and Combs, 1975; Einsele, 1992; Marsaglia, 1995).

Although exploration has been performed by various oil companies, little has been published on the petroleum geology of the southern Black Sea margin (Gedik and Korkmaz, 1984; Sonel et al., 1989, 1992; Aydın et al., 1995; Robinson et al., 1996). The published literature is either about the general geology of the various parts of the Pontides (Tokay, 1952; Ketin, 1962; Aydın et al., 1986, 1987; Tüysüz, 1990, 1993; Robinson et al., 1995) or focuses entirely on the formation of the Black Sea Basin itself (Görür, 1988; Görür et al., 1993; Okay et al., 1994). The aim of this chapter is to bring together data and interpretations from various sources in order to give an overview of the petroleum potential of the Turkish Black Sea shelf.

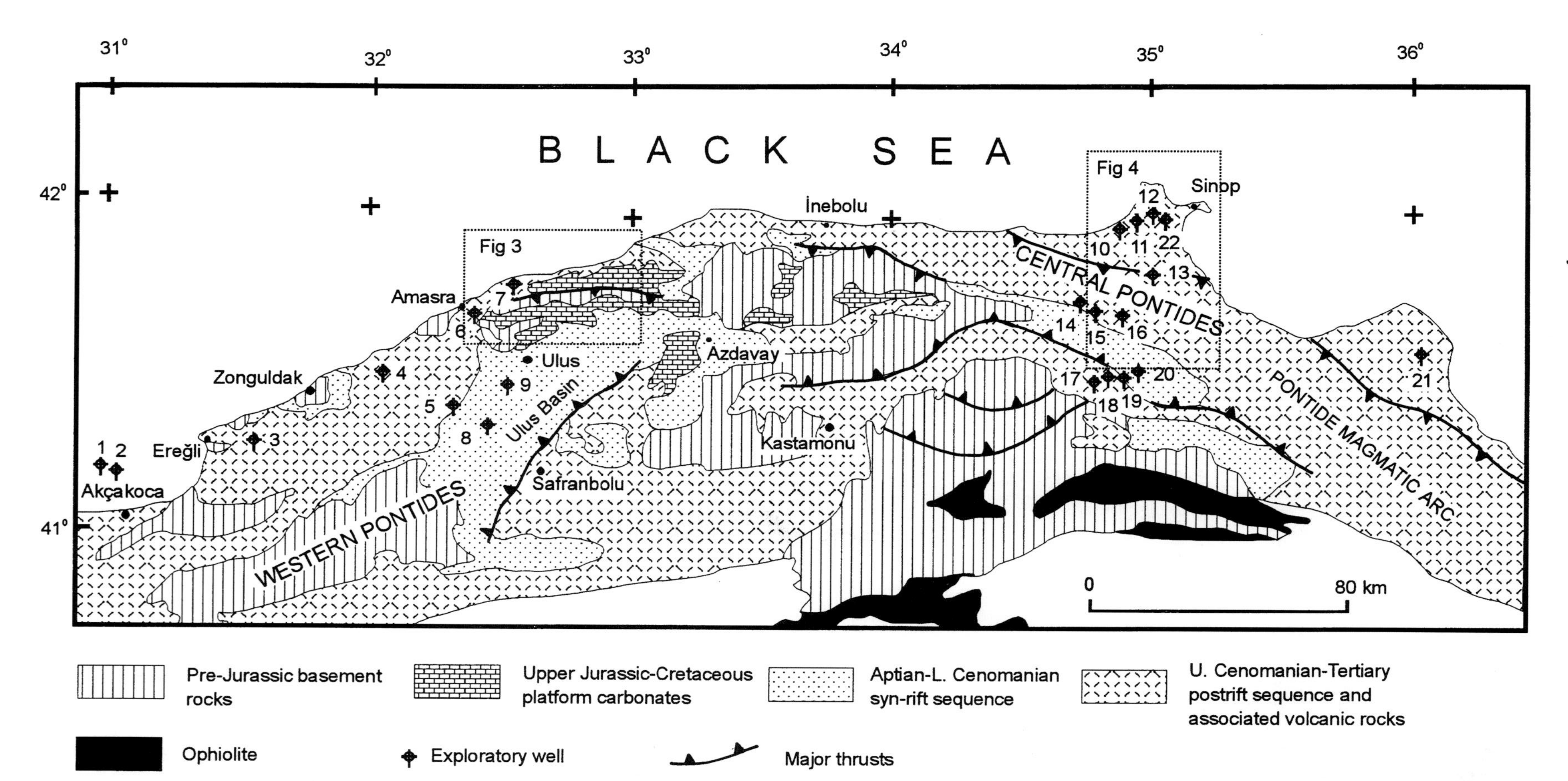

Figure 1. Simplified geological map of the Zonguldak-Sinop region. Framed areas are shown in detail in Figures 3 and 4. 1 = Akçakoca-1, 2 = Akçakoca-2, 3 = Ereğli-1, 4 = Filyos-1, 5 = Bartin-1, 6 = Amasra-1, 7 = Çakraz-1, 8 = Gegendere-1, 9 = Ülüs-1, 10 = Sinop-3, 11 = Karasu-1, 12 = Sinop-1, 13 = Erfelek-1, 14 = Akveren-1, 15 = Fasilli-1, 16 = Soğuksu-1, 17 = Boyabat-1, 18 = Boyabat-2, 19 = Boyabat-3, 20 = Boyabat-4, 21 = Badut-1, 22 = Sinop-2. (Offshore wells Karadeniz-1 and Iğneada-1 are not on the map). The İstanbul and Sakarya zones are not differentiated.

HISTORY OF EXPLORATION DRILLING

Hydrocarbon exploration in the Pontides started in the 1960s. Since then, about 24 wells have been drilled throughout the Western and Central Pontides (Figure 1); 20 are onshore and the remainder are offshore. The onshore wells are located in the Zonguldak-İnebolu and the Sinop regions; the offshore ones were drilled in the Black Sea shelf off Akçakoca and Iğneada. The majority of the wells were drilled by the Turkish Petroleum Company (TPAO), in some cases with outside participation. These wells appear to have had mostly Lower Cretaceous synrift sediments as a drilling objective, although some of them (e.g., Çakraz-1, Bartın-1, Amasra-1, and Ereğli-1) aimed only at the Devonian rocks. They were drilled mostly on surface structures and, with the exception of the offshore wells west of Zonguldak (e.g., Akçakoca-1 and 2) and three of the onshore wells in the Sinop region (e.g., Badut-1, Fasili-1, and Boyabat-2) that had hydrocarbon shows in Cretaceous to Eocene sediments, were abandoned as dry holes (Teknica, 1984; Scott Pickford and Associates Ltd. and Aksan, 1987, 1988; Gümüş and Altan, 1995) (Figure 1). The Turkish Petroleum Company still continues its exploration activity along the coastal areas of the Western and Central Pontides, one of the more prospective regions of the Black Sea margin.

TECTONOSTRATIGRAPHIC EVOLUTION

The Black Sea Basin is a small ocean located behind the Pontide magmatic arc that resulted from the consumption of the Neotethys Ocean to the south (Hsü et al., 1977; Letouzey et al., 1977; Şengör and Yılmaz, 1981; Okay et al., 1994). This back-arc basin consists of two oceanic depressions: the Western and Eastern Black Sea basins (Figure 2a). These basins are separated by a thinned continental ridge (the Mid-Black Sea High) and have different structural and stratigraphic features. They opened during the Aptian to Cenomanian as a result of a complex interplay between rifting, transform faulting, and block rotation (Figure 2b) (Görür et al., 1993; Okay et al., 1994).

The Western Black Sea Basin formed by tearing, along the juvenile Pontide magmatic arc, a Hercynian continental sliver, the İstanbul Zone (Okay, 1989), from the southern margin of Laurasia (Figure 2b). The İstanbul Zone consists mainly of a sedimentary sequence, ranging in age from Ordovician to Cretaceous (Abdüsselamoğlu, 1977; Dean et al., 1990–1992); the Ordovician to Carboniferous part corresponds with a typical Atlantic-type continental margin facies (Abdüsselamoğlu, 1977). It moved south during the Late Cretaceous to Paleocene along two transform faults, opening in its wake the Western Black Sea Basin (Figure 2b). The İstanbul Zone collided at the end of the early Eocene with a Cimmeride zone, the Sakarya Zone (Okay, 1989), obliterating the arm of the Neotethys Ocean in between [the Intra-Pontide Ocean (Şengör and Yılmaz, 1981)] and ending the extension in the Western Black Sea Basin (Okay et al., 1994). The base of the Sakarya Zone of pre-Jurassic metamorphic and accretionary complex rocks is unconformably overlain by Jurassic to Cretaceous sediments (Şengör and Yılmaz, 1981; Okay et al., 1991).

The Eastern Black Sea Basin resulted from the counterclockwise rotation of an Eastern Black Sea block around a rotation pole located north of Crimea (Figure 2b). This rotation was coeval with the opening of the Western Black Sea Basin, but continued until the Miocene (Okay et al., 1994). Details of these two openings are discussed extensively in Görür (1988, 1989), Görür et al. (1993), Okay et al. (1994), and Görür (this volume); therefore, we will not discuss them here.

Stratigraphic evolution of the Western Black Sea Basin is clearly demonstrated by the Cretaceous to Lower Tertiary rocks of both the İstanbul and the Sakarya zones exposed between Zonguldak and Sinop (Figures 1, 3, and 4). The stratigraphic record of the Eastern Black Sea Basin is poor in the Eastern Pontides, because this region is underlain entirely by the Upper Cretaceous to Eocene Pontide magmatic arc. The continental margin sediments of this basin must be farther north, below the sea. Therefore, this chapter deals essentially with the southern margin of the Western Black Sea Basin.

The synrift sediments of the Black Sea Basin (≤1300-m-thick) range in age from Aptian to Lower Cenomanian (the Çağlayan Group) (Ketin and Gümüş, 1963; Görür et al., 1993; Görür, this volume) (Figure 5). In some localities, lagoonal and organic-rich black shales and marls formed much of the early fill on the rift floor (the Kilimli Formation; Charles, 1930) (Figure 5). In the Western Pontides, the rift floor was constituted by the pre-Aptian sequence of the İstanbul Zone; in both the Central and Eastern Pontides, it is represented by the Sakarya Zone. When the block faulting accelerated in the Albian, the rift floor subsided further and deposited marginal marine glauconitic sandstones, passing up to deeper marine blue to black shales, turbiditic sandstones, and sandy limestones, in part with boulder beds, debris flows, and slumps (the Velibey and the Sapça formations; Tokay, 1952; Siyako et al., 1981) (Figure 5). These mass-flow deposits contain huge exotic blocks derived mostly from the rift basement. They were deposited, together with the proximal turbidites, in the areas adjacent to the actively rising fault blocks (Görür et al., 1993). As the rift basin was further attenuated and subsided to considerable depths, it accumulated organic-rich black shales and subordinate limestones interrupted sporadically by coarse mass-flow deposits (the Tasmaca Formation) (Siyako et al., 1981) (Figure 5). Occurrence of the organic-rich black shales in the synrift sequence records that the waters in the rift were anoxic during this stage of the rifting. The anoxia probably resulted from the restricted water circulation, although high primary organic production may also have played an important role in the accumulation of these sediments (Pedersen and Calvert, 1990; Görür et al., 1993).

In the Western Black Sea Basin, the rift-drift transition is marked by a drastic change in sedimentation

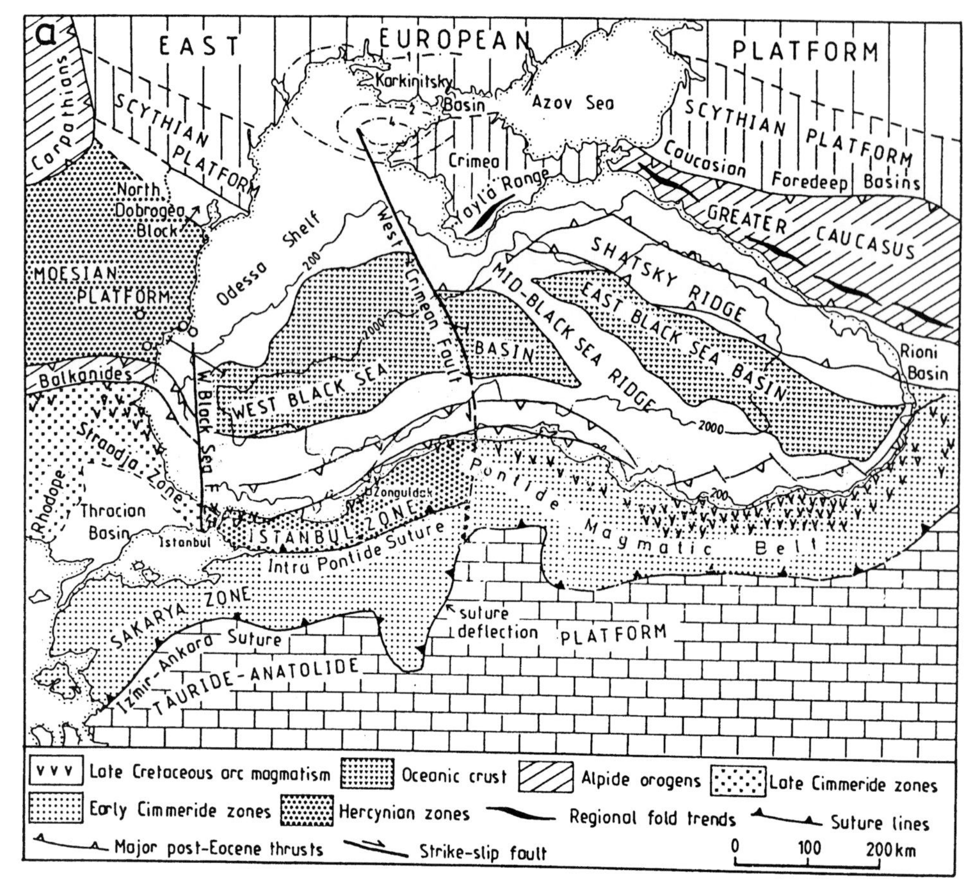

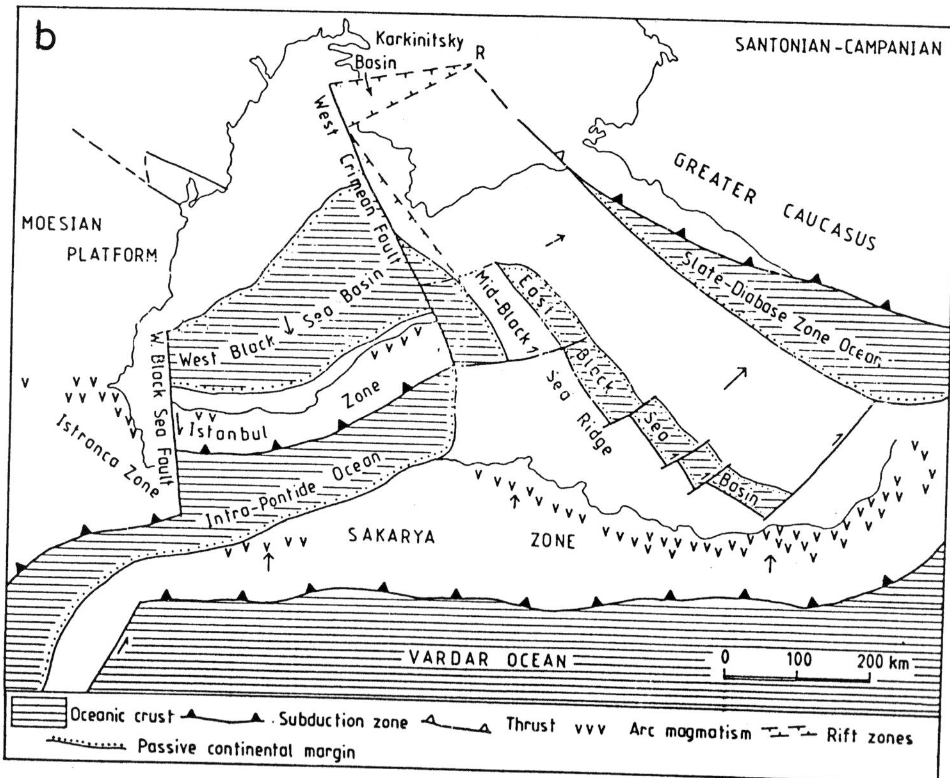

Figure 2. (a) Tectonic setting of the Black Sea Basin. (b) Tectonic evolution of the Western and the Eastern Black Sea basins during the Cretaceous. R = rotation pole of the East Black Sea block (Okay et al., 1994). Reproduced with changes with the permission of the Geological Society of America, Inc.

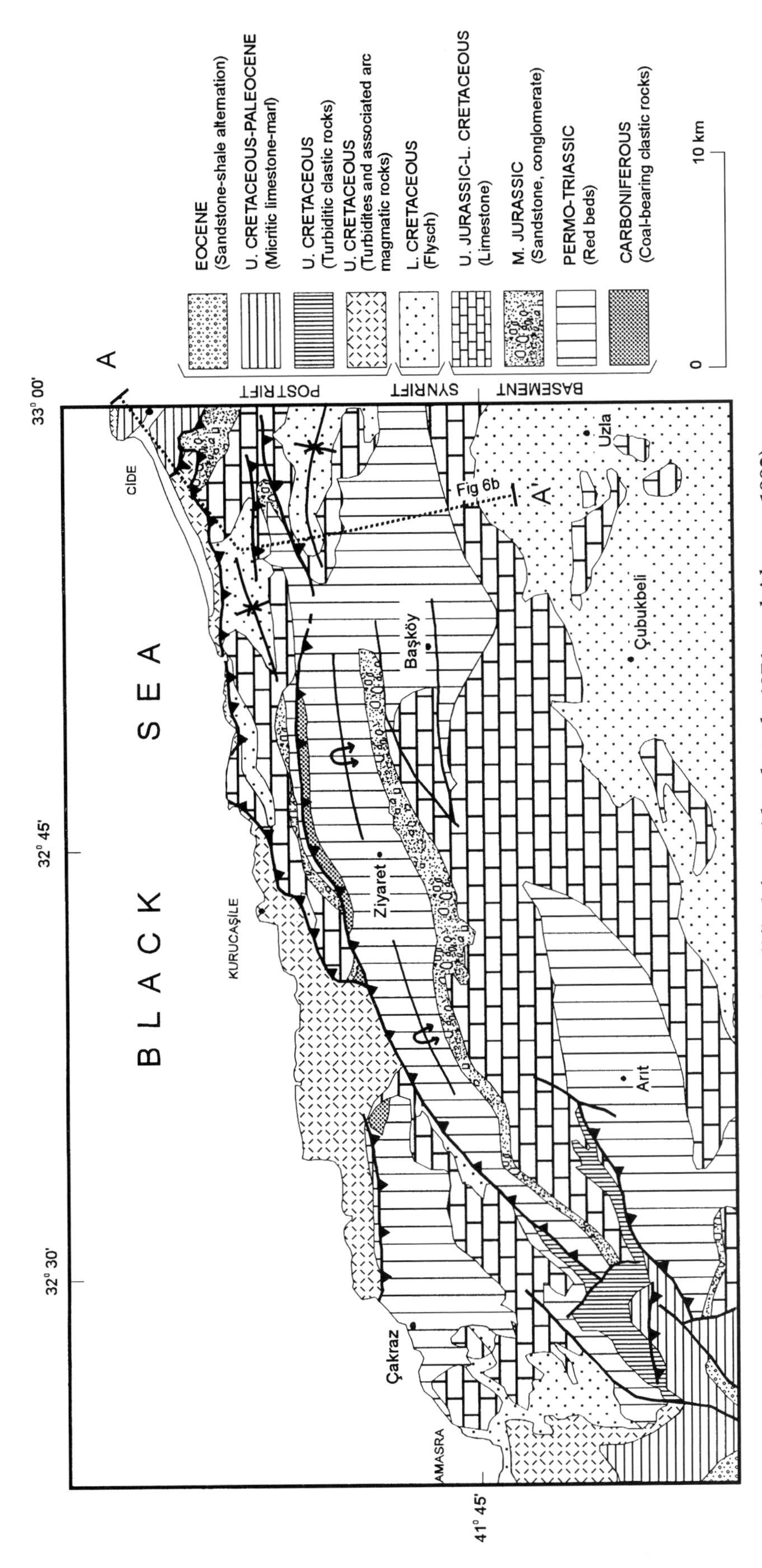

Figure 3. Geological map of the Amasra-Cide area (modified from Akyol et al., 1974, and Akman, 1992).

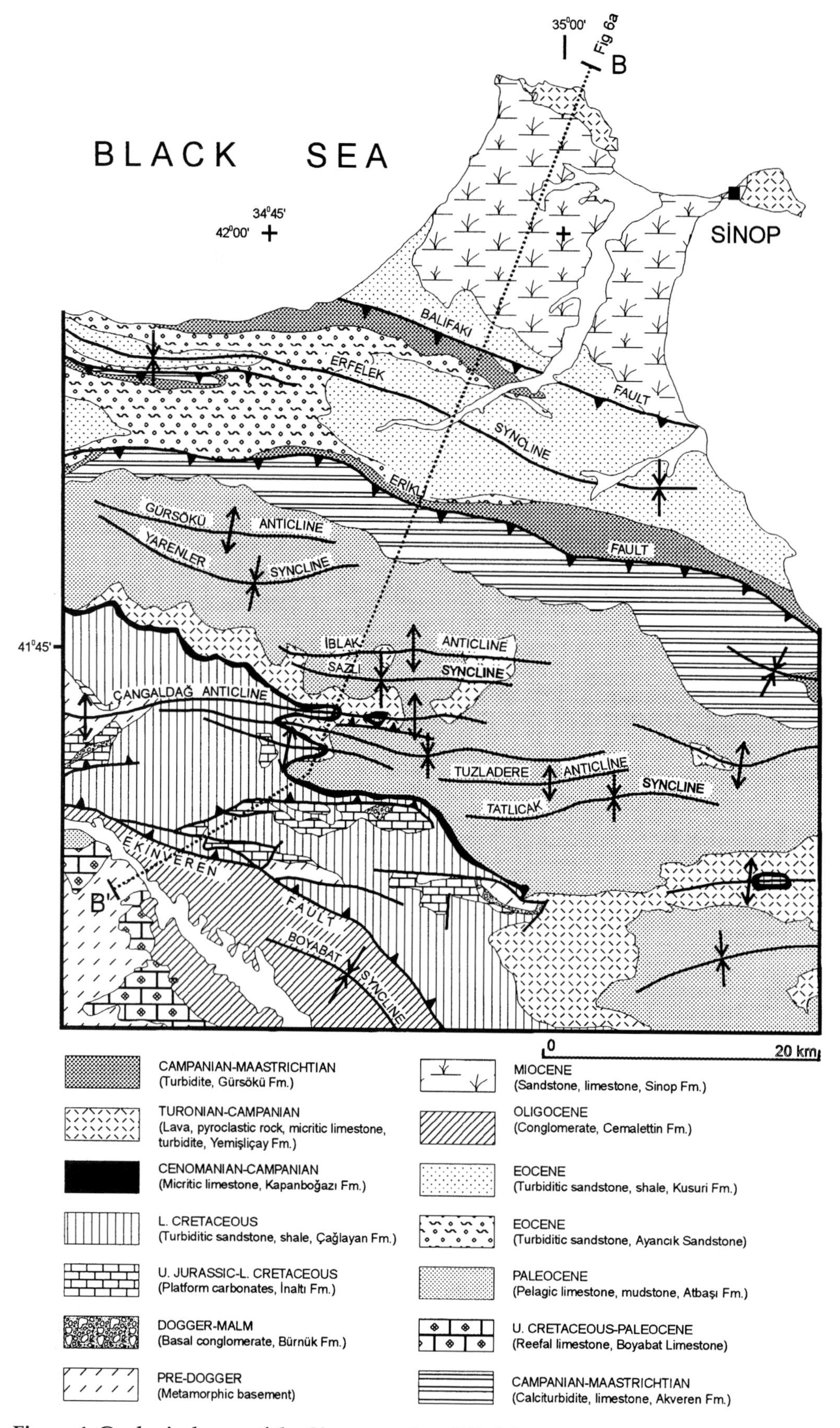

Figure 4. Geological map of the Sinop area (modified from Gedik and Korkmaz, 1984).

during the late Cenomanian. Deposition of the organic-rich black shales ceased, and accumulation of red pelagic carbonates and marls started (the Kapanboğazı Formation) (Ketin and Gümüş, 1963) (Figure 5). These carbonates were laid down above the synrift sequence with a slightly angular unconformity. This postbreakup unconformity and the drastic change in sedimentation probably indicate the onset of sea-floor spreading in the Western Black Sea Basin during the late Cenomanian (Görür et al., 1993). Following the 20-m-thick red pelagic carbonate accumulation, the sedimentation on the southern margin of this basin became dominated by ≤8000-m-thick volcanogenic turbidites (both terrigeneous and carbonate) and deep-water clastic and carbonate rocks (the Yemişliçay, Gürsökü, Akveren, Atbaşı, and Kusuri formations) (Badgley, 1959; Ketin and Gümüş, 1963) (Figure 5). The Pontide magmatic arc, which had been developing in the Pontides since the Aptian–Albian, was the main source for the volcanic material in the turbidites (Hsü et al., 1977; Letouzey et al., 1977; Şengör and Yılmaz, 1981; Aydın et al., 1986). Toward the end of the Eocene, an overall shallowing occurred over the whole of the southern margin, probably due to the early Eocene collision between the İstanbul and Sakarya zones in the south (Şengör and Yılmaz, 1981; Okay et al., 1994). This collision and the continuing intracontinental convergence resulted at the end of the Eocene in both deformation (Figure 6) and erosion of the sediments on the margin. Because of this tectonic activity, younger sediments are not significantly represented everywhere.

PETROLEUM GEOLOGY

Prospective hydrocarbon targets range from the Lower Paleozoic to the Lower Tertiary in the Pontides. Along the Black Sea coast, Paleozoic formations have good source and reservoir rock potential in Devonian and Carboniferous facies, but are highly deformed. The Devonian rocks also display oil seeps in the Zonguldak region. Despite this potential for generation and trapping of hydrocarbons, the Paleozoic sediments are not evaluated in this chapter, because the primary interest here is the arc margin sequence of the Black Sea Basin. Therefore, only the petroleum potential of the Cretaceous to Eocene syn- to postrift sediments is treated in the following paragraphs.

Potential Source Rocks

Rock-Eval pyrolysis and total organic carbon (TOC) analyses indicate that the southern continental margin sequence of the Black Sea Basin contains fair to good potential source rocks in various stratigraphic levels (Aydın et al., 1995; Robinson et al., 1996) (Figures 5, 7, and 8). In the synrift part of the sequence, these rocks constitute the Kilimli, Sapça, and Tasmaca formations, whereas in the postrift part, they occur mostly in the Kusuri Formation of the Eocene (Gedik and Korkmaz, 1984; Korkmaz, 1992; Sonel et al., 1992).

The Kilimli Formation of Aptian age crops out discontinuously in the Western Pontides between Zonguldak and İnebolu. It consists mainly of ≤200-m-thick dark gray to black lagoonal shales, rich in organic matter and glauconite. These locally well-bioturbated shales contain common gastropods, brachipods, and some nannofossils (Akman, 1992). Similar organic-rich shales are found in the Albian Sapça Formation (Figure 5). Within this formation, they alternate with turbiditic sandstones, marls, and sandy limestones (Tokay, 1952; Aydın et al., 1987). Geochemical analyses of a number of surface and core samples of these shales from the area between Zonguldak and Sinop show that they can have enough organic matter to be considered a potential source rock for petroleum (Teknica, 1984; Gedik and Korkmaz, 1984; Scott Pickford and Associates Ltd. and Aksan, 1987, 1988; Korkmaz, 1992; Sonel et al., 1992; Aydın et al., 1995; Robinson et al., 1996). The organic matter is mainly of algal origin (Type I and II kerogen) and the TOC content ranges mostly from 0.5 to 1.5 wt%. Vitrinite reflectance (R_0) values are generally >0.6, indicating that these organic-rich shales have reached the oil window (Dow, 1977; Dow and O'Conner, 1979; Tissot and Welte, 1984; Selley, 1985) (Figure 5). The synrift sequence is terminated with the Cenomanian Tasmaca Formation, comprising a 100 m- to 400-m-thick uniform sequence of blue to black, relatively deeper marine shales and clayey limestones, in part with abundant slumps and exotic blocks of various sizes (Figure 5). The shales are also organic rich with Type II kerogen and have TOC values similar to those of the shales of the Kilimli and the Sapça formations below, although the R_0 values are generally 0.5 to 0.6, implying that they are immature (Scott Pickford and Associates Ltd. and Aksan, 1987, 1988) (Figure 5).

The division of the synrift sequence into various formations was established only in the Zonguldak-İnebolu region (Figure 1); such division seems difficult elsewhere (Görür, this volume). Therefore, in the Ulüs Basin to the south and the Sinop region to the east, all the synrift sediments are collected under the Ülüs and the Çağlayan formations, respectively (Figures 1, 5). The shales in the Ülüs Formation contain Type II and III kerogen and generally have a TOC varying from 0.3 to 1.9 wt %. Maturation level of these organic-rich sediments seems low as indicated by the R_0 values of ~0.5 (Scott Pickford and Associates Ltd. and Aksan, 1987, 1988). On the contrary, the shales of the Çağlayan Formation of the Sinop region show R_0 values mostly between 0.5 and 1.3 and are, therefore, mature (Gedik and Korkmaz, 1984; Korkmaz, 1992; Aydın et al., 1995) (Figure 7a). They have Type II and III kerogen with a TOC content between 0.6 and 1.5 wt % (Gedik and Korkmaz, 1984; Korkmaz, 1992; Sonel et al., 1992) (Figure 7b).

Analytical data derived from the postrift sequence indicate that the Eocene Kusuri Formation (Ketin and Gümüş, 1963) is the main unit of this sequence containing potential source rocks. This formation is a thick (800–1200 m) shallowing-upward unit of turbiditic sandstones, shales, marls, and limestones, containing tuffs, agglomerates, and lavas toward the Southern Pontides (Figure 5). The shales of this sequence mostly contain Type III kerogen (Figure 8a) and have a TOC mostly between 0.15 and 0.60 wt % (Figure 8b) (Aydın et al.,

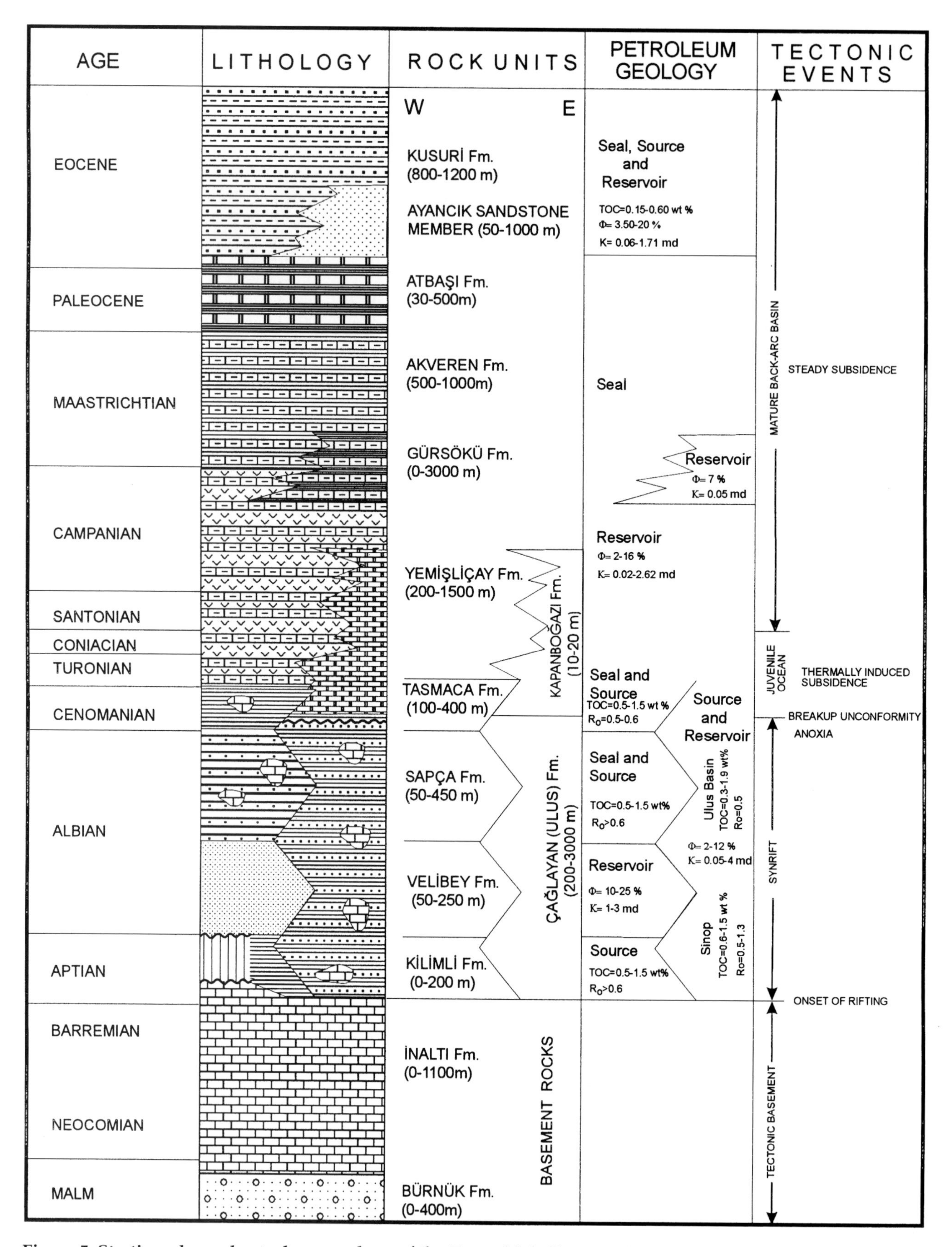

Figure 5. Stratigraphy and petroleum geology of the Zonguldak-Sinop region with major Cretaceous tectonic events.

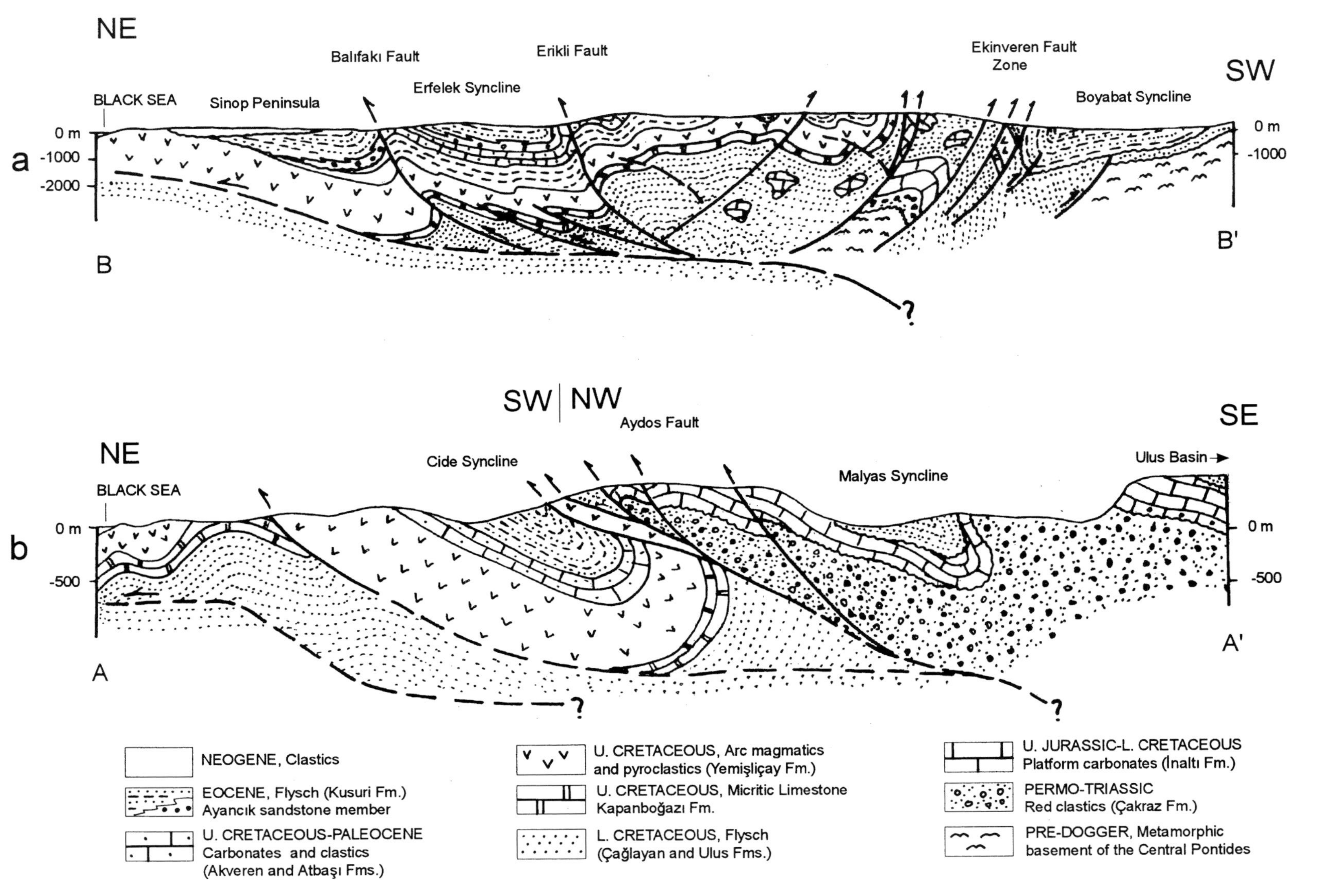

Figure 6. Potential structural fault and fold traps formed in (a) the Sinop and (b) the Amasra-Cide areas during the Eocene compressional tectonics (modified from Akyol et al., 1974). See Figures 3 and 4 for section localities.

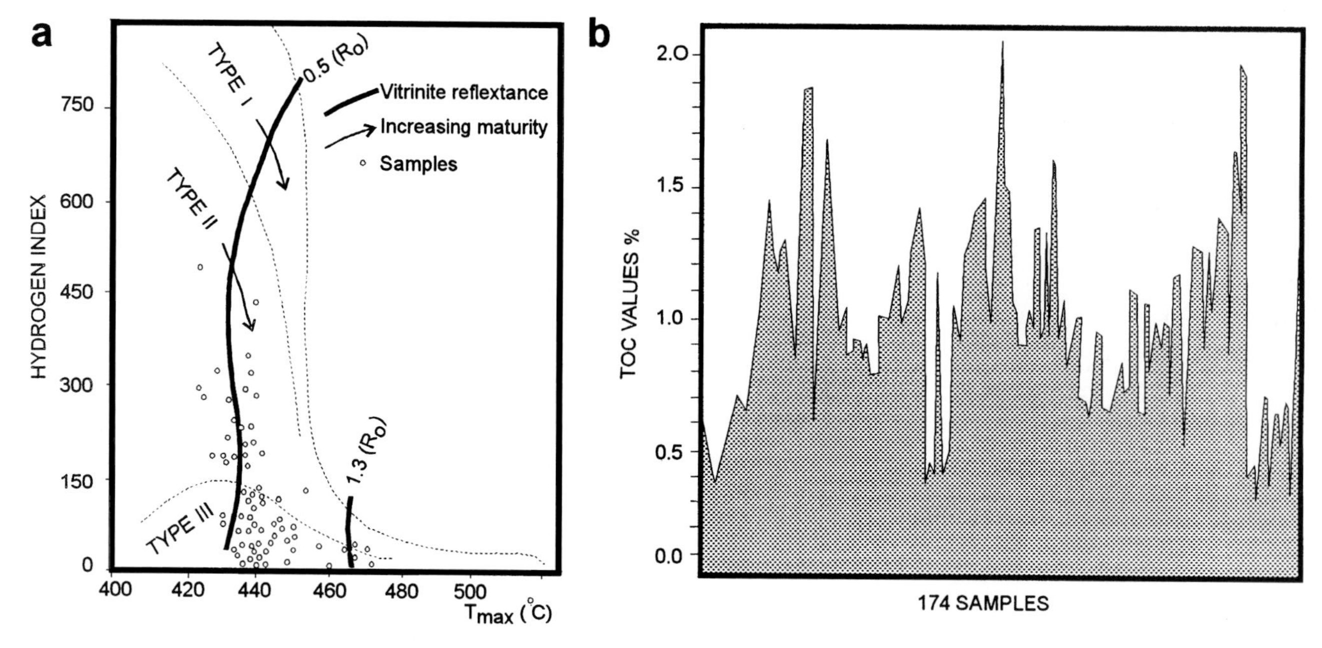

Figure 7. (a) Rock-Eval pyrolysis and (b) total organic carbon (TOC) analyses of the shales of the Çağlayan Formation from the Sinop region (after Aydin et al., 1995).

1995). In the Zonguldak region, these source rocks are not sufficiently buried to have reached the oil window, but in the Sinop region they seem to have been deeply buried enough to have acted as a productive source rock (Figure 8a). This is also indicated by the gas shows at the base of this formation in well Boyabat-2 (Scott Pickford and Associates Ltd. and Aksan, 1987, 1988).

Potential Reservoir Rocks

Potential reservoir rocks in the arc margin sequence of the Black Sea Basin are represented mainly by clastic sediments. They exist mostly in the synrift Çağlayan Group and the postrift Yemişliçay, Gürsökü, and Kusuri formations (Figure 5).

The best reservoir rocks in the Çağlayan Group are the sandstones of the Albian Velibey Formation. This formation consists mainly of medium to thickly bedded (locally cross-bedded) sandstones, in part with conglomerates and sandy limestones (Figure 5). The sandstones are variable, but are generally composed of medium- to coarse-grained, well-sorted, glauconitic quartz arenite to quartzose litharenite (Folk, 1974). Generally, they are mineralogically and texturally mature. The sand grains include quartz and lithic fragments with minor amounts of feldspars, mica, and glauconites. Lithic fragments are formed from sedimentary, volcanic, and metamorphic rocks derived from the basement rocks. Glauconites, having little or no internal structure, occur in moderate amounts within the sandstone beds in the upper part of the formation (Görür et al., 1993). The cement consists of quartz and minor amounts of calcite, siderite, and chlorite. The degree of cementation varies from place to place and apparently controls the amount of the porosity. In the Zonguldak region, the Velibey sandstones may have ≤25% porosity (Scott Pickford and Associates Ltd. and Aksan, 1987); in the Sinop area, the equivalent sandstones, which form 150- to 200-m-thick turbiditic units, have low porosity values, ranging from 2% to 12% (Gedik and Korkmaz, 1984; Sonel et al., 1992). In the latter area, the permeability of the sandstones is also low, varying between 0.05 and 4 md (Gedik and Korkmaz, 1984; Teknica, 1984; Sonel et al., 1992) (Figure 5).

To the east of Amasra, the Çağlayan clastic sequence is capped with an angular unconformity by the deep marine carbonates of the synbreakup Kapanboğazı Formation, which is in turn overlain by the Turonian to Campanian postrift Yemişliçay Formation (Figure 5). No potential reservoirs have been observed in the Kapanboğazi limestones, which appear to be uniformly impermeable, with some marly interbeds. The Yemişliçay Formation is essentially a 1500-m-thick volcanogenic turbidite assemblage, comprising alternations of volcanic rocks, volcaniclastic conglomerates and sandstones, shales, marls, and pelagic limestones (Figure 5). The turbiditic coarse clastic units seem to have some reservoir potential, particularly in the upper part of the formation (i.e., the Erikli Sandstone; Kaya et al., 1983). In well Badut-1, the units contain small amounts of gas at depths of 1500 m and 1650 m (Gedik and Korkmaz, 1984; Teknica, 1984). However, these units are mostly compositionally immature, clay rich, and contain volcanic detritus, and therefore have low porosity and permeability. In the Sinop region, the measured porosity and permeability range from 2% to 16% and 0.02 to 2.62 md, respectively (Akarsu and Aydın, 1979; Gedik and Korkmaz, 1984).

In the Zonguldak region, the Yemişliçay Formation is overlain with a sharp contact by the Maastrichtian Akveren Formation (Figure 5). Toward Sinop, the Gürsökü formation of late Campanian to early

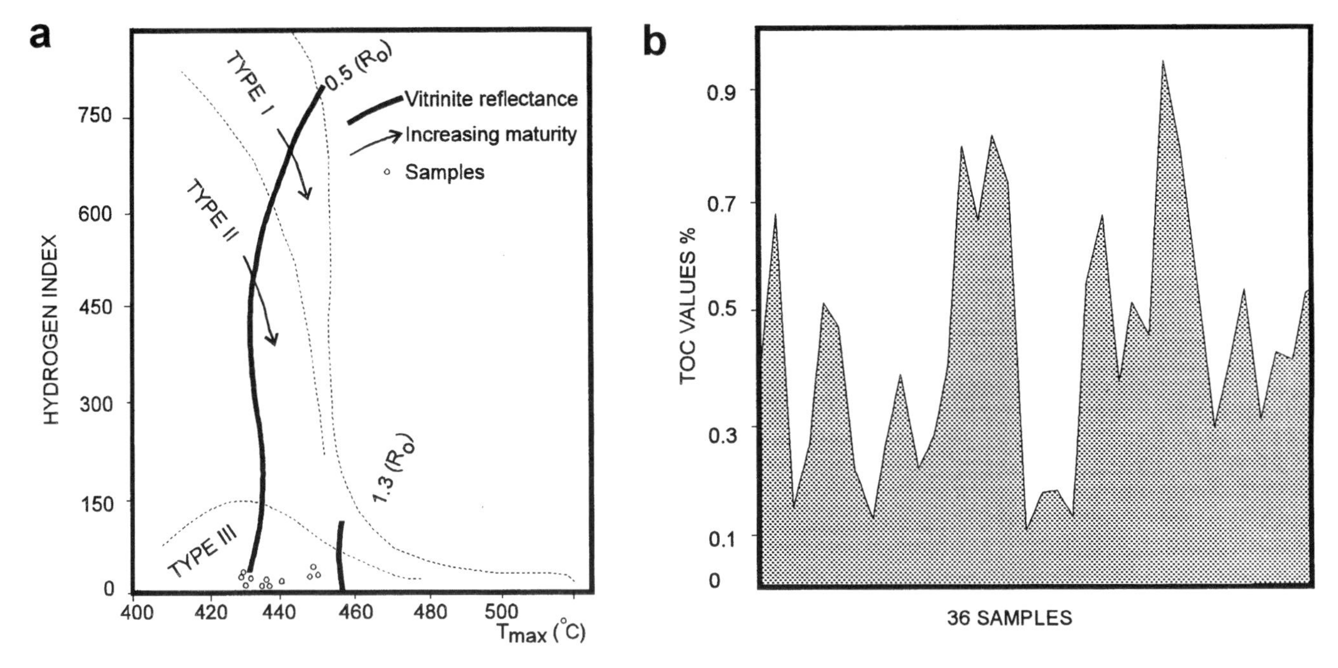

Figure 8. (a) Rock-Eval pyrolysis and (b) total organic carbon (TOC) analyses of the shales of the Kusuri Formation from the Sinop region (after Aydın et al., 1995).

Maastrichtian age occurs in between. The Gürsökü Formation consists of thick (≤3000 m) deep-water turbidites (mostly calciturbidites) characterized by the alternations of shales, marls, and sandstones with no volcanics (Akarsu and Aydın, 1979; Aydın et al., 1986) (Figure 5). Reservoir rocks may be locally provided by the sandstone units within this formation, although in most cases their porosity and permeability seem to be low. Sonel et al. (1992) reported porosity of 7% and permeability of 0.05 md from the Bürnük region, south of Sinop.

Above the Gürsökü Formation lies a thick (≤1500 m) sequence of dominantly calciturbidites of both the Akveren and the overlying Atbaşı formations of Maastrichtian to Lower Eocene age (Badgley, 1959; Ketin and Gümüş, 1963; Gedik and Korkmaz, 1984). The limestone interbeds of these formations are not expected to have reservoir potential, because they are finely textured, tight, and clayey throughout the Pontides. Potential reservoir rocks can be recognized in the thickly bedded turbidite sandstones of the overlying Eocene Kusuri Formation (i.e., the Ayancik Sandstone Member) (Badgley, 1959; Ketin and Gümüş, 1963), although field observations indicate that they are both compositionally and texturally immature (Figure 5). Porosity and permeability values measured in the Sinop region vary from 3.50% to 20% and 0.06 to 1.71 md, respectively (Gedik and Korkmaz, 1984; Sonel et al., 1992).

Potential Cap Rocks

Regional and local lithologic seals with respect to the reservoir rocks described above are furnished by the Sapça, Tasmaca, Akveren, and Kusuri formations (Gedik and Korkmaz, 1984; Scott Pickford and Associates Ltd. and Aksan, 1987; Sonel et al., 1992) (Figure 5).

The reservoir sandstones of the Velibey Formation pass laterally and upward into the thick sequence of shales, marls, and argillaceous sands of the Sapça Formation, and then into the shales and clayey limestones of the Tasmaca Formation. These two formations have a total thickness of 850 m, and therefore should provide a good seal.

The Akveren Formation sits on the Yemişliçay Formation in the Zonguldak region and on the Gürsökü Formation in the Sinop region. This 500- to 1000-m-thick sequence of tight calciturbidites with interbedded shales should provide adequate sealing for any reservoir development in both the Yemişliçay and the Gürsökü formations (Scott Pickford and Associates Ltd. and Aksan, 1987) (Figure 5).

The Eocene reservoirs may be sealed by the thick interturbidite shales, marls, and volcanics within the Kusuri Formation (Figure 5). The volcanics may act as an effective seal, particularly when they are weathered and altered to clay minerals.

Potential Traps

Good possibilities exist for the development of stratigraphic and structural traps in the southern margin of the Black Sea Basin. The stratigraphic traps are expected in those areas where the reservoir rocks interfinger with or are enclosed by impermeable shaley units. In the synrift sequence, they may have formed where the reservoir sandstones of the Velibey Formation pass laterally and vertically into the dark-colored shales of the Sapça and Tasmaca formations. In the postrift sequence, these traps may have formed through the thick turbiditic sandstones of the Yemişliçay, Gürsökü, and Kusuri formations sealed by the interturbidite shales.

Several types of extensional and compressional structures may constitute hydrocarbon traps in the Black Sea margin. The prospective ones are categorized as normal fault, rotated fault block, drape fold, and compressional fault and fold traps (Aydın et al., 1995; Robinson et al., 1996). Normal fault and rotated fault-block traps are related to the rifting and graben formation during the opening of the Black Sea Basin. Therefore, they are commonly associated with the Cretaceous synrift sediments and may be the most prospective deep structural traps in the basin. Drape-fold traps may have developed in the sediments overlying the upthrown side of the normal faults. Compressional fault and fold traps formed during or after the early Eocene compressional tectonics. This phase of tectonics reactivated major Cretaceous normal faults with reverse displacement (i.e., the Ekinveren Fault in the Sinop region) (Tüysüz et al., 1990) and created low-angle thrust faults with both north and south vergence (Figures 3, 4, and 6). The thrusts are sometimes arcuate and can be traced laterally for tens of kilometers. They strike to the east and are associated mostly with overturned folds, which have formed up to now the main target of the onshore explorations in the Black Sea region (Figures 3, 4, and 6). Not all the folds are fault-related. Quite a number of them developed independent of the thrusting. For example, there is a series of roughly symmetrical folds along the Black Sea coast (e.g., the Gürsökü, Iblak, Çangaldağ, and Tuzladere anticlines of the Sinop region) (Gedik and Korkmaz, 1984) (Figure 4). These folds mostly trend east-west, parallel to the thrust fault patterns. They extend from Zonguldak to Sinop, with anticline axes ranging in length from 8 to 42 km and half-wavelengths of ~4 km, which make them the most prospective traps in the region, because folds have developed above a decollement which, in the south (north of the Çangaldağ Anticlinorium), develops along the Çağlayan Formation and northward rises to the base of the Tertiary succession (Şengör, 1995) (Figures 3, 4, and 6). This decollement may provide an excellent trap for the reservoirs below it and the folds above it.

SUMMARY AND CONCLUSIONS

The arc margin of the Black Sea Basin is represented by a thick (>9000 m) sedimentary sequence with various rock types deposited throughout the rifting of this basin. During the Aptian to early Cenomanian, a deepening-upward synrift sequence accumulated in lagoonal to deep-marine environments of the restricted rift trough. During the late Cenomanian, the rift trough turned into a proto-ocean with an increase in the activity of the Pontide magmatic arc. This phase of rifting led, between the late Cenomanian and the early Eocene, to the thick accumulation of volcaniclastic turbidites, shales, and pelagic limestones on the arc margin of the Black Sea Basin. The margin was subjected to compressional tectonics at the end of the early Eocene to Oligocene, related to the closure of the Neotethys Ocean to the south. These tectonics resulted in deformation and erosion of the margin until the end of the Oligocene. It was again transgressed by shallow marine to terrestrial clastic sediments in the Miocene.

Although no economic hydrocarbon accumulation has yet been discovered, we believe that there is the geological potential for commercial volumes of oil in the southern continental margin of the Black Sea Basin because:

1. The margin contains a large volume of sediments.
2. Sandstones favorable for reservoir are widespread, particularly in the Lower Cretaceous synrift sequence, although the Upper Cretaceous to Eocene turbiditic sandstones of the postrift sequence also have some potential.
3. Fair to good source rocks are present in the lagoonal to marine shales of the rift sequence.
4. Shales with seal potential are common in both the Cretaceous and the Tertiary facies.
5. Sedimentological and tectonic development of the margin between the Cretaceous and the Tertiary enhanced hydrocarbon maturation, migration, and trapping.
6. Several gas and oil shows were reported from both some of the wells and the surface (e.g., along the Ekinveren Fault).
7. The area studied is basically underexplored and in the youthful exploration stage.

The critical problem in the exploration potential of the Southern Black Sea margin is the timing of the hydrocarbon generation, because most of the prospective traps formed concurrently with the deformation of this margin during the early Eocene compression. If large quantities of hydrocarbon had been generated and expelled before this period, they would mostly be lost to the surface during the Eocene thrusting. On the contrary, if the hydrocarbon generation took place during or after this tectonic event, their entrapment would be possible. Vitrinite reflectance analysis of many Cretaceous surface samples shows that these source rocks are early-mature to mature, indicating that potential for hydrocarbon generation during or after the early Eocene existed in the subsurface (Gedik and Korkmaz, 1984; Scott Pickford and Associates Ltd. and Aksan, 1987; Sonel et al., 1992; Aydın et al., 1995).

On the basis of both the kerogen type and the nature of the hydrocarbon shows, it may be concluded that the Eocene is promising in terms of gas, whereas the older sediments should be tested for oil. Maturation analyses indicate that main hydrocarbon generation postdated the formation of the structural traps and, therefore, no oil was lost to the surface during the early Eocene deformation.

ACKNOWLEDGMENTS

This study is supported by a Türkiye Bilimsel ve Teknik Arastirma Kurumu (TÜBITAK)-GloTek grant. Constructive reviews by P. Nixon and A.G. Robinson are acknowledged.

REFERENCES CITED

Abdüsselamoğlu, S., 1977, The Palaeozoic and Mesozoic in the Gebze region: explanatory text and excursion guidebook, 4th Colloquium on Geology of the Aegean Region, Excursion 4, Western Anatolia and Thrace, 16 p.

Akarsu, I., and M. Aydın, 1979, Sinop-İnebolu-Küre-Kastamonu-Tasköprü-Boyabat-Durağan yerlesme merkezleri ile çevrili sahanin genel jeoloji raporu: Türkiye Petrolleri company report 1323, 48 p.

Akman, A.Ü., 1992, Amasra-Arit arasinin jeolojisi: Ph.D. thesis, Ankara University, 209 p.

Akyol, Z., E. Arpat, B. Erdoğan, F. Saroğlu, E. Göğer, Y. Güner, I. Sentürk, K. Tütüncü, and S. Uysal, 1974, Cide-Kurucasile Dolayinin Jeoloji Haritasi: Maden Tetkik ve Arama Enstitüsü, Ankara, 1: 50,000 ölçekli Türkiye jeoloji haritasi serisi.

Aydın, M., O. Demir, H.S. Serdar, S. Özaydın, and B. Harput, 1995, Tectono-sedimentary evolution and hydrocarbon potential of the Sinop-Boyabat Basin, north Türkiye, *in* A. Erler, T. Ercan, E. Bingöl, and S. Örçen, eds., Geology of the Black Sea region: General Directorate of Mineral Research and Exploration and Chambers of Geological Engineers, Turkey, p. 254–263.

Aydın, M., Ö. Sahintürk, H.S. Serdar, I. Özçelik, Y. Akarsu, A. Üngör, R. Çokuğras, and S. Kasar, 1986, Ballıdağ-Çangaldağ (Kastamonu) arasindaki bölgenin jeolojisi: Türkiye Jeoloji Kurumu Bülteni, v. 29, p. 1–16.

Aydın, M., H.S. Serdar, Ö. Sahintürk, M. Yazman, R. Çokuğras, O. Demir, and Y. Özçelik, 1987, Çamdağ (Sakarya)-Sünnicedağ (Bolu) yöresinin jeolojisi: Türkiye Jeoloji Kurumu Bülteni, v. 30, p. 1–14.

Badgley, P.C., 1959, Stratigraphy and petroleum possibilities of the Sinop region: Tidewater Oil Co. report, Petrol Isleri Genel Müdürlüğü arsivi, 38 p.

Charles, F., 1930, Contribution à l'étude des terrains crétacés du Nord de l'Anatolie (Asie Mineure): Comptes Rendus et Sommaires de la Société Géologique de France, 191 p.

Dean, W.T., F. Martin, and O. Monod, 1990–1992, Field program with TPAO in northern and southern Turkey: Türkiye Petrolleri company report 10, 64 p.

Dow, W.G., 1977, Kerogen studies and geological interpretations: Journal of Geochemical Exploration, v. 7, p. 79–99.

Dow, W.G., and D.I. O'Conner, 1979, Vitrinite reflectance—what, how, and why: AAPG Bulletin, v. 63, p. 441–452.

Einsele, G., 1992, Sedimentary basins: Berlin, Springer-Verlag, 628 p.

Folk, R. L., 1974, Petrology of sedimentary rocks: Austin, Texas, Hemphill Publishing Company, 182 p.

Gedik, A., and S. Korkmaz, 1984, Sinop Havzasinin jeolojisi ve petrol olanaklari: Jeoloji Mühendisliği, v. 19, p. 53–79.

Görür, N., 1988, Timing of opening of the Black Sea Basin: Tectonophysics, v. 147, p. 247–262.

Görür, N., 1989, Timing of opening of the Black Sea: sedimentological evidence from the Rhodope-Pontide fragment, *in* A.M.C. Şengör, ed., Tectonic evolution of the Tethyan region: Dordrecht, Kluwer Academic Publishers, 698 p.

Görür, N., 1991, Aptian–Albian palaeogeography of Neotethyan domain: Palaeogeography, Palaeoclimatology, Palaeoecology, v. 87, p. 267–288.

Görür, N., this volume, Cretaceous syn- to postrift sedimentation on the southern continental margin of the Western Black Sea Basin, *in* A. Robinson, ed., Regional and petroleum geology of the Black Sea and surrounding region: AAPG Memoir 68, p. 227–239.

Görür, N., O. Tüysüz, A. Aykol, M. Sakinç, E. Yiğitbaş, and R. Akkök, 1993, Cretaceous red pelagic carbonates of northern Turkey: their place in the opening history of the Black Sea: Eclogae Geologica Helvetica, v. 86, p. 819–838.

Gümüş, Ö., and Y. Altan, 1995, History of petroleum and oil wells drilled in Turkey: Ankara, General Directorate of Petroleum Affairs, 196 p.

Hsü, K.J., I.K. Nacev, and V.T. Vucev, 1977, Geologic evolution of Bulgaria in the light of plate tectonics: Tectonophysics, v. 40, p. 245–256.

Kaya, O., A. Dizer, I. Tansel, and E. Meriç, 1983, Stratigraphy of the Cretaceous in the Ereğli area, Zonguldak: Bulletin of Mineral Research and Exploration Institute of Turkey, v. 99/100, p. 1–16.

Ketin, I., 1962, Türkiye Jeoloji Haritasi, Sinop Paftasi ve Izahati: Maden Tetkik ve Arama Enstitüsü, Ankara, Ölçek 1:500,000.

Ketin, I., and Ö. Gümüş, 1963, Sinop-Ayancik arasindaki III. Bölgeye dahil sahalarin jeolojisi hakkinda rapor, 2. Kisim, Jura ve Kretase Formasyonlarinin etüdü: Türkiye Petrolleri company report 213–288, 118 p.

Korkmaz, S., 1992, Sinop Havzasinda kaynak kaya fasiyesi, organik olgunlasma ve petrol olusumuna volkanizma ve çökelme ortami açısından yeni bir yaklasim: Türkiye Petrol Jeologlari Derneği Bülteni, v. 4, no. 1, p. 35–45.

Letouzey, J., B. Biju-Duval, A. Dorkel, R. Gonnard, K. Kristchev, L. Montadert, and O. Sungurlu, 1977, The Black Sea: a marginal basin; geophysical and geological data, *in* B. Biju-Duval and L. Montadert, eds., International symposium on the structural history of the Mediterranean basins: Paris, Editions Technip, p. 363–376.

Marsaglia, K.M., 1995, Interarc and backarc basins, *in* C.J. Busby and R.V. Ingersoll, eds., Tectonics of sedimentary basins: Cambridge, Massachusetts, Blackwell Science, 579 p.

Okay, A.I., 1989, Tectonic units and sutures in the Pontides, northern Turkey, *in* A.M.C. Şengör, ed., Tectonic evolution of the Tethyan region: NATO Advanced Science Institute (ASI) Series, C 259, p. 109–116.

Okay, A.I., A.M.C. Şengör, and N. Görür, 1994, Kinematic history of the opening of the Black Sea and its effect on the surrounding regions: Geology, v. 22, p. 267–270.

Okay, A.I., M. Siyako, and K.A. Bürkan, 1991, Geology and tectonic evolution of the Biga Peninsula, Northwest Turkey: Bulletin of the Technical University of İstanbul, v. 44, p. 191–256.

Pedersen, T.F., and S.E. Calvert, 1990, Anoxia vs. productivity: what controls the formation of organic-rich sediments and sedimentary rocks?: AAPG Bulletin, v. 74, p. 454–466.

Robinson, A.G., C.J. Banks, M.M. Rutherford, and J.P.P. Hirst, 1995, Stratigraphic and structural development of the Eastern Pontides, Turkey: Journal of the Geological Society, London, v. 152, p. 861–872.

Robinson, A.G., J.H. Rudat, C.J. Banks, and R.L.F. Wiles, 1996, Petroleum geology of the Black Sea: Marine and Petroleum Geology, v. 13, p. 195–223.

Schlanger, S.O., and J. Combs, 1975, Hydrocarbon potential of marginal basins bounded by an island arc: Geology, v. 3, p. 397–400.

Scott Pickford and Associates Ltd. and Aksan, AS, 1987, Exploration evaluation of the Western Black Sea, onshore area (Turkey): a commercial report, 75 p.

Scott Pickford and Associates Ltd. and Aksan, AS, 1988, Exploration evaluation of the Black Sea Sinop onshore area (Turkey): a commercial report, 50 p.

Selley, R.C., 1985, Elements of petroleum geology: New York, W.H. Freeman and Company, 449 p.

Şengör, A.M.C., 1995, The larger tectonic framework of the Zonguldak Coal Basin in northern Turkey: an outsider's view, *in* M.N. Yalçin and G. Gürdal, eds., Zonguldak Havzasi Araşturma Kuyulan-1: TÜBITAK, p. 1–26.

Şengör, A.M.C., and Y. Yılmaz, 1981, Tethyan evolution of Turkey: a plate tectonic approach: Tectonophysics, v. 75, p. 181–241.

Siyako, M., Z. Aksoy, K.A. Bürkan, and O. Demir, 1981, Zonguldak dolayinin jeolojisi ve hidrokarbon olanaklari: Türkiye Petrolleri company report 1536, 72 p.

Smith, G.A., and C.A. Landis, 1995, Intra-arc basins: Cambridge, Massachusetts, Blackwell Science, 579 p.

Sonel, N., A.M. Albayrak, and A. Sari, 1992, Bürnük (Boyabat-Sinop) civarının petrol olanaklari: Doğa-Türkiye Yerbilimleri Dergisi, v. 1, p. 17–35.

Sonel, N., A. Sari, B. Coskun, and E. Tozlu, 1989, Boyabat (Sinop) Havzasi Ekinveren Fayinin petrol aramalarindaki önemi: Türkiye Jeoloji Bülteni, v. 32, p. 39–49.

Teknica, 1984, Evaluation of hydrocarbon in the Turkish sector of the Black Sea: Türkiye Petrolleri company report 1950/2, 13 p.

Tissot, B.P., and D.H. Welte, 1984, Petroleum formation and occurrence: Berlin, Springer-Verlag, 699 p.

Tokay, M., 1952, Contribution à l'étude géologique de la région comprise entre Ereğli, Alapli, Kiziltepe et Alacaağzi: Maden Tetkik ve Arama Enstitüsü Mecmuasi, Sayi, v. 42–43, p. 37–78.

Tüysüz, O., 1990, Tectonic evolution of a part of the Tethyside orogenic collage: the Kargı Massif, northern Turkey: Tectonics, v. 9, p. 141–160.

Tüysüz, O., 1993, Karadeniz'den Orta Anadolu'ya bir jeotravers: Kuzey Neo-Tetisin tektonik evrimi: Türkiye Petrol Jeologlari Derneği Bülteni, v. 5, no. 1, p. 1–33.

Tüysüz, O., E. Yiğitbaş, Y. Yılmaz, and H.S. Serdar, 1990, Orta Pontidlerde Üst Jura-Alt Kretase stratigrafisi ve tektonik anlami: Türkiye 8 Petrol Kongresi Jeoloji Bildiriler, p. 340–350.

Weissert, M., J. McKenzie, and P. Hochuli, 1979, Cyclic anoxic events in the early Cretaceous Tethys Ocean: Geology, v. 7, p. 147–151.

Ustaömer, T., and A. Robertson, 1997, Tectonic-sedimentary evolution of the North Tethyan margin in the Central Pontides of Northern Turkey, *in* A.G. Robinson, ed., Regional and petroleum geology of the Black Sea and surrounding region: AAPG Memoir 68, p. 255–290.

Chapter 14

Tectonic-Sedimentary Evolution of the North Tethyan Margin in the Central Pontides of Northern Turkey

Timur Ustaömer
İstanbul University
İstanbul, Turkey

Alastair Robertson
University of Edinburgh
Edinburgh, Scotland, United Kingdom

ABSTRACT

The Central Pontides of northern Turkey is one of the best exposed segments of the southern margin of Eurasia adjacent to the Tethys Ocean, at least from the Paleozoic onward, and its history can be taken as a guide to the tectonic evolution of the Pontides as a whole. A number of east-west–trending tectonic units record subduction-accretion and the growth of the south Eurasian margin. The Central Pontides also document Lower Cretaceous lithospheric extension related to opening of the Black Sea during the Late Mesozoic–Early Tertiary, and a later active margin and collisional history.

Three time intervals exemplify the tectonic evolution of the Central Pontides. During the Late Paleozoic–Mid-Jurassic, Tethys was subducted northward, with development of an oceanic arc (the Çangaldağ Complex) and rifting of a continental fragment (İstanbul and Devrekani units), related to transform and/or active margin processes, to form a back-arc basin system (the Küre Complex and equivalents) in latest Paleozoic–earliest Triassic times. This was followed in the Lower Triassic by collision of a seamount (the Kargı Complex) with the active Eurasian margin, leading to deep burial beneath accreted units, including ophiolitic rocks. This collision possibly triggered collapse of the Küre back-arc basin further north, also in the Lower Triassic. Southward closure of the Küre Basin by the Upper Jurassic finally led to accretion of the entire tectonic stratigraphy to the southern margin of Eurasia during the "Cimmerian orogeny."

During the Late Jurassic–Early Cretaceous, the recently formed orogen subsided, possibly triggered by renewed northward subduction of Tethys, and carbonate platform sedimentation ensued during the Late Jurassic–Early Cretaceous. Crustal extension of the active margin then took place in the Early

This chapter is dedicated to the memory of Prof. Dr. Ihsan Ketin.

Cretaceous. The carbonate platform was dissected into half grabens, into which turbidites, debris flows, and olistoliths were shed. Early Cretaceous extension also activated exhumation of high-grade metamorphic rocks in the Central Pontides as a precursor to opening of the Western Black Sea marginal basin.

During the Late Cretaceous–Early Tertiary, the Western Black Sea Basin underwent sea-floor spreading, while the southern margin rapidly subsided, associated with northward emplacement of ophiolites and ophiolitic melange. During the Early Tertiary, the Pontides were sutured to the Anatolides to the south, resulting in south-vergent reimbrication of the Paleotethyan basement, especially in southerly areas, and north-vergent compression near the Black Sea coast.

INTRODUCTION

The Alpine-Himalayan mountain chain is located between stable Laurasia to the north and Africa-Arabia-India (Gondwana) to the south. The Tethyan orogenic collage was formed by rifting, subsequent drifting, and final accretion of Gondwana-derived fragments of different sizes to the northern active margin of Tethys, namely Laurasia (Robertson and Dixon, 1984; Şengör, 1984). Rifting of continental fragments along the Gondwana margin created new oceanic basins behind them. The new oceanic basins, located in the south, are termed "Neotethys," while the northerly, older basin is known as "Paleotethys." Progressive welding of subduction-accretion complexes to the southern margin of Laurasia resulted in gradual southward migration of a subduction front and associated magmatism (Şengör et al., 1988, 1991). Collision of Africa and Laurasia in the Miocene greatly reduced the Tethys, and now only the Eastern Mediterranean Sea remains, itself being consumed northward along the Crete-Cyprus active margin (Figure 1) (Robertson and Grasso, 1995; Robertson et al., 1996).

The Pontide tectonic belt of northern Turkey (Ketin, 1966) comprises an ~1500-km-long segment of the Alpine-Himalayan chain and is widely believed to have been part of the south Eurasian margin, adjacent to Paleotethys from the Paleozoic onward. A number of tectonic models have been proposed for the evolution of the Tethyan Ocean and its margins (Dewey et al., 1973; Stocklin, 1974; Adamia et al., 1977; Hsü and Bernoulli, 1978; Şengör, 1979, 1984; Robertson and Dixon, 1984). However, a debate still persists, particularly as to the location of the Paleotethyan suture and its subduction polarity. Recently acquired field data have refined the understanding of the tectonic evolution of pre-Late Jurassic Tethys, leading to new tectonic models (Yılmaz and Şengör, 1985; Yılmaz and Boztuğ, 1986; Dercourt et al., 1986, 1993; Tüysüz, 1985, 1990; Ustaömer and Robertson, 1990, 1993, 1994; Stampfli et al., 1991; Okay et al., 1994; Boztuğ et al., 1995; Robinson et al., 1995; Banks and Robinson, this volume).

Two fundamentally different schools of thought still exist: One envisions that the north Tethyan margin was passive until the Late Jurassic. Paleotethys was subducted southward during the Paleozoic, under the active margin of Gondwana in this model (Dewey et al., 1973; Şengör, 1984, Şengör et al., 1984). A continental sliver was rifted off (i.e., the Cimmerian continent) as a result of back-arc extension, opening a new oceanic basin system to the south (Neotethys). This continental sliver later collided with Laurasia, resulting in total elimination of Paleotethys by the Upper Jurassic during the Cimmerian orogeny (Şengör, 1984). In this model, the Pontides were initially thought of as part of the Cimmerian continent. However, more recently, at least one unit in the west, the İstanbul Unit (Ustaömer and Robertson, 1993), was reassigned to the southern margin of Eurasia (Okay et al., 1994).

The second school of thought envisions the southern margin of Eurasia as an active continental margin associated with terrane displacement, marginal basin formation, and arc genesis (Adamia et al., 1977; Robertson and Dixon, 1984; Dercourt et al., 1986, 1993). In this model, only one progressively evolving Tethys Ocean existed. Continental slivers were rifted off Gondwana, drifted northwest, and were later accreted to the northern margin of Eurasia.

GEOLOGICAL SETTING

The Pontide tectonic belt of northern Turkey (Figure 1) comprises a number of pre-Late Jurassic tectonostratigraphic units, bordered to the south by Late Mesozoic ophiolites, ophiolitic melanges, and other units of the mainly Mesozoic Anatolides and Taurides (Şengör and Yılmaz, 1981). Within the Pontides, pre-Jurassic continental units (Şengör et al., 1980) are exposed in the northwest (the İstranca Massif), west (the İstanbul Unit), and east (the Bayburt Fragment). In other areas of the Pontides, mainly flysch and volcanics are interpreted as subduction-accretion complexes that were amalgamated with Eurasia during the Late Paleozoic–Early Mesozoic

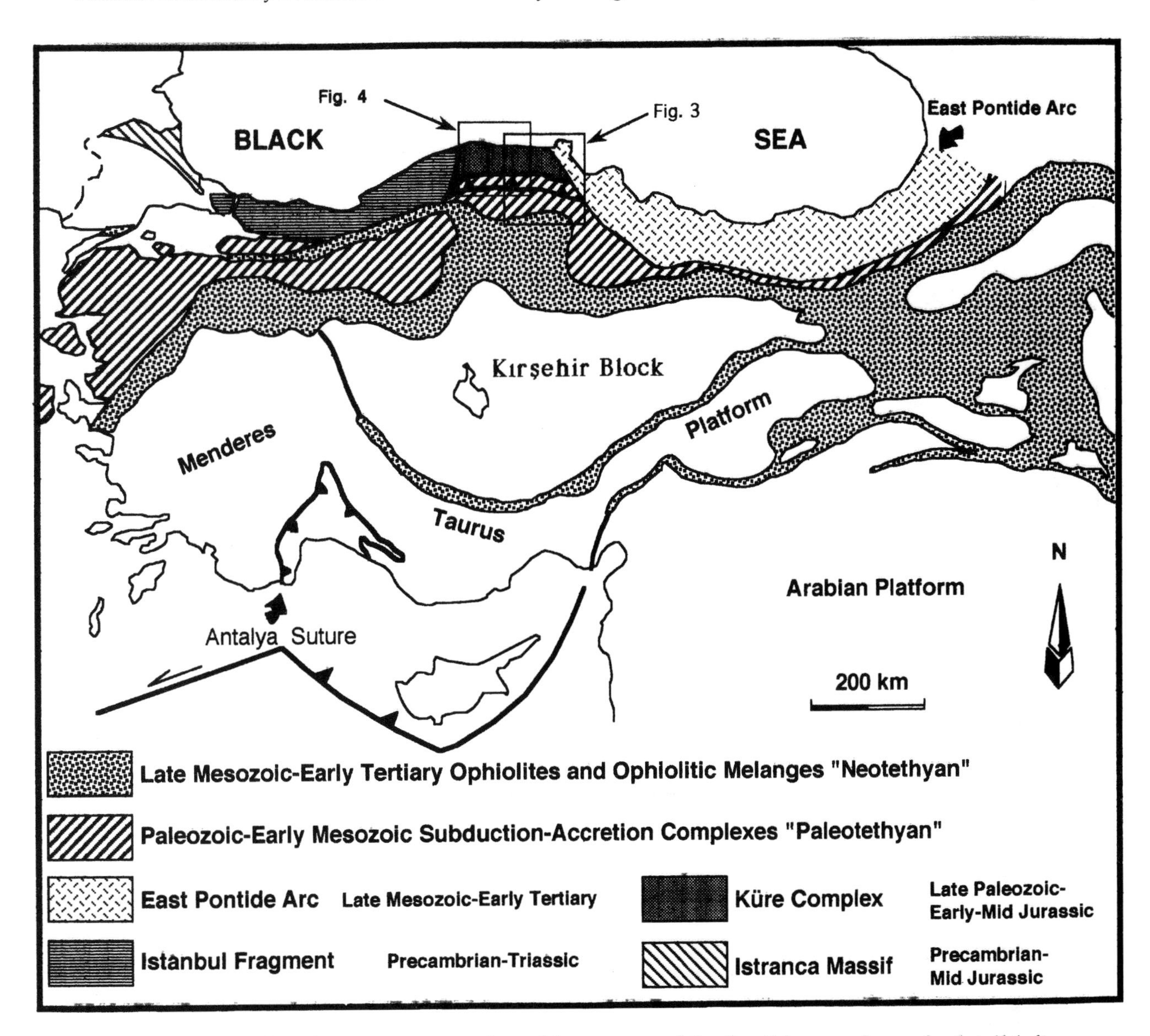

Figure 1. Suture map of Turkey. Tectonostratigraphic terranes of the Pontides are shown in detail (after Ustaömer and Robertson, 1993). Boxes indicate the locations of the geological maps shown in Figures 3 and 4.

(Okay et al., 1991; Pickett et al., 1992, 1995; Pickett and Robertson, in press) (Figure 1). Detailed geological studies of the Central Pontides (Eren, 1979; Güner, 1980; Yılmaz, 1980; Yılmaz and Sengör, 1985; Tüysüz, 1985, 1990; Ustaömer and Robertson, 1990, 1993, 1994, 1995) have revealed remnants of two different pre-Jurassic oceanic basins: the one in the south is interpreted as the main Tethys (Paleotethys), while another in the north (the Küre Basin) is viewed as a marginal oceanic basin developed north of Paleotethys. Paleotethyan units are also exposed in the Eastern Pontides and form the basement of the Sakarya Continent (Şengör and Yılmaz, 1981). Our work in the Central Pontides indicates that subduction of Paleotethys in the Late Paleozoic–Early Mesozoic was dominantly northward, under the active southern continental margin of Eurasia (Figure 2). This subduction gave rise to Late Paleozoic volcanic arcs sited along the south Eurasian margin and within the adjacent Tethys Ocean. These arcs include the Çangaldağ Complex of the Central Pontides (Ustaömer and Robertson, 1990), and possibly also other arc units exposed in the Armutlu Peninsula, Western Pontides, and the Ağvanis mountains, Eastern Pontides (Okay, 1984) (Figure 2).

Our study focuses on the Central Pontides because this area displays the most complete tectonostratigraphy and has the most extensive database. With its central location in the Central Pontides, this area can be considered as representative of the Pontides as a whole.

The Central Pontides region comprises several tectonic units (Figures 3, 4) (Eren, 1979; Yılmaz, 1980; Yılmaz and Şengör, 1985; Aydın et al., 1986; Tüysüz, 1985, 1990; Ustaömer and Robertson, 1990, 1993, 1994).

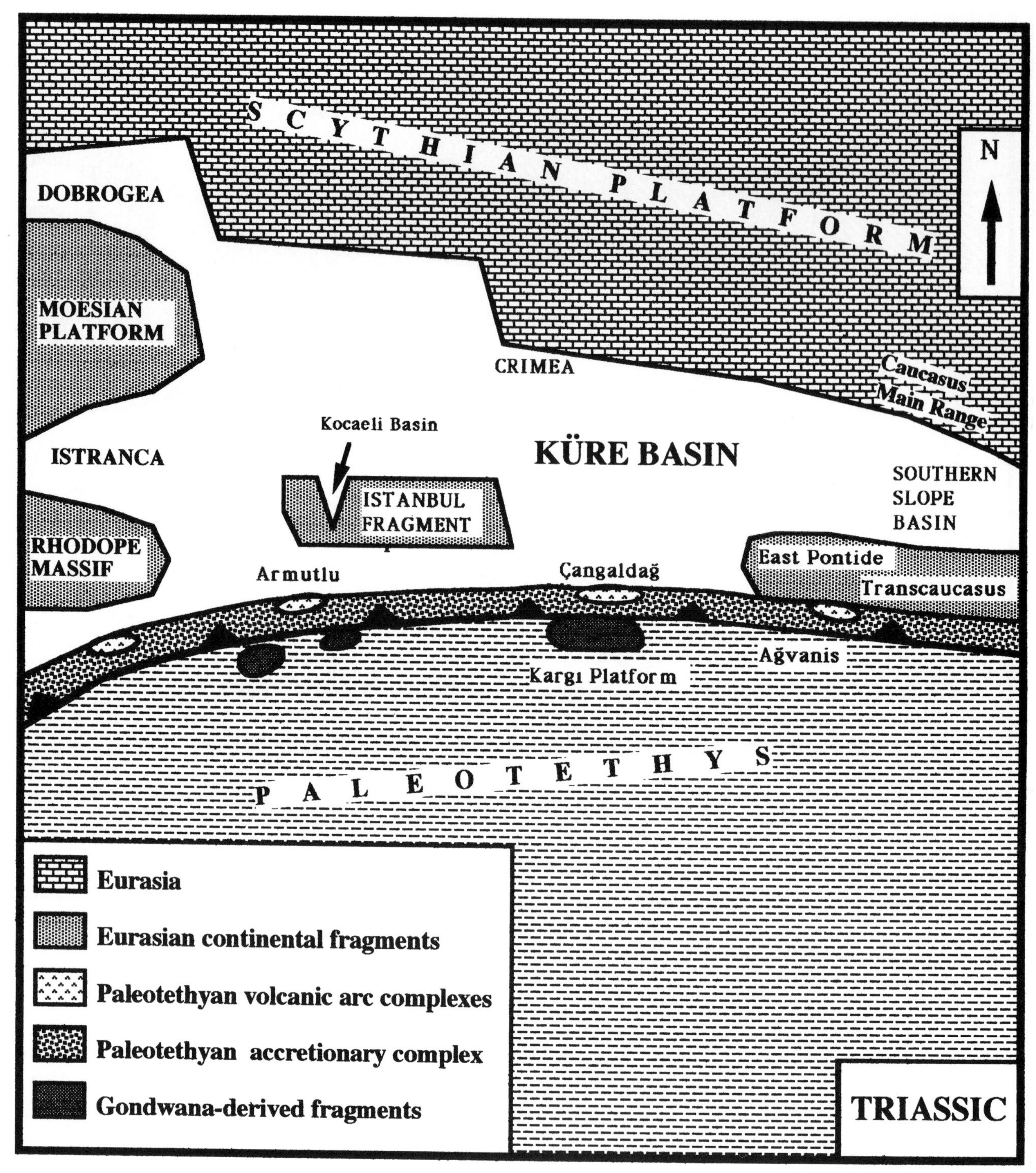

Figure 2. Paleogeographic map of the North Tethyan margin in the Eastern Mediterranean region, showing the Triassic Paleotethyan marginal basin complex that opened related to transform and/or active margin processes. This basin complex closed by southward underthrusting by the Late Jurassic, while Paleotethys remained open to the south. Following closure of the marginal basin complex, further compression was taken up by initiation of a new subduction system along the southern margin of Eurasia (after Ustaömer and Robertson, 1993).

Along the Black Sea coast in the north, volcano-sedimentary units of the Late Mesozoic–Early Tertiary Black Sea marginal basin are exposed. The Istanbul Unit is located in the west. Low-angle thrust sheets of the Paleozoic sediments of the Istanbul Unit are found floating over the Küre Complex (Aydın et al., 1986; Ustaömer and Robertson, 1993, 1994), representing a major Late Paleozoic–Early Mesozoic unit exposed in

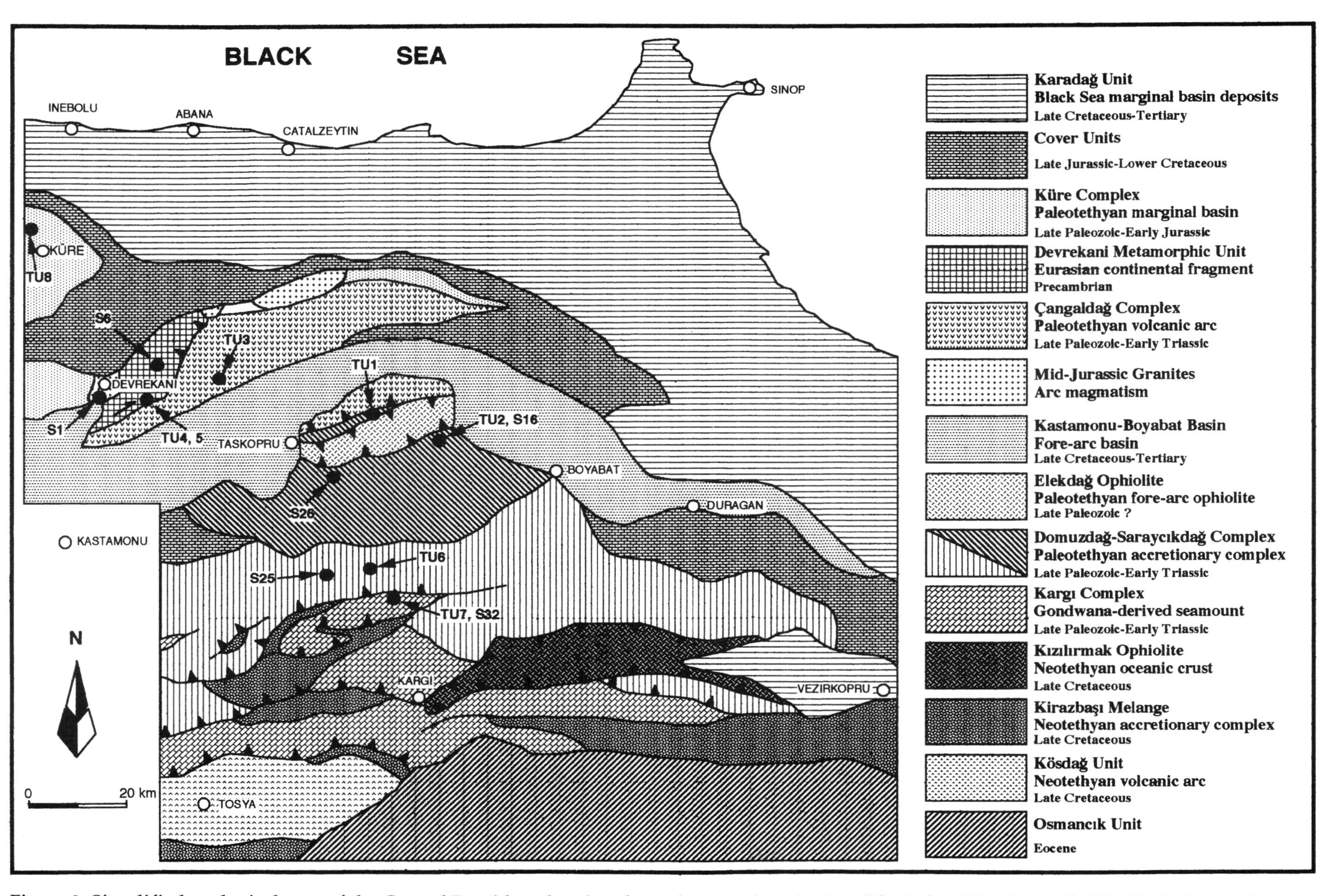

Figure 3. Simplified geological map of the Central Pontides, showing the main tectonic units (modified after Tüysüz, 1990). The black dots indicate the locations and the numbers of the samples that were radiometrically dated during this study (Table 1).

the northern areas (Figure 4). In the middle of the area is the east-west–trending Late Cretaceous–Tertiary Kastamonu-Boyabat basin (Saner, 1980), which dissects the Çangaldağ Complex, a Late Paleozoic volcanic arc unit. Exposed between the Küre Complex and the Çangaldağ Complex is the Devrekani metamorphic unit, a continental sliver of inferred Precambrian age metamorphosed to amphibolite facies. These units are unconformably overlain by Upper Jurassic–Lower Cretaceous platform carbonates, then by Lower Cretaceous flysch. To the south of the Kastamonu-Boyabat Basin is a south-vergent, imbricated zone of east-west–trending metaophiolites, melanges, and slivers of a carbonate platform and its marginal sequences, of Late Paleozoic–Early Triassic age, together with Late Mesozoic ophiolites and ophiolitic melanges (Tüysüz, 1990). In the southernmost areas, a Late Mesozoic arc sequence is exposed (Tüysüz, 1990).

The tectonic evolution of the Central Pontides can be conveniently divided into three time intervals: (1) pre-Late Jurassic, (2) Late Jurassic–Early Cretaceous, and (3) Early Cretaceous–Tertiary. In this chapter, we focus on the pre-Late Jurassic tectonic history. We begin with post-Late Jurassic events that must be disentangled before the earlier tectonic history of the southern margin of Eurasia can be deciphered. Our discussion of the Paleotethyan units is aided by new field and laboratory chemical analytical results and new radiometric age data from metamorphic and magmatic units.

PREVIOUS WORK

Numerous studies have been carried out on oceanic and continental units of the Central Pontides, and extensive data have been accumulated for nearly a century. Most work in the Küre area concentrated on economic massive sulfide deposits (Nikitin, 1926; Kovenko, 1944; Çağatay et al., 1980; Güner, 1980). Detailed mapping of the northern areas was carried out by the Turkish Geological Survey (MTA) (Ketin, 1962), Turkish Petroleum Company (TPAO) (Ketin and Gümüş, 1963; Aydın et al., 1986, 1995; TPAO unpublished reports), and by academic earth scientists (Eren, 1979; Yılmaz, 1980; Yılmaz and Şengör, 1985; Yılmaz and Boztuğ, 1986). As a result, the stratigraphy of the region became well known, especially for post-Late Jurassic units, while important data were also collected from the pre-Late Jurassic, mostly metamorphosed volcanic-sedimentary units and ophiolites. In particular, the southern part of the Central Pontides (i.e., the Kargı Massif) was mapped by Tüysüz (1985, 1990). He recognized, for the first time, several pre-Late Jurassic oceanic and continental units that are tectonically imbricated with Late Mesozoic ophiolites and ophiolitic melanges.

Data collected from the pre-Late Jurassic units of the Central Pontides have already been used to support the two contrasting tectonics models involving either southward subduction or mainly northward subduction. Tüysüz (1985, 1990) and Aydın et al. (1986) supported Şengör's model in which Paleotethys was subducted southward and a back-arc basin opened in southerly areas (Tüysüz, 1990). Yılmaz and Boztuğ (1986), on the other hand, favored northward subduction of Paleotethys, citing evidence of mid-Jurassic arc magmatism (i.e., the Kastamonu granitoid belt) to the north of the Paleotethyan ophiolites.

Our work has concentrated on pre-Late Jurassic units of the Central Pontides, with the aim of testing alternative tectonic models (Ustaömer and Robertson, 1993, 1994, 1995). We have collected structural, geochemical, and stratigraphical-sedimentological data from all the pre-Late Jurassic units. Critical areas were mapped on 1:25,000 scale, and numerous structural traverses were made in the region. More than 200 samples of mainly igneous and sedimentary rocks from all the tectonic units were geochemically analyzed by high-quality XRF techniques for major and trace elements at Edinburgh University. Microprobe work was carried out on 50 samples (lavas, ultrabasics, granites, greenschists, blueschists, amphibolites, eclogites, and massive sulfides), and more than 2000 mineral chemical analyses were performed. In addition, 14 samples were radiometrically dated by the K/Ar method.

POST-LATE JURASSIC: NEOTETHYAN VS. PALEOTETHYAN TECTONIC HISTORY

The Central Pontides include extensive post-Late Jurassic volcanic-sedimentary units that unconformably overlie Paleotethyan basement and Late Mesozoic ophiolites and ophiolitic melanges. The post-Late Jurassic units are already relatively well documented (Ketin, 1962; Ketin and Gümüş, 1963; Yılmaz, 1980; Gedik and Korkmaz, 1984; Tüysüz, 1985; Aydın et al., 1986; Görür, 1988; Yılmaz and Tüysüz, 1988; Tüysüz, 1991; Yılmaz and Tüysüz, 1985; Görür, 1991; Tunoğlu, 1991; Görür et al., 1993; Aydın et al., 1995; Derman et al., 1996; Derman and Norman, 1996), and a consensus has largely been reached regarding the tectonic setting of these units in relation to the Pontide margin.

A key question is the extent to which post-Upper Jurassic tectonic events have resulted in disruption and dispersal of the original Paleotethyan basement. For example, if post-Upper Jurassic events included major terrane migration or regional-scale thrusting, this would effectively preclude realistic tectonic reconstruction of the Paleotethyan basement. In the following section, we show that, although complex, the post-Upper Jurassic history is sufficiently well understood for its effects to be identified and subtracted from the earlier tectonic history.

In the north, the Karadağ Unit is exposed along the Black Sea coast (Tüysüz, 1985, 1990; Aydın et al., 1986) (Figures 3, 4). This unit comprises a Late Cretaceous–Tertiary volcanic-sedimentary sequence associated with opening of the Black Sea as a marginal basin (Görür, 1988). A Late Jurassic–Early Cretaceous sedimentary succession transgressively overlies the northern basement units of the Central Pontides (Ketin, 1962) and reflects the initial stages of opening of the

Black Sea. Farther south, the Kastamonu-Boyabat Basin (Figures 4, 5) is made up of Late Cretaceous–Tertiary volcano-sedimentary successions, deposited in a forearc basin (Saner, 1980). In the south, a Late Cretaceous ophiolite and ophiolitic melange is imbricated with the basement units (Tüysüz, 1990). A third unit, the Kösdağ, exposed in southernmost areas (Figures 3, 5), is dominated by Late Mesozoic basic and acidic volcanics; is intruded by granites, with minor sediments; and is interpreted as an emplaced fragment of a Neotethyan arc (Tüysüz, 1990; Tüysüz et al., 1993, 1995).

Late Jurassic–Early Cretaceous Sedimentary Cover

This is well exposed in northerly areas (north of the Kastamonu-Boyabat Basin) (Figures 4, 5), but is also locally exposed in the south. The cover units unconformably overlie the northern basement units and are represented by Late Middle–Upper Jurassic, red, coarse-grained clastics of fluvial origin (the Bürnük Formation) (Ketin and Gümüş, 1963; Yılmaz, 1980; Aydın et al., 1986; Tüysüz, 1990; Derman et al., 1996). This unit is overlain by shallow-marine platform carbonates of Late Jurassic–earliest Cretaceous age (the İnaltı Formation) (Ketin and Gümüş, 1963). In its upper part, this unit passes into a calcareous mudstone sequence, alternating with thin layers of calciturbidites and turbiditic sandstones (the Çağlayan Formation) (Ketin and Gümüş, 1963). The Early Cretaceous Çağlayan Formation is made up of turbiditic sandstone–shale alternations, with blocks of limestones, and debris flows in the upper part. The unit is very similar lithologically to the Paleotethyan Küre Complex (see below) in some areas, which has caused some confusion in the past. Blocks of limestones (a few hundred meters across) and red conglomerates are likely to have been derived from the basal part of the sequence. Turbiditic facies of the Çağlayan Formation contain numerous well-developed sedimentary structures in contrast to the Küre Complex sandstones. For example, flute and groove casts and load structures are widely seen at the base of individual beds. Complete Bouma sequences are rarely observed, but Ta-Tb-Te and Td-Te beds are common. Both fining- and coarsening-upward sequences are found within turbidites.

Interpretation

Marine transgression occurred in the Late Jurassic, and a carbonate platform was established (Yılmaz and Tüysüz, 1988; Görür et al., 1993) (Figure 6). The Pontide margin experienced crustal extension in the Late Jurassic–Early Cretaceous, resulting in block faulting of the carbonate platform (A. Robinson, C. Banks, and S. Hall, 1992, personal communication; Görür et al., 1993; Ustaömer, 1993). North-facing half-grabens formed in the north and were filled by turbiditic sediments, debris flows, and limestone blocks derived both from the carbonate platform and from the Paleotethyan basement. This tectonic extension also gave rise to the Kastamonu-Boyabat Basin as an initially south-facing half graben, which later became inactive and gradually filled with shallow-marine to continental sediments. Early Cretaceous extension developed above a northward-dipping subduction zone and was a precursor to opening of the Black Sea from a back-arc basin in the Late Mesozoic–Early Tertiary (Görür, 1988). Early Cretaceous extension was possibly also responsible for exhumation of deeply buried Paleotethyan units (e.g., blueschists) in the Central Pontides.

Black Sea Marginal Basin Deposits—Karadağ Unit

This unit is exposed along the Black Sea coast (Tüysüz, 1985; Aydın et al., 1986) (Figures 3, 4), where it unconformably overlies deformed flysch of the Küre Complex, and locally conformably overlies Lower Cretaceous flysch (the Çağlayan Formation).

At its stratigraphic base, there are red micritic pelagic limestones of Cenomanian–Turonian age (Kapanboğazı Formation) (Ketin and Gümüş, 1963; Aydın et al., 1986) directly overlying the Küre flysch. Upwards, these sediments alternate with green tuffs, with large north-verging slump folds. Still further upwards, volcanic debris flow deposits, volcaniclastic sandstones, columnar-jointed lavas, and sills are seen. The age of this sequence (the Yemişliçay Formation) (Ketin and Gümüş, 1963) is Coniacian–Campanian, based on pelagic foraminifera (Aydın et al., 1986). It is overlain by gray-green marls and shales, alternating with turbiditic sandstones and thin limestones, with north-verging slump folds. The age of this (nonvolcanogenic) sequence (the Gürsökü Formation) (Gedik and Korkmaz, 1984; Aydın et al., 1986) is Campanian–early Maastrichtian, based on pelagic foraminifera (Aydın et al., 1986). Further up, there are white-gray marls alternating with dominantly thin horizons of calciturbidites and turbiditic sandstones. A Late Cretaceous–Early Paleocene age is assigned to this formation (the Akveren Formation) (Aydın et al., 1986). Finally, red marl–calciturbidite alternations with thin-turbiditic sandstones are dated as Mid-Paleocene–early Eocene (Aydın et al., 1986).

Interpretation

Extension and collapse of the north Pontide margin culminated in the Late Cretaceous (Görür et al., 1993). Deep-water sediments accumulated in submerged half-grabens, associated with intrusion of sills and extrusion of lava flows. Extension also triggered large-scale slumping of previously deposited deep-water sediments.

Overall, the Karadağ Unit is interpreted as an Late Cretaceous–Eocene back-arc basin (Görür, 1988, 1991; Yılmaz and Tüysüz, 1988; Görür et al., 1993) (Figure 6). Extensional sills and north-verging slumps characterized the opening of this basin to form the Black Sea marginal basin in the Upper Cretaceous (Görür, 1988). The volcanogenic material was derived from a well-developed ensialic arc, exposed to the southeast, along the Eastern Black Sea coast.

Kastamonu-Boyabat Basin

The Kastamonu-Boyabat Basin forms a roughly east-west–trending belt (Figures 3, 4). The basin contains a Late Cretaceous–Oligocene volcano-sedimentary

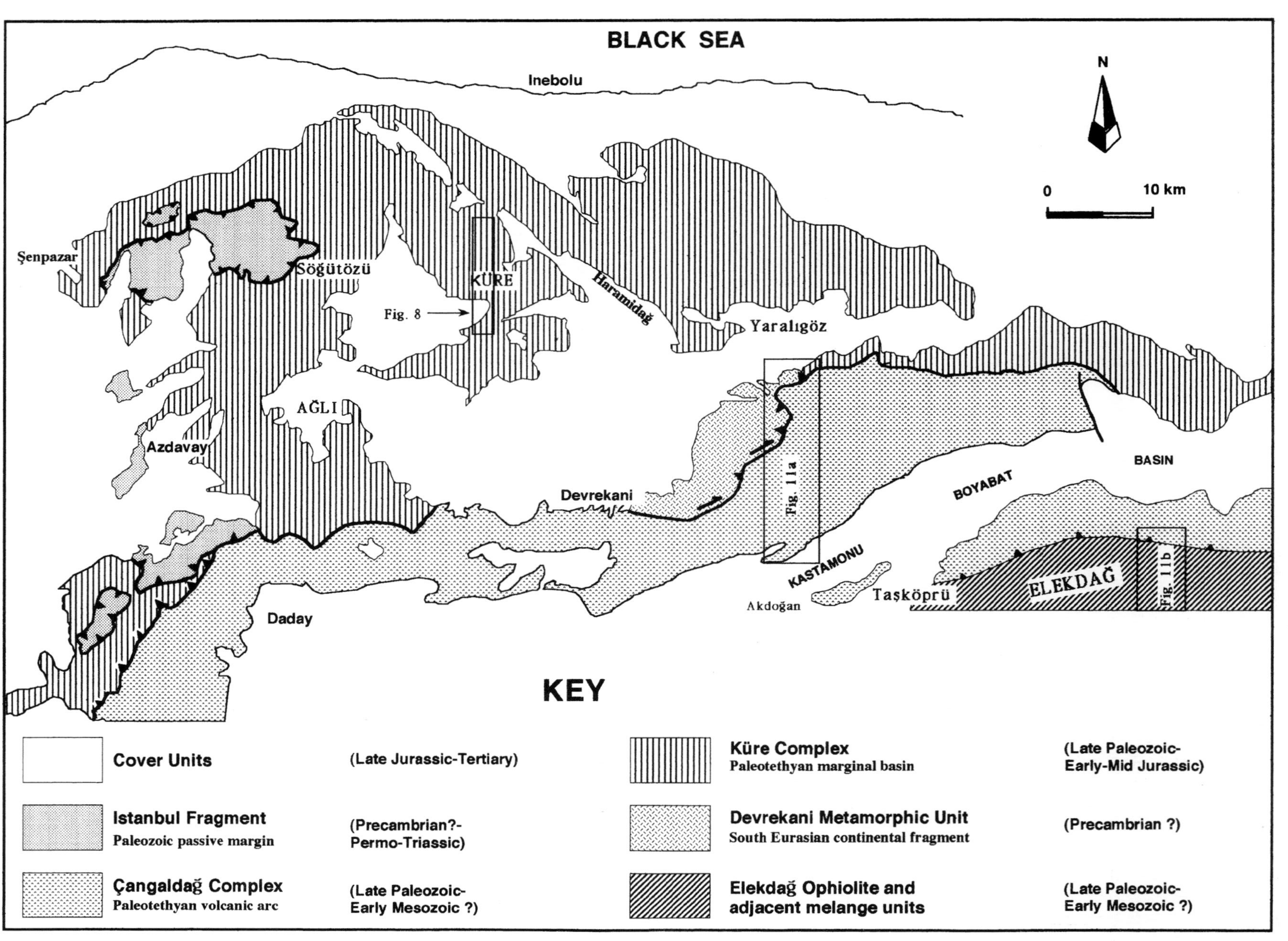

Figure 4. Simplified geological map of the northern Central Pontides, showing the distribution of the Pre-Late Jurassic units and the Late Mesozoic–Tertiary Kastamonu-Boyabat Basin (modified after Aydın et al., 1986). Boxes indicate the location of Figures 8 and 11a, b.

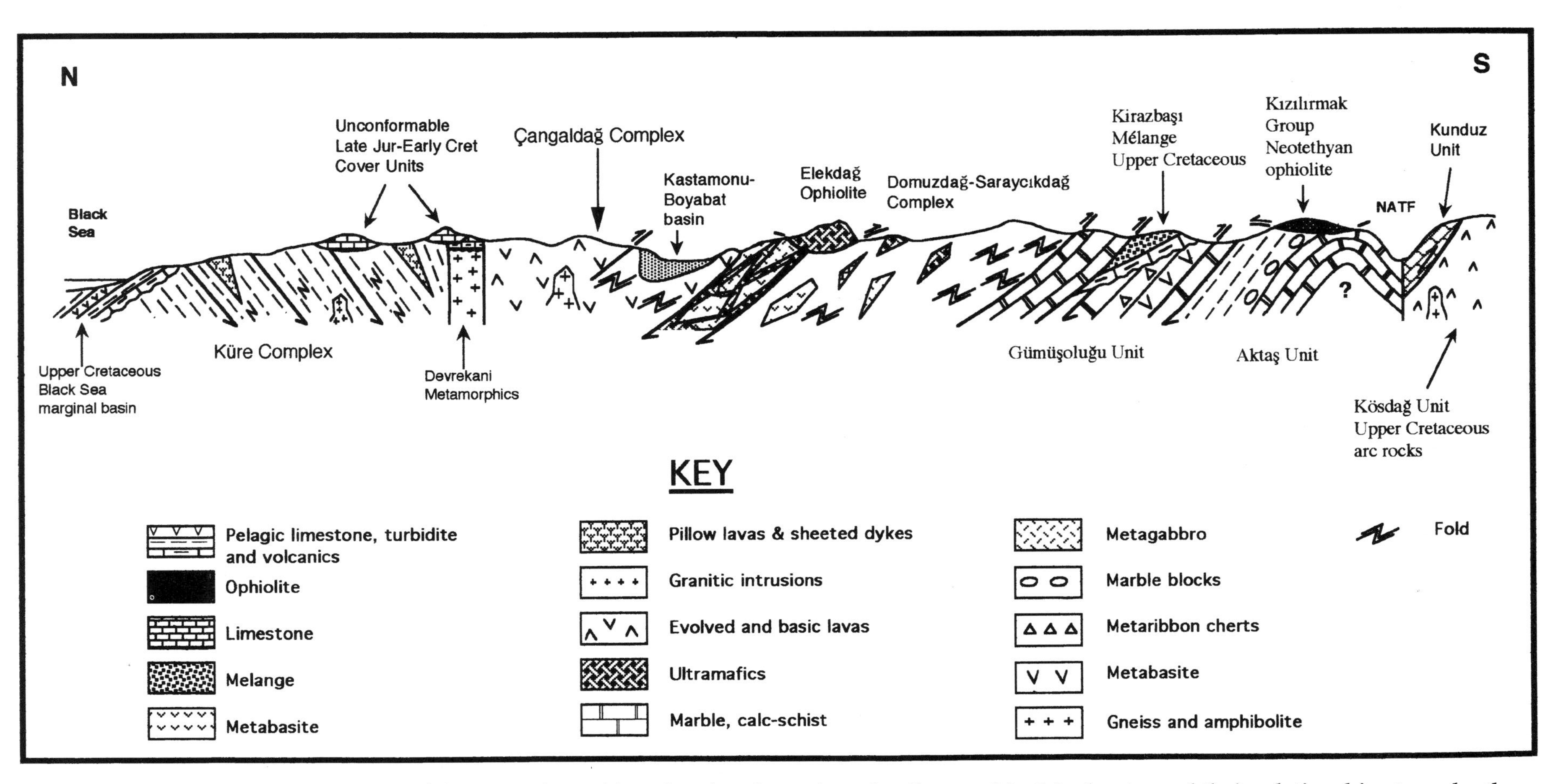

Figure 5. Simplified N-S cross section of the Central Pontides, showing the main units discussed in this chapter and their relationships to each other. The section is based on this study and also builds on earlier work by Tüysüz (1990).

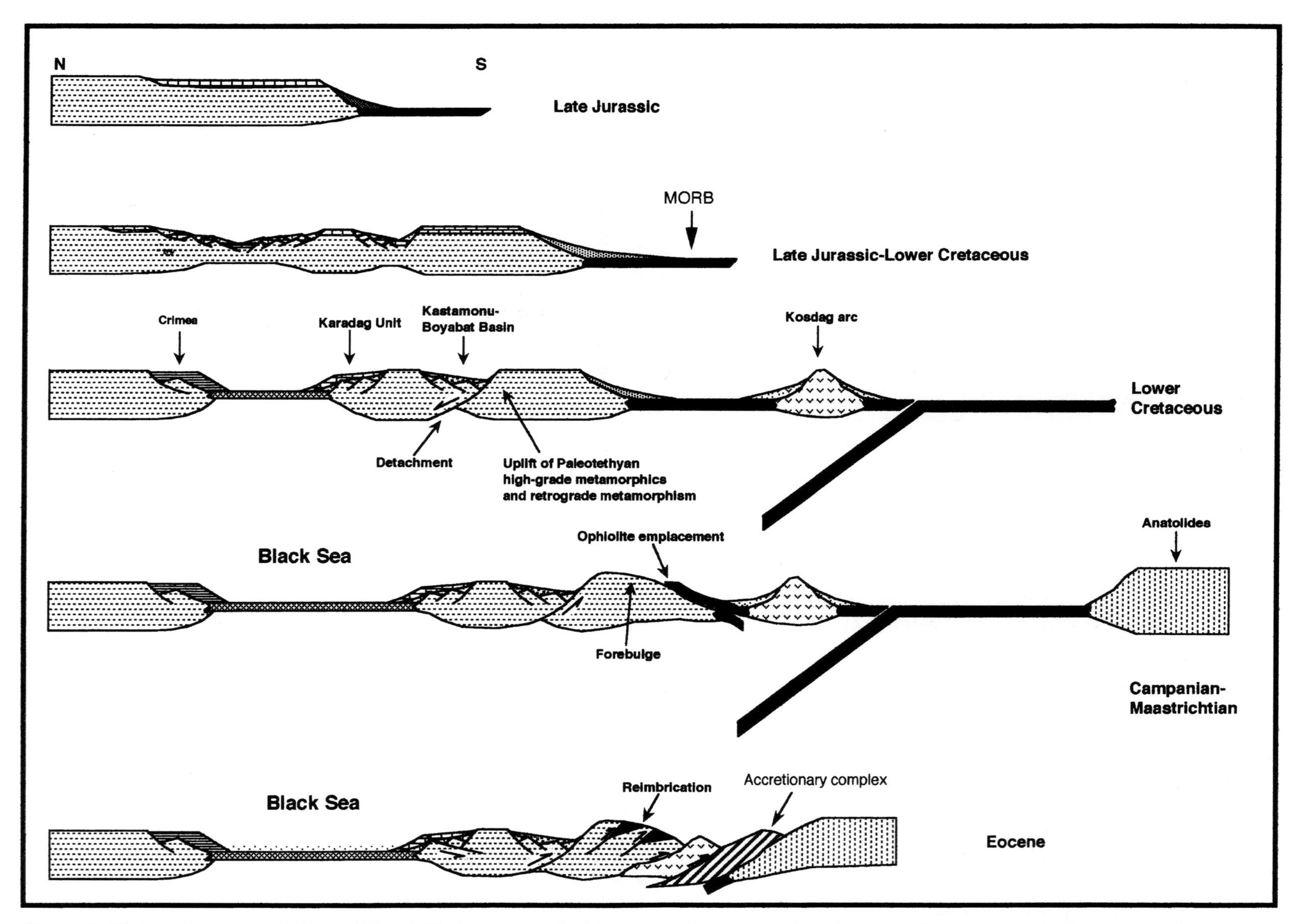

Figure 6. Plate tectonic evolution of North Tethyan margin in the post Late Jurassic. The ages of events are well constrained by fossil ages, as most units are unmetamorphosed. New radiometric age data highlight the inferred role of extensional faulting and exhumation related to opening of the Western Black Sea Basin, which then resulted in thermal resetting to produce Early Cretaceous ages. The thermal resetting effects of collisional events in the Late Cretaceous and Eocene are also reflected in the ages. MORB = mid-ocean rich basalt.

sequence that dissects the Paleotethyan basement and is interpreted as a fore-arc basin (Saner, 1980; Tüysüz, 1990). The basin has an asymmetrical structure, with the northern limb being vertical and locally overturned toward the south, while the southern limb is relatively flat and dips northward with a low angle (Yılmaz and Tüysüz, 1991). The succession commences with Paleocene–lower Eocene lithologies on the southern limb, following a depositional hiatus (Yılmaz and Tüysüz, 1991).

Early Cretaceous flysch is unconformably overlain by Upper Cretaceous red pelagic limestones. Along the contact, there is a thin (up to 1 m thick) gray to white conglomerate and medium-bedded, coarse sandstones. The red limestones (the Kapanboğazı Formation) are somewhat similar to the lowermost formation of the Black Sea marginal basin sediments (the Karadağ Unit) in terms of lithology, except volcanogenic intercalations are absent. Upwards, red pelagic limestones (Ammonitico Rosso facies) are seen, with thin shale interbeds, followed by deposition of silty limestones. Bedding surfaces exhibit trace fossils (e.g., Thalassinoides). Volcanogenic sedimentation follows upsection, comprising volcaniclastic sandstones, occasional channelized debris flows (in which the clasts are subrounded to rounded), volcanics, tuffs, and red-green shales. Slump folds in this section verge southward, toward the basin axis. Associated with the volcanogenic sequence are columnar-jointed lavas and lahar-type breccias, which contain hornblende-bearing andesitic blocks up to 1 m long. These volcanogenic deposits are overlain by subvertical bioclastic limestones, with rhodolites, followed by turbiditic sandstones. Paleocene and Eocene units are represented by nummulite- and *Alveolina* sp.-bearing shallow-marine limestones and shales. Oligocene fluvial sediments then fill the basin (Yılmaz and Tüysüz, 1991).

Interpretation

The Kastamonu-Boyabat Basin was previously interpreted as a fore-arc basin located within a Late Cretaceous–Early Tertiary subduction-accretion complex (Saner, 1980; Yılmaz and Tüysüz, 1988, 1991; Tüysüz, 1990). However, the basement is the intact Late Paleozoic–Early Mesozoic Çangaldağ Complex, rather than melange. Also, a Late Mesozoic volcanic arc is not developed to the north of the Kastamonu-Boyabat Basin in the Central Pontides. Upper Cretaceous lavas and volcaniclastic sediments are present in the Yemişliçay Formation of the Karadağ Unit (see above), but they are thin (a few meters thick) and are seen to be interbedded with deep-water sediments. A thick arc-type volcanic pile, as in the Eastern Pontides, is not developed. This could reflect erosion of volcanic arc units, or any continuation of the Eastern Pontide arc that lies in the Black Sea to the north. Erosion of the volcanic pile is an unlikely explanation, as Upper Cretaceous–Eocene shallow-water sediments are preserved, but lack volcanics. If the Eastern Pontide arc continues into the Black Sea, the Karadağ Unit would be interpreted as a fore-arc basin, rather than a back-arc basin. Alternatively, the Pontide margin may have existed as an obliquely subducting margin in the Central Pontides, so that strike-slip displacement exceeded subduction and a volcanic gap could have existed between the Eastern and Western Pontides.

We propose that the Kastamonu-Boyabat Basin originated as one in a series of Early Cretaceous half grabens (Figure 6). Rapid subsidence, deep-water sediment accumulation, and slumping took place in the Late Cretaceous southward, toward the basin axis, in this case. The main difference from the otherwise similar Karadağ Unit is the occurrence of a thick sequence of volcaniclastic sediments in the Kastamonu-Boyabat Basin, interpreted as of deep-water fan-delta origin. The volcaniclastics were possibly derived from the Eastern Pontide arc. After this period, further extension possibly migrated northward, associated with opening of the Black Sea, while rifting of the Kastamonu-Boyabat Basin failed, followed by sediment infilling. The asymmetric geometry of the basin, with the northern limb steep and locally overturned, is interpreted as a result of Early Tertiary compression.

In summary, the Kastamonu-Boyabat Basin is interpreted as having originated as a Late Jurassic–Early Cretaceous half graben that later evolved into a fore-arc basin (Saner, 1980).

Late Cretaceous Dismembered Ophiolite and Ophiolitic Melange

In the southern part of the Central Pontides, to the south of the Kastamonu-Boyabat Basin, unmetamorphosed, dismembered ophiolites and ophiolitic melanges are exposed within an Eocene imbricate zone (Tüysüz, 1985, 1990). These units were first described by Tüysüz (1985); the ophiolite was termed the Kızılırmak Group, and the ophiolitic melange, the Kirazbaşı melange. The ophiolite occurs as an east-west–trending klippe over basement lithologies (Tüysüz, 1990) (Figures 3, 5).

The ophiolite is represented by massive serpentinized ultramafics (i.e., harzburgite), microgabbro, and a sheeted dyke complex in which the dykes trend north-south and dip westward. Rodingite is developed in the ultramafics. Above this are vesicular pillow lavas, red radiolarian cherts, and shales, with volcaniclastic sandstone interbeds and finally pelagic limestones. The ophiolite is internally imbricated, and exhibits south-verging thrust faults (Tüysüz, 1990; Yılmaz and Tüysüz, 1991). Based on structural data, this unit was emplaced from the south-southwest toward the north-northeast.

The ophiolitic melange (i.e., the Kirazbaşı Melange) (Tüysüz, 1985) is part of an extensive "colored melange" belt in northern Turkey. The unit forms north-dipping thrust wedges within an imbricate zone, in which the southern contacts are sedimentary, while the northern contacts are thrusts (Tüysüz, 1985, 1990).

At the base, this unit is represented by thin (<1 m) pelagic *Globotruncana*- and radiolarian-bearing limestones, unconformably overlying Paleotethyan basement (i.e., the Kargı Complex). Above this basal unit are highly sheared brown to black shales, phacoidal, siliciclastic sandstones, and debris flows. The upper part of the section is tectonic melange, with blocks of serpentinite, pillow lava, red shales, cherts, and metamorphics (derived from the basement). The size of these tectonic blocks is variable, but locally they reach up to several tens of meters in diameter. Volcaniclastic sediments are also seen as interbeds in red shales and cherts; these are interpreted as having been derived from the Kösdağ arc.

A Campanian age was determined for the basal pelagic limestones (Tüysüz, 1990). Paleocene sediments in the north and early Eocene sediments in the south unconformably overlie this ophiolitic melange and its basement; this limits the age of genesis and emplacement of the melange as Campanian to early Eocene (Tüysüz, 1990).

The Kösdağ Unit

This unit, first described by Tüysüz (1990), is exposed in the southernmost areas of the Central Pontides along the North Anatolian transform fault (Figures 3, 5). The northern contact of the unit is a low-angle thrust along which the basement units and the Late Cretaceous ophiolitic melanges were emplaced from the north. The unit comprises north-dipping, foliated, basic lavas, tuffs, and volcaniclastic sediments, intercalated at the base with pelagic limestones and cherts. The pelagic limestones contain a Late Cretaceous fauna (Tüysüz, 1990). Above this basal sequence comes a dominantly acidic lava pile, with tuff and volcaniclastic sediment intercalations. The upper part of the unit is represented by volcaniclastic turbidites (Tüysüz, 1990). Small granitic intrusions are also reported (Yılmaz and Tüysüz, 1988). The unit is affected by low-pressure greenschist facies metamorphism at the base; this decreases upward and then disappears (Tüysüz, 1990).

Interpretation

Cretaceous ophiolitic melange slices and ophiolite nappes are exposed to the south of the Paleotethyan ophiolitic melange and accretionary complex (i.e., the Domuzdağ-Saraycıkdağ Complex). There is no evidence for the existence of a Late Mesozoic oceanic basin to the north of this area that could have been the root zone for these ophiolite and related melange units. Structural data indicate that the Late Cretaceous ophiolite was emplaced from the south to the north (Tüysüz, 1990; Yılmaz and Tüysüz, 1991). Therefore, the ophiolite and melange must have originated in a Late Mesozoic ocean basin (i.e., Neotethys) to the south of Paleotethyan units in the Central Pontides (e.g., the Kargı Massif) (Yılmaz and Tüysüz, 1991).

Tüysüz (1990), Yılmaz and Tüysüz (1988, 1991), and Yiğitbaş et al. (1990) interpreted the cover units to the south of Kastamonu-Boyabat Basin (Figure 5) as an imbricate belt (an accretionary complex) that developed as a result of northward subduction of Neotethys during the Late Mesozoic. A Late Cretaceous ophiolite (i.e., the Kızılırmak Group), a sliver of Neotethyan oceanic crust, was obducted onto the Pontide margin from south to north, as a result of backthrusting (i.e., "retrocharriage"). These researchers thought that imbrication of the Pontide margin took place in a deep-sea environment, as shown by the occurrence of thin transgressive *Globotruncana*-bearing limestones.

We propose an alternative model (Figure 6) in which Late Mesozoic subduction of Tethys was dominantly northward, and an oceanic volcanic arc, Kösdağ arc, developed above an intra-oceanic subduction zone, leaving a Neotethyan Ocean strand to the north, adjacent to a newly established active continental margin. The basement of this basin was either suprasubduction zone oceanic crust or trapped mid-ocean rich (MOR)-type oceanic crust. Southward closure of this narrow oceanic basin was possibly coupled with rapid subsidence of the southern margin of the Paleotethyan basement terrane in the Late Cretaceous. Subsidence possibly began with deposition of a thin transgressive cover unit (<1 m) of *Globotruncana*-bearing pelagic limestones, followed by turbidite deposition in a foreland basin setting. Neotethyan ophiolites and related units (e.g., Kösdağ arc) (Tüysüz, 1990) were then emplaced northward onto the south-Eurasian continental margin in the Late Cretaceous, followed by complete closure of Neoethys in the Eocene, when the Kırşehir Block collided with the active continental margin along the İzmir-Ankara-Erzincan suture. This collision caused southward reimbrication of the previously emplaced Late Mesozoic–Early Tertiary ophiolites and ophiolitic melanges and underlying Paleotethyan units. The advantages of this model are as follows: (1) It explains the present outcrop geometry and occurrence of Neotethyan melanges as north-dipping thrust wedges within an Early Tertiary zone of reimbrication; (2) it helps explain the kinematic difficulty of northward (i.e., toward arc) emplacement of oceanic slices in a northward subduction system; and (3) it does not require intense imbrication of the continental margin (the backstop) during northward subduction in the Late Mesozoic, as the trench was located farther south within a marginal basin located between the trench and a backstop.

SUMMARY OF NEOTETHYAN EVOLUTION

The post-Late Jurassic volcanic-sedimentary units of the Central Pontides reflect active margin processes related to the northward subduction of the Jurassic–Cretaceous Neotethys. The northern basement units were transgressed in the Late Jurassic and platform-type carbonate sedimentation began (i.e., the İnaltı Formation). Lithospheric extension occurred in the Early Cretaceous, and this eventually led to the breakup of the platform to form half grabens. Offsets during extension were sufficient to expose basement, particularly on horsts. Turbidites and debris flows (i.e., the Çağlayan Formation) accumulated in the grabens, locally in direct contact with basement lithologies (i.e., the Küre Complex), which has caused some confusion in the past concerning how to separate these two superficially similar terrigenous turbiditic sequences (e.g., Aydın et al., 1995). The Kastamonu-Boyabat Basin represents one of these half grabens that later filled with deep-marine to continental sediments. Extension continued until the end of the Campanian, as evidenced by the presence of reworked megabreccias (from the İnaltı and Bürnük formations) (Derman and Norman, 1996). This extension culminated in the formation of the Western Black Sea as a type of marginal basin in the Upper Cretaceous (Görür, 1988). Exhumation of southerly basement units to the south of Kastamonu-Boyabat Basin also occurred during the Early Cretaceous extensional event.

Neotethys was subducted northward under the Pontide margin of Eurasia during the Late Mesozoic–Early Tertiary. A magmatic arc (i.e., the Kösdağ Unit) was formed to the south of the continental margin, in response to Late Cretaceous subduction. Southward closure of the remaining ocean resulted in regional compression. Ophiolites were emplaced from the south, together with ophiolitic melanges, leading to rapid collapse of the Central Pontide continental margin in the south to form a foredeep. The Kösdağ arc collided with the margin after the intervening oceanic lithosphere was subducted (Figure 6). The dextral North Anatolian transform fault was subsequently initiated in the Miocene, causing further structural complexity in its immediate vicinity (Andrieux et al., 1995).

The Pontides collided with the Anatolides in the Eocene when the Neotethys was totally consumed (Şengör and Yılmaz, 1981). This collision resulted in intense south-vergent imbrication of the southern part of the Central Pontides and in less intense north-vergent imbrication of the Black Sea coastal area (Şengör, 1995). As discussed below, pre-Upper Jurassic structural vergences were similar; that is, northward in the north, but southward in the south. However, the Paleotethyan and Neotethyan structures can be clearly separated by examining deformation styles and intensity of both basement and cover units. For example, the Paleotethyan Küre Complex in the north is characterized by intense north-vergent sheared chevron folds, shear zones, and duplex structures, while cover units are characterized by only high-amplitude open folds and rare thrusts. Post-Late Jurassic units are unmetamorphosed, whereas basement units are metamorphosed to greenschist, blueschist, or amphibolite facies. The basement units in the southern areas have undergone south-vergent ductile to brittle deformation with development of foliation, mineral orientation, stretching lineation, isoclinal-chevron folding, and thrusting. None of these structures are observed in the post-Late Jurassic Central Pontide units. The Tertiary imbrication in the Central Pontides exploited pre-Late Jurassic zones of weakness. However, this deformation is well understood and did not involve indiscriminate disruption of Paleotethyan units (e.g., by large-scale strike slip). Taking account of the Neotethyan deformation, the Paleotethyan basement of the Central Pontides can therefore be analyzed and interpreted in terms of plate tectonic processes, as discussed below.

PRE-LATE JURASSIC TECTONIC UNITS OF THE CENTRAL PONTIDES

A number of east-west–trending tectonic units, differing in lithology, stratigraphy, structure, and geochemistry, are exposed beneath the Upper Jurassic–Tertiary cover units (Figures 3–5). Most of these units were first described by Tüysüz (1985, 1990). We have used Tüysüz's (1990) stratigraphic terminology for the most part, although we introduce new data and propose alternate interpretations. Each of the basement tectonic units from north to south, starting with the Paleotethyan Küre Complex, is summarized below.

Küre Complex

The Küre Complex comprises a structurally thickened (>20 km) wedge of thrust-imbricated siliciclastic sediments [which largely corresponds to the Akgöl Formation of Ketin (1962)], interleaved with tectonic slices of a dismembered ophiolite (Figures 4, 5). Late Carboniferous–Permian, Triassic–Mid-Jurassic fossils have been identified (Aydın et al., 1986, 1995). However, Late Paleozoic palynomorphs could be entirely reworked from the adjacent İstanbul Unit (Yılmaz and Şengör, 1985). Potassium/argon dating of basalts suggested Middle Jurassic ages (Aydın et al., 1995), but these are not considered reliable in view of their low potassium content and hydrothermally altered nature. In the north, a Late Cretaceous–Early Tertiary volcanic-sedimentary succession (the Karadağ Unit) unconformably overlies the Küre Complex along the Black Sea coast (Figure 4). In the west, low-angle thrust sheets of the İstanbul Unit are emplaced over the Küre Complex. In the south, two units, the Devrekani metamorphics and the Çangaldağ Complex, are in tectonic contact with the Küre Complex. Mid-Jurassic granites and associated felsic lavas intrude the Küre Complex and adjacent units to the south. In this area, Upper Jurassic–Lower Cretaceous shallow-marine carbonates with basal continental red conglomerates unconformably overlie the Küre Complex.

The dismembered Küre ophiolite (Figures 7a, 8) is reconstructed as follows: serpentinized peridotite at the base is overlain by layered cumulate gabbros, exposed directly south of the town of Küre. The cumulates pass upward into isotropic microgabbro, cut by diabase dykes. The dyke percentage increases up sequence and passes into a true sheeted dyke complex (i.e., 100% dykes). The sheeted dykes are stratigraphically overlain by alternations of pillow lava, massive lava, and lava breccias. Individual intact successions in the vicinity of Küre range from 100 to 200 m thick; elsewhere, detached blocks range from a few meters to tens of meters in size, and are found within sheared Küre Complex sediments (Figure 9). Small volumes of interpillow sediment comprise devitrified, chloritized volcanic glass and shale. Pillow lavas are locally overlain by lava breccias and devitrified hyaloclastites. Both the lavas and lava breccias, in several different slices, are depositionally overlain by shales, interpreted as hemipelagic sediments (Figures 8, 9). In several thrust sheets, "Cyprus-type"

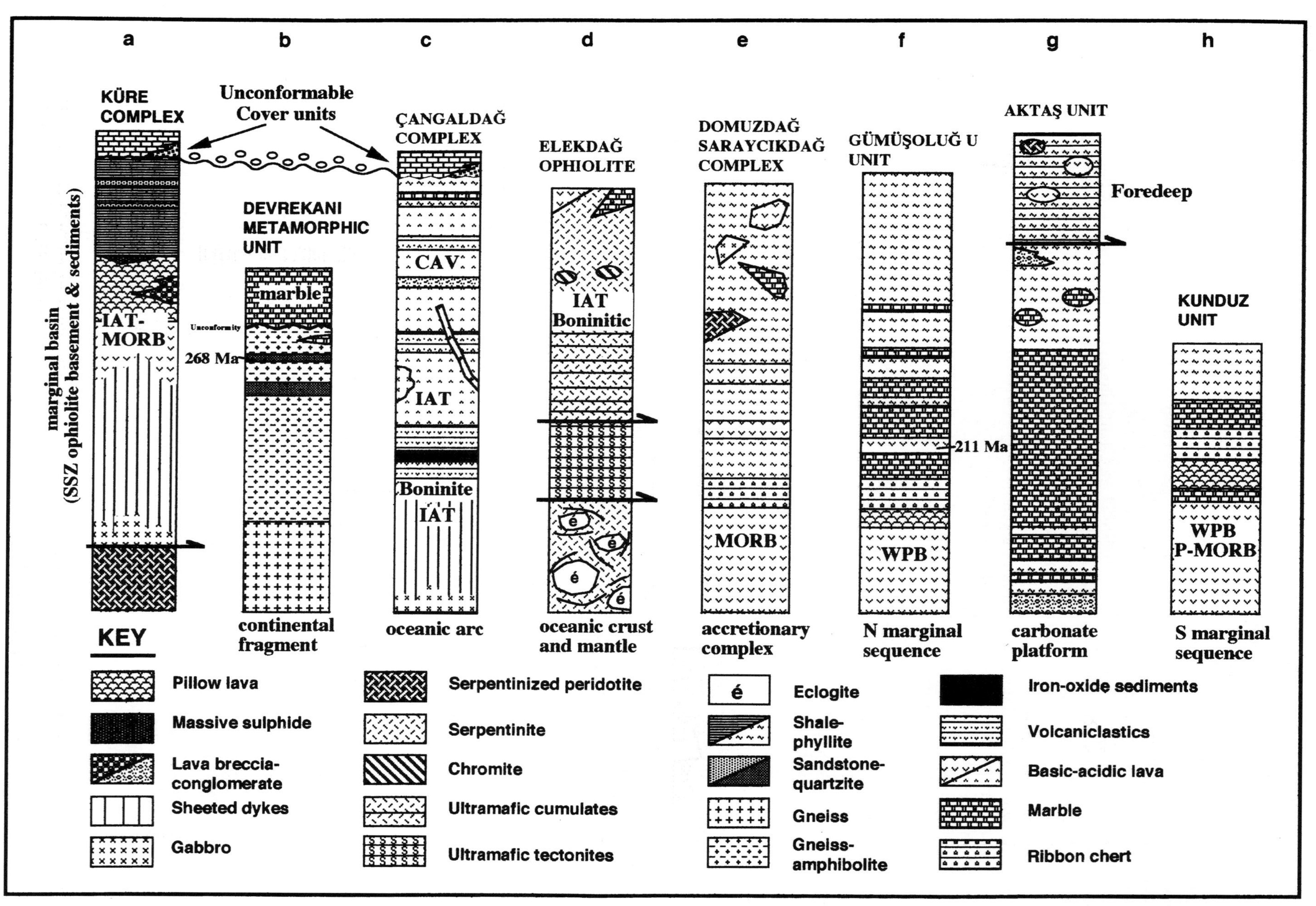

Figure 7. Composite successions of the main pre-Late Jurassic tectonic units described in this chapter. Compare this with Tüysüz (1990).

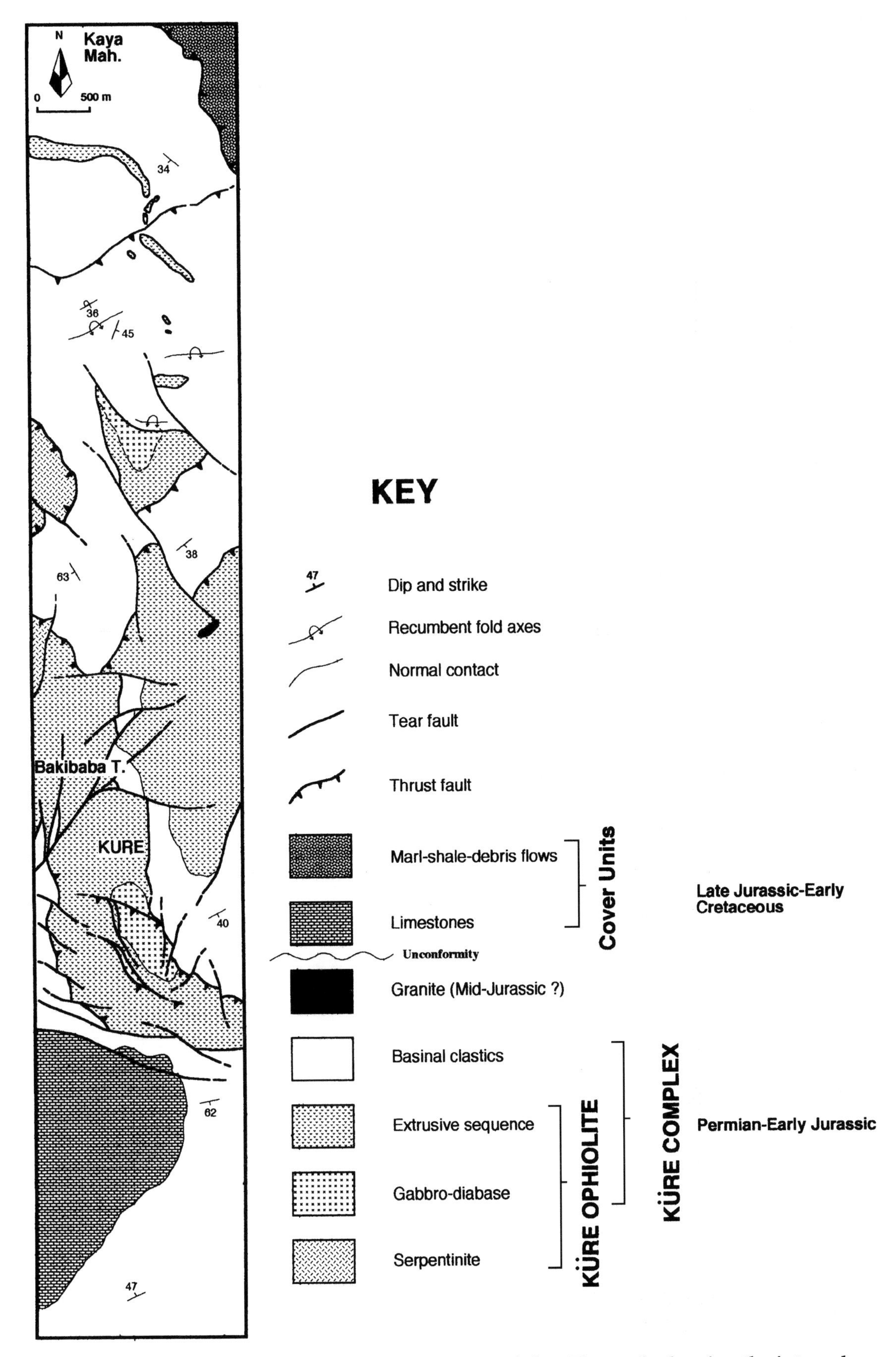

Figure 8. Geological map of the Küre area in the north (see Figure 4), showing the internal structure, distribution of the ophiolites, the matrix of the Küre Complex, and the cover units (after Ustaömer and Robertson, 1994).

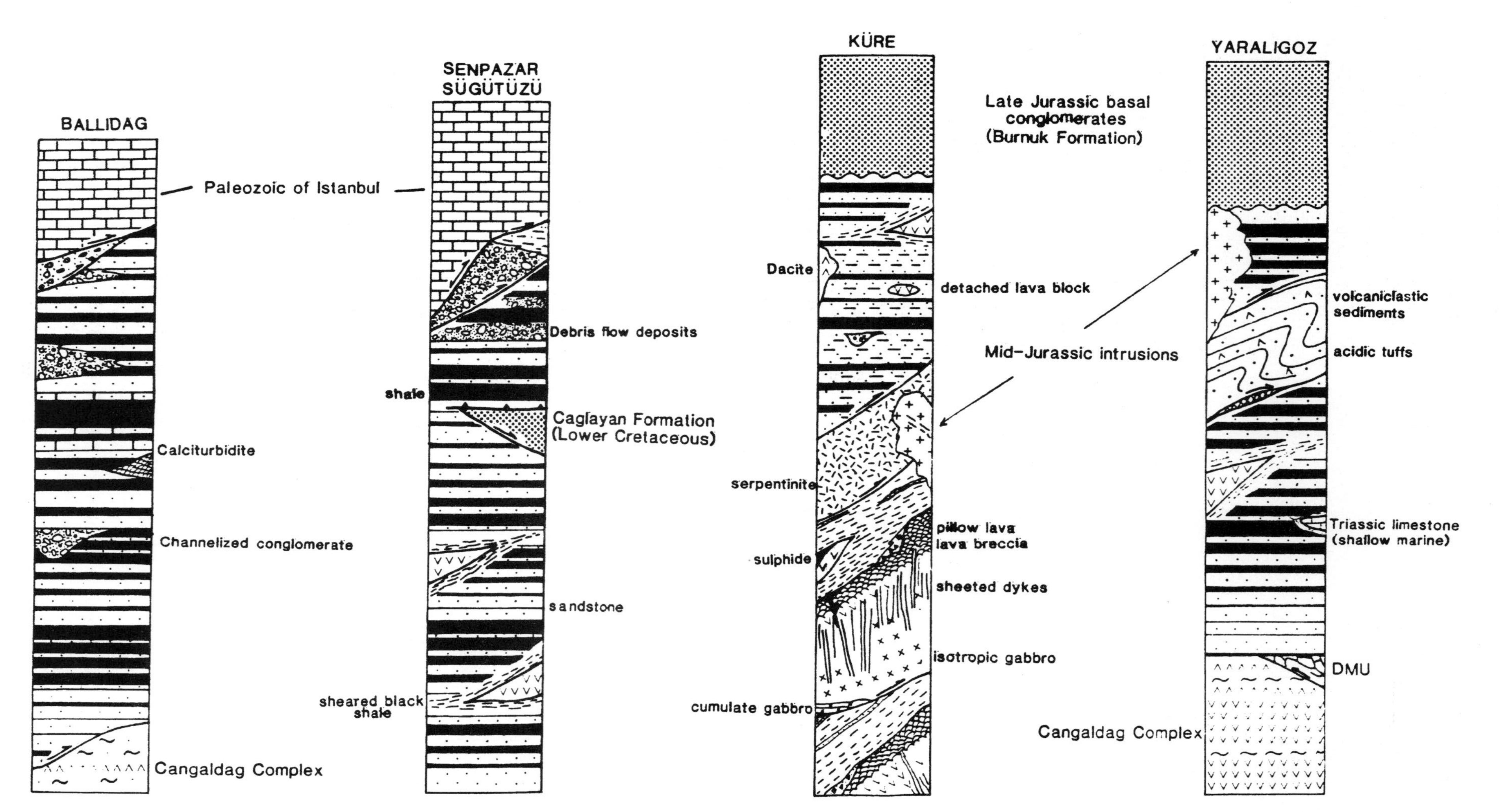

Figure 9. Generalized stratigraphic logs from the Küre Complex, showing the internal structure, deformation, and stratigraphy of the unit, and its relationship with adjacent tectonic units, as exposed in Daday-Azdavay (Ballidağ), Senpazar-Süğütüzü, Küre, and Yaraligoz areas (after Ustaömer, 1993).

cupriferous pyrite deposits are found along the lava–sediment contact, both as disseminated and massive ores (Güner, 1980). Adjacent sediments, often black shales, are unmineralized. Immobile element geochemistry of the basalts (35 samples) indicates both MOR and island-arc tholeiite (IAT) compositions and implies a suprasubduction zone eruptive setting. The mean Cr/(Cr + Al) ratio of the chrome spinels in the serpentinized peridotite is >0.60, which is consistent with an above-subduction zone setting. Pyroxene chemistry of the lavas also confirms the presence of a subduction influence (Ustaömer and Robertson, 1994).

Sediments depositionally overlying the Küre ophiolitic lavas are mainly shales, alternating with terrigenous sandstones (Figures 9, 10). Greenschist facies volcaniclastic sediments occur in local thrust sheets, mainly in the south. An unconformable contact relation of the Küre flysch over these volcaniclastic sediments was recently proposed locally (i.e., from northeast of Haramidağ) (Aydın et al., 1995). We have interpreted these volcaniclastics as the deeply buried northern sedimentary apron of the Çangaldağ arc (Ustaömer and Robertson, 1994); thus, local unconformities are to be expected. Conglomerates, mainly debris flows up to 50 m thick, are intercalated with sandstones and shales in the vicinity of the overriding "Paleozoic of İstanbul" thrust sheets (i.e., the İstanbul Unit) (Figure 9). Petrographic work on the sandstones indicates acidic to intermediate igneous and metamorphic source areas; the geochemistry of the shales (24 samples) suggests both mafic and acid igneous provenance.

Intense zones of deformation and faulting up to 10 m thick, commonly separate more coherent successions up to several hundred meters thick (Figure 10). Shear zones mainly dip southward. Individual thrust packets are internally deformed by small-scale reverse faults, thrust faults, and larger duplex structures. Small-scale thrust faults indicate relative northward overthrusting throughout the Küre Complex.

At their base, individual ophiolitic thrust slices are marked by southward-dipping zones of sheared black shales with scaly fabrics. By contrast, the upper contacts of these thrust sheets are commonly depositional (Figure 10). Detached lava blocks are also locally present in the Küre Complex, surrounded by sheared shale. Occasionally, exposed slickensides indicate mainly northward-directed movement within these shear zones. North-verging, north-facing folds range from tight, asymmetrical folds to chevron folds and, more rarely, open folds. Most folds are sheared, but coherent folds preferentially occur in more sandstone-dominated successions. There is a wide variation in fold axial trends, but northwest-southeast directions dominate.

The Küre Complex is interpreted as a Triassic to Early–Mid-Jurassic subduction-accretion complex of southward polarity, related to closure of a Paleotethyan marginal basin (Ustaömer and Robertson, 1990, 1993, 1994, 1995). As discussed below, this is believed to have formed above a northward-dipping, Paleotethyan subduction zone.

Devrekani Metamorphic Unit

The Devrekani metamorphic unit is exposed as a fault-bounded tectonic block that crops out between the Küre Complex to the north and the Çangaldağ Complex to the south (Figures 4, 5, and 7b). The metamorphic assemblage comprises high-grade gneisses and amphibolites at the base, transgressively overlain by metamorphosed carbonates (Figure 7b). The Devrekani metamorphic unit is intruded by a Mid-Jurassic granite (Yılmaz, 1980), and both this and the metamorphic basement are unconformably overlain by Late Jurassic–Early Cretaceous cover sediments (Tüysüz, 1990). Both Precambrian (Yılmaz, 1980) and early Paleozoic ages (Tüysüz, 1990) have been suggested, based on correlations with Cambrian to Silurian sequences of the Paleozoic of the İstanbul Unit (Tüysüz, 1990). Aydın et al. (1995) obtained a Mid-Carboniferous K/Ar age (311 ±6.2 Ma) from a gneiss sample, 6 km east of Devrekani. Potassium/argon radiometric dating of two gneiss samples (whole rock) and an amphibolite (mineral separate) during this study gave Early Cretaceous and Early Permian ages, respectively (Table 1). The amphibolite is from a rare sill, 25 cm thick, intruded into quartzo-felsic gneiss in the upper part of the Devrekani metamorphic unit, below a transgressive metacarbonate cover. This sill gave a 248 Ma age (Late Permian), but this is uncertain due to the presence of nonradiogenic argon. The Devrekani metamorphic unit is inferred to have rifted from the south Eurasian margin to open the Küre marginal basin in the latest Permian (Ustaömer and Robertson, 1990, 1993). The radiometrically determined Early Cretaceous ages can be explained in terms of the important regional extension that took place during this time, as a precursor to opening of the Western Black Sea Basin in the Late Cretaceous–early Tertiary, as summarized earlier. The Devrekani metamorphic unit is very similar, in both lithology and stratigraphy, to Precambrian continental basement units of the Rhodope-Pontide belt and similar units in the Caucasus (Ustaömer and Robertson, 1993). These units experienced collisional deformation in the Mid-Late Carboniferous, associated with granitic intrusion. The Mid-Carboniferous age obtained from a gneiss sample could thus be interpreted as a thermal resetting age.

The contact of the Devrekani metamorphic unit with the Çangaldağ Complex to the south is a high-angle fault zone, characterized by thick (≤50 m) mylonites in southwest-northeast–trending segments, while more north-south–trending segments exhibit mainly low-angle shear zones (Figure 4). Small lens-shaped protrusions of sheared, mylonitized serpentinite, with high-angle fabrics, are seen along southwest-northeast–trending contacts. The base of the low-angle thrust segments is often sharp, but in places includes up to 1-m-thick shear zones, with phacoids derived from wall rocks. The high-angle segments are interpreted as strike-slip faults, essentially lateral ramps, and the low-angle segments as thrusts. The final emplacement direction of the Devrekani sliver was from west-southwest to east-northeast. However, two different shear events are

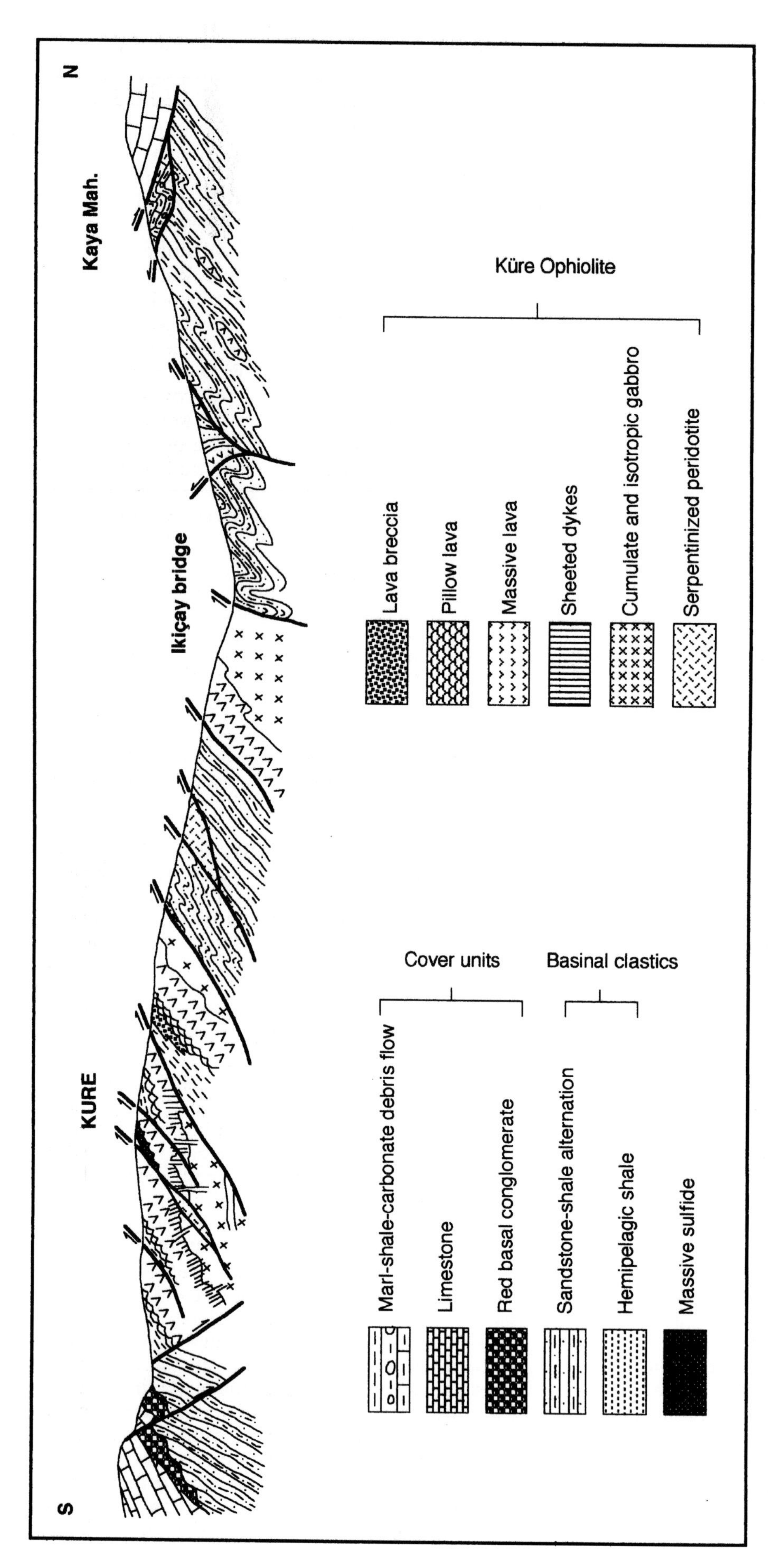

Figure 10. Composite N-S geological cross section of the transect mapped (Figure 8). Note the sliced nature and the presence of sediments depositionally overlying mafic extrusives.

Table 1. Results of K/Ar Radiometric Dating of Magmatic and Metamorphic Units of the Central Pontides.*

Sample	K (wt%)	$^{40}Ar^{*}/10^{-10}mol/g$	$\%^{40}Ar^{*}$	Age (Ma)	Mineral Type
TU-1	0.146	0.174	6.83	67.6 ± 13.0	W. Rock
TU-2	0.141	0.093	6.83	37.4 ± 3.3	W. Rock
TU-3	0.659	1.107	36.78	94.3 ± 3.3	W. Rock
TU-4	0.639	1.541	48.81	133.9 ± 3.8	W. Rock
TU-5	4.60	10.960	87.45	132.4 ± 2.8	W. Rock
TU-6	0.098	0.187	14.70	106.7 ± 8.9	W. Rock
TU-7	2.18	5.343	85.18	136.0 ± 2.9	W. Rock
TU-8	2.22	3.135	70.49	79.6 ± 1.8	W. Rock
S-1	1.49	2.29	25.26	86.3 ± 4.2	Feldspar
S-1	0.37	0.75	22.75	113.5 ± 6.1	Hornblende
S-6	1.02	4.72	5.04	248.8 ± 68.9	Hornblende
S-16	5.93	8.82	10.76	83.7 ± 9.7	Muscovite
S-25	0.21	0.18	12.96	47.4 ± 4.5	W. Rock
S-26	3.87	7.38	28.36	106.8 ± 4.7	Glaucophane
S-32	0.32	1.25	13.85	211.7 ± 18.7	Hornblende

*Sample locations are shown on Figure 3. Potassium/argon dating was carried out on 14 whole-rock samples (W. Rock) and mineral separates (as indicated) of metamorphic and igneous rocks from the Central Pontides. Samples were collected from each of the main tectonic units (except the Küre Complex) and examined under the microscope. Fourteen of the most suitable lithologies (based on mineralogy and degree of alteration) were then analyzed, using the K/Ar technique, at the Scottish Universities Research and Reactor Centre. Whole-rock analyses were made on 8 samples, while mineral separates were used for 6 samples. Samples TU-8 and S-1 = granites; TU-4, TU-5, and S-6 = Devrekani Metamorphic Unit; TU-3 = Çangaldağ Complex; TU-1, TU-2, TU-6, S-16, S-25, and S-26 = Domuzdağ-Saraycıkdağ Complex; TU-7 and TU-32 = Gümüşoluğu Unit. The radiometric ages determined from various units of the Central Pontides range from 248–37 Ma (Permian–Eocene). The oldest ages are from banded amphibolites. Samples 1, 2, 6, and 25 show low potash values; hence, ages are not considered reliable. Since the region has undergone low-temperature/low-pressure metamorphism, the most reliable ages are expected from higher-grade amphibolites and unmetamorphosed granites.

observed in these zones; an earlier sinistral and a later dextral one. The contact of the Devrekani metamorphic unit with the Küre Complex to the north is not exposed.

The Devrekani metamorphic unit is interpreted as a fragment of the south Eurasian margin that was rifted off to form a crustal sliver within Paleotethys and later reamalgamated to Eurasia (Ustaömer and Robertson, 1990).

Çangaldağ Complex

Farther south, the Çangaldağ Complex is an approximately 10-km-thick, imbricated pile of basic and evolved volcanics and volcaniclastics, overlying an ophiolitic basement made up of sheeted dykes and basic lavas (Figures 4, 7c). The complex is metamorphosed to greenschist facies. The east-west–trending, Late Creteceous–Tertiary Kastamonu-Boyabat Basin splits the outcrop. The southern margin abuts melange composed mainly of metabasite and micaschist (i.e., the Bayam melange, Figure 11). Mid-Jurassic granites intrude the Çangaldağ Complex in the north and are unconformably overlain by Upper Jurassic conglomerates, passing into neritic carbonates, thus confirming a pre-Middle Jurassic age for the Çangaldağ Complex. In this study, one sample of a gabbro gave a Cenomanian–Late Cretaceous whole-rock age using the K/Ar method (94.3 ±3.3), but this is probably unreliable in view of its hydrothermally altered nature.

Mapping and regional reconnaissance of the Çangaldağ Complex have revealed the following units, in a generally ascending order: (1) an ophiolitic basement, exposed in the northwest and along the northern margin of the Kastamonu-Boyabat Basin; (2) a volcanic-sedimentary sequence, mainly exposed in the south and east; (3) a volcanic sequence, to the north of the Kastamonu-Boyabat Basin; and (4) a "collapse sequence," in northerly areas (Figures 4, 11, and 12).

1. Ophiolitic rocks are locally exposed as north-dipping thrust sheets, imbricated with volcanic-sedimentary and volcanic sequences (Figure 12a). A well-developed sheeted dyke complex is exposed as a fault-bounded unit beneath mafic lavas. The sheeted dykes are fine-grained, dark green, typically 20–25 cm wide, and have millimeter-thick chilled margins. Small gabbroic intrusions, ≤100 m across, and in places pegmatitic, are common near the contact between the sheeted dykes and the overlying lavas. Basic lavas are seen above the sheeted dykes. Flattened basic pillow lavas are locally overlain and interbedded with thin (<2 m) volcaniclastic sediments and intervals of ferruginous sediments and green, recrystallized radiolarian cherts. Depositionally above are 400 m of northward-dipping, greenish to brownish volcaniclastic sandstones; these are thin- to medium-bedded, fine- to medium-grained, and exhibit sharp bases and graded tops. Tuffaceous sediments, ≤5 cm thick, are interbedded throughout.
2. An overlying volcanic-sedimentary sequence, ≤5 km thick in the east, consists mainly of fine-grained volcanogenic sediments (phyllites), with subordinate lavas and volcaniclastics (Figure 12b). Volcaniclastic sediments are mainly fine to medium grained, laterally discontinuous, and form interbeds ≤10 m thick. Sedimentary structures, including parallel lamination, convolute lamination, and grading are preserved in places.

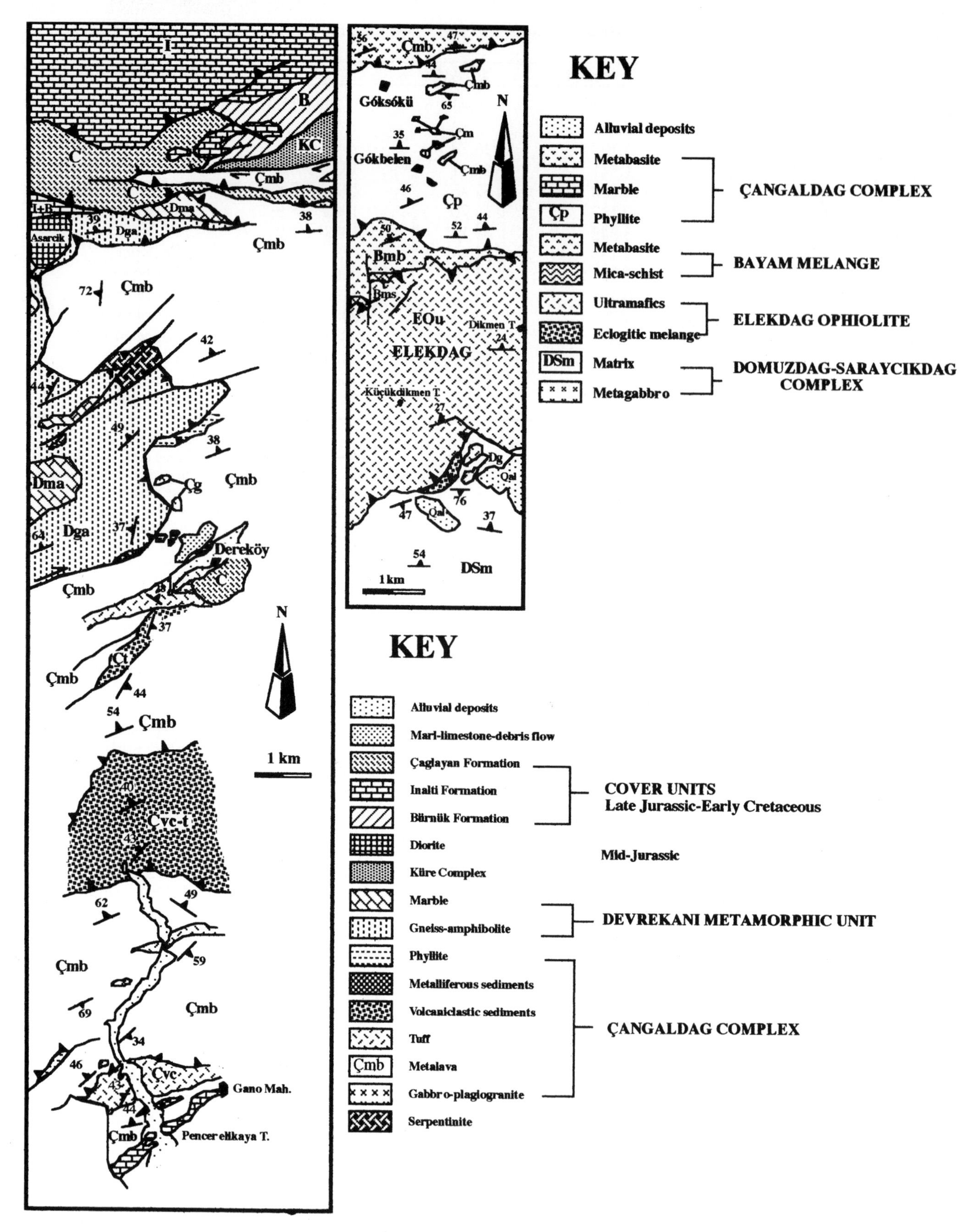

Figure 11. Geological maps of the Çangaldağ Complex and adjacent units. Locations are shown in Figure 4. (A) Northerly part of the Çangaldağ Complex; (B) Southerly part of the Çangaldağ Complex. Modified after Yılmaz (1980) and Eren (1979).

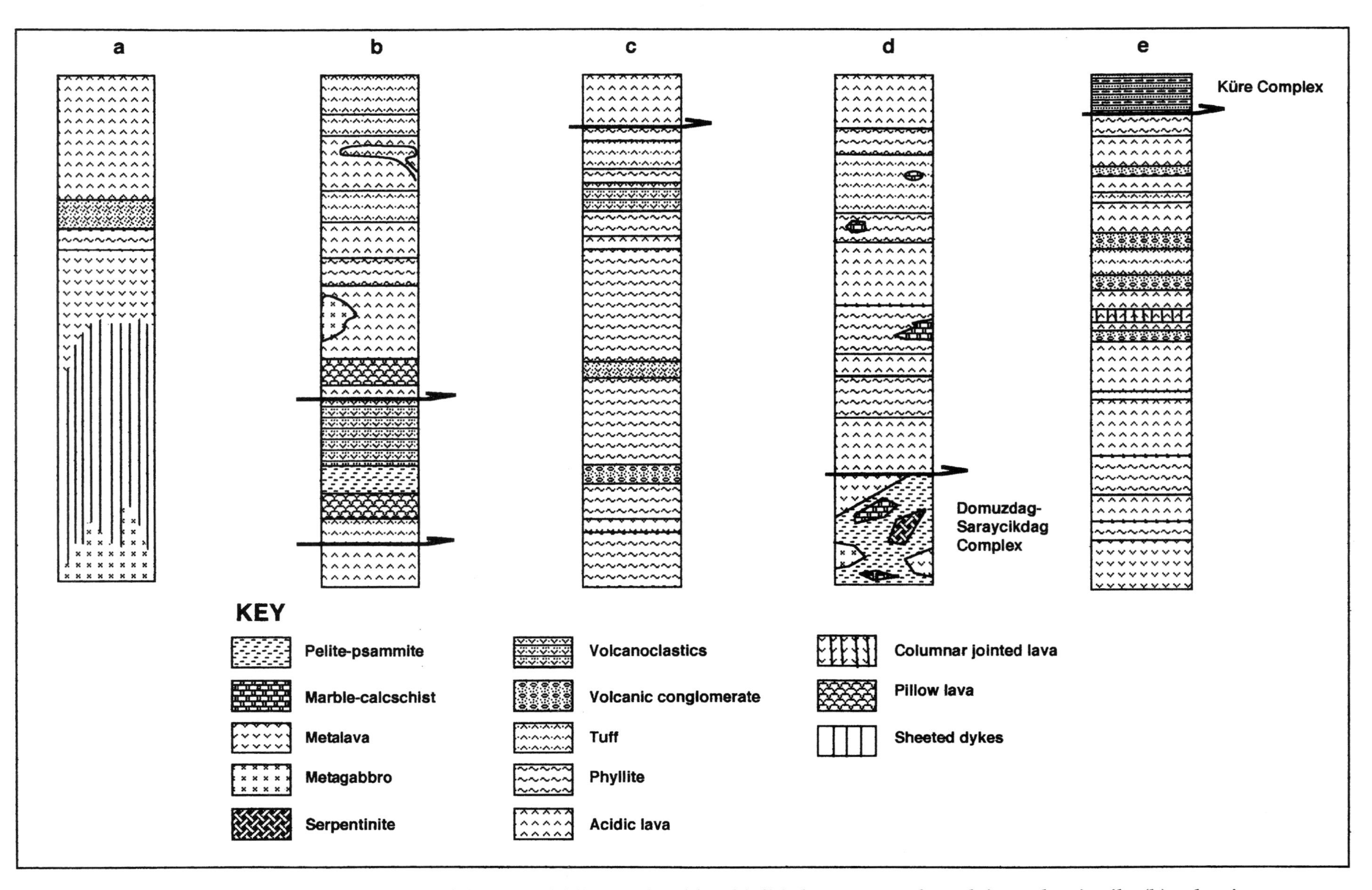

Figure 12. Composite stratigraphic successions of the Çangaldağ Complex. (a) ophiolitic basement and overlying volcanic pile, (b) volcanic sequence (western area), (c, d) volcano-sedimentary sequence (northern and southern areas, respectively), and (e) volcanic sequence (eastern area).

Volcanic-sedimentary lithologies to the south of the Kastamonu-Boyabat Basin reappear on the northern slopes of Elekdağ (Figures 4, 12c), where volcaniclastic sediments dominate, with subordinate lava flows and phyllites. Upsequence, tuffaceous sediments, ≤100 m thick, exhibit well-developed, laterally continuous sedimentary bedding (typically 5 cm thick), marked by color banding and parallel lamination. Overlying lavas and volcaniclastics, ≤1000 m thick, are probably structurally repeated. Phyllites range from dark brown to reddish brown and locally black, and include numerous recrystallized thick-bedded limestone lenses and blocks up to several tens of meters wide.

3. The overlying volcanic sequence comprises porphyric andesites, basaltic andesites, rhyolites, rhyodacites, and dacites, associated with tuffs and volcaniclastic sediments that are locally silicified (Figure 12d). Numerous small gabbroic-plagiogranitic and felsic intrusives (<100 m across) are exposed, while coarse-grained dykes up to several meters wide are seen throughout the sequence. Phyllites occur at several structural levels and dominate the upper part of the sequence, with interbeds of thin-bedded, recrystallized limestones and volcanic-derived matrix-supported conglomerates. Columnar-jointed and vesicular lavas are exposed higher in the succession. Flow-banded lavas and tuffs contain occasional volcanic-derived clast-supported conglomerates, ≤2 m thick. Above this is a sequence of columnar-jointed, vesicular basaltic andesites, rare pillow lavas, acidic tuffs, tuffaceous sediments, and acidic lavas, intercalated with alternations of volcanic-derived, matrix-supported conglomerates (~3000 m thick, total). White rhyolitic lavas dominate the upper part of the succession. Individual flows are characterized by dark-brown, chilled margins, ≤1 cm thick.
4. Schistose black phyllites stratigraphically overlie the uppermost lavas of the mainly volcanic sequence. Thin (<15 cm) interbeds of recrystallized limestones are seen within black phyllites, with additional lava flows. These individual lava flows are thin (<70 cm), aphyric, or locally plagioclase-phyric. Sedimentary structures (fine lamination) are well exposed in the upper part of this unit. An albite + epidote + tremolite + actinolite + chlorite + calcite + quartz + opaque greenschist mineral assemblage is developed throughout the volcanic sequence (Yılmaz, 1980). Prehnite and pumpelliite are locally found as vein and vesicle fills.

A total of 80 samples of lava and phyllite were analyzed for major and trace elements. Geochemical discrimination plots indicate that the ophiolitic basement of the Çangaldağ Complex is of MORB and IAT type in the northern areas, but boninitic in the south. The calc-alkaline nature and occurrence of boninite-type lavas suggests an above-subduction zone eruptive setting. An arc-related setting for the volcanic-sedimentary and volcanic units above the ophiolitic basement is shown by MORB-normalized plots. LIL-element enrichment (large ion lithophile), Nb depletion relative to Ce, P enrichment, and Zr and Ti depletion are all characteristics of calc-alkaline lavas erupted above subduction zones (Pearce, 1980). The Çangaldağ Complex is interpreted as a south-facing oceanic volcanic arc of Late Paleozoic–Early Mesozoic age. The ophiolitic basement is interpreted as the result of initial subduction and extension before any arc formed. During the earlier stages of arc genesis, tholeiitic lavas were erupted; a volcanic-volcaniclastic sequence was then shed over the fore-arc basin (Figure 13a, b). This was followed by progradation of a mature arc over the fore-arc, associated with calc-alkaline lava eruption and volcaniclastic sedimentation (Figure 13c). The uppermost part of the tectonostratigraphy is composed of black phyllites interbedded with deep-water limestones; occasional lava flows could represent collapse of the arc, related to opening of the inferred Küre back-arc basin to the north (Figure 13d). Occurrences of blocks of thick-bedded limestone blocks in the volcanic-sedimentary sequence to the south of the Kastamonu-Boyabat Basin suggest that a carbonate platform (now eroded) was established along the margins of the arc (Figure 13c). This could also explain the origin of shallow-marine limestone blocks within the Küre Complex in the north.

Elekdağ Ophiolite

The undated Elekdağ ophiolite (Eren, 1979; Tüysüz, 1985, 1990) crops out as a southwest-northeast–trending, largely north-dipping huge tectonic slice (Figures 4, 5, and 7d), comprising an ultramafic tectonite at the base, followed by ultramafic cumulates and massive serpentinized peridotites, with podiform chromites in the upper levels. Tectonic blocks of blueschists are common. The ophiolite is thrust over melange units in the south (see below), and similar melange is also exposed along its northern margin (the Bayam melange) (Figure 11). The northern contact of the ophiolite is with the Domuzdağ-Saraycıkdağ Complex; the Çangaldağ Complex is a thrust that locally dips southward, suggesting that the Elekdağ ophiolite is a klippe (Figure 11).

The base of the ophiolite proper comprises ultramafic tectonites, ≤200 m thick. Foliations dip northward, parallel to the basal thrust plane. Above comes an ultramafic cumulate sequence, 100 m thick. Although greatly serpentinized and deformed, laterally continuous color banding corresponds to primary layering. Serpentinized ultramafics (massive peridotites) form the highest level of the exposed ophiolite section. At several localities, economic podiform chromite ores are present in the upper part of the ophiolite. The Cr/(Cr + Al) ratio of the chrome spinels (≤0.84) departs from typical MORB values (<0.60), suggesting an above-subduction setting (i.e., IAT to boninitic) (Ustaömer, 1993). The Elekdağ ophiolite is locally structurally overlain by blocks of metabasites, metacarbonates (marbles, calc-schists, and metacarbonate debris flows), and metaclastics, all metamorphosed to blueschist facies (Eren, 1979).

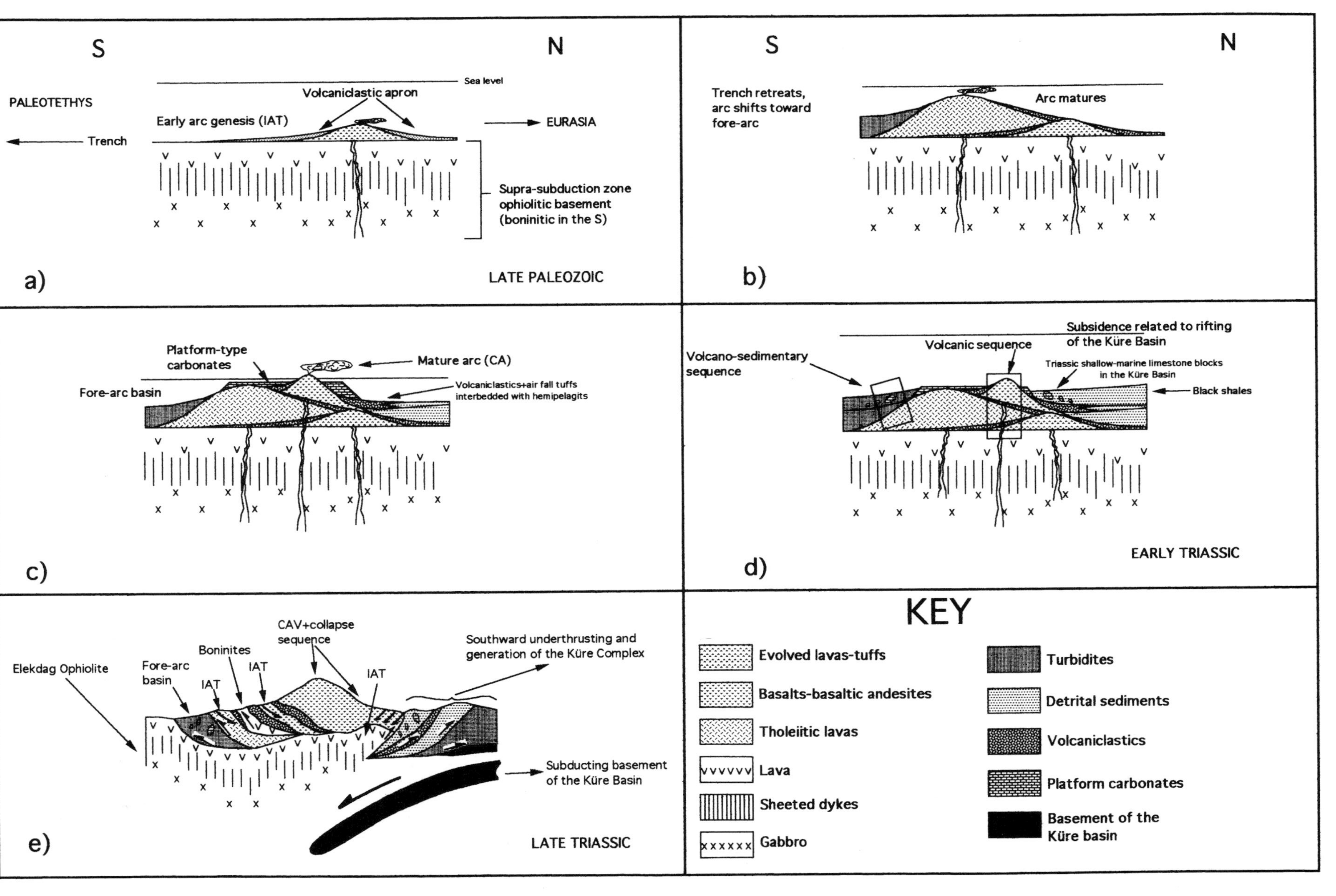

Figure 13. Schematic drawings showing the inferred genesis of the Çangaldağ volcanic arc (see Figure 4) and its later accretionary evolution. IAT = island-arc tholeiites, CA = calc-alkaline lavas. Not drawn to scale.

The Elekdağ ophiolite plays an important role in existing tectonic models (Şengör, 1984; Şengör et al., 1984; Tüysüz, 1985, 1990; Yılmaz and Şengör, 1985). Tüysüz (1985, 1990) regarded the Elekdağ ophiolite as a complete, but moderately disrupted, ophiolite, ranging from ultramafics at the base to lavas and ophiolite-related sediments at the top. This ordered ophiolite was thought to be exposed as a double anticline (i.e., Yılanlı Group; Tüysüz, 1990). Eren (1979) mapped the unit as a serpentinized ultramafic sliver. Our mapping opposes the view of the Elekdağ ophiolite as a complete ophiolite with ordered ultramafic-gabbro-diabase-lava-sediment sequences. It is instead dominated by serpentinized ultramafics, together with tectonic blocks of blueschists. Both the northern and southern margins of the ophiolitic units are tectonic contacts, which also expose eclogites. The ophiolite is thrust over an ophiolitic melange along its southern contact, above the Çangaldağ Complex, and ophiolitic melange along the northern contact. The melange contains slices of gabbro and metabasites in a phyllitic matrix, but these are not part of the ophiolite. The Elekdağ ophiolite was interpreted as a sliver of Paleotethyan basement (Yılmaz and Şengör, 1985; Tüysüz, 1990). Based on analytical data, we interpret the Elekdağ ophiolite as mainly an eroded remnant of suprasubduction zone Paleotethyan oceanic mantle (Ustaömer and Robertson, 1990).

Eclogitic Melange

Tectonic lenses of eclogitic melange are present along both the northern and southern margins of the Elekdağ ophiolite (Eren, 1979).

In the south, the base of the ophiolite is marked by a shear zone, ≤50 m thick. At several localities, blueschist eclogite blocks are enclosed in sheared serpentinite and appear as lenses directly above the basal thrust (Figure 11). The eclogite blocks are generally 2 to 3 m across, but larger blocks also occur (≤15 m across; Eren, 1979). Blocks are green, mineralogically zoned, and generally spherical. Tourmaline rinds (5 cm long) are well developed, together with garnet, chlorite, actinolite, glaucophane, epidote, quartz, and sphene. A garnet + omphacite assemblage is developed in the cores of blocks (Eren, 1979). Immobile element geochemistry of the eclogites (15 samples) indicates a MORB affinity, although this must be treated with caution, as some mobility of trace elements may have taken place (Ustaömer, 1993).

We interpret the eclogites (Eren, 1979) as deeply subducted oceanic fragments, which were intensely sheared to form melange and later uplifted in a fore-arc setting, accompanied by retrograde metamorphism.

Domuzdağ-Saraycıkdağ Complex

Farther south again, the Domuzdağ-Saraycıkdağ Complex comprises, in the north, a unit of north-dipping melange (the Domuzdağ melange) 10 km thick (estimated from dip of schistosity) and, in the south, slices of metabasites and pelite/psammite, all metamorphosed to blueschist facies (retrograded to greenschist facies) (Eren, 1979; Tüysüz, 1990). The complex is bounded to the north by the Elekdağ ophiolite (and its basal eclogitic melange) and locally by the Çangaldağ Complex. A Permian carbonate platform (Kargı Complex) lies to the south (Figures 4, 5, and 7e). Slices of Late Cretaceous ophiolitic melanges occur in the more southerly outcrops (Tüysüz, 1990). The complex is unconformably overlain by Lower Cretaceous sediments in the southeast (Tüysüz, 1990). Six samples of blueschist and greenschist were dated by the K/Ar method (Table 1); they range in age from Late Cretaceous to Eocene. These are apparently anomalous for the Central Pontide metamorphic basement; they are best interpreted in terms of thermal resetting of older ages in response to tectonic events that included emplacement of ophiolites in the latest Cretaceous and final suturing of Neotethys during the Early Tertiary.

In northerly outcrops, the tectonic melange comprises slices of dominantly metabasite and serpentinite, with minor sedimentary rocks ~100 m thick (Eren, 1979). Southward, the melange is of block-in-matrix type, separated by west-southwest– to east-northeast–trending zones of tectonic melange (Tüysüz, 1990). Ophiolitic blocks (often >10 m in size) include serpentinite, gabbro, and metabasites, with marble and blueschist. The matrix is pelitic and psammitic, with some metatuff, red metasiliceous mud, and calc-schist intercalations. In some metabasite blocks, boulders of metacarbonates are embedded in a metabasite matrix. Serpentinite schist (≤1 m thick) locally forms the matrix of the tectonic melange; however, this matrix is sometimes absent. Immobile element geochemistry (43 samples) of the metabasites in the northern tectonic melange indicates IAT- to boninitic-type tectonic affinities, while metabasite blocks in the southerly melange outcrops are of MORB type (Ustaömer, 1993).

Toward the south, blocks gradually disappear, and the unit passes into a north-dipping "diabase-phyllite" unit (i.e., the Bekirli metamorphics of Tüysüz, 1985). The exposed basement of this unit is represented by metabasite slices, overlain by metacherts (with glaucophane) and pelitic sediments, and then by metabasites intersliced with pelites and psammites.

The structurally lowermost metabasites are massive and weakly foliated, with albite porphyroblasts. Upward, thin pelites and black folded cherts, ≤20 m thick, are locally present. Black psammitic-pelitic metasediments contain large garnets. Overlying brown metaclastics contain slices of porphyroblastic metabasites; metabasite slices then decrease upward and pelitic-psammitic sediments dominate. The metabasites are of the MORB type, without an identifiable subduction component. They are, however, more enriched in high-field-strength elements, relative to metabasites in the structurally higher, more northerly outcrops. Mesoscopic structures, including tight asymmetrical folds, chevron folds, isoclinal folds, and stretching lineations, indicate dominantly southward-directed emplacement (Ustaömer, 1993).

The Domuzdağ-Saraycıkdağ Complex was previously considered as two separate units: the Domuzdağ ophiolitic melange in the north and the Bekirli metamorphics in the south (Tüysüz, 1985; Yılmaz and

Şengör, 1985). The Domuzdağ melange was interpreted as a Paleotethyan subduction complex. The Bekirli metamorphic unit (equivalent to the diabase-phyllite unit) was described as a layer-cake succession of lava–sediment alternations that were thought to be part of the the Paleotethyan ophiolite (i.e., the Yılanlı group; Tüysüz, 1985, 1990). Tüysüz (1990) correlated this unit with exposures in the Küre and Çangaldağ areas. Our work has shown that the Bekirli unit is, in fact, a north-dipping lava–sediment tectonic slice complex, rather than an intact stratigraphic succession. The geochemistry of the lavas within this unit indicates normal- and enriched-MORB-type settings, very dissimilar to the lavas of the Küre and Çangaldağ areas, which are of suprasubduction type. Also, the stratigraphy of these three areas differs markedly, as described above. The Domuzdağ melange was thought to have developed through combined sedimentary and tectonic processes, with the ophiolitic blocks being derived from the Elekdağ Ophiolite (i.e., the Yılanlı Group of Tüysüz, 1990). Our geochemical data from the ophiolitic melange show that only the northernmost metabasites are of suprasubduction type (IAT to boninitic), in common with the probable origin of the Elekdağ ophiolite. The presence of IAT to boninitic metabasites at the structurally highest levels (i.e., the northern melange) could be explained by tectonic erosion of the hanging wall of the adjacent fore-arc (i.e., the Elekdağ ophiolite) during the early stages of Paleotethyan subduction. By contrast, the metabasite blocks in the south are of MORB type; these are thought to have been detached from subducting Paleotethyan normal-MORB crust and accreted to the fore-arc to the north. We interpret the southerly diabase-phyllite complex as a Paleozoic–earliest Mesozoic accretionary complex that was assembled during northward subduction of Paleotethys (Ustaömer and Robertson, 1990).

The Kargı Complex

A carbonate-dominated sequence, termed the Kargı Complex, structurally underlies the Domuzdağ-Saraycıkdağ Complex (Figures 4, 5, and 7f–h). The Kargı Complex consists of three structurally assembled tectonostratigraphic units: the Gümüşoluğu unit in the north (structurally highest), the Aktaş unit, and the Kunduz unit in the south (structurally lowest).

Benthic foraminifera (i.e., *Fusulinida*) are observed in the Aktaş unit limestones and overlying pelitic sediments. A Late Carboniferous–Permian age for the platform unit was determined from occurrences of *Hemigordius* sp., *Tetrataxis* sp., *Fusulina* sp., *Schwagerina* sp., and *Mizzia velebitana* (Tüysüz, 1990). Potassium/ argon dating of two amphibolite samples from the northern unit complex during this study (Table 1) gave Late Triassic (211.7 ±18.7) and Early Cretaceous (136.0 ±2.9) ages. We interpret the Late Triassic age as the time when the Kargı Complex was accreted and metamorphosed at the Eurasian active margin. The Early Cretaceous age can be interpreted in terms of thermal resetting related to crustal extension of the Pontide margin.

Gümüşoluğu Unit

The Gümüşoluğu Unit (Tüysüz, 1985), at the highest levels, is dominated by south-vergent, thrust-imbricated, folded metabasites and deep-sea sediments (Figure 7f). The metabasic rocks are dominantly massive, foliated amphibolites. In places, deformed pillow structures are preserved. The thickness of the metabasite lithologies varies from 1 to 50 m in different slices. Lenses of limestones occur in some metabasites. The metabasites are depositionally overlain by ribbon cherts and redeposited limestones, with fine laminations and medium to thin bedding in the upper parts. Limestone conglomerates in the lower thrust slices are debris flows (each ≤1 m thick) comprising deformed limestone clasts (≤10 cm long) set in a reddish shaley matrix. In structurally higher slices, limestones contain thin partings (1–2 cm thick) of green metabasic volcaniclastics. These metabasites are overlain by ribbon cherts (now quartzite). In some thrust slices, these cherts are thin bedded (≤4 cm thick), white to reddish, and in places contain red pelite interbeds a few millimeters thick. Individual ribbon cherts are ≤2 m thick, where they are not folded. The ribbon cherts are stratigraphically overlain by metacarbonates in the structurally lower slices and by phyllites in the upper slices. The metacarbonates are dominantly massive, but in places are conglomeratic. Farther up sequence, the metacarbonates become thinner bedded and decrease in abundance, while pelitic intercalations increase. Thin metacarbonate horizons alternate with pelitic sediments in these intervals. The upper part of the sequence is dominantly phyllitic. The uppermost slices are mainly metabasite, ribbon chert, and phyllite together with grayish-black metalliferous sediments.

The metabasites commonly comprise an assemblage of albite + blue-green amphibole + hornblende + epidote + chlorite + biotite + sphene + opaque minerals. Omphacite, glaucophane, and clinoenstatite are seen in some thin sections. Occurrences of omphacite together with glaucophane in the Gümüşoluğu Unit indicate high-grade blueschist facies metamorphism. This was followed by epidote-amphibolite facies metamorphism and finally by a retrograde greenschist facies metamorphism.

Aktaş Unit

Structurally beneath the Gümüşoluğu Unit is the Aktaş Unit (Tüysüz et al., 1993), made up of folded platform-type carbonates at the base passing upward into a clastic succession, with blocks of limestones and debris flows composed of limestone clasts (Figure 7g). This, in turn, is structurally overlain by black pelitic sediments, with blocks of metabasite and metaserpentinite. The Aktaş Unit is unconformably overlain by Upper Cretaceous *Globotruncana*-bearing limestones and an overlying succession of sheared flysch and Upper Cretaceous colored melange.

At the exposed base of the unit, there are laterally discontinuous, quartz-rich metaconglomerates, ≤1 m thick, followed by a finer grained metaclastic succession, mainly psammites and pelites, ≤20 m thick

(Tüysüz, 1985, 1990). Upwards, thin beds of limestones alternate with the black pelitic sediments. This pelite–carbonate alternation gradually gives way to carbonates, without shaley partings, over a distance of 50 m. The recrystallized carbonates are grayish-black to gray, thick bedded, and >1000 m in total thickness. Fusulinids are observed in the carbonate succession, indicating a Late Carboniferous–Permian age (Tüysüz, 1990). Farther upward, the carbonates become thinner bedded, with thin shaley (pelitic) partings. Gradually the carbonate intercalations disappear and the sequence becomes totally clastic, at first as black pelitic sediments, with brown psammitic interbeds, ≤5 m thick, then with alternations of black pelites. Recrystallized limestone blocks, interpreted as olistoliths, are present in this part of the sequence. These are generally lens-shaped and variable in dimension, up to 200 × 500 m in size in the type area: kilometer-sized blocks are common in other areas. The limestone blocks are thick bedded and crystalline, without shaley partings, and are similar to the limestones at the base of the Aktaş Unit. No fossils have been found in these limestone blocks. The uppermost part of the sequence is represented by pelite and psammite alternations, with interbeds of debris flows and calciturbidites, ≤30 cm thick. The debris flows are generally ≤1 m thick, with a pelitic matrix. Clasts are highly sheared and phacoidal, recrystallized limestone. Individual clasts range from coarse pebble to boulder size. The matrix is cleaved, parallel to bedding.

A >1000-m-thick, black, pelitic sequence structurally overlies the above succession. The contact is marked by discontinuous quartz veins ≤2 m thick. The black pelites contain blocks of metabasites, limestones, and serpentinites. The individual blocks are smaller (up to a few meters long and a few meters wide) than the limestone blocks in the basal sequence, and they are more lenticular. Calciturbidite interbeds are also present.

Kunduz Unit

South of the Aktaş Unit, in the vicinity of the North Anatolian transform fault, another sequence is seen: this is similar to the overlying Gümüşoluğu Unit in tectonostratigraphy, but has a lower metamorphic grade. The Kunduz Unit (Tüysüz, 1985) consists of thrust slices of low-grade metalavas, ribbon cherts, redeposited carbonates, and clastic sediments (Figure 7h).

A volcanic sequence, exposed at the base, is represented by mainly aphyric, weakly foliated massive lavas. These lavas are locally stratigraphically overlain by metalliferous sediments, a few centimeters thick, then by limestones alternating with reddish-brown shales (≤200 m thick). Individual graded limestones, ≤1 m thick, are interpreted as calciturbidites. Lamination and grading indicate upward movement. Above are green shale–phyllite and volcaniclastic sediments, alternating with calciturbidites, ≤2 m thick. These limestones are intruded by diabase dykes 50 to 70 cm wide. The volcaniclastic sediments contain calciturbidite interbeds ranging from 5 to 50 cm thick. There are also amalgamated calciturbidites, ≤5 m thick, locally containing a few centimeter-thick volcaniclastic partings. The volcaniclastics are green, well foliated, with albite porphyroblasts. Chlorite is abundant on foliation planes that are parallel to bedding.

Pillow lavas are vesicular, 40 to 60 cm long, and flattened, with dark-green chilled margins a few millimeters thick. The upper part of the pillow lavas contains chlorite-rich tuff and limestone, forming interpillow matrix. Diabasic dykes intrude the pillow lavas, which are then overlain by massive lavas with blocks of recrystallized limestones. The massive lavas are in turn overlain by white to reddish ribbon cherts (~70 cm thick). Farther upsequence, limestones and phyllites dominate. The structurally lowest slices are represented by phyllites, alternating with quartz-rich psammitic interbeds, 40 to 50 cm thick, of possible turbiditic origin. Black cherts are also present within this upper part of the succession, associated with psammites.

The Kargı Complex metabasites consist of within-plate-type alkaline lavas (29 samples) (Ustaömer, 1993). Accordingly, the metabasites might have been erupted in a rift (i.e., stretched continental crust) or intra-oceanic (i.e., hot spot) related setting. Although lavas in both settings are compositionally similar, Thompson et al. (1983) used a La_n/Nb_n ratio (elements normalized to primordial mantle abundances) to highlight differences between these two eruptive tectonic settings. The ratio in continental intraplate basalts ranges from 1 to 5.5 (average 1.2). Ocean island basalts, on the other hand, have a more limited range between 0.2 and 1.2 (average 0.6–0.7). The Kargı metabasites exhibit a limited range of La_n/Nb_n ratio between 0.2 and 0.75, compatible with an intra-oceanic rather than a rift-related eruptive setting.

The metabasites do not show any relative Nb depletion on MORB-normalized plots that, together with the light rare-earth–element enrichment, are characteristic of suprasubduction zone volcanism. This is inconsistent with earlier tectonic models that invoked back-arc basin opening above a southward-subducting Paleotethys (Tüysüz, 1990).

In summary, the geochemistry of the Kargı Complex metabasites is suggestive of P-MOR (plume mid-ocean ridge) to within-plate–type intra-oceanic eruptive settings.

Both the Gümüşoluğu and the Kunduz units were interpreted as intact metabasite-metacarbonate-phyllite successions that formed the upper levels of units associated with the Elekdağ ophiolite (Tüysüz, 1985). The Aktaş Unit was seen as stratigraphically underlying the Gümüşoluğu Unit and was interpreted as a Late Carboniferous–Permian carbonate platform that rifted in the Permian–Triassic above a southward-dipping subduction zone to open a back-arc basin, represented by the Kunduz Unit (Tüysüz, 1990). Ophiolitic blocks in these units were derived from the Elekdağ ophiolite, following its tectonic emplacement (Tüysüz, 1985, 1990). The new data presented here favor a quite different interpretation of the Kargı Complex. First, the northerly Gümüşoluğu Unit and the southerly Kunduz Unit represent north-dipping slice complexes rather than layer-cake successions. The higher thrust sheets within the Gümüşoluğu Unit comprise distal-type facies, consistent with sequential-type (piggyback) thrusting of a proximal (southerly) to distal (northerly) facies transition away from the carbonate platform (i.e., the Aktaş Unit). The opposite is observed for the Kunduz Unit, with more distal units in structurally lower slices being sequentially thrust beneath the Aktaş Platform unit. Secondly, the contact between the platform and base of the northerly slice complex is tectonic rather than depositional, marked by exposures of black phyllites with ophiolitic embedded blocks. The Aktaş-Kunduz Formation transition could be interpreted in terms of either (1) rifting of a carbonate platform or (2) subsidence of the platform related to crustal loading in a foredeep setting. The tectonic position of the Kargı Complex, structurally beneath an inferred accretionary complex (i.e., the Domuzdağ-Saraycıkdağ Complex), and its internal tectonostratigraphy clearly favor the second alternative.

The Gümüşoluğu unit is interpreted as the northerly passive margin of a carbonate platform, represented by the Aktaş Unit. Inferred depositional environments range from platform edge (massive limestones, pelitic sediments), to slope (the calciturbidites, ribbon cherts), to base of slope (calciturbidites, debris flows, and pelitic sediments), to abyssal (ribbon cherts and pelitic sediments). The Aktaş Unit is interpreted as a Permian carbonate platform (Tüysüz, 1990) that later collapsed, becoming a foredeep related to southward overthrusting of a Paleotethyan subduction-accretion complex (i.e., Domuzdağ-Saraycıkdağ Complex). The continental fragment that was rifted from Gondwana in the Late Paleozoic was later amalgamated to the southern margin of Eurasia (Ustaömer and Robertson, 1990). The Kunduz Unit is interpreted as the southern passive margin of the Kargı carbonate platform, which was later imbricated and underthrust, related to northward subduction of Paleotethys.

Magmatism

Several granitic intrusions are exposed to the north of the Kastamonu-Boyabat Basin (Figure 4), associated with dacitic volcanics. These are locally overlain by Upper Jurassic red, basal conglomerates, rich in granite clasts, and are collectively assigned to the "Kastamonu granitoid belt" (Yılmaz and Boztuğ, 1986; Boztuğ et al., 1995). One of these intrusions was dated as Mid-Jurassic (165 Ma) by the Rb/Sr whole-rock method.

One view is that these granites relate to northward subduction of Paleotethys (Yılmaz and Boztuğ, 1986) and are "I-type" granites reflecting continental crust contamination (Boztuğ et al., 1984). Another possibility is that these are "Tibetan-type" granites (Yılmaz and Şengör, 1985), related to crustal thickening following suturing of Paleotethys. A third possibility is that the granites relate to southward subduction and closure of the Küre marginal oceanic basin located to the north (Ustaömer and Robertson, 1992).

Two of the intrusions were geochemically analyzed, one in the north (Battallar, NW of the town of Küre), and the other in the south (Devrekani granite). The first is a peraluminous monzoquartz-diorite, and the second is a metaluminous quartz monzonite (Debon and Le Fort, 1982). On several discrimination diagrams, these granitic rocks plot in the VAG (volcanic arc granite) field (Ustaömer and Robertson, 1994).

Two granite samples dated by the K/Ar method gave Late Cretaceous ages (79.6 ±1.8 and 86.3 ±4.2) (Table 1). This is potentially important, as it suggests that the Kastamonu granitic rocks are not all Mid-Jurassic in age, as previously thought. These granitic rocks are believed to relate to northward subduction beneath the southern margin of Eurasia, a process that was possibly more long-lived than previously believed.

İstanbul Unit

The last unit we will consider is the İstanbul Unit (Ustaömer and Robertson, 1993) that is mainly exposed farther west, in the Western Pontides. The İstanbul Unit is the equivalent of the İstanbul Zone of Okay (1989) and corresponds to part of the İstanbul-Balkan Unit of Şengör (1987). The pre-Jurassic successions of the İstanbul Unit comprise a transgressive Paleozoic sequence, known as the Palaeozoic of İstanbul (Abdüsselamoglu, 1977). Unconformable above this is a Triassic marine succession termed the Kocaeli Basin (Özdemir et al., 1973). Elsewhere, the Triassic sediments are represented by continental red clastics. Low-angle thrust sheets of the Paleozoic of İstanbul are emplaced over the Küre Complex in the Süğütüzü, Daday-Azdavay, and Ballıdağ areas (Figure 4). The Paleozoic sequence there is characterized by south-vergent recumbent folds. Beneath the thrust planes are lenticular debris flows, derived from the Paleozoic sequence. Channelized conglomerates are present within the Küre Complex close to the Paleozoic of İstanbul klippes. These conglomerates contain abundant crinoidal limestone, quartzite, purple mudstone, and red siltstone pebbles, and are considered to have been derived from the Paleozoic of İstanbul sequence. The importance of these observations is the implication that the Paleozoic of İstanbul was located north of the Küre Complex, and that it was finally emplaced prior to complete closure of the Küre marginal basin by the Late Jurassic.

Paleozoic Sequence

In the west, the Paleozoic of İstanbul succession (Figures 4, 14) begins with continentally derived Cambro-Ordovician clastics (>2000 m) that unconformably overlie a migmatitic basement, including granites and volcanics, as exposed in the Bolu area (Cerit, 1990; Ustaömer, 1996). Above these are Early Ordovician–Early Silurian quartzites (50 m) and siliceous, laminated shales, often with lenses of orthoquartzite (1000 m). Overlying shallow-marine limestones (50–500 m) and then fossiliferous shales, interbedded with calciturbidites of Late Silurian–Early Devonian age (400 m). These sediments pass upward into nodular limestones of Late Devonian age (250 m) and are, in turn, conformably overlain by radiolarian cherts with phosphatic nodules of Early Carboniferous age (50 m). A thick sequence (>2000 m) of Lower Carboniferous turbidites with cherty limestones blocks then follows.

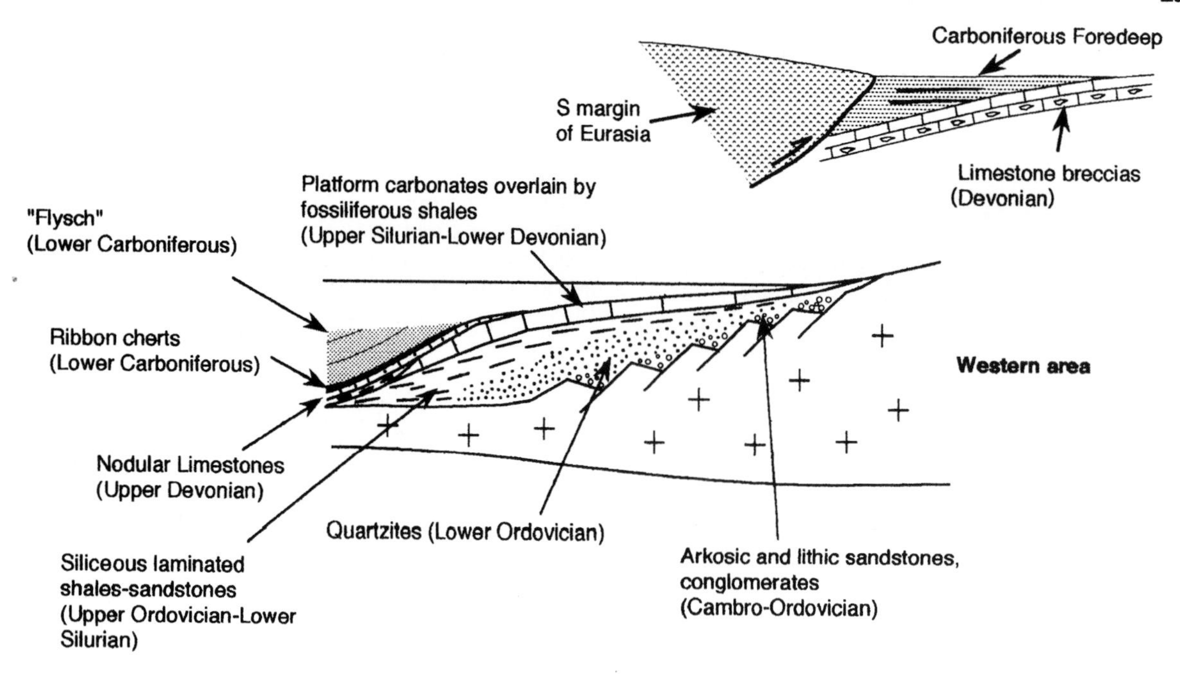

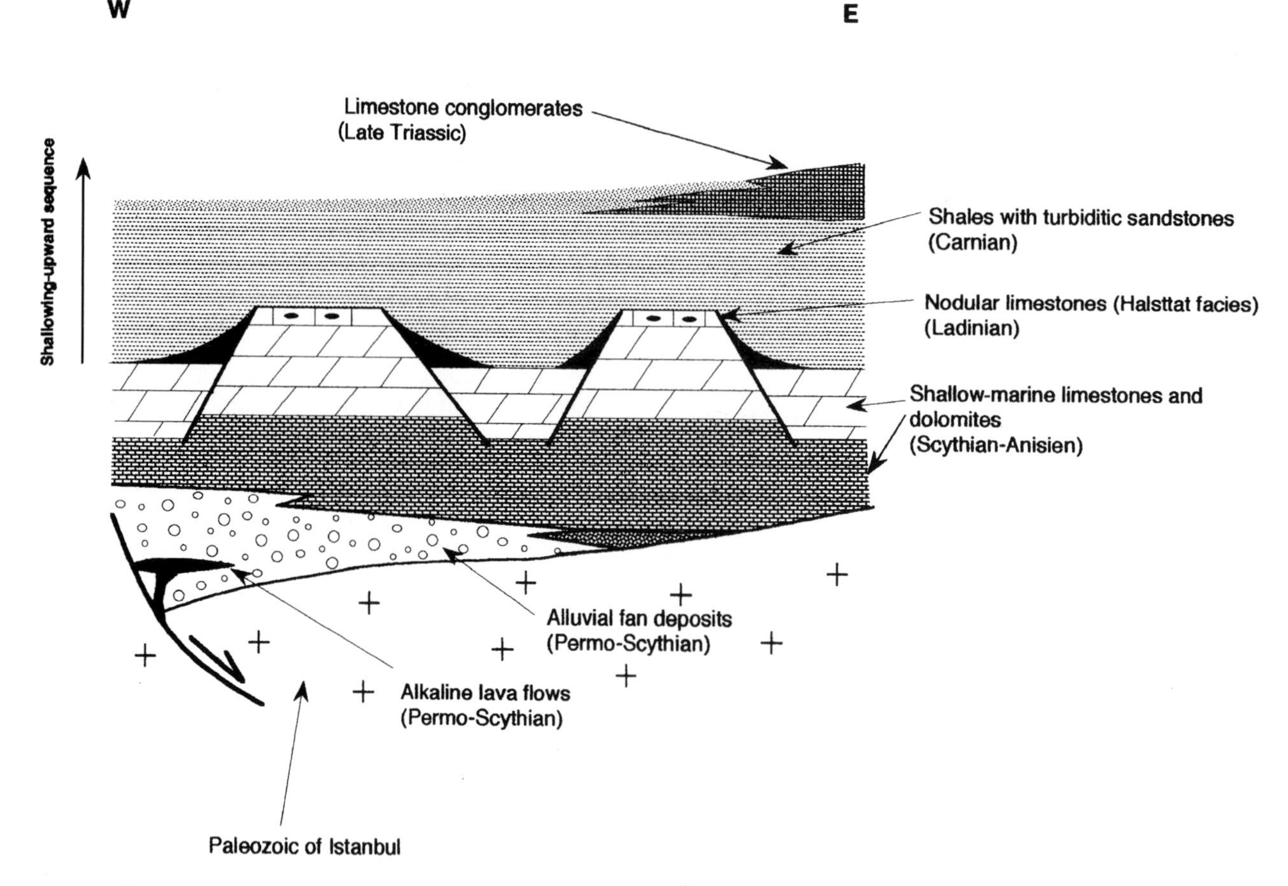

Figure 14. Schematic interpretations of different parts of the İstanbul Unit. (A) Stratigraphy and interpretation of the Paleozoic of İstanbul. Note the differences between the Paleozoic sequences in the west and east. The Late Paleozoic sediments are deep marine in the west, but shallow to continental in the east. (B) Stratigraphy and interpretation of the Triassic Kocaeli Basin. Note that the western margin of the basin is faulted, associated with alkaline lava flows.

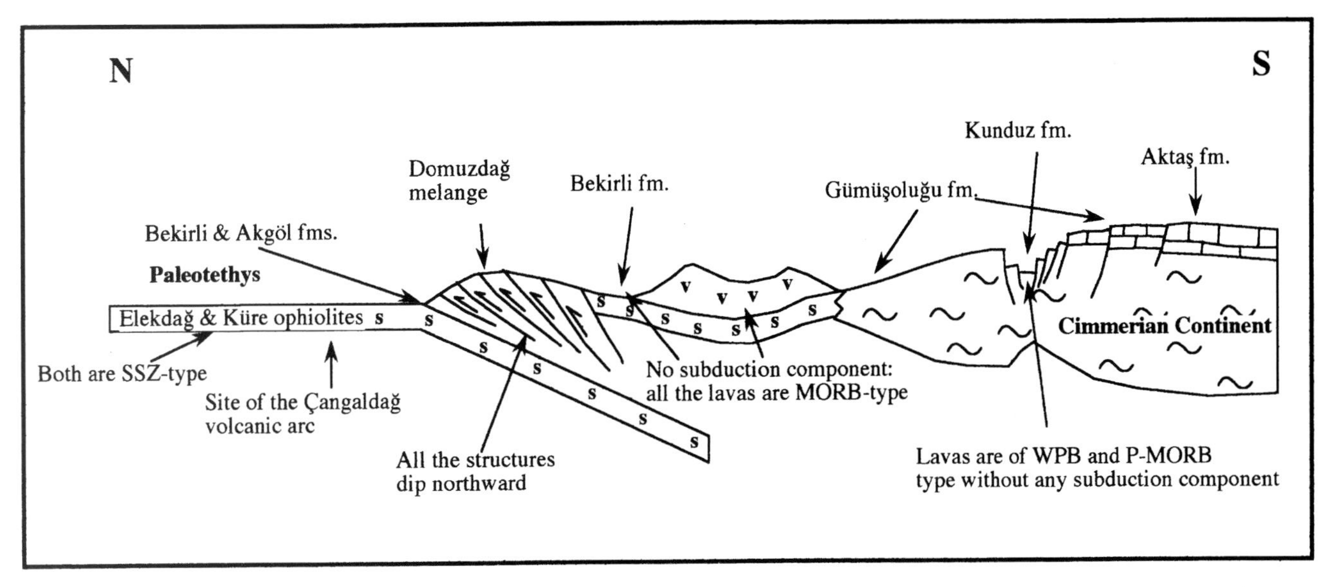

Figure 15. Sketch to show the inferred tectonic settings of units in the Central Pontides as predicted by the southward-subduction model (Yilmaz et al., this volume). Some obvious problems with this interpretation are highlighted and discussed in the text. MORB = mid-ocean rich basalt.

The stratigraphy is somewhat different in the more easterly areas. Differences are first apparent in the Devonian sediments, which are represented by black limestone breccias. The uppermost part of the sequence is shallow marine to continental, with coal measures of Carboniferous age.

The Paleozoic of İstanbul is widely interpreted as a south-facing Paleozoic passive margin (Şengör and Yılmaz, 1981). The Silurian–Devonian sequence is taken to be a carbonate platform. This platform rapidly subsided in the latest Devonian–Early Carboniferous, with deposition of radiolarian cherts, and then turbidites. We interpret the turbiditic sequence as a foreland basin–type sequence associated with collision of the İstanbul Unit with a continental margin to the north (Figure 14). The sequence in the easterly areas was shallow-marine to continental in the Late Paleozoic. The easterly area is located farther north than the İstanbul area (i.e., present geographic coordinates). In the east, there are thick limestone breccias (Bolu-Zonguldak-Kastamonu areas) of Devonian age that we interpret as a collapse sequence. These breccias are followed by shallow-marine limestones and then by deltaic to limnic clastic sediments with coal measures (Kerey, 1984). We suggest that this area represented a promontory of the İstanbul Unit that collided with the Eurasian continental margin to become a foreland basin (Figure 14). Kerey (1984) reported occurrences of volcanic clasts in this basin. The continental margin with which the İstanbul Unit collided in the Late Paleozoic was possibly then one of Andean type. The Early Carboniferous turbidite basin of the western area might represent a remnant basin related to collision of an irregular İstanbul Unit with the Eurasian margin to the north (Ustaömer and Robertson, 1993).

Triassic Kocaeli Basin

Farther west, in the Kocaeli Peninsula, a north-south–trending Permo–Triassic Basin (the Kocaeli Basin) is floored by the Paleozoic of İstanbul (Özdemir et al., 1973) (Figure 14). The sequence starts with red fluvial clastics, intercalated, in the upper part, with alkaline lava flows. Transgression began in the early Scythian with deposition of dolomitic limestones, carbonate grainstones, and shale. Above is a micritic, marly limestone succession, with occasional oolitic interbeds. This is overlain by Upper Scythian dolomitic limestones with neptunian dykes, and in turn passes into nodular limestones (i.e., Halstatt facies), a few meters thick, of Ladinian age. This is followed by a thick sequence (>1000 m) of Carnian turbidites, rich in *Halobia* within shaley partings. The Kocaeli Basin apparently closed by the end of the Late Triassic, marked by a shallowing-upward sequence and deposition of limestone conglomerates. Cretaceous conglomerates then unconformably overlie the Triassic layer without known Jurassic facies.

The formation of the north-south–trending Kocaeli Basin could relate to east-west rifting of the Küre basin farther northeast. We suggest that the Triassic Kocaeli Basin may represent a failed rift, associated with the opening of the Küre basin, which later closed in the Late Triassic–Early Jurassic with the Küre basin (Figures 2, 14).

PRE-LATE JURASSIC TECTONIC EVOLUTION: NORTHWARD VS. SOUTHWARD SUBDUCTION POLARITY OF PALEOTETHYS

Tectonic models proposed for the pre-Late Jurassic mainly differ in subduction polarity of Paleotethys. We discuss the alternative southward and northward polarity models and conclude with our favored interpretation. We use the stratigraphic terminology of Tüysüz (1985, 1990) when discussing the southward polarity model, and our own modified nomenclature when we consider the northward polarity model.

In the southward-subduction model (Figure 15), the Permian carbonate platform and related units (i.e., the Kargı Complex) originated along the southern margin of Paleotethys as part of the northern margin of the Cimmerian continent. The Bekirli Formation (our southerly diabase-phyllite unit) is assigned to both fore-arc and trench settings. The Domuzdağ melange is seen as an accretionary complex. The Akgöl Formation (equivalent to our Küre Complex) is interpreted, together with the Bekirli Formation, as trench-type assemblages. The Elekdağ and Küre ophiolites are interpreted as remnants of southward-subducted Paleotethyan oceanic crust and mantle. A back-arc basin (Karakaya Basin) opened in the south above southward-subducting Paleotethys, represented by the Kunduz Unit.

There are a number of serious problems with this tectonic model:

1. Both the Küre and Elekdağ ophiolites are of suprasubduction type based on geochemical evidence and are thus unlikely to represent open-ocean Paleotethyan crust and mantle.
2. The Bekirli (i.e., diabase-phyllite) and Akgöl (i.e., Küre) "formations" are very dissimilar lithologically and geochemically and cannot be correlated as part of a single ophiolite-related unit. Indeed, it is not appropriate to consider these as true stratigraphic formations in the first place. The Bekirli "formation" comprises intersliced metabasites and phyllites, in which the metabasites are of MORB type without any identifiable subduction component. The Akgöl Formation, on the other hand, is characterized by structurally thickened siliciclastic sediments, interleaved with suprasubduction-type ophiolite slices.
3. There is no evidence for the existence of a major subduction-related magmatic arc located between the Domuzdağ Melange trench-accretionary complex in the north and the Kunduz Unit inferred back-arc basin in the south. The Kösdağ Unit is part of a younger, Late Mesozoic magmatic arc (Tüysüz, 1990) and is, in any case, to the south of the Kunduz Unit (i.e., south of the inferred back-arc basin).
4. In a southward-subduction polarity model, the Kunduz Unit represents a Karakaya back-arc basin, while the Gümüşoluğu and the Aktaş units preserve parts of its rifted margin (e.g., rifted Permian platform). However, geochemical data indicate that both the Kunduz and Gümüşoluğu metabasites are of P-MORB and WPB (within plate basalt), without any identifiable subduction component, as expected in an above-subduction-zone marginal basin.
5. The implied structural vergences in the southward-dipping subduction model do not fit the actual field structural data. Dominantly southward-dipping thrusts, foliation, and axial planes of folds would be expected. However, all the more-southerly basement units (from the southern margin of the Kastamonu-Boyabat Basin southward) exhibit a consistently northward-dipping foliation. Axial planes of folds and thrust planes also dip northward. As a result, the southward-subduction model would produce a tectonostratigraphy that is the reverse of that actually observed (i.e., with the Akgöl Unit at the base and the Kunduz Unit at the top). The possibility that the actual, opposite tectonostratigraphy could have resulted entirely from Neotethyan restacking can be discounted as: (1) all preexisting north-vergent structures would have had to have been totally obliterated, which is not credible; (2) Neotethyan structures are of high-level brittle type, quite unlike the commonly ductile deformation of the basement units; (3) absolute dating of basement structures is difficult in the southern Central Pontides as cover units are mainly absent. However, the basement is locally unconformably overlain by Campanian limestones, which are unmetamorphosed, in strong contrast to the amphibolite or blueschist facies metamorphism of the southern Central Pontides basement.

In our alternate northerly subduction polarity model (Figure 16), the North Tethyan margin in the Central Pontides is interpreted as an active margin, similar to parts of the southwest Pacific region. Southerly and northerly parts of the Central Pontides originated in separate, but related, Paleotethyan oceanic basins. The southerly basin (represented by the Domuzdağ-Saraycıkdağ Complex) corresponds to the main Paleotethys, and the northerly oceanic basin (represented by the Küre Complex) to a Paleotethyan back-arc marginal basin. Paleotethys was located in the south and was subducted northward during the Late Paleozoic–Early Mesozoic, giving rise to a back-arc marginal basin system within the south Eurasian continental margin (Ustaömer and Robertson, 1993). This marginal basin system possibly opened as a result of subduction rollback, activating extension of the hanging wall of the Paleotethyan subduction system.

A continental sliver (the Kargı Complex) rifted off the northern margin of Gondwana and drifted northward across Paleotethys during the Permian. The Kargı Complex records a transition from a carbonate platform to a foredeep, interpreted as the result of collision with the trench near the southern margin of Eurasia in the Late Permian–earliest Triassic. Northerly passive marginal sediments (i.e., limestones, cherts) were detached, together with oceanic extrusives (i.e., metabasites), and accreted to the toe of the accretionary complex in a piggyback fashion. The carbonate platform was then thrust into the trench and collapsed under the thrust load to form a foredeep. Limestone olistoliths, carbonate debris flows, and calciturbidites were shed into the foreland basin from the disintegrating platform. Ophiolitic blocks were possibly also shed into the foredeep from the accretionary complex. The foredeep succession was later overridden by the advancing thrust stack and internally imbricated. Finally, the southern passive margin of the platform entered the trench and was thrust-imbricated (Figure 16).

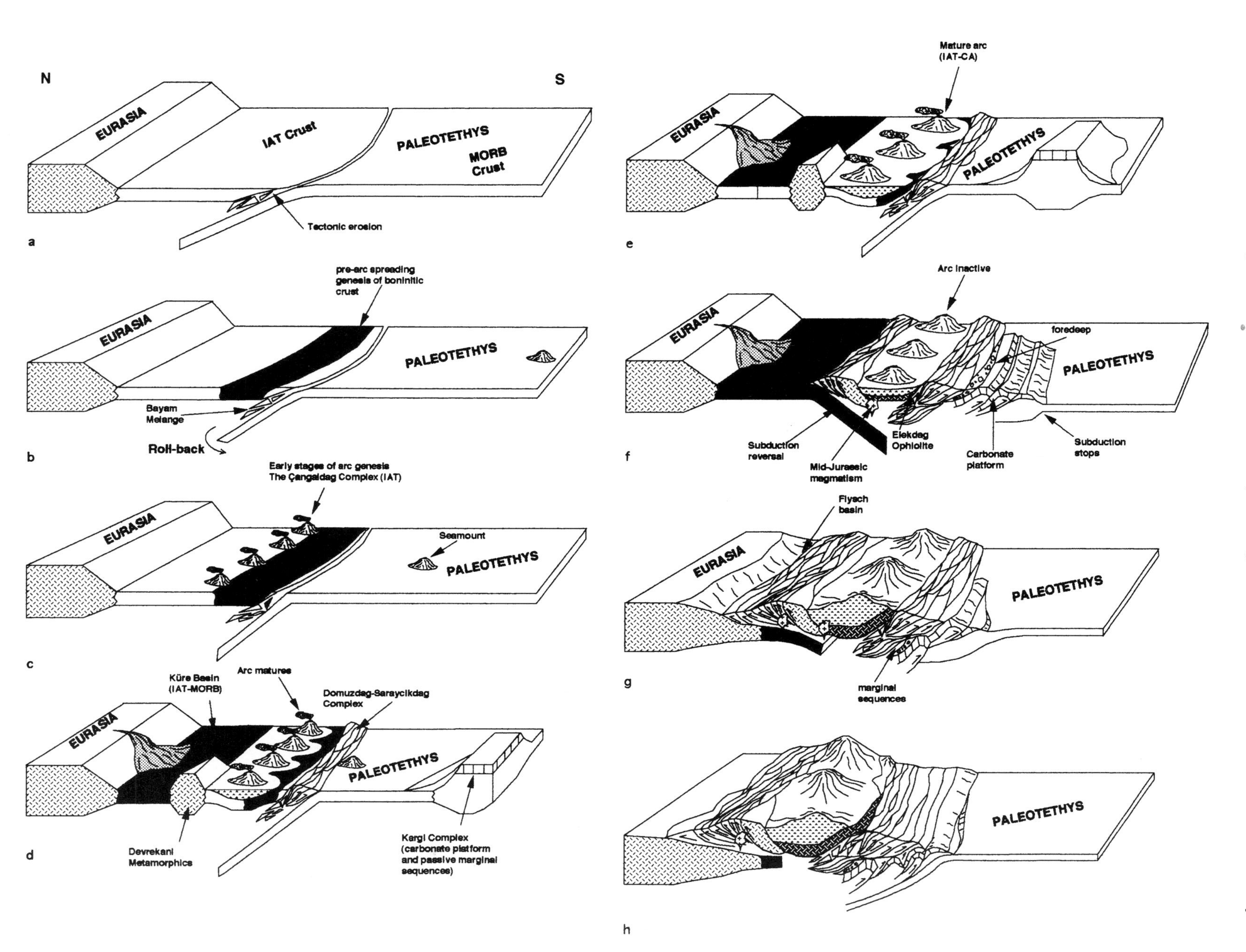

Figure 16. Pre-Late Jurassic tectonic evolution of the North Tethyan margin in the Central Pontides. The rationale for these reconstructions and the termporal framework are discussed in the text. MORB = mid-ocean rich basalt.

A different picture emerges for units north of the Kastamonu-Boyabat Basin (i.e., mainly the Küre Complex). Geochemical evidence indicates an above-subduction-zone origin for the Küre ophiolitic slices, and this, together with the absence of open-ocean sediments (e.g., ribbon radiolarites), favors an origin in a marginal basin setting near the Eurasian continental margin. However, the structural evidence unambiguously indicates emplacement by northward overthrusting. We interpret the Küre unit as a subduction-accretion complex, in which all but slivers of the lavas and sediments and minor ultramafic rocks were subducted. In this case, subduction was southward, in contrast to the more southerly areas of the Central Pontides discussed above. In other words, a subduction polarity reversal must exist within the Central Pontides. We explain this in terms of northward subduction of the main Paleotethys to the south, whereas the Küre marginal basin to the north finally closed by southward subduction. Southward subduction was possibly activated by collision of the Kargı carbonate platform with the trench in the Early Triassic. We tentatively interpret the Mid-Jurassic granites and volcanics of the Central Pontides as arc magmatism related to southward subduction of the Küre marginal basin. Total consumption of the Küre marginal basin culminated in accretion of the entire thrust stack to the southern margin of Eurasia by the Late Jurassic. This event was the possibly the driving force of the Cimmerian orogeny (Figure 14h).

CONCLUSIONS

Our main conclusions regarding the tectonic evolution of the Central Pontides are as follows.

The north-south traverse of the Central Pontides, the best exposed part of the Pontide Chain in northern Turkey, shows that remnants of two separate, but related, Paleotethyan Ocean basin systems were preserved in different areas. The greater part of the tectonostratigraphy (exposed in the south) originated farther south in the main Paleotethys during the Late Paleozoic–Early Mesozoic. A smaller part of the tectonostratigraphy (exposed in the north) formed within a coeval Paleotethyan back-arc marginal basin located along the southern margin of Eurasia (Küre basin).

Late Cretaceous–Early Tertiary (Neotethyan) deformation is well understood, and its influence can effectively be subtracted from the Paleotethyan basement structure. This basement preserves structurally ordered units and is not merely the result, for example, of later terrane amalgamation of diverse units.

From the structural base in the south to the structural top in the north, the tectonic origin of individual Paleotethyan basement units was as follows:

- The Kargı Complex is interpreted as a sliver of continental crust rifted from Gondwana, which drifted across Paleotethys during the Permian as a carbonate platform bordered by deep-water sediments. The platform-slope assemblage was then accreted at a trench, associated with development of a foredeep in the Late Permian to earliest Triassic.
- The Domuzdağ-Saraycıkdağ Complex comprises tectonic slices of oceanic sediments (e.g., ribbon cherts) and MORB-type extrusives, metamorphosed to blueschist facies. Structural evidence indicates northward underthrusting. This unit is interpreted as an accretionary wedge largely composed of seamount-type volcanics and deep-sea sediments related to northward subduction of the main Paleotethys.
- The Elekdağ ophiolite is a huge klippe that is dominated by serpentinized ultramafic rocks, with subordinate blueschist blocks. The ophiolite formed in a suprasubduction zone setting, based on geochemical evidence; it was later subducted and underwent high-pressure metamorphism. This was followed by exhumation, possibly related to regional crustal extension in the Early Cretaceous. The Elekdağ ophiolite possibly originated as upper mantle and lower crust of a Paletethyan fore-arc that was sited between the Çangaldağ arc to the north and the trench-accretionary complex to the south.
- The Çangaldağ Complex is floored by an ophiolite with a boninitic-type composition in the south and an IAT composition in the north. The former is interpreted as fore-arc crust that possibly was originally contiguous with the Elekdağ ophiolite to the south. The ophiolitic basement units are depositionally overlain by a mature calc-alkaline arc-type volcanics and minor sediments. The Çangaldağ Complex is interpreted as an oceanic arc sited near the south Eurasian continental margin. Its highest levels show evidence of tectonic collapse, which could be related to opening of the Küre marginal basin to the north.
- The laterally discontinuous Devrekani metamorphic unit is interpreted as a sliver of the south Eurasian continental margin (i.e., basement of the İstanbul Unit), as suggested by occurrences of similar basement rocks throughout the circum-Black Sea region. This unit crops out as a fault-bounded crustal sliver, and its present location between the Küre Complex to the north and the Çangaldağ Complex to the south may have been influenced by the strike-slip in the post-Late Jurassic.
- The Küre Complex in the north opened in the latest Paleozoic–earliest Mesozoic, above a subduction zone, as evidenced by the presence of IAT- to MORB-type extrusives and a depleted mantle sequence. The sedimentary fill of this basin is terrigenous and lacks true open-oceanic sediments (i.e., radiolarites). The oceanic basin was probably quite narrow (i.e., a few hundred kilometers) and developed above a N- to NW-dipping subduction zone. Structural evidence supports the emplacement of the Küre Complex as an accretionary prism related to southward subduction of the

marginal basin, followed by suturing during the Cimmerian orogeny.

The data presented in this chapter shed light on the paleogeography of the pre-Late Jurassic southern margin of Eurasia, adjacent to the Paleotethyan Ocean to the south. The south Eurasian margin evolved as a Pacific-type active margin throughout its history. Structural vergence and tectonic facies patterns (e.g., Robertson, 1994) support the existence of a large ocean to the south of the Pontides, which was subducted northward in the Late Paleozoic–Early Mesozoic. This was the main Paleotethys. The Küre Basin, on the other hand, is interpreted here as one of several circum-Black Sea marginal basins of Late Paleozoic–Early Mesozoic age that opened above a northward-subducting Paleotethys. Gondwana-derived carbonate platform slivers (e.g., Kargı Complex) were accreted to the northerly active margin, causing compression and eventual collapse of the Küre marginal basin, which then closed by southward underthrusting.

After elimination of marginal oceanic basins (i.e., Küre and equivalents), the Eurasian margin stabilized in the Late Jurassic, and carbonate platform sedimentation ensued; Neotethys remained open to the south. Extension ensued, with basin formation in the Lower Cretaceous. Deeply buried units to the south of the Çangaldağ Complex were possibly detached and uplifted at this stage. During the Late Cretaceous–Early Tertiary, northward subduction of Neotethys then gave rise to the Black Sea as a form of back-arc marginal basin within the Eurasian active continental margin, more or less in the same area as its Paleotethyan precursor. Neotethys in the Central Pontides closed by northward subduction associated with emplacement of ophiolite-related units onto the Eurasian margin in the Late Cretaceous, culminating in final continental collision in the Early Tertiary.

ACKNOWLEDGMENTS

The authors would like to thank Dr. A.G. Robinson for inviting us to write this paper. We also thank him for his interest in our work. T. Ustaömer thanks the Turkish Ministry of Education for a Ph.D. grant. A.H.F. Robertson acknowledges a N.E.R.C. Small Grant. We thank A.M.C. Şengör for his encouragement, discussions, and logistical support. We also benefited from discussions with many colleagues, including J.E. Dixon, P. Clift, E. Pickett, Y. Yılmaz, A.G. Robinson, C. Banks, P.A. Ustaömer, and A. Collins. Critical appraisals of this manuscript were made by O. Tüysüz and an anonymous reviewer. Logistical support for our fieldwork, provided by M. and O. Güçlü, is much appreciated. Dr. Dodie James assisted with XRF analysis, and Dr. S. Kearns with microprobe analysis. We also thank BP for financial support to perform radiometric dating at the Scottish Universities Research and Reactor Centre, East Kilbride, Scotland.

REFERENCES CITED

Abdüsselamoğlu, M.S., 1977, The Palaeozoic and Mesozoic in the Gebze region—explanatory text and excursion guidebook: 4th Colloquium on the Aegean Region, Exc. 4, İstanbul Teknik Üniversitesi Maden Fakultesi, İstanbul, 16 p.

Adamia, Sh.A., M.B. Lordkipanidze, and G.S. Zakariadze, 1977, Evolution of an active continental margin as exemplified by the Alpine history of the Caucasus: Tectonophysics, v. 40, p. 183–199.

Andrieux, J., S. Over, A. Poisson, and O. Bellier, 1995, The North Anatolian fault zone: distributed Neogene deformation in its northward convex part: Tectonophysics, v. 243, p. 135–154.

Aydın, M., O. Sahintürk, H.S. Serdar, Y. Ôzçelik, I. Akarsu, A. Üngör, R. Çokuğraş, and S. Kaçar, 1986, The geology of the area between Ballıdağ and Çangaldağ (Kastamonu) (in Turkish): Bulletin of the Geological Society of Turkey, v. 29, p. 1–16.

Aydın, M., O. Demir, Y. Ôzçelik, N. Terzioğlu, and M. Satir, 1995, A geological revision of Inebolu, Devrekani, Ağlı and Küre areas; new observations in Paleotethys–Neotethys sedimentary successions, *in* A. Erler, T. Ercan, E. Bingöl, and S. Orçen, eds., Geology of the Black Sea Region: Proceedings of the International Symposium on the Geology of the Black Sea Region, Mineral Research and Exploration Institute (MTA), p. 33–38.

Banks, C.J., and A.G. Robinson, this volume, Mesozoic strike-slip back-arc basins of the Western Black Sea region, *in* A.G. Robinson, ed., Regional and petroleum geology of the Black Sea and surrounding region: AAPG Memoir 68, p. 53–62.

Boztuğ, D., F. Debon, P. Le Fort, and O. Yılmaz, 1984, Geochemical characteristics of some plutons from the Kastamonu granitoid belt (northern Anatolia, Turkey): Schwezerische Mineralogische und Petrographische Mitteilungen, v. 64, no. 3, p. 389–403.

Boztuğ, D., F. Debon, P. Le Fort, and O. Yılmaz, 1995, High compositional diversity of the Middle Jurassic Kastamonu plutonic belt, northern Anatolia, Turkey: Turkish Journal of Earth Sciences, v. 4, no. 2, p. 67–86.

Çağatay, A., H. Pehlivanoğlu, and Y. Altun, 1980, Küre piritli bakır yataklarının kobalt-altin mineralleri ve yataklarin bu metaller açısından ekonomik değeri: Maden Tetkik Arama Enstitüsü Dergisi, 93/94, p. 110–117.

Cerit, O., 1990, Bolu Masifinin jeolojik ve tektonik incelenmesi: Ph.D. thesis (unpublished), Hacettepe Üniversitesi Fen Bilimleri Enstitüsü, 197 p.

Debon, F., and P. Le Fort, 1982, A chemical-mineralogical classification of common plutonic rocks and associations: Transactions of the Royal Society of Edinburgh: Earth Sciences, v. 73, p. 135–149.

Dercourt, J., et al., 1986, Geological evolution of the Tethys belt from the Atlantic to the Pamirs since the Lias: Tectonophysics, v. 123, p. 241–315.

Dercourt, J., L.E. Ricou, and B. Vrielynck, eds., 1993, Atlas of Tethys palaeoenvironmental maps:

Paris, Gauthier-Villars, 307 p.
Derman, A.S., Y. Ôzçelik, S. Kibici, N.Y. Bragin, and F. Kuru, 1996, Late Jurassic paleogeography of Western Black Sea (in Turkish): Türkiye 11, Petrol Kongresi Bildiriler, p. 75–80.
Derman, A.S., and T. Norman, 1996, Importance of recognition of megabreccias: examples from Black Sea Region: Turkiye 11, Petrol Kongresi Bildiriler, p. 83–90.
Dewey, J.F., W.C. Pitman, III, W.B.F. Ryan, and J. Bonnin, 1973, Plate tectonics and the evolution of the Alpine system: Geological Society of America Bulletin, v. 84, p. 3137–3180.
Eren, R.H., 1979, Kastamonu-Taşköprü bölgesi metamorfitlerinin jeolojik ve petrografik etudu: Ph.D. thesis, İstanbul Technical University, 143 p.
Gedik, A., and S. Korkmaz, 1984, Sinop Havzasinin jeolojisi ve petrol olanaklari: Jeoloji Mühendisliği, v. 19, p. 53–80.
Görür, N., 1988, Timing of opening of the Black Sea Basin: Tectonophysics, v. 147, p. 247–262.
Görür, N., 1991, Aptian–Albian palaeogeography of Neotethyan domain: Palaeogeography, Palaeoclimatology, Palaeoecology, v. 87, p. 267–288.
Görür, N., O. Tüysüz, A. Aykol, M. Sakinç, E. Yiğitbas, and R. Akkök, 1993, Cretaceous red pelagic carbonates of northern Turkey: their place in the opening history of the Black Sea: Eclogea Geologica Helvetia, v. 86, no. 3, p. 819–838.
Güner, M., 1980, Küre civarının masif sulfit yataklari ve Jeolojisi, Pontidler (Kuzey Türkiye)—massive sulfide ores and geology of the Küre area, Pontides (N Turkey): Maden Tetkik ve Arama Enistitüsü Bulteni, v. 93/94, p. 65–109.
Hsü, K.J., and D. Bernoulli, 1978, Genesis of the Tethys and the Mediterranean: Initial Reports of the Deep Sea Drilling Project, v. 42, no. 1, p. 943–949.
Kerey, E., 1984, Facies and tectonic setting of the Upper Carboniferous rocks of northwestern Turkey, *in* J.E. Dixon and A.H.F. Robertson, eds., The geological evolution of the Eastern Mediterranean: Geological Society of London Special Publication 17, p. 123–128.
Ketin, I., 1962, 1:500,000 olçekli Türkiye Jeoloji Haritasi izahnamesi (Sinop): Maden Tetkik Arama Enstitüsü yayini, Ankara, 111 p.
Ketin, I., 1966, Tectonic units of Anatolian Asia Minor (in Turkish): MTA Bulletin, v. 66, p. 20–34.
Ketin, I., and O. Gümüş, 1963, Sinop-Ayancik güneyinde III. bölgeye dahil sahalarin jeolojisi hakkinda rapor II: Turkish Petroleum Oil Company Report, v. 228, 37 p.
Kovenko, V., 1944, Metallogeny of the old copper body and recently discovered Asikoy body, and central and eastern part of coastal regions of Black Sea: Maden Tetkik ve Arama Enstitüsü Bülteni, v. 32, no. 2, p. 180–212.
Nikitin, V., 1926, Küre copper ore, unpublished report, Maden Tetkik Arama Enstitüsü, Ankara.
Okay, A.I., 1984, The geology of the Ağvanis metamorphic rocks and neighboring formations: Bulletin of the Mineral Research and Exploration Institute (MTA), v. 99/100, p. 16–36.
Okay, A.I, 1989, Tectonic units and sutures in the Pontides, Northern Turkey, *in* A.M.C. Şengör, ed., Tectonic evolution of the Tethyan region: NATO Advanced Science Institute (ASI) Series, C259, p. 109–116.
Okay, A.I., M. Siyako, and K.A. Bürkan, 1991, Geology and tectonic evolution of the Biga Peninsula, Northwest Turkey: Bulletin of the Technical University of İstanbul, Special Issue on Tectonics, v. 44, p. 191–256.
Okay, A.I., A.M.C. Şengör, and N. Görür, 1994, Kinematic history of the opening of the Black Sea and its effects on the surrounding regions: Geology, v. 22, p. 267–270.
Özdemir, U., G. Talay, and A. Yurtsever, 1973, Kocaeli Triyasi Projesi "Kocaeli Triyasinin Biyostratigrafik Etüdü": Congress Proceedings on Earth Science, 50th Anniversary of the Turkish Republic, 1973, Maden Tetkik Arama Enstitüsü, p. 115–130.
Pearce, J.A., 1980, Geochemical evidence for the genesis and eruptive setting of lavas from Tethyan ophiolites, *in* A. Panayiotou, ed., Proceedings of the International Ophiolite Symposium, Cyprus, 1979, p. 261–272.
Pickett, E.A., A.H.F. Robertson, J.E. Dixon, and A.I. Okay, 1992, Palaeotethyan subduction-accretion: evidence from the Karakaya Complex, NW Turkey (abs.): International Workshop on the Geology of Turkey, p. 53.
Pickett, E.A., and A.H.F. Robertson, 1996, Tectonic-sedimentary setting of the Karakaya Complex, NW Turkey: Journal of the Geological Society, London.
Robertson, A.H.F., 1994, Role of the tectonic facies concept in orogenic analysis and its application to Tethys in the Eastern Mediterranean region: Earth-Science Reviews, v. 37, p. 139–213.
Robertson, A.H.F., and J.E. Dixon, 1984, Introduction: aspects of the geological evolution of the Eastern Mediterranean, *in* J.E. Dixon and A.H.F. Robertson, eds., The geological evolution of the Eastern Mediterranean: Geological Society of London Special Publication 17, p. 1–74.
Robertson, A.H.F., and M. Grasso, 1995, Overview of the Late Tertiary tectonic and palaeo-environmental development of the Mediterranean region, *in* A.H.F. Robertson and M. Grasso, eds., Special issue—Later Tertiary–Quaternary Mediterranean tectonics and palaeo-environments: Terra Nova, v. 7, p. 114–127.
Robertson, A.H.F., J.E. Dixon, S. Brown, A. Collins, A. Morris, E. Pickett, I. Sharp, and T. Ustaömer, 1996, Alternative tectonic models for the Late Palaeozoic–Early Tertiary development of Tethys in the eastern Mediterranean region, *in* A. Morris and D.H. Tarling, eds., Palaeomagnetism and tectonics of the Mediterranean region: Geological Society Special Publication 105, p. 239–263.
Robinson, A.G., C.J. Banks, M.M. Rutherford, and J.P.P. Hirst, 1995, Stratigraphic and structural development

of the Eastern Pontides, Turkey: Journal of the Geological Society of London, v. 152, no. 5, p. 861–872.

Saner, S., 1980, Bati Pontidlerin ve komsu havzalarin olusumlarinin levha tektoniği kuramiyla açiklanmasi, Kuzeybati Türkiye: MTA Enistitüs Dergisi, v. 93/94, p. 1–19.

Şengör, A.M.C., 1979, Mid-Mesozoic closure of Permo-Triassic Tethys and its implications: Nature, v. 279, p. 590–593.

Şengör, A.M.C., 1984, The Cimmeride orogenic system and the tectonics of Eurasia: Geological Society of America Special Paper 195, 81 p.

Şengör, A.M.C., 1987, Tectonics of the Tethysides: orogenic collage development in a collisional setting: Annual Reviews of Earth and Planetary Science, v. 15, p. 213–244.

Şengör, A.M.C., 1995, The larger tectonic framework of the Zonguldak Coal Basin in northern Turkey: an outsider's view, *in* M.N. Yalçin and G. Gürdal, eds., Zonguldak Havzasi Araştırma Kuyulan-1: TÜBITAK, p. 1–26.

Şengör, A.M.C., and Y. Yılmaz, 1981, Tethyan evolution of Turkey: a plate tectonic approach: Tectonophysics, v. 75, p. 181–241.

Şengör, A.M.C., Y. Yılmaz, and I. Ketin, 1980, Remnants of a pre-Late Jurassic ocean in northern Turkey: fragments of Permian–Triassic Palaeotethys?: Bulletin of the Geological Society of America, v. 91, no. 1, p. 599–609.

Şengör, A.M.C., Y. Yılmaz, and O. Sungurlu, 1984, Tectonics of the Mediterranean Cimmerids: nature and evolution of the western termination of Palaeotethys, *in* J.E. Dixon and A.H.F. Robertson, eds., The geological evolution of the Eastern Mediterranean: Geological Society of London Special Publication 17, p. 77–112.

Şengör, A.M.C., D. Altiner, A. Cin, T. Ustaömer, and K.J. Hsü, 1988, Origin and assembly of the Tethyside orogenic collage at the expense of Gondwana Land, *in* M.G. Audley-Charles and M.G. Hallam, eds., Gondwana and Tethys: Geological Society of London Special Publication 37, p. 119–181.

Şengör, A.M.C., A. Cin, D.B. Rowley, and N. Shangyou, 1991, Magmatic evolution of the Tethysides: a guide to reconstruction of collage history: Palaeogeography, Palaeoclimatology, Palaeoecology, v. 87, p. 411–440.

Stampfli, G., J. Marcoux, and A. Baud, 1991, Tethyan margins in space and time: Palaeogeography, Palaeoclimatology, Palaeoecology, v. 87, p. 373–409.

Stocklin, J., 1974, Possible ancient continental margins in Iran, *in* C.A. Burk and C.L. Drake, eds., The geology of continental margins: Berlin, Springer-Verlag, p. 873–887.

Tompson, R.N., M.A. Morrison, A.P Dickin, and G.L. Headry, 1983, Continental flood basalts...arachnids rule OK?, *in* C.J. Hawkesworth and M.J. Norry, eds., Continental basalts and mantle xenoliths: Shiva Geology Series, p. 158–185.

Tunoğlu, C., 1991, Microfacies analysis of the Upper Jurassic–Lower Cretaceous carbonate sequence of Devrekani Basin (northern Kastamonu) (in Turkish): Türkiye Petrol Jeolojisi Bülteni, v. 3, no. 1, p. 75–86.

Tüysüz, O., 1985, Kargı masifi ve dolayindaki tektonik birliklerin ayirdi ve arastirilmasi (Petrolojik inceleme): Ph.D. thesis, İstanbul Universitesi Fen Bilimleri Enstitüsü, 431 p.

Tüysüz, O., 1990, Tectonic evolution of a part of the Tethyside orogenic collage: the Kargı Massif, northern Turkey: Tectonics, v. 9, no. 1, p. 141–160.

Tüysüz, O., 1993, Karadenizden Orta Anadolu'ya bir Jeotravers: Kuzey Neo-Tetisin Tektonik evrimi: Turkiye Petrol Jeolojisi Bülteni, v. 5, no. 1, p. 1–33.

Tüysüz, O., E. Yiğitbaş, and H. Serdar, 1993, An approach to the early Mesozoic evolution of the Central Pontides, the Palaeotethys-Karakaya marginal basin problem: 8th Petroleum Congress of the Turkish Association of Petroleum Geologists, p. 351–362.

Tüysüz, O., A.A. Dellaloğlu, and N. Terzioglu, 1995, A magmatic belt within the Neotethyan suture zone and its role in the tectonic evolution of northern Turkey: Tectonophysics, v. 243, p. 173–191.

Ustaömer, T., 1993, Pre-Late Jurassic tectonic-sedimentary evolution of North Tethys: Central Pontides, N. Turkey: Ph.D. thesis, University of Edinburgh, 391 p.

Ustaömer, T., and A.H.F. Robertson, 1990, Palaeotethys versus Neotethys: Late Palaeozoic–Early Tertiary tectonic evolution of the Central Pontides, N. Turkey (abs.): Abstracts—International Earth Science Congress on the Aegean Regions, October 1–6, İzmir, p. 197.

Ustaömer, T. and Robertson, A.H.F., 1992, Palaeotethyan tectonic evolution of the north Tethyan margin in the Central Pontides, International Workshop: Work in Progress on the Geology of Türkiye, Keele, Abstracts, p. 73–74.

Ustaömer, T., and A.H.F. Robertson, 1993, Late Palaeozoic-Early Mesozoic marginal basins along the active southern continental margin of Eurasia: evidence from the Central Pontides (Turkey) and adjacent regions: Geological Journal, v. 28, no. 3/4, p. 219–238.

Ustaömer, T., and A.H.F. Robertson, 1994, Late Palae-ozoic marginal basin and subduction-accretion: evidence from the Palaeotethyan Küre Complex, Central Pontides, N. Turkey: Bulletin of the Geological Society of London, v. 151, no. 2, p. 291–306.

Ustaömer, T., and A.H.F. Robertson, 1995, Paleotethyan tectonic evolution of the north Tethyan margin in the Central Pontides, N. Turkey, *in* A. Erler, T. Ercan, E. Bingol, and S. Orçen, eds., Geology of the Black Sea region: Proceedings of the International Symposium on the Geology of the Black Sea Region, MTA, p. 24–32.

Yılmaz, O., 1980, Daday-Devrekani Masifinin kuzeydoğu kesiminin litostratigrafik birimleri ve tektoniği (Bati Pontidler, Türkiye)—Lithostratigraphic units and tectonics of northeastern part of the

Daday-Devrekani Massif (Western Pontides, Turkey): Yerbilimleri, v. 5–6, p. 101–135.
Yılmaz, O., and D. Boztuğ, 1986, Kastamonu granitoid belt of Turkey: first arc plutonism product related to the subduction of the Paleotethys: Geology, v. 14, p. 179–182.
Yılmaz, Y., O. Tüysüz, E. Yiğitbaş, Ş. Can Genç, and A.M.C. Şengör, this volume, Geology and tectonic evolution of the Pontides, *in* A. Robinson, ed., Regional and petroleum geology of the Black Sea and surrounding region: AAPG Memoir 68, p. 183–226.
Yılmaz, Y., and A.M.C. Şengör, 1985, Paleotethyan ophiolites in northern Turkey: petrology and tectonic setting: Ofioliti, v. 10, no. 2/3, p. 485–504.
Yılmaz, Y., and O. Tüysüz, 1988, An approach to the problem of reconstructing the Mesozoic tectonic units in the Kargı Massif and its surroundings (in Turkish): Turkish Association of Petroleum Geologists Bulletin, v. 1/1, p. 73–86.
Yılmaz, Y., and O. Tüysüz, 1991, Anatomy of an imbricated zone: geology of the Kargı Massif, Central Pontides: Bulletin of the Technical University of İstanbul, v. 44, no. 1–2, p. 279–299.
Yiğitbaş, E., O. Tüysüz, and H.S. Serdar, 1990, Orta Pontidlerde Üst Kretase yasli aktif kita kenarinin jeolojik özellikleri: Türkiye 8 Petrol Kongresi, Bildiriler, p. 141–151.

Okay, A.I., and Ö. Şahintürk, 1997, Geology of the Eastern Pontides, *in* A.G. Robinson, ed., Regional and petroleum geology of the Black Sea and surrounding region: AAPG Memoir 68, p. 291–311.

Chapter 15

Geology of the Eastern Pontides

Aral I. Okay
İstanbul Technical University (İ.T.Ü)
İstanbul, Turkey

Ömer Şahintürk
Turkish Petroleum Company
Ankara, Turkey

ABSTRACT

The 500-km-long Eastern Pontide belt shows several common stratigraphic features resulting from a common Mesozoic–Tertiary tectonic history. There is a heterogeneous pre-Jurassic basement comprised of Devonian? high-grade metamorphic rocks, Lower Carboniferous granodiorites and dacites, Upper Carboniferous–Lower Permian shallow-marine to terrigeneous sedimentary rocks and an allochthonous Permo–Triassic metabasite-phyllite-marble unit. The Mesozoic sedimentary sequence starts with a widespread Liassic marine transgression coming from the south. The Lower and Middle Jurassic rocks of the Eastern Pontides make up a 2000-m-thick sequence of tuff, pyroclastic rock, lava, and interbedded clastic sedimentary rock; the volcanism is probably related to rifting leading to the opening of the Neotethyan Ocean in the south. The Upper Jurassic–Lower Cretaceous is characterized by carbonates, showing a transition from platform carbonate deposition in the north to pelagic carbonates and calciturbidites in the south; this indicates the development of a south-facing passive continental margin. During the Cenomanian, there was uplift and erosion throughout the Eastern Pontides. Rocks of this stage are not present, and in many localities the Senonian deposits lie unconformably over Jurassic carbonates and even over the Carboniferous granitic basement. This compressive event is associated with the northward emplacement of an ophiolitic melange over the passive continental margin of the Eastern Pontides. The obduction of the ophiolitic melange is probably caused by the partial subduction of the Eastern Pontides continental margin in a south-dipping intra-oceanic subduction zone. This was followed by the flip of the subduction polarity during the Cenomanian–Turonian, which led to the development of a Senonian volcanic arc in the outer Eastern Pontides above the northward-subducting Tethyan Ocean floor. The volcanic arc is represented by >2-km-thick succession of volcanic and volcaniclastic rocks and interbedded limestones and marls. There are also intrusive granodiorite plutons with isotopic ages of 95 to 65 m.y. The volcanism shows a general silica enrichment, with time, ranging from basalts and andesites to dacites. The

Senonian sequence in the inner Eastern Pontides is made up of a tuffaceous flyschoid series representing the fore-arc succession. The Eastern Black Sea Basin probably opened during the Maastrichtian through the rifting of the volcanic arc axis.

During the late Paleocene–early Eocene, there was north-vergent thrust imbrication of the inner Eastern Pontides with the development of a major foreland flysch basin in front of the northward moving thrust sheets. Folding and uplift occurred in the outer Eastern Pontides during this period. This compressive deformational event, the strongest Mesozoic–Tertiary orogenic phase in the Eastern Pontides, was probably caused by the collision between the Pontide arc and the Tauride microplate in the south.

Widespread calc-alkaline volcanism and shallow-marine sedimentation occurred throughout the Eastern Pontides during the middle Eocene. The middle Eocene rocks are essentially undeformed and lie unconformably over a folded and thrust-faulted basement. This major middle Eocene extensional event is probably related to an accelarated phase of opening of the Eastern Black Sea Basin. From the end of the middle Eocene onward, the Eastern Pontides stayed largely above sea level, with minor volcanism and terrigeneous sedimentation.

INTRODUCTION

The Eastern Pontides form a mountain chain 500 km long and 100 km wide along the southeastern coast of the Black Sea. Geologically, the Eastern Pontides are well known as one of the best preserved examples of a paleo-island arc (e.g., Akin, 1978; Şengör and Yılmaz, 1981; Akıncı, 1984), which was formed during the Senonian above the northward-subducting Tethyan Ocean floor. The object of this chapter is to document the evolution of the Eastern Pontides from its position along the southern continental margin of Laurasia, its transformation into an active continental margin, and its eventual deformation during the Early Tertiary continental collision.

Geographically, the Eastern Pontides is a loosely defined term used for the region skirting the Eastern Black Sea coast of Turkey. Its western boundary is taken arbitrarily either as the Yeşılırmak or Kızılırmak river near Samsun. Tectonically, it forms the eastern part of the Sakarya Zone of the Pontides (Figure 1) (Okay, 1989). It is bounded in the south by the Ankara-Erzincan Neotethyan suture and in the north by the East Black Sea Basin; in the east, it extends without a break into the Lesser Caucasus, where it can be correlated with the Achara-Trialet (Banks et al., this volume) and Artvin-Karabakh zones (Figure 1) (Khain, 1975). Its western geological boundary with the Central Pontides is stratigraphic and corresponds to a facies change in the Cretaceous sequence.

The Sakarya Zone, which includes the Eastern Pontides, is characterized by a general absence of in-situ Paleozoic sedimentary rocks, by the presence of Paleotethyan Permo–Triassic accretion-subduction complexes (the Karakaya Complex), and by a ubiquitous Liassic transgression (Okay, 1989; Okay et al., 1996a). In contrast, the Taurides in the south show a well-developed Paleozoic sedimentary succession and do not comprise Paleotethyan accretion-subduction complexes. In northeast Turkey, these two paleogeographic realms are separated by the Ankara-Erzincan suture zone, which is marked by large bodies of peridotite and ophiolitic melange (Figure 2).

The Eastern Pontides is commonly divided into an inner/southern and an outer/northern part (Akin, 1978; Gedikoğlu et al., 1979; Özsayar et al., 1981). The outer Eastern Pontides are dominated by Senonian and middle Eocene volcanic and volcaniclastic rocks, which hide much of the pre-Senonian geology (Figure 2). On the other hand, pre-Senonian rocks are widely exposed in the inner Eastern Pontides, which occupied a fore-arc position during the Senonian and underwent much more intensive deformation than did the outer Eastern Pontides during the Early Tertiary continental collison. The transitional boundary between these two parts follows approximately the Niksar-Gümüşhane-Ardanuç line (Figure 2).

THE PRE-JURASSIC BASEMENT OF THE EASTERN PONTIDES

The isolated exposures of the pre-Jurassic basement in the Eastern Pontides can be grouped into four types: a high-grade metamorphic complex of pre-Carboniferous age, an early Carboniferous granodiorite-dacite complex, an Upper Carboniferous–Lower Permian shallow-water to terrigeneous sedimentary sequence, and a Permo–Triassic metabasite-phyllite-marble unit.

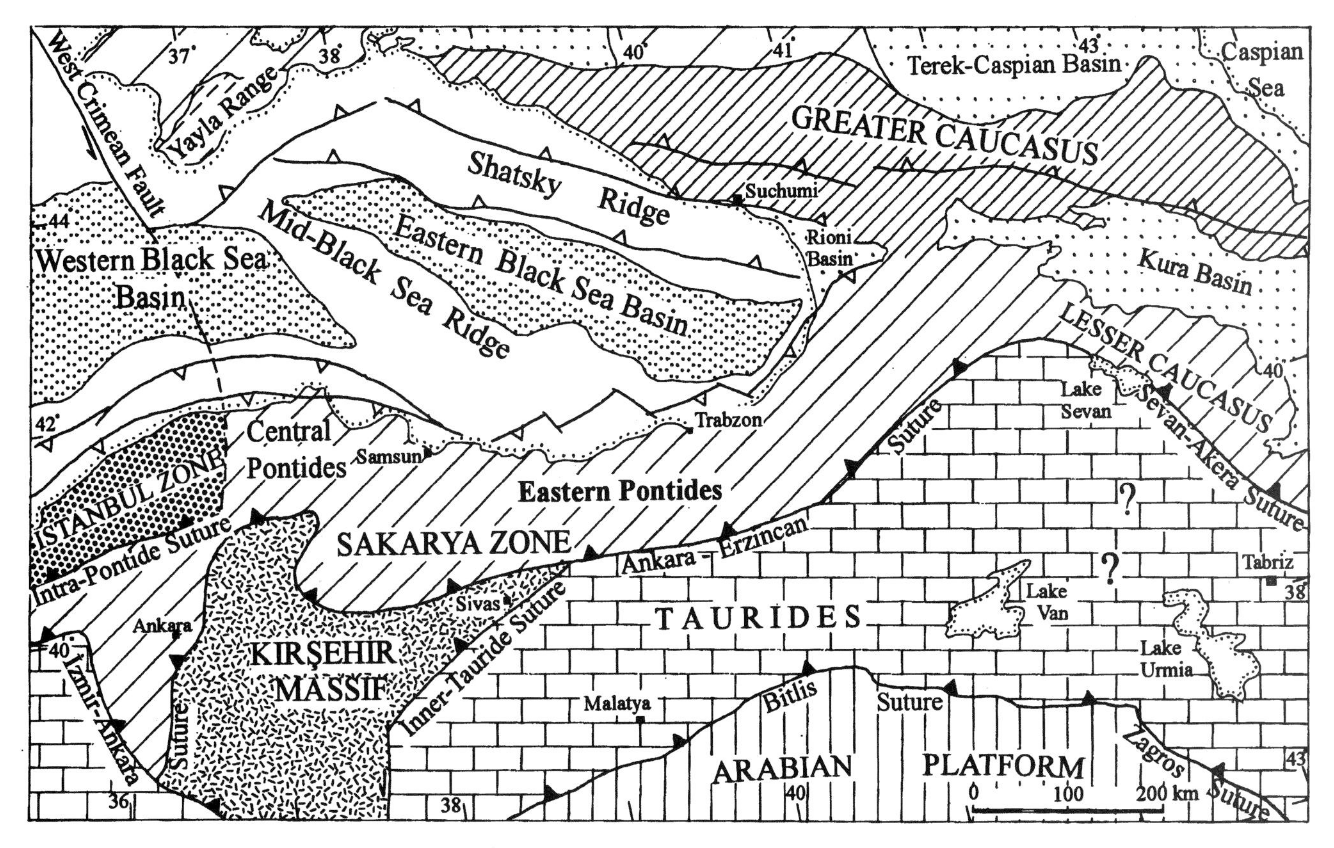

Figure 1. Tectonic map of the Eastern Black Sea region. Lines with black triangles indicate Neotethyan sutures with the original subduction polarity. Lines with open triangles are major post-Eocene thrusts.

High-Grade Metamorphic Complex—Pulur Massif

A heterogeneous crystalline basement of cordierite-sillimanite-garnet gneiss, microgneiss, migmatite, metaquartzite, banded amphibolite, diopside-plagioclase rock, and metadiorite is exposed in a major north-vergent Eocene thrust slice in the inner Eastern Pontides (Figures 2, 3). This metamorphic complex, called the Pulur Massif, outcrops in a 5–10 km wide and 60 km long northeast-trending belt and is overlain unconformably by the Liassic volcanosedimentary rocks (Ketin, 1951; Tanyolu, 1988; Keskin et al., 1989; Okay, 1996). The high-grade metamorphic rocks of the Pulur Massif are associated with medium-grained, banded metagranitic rocks that may represent synmetamorphic granites. In the Pulur Massif, there are also rare metadunite and metaharzburgite bands, a few meters thick, interlayered with amphibolites (Okay, 1996). The metamorphic rocks of the Pulur Massif are extensively mylonitized during the Alpide events and are intruded by Eocene dioritic and andesitic stocks, dykes, and sills. The gneisses and amphibolites, which form small outcrops under the Jurassic volcanosedimentary rocks south of Artvin (Figure 2) (Maden Tetkik ve Arama Enstitüsü, 1977; Tarhan, 1982), are probably part of the same high-grade metamorphic complex.

Lower Carboniferous Granodiorite-Dacite Complex—Gümüşhane and Köse Granodiorites

Granitic rocks occupy large areas south of Gümüşhane forming the Gümüşhane and Köse composite plutons (Figures 2, 3). They are generally hornblende-biotite granodiorites (Zankl, 1962a; Yılmaz, 1976) and intrude a metasedimentary basement of greenschist facies schists and phyllites of unknown age (Yılmaz, 1972, 1977). The Köse pluton has yielded a well-defined earliest Carboniferous (360 ±2 Ma) Rb/Sr isochron age (Bergougnan, 1987).

Probable extrusive equivalents of the Gümüşhane and Kelkit granodiorites occur south of the Olur region, where Yılmaz (1985) and Bozkus (1992a) describe a thick sequence of dacite, rhyodacite, and rhyolite lavas and tuffs unconformably overlain by the Jurassic volcaniclastic rocks (Figure 2).

Upper Carboniferous–Lower Permian? Sedimentary Sequence

A coherent and thick Upper Carboniferous sequence is exposed in two thrust sheets in the inner Eastern Pontides (Figure 3). The sequence shows a simple monoclinal structure and is unconformably overlain by Jurassic sandy limestones. The base of the sequence is not exposed, but probably lies over the high-grade metamorphic rocks of the Pulur Massif, which outcrops in the overlying thrust sheet. This Upper Paleozoic sequence, known since Ketin (1951), has been studied by several geologists with conflicting views regarding its stratigraphy and age (Ağar, 1977; Akdeniz, 1988; Keskin et al., 1989; Okay, 1993; Robinson et al., 1995). A map and cross section of the

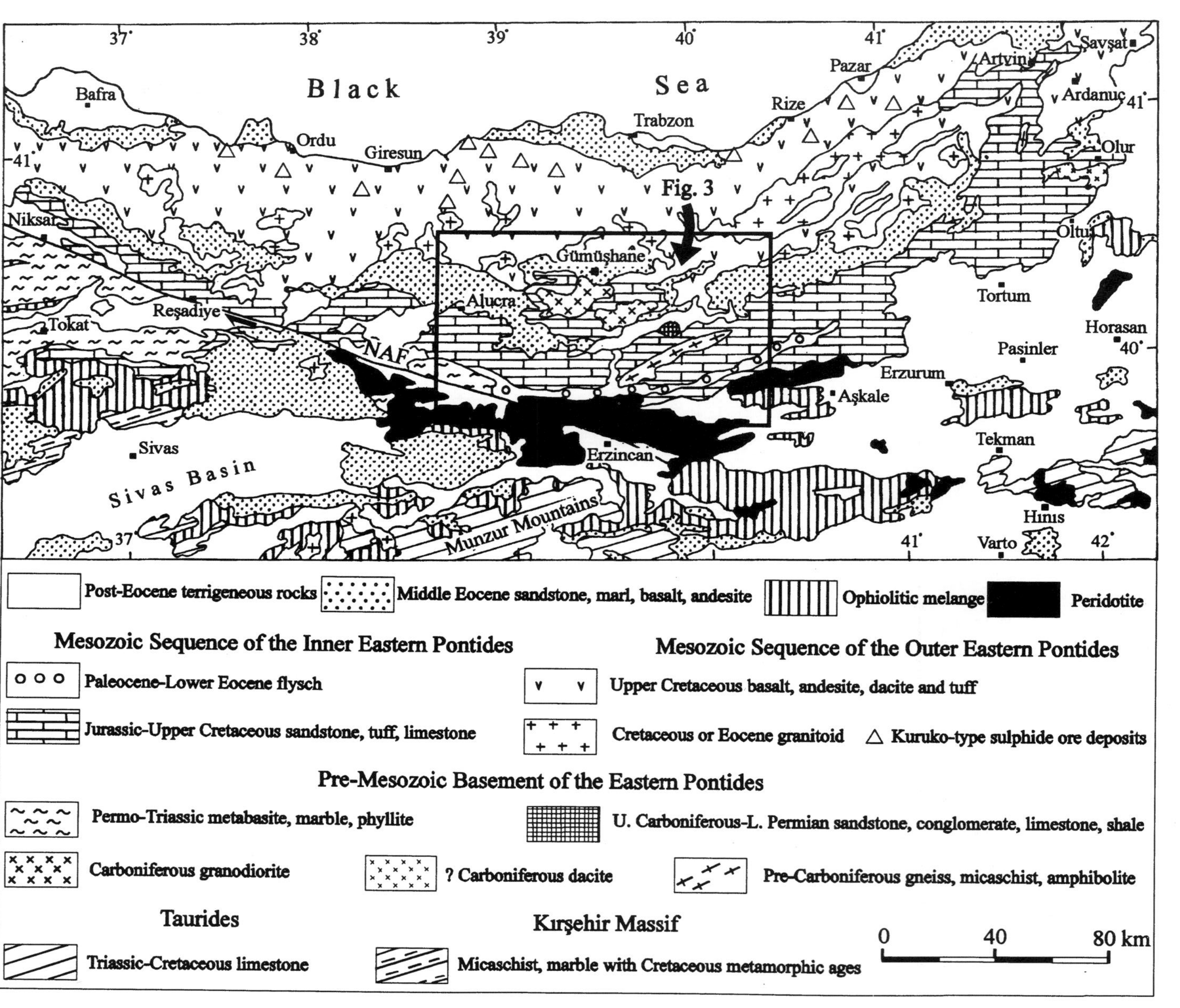

Figure 2. Simplified geological map of the Eastern Pontides. For clarity, no tectonic boundaries, except the North Anatolian fault (NAF), are shown. The locations of the sulfide deposits are from Pejatovic (1979) and Akıncı (1984). The region shown in Figure 3 is outlined.

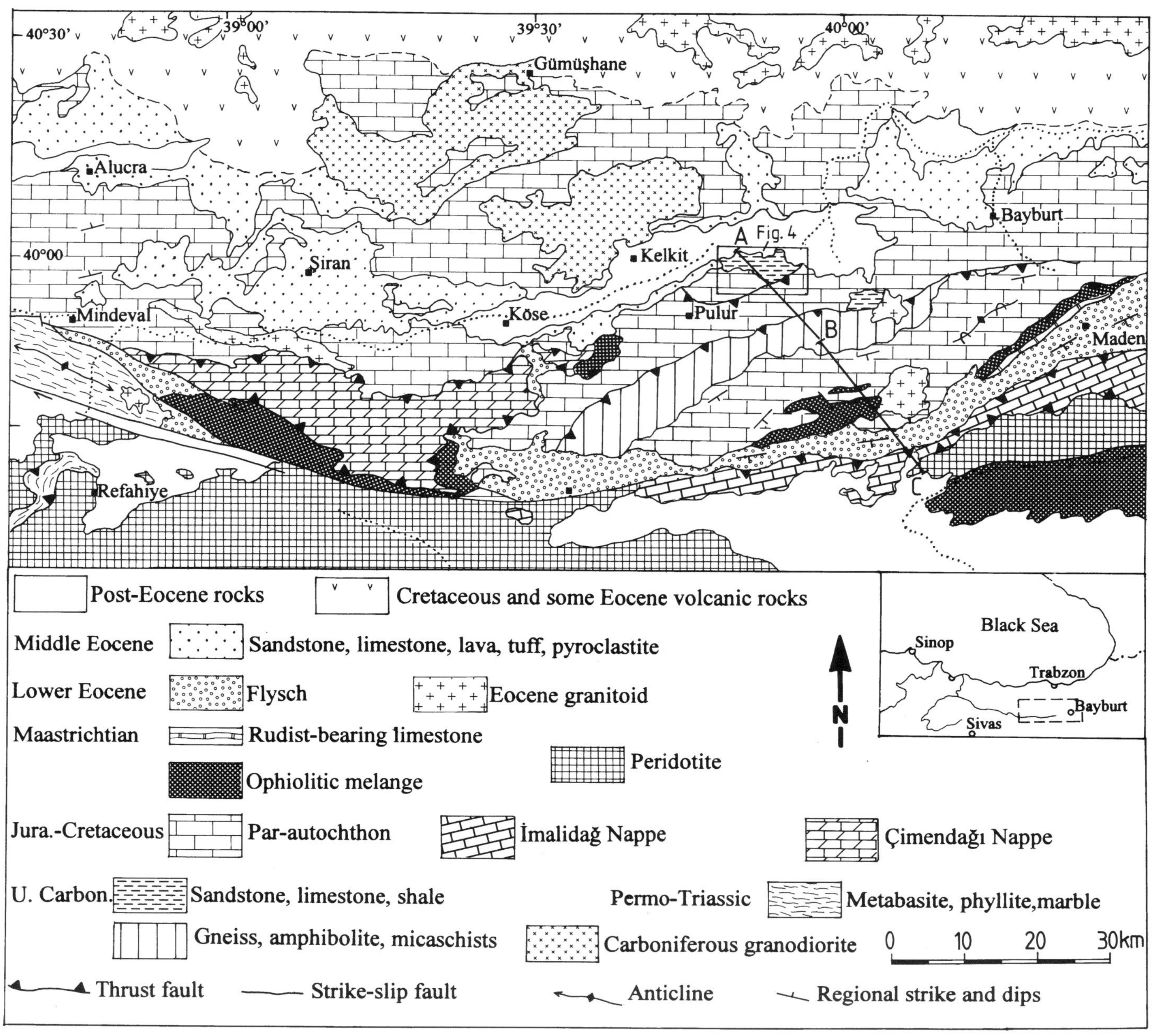

Figure 3. Geological map of the inner Eastern Pontides. For location, see Figure 2. Lines of sections refer to Figure 8.

region, based on recent mapping (Okay, 1993; Okay et al., in press), are shown in Figure 4. The Paleozoic sequence starts near Çatalçeşme with a ~1100-m-thick, heterogeneous series of sandstone, pebbly sandstone, quartzite, dark limestone, siltstone, and shale with rare thin coal seams; these lithologies are intimately intercalated on a few meters to a few tens of meters scale. The sandstones are medium to thickly bedded arkosic arenites with well-rounded pebbles of acidic magmatic rocks, possibly derived from the equivalents of the Gümüşhane granodiorite and Olur dacites. They are intercalated with medium to thickly bedded, dark-gray to black limestones locally rich in brachiopods, coral, gastropod, algae, and fusulinids. Thinly bedded, bioturbated siltstones with plant fragments and black-gray shale, with a few centimeter thick discontinuous coal seams, occur locally between the limestone beds. The fusulinid fauna in the limestones conclusively indicate a Late Carboniferous (Upper Kasimovian–Lower Gzelian) age. The diagnostic fusulinid species include *Eostafella* sp., *Ozawainella* cf. *angulata* (Colani) sp., *O. nikitovkensis* (Brazhnikova), *Pseudoendothyra* cf. *timanica* (Rauser), *Schubertella obscura* Lee & Chen, *S. pseudomagna* Putrya & Leont, *S. parvifusiformis* Lin, *Quasifusilina* ex gr. *longissima* (Moeller), *Q.* cf. *praecursor* Rauser, *Triticites gissaricus* Bensch, *T.* cf. *sinuosus* Rosovskaya, *T.* aff. *simplex* Schellwien, *T. petschoricus* Rauser, *T.* ex gr. *karlensis* Rosovskaya *Rugofusulina prisca ovoidea*, and *R. cf. praevia* Shlykova (Okay and Leven, 1996).

This heterogeneous Upper Carboniferous series is conformably overlain by ~1000-m-thick monotonous red terrigenous sandstones (Figure 4). The sandstones are thickly bedded to massive arkosic arenites and pebbly arenites. The pebbles in the sandstones are generally 2–5 cm large and consist of quartz and acidic magmatic rocks. No fossils have been found in the sandstones; however, considering that even the uppermost parts of the heterogeneous series are of Kasimovian–early Gzelian age, these conformably overlying terrigenous sandstones should be latest Carboniferous (Gzelian) and possibly earliest Permian in age.

Permo–Triassic Metabasite-Marble-Phyllite Unit—Ağvanis and Tokat Massifs

A thick sequence of closely intercalated metabasite, marble and phyllite forms a 35-km-long by ~8-km-wide metamorphic block, called Ağvanis Massif, immediately north of the Ankara-Erzincan suture north of Refahiye (Figures 2, 3) (Nebert, 1961; Okay, 1984). The metamorphic rocks form a large anticlinorium and are bounded in the north and south by strike-slip faults of the North Anatolian fault zone.

The Ağvanis Massif is dominated by metabasic rocks (60%–70% of the sequence), largely metatuffs and metalavas, locally with preserved pillow structures. The metabasic rocks are intimately intercalated with marble and phyllite horizons, each horizon usually <50 m thick. There are also very rare serpentinite lenses, which are a few tens of meters long (Okay, 1984). The total structural thickness is ~4.5 km. The whole sequence has undergone a greenschist facies metamorphism with the development of actinolite/barroisite-albite-epidote-chlorite-sphene paragenesis in the metabasic rocks.

The metamorphic rocks of the Ağvanis Massif are unconformably overlain by a Paleocene olistostrome formation. It is likely that the metamorphic rocks also form the basement to the Liassic sedimentary and volcanic rocks exposed north of the massif, although a post-Miocene strike-slip fault now constitutes the surface contact between these two formations (Figure 3).

No fossils are found in the Ağvanis Massif. Similar metabasite-marble-phyllite sequences occur in the Tokat Massif in the west (Blumenthal, 1950; Alp, 1972; Özcan et al., 1980; Tutkun and Inan, 1982; Aktimur et al., 1992) and are widespread in the western part of the Sakarya Zone forming part of the Karakaya Complex (the Nilüfer Unit of Okay et al., 1991, 1996a). In the Tokat Massif, metaclastic rocks locally comprise Permian and Triassic limestone blocks (Blumenthal, 1950; Öztürk, 1979; Özcan et al., 1980) indicating Permo–Triassic depositional and latest Triassic metamorphic ages.

The close intercalation of basic volcanic rock and tuff with limestone and shale, and absence of sheeted dyke complex or gabbro, indicates that the deposition of the Ağvanis Massif occurred in an arc-related basin, where there is close intermingling of volcanic and sedimentary rocks. This interpretation is in contrast to the ophiolite interpretation of the Ağvanis Massif by Şengör et al. (1980).

PRE-JURASSIC EVOLUTION OF THE EASTERN PONTIDES

The high-grade metamorphic basement of the Eastern Pontides is exposed in the Pulur Massif. This basement was intruded by granodiorites during the earliest Carboniferous, represented by the Gümüşhane and Köse plutons. Acidic volcanism as observed in the Olur region (Figure 5) was also associated with the granitic intrusions. The high-grade metamorphism could plausibly be associated with the thermal event that produced the calc-alkaline magmatism, and hence could be of Devonian or earliest Carboniferous age. The high-temperature–low-pressure metamorphic rocks and the calc-alkaline magmatic rocks probably formed in a Late Devonian–Early Carboniferous magmatic arc, although the polarity of subduction and the setting of the magmatic arc are obscure. In the Late Carboniferous, shallow-marine to fluviatile sedimentary rocks transgressed over the metamorphic-magmatic basement. Plant fossils in the Upper Carboniferous sequence show Euroamerican affinities (Şengör, 1990). Similar Upper Carboniferous–Lower Permian facies are widespread in the Greater Caucasus and represent molasse deposition at the end of the Hercynian orogeny (Khain, 1975; Adamia et al., 1982), and can be compared with the Rotliegende of Europe. Furthermore, early Hercynian sillimanite-cordierite-bearing gneisses, migmatites, and intrusive plutons (similar to those from the basement of the Eastern Pontides) are reported from the Greater

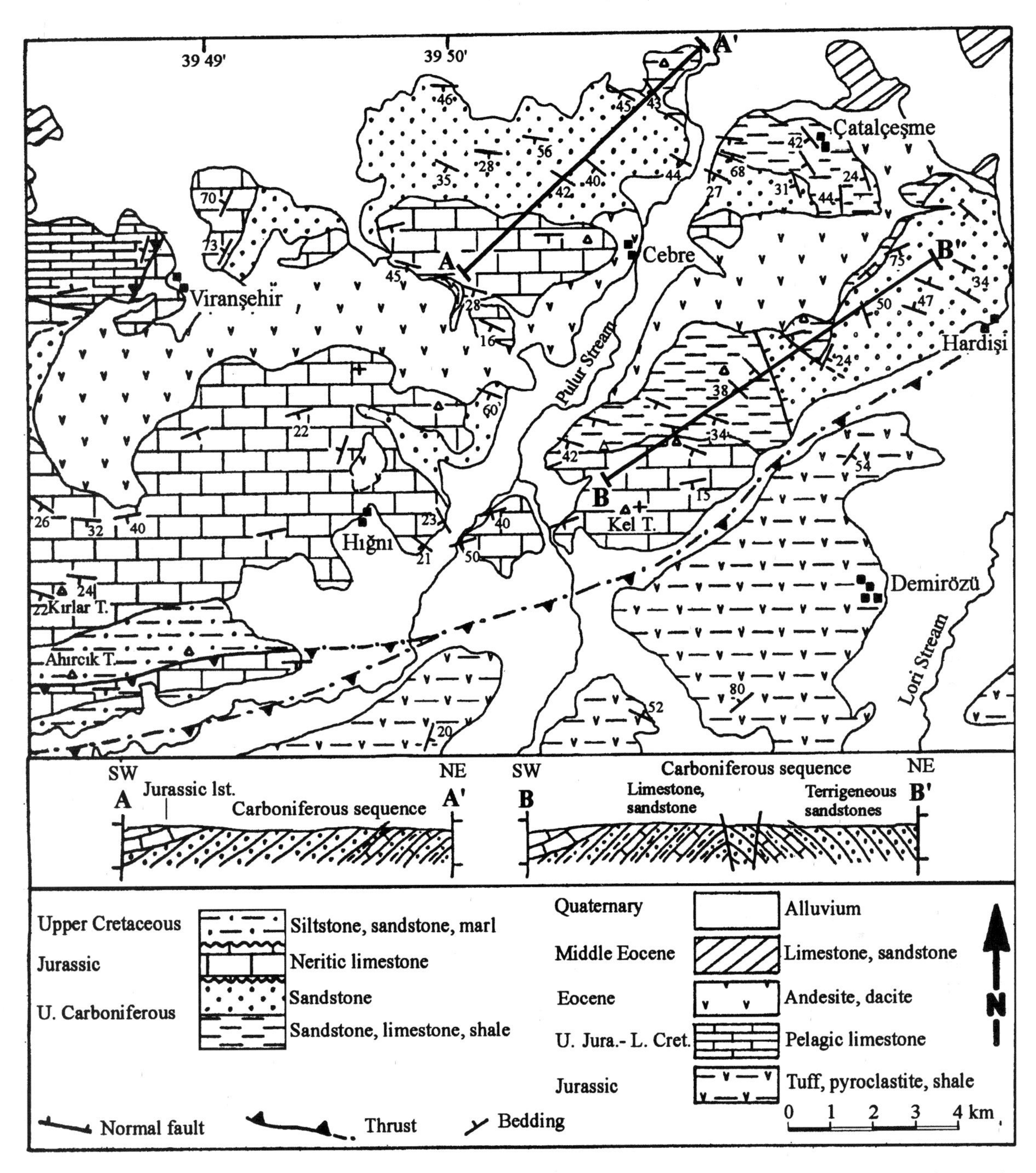

Figure 4. Geological map and cross sections of the Demirözü region showing the stratigraphic and tectonic setting of the Upper Carboniferous sequence. For location see Figure 3.

Caucasus (fore-range and main range zones) and from the Dzirula, Khrami, and Loki salients of the Transcaucasian Median Massif (Abesadze et al., 1982; Adamia et al., 1982, 1983). In contrast, no Hercynian metamorphism or magmatism is known in the Taurides, indicating that during the Late Paleozoic, the Eastern Pontides were possibly part of the Caucasian realm located along the southern margin of Laurasia (Adamia et al., 1982; Robinson et al., 1995). A contrasting view is given by Şengör (1990), who places the Eastern Pontides and the Dzirula, Khrami, and Loki salients at the northern margin of Gondwana. This is largely based on a continuous Middle Devonian to Middle Triassic clastic series (the Dizi Series, Adamia et al., 1982), with no record of a late Paleozoic deformation, located in the Greater Caucasus north of the Transcaucasian Median Massif. However, the Dizi Series could be completely allochthonous and derived from the south during the Late Triassic.

The Permian and Triassic events are poorly recorded in the Eastern Pontides. The various reports of the presence of Permo–Triassic ophiolites in the

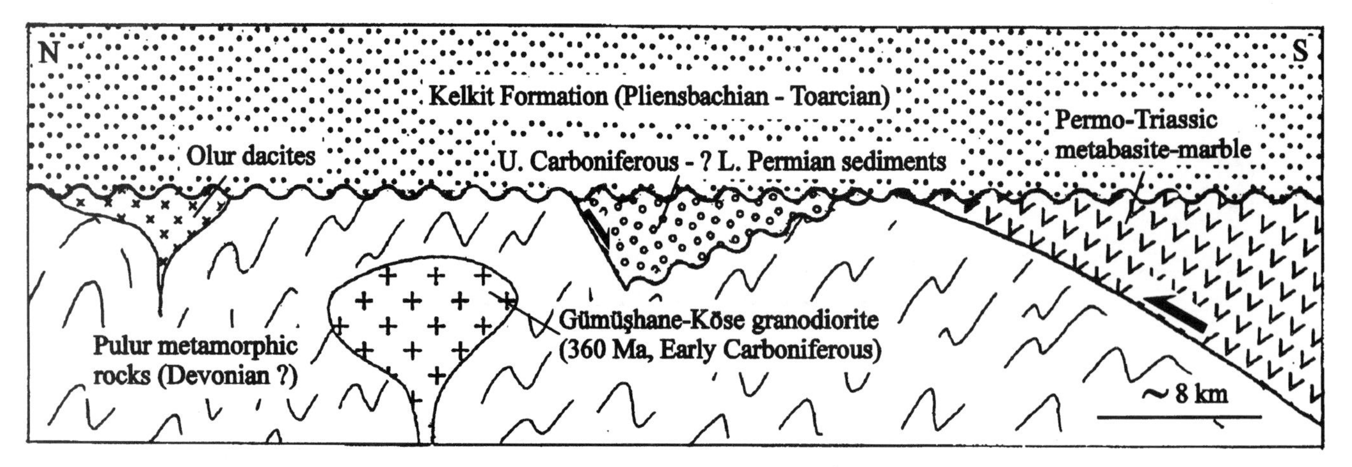

Figure 5. Speculative sketch illustrating possible relations among the pre-Jurassic basement units of the Eastern Pontides.

Eastern Pontides (Seymen, 1975; Bektas et al., 1984; Koçyiğit, 1990) are not verified. In the Biga Peninsula in the western part of the Sakarya Zone, a Permo-Triassic metabasite-phyllite-marble unit, similar to the Ağvanis Massif, tectonically overlies a high-grade metamorphic basement with mid-Carboniferous (308 ±16 Ma) zircon Pb ages (Okay et al., 1996a). This relationship is interpreted as the tectonic emplacement of a Permo–Triassic ensimatic fore-arc sequence over a continental margin during the latest Triassic final closure of the Paleotethys (Okay et al., 1996a). A similar tectonic relationship and interpretation can be envisaged for the Eastern Pontides. The location of the Paleotethyan fore-arc sequences along the inner margin of the Eastern Pontides and their apparent absence in the north suggest that the Paleotethys was located to the south of the Eastern Pontides. However, using the available data from the Eastern Pontides, little else can be said about the initiation, subduction polarity, and destruction of the Paleotethys.

JURASSIC–EARLY CRETACEOUS—EVOLUTION OF A SOUTH-FACING PASSIVE CONTINENTAL MARGIN

Lower–Middle Jurassic Rift Sequence—The Kelkit Formation

Triassic sedimentary rocks are virtually absent in the Eastern Pontides, and the Mesozoic deposits begin with a major Liassic transgression coming from the south (Akin, 1978). The Jurassic in the Eastern Pontides is characteristically represented by a predominantly volcaniclastic formation (the Kelkit Formation), which rests unconformably over a heterogeneous basement. It consists of basaltic and andesitic lithic tuffs, volcanogenic sandstone, shale, basaltic and andesitic lavas, and conglomerate. There are also thin, discontinuous coal and ammonitico rosso horizons within the sequence (Figure 6). Although the sequence is dominated by volcanogenic sandstones, there are also true pyroclastic rocks and basaltic and andesitic lava flows (Bergougnan, 1976, 1987). The clinopyroxene composition from the pyroclastic rocks and lavas suggests a tholeiitic parent magma (Bergougnan, 1987). The Kelkit Formation has a very wide distribution in the Eastern Pontides and extends from the Destek-Reşadiye area (Seymen, 1975; Öztürk, 1979; Aktimur et al., 1992) 500 km eastward to the Olur and Yusufeli regions (Maden Tetkik ve Arama Enstitüsü, 1977; Yılmaz, 1985; Bozkus, 1992a). Its northward extension is largely concealed by the Cretaceous and Eocene deposits north of Gümüşhane; however, small inliers in this region (Tasli, 1984; Bektas et al., 1987; Korkmaz, 1993) show that a similar facies, albeit richer in volcanic rocks, characterizes the Lower–Middle Jurassic throughout the Eastern Pontides (Figure 7A).

The Kelkit Formation is ~1500 to 2000 m thick (Ketin, 1951; Nebert, 1961; Pelin, 1977; Bergougnan, 1987; Gürsoy, 1989; Okay, 1993) and shows vertical and lateral facies changes. Three main facies are recognized: (1) a turbiditic volcaniclastic sandstone-shale unit showing graded bedded and flow and slump structures (Okay, 1984), (2) a widespread lithic tuff-volcaniclastic sandstone-conglomerate unit including several coal horizons representing a paralic environment (Pelin, 1977), and (3) the ammonitico rosso facies showing condensed deposition on top of seamounts. The Kelkit Formation becomes generally finer grained and deeper marine toward the south (Yılmaz, 1985; Okay, 1993). For example, south of Pulur, the basal Kelkit Formation overlies the high-grade metamorphic rocks of the Pulur Massif containing a 20-m-thick horizon of pebbly arenites with thin coal seams and grades up into a 1500-m-thick sequence of interbedded fine-grained dark tuff and shale; this includes Jurassic limestone blocks several hundred meters large (Okay, 1993). The deposits south of Pulur do not include the volcaniclastic sandstones and coarse pyroclastics common in the Kelkit Formation farther north.

The age of the Kelkit Formation is largely based on ammonites from the ammonitico rosso horizons, which show the presence of all the Liassic stages from Early Pliensbachian to Toarcian (Otkun, 1942;

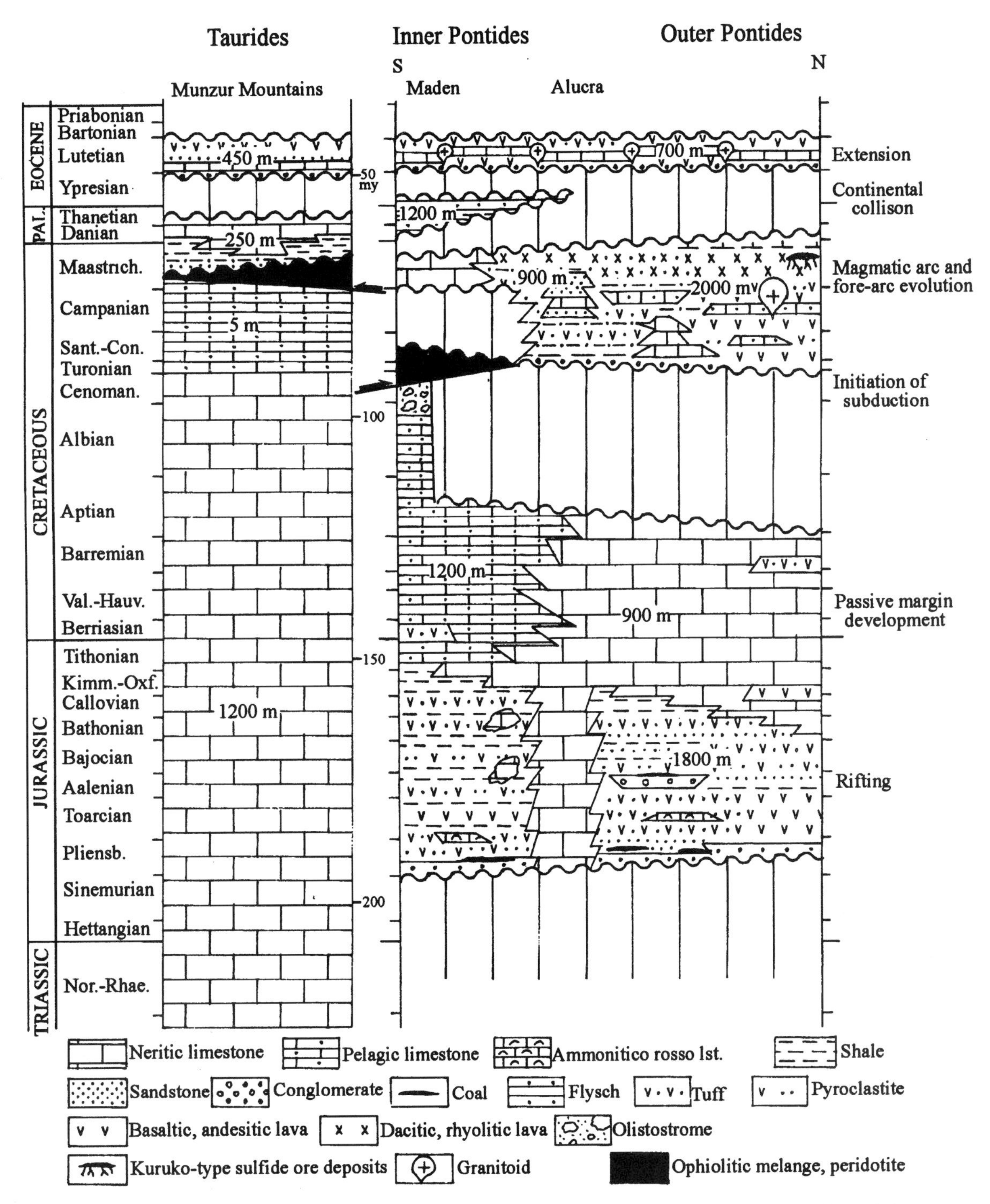

Figure 6. Stratigraphic columns for the Eastern Pontides and the Munzur Mountains of the Taurides. The stratigraphy of the Taurides in the Munzur Mountains is based on Özgül and Tursucu (1984), for the numerous stratigraphic data on the Eastern Pontides, see the text.

Stchepinsky, 1945; Ketin, 1951; Alp, 1972; Yılmaz, 1972; Bassoullet et al., 1975; Özer, 1984; Bergougnan, 1987). In addition, palynology of separate coal horizons gives Liassic (Agrali et al., 1966; Pelin, 1977) and Dogger ages (Agrali et al., 1965). The presence of Dogger age is further suggested by rare macrofossils (Wedding, 1963) and by the recent determination of dinoflagellate and palynomorph assemblages (Robinson et al., 1995). Thus, the age span of the Kelkit Formation is from early Pliensbachian up to at least the end of the Bathonian.

A different Jurassic facies occurs in the Pulur region in the relative authochthon at the base of the thrust sheets. Here, Liassic shallow-water sandy limestones

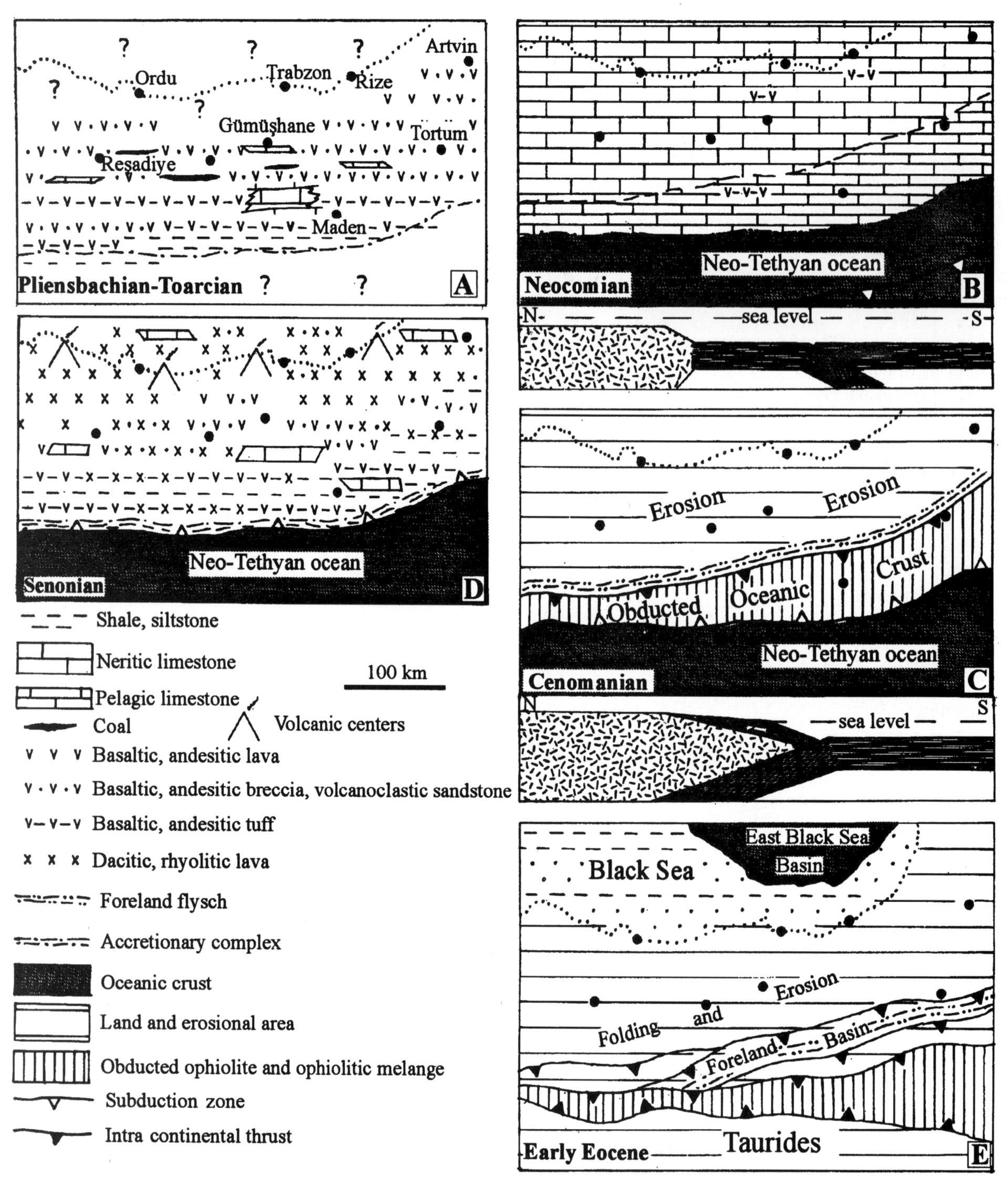

Figure 7. Mesozoic paleogeographic and tectonic maps of the Eastern Pontides. The scale is only for the continental crust, assuming a conservative 50% crustal shortening in the inner Eastern Pontides. (A) Pliensbachian–Toarcian, ≤2000-m-thick volcaniclastic rocks with basic lavas characterize much of the Eastern Pontides. Associated with the basic volcaniclastic rocks are thin coal seams and ammonitico rosso-type limestones. In contrast, neritic limestone deposition occurs in a major horst south of Gümüşhane. The paralic to shallow-marine environment in the north changes to deeper marine conditions in the south. Possible rifting leading to the development of the Neotethyan Ocean in the south. (B) Neocomian, extensive carbonate deposition over the whole of the Eastern Pontides. The carbonates range from neritic to pelagic toward the south and suggest the development of a south-facing passive continental margin. Minor tuff deposition from a possible intra-oceanic subduction zone to the south. (C) Cenomanian, obduction of oceanic crust and accretionary complex is caused by the partial subduction of the Eastern Pontides continental margin in an intra-oceanic subduction zone. This is followed by the flip of the subduction polarity. Uplift and erosion characterize the outer Eastern Pontides. (D) Senonian, a volcanic arc forms above the northward-subducting Tethyan Ocean floor. The Eastern Black Sea Basin develops during the Maastrichtian through the splitting of the arc axis. (E) Early Eocene, continental collision with the Taurides results in the thrust imbrication of the inner Eastern Pontides continental margin. A major foreland flysch basin develops in front of the north-vergent thrust sheets. Strong uplift and folding in the Eastern Pontides.

(Akdeniz, 1988; Okay, 1993; Robinson et al., 1995) lie unconformably over the Carboniferous sedimentary sequence (Figure 4). They grade up through an oolitic limestone horizon to thickly bedded, cherty micrites. The whole sequence is ~750 m thick and ranges in age from Liassic to Berriasian–Valanginian. It is unconformably overlain by Senonian deep-water sediments (Akdeniz, 1988; Okay et al., in press). Lower and Middle Jurassic rock in the overlying thrust sheets is developed in the volcaniclastic facies, suggesting that the Pulur Jurassic rocks are deposited on top of a horst and thus avoided the volcaniclastic influx (Figure 6).

The similarity in the Mesozoic stratigraphy between the Eastern Pontides and the Caucasus, as shown by the general absence of Triassic deposits and similar volcanic and coal-bearing Jurassic facies (Khain, 1975; Adamia et al., 1982), indicates, contrary to some suggestions (Bektas et al., 1984), that the Eastern Pontides were located along the southern margin of Laurasia before the opening of the Eastern Black Sea Basin in the Maastrichtian.

Görür et al. (1983) interpreted the Kelkit Formation of the Eastern Pontides as a rift facies related to the opening of the Neotethyan Ocean in the south. The lateral facies and thickness changes in the Kelkit Formation support this interpretation. The southward deepening inferred from the Kelkit Formation is probably related to the opening of the Neotethyan Ankara-Erzincan Ocean in the south (Görür et al., 1983). However, a discrepancy arises in this interpretation due to the dissimilarity of the pre-Jurassic stratigraphy between the Eastern Pontides and the Taurides to the south. In the Munzur and Keban units of the Taurides there is a well-developed Triassic and Permian carbonate succession not seen anywhere in the Pontides (Figure 6) (Özgül and Tursucu, 1984). Furthermore, during the Liassic, there were faunal differences between the two sides of the suture (Bassoullet et al., 1975; Enay, 1976); Liassic ammonites from the Pontides are similar to those from the southern Laurasian margin, whereas Liassic fauna from the Munzur Mountains of the Taurides resemble those from the southern margin of the Tethys. It is quite possible that there was major post-Liassic strike-slip movement along the southern margin of Laurasia, so that the Taurides were not contiguous with the Eastern Pontides during the pre-Liassic. One possibility is that the Sanandaj-Sirjan Zone in Southwest Iran, which shows evidence for Paleozoic and Triassic orogenic activity and has an uppermost Triassic to Middle Jurassic unconformable cover of thick coal-bearing clastic rocks, similar to the Kelkit Formation of the Eastern Pontides (Stöcklin, 1968; Şengör, 1990), could represent the continental fragment that rifted off from the Eastern Pontides during the Jurassic.

Upper Jurassic–Lower Cretaceous Carbonate Platform

The Upper Jurassic–Lower Cretaceous carbonates, which conformably overlie the Kelkit Formation, outcrop throughout the Sakarya Zone. In the Eastern Pontides, the carbonate deposition begins slightly earlier in the north (Oxfordian–Tithonian), where it is represented by a ~900-m-thick neritic limestone and dolomite (Pelin, 1977, 1981; Gürsoy, 1989; Yılmaz, 1992; Robinson et al., 1995), than in the south (Tithonian–Berriasian), where there is a >1000-m-thick pelagic radiolarian biomicrite and calciturbidite sequence (Ketin, 1951; Bursuk, 1975, 1981; Tutkun and Inan, 1982; Okay et al., in press). Minor and local basic volcanism during the Late Jurassic–Early Cretaceous is evidenced by thin tuff beds in the limestone sequence north of Gümüşhane (Zankl, 1962b) and south of Pulur (Okay et al., in press). In the Late Jurassic, there is a clear facies differentiation between the outer and inner Eastern Pontides. The boundary between these two realms follows approximately the Niksar-Demirözü-Bayburt-Tortum line (Figure 2). The picture is that of a carbonate platform passing southeast into a carbonate ramp representing the south-facing continental margin of Laurasia (Figure 7B) (Görür, 1988). This phase in the Eastern Pontides represents the development of a south-facing passive carbonate continental margin.

The Upper Jurassic–Lower Cretaceous carbonates are bounded above by a major Senonian unconformity associated in places (for example, in parts of the Alucra region) (Pelin, 1977) with the erosion of the whole carbonate sequence. The carbonates are karstified with locally developed paleovalleys removing the complete carbonate sequences. The uppermost age of the preserved carbonate sequence is late Barremian in the north (Pelin, 1977; Bergougnan, 1987) and Aptian in the south (Bursuk, 1981; Okay et al., in press). Albian ages from the pelagic carbonates are only reported from the Maden region near the suture zone (Elmas, 1994; Robinson et al., 1995).

CENOMANIAN–TURONIAN—REGIONAL UPLIFT RELATED TO THE EMPLACEMENT OF OPHIOLITIC MELANGE

The Cenomanian represents a major episode of uplift and erosion throughout the Eastern Pontides (Ketin, 1977; Pelin et al., 1982), which is associated with the northward emplacement of an ophiolitic melange over the inner Eastern Pontides (Figure 7C). Cenomanian deposits are absent throughout the Eastern Pontides, and in most localities Campanian limestones lie unconformably over Jurassic sediments (Pelin, 1977; Yılmaz, 1985; Bergougnan, 1987; Gürsoy, 1989; Robinson et al., 1995); in the Gümüşhane region, Senonian rocks rest directly on the Carboniferous granites (Yılmaz, 1972). In this respect, the Eastern Pontides differ from the central Pontides, where the Aptian–Albian is characterized by shallow to deep marine clastic rocks interpreted as synrift deposits associated with the opening of the Western Black Sea Basin (Görür, 1988; Robinson et al., 1995).

The ophiolitic melange in the inner Eastern Pontides forms a 200-km-long thrust sheet from north of Erzincan to north of Tortum (Figure 3) and rests tectonically over the Lower Cretaceous pelagic carbonates (Bilgin, 1984; Bergougnan, 1987; Inan, 1988; Okay et al., in press). Due to the Early Tertiary erosion, the ophiolitic melange is preserved as small klippen over the Neocomian pelagic carbonates, which contrasts with the large peridotite and ophiolitic melange masses in the suture zone and in the Taurides (Figure 2). Locally, an olistostromal foreland flysch sequence occurs between the melange and the carbonates. The youngest age recorded in the carbonates underneath the melange is Late Albian in the Maden region (Elmas, 1994). The ophiolitic melange is composed of, in order of abundance, spilitized basalt, radiolarian chert, pelagic and neritic limestone, sandstone, shale, siltstone, and serpentinite blocks. It includes lithologies from both the oceanic crust and the passive continental margin of the Eastern Pontides. The various blocks in the melange are juxtaposed along fault contacts without any discernible matrix. Pelagic limestone blocks in the melange, derived from the Eastern Pontides continental margin, range in age up to Aptian (Okay et al., in press), and the melange is unconformably overlain by Maastrichtian rudist-bearing neritic limestones in the Maden region (Figure 3) (Ketin, 1951; Fenerci, 1994). Farther south in the Askale region (Bozkus, 1992b) and northwest of Erzurum (Inan, 1988), Maastrichtian pelagic limestones and calciturbidites lie unconformably over the melange. This constrains the age of the melange formation and its emplacement onto the continental margin to the Cenomanian–Campanian (Figure 6). Considering that the Late Cretaceous transgression in the Eastern Pontides starts in the Turonian–Coniacian, the emplacement age of the melange is further constrained to Cenomanian–Turonian (Figure 6). The ophiolitic melange thrust sheet apparently did not reach farther north than the line connecting Siran-Kelkit-Bayburt (Figure 3), although the compression was felt throughout the Eastern Pontides as a period of major uplift and erosion (Figure 7C). In the west, in the region of the Tokat Massif, Aktimur et al. (1992) also describe the emplacement of an ophiolitic melange during this time. In the Lesser Caucasus, ophiolite and ophiolitic melange were emplaced northward over the Sevan-Akera Zone also during the Cenomanian–Coniacian (Knipper, 1980).

Thus, oceanic crust and/or oceanic accretionary complex were obducted northward over the 1000-km-long Eastern Pontides–Lesser Caucasus continental margin during the Cenomanian–Turonian. This obduction may be related to the partial subduction of the Eastern Pontides passive continental margin in a south-dipping juvenile intra-oceanic subduction zone (Figure 7C). This was probably followed by the flip of the subduction polarity from a south-to-north–dipping subduction, which explains the close temporal relation between the obduction of the ophiolitic melange and the start of the northward-dipping subduction as deduced from the Turonian subduction-related volcanic activity in the outer Eastern Pontides. An alternative mechanism for the emplacement of the melange is the back-thrusting of the accretionary complex (Silver and Reed, 1988) above a northward-dipping subduction zone, which has been suggested for the Eastern Pontides by Elmas (1995). However, this mechanism is unlikely in the present case, as there is little evidence for subduction activity in the Eastern Pontides prior to the emplacement of the ophiolitic melange.

SENONIAN—BUILDUP OF THE PONTIDE MAGMATIC ARC

In the outer Eastern Pontides, which is dominated by Senonian and Eocene volcanic and sedimentary rocks, there is no clear break between the Lower and Upper Cretaceous. In the inner Eastern Pontides, the Senonian transgression youngs southward from Late Turonian–Coniacian in Alucra (Schiftah, 1967; Pelin, 1977; Robinson et al., 1995), to Coniacian–Santonian in the Kelkit (Gürsoy, 1989) and finally to Early Maastrichtian in the Maden region (Ketin, 1951; Fenerci, 1994), suggesting that the transgression came from the north.

A >2-km-thick Cretaceous volcano-sedimentary sequence, representing the upper surficial deposits of a magmatic arc (Dewey et al., 1973; Boccaletti et al., 1974; Akin, 1978), outcrops throughout the outer Eastern Pontides (Figure 6). Although the outer Eastern Pontides region is heavily vegetated, it has been intensely studied due to the widespread polymetallic sulfide mineralization in the volcanic rocks. The structure of the Mesozoic series of the outer Eastern Pontides is characterized by block-faulting and gentle seaward dips. To date, no major folds or thrusts have been mapped. The steep-dipping faults defining complex horsts and grabens are generally conjugate and follow NE and NW directions (Schultze-Westrum, 1962; Zankl, 1962a; Kronberg, 1970; Buser and Cvetic, 1973; Akin, 1978; Gedikoğlu, 1978).

The Cretaceous volcanic cycle in the outer Eastern Pontides starts with basaltic and andesitic lavas and passes up to dacitic and rhyolitic lavas, breccias, and tuffs with minor limestone intercalations (Schultze-Westrum, 1962; Zankl, 1962a; Eğin et al., 1979; Özsayar et al., 1982; Ercan and Gedik, 1983; Akıncı, 1984; Gedik et al., 1992; Korkmaz, 1993). The cycle ends with intercalations of mudstone, tuff, radiolarian chert, marl, and limestone from which a late Maastrichtian to Danian pelagic fauna was described (Hirst and Eğin, 1979; Korkmaz, 1993). Although there is some evidence for local basic volcanism during the Early Cretaceous (Zankl, 1962b; Okay, 1993), in most regions the volcanic and volcaniclastic rocks unconformably overlie neritic limestones of Kimmeridgian to Neocomian age and are thus younger than Cenomanian (Pelin, 1977; Terlemez and Yılmaz, 1980; Tasli, 1984; Korkmaz, 1993). The basal parts of the volcanic sequence are precisely dated by Taner and Zaninetti (1978), who describe a pelagic Middle Turonian fauna in the limestones intercalated with the basic volcanic rocks stratigraphically 1500 m below the dacites. Farther up in the sequence, all the stages of the Senonian are recognized in the intercalated limestones (Özsayar, 1971), such that the volcanism was continuous up to the end of the Maastrichtian and in places passes into the Early Paleocene (Korkmaz and Gedik, 1988; Korkmaz, 1993).

Thus, contrary to many views, which initiate the subduction under the Eastern Pontides during the Jurassic and earlier (Adamia et al., 1977; Kazmin et al., 1986), we follow Şengör and Yılmaz (1981) and Görür (1988) in placing the beginning of subduction into the Cenomanian–Turonian.

The thickness of the Cretaceous volcanic cycle is >2000 m; the volcanism was wholly submarine and, judging from the intercalated *Globotruncana*-bearing pelagic and rudist-bearing neritic limestone lenses, occurred over an uneven submarine topography. Possible volcanic centers were separated by deep marine basins (Robinson et al., 1995). Numerous massive and stockwork-type polymetallic (Fe, Cu, Pb, and Zn) sulfide ore deposits occur within the dacitic-rhyolitic lava, breccia, and tuff in the Maastrichtian part of the volcanic sequence (Figure 2). These deposits are intensely studied (Kraeff, 1963; Koprivica, 1976; Altun, 1977; Eğin et al., 1979; Hirst and Eğin, 1979; Pejatovic, 1979; Çağatay and Boyle, 1980; Akıncı, 1984). They are remarkably similar to the Japanese Miocene Kuruko sulfide ores (Akin, 1978), formed during arc volcanism around the volcanic centers (Mitchell and Garson, 1976). The sulfide ores are usually overlain by exhalative-sedimentary manganese deposits thought to be produced by volcanic hot springs discharging directly onto the sea floor (Hirst and Eğin, 1979). The distribution of the Kuruko-type sulfide ores in the Eastern Pontides (Vujanovic, 1974; Pejatovic, 1979) gives an indication of the volcanic centers during the Senonian, and shows that the Maastrichtian volcanic axis was located close to the present-day Black Sea margin (Figure 2). The sulfide mineralization was partly controlled by the NE-SW– and NW-SE–trending conjugate faults (Schultze-Westrum, 1962; Koprivica, 1976; Hirst and Eğin, 1979).

Cretaceous volcanic rocks are generally subalkaline and give typical island-arc geochemical signatures (Peccerillo and Taylor, 1975; Akin, 1978; Gedikoğlu, 1978; Eğin et al., 1979; Eğin and Hirst, 1979; Manetti et al., 1983; Akıncı, 1984; Köprübasi, 1993). Only toward the end of the volcanic cycle was there a minor alkaline, shoshonitic basic volcanism producing leucite and nepheline-bearing basanites and tephrites (Gümüs, 1978; Korkmaz et al., 1993).

Associated with the Cretaceous volcanism was the intrusion of a large number of granitoids (Figure 2). Their isotopic ages range from ~95 to 65 m.y. (Taner, 1977; Gedikoğlu, 1978; Moore et al., 1980). Although they show a wide modal scatter, they are dominantly hornblende-biotite, granodiorite, and quartz-diorite; geochemically, the granitoids show a typical calc-alkaline trend (Çoğulu, 1975; Taner, 1977; Gedikoğlu, 1978; Moore et al., 1980). The granitoids generally intrude the lower basic volcanic rocks and are locally overlain by dacitic lavas.

During the Senonian, the inner Eastern Pontides were in a fore-arc position. In some places, such as north of Kelkit, there was a ridge between the arc and fore-arc, characterized by the deposition of shallow-marine sandstones and rudist-bearing limestones (Schiftah, 1967; Gürsoy, 1989). However, in most regions, the transition was gradual, with a southward decrease in the amount of lava flows at the expense of volcaniclastic rocks. The Senonian, in the inner Eastern Pontides is characteristically represented by a 500- to 900-m-thick tuffaceous flyschoid sequence with pelagic limestone intercalations (Seymen, 1975; Pelin, 1977; Yılmaz, 1985; Gürsoy, 1989; Okay et al., in press).

The Senonian volcanic arc of the Eastern Pontides was an extensional arc, as shown by the submarine nature of the volcanism. The marginal basins behind extensional arcs usually develop by the splitting of the volcanic arc axis (Karig, 1971). The distribution of the Kuruko-type ore deposits in the Eastern Pontides shows that during the Maastrichtian, the volcanic arc axis was located close to the present-day Black Sea coast. Thus, the Eastern Black Sea Basin probably started to open during the Maastrichtian by the splitting of this arc axis. An earlier opening of the Eastern Black Sea Basin would have resulted in a major volcanic and volcaniclastic apron to the north of the present-day volcanic axis, which is not observed in the very narrow Black Sea shelf to the north of the Eastern Pontides.

PALEOCENE–EARLY EOCENE THRUST IMBRICATION—CONTINENTAL COLLISION

During the Paleocene–early Eocene, there was major shortening along the inner Eastern Pontides, and the continental margin was telescoped into a series of stacked north-vergent thrust slices. The thrusting did not reach farther north than the Bayburt-Kelkit-Mindeval line (Figure 3). In the Alucra region, which is located between the inner and outer Pontides, there was upright folding and a major break in sedimentation during the Paleocene–early Eocene. Lutetian limestones, marls, and sandstones in this region lie with the angular unconformity on folded Jurassic and Cretaceous sediments (Nebert, 1961; Pelin, 1977) and even overlie the metamorphic basement of the Ağvanis Massif (Okay, 1984). In the outer Eastern Pontides, sedimentary or volcanic rocks of Late Paleocene–early Eocene age are also not recognized, and Lutetian volcano-sedimentary rocks lie unconformably over the Senonian rocks (Gedikoğlu et al., 1982; Korkmaz and Gedik, 1988; Korkmaz, 1993), suggesting that the entire Eastern Pontides was above sea level during the Paleocene–Early Eocene.

South of the town of Kelkit, three north-vergent thrust slices are recognized (Figure 3) (Okay et al., in press). The basement rocks were involved in thrusting, and the high-grade Pulur metamorphic rocks were emplaced over the Jurassic Kelkit Formation (Figure 8). The topmost thrust slice in the structural sequence is rootless and is named the Çimendaği nappe in the west and the İmalidağ nappe in the east (Figure 3) (Bergougnan, 1975, 1976). The Çimendaği nappe consists mainly of Oxfordian to Berriasian shallow-water carbonates overlain unconformably by Santonian to Campanian red pelagic limestones, while the İmalidağ nappe is made up of Tithonian flysch overlain by Neocomian radiolarian biomicrites (Bergougnan, 1976,

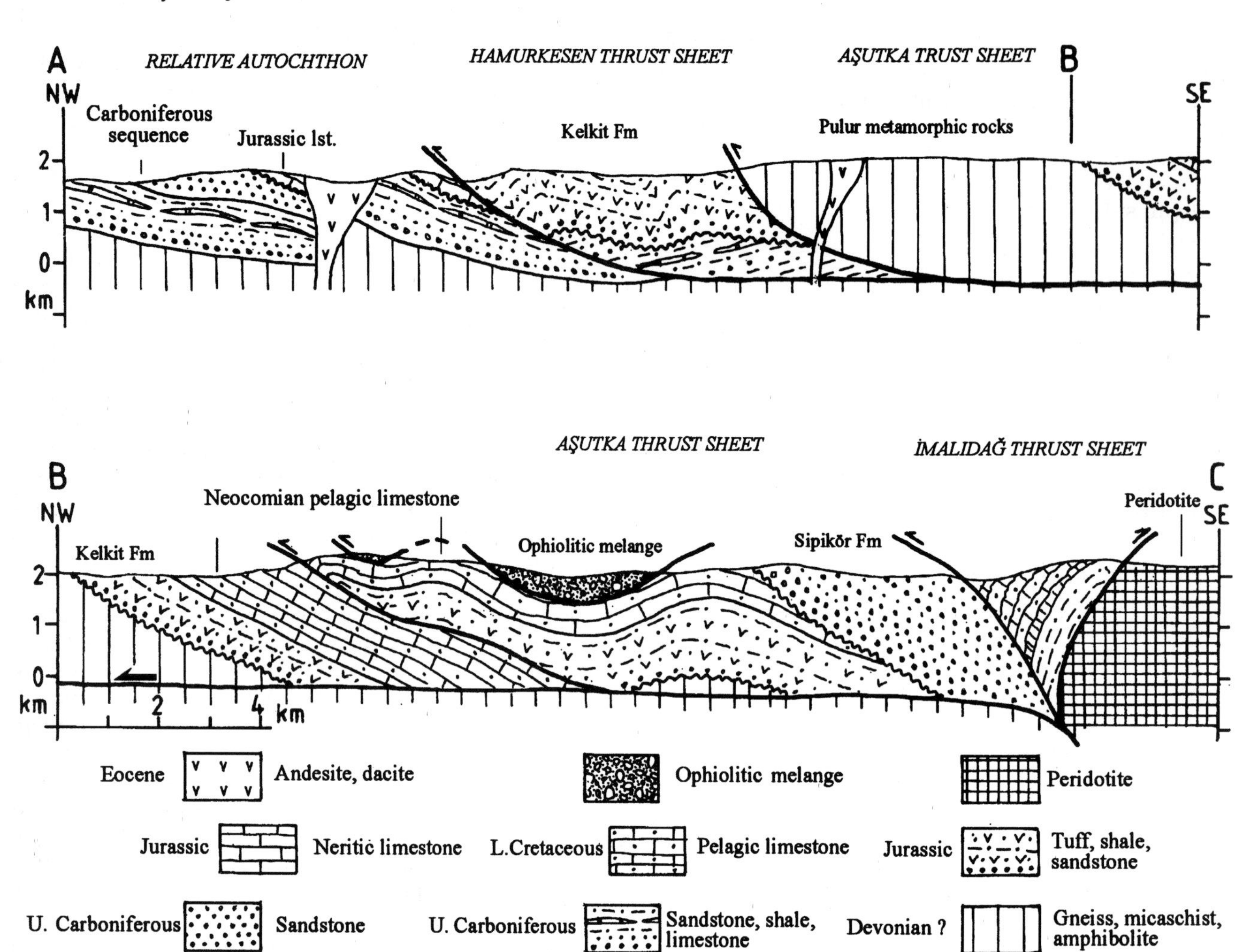

Figure 8. Geologic cross sections across the inner Eastern Pontides. For the location of the cross section, see Figure 3. Note the overlap between the top and bottom cross sections.

1987; Okay, 1984; Yılmaz, 1985). A major clastic foreland basin developed in front of these two northward-moving nappes (Figures 7, 8). Judging from its isolated outcrops, the foreland basin must have originally extended at least up to the Köse region (Gürsoy, 1989); however, it is now largely preserved as an 180-km-long and 3–5-km-wide east-to-northeast–trending belt below the İmalidağ and Çimendaği nappes (Figure 3). The basin fill consists of a few hundred-meters-thick conglomerates overlain by a >1000-m-thick upper Paleocene–lower Eocene turbidite sequence with large limestone olistoliths derived from the overlying nappes (Ketin, 1951; Bergougnan, 1976; Norman, 1976). Norman (1976) made a systematic study of the paleocurrent directions in the turbidites (the Spikör Formation) and showed that the currents in the basin were largely axial and were coming from the southwest. These data imply that the collision probably occurred along a northeast-southwest direction, which is oblique to the continental margin.

This major Paleocene/early Eocene compressive event, the strongest post-Jurassic deformational event in the Eastern Pontides, is probably related to the collision of the Eastern Pontides island arc with the Anatolides–Taurides along the Ankara–Erzincan suture in the south (Figure 7E). There is a clear northward decrease in deformation from a thrust belt in the south to a region of upright folding in the Alucra-Gümüşhane area and finally to a subtle unconformity in the outer Eastern Pontides in the north. Regional uplift caused deep erosion, which in places removed sections down to the pre-Mesozoic basement. All these are typical features of a continental collision: however, most workers (Tokel, 1977; Akin, 1978; Robinson et al., 1995) relate the Lutetian calc-alkaline magmatism to the northward subduction of the Tethys Ocean and consider the continental collision to be of Oligocene age. Others (Şengör and Yılmaz, 1981) initiate the collision in the Paleocene–early Eocene, but still relate the Lutetian magmatism to ongoing subduction. However, Lutetian rocks are largely undeformed and lie with a major angular discordance over all the older units, indicating that there was no major regional compression in the Eastern Pontides after the middle Eocene, which is difficult to believe if the continental collision had occurred in the Oligocene. The Senonian arc volcanism is confined to a relatively narrow belt, a characteristic feature of the present-day arc volcanism (Hamilton, 1995). In contrast, Lutetian magmatism, although much more restricted in time, is spread over the 100 km breadth of the Eastern Pontides and extends south to the Ankara-Erzincan Tethyan suture. Such a diffuse magmatism cannot be related to the activity of a single subduction system over a restricted time. A third line of evidence comes from the Kösedağ syenite pluton of middle-late Eocene age (42–37 Ma Rb/Sr whole-rock age) (Kalkanci, 1974) located northeast of Sıvas (Figure 2). It is an alkaline pluton with within-plate and postorogenic geochemical features (Boztuğ et al., 1994), and intrudes the suture zone. Thus, the weight of the geological evidence is for a Paleocene–early Eocene collision between the Pontides and the Anatolide-Tauride Platform (Elmas, 1995).

MIDDLE EOCENE—A NEW SEDIMENTARY AND VOLCANIC CYCLE

In the Eastern Pontides, Lutetian deposits transgressed over an existing folded and thrust-faulted surface (Figure 6). The Lutetian deposits are generally not folded and are not involved in thrust faults. They mark a new cycle of marine sedimentation and volcanism, with ages confined largely to the Lutetian. Lutetian rocks in the Eastern Pontides were deposited in shallow-water and are characterized by the presence of abundant nummulites in the limestones and sandstones intercalated with the volcanic rocks. The volcanism was more basic in composition than the Senonian volcanism, and occurred throughout the Eastern Pontides. The base of the Eocene transgression is generally dated as Lutetian (Ketin, 1951; Nebert, 1964; Bergougnan, 1987; Elmas, 1995), although in some regions it might have been as early as late Ypresian (Bursuk, 1975). The Lutetian in the inner Eastern Pontides is represented by ~700-m-thick shallow-marine succession consisting of basal conglomerates overlain by nummulite-bearing sandy limestones and sandstones, which pass up to a volcaniclastic series of sandstone, siltstone, basaltic and andesitic tuff, marl and rare basaltic flows (Ketin, 1951; Nebert, 1961; Ağar, 1977; Pelin, 1977; Özer, 1984; Gürsoy, 1989; Bozkus, 1992a). In the outer Eastern Pontides, a similar sequence, ~1000 m thick but richer in volcanic rocks, constitutes the Lutetian sequence (Tokel, 1977; Korkmaz and Gedik, 1988; Korkmaz, 1993). Lutetian volcanic rocks represent a short-lived volcanic cycle known as the Upper Basic Series (Schultze-Westrum, 1962; Zankl, 1962a; Tokel, 1977; Akıncı, 1984) and show a similar but less pronounced silica enrichment with time as the Senonian volcanic cycle. Geochemically, Lutetian volcanic rocks in the outer Eastern Pontides are calc-alkaline and fall in the field of island-arc basalts and andesites (Tokel, 1977; Eğin et al., 1979; Eğin and Hirst, 1979; Akıncı, 1984; Terzioğlu, 1984). Several hornblende-biotite granodiorites, which intrude Eocene sediments and volcanics, constitute the plutonic members of this magmatic cycle (Schultze-Westrum, 1962; Zankl, 1962a). The few isotopic ages from these granitoids range from 45 to 30 m.y. (Çoğulu, 1975; Moore et al., 1980). However, unlike the Senonian magmatism, the Lutetian magmatic rocks are not restricted to the outer Eastern Pontides but occur throughout the Eastern Pontides and adjacent Taurides. They intrude the late Paleocene–early Eocene thrust contacts in the inner Eastern Pontides north of Erzincan (Figure 3). In the Ankara-Erzincan suture zone northeast of Sıvas, the middle–late Eocene (42–37 m.y.) Kösedağ pluton (Kalkanci, 1974) intrudes the Lutetian volcano-sedimentary formations (Figure 2). Lutetian deposits south of the Ankara-Erzincan suture also comprise andesitic lavas, tuffs, and pyroclastic rocks intercalated with shallow-water sedimentary rocks (Özgül, 1981; Yılmaz, 1985). This and the major Paleocene–early Eocene unconformity show that the Senonian and Lutetian volcanic sequences represent two distinct cycles (Manetti et al., 1983, 1988).

The cause of the widespread Lutetian volcanism is not clear. A Tibetan-type postcollisional magmatism triggered by crustal thickening is unlikely, as the Lutetian magmatism was wholly submarine, suggesting regional extension only a few million years after the collision. This regional extension and the associated magmatism could have been related to the accelerated opening of the oceanic Eastern Black Sea Basin. Okay et al. (1994) suggested that the Eastern Black Sea Basin has opened by the counterclockwise rotation of a large continental block north of the Eastern Pontides. Although the rotation and thus the opening of the Eastern Black Sea Basin probably started in the latest Cretaceous, an increase in the rotation rate during the Lutetian might have resulted in the extension and magmatism throughout the Eastern Pontides. However, Eocene magmatism is also very widespread in the Lesser Caucasus and Iran (Kazmin et al., 1986), which suggests a more global cause for this enigmatic magmatic event.

OLIGOCENE AND YOUNGER DEPOSITS

None of the marine sequences in the Eastern Pontides reach to the late Eocene, showing that the Eastern Pontides were uplifted en bloc by the end of the mid-Eocene and have stayed largely above sea level since the middle Eocene, except for an Early Miocene marine incursion along the Ankara-Erzincan suture zone (Gedik, 1985; Inan, 1988; Yılmaz et al., 1988; Gökten, 1993). To the north of the Eastern Pontides, minor marine deposits of late Miocene (Sarmatian) and early Pliocene (Pontian) ages form small outcrops along the present-day Black Sea coast and represent small bays of the Paratethys (Özsayar, 1971, 1977).

The Oligocene to early Miocene history of northeastern Turkey is characterized by continuing compression caused by the ongoing collision of Gondwana and Laurasia after the complete elimination of the intervening oceanic basins. Most of this compression was accommodated by general south-vergent thrusting and folding along the Ankara-Erzincan suture to the south of the inner Eastern Pontides (Aktimur et al., 1990; Bozkus, 1992b). Small foreland basins, characterized by terrigenous sedimentation, developed during the Oligocene and Miocene in front of these thrust slices along the Ankara-Erzincan suture (Inan, 1988). There was also largely basaltic alkaline volcanism, which lasted up to the Recent (Terzioğlu, 1985). In the middle Miocene, the continuing compression resulted in the initiation of the North Anatolian fault, which started the westward escape of the Anatolian block, a tectonic regime that continues today (Şengör, 1979).

THE OTHER SIDE OF THE TETHYS OCEAN— THE TAURIDE MARGIN

Further insight on the evolution of the Tethyan Ocean south of the Eastern Pontides can be gained from the geology of the northern margin of the Taurides, south of the Tethyan suture. Pre-Tertiary lithologies south of the suture occur intermittently from south of Sıvas to south of Erzincan (Figure 2). They are best exposed in the Munzur Mountains southwest of Erzincan, where the Mesozoic is represented by Upper Triassic–Cenomanian platform carbonates overlain by Turonian–upper Campanian pelagic biomicrites (Figure 6) (Özgül 1981; Özgül and Tursucu, 1984). In the early Maastrichtian, ophiolitic melange with large peridotite slices was emplaced over the carbonates, and the carbonate platform was internally sliced along major south-vergent thrusts. In a 350-km-long region between south of Sıvas and Horasan, the ophiolitic melange and the peridotite slices are unconformably overlain by Maastrichtian to upper Paleocene shallow-water limestones (Özgül, 1981; Gedik, 1985; Yılmaz et al., 1988; Inan et al., 1993). In the Munzur region, this was followed by a period of uplift and erosion, and the Lutetian sandstone, limestone, tuff, basalt, and andesites unconformably overlie all the older units (Figure 6). In the Munzur region, the upper Eocene rocks are not present as in the Pontides, and the Oligocene is made up of terrigenous clastics and evaporites; the marine sequence starts again with Lower Miocene shallow-marine deposits (Gökten, 1993).

Geology of the northern margin of the Tauride block does not well constrain the age of the collision with the Eastern Pontides. Here, the major compressive event is of late Campanian–early Maastrichtian age and is related to the obduction of ophiolite and ophiolitic melange. This deformational event is precollisional and is similar to that observed in Oman, where the emplacement of the Semail ophiolite led to the imbrication of the Arabian continental margin (Robertson and Searle, 1990; Michard et al., 1991). Based on data from the Taurides, the collision with the Eastern Pontides could have been either during the early Eocene or in the late Eocene–Oligocene, during which there was folding and regional uplift.

CONCLUSIONS

The major stratigraphic and tectonic features of the Eastern Pontides can be summarized as follows.

There is a heterogeneous pre-Jurassic basement consolidated during the early Hercynian and Cimmeride orogenic events. Triassic sedimentary rocks are absent, possibly due to metamorphism during the Cimmeride orogeny. The Mesozoic sequence starts with a widespread Liassic transgression and continues essentially uninterrupted until the mid-Cretaceous, when there is a major break in sedimentation, with uplift and erosion of the entire Eastern Pontides. This compressive event caused the emplacement of an ophiolitic melange over the southern continental margin of the Eastern Pontides during the Cenomanian–Turonian. The compression and obduction of the melange is probably related to the partial subduction of the Eastern Pontides passive continental margin in a south-dipping intra-oceanic subduction zone. This was followed by a flip in the subduction polarity and, consequently, a volcanic arc developed during the Turonian to Maastrichtian-Danian in the outer Eastern Pontides above the northward-subducting Tethyan Ocean floor. The volcanic arc was extensional and wholly submarine. The inner parts of the Eastern Pontides were in a fore-arc position during the Senonian. The Eastern Black Sea Basin probably started to open during the Maastrichtian through the splitting of the volcanic arc axis.

Major thrust imbrication of the southern continental margin of the Eastern Pontides occurred during the late Paleocene–early Eocene. The thrusting involved the pre-Jurassic basement; thick foreland flysch basins have developed in front of the northward-moving nappes. In the outer Eastern Pontides, the late Paleocene–early Eocene is characterized by folding, uplift, and erosion. This orogenic event, the strongest in the Eastern Pontides during the Mesozoic and Tertiary, marks the continental collision between the Eastern Pontide arc and the Taurides.

Essentially undeformed basaltic and andesitic volcanic rocks and shallow-marine sedimentary rocks of Middle Eocene age occur throughout the Eastern Pontides; these are transgressive over a folded and thrust-faulted basement. They mark a regional extension, probably related to an accelerated phase of the opening of the Eastern Black Sea Basin. From the middle Eocene onward, the Eastern Pontides stayed above sea level, with minor volcanism and terrigenous sedimentation.

The Eastern Pontides stratigraphic sequence is rich in volcanic and volcaniclastic rocks. Three major Mesozoic–Tertiary magmatic cycles are recognized. The first cycle is Early to Mid-Jurassic, is probably of tholeiitic character, and is probably related to rifting. The second cycle is Turonian–Maastrichtian, is dominantly subalkaline, and is subduction related. The third cycle is Middle Eocene, is calc-alkaline, and is probably related to a regional extension.

ACKNOWLEDGMENTS

We thank Necdet Özgül, Celal Şengör, and Okan Tüysüz for discussions on the geology of the Eastern Pontides and the neighboring Taurides. Nilgün Okay and two anonymous referees are thanked for a constructive review of the manuscript. Turkish Petroleum Company (TPAO) and Mineral Research and Exploration Institute (MTA) are thanked for supporting fieldwork in the Eastern Pontides.

REFERENCES CITED

Abesadze, M., S. Adamia, T. Chkotua, M. Kekelia, I. Shavishvili, M. Somin, and G. Tsimakuridze, 1982, Pre-Variscan and Variscan metamorphic complexes of the Caucasus: IGCP Project No. 5, Newsletter No. 4, p. 5–12.

Adamia, S., A.A. Belov, M. Lordkipanidze, and M.L. Somin, 1982, Project No. 5 IGCP "Correlation of Prevariscan and Variscan events in the Alpine Mediterranean Mountain Belt": Guidebook for the Field Excursion for the International Working Meeting in the Caucasus, Tblisi, 82 p.

Adamia, S., M. Kekelia, and G. Tsimakuridze, 1983, Pre-Variscan and Variscan granitoids of the Caucasus: International Geologic Correlation Programme (IGCP) Project No. 5, Newsletter No. 5, p. 5–12.

Adamia, S.A, M.B. Lordkipanidze, and G.S. Zakariadze, 1977, Evolution of an active continental margin as exemplified by the Alpine history of the Caucasus: Tectonophysics, v. 40, p. 183–199.

Ağar, Ü., 1977, Geology of the Demirözü (Bayburt) and Köse (Kelkit) region (in Turkish): Ph.D. thesis, University of İstanbul, İstanbul, Turkey, 59 p.

Agrali, B., E. Akyol, and Y. Konyali, 1965, Prevues palynologiques de l'existence du Dogger dans la région de Bayburt: Bulletin of the Mineral Research and Exploration Institute of Turkey, v. 65, p. 45–57.

Agrali, B., E. Akyol, and Y. Konyali, 1966, Paleontological study of three coal seams in the Kelkit-Bayburt Jurassic (in Turkish): Türkiye Jeoloji Kurumu Bülteni, v. 10, p. 149–155.

Akdeniz, N., 1988, The regional tectonic framework of the Permo–Carboniferous of the Demirözü area (in Turkish): Türkiye Jeoloji Bülteni, v. 31, p. 71–80.

Akin, H., 1978, Geologie, Magmatismus und Lagerstaettenbildung im ostpontischen Gebirge-Türkei aus der Sicht der Plattentektonik: Geologische Rundschau, v. 68, p. 253–283.

Akıncı, Ö.T., 1984, The Eastern Pontide volcano-sedimentary belt and associated massive sulphide deposits, *in* J.E. Dixon and A.H.F. Robertson, eds., The geological evolution of the Eastern Mediterranean: Geological Society of London Special Publication 17, p. 415–428.

Aktimur, T., S. Ates, M.E. Yurdakul, M.E. Tekerli, and M. Keçer, 1992, Geology of the Niksar-Erbaa and Destek region (in Turkish): Maden Tetkik ve Arama Dergisi, v. 114, p. 25–36.

Aktimur, T., M.E. Tekirli, and M.E. Yurdakul, 1990, Geology of the Sıvas-Erzincan Tertiary basin (in Turkish): Maden Tetkik ve Arama Dergisi, v. 111, p. 25–36.

Alp, D., 1972, Geology of the Amasya region (in Turkish): İstanbul Üniversitesi Fen Fakültesi Monografileri, no. 22, 101 p.

Altun, Y., 1977, Geology of the Çayeli-Madenköy copper-zinc deposits and the problems related to mineralization: Bulletin of the Mineral Research and Exploration Institute of Turkey, v. 89, p. 10–23.

Banks, C.J., A.G. Robinson, and M.P. Williams, this volume, Structure and regional tectonics of the Achara-Trialet Fold Belt and the Adjacent Rioni and Kartli Foreland Basins, Republic of Georgia, *in* A.G. Robinson, ed., Regional and petroleum geology of the Black Sea and surrounding region: AAPG Memoir 68, p. 331–346.

Bassoullet, J.-P., H. Bergougnan, and R. Enay, 1975, Répartition des faunas et faciès liasiques dans l'Est de la Turquie, région du Haut-Euphrate: Comptes Rendus Academie Science Paris, v. 280, p. 583–586.

Bektas, O., S. Pelin, and S. Korkmaz, 1984, Back-arc mantle diaparism in the Eastern Pontides and polygenetic ophiolites (in Turkish): Geological Society of Turkey, Proceedings of the Ketin Symposium, Ankara, p. 175–188.

Bektas, O., A. Van, and S. Boynukalyn, 1987, Jurassic volcanism and its geotectonics in the Eastern Pontides (Northeastern Turkey) (in Turkish): Türkiye Jeoloji Bülteni, v. 30, p. 9–18.

Bergougnan, H., 1975, Relations entre les edifices pontique et taurique dans le Nord-Est de l'Anatolie: Bulletin de la Société Géologique de France, v. 12, p. 1045–1057.

Bergougnan, H., 1976, Structure de la Chaine pontique dans le haut-Kelkit (Nord-Est de l'Anatolie): Bulletin de la Société Géologique de France, v. 13, p. 675–686.

Bergougnan, H., 1987, Études geologiques dans l'Est-Anatolien: Ph.D. thesis, University Pierre et Marie Curie, Paris, France, 606 p.

Bilgin, A., 1984, Stratigraphy of the Serçeme Creek (Erzurum) and surrounding area (in Turkish): Jeoloji Mühendisliği, v. 18, p. 35–44.

Blumenthal, M.M., 1950, Beiträge zur Geologie des landschaften am Mittleren und unteren Yesilırmak (Tokat, Amasya, Havza, Erbaa, Niksar): Publication of the Mineral Research and Exploration Institute of Turkey, Ser. D, no. 4, 153 p.

Boccaletti, M., P. Gocev, and P. Manetti, 1974, Mesozoic isopic zones in the Black Sea region: Boll. Soc. Geol. Italiana, v. 93, p. 547–565.

Bozkus, C., 1992a, Stratigraphy of the Olur (Erzurum) region (in Turkish): Türkiye Jeoloji Bülteni, v. 35, p. 103–119.

Bozkus, C., 1992b, The stratigraphy of the Çayyrli-Tercan Tertiary basin (in Turkish): Türkiye Jeoloji Kurultayi Bülteni, v. 7, p. 97–107.

Boztuğ, D., S. Yılmaz, and Y. Keskin, 1994, Petrography, petrochemistry and petrogenesis of the eastern part of Kösedağ pluton from the central-eastern Anatolian alkaline province (in Turkish): Türkiye Jeoloji Bülteni, v. 37, p. 1–14.

Bursuk, A., 1975, Stratigraphic and micropaleontological study of the Bayburt region (in Turkish):

Ph.D. thesis, University of İstanbul, Turkey, Karadeniz Teknik Üniv. Matbaasi, 196 p.
Bursuk, A., 1981, Calpionellid biozones in the Askale-Bayburt region (NW Erzurum) (in Turkish): Karadeniz Teknik Üniversitesi Yer Bilimleri Dergisi Jeoloji, v. 1, p. 21–28.
Buser, S., and S. Cvetic, 1973, Geologie der Umgebung der Kupfererzlagerstätte Murgul in der Türkiye: Bulletin of the Mineral Research and Exploration Institute of Turkey, v. 81, p. 1–25.
Çağatay, M.N., and D.R. Boyle, 1980, Geology, geochemistry and hydrothermal alteration of the Madenköy massive-sulfide deposit, Eastern Black Sea region, Turkey, *in* J. D. Ridge, ed., International Association of the Genesis of Ore Deposits (IAGOD) 5th Symposium Proceedings: E. Schweizerbart'sche Verlagsbuchhandlung, Stuttgart, Germany, p. 653–678.
Çoğulu, E., 1975, Petrological and geochronological studies in the Gümüşhane and Rize regions (in Turkish): Teknik Üniversite Matbaasi, İstanbul, 112 p.
Dewey, J.F., W.C. Pitman, III, W.B.F. Ryan, and J. Bonnin, 1973, Plate tectonics and evolution of the Alpine system: Geological Society of America Bulletin, v. 84, p. 3137–3180.
Eğin, D., and D.M. Hirst, 1979, Tectonic and magmatic evolution of volcanic rocks from the northern Harsit River area, NE Turkey: Proceedings of the 1st Geological Congress of the Middle East (GEOCOME), p. 56–93.
Eğin, D., D.M. Hirst, and R. Phillips, 1979, The petrology and geochemistry of volcanic rocks from the northern Harsit River area, Pontid volcanic province, Northeast Turkey: Journal of Volcanology and Geothermal Research, v. 6, p. 105–123.
Elmas, A., 1994, Stratigraphic data on the Late Cretaceous-Tertiary nappe tectonics in the Eastern Pontides (north of the Kop Daği) (in Turkish): Proceedings of the 10th Petroleum Congress of Turkey, p. 276–289.
Elmas, A., 1995, Geology of the Kop Daği area (Bayburt, Erzurum): evolution of a fore-arc basin (in Turkish): Türkiye Petrol Jeologlari Derneği Bülteni, v. 6, p. 19–37.
Enay, R., 1976, Faunes anatoliennes (*Ammonitina*, Jurassique) et domaines biogéographiques nord et sud Téthysiens: Bulletin de la Société Géologique de France, v. 18, p. 533–541.
Ercan, T., and A. Gedik, 1983, Volcanism of the Pontide Belt (in Turkish): Jeoloji Mühendisliği, v.18, p. 3–22.
Fenerci, M., 1994, Rudists from Maden (Bayburt) area (NE Turkey): Turkish Journal of Earth Sciences, v. 3, p. 1–12.
Gedik, A., 1985, Geology and petroleum potential of the Tekman (Erzurum) basin (in Turkish): Maden Tetkik ve Arama Dergisi, v. 103/104, p. 1–24.
Gedik, A., T. Ercan, S. Korkmaz, and S. Karatas, 1992, Petrology of the magmatic rocks in the area between Rize, Findikli and Çamlihemsin (Eastern Black Sea region) and their distribution in the Eastern Pontides (in Turkish): Türkiye Jeoloji Bülteni, v. 35, p. 15–38.
Gedikoğlu, A., 1978, Harsit granite complex and neighboring rocks (Giresun–Doğankent): Habilatation thesis, Black Sea Technical University, Trabzon, Turkey, 161 p.
Gedikoğlu, A., S. Pelin, and T. Özsayar, 1979, The main lines of geotectonic development of the east Pontids in the Mesozoic era: Proceedings of the 1st Geological Congress of the Middle East (GEOCOME), p. 555–580.
Gedikoğlu, A., T. Özsayar, and S. Pelin, 1982, A paleocaldera in Gölköy (Ordu) region and its relation with the mineralization (in Turkish): Karadeniz Üniversitesi Yerbilimleri Dergisi Jeoloji, v. 2, p. 117–130.
Gökten, E., 1993, Geology of the southern boundary of the Sıvas Basin east of Ulas (Sıvas–Central Anatolia), tectonic development related to the closure of the inner Tauride Ocean (in Turkish): Türkiye Petrol Jeologlari Derneği Bülteni, v. 5, p. 35–55.
Görür, N., 1988, Timing of opening of the Black Sea Basin: Tectonophysics, v. 147, p. 247–262.
Görür, N., A.M.C. Şengör, R. Akkök, and Y. Yılmaz, 1983, Sedimentological data regarding the opening of the northern branch of the Neotethys (in Turkish): Türkiye Jeoloji Kurumu Bülteni, v. 26, p. 11–19.
Gümüs, A., 1978, La pétrologie et l'age radiométrique des laves a feldspathoides des environs de Trabzon (Turquie): Geologica Balcanica, v. 8, p. 17–26.
Gürsoy, H., 1989, Tectonics and stratigraphy of the Kelkit (Gümüshane) region (in Turkish): Ph.D. thesis, Cumhuriyet Üniversitesi, Sıvas, Turkey, 140 p.
Hamilton, W.B., 1995, Subduction systems and magmatism, *in* J.L. Smellie, ed., Vulcanism associated with extension at consuming plate margins: Geological Society of London Special Publication 81, p. 3–28.
Hirst, D.M., and D. Eğin, 1979, Localization of massive, polymetallic sulfide ores in the northern Harsit River area, Pontid volcanic belt, Northeast Turkey: Annales de la Société Géologique de Belgique, v. 102, p. 465–484.
Inan, S., 1988, Tectonic evolution of the Erzurum-Askale-Tortum region (in Turkish): Cumhuriyet Üniversitesi Mühendislik Fakültesi Dergisi, Yerbilimleri, v. 5, p. 37–48.
Inan, S., A. Öztürk, and H. Gürsoy, 1993, Stratigraphy of the Ulas-Sincan (Sıvas) region: Doga–Türk Yerbilimleri Dergisi, v. 2, p. 1–15.
Kalkanci, S., 1974, Etude géologique et pétrochimique de sud de la region de Susehri, géochronologie de massif syenitique de Kösedağ (NE de Sıvas, Turquie): Ph.D. thesis, University of Grenoble, France, 135 p.
Karig, D.E., 1971, Origin and development of marginal basins in the Western Pacific: Journal of Geophysical Research, v. 76, p. 2542–2561.
Kazmin, V.G., I.M. Sbortshikov, L.-E. Ricou, L.P. Zonenshain, J. Boulin, and A.L. Knipper, 1986, Volcanic belts as markers of the Mesozoic–Cenozoic active margin of Eurasia: Tectonophysics, v. 123, p. 123–152.
Keskin, I., S. Korkmaz, I. Gedik, M. Ates, L. Gök, Ö. Küçümen, and T. Erkal, 1989, Geology of the region around Bayburt: Report of the Maden Tetkik ve Arama Genel Müdürlüğü, no. 8995, 128 p.
Ketin, I., 1951, Über die Geologie der Gegend von Bayburt in Nordost-Anatolien: İstanbul Üniversitesi Fen Fakültesi Mecmuasi, Seri B, v. 16, p. 113–127.
Ketin, I., 1977, Main orogenic events and paleogeographic evolution of Turkey: Bulletin of the Mineral

Research and Exploration Institute of Turkey, v. 88, p. 1–4.
Khain, V.E., 1975, Structure and main stages in the tectono-magmatic development of the Caucasus: an attempt at geodynamic interpretation: American Journal of Science, v. 275-A, p. 131–156.
Knipper, A.L., 1980, The tectonic position of ophiolites of the Lesser Caucasus: Proceedings of the International Ophiolite Symposium, Cyprus, p. 372–376.
Koçyiğit, A., 1990, Structural relations of three suture belts west of Erzincan (northeast Turkey), Karakaya, Intra-Tauride, and Erzincan sutures (in Turkish): Proceedings of the 8th Petroleum Congress of Turkey, p. 152–160.
Koprivica, D., 1976, Geology, structural features and sulfide and manganese occurrences of the Hopa-Arhavi (Northeast Turkey): Bulletin of the Mineral Research and Exploration Institute of Turkey, v. 87, p. 1–10.
Köprübaşi, N., 1993, Petrology and geochemistry of the Jurassic–Cretaceous magmatic rocks between Tirebolu-Harsit Giresun (in Turkish): Türkiye Jeoloji Bülteni, v. 36, p. 139–150.
Korkmaz, S., 1993, Stratigraphy of the Tonya-Düzköy area (southwest of Trabzon) (in Turkish): Türkiye Jeoloji Bülteni, v. 36, p. 151–158.
Korkmaz, S., and A. Gedik, 1988, Geology of the Rize-Findikli-Çamlihemsin area and petroleum occurrences (in Turkish): Jeoloji Mühendisliği, v. 32–33, p. 5–15.
Korkmaz, S., M.B. Sadyklar, A. Van, N. Tüysüz, and T. Ercan, 1993, Geochemical characteristics and geotectonic implications of the Upper Cretaceous Saraf Tepe (Trabzon) basanite, NE Turkey (in Turkish): Türkiye Jeoloji Bülteni, v. 36, p. 37–44.
Kraeff, A., 1963, Geology and mineral deposits of the Hopa-Murgul region: Bulletin of the Mineral Research and Exploration Institute of Turkey, v. 60, p. 44–59.
Kronberg, P., 1970, Photogeologische Daten zur Tektonik im ostpontischen Gebirge (NE Türkei): Bulletin of the Mineral Research and Exploration Institute of Turkey, v. 74, p. 24–33.
Maden Tetkik ve Arama Enstitüsü, 1977, 1:50,000 scale geological map series, Tortum G47-a sheet: Maden Tetkik ve Arama Enstitüsü, Ankara.
Manetti, P., M. Boccaletti, and A. Peccerillo, 1988, The Black Sea, remnant of a marginal basin behind the Srednogorie-Pontides island-arc system during the Upper Cretaceous–Eocene times: Bolletino di Geofisica Teorica ed Applicata, v. 30, p. 39–51.
Manetti, P., A. Peccerillo, G. Poli, and F. Corsini, 1983, Petrochemical constraints on the models of Cretaceous-Eocene tectonic evolution of the Eastern Pontic chain (Turkey): Cretaceous Research, v. 4, p. 159–172.
Michard, A., F. Boudier, and B. Goffé, 1991, Obduction versus subduction and collision in the Oman case and other Tethyan settings, *in* T. Peters, A. Nicolas, and R.G. Coleman, eds., Ophiolite genesis and evolution of the oceanic lithosphere: Ministry of Petroleum and Minerals in Oman, Masqat, Kluwer Academic Publications, Dordrecht, p. 447–467.
Mitchell, A.H.G., and M.S. Garson, 1976, Mineralization at plate boundaries: Mineral Science and Engineering, v. 8, p. 129–169.
Moore, W.J., E.H. McKee, and Ö. Akıncı, 1980, Chemistry and chronology of plutonic rocks in the Pontid Mountains, northern Turkey: European Copper Deposits, p. 209–216.
Nebert, K., 1961, Der Geologische Bau der Einzugsgebiete Kelkit Çay und Kızılırmak (NE-Anatolien): Bulletin of the Mineral Research and Exploration Institute of Turkey, v. 57, p. 1–51.
Nebert, K., 1964, Zur Geologie des Kelkit Çay-Oberlaufs südwestlich von Siran (Nordostanatolien): Bulletin of the Mineral Research and Exploration Institute of Turkey, v. 62, p. 42–59.
Norman, T., 1976, Paleocurrent directions in the Lower Tertiary basin south of Bayburt (in Turkish): Türkiye Jeoloji Kurumu Bülteni, v. 19, p. 23–30.
Okay, A.I., 1984, The geology of the Ağvanis metamorphic rocks and neighboring formations: Bulletin of the Mineral Research and Exploration Institute of Turkey, v. 99/100, p. 16–36.
Okay, A.I., 1989, Tectonic units and sutures in the Pontides, Northern Turkey, *in* A.M.C. Şengör, ed., Tectonic evolution of the Tethyan region: NATO ASI Series C259, Kluwer, Dordrecht, p. 109–116.
Okay, A.I., 1993, Geology and tectonic evolution of the Pulur (Bayburt) region (in Turkish): Report of the Turkish Petroleum Exploration Division, Ankara, no. 3415, 86 p.
Okay, A.I., 1996, Granulite facies gneisses from the Pulur region, Eastern Pontides: Turkish Journal of Earth Sciences, v. 5, p. 55–61.
Okay, A.I., and E.Ja. Leven, 1996, Stratigraphy and paleontology of the Upper Paleozoic sequence in the Pulur (Bayburt) region, Eastern Pontides: Turkish Journal of Earth Sciences, v. 5, p. 145–155.
Okay, A.I., Ö. Sahintürk, and H. Yakar, in press, Stratigraphy and tectonics of the Pulur region (Bayburt, Eastern Pontides) (in Turkish): Maden Tetkik ve Arama Bülteni.
Okay, A.I., M. Satyr, H. Maluski, M. Siyako, P. Monie, R. Metzger, and S. Akyüz, 1996, Paleo- and Neotethyan events in northwest Turkey, *in* A. Yin and M. Harrison, eds., Tectonics of Asia: Cambridge University Press, p. 420–441.
Okay, A.I., A.M.C. Şengör, and N. Görür, 1994, Kinematic history of the opening of the Black Sea and its effect on the surrounding regions: Geology, v. 22, p. 267–270.
Okay, A.I., M. Siyako, and K.A. Bürkan, 1991, Geology and tectonic evolution of the Biga Peninsula, *in* J.F. Dewey, ed., Special issue on tectonics: Bulletin of the Technical University of İstanbul, v. 44, p. 191–255.
Otkun, G., 1942, Etude paléontologique de quelques gisements du Lias d'Anatolie: Publications de l'Institut d'Etudes et de Recherches Minières de Turquie, Serie B, no. 8, 41 p.
Özcan, A., F. Armağan, E. Keskin, A. Oral, S. Özer, M. Sümengen, and O. Tekeli, 1980, Geology of the region between the Tokat Massif and the North Anatolian fault: Report of Maden Tetkik ve Arama Enstitüsü, no. 6722, 146 p.

Özer, E., 1984, The geology of the Bayburt (Gümüshane) region (in Turkish): Karadeniz Teknik Üniversitesi Dergisi Jeoloji, v. 3, p. 77–89.

Özgül, N., 1981, Geology of the Munzur Mountains (in Turkish): Report of the Maden Tetkik ve Arama Enstitüsü, no. 6995, 136 p.

Özgül, N., and A. Tursucu, 1984, Stratigraphy of the Mesozoic carbonate sequence of the Munzur Mountains (Eastern Turkey), *in* O. Tekeli and M.C. Göncüoğlu, eds., Geology of the Taurus Belt: Maden Tetkik ve Arama Enstitüsü, Ankara, p. 173–181.

Özsayar, T., 1971, Paläontologie und Geologie des Gebietes östlich Trabzon (Anatolien): Ph.D. thesis, Giesener Geologische Schriften, Heft 1, 138 p.

Özsayar, T., 1977, A study of Neogene formations and their molluskan fauna along the Black Sea coast (in Turkish): Publication of the Karadeniz Teknik Üniversitesi, no. 79, 80 p.

Özsayar, T., S. Pelin, and A. Gedikoğlu, 1981, Cretaceous in the Eastern Pontides (in Turkish): Karadeniz Teknik Üniversitesi Yerbilimleri Dergisi Jeoloji, v. 1, p. 65–114.

Özsayar, T., S. Pelin, A. Gedikoğlu, A.A. Eren, and S. Çapkynoğlu, 1982, The geology of the Ardanuç (Artvin) region (in Turkish): Karadeniz Üniversitesi Yerbilimleri Dergisi Jeoloji, v. 2, p. 21–38.

Öztürk, A., 1979, Stratigraphy of the Ladik-Destek region (in Turkish): Türkiye Jeoloji Kurumu Bülteni, v. 22, p. 27–34.

Peccerillo, A., and S.R. Taylor, 1975, Geochemistry of Upper Cretaceous volcanic rocks from the Pontide chain, northern Turkey: Bulletin Volcanologique, v. 39, p. 1–13.

Pejatovic, S., 1979, Metallogeny of the Pontide-type massive sulfide deposits (in Turkish): Publication of the Mineral Research and Exploration Institute of Turkey, no. 177, 100 p.

Pelin, S., 1977, Geological study of the area southeast of Alucra (Giresun), with special reference to its petroleum potential (in Turkish): Karadeniz Teknik Üniversitesi, yayin no. 87, Trabzon, 103 p.

Pelin, S., 1981, Microfacies analysis of the carbonate shelf in the Berdiga Mountains (in Turkish): Karadeniz Teknik Üniversitesi Yer Bilimleri Dergisi Jeoloji, v. 1, p. 15–20.

Pelin, S., T. Özsayar, A. Gedikoğlu, and E. Tülümen, 1982, The origin of the Upper Cretaceous red biomicrites in the Eastern Pontides (in Turkish): Karadeniz Üniversitesi Yer Bilimleri Dergisi Jeoloji, v. 2, p. 69–80.

Robertson, A.H.F., and M.P. Searle, 1990, The northern Oman Tethyan continental margin, stratigraphy, structure, concepts and controversies, *in* A.H.F. Robertson, M.P. Searle, and A.C. Ries, eds., The geology and tectonics of the Oman Region: Geological Society of London Special Publication 49, p. 3–26.

Robinson, A.G., C.J. Banks, M.M. Rutherford, and J.P.P. Hirst, 1995, Stratigraphic and structural development of the Eastern Pontides, Turkey: Journal of the Geological Society of London, v. 152, p. 861–872.

Schiftah, S., 1967, Eine Oberkreidefauna des Sensuyu-Gebietes (Kelkit, NE Anatolien): Ph.D. thesis, University of München, Germany, 141 p.

Schultze-Westrum, H.H., 1962, Das geologische Profil des Aksudere bei Giresun (Nordost-Anatolien): Abhandlungen von Bayerische Akademie der Wissenschaften, Mathematische-Naturwissenschaftliche Klasse, v. 109, p. 23–58.

Şengör, A.M.C., 1979, The North Anatolian transform fault, its age, offset and tectonic significance: Journal of the Geological Society of London, v. 136, p. 269–282.

Şengör, A.M.C., 1990, A new model for the late Paleozoic–Mesozoic tectonic evolution of Iran and implications for Oman, *in* A.H.F. Robertson, M.P. Searle, and A.C. Ries, eds., The geology and tectonics of the Oman region: Geological Society Special Publication 49, p. 797–831.

Şengör, A.M.C., and Y. Yılmaz, 1981, Tethyan evolution of Turkey, a plate tectonic approach: Tectonophysics, v. 75, p. 181–241.

Şengör, A.M.C., Y. Yılmaz, and I. Ketin, 1980, Remnants of a pre-Late Jurassic ocean in northern Turkey, fragments of Permo-Triassic Paleotethys?: Geological Society of America Bulletin, v. 91, p. 599–609.

Seymen, I., 1975, Tectonic features of the North Anatolian fault zone in the Kelkit Valley (in Turkish): Ph.D. thesis, İstanbul Teknik Üniversitesi, Turkey, Matbaa Teknisyenleri Basimevi, 192 p.

Silver, E.A., and D.L. Reed, 1988, Backthrusting in accretionary wedges: Journal of Geophysical Research, v. 93, p. 3116–3126.

Stchepinsky, V., 1945, Stratigraphie du basin superieur de la Kelkitçayi: Maden Tetkik ve Arama Enstitüsü Mecmuasi, v. 33 , p. 133–152.

Stöcklin, J., 1968, Structural history and tectonics of Iran—a review: AAPG Bulletin, v. 52, p. 1229–1258.

Taner, M.F., 1977, Etude geologique et petrographique de la region de Güneyce-Ykizdere, situee au sud de Rize (Pontides Orientales, Turquie): Ph.D. thesis, Universite de Geneve, Switzerland, 180 p.

Taner, M.F., and L. Zaninetti, 1978, Etude paleontologique dans le Cretace volcano-sedimentaire de Güneyce (Pontides orientales, Turquie): Rivista Italiana di Paleontologia e Stratigrafia, v. 84, p. 187–198.

Tanyolu, E., 1988, Geology of the eastern part of the Pulur Massif: Maden Tetkik ve Arama Dergisi, v. 108, p. 1–17.

Tarhan, F., 1982, Engineering geology of the Artvin granite (in Turkish): Thesis (unpublished), Karadeniz Teknik Üniversitesi, Trabzon, Turkey, 148 p.

Tasli, K., 1984, The geology of the Hamsiköy (Trabzon) region (in Turkish): Karadeniz Üniversitesi Yerbilimleri Dergisi Jeoloji, v. 3, p. 69–76.

Terlemez, I., and A. Yılmaz, 1980, Stratigraphy of the area between Ünye-Ordu-Koyulhisar-Resadiye (in Turkish): Türkiye Jeoloji Kurumu Bülteni, v. 23, p. 179–192.

Terzioğlu, M.N., 1984, Geochemistry and petrology of the Eocene Bayirköy volcanic rocks from south of Ordu: Cumhuriyet Üniversitesi Mühendislik Fakültesi Dergisi, Ser. A., v. 1, p. 43–60.

Terzioğlu, M.N., 1985, Petrology and genesis of the

Upper Miocene Kuyucak basalt, Mesudiye (Ordu, Northern Turkey) (in Turkish): Yerbilimleri, v. 12, p. 53–67.

Tokel, S., 1977, Eocene calc-alkaline andesites and geotectonism in the Eastern Black Sea region (in Turkish): Türkiye Jeoloji Kurumu Bülteni, v. 20, p. 49–54.

Tutkun, S.Z., and S. Inan, 1982, Geology of the Niksar-Erbaa (Tokat) region (in Turkish): Karadeniz Üniversitesi Yerbilimleri Dergisi Jeoloji, v. 2, p. 51–68.

Vujanovic, V., 1974, The basic mineralogical, paragenetic and genetic characteristics of the sulphide deposits exposed in the Eastern Black Sea coastal region (Turkey): Bulletin of the Mineral Research and Exploration Institute of Turkey, v. 82, p. 21–36.

Wedding, H., 1963, Beiträge zur Geologie der Kelkitlinie und zur Stratigraphie des Jura im Gebiet Kelkit-Bayburt (Gümüşhane): Bulletin of the Mineral Research and Exploration Institute of Turkey, v. 61, p. 31–37.

Yılmaz, A., 1985, Structural evolution and geology of the region between the Kelkit River and Munzur Mountains (in Turkish): Türkiye Jeoloji Kurumu Bülteni, v. 28, p. 79–92.

Yılmaz, A., Y. Terlemez, and S. Uysal, 1988, Some stratigraphic and tectonic characteristics of the area around Hynys (southeast of Erzurum): Bulletin of the Mineral Research and Exploration Institute of Turkey, v. 108, p. 1–22.

Yılmaz, C., 1992, Stratigraphy of the Kelkit (Gümüşhane) region (in Turkish): Jeoloji Mühendisliği, v. 40, p. 50–62.

Yılmaz, H., 1985, Geology of the Olur (Erzurum) region (in Turkish): Karadeniz Teknik Üniversitesi Yerbilimleri Dergisi, v. 4, p. 23–43.

Yılmaz, Y., 1972, Petrology and structure of the Gümüşhane granite and the surrounding rocks, N.E. Anatolia: Ph.D. thesis, University College London, England, 284 p.

Yılmaz, Y., 1976, Geology of the Gümüşhane granite (petrography): İstanbul Üniversitesi Fen Fakültesi Mecmuasi, Seri B, v. 39, p. 157–172.

Yılmaz, Y., 1977, Petrogenetic problems of the Kurdoğlu contact metamorphic zone (in Turkish): Türkiye Jeoloji Kurumu Bülteni, v. 20, p. 63–68.

Zankl, H., 1962a, Magmatismus und Bauplan des Ostpontischen Gebirges im Querprofil des Harsit-Tales: Abhandlungen von Bayerische Akademie der Wissenschaften, Mathematische-Naturwissenschaftliche Klasse, v. 109, p. 59–91.

Zankl, H., 1962b, Magmatismus und Bauplan des Ostpontischen Gebirges im Querprofil des Harsit-Tales, NE Anatolien: Geologische Rundschau, v. 51, p. 218–239.

Derman, A.S., and Y.H. İztan, 1997, Results of geochemical analysis of seeps and potential source rocks from Northern Turkey and the Turkish Black Sea, *in* A.G. Robinson, ed., Regional and petroleum geology of the Black Sea and surrounding region: AAPG Memoir 68, p. 313–330.

Chapter 16

Results of Geochemical Analysis of Seeps and Potential Source Rocks from Northern Turkey and the Turkish Black Sea

A. Sami Derman
Y. Haluk İztan
Turkish Petroleum Corp.
Ankara, Turkey

ABSTRACT

Hydrocarbon shows have been known in northern Turkey for more than 100 years. Close to the Black Sea, several source rock units, mainly from outcrops but also from wells, have been tested for source rock potential. Organic geochemical studies on subsurface and surface samples indicate that there are several potential hydrocarbon source rock units in the region: the Kartal Formation (Early Devonian), Yılanlı Formation (Middle Devonian–Early Carboniferous), Alacaağzı and Zonguldak Formations (Carboniferous), Himmetpaşa Formation (Middle Jurassic), Çağlayan and Ülüs Formations (Cretaceous), Yemişliçay Formation (Late Cretaceous) and Kusuri Formation (Eocene). The Zonguldak and Himmetpaşa formations are composed of predominantly gas-prone vitrinite macerals. The coal samples from the Alacaağzı Formation have a different maceral composition consisting predominantly of sporinite, which is capable of producing oil. Four surface oil seeps, one seep from offshore of Rize, one oil show from Iğneada-1 well, one gas seep from the Ülüs Basin, and one gas sample from the Akçakoca-1 well, have been analyzed using classical organic geochemical techniques (pyrolysis, gas chromatography, and gas chromatography-mass spectrometry). An attempt has been made to correlate possible source rock in the area with the Armutçuk oil seep. Results of geochemical analysis of the oil seeps from different localities in the Black Sea region indicate that they have been derived from different units.

INTRODUCTION

The subject area includes the Turkish sector of the Black Sea and adjacent parts of northern Turkey. It extends from the Bulgarian border in the west to the Georgian border in the east, covering approximately 190,000 km^2 onshore and 140,000 km^2 offshore (Figure 1). Considering its size, the Turkish sector of the Black Sea is underexplored, due to a lack of understanding of the geology of the area and the cost of exploration.

The first article published about this area was by Spratt (1877), who wrote about coal mines around Zonguldak. Most of the later studies have concentrated on the Zonguldak area, due to the coal mining from Carboniferous clastics (Ralli, 1933; Lucius, 1935; Arni, 1936; Graning, 1936; Egeman, 1945; Ziljstra, 1952; Patijn, 1953; Fratschner, 1956; Wedding, 1967, 1969). Exploratory studies for oil started in 1957 (Ketin and Gümüs, 1963; Ketin, 1965); commencing as field mapping. There have been subsequent studies by many workers (Akyol et al., 1974; Arpat et al., 1978; Saner et al., 1979, 1981; Güven, 1980; Şengör and Yılmaz, 1981; Kerey, 1982; Şengör, 1984; Şengör et al., 1984; Derman, 1990; Derman and Özçelik, 1991; Alisan and Derman, 1992; Derman and Sayılı, 1992; Derman et al., 1992; Sayılı et al., 1992).

This chapter evaluates the results of geochemical data obtained over the years from analysis of both drilling and surface samples. Our aim is to review the geochemical data and relate them to the hydrocarbon potential in the Turkish sector of the Black Sea (Görür and Tüysüz, this volume) and adjacent onshore areas. We also present some of the problems related to oil exploration in this area.

Four oil seeps (Zonguldak, Armutçuk, Pusacik, and Ekinveren) from the onshore, and one seep (Rize) from the offshore areas of the Black Sea region (Figure 1) have been collected and analyzed geochemically in order to determine their physical properties, chemical composition and most probable source rocks.

EXPLORATION HISTORY

Hydrocarbon shows have been known in northern Turkey for more than 100 years. Some of them have been collected for medical purposes. Six hydrocarbon seeps are known in the Black Sea and adjacent onshore areas (Figure 1). Carbonates of the Yılanlı Formation (Middle Devonian–Visean) and sandstones of the Alacaağzı Formation (Namurian) contain two oil seeps in the Zonguldak area. Gas is seeping out ~5 km west of Ülüs from turbidite sediments of Cretaceous age (Aslancı seep). Another oil seep, the Ekinveren seep, is located near Boyabat in the Central Pontides in a Cretaceous sandstone, along a fault zone (Figure 1). Offshore, there are two seeps: Çayeli (oil) and Inceburun (gas) (Norman and Atabey, 1992).

The first exploratory well (Boyabat-1) was drilled in 1960, targeting the İnaltı Formation of Late Jurassic–Early Cretaceous age (Figure 1). Six years later, a second well was drilled to test Lower Cretaceous and Tertiary units (Badut-1). Gas shows were encountered in the volcaniclastic Yemişliçay Formation, and the well was abandoned. In 1967 and 1968, Fasıllı-1 and Karasu-1 wells were drilled and abandoned as dry holes. In 1970 and 1971, two offshore wells were drilled in the western part of the Black Sea (Iğneada-1 and Karadeniz-1) (Figure 1). In spite of minor oil shows, both were abandoned as dry holes. In 1975 and 1976, three wells were drilled in the Central Pontides to test some surface structures and the stratigraphy in the area. In the same year, Akçakoca-1 and 2 wells were drilled to test one structure offshore Ereğli. In Akçakoca-1, gas shows were encountered in Eocene sands, and 2.5 MMCFGD (million cubic feet of gas per day) was tested. Between 1986 and 1994, 14 more onshore wells were drilled, penetrating different formations ranging in age from Carboniferous to Cretaceous. Of these, six wells (Gegendere-1, Bartin-1, Filyos-1, Soğuksu-1, and Boyabat-3 and 4) have gas shows; the remaining eight wells were abandoned as dry holes.

STRATIGRAPHIC SUMMARY

The oldest rocks are amphibolites, banded gneiss, meta-acidic and metabasic igneous rocks of the Yedigöller Formation of Precambrian age cropping out in two areas: around Çamdağ and Eflani (Arpat et al., 1978; Kaya, 1982; Serdar and Demir, 1983) (Figure 1). The first sedimentary unit overlying the Yedigöller Formation is dark gray shales of the Kocatöngel Formation (Figure 2) of Late Cambrian–Ordovician age (Aydın et al., 1984). This grades upward into the Bakacak Formation (coarse-grained, large-scale cross-bedded sandstone and conglomerate with reddish-colored mudstones of possibly continental origin) of Ordovician age (Yazman and Çokuğras, 1983), indicating a shallowing-upward character. Silurian sediments are probably not present in the Çamdağ area, but are represented in the İstanbul, Zonguldak, and Eflani areas (Figure 2), suggesting an erosional event in the Çamdağ area. The sediments are unconformably overlain by Devonian sediments, which are divided into three formations separated by unconformities (Derman and Özçelik, 1991): shales and sandstones of the Kabalakdere Formation at the bottom, red mudstones, shale and sandstone of the Kartal Formation in the middle (Lower Devonian), and carbonates and shales of the Yılanlı Formation at the top (Middle Devonian–Visean). No clastic Carboniferous sediments are present, and the Yılanlı Formation is overlain by continental clastics of Late Permian age in the Çamdağ area (Alisan and Derman, 1992). Carbonates of the Yılanlı Formation grade upward into the Alacaağzı Formation of Namurian age, and form a coarsening-upward sequence of deltaic character in Zonguldak (Derman et al., 1985). The Alacaağzı Formation is overlain by the Zonguldak Formation, a delta plain sequence consisting of coarse-grained, coal-bearing clastics of Westfalian age (Saner et al., 1980; Kerey, 1982; Derman, 1985; Derman et al., 1985). Volcanic tuff horizons are present in the Zonguldak Formation clastics. There are no proven Permian sediments in this area.

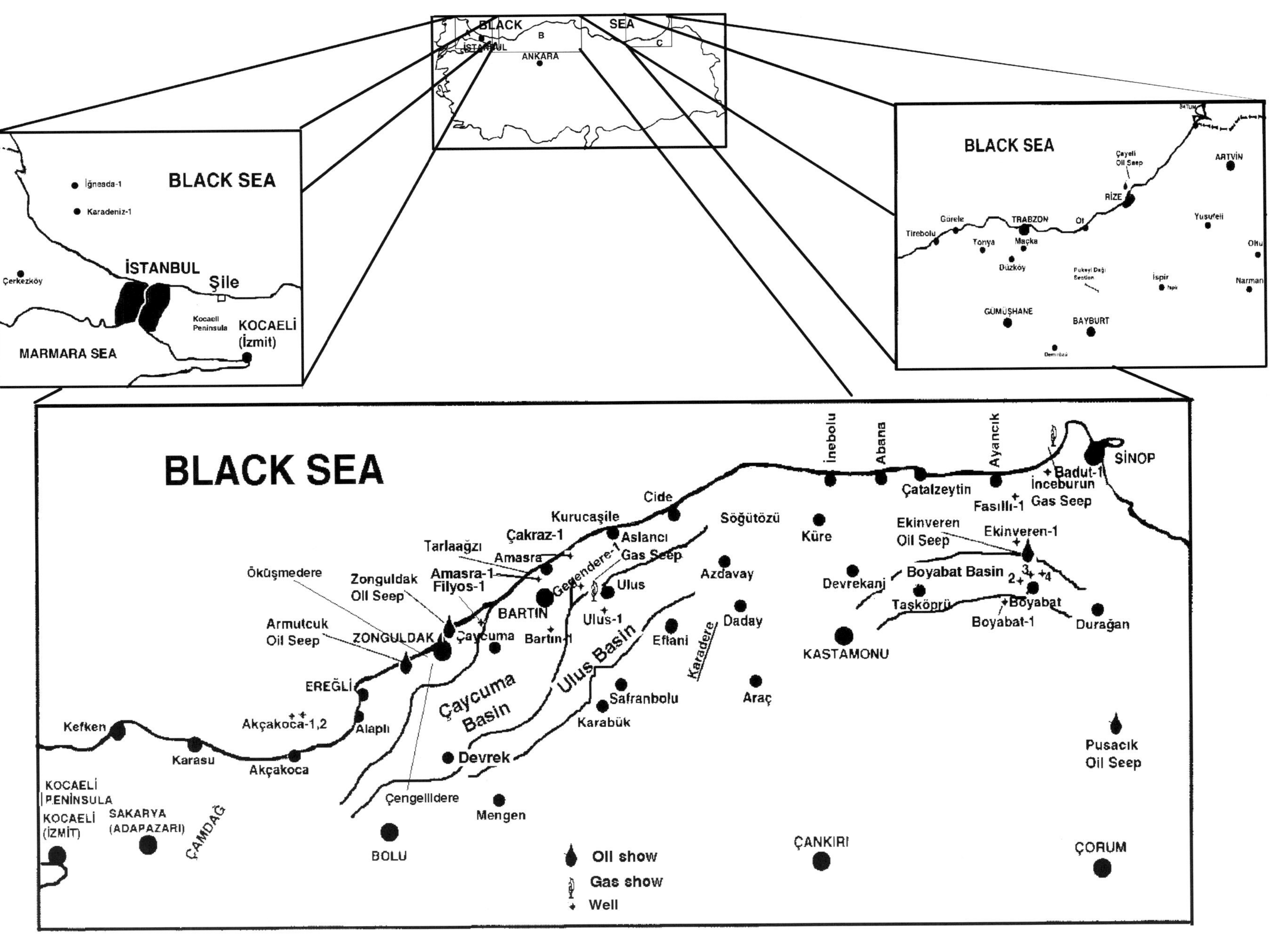

Figure l. Location map.

Carboniferous sediments, composed of conglomerate, sandstone, shale, and limestone of possibly continental origin, are exposed in the Eastern Pontides, around Bayburt and Gümüşhane, unconformably overlying the granitic metamorphic basement. They are overlain by shallow marine sediments of Early Permian age that consist of conglomerates and red-colored sandstones at the base, grading upward into sandstone, shale, and limestone of shallow marine origin, and finally into continental red clastics (Akdeniz et al., 1992; Korkmaz et al., 1992; Robinson et al., 1996).

In the Kocaeli Peninsula west of the Çamdağ area, Mesozoic sediments underlain by red-colored continental sediments have been interpreted as Triassic (Özdemir, 1971, 1975), but this unit is overlain by Triassic sediments made of mostly carbonate with a transgressive base. This brings the possibility that these red clastics could well be Permian. Limestone of Campanian age overlies Triassic sediments in the Kocaeli Peninsula (Altınlı et al., 1970) and Permian sediments in the Çamdağ area (Derman and Özçelik, 1991; Alisan and Derman, 1992).

Carboniferous rocks are unconformably overlain by the Çakraz Group of Late Triassic age between the towns of Amasra and Cide (Figure 1). The Çakraz Group comprises, from, bottom to top, the following: (1) Değirmendere Formation, red-colored lensoid sandstone and conglomerate enclosed in red-colored mudstones representing fluvial channel and arid flood plain deposits; (2) Çakrazboz Formation, red- to orange-colored, large-scale, high-angle cross-laminated quartz sandstone, representing eolian sand deposits; and (3) Basköy Formation, gray to white, pink to green varicolored clay, marl, and argillaceous limestone, representing lake deposits that grade into red-colored mudstones laterally and vertically (Figure 2). It has abundant spore and pollens indicating a Late Triassic age (Alisan and Derman, 1992). These sediments were not developed in areas to the west of Amasra.

The Himmetpaşa Formation (Bajocian–Bathonian) rests with an angular unconformity on the different stratigraphic levels of the Çakraz Group. It begins with sandstones and conglomerates, including coalified plant fragments, and shows an upward-deepening character, containing belemnites and ammonites. Farther up, it shallows, ending with coal and petrified wood fragment-bearing black mudstone and channel sands. It forms a marine wedge in this area, wedging out in the southwest of Kurucaşile. Palynological analysis of the Himmetpaşa Formation yields spores indicating a Middle?–Late Jurassic age (Alisan and Derman, 1992), while nannoplankton give a Bajocian–Bathonian age. This formation may extend farther east than actually exposed (Derman et al., 1992). Upward, it grades into the Bürnük Formation, comprising continental clastics with occasional evaporites. The Bürnük Formation is not developed west of Amasra (Figures 1, 2).

The İnaltı Formation of Late Jurassic–Early Cretaceous (Berriasian) age, is made up of shales, marls, and sandy limestone at the base, followed by limestone and dolomites. It unconformably overlies the Bürnük Formation, with a thin sandstone and/or shale and marls in the Cide area. The İnaltı Formation represents a platform-type carbonate and can be used as a key unit to reconstruct the stratigraphy (Derman, 1990, 1995a; Derman and Sayılı, 1992; Sayılı et al., 1992; Derman et al., 1996). During earlier mapping, all carbonates deposited during the Late Jurassic and Early Cretaceous were considered as one unit (Saner et al., 1980). Later studies indicated that an important unconformity exists within the İnaltı Formation, between Tithonian and Barremian age in the Zonguldak area (Derman, 1990). No Berriasian age is found in the İnaltı carbonates. On the other hand, transported megabreccias in the younger Ülüs and Çağlayan formations contain limestone blocks of Berriasian age. Therefore, the İnaltı Formation is considered to be Late Oxfordian–Berriasian (Derman, 1995a).

Around Zonguldak, the İnaltı Formation is unconformably overlain by red-colored continental clastics of the Inciğez Formation (possibly of Berriasian–Hauterivian age), which, in turn, are overlain by rudist-bearing limestone of the Öküsmedere Formation, sandstone–limestone interbeds of the Çengellidere Formation (Barremian–Early Aptian), and dominantly quartz arenites of the Velibey sandstone of Late Aptian–Early Albian age (Özer, 1986; Derman, 1990). The Velibey sandstone grades upward into glauconitic carbonate sandstone of the Sapca Formation (Albian), which then grades into marls of the Tasmaca Formation of Late Cretaceous age (Saner et al., 1980; Derman, 1990). The volcaniclastic Yemişliçay Formation of Late Cretaceous (Coniacian–Early Campanian) age has a gradational relationship with underlying units. Its stratigraphic relations with underlying units around Zonguldak suggest that deposition of the Yemişliçay Formation began in the Coniacian in this area. The Akveren Formation, of Late Campanian–early Paleocene age, consisting of limestone, sandy limestone, marl, shales, and calciturbidites, unconformably overlies all formations older than Late Campanian.

Around Cide and in Ülüs Basin, the İnaltı Formation is unconformably overlain by the Ülüs Formation, of Late Valanginian–Early Campanian age. Due to the onlapping nature of the formation, the lowermost part is not exposed at the surface. In Ülüs-1 well, however, basalts of Neocomian age are overlain by black shales and evaporites (core sample), followed by very thick megabreccias (2800 m) and turbiditic sandstone and shales (650 m) of the Ülüs Formation. The megabreccias contain blocks of limestone of the İnaltı Formation and the Yılanlı Formation, and coal-bearing clastics of the Alacaağzı and Zonguldak Formations. Çağlayan and Ülüs formations have a similar character: the Çağlayan Formation was defined from the Eastern and Central Pontides (Ketin and Gümüs, 1963), and the Ülüs Formation was originally defined from the Western Pontides. Velibey, Sapça, and Tasmaca formations are separate units as originally defined by Saner et al. (1980), and should not be confused with other units, as suggested by some authors (Aydın et al., 1986; Görür et al., 1993). The Ülüs Formation is overlain by Late Campanian sediments that begin with 2–3 m of sandstone followed by pelagic limestones, and continue with turbiditic sediments of the Akveren Formation (Derman, 1990, 1995a). The Çağlayan Formation is overlain by the Kapanboğazı Formation (Ketin and Gümüs, 1963; Aydın et al., 1986).

There are no proven Triassic sediments in the Eastern Pontides (although they may be present but not reported). The stratigraphic relationships of Jurassic sediments vary from one area to another. In the vicinity of Bayburt, Liassic sediments, which comprise coal-bearing clastics and some carbonates, overlie Lower Permian shallow marine to continental sediments. In the northern zone of the Eastern Pontides, the granitic-metamorphic basement is unconformably overlain by Liassic sediments (Akdeniz et al., 1992) that grade upward into carbonates of Dogger–Early Cretaceous age. In the vicinity of Bayburt, the coal-bearing clastics of Liassic age are reported to pass upward into reefal limestone of Malm–Early Cretaceous age by Akdeniz et al. (1992) without mentioning the presence of any Dogger sediments. Korkmaz et al. (1992) report that the Lower and Middle Jurassic are dominated by volcanics and volcano-sedimentary series, locally comprising limestone and continental deposits. These units are conformably overlain by carbonates of late Dogger–Early Cretaceous age. Robinson et al. (1996), however, describe Bajocian–Bathonian sediments as unconformably or disconformably overlying rocks as old as metamorphic basement. The Upper Jurassic is considered gradational from the Middle Jurassic (Akdeniz et al., 1992; Korkmaz et al., 1992). Late Jurassic–Early Cretaceous ages are represented by mostly shallow water carbonates, assigned to the Callovian?–Berriasian (Robinson et al., 1996). In the Olür area, however, Late Jurassic–Early Cretaceous ages are represented by deltaic-turbiditic units of Portlandian–Berriasian age (Konak et al., 1992). All these indicate that there is not a good understanding of the Jurassic stratigraphy of the Eastern Pontides, but published data indicate that the Late Jurassic sediments begin with a transgressive base and continue into Berriasian sediments. Middle and Upper Cretaceous sediments are mostly clastic with volcaniclastic intercalations.

Tertiary units have a patchy distribution and show much facies variation in the region (Figure 2). In the Çaycuma Basin, the Akveren Formation of Late Campanian–early Paleocene age grades into thin sandstone and interbedded marls and shales of the Atbaşı Formation (Paleocene). The Kusuri Formation of Eocene age, consisting of sandstone, marl, tuffs, tuffites, lavas, and agglomerates, unconformably overlies the Atbaşı and İnaltı formations (Şahintürk and Özçelik, 1983). There are more than 4000 m of *Globigerina*-bearing marls in the Çaycuma Basin (well data).

In the Eflani area, marls and limestone interbedding of the shallow marine Safranbolu Formation, of late Paleocene–middle Eocene age, unconformably overlie all older units. These limestones and marls extend from Karabük to Devrekani to the north of Kastamonu. In the Boyabat Basin, the stratigraphic succession begins on the metamorphic basement, with thin sandstone overlain by pelagic limestone of late Campanian age, and continues into turbiditic sandstone–shale interbedding (Boyabat-2 well). On the marginal areas, the sequence begins with shallow marine limestone of Paleocene–Eocene age. There are no Tertiary volcanics present.

The stratigraphic succession ends with middle Eocene sediments in all areas. No Oligocene or younger sediments (except alluvial sediments) are encountered in this region onshore. Sediments younger than middle Eocene are present offshore, however. On the continental margin, middle Eocene sediments are overlain by either Oligocene or Miocene sediments, due to the onlapping relations of these units. Therefore, upper Eocene sediments are not penetrated in Akçakoca-1 well, although its depositional limit is to the north of the Akçakoca wells.

In the Eastern Pontides, Tertiary (Paleocene–middle Eocene) sediments have a volcaniclastic content, while the Oligocene and Miocene are represented by continental clastics.

GEOCHEMICAL ANALYSIS OF SOURCE ROCKS

Western and Central Pontides

Organic geochemical studies on subsurface and surface samples indicate that there are several potential hydrocarbon source rock units in the region (Table 1). The Kartal Formation (Early Devonian), Yılanlı Formation (Middle Devonian–Early Carboniferous), Alacaağzı and Zonguldak formations (Carboniferous), Himmetpaşa Formation (Middle Jurassic), Çağlayan and Ülüs formations (Cretaceous), Tasmaca Formation (middle Cretaceous), Yemişliçay Formation (Late Cretaceous), and Kusuri Formation (Eocene) are all considered to be potential hydrocarbon source rocks.

The Kartal Formation is exposed in a few places in the Western Pontides. No well has penetrated this formation in the sub-surface. The unit is composed of predominantly clastics and some carbonates. Total organic carbon (TOC) values range from 0.12 to 2.35 wt %. The organic matter is generally Types III and IV, and in some places Type II (Harput et al., 1993). The SCI measurements indicate that the maturity level of the unit changes from middle mature around Bartin and the Çaycuma Basin (Figure 1) to overmature in areas 25 km to the east of Mengen (SCI = 7.5 and 10, respectively). This means that maturity increases from north to south.

The Yılanlı Formation is a carbonate unit with thin beds of black shales that contain up to 7.92 wt % TOC (Harput, 1993). The kerogen is mostly Type II and the maturity level of the unit changes from middle mature around the Zonguldak and Bartin areas to overmature in other areas, based on the surface samples [R_o = 0.72–2.0%, SCI (spore coloration index) = 6.2–9.0]. This unit is present from İstanbul to the Bartin area; in most areas, it is exposed at the surface. It shows oil potential in a few areas between Bartin and Cide (onshore) where it is covered by younger sediments. The Yılanlı Formation shows a similar maturity trend as the Kartal Formation.

Table 1. Results of Geochemical Analyses of Samples from the Western and Central Pontides.

Formation	TOC (wt %)	P2 (PY) (ppm) (max)	HI mg HC/g TOC (max)	T_{max} (°C)	SCI	R_o (%)	OM Type
Kartal	0.12–2.35	14–3747	3–196	439(?)	7.5–10	0.65–0.80	IV, III, II
Yılanlı	0.10–7.92	408–13,527	35–305	434–473	6.2–9.0	0.72–2.0	II
Alacaağzı (shale)	0.22–8.03	120–22,492	12–315	412–486	5.0–8.5	0.55–1.33	II, III
Alacaağzı (coal)	30–70	12,600–206,000	22–598	422–447	–	0.75–0.85	II, IV
Zonguldak	0.07–8.03	60–2890	12–51	436–494	5.5–7.5	0.45–1.20	III
Himmetpaşa	0.25–3.92	60–1170	4–68	428–475	6.0–7.5	0.68–0.86	IV, III, II
Çağlayan	0.09–2.14	8–8742	3–417	423–471	3.0–9.0	0.35–1.40	III, II, IV, I
Ülüs	0.25–1.84	10–2494	5–229	427–498	4.0–10.0	0.44–1.70	II, III, IV
Tasmaca	0.35–1.46	1376–4751	110–379	430–443	4.5–6.0	0.45–0.55	II
Yemişliçay	0.29–1.12	–	152–225	443–447	6.5	0.88–0.94	II, III
Kusuri	0.08–0.93	67–661	13–34	432–453	2.5–7.5	0.31–0.33	III

The Alacaağzı Formation is prodelta and delta front shale, which contains in its lower part up to 8.03 wt % TOC. It has both Type II and Type III organic matter (Harput, 1993). The maturity level of the organic matter ranges from middle mature in general to postmature in one locality around Bartin, which may be related to Tertiary volcanics (R_o = 0.55–1.33%; SCI = 5.0–8.5; T_{max} = 412–486°C) (Table 1).

The Alacaağzı Formation is present between the Zonguldak and Cide areas. It crops out in the Zonguldak area, but it is under cover between Bartin and Cide. Coal samples taken from this formation have also been analyzed. The analytical data (Table 1) show that samples have high petroleum (oil + gas) source rock potential as indicated by high TOC (30–70 wt %), high HI (222–598 mg HC/g), high petroleum yield (PY) (12,600–206,000 ppm), R_o (0.75–0.85), and T_{max} (422–447°C) values.

The Zonguldak Formation consists of shale, sandstone, and conglomerate of delta plain origin. This formation is present between Zonguldak and Cide. Outcrop samples show up to 5.42 wt % TOC. The kerogen is mostly Type III, which is capable of producing mainly gas (Tissot et al., 1980), but Type II kerogen is also present. The R_o, SCI, and T_{max} values vary from 0.45–1.2 wt %, 5.5–7.5, and 436–494°C, respectively (Table 1), which indicates moderate maturity. Maturity increases from moderately mature in Tarlaağzı to postmature in the Söğütözü area, where the Carboniferous is present as debris flow. In the Amasra-1 well, TOC values of the shaly sections range from 0.07–2.66%. The R_o values, on the surface, range from 0.65–1.2% throughout the unit in the well, which indicates moderate maturity. The Zonguldak Formation is present between Zonguldak and Cide.

In the Çakraz-1 well, the Alacaağzı and the Zonguldak Formations are mature enough (R_o = 0.62–0.94%; SCI = 5.5–7.5) to generate hydrocarbons, but the kerogen type indicates that organic matter is mostly gas prone (Type III and Type IV). In the Gegendere-1 well, the shales of the Zonguldak and the Alacaağzı formations are rich in organic content (TOC = 1.76–8.03 wt %). Maturity level increases uniformly with depth (R_o values increase from 0.7 to 1.3%), although three reverse faults have been cut. This indicates that maturity level has been reached after faulting. The faulting is probably of post-middle Eocene age (Derman and Norman, in press).

The Himmetpaşa Formation is made up of sandstones at the bottom, dark-gray shales in the middle, and coal and some sandstones at the top. It is not present to the west of Kurucaşile (Derman, 1995a). Organic matter measurements from shaly intervals give high TOC values ≤3.92 wt %. Kerogen is predominantly Types III and IV at the bottom and at the top, but Type II has been observed in the middle part of the formation. The unit is early mature to postmature in the south of Cide based on R_o (0.68–0.86%), SCI (6.0–7.5), and T_{max} (428–475°C) values.

In order to understand the oil potential of the coal beds in the area, organic petrographic analyses have been performed on several coal samples from three coal-bearing units: the Alacaağzı, Zonguldak, and Himmetpaşa formations. The coal samples from the Zonguldak and Himmetpaşa formations are composed of predominantly gas-prone vitrinite macerals. The coal samples from the Alacaağzı Formation have different maceral compositions, consisting predominantly of sporinite (60–70%), which is capable of producing oil. Also, high amounts of extract (≤33,900 ppm) taken from the Alacaağzı coals support this finding.

The Çağlayan Formation is a turbiditic unit made up of shale–sandstone interbedding. It is a very extensive unit in the central and eastern Pontide region. Due to its turbiditic character and variable burial history in different parts of the region, organic geochemical parameters change drastically from one area to another. The TOC values range from 0.09–2.14 wt %, averaging 0.60 wt %. Organic matter varies from Type I to Type IV, but is mainly Types II and III (Table 1). Maturity values also show great diversity, which is the result of volcanic and magmatic intrusions during the Late Cretaceous and Eocene, and variable burial history. The R_o, SCI, and T_{max} values vary from 0.35 to 1.40%, 3.0 to 9.0,

Table 2. Results of Geochemical Analyses of Samples from the Eastern Pontides.

Age	TOC (wt %)	P2 (PY) (ppm)	HI	T_{max} (°C)	SCI	R_o (%)	OM Type
Liassic	0.12–1.53	10–3070	3–290	407–498	7.5–9.0	0.82–1.30	III, IV
Cretaceous	0.13–0.79	30–200	7–41	432–485	6.0–8.0	0.88–1.22	III, IV
Eocene	0.47–1.69	140–540	8–80	457–482	6.0–7.0	0.75–0.88	III
Miocene	0.73–1.61	960–8380	55–520	416–437	3.0–3.51	–	II

and 423 to 471°C, respectively, suggesting that the unit is immature between Sinop and Boyabat to overmature in the İnebolu-Abana area.

The Ülüs Formation is also a turbiditic unit and is mostly developed in and around the Ülüs basin. The content of organic matter depends on the amount of sand and silt-sized material present. To the west of the Ülüs Basin, inflow of abundant coarse clastics and suspended matter has probably diluted the basinal sediments with respect to organic content. Similar to the Çağlgayan Formation, TOC contents, the type of organic matter, and maturity of the unit change frequently in short distances, depending on the turbiditic character of the sediments, magmatic activity, proximity to faults, and burial history, across the basin. The TOC content of the unit varies from 0.25 to 1.84 wt % (Harput, 1993). The organic matter type changes from Type II to Type IV. R_o, SCI, and T_{max} values are between 0.44 and 1.70%, 4 and 10, and 427 and 498°C, respectively. Maturity increases from west to east and from the margin toward the center of the Ülüs Basin.

The Tasmaca Formation consists of bluish-gray colored marl. It has up to 1.46 wt % TOC values, most of which are ~1.0 wt %. The unit has Type II organic matter, which is early mature–marginally mature in surface exposures around Zonguldak. Maturity level increases from south to north, with R_o values changing from 0.45 to 0.55%. Average SCI and T_{max} values are 5.5 and 435°C, respectively.

The Yemişliçay Formation has not been considered a potential source rock due to its volcaniclastic nature. In Filyos-1 well, however, it has a 400-m-thick shaly level which has up to 1.12 wt % organic carbon content. The organic matter is Types II, and III, and the kerogen is mature in this interval (R_o = 0.88–0.94 wt %; SCI = 6.5; T_{max} = 443–447°C). Additionally, C_1–C_4 gas reading recorded during drilling in this interval shows that the C_2+ wet gas ratio is about 80%, which indicates that this zone is in the oil window. Other levels in the Yemişliçay Formation do not have any source rock potential in the well.

The Kusuri Formation has TOC values between 0.08 and 0.93 wt %. The organic matter is predominantly Type III, and the maturity level changes from early to middle mature (R_o = 0.31–0.33 wt %; SCI = 2.5–7.5; T_{max} = 432–453°C) (Table 2). Thus, the unit is considered to be a potential source rock for only gas.

Eastern Pontides

In the Eastern Pontides, samples ranging in age from Liassic to Miocene have been evaluated geochemically in order to find out their source rock potential (Table 2).

Most of the samples taken from Liassic outcrops around Bayburt have low organic matter content (0.12–1.53 wt %), low P2 (10–3190 ppm) values, and show high maturity levels (T_{max} = 470°C; SCI = 7.5–9.0; R_o = 0.82–1.3%). In one measured section to the north of Bayburt (Pukeyi Dağı), the unit has been found to be early mature (T_{max} = 425–435°C; SCI = 4.5–6.0; R_o = 0.55–0.65%). The unit has no source rock potential in this area.

The Cretaceous unit equivalent to the Çağlayan Formation also has low TOC (0.13–0.79 wt %) and P2 (30–200 ppm) values. The HI values are also very low (7–41 mg HC/g TOC). The maturity level of the unit ranges from middle to postmature (T_{max} = 432–485°C, SCI = 6.0–8.0%; R_o = 0.88–1.22%). Therefore, this unit does not have source potential.

The Eocene samples are relatively rich in organic matter, ranging from 0.47–1.69 wt %, averaging 1.0 wt %. However, low P2 (140–540 ppm) and HI values (8–80 mg HC/g TOC) indicate that this unit cannot be considered as a potential source rock. The maturity level of the unit is middle mature–postmature (T_{max} = 457–482°C, SCI = 6.0–7.0; R_o = 0.75–0.88%).

The Miocene samples have enough organic matter to be a source rock, ranging from 0.73–1.61 wt %. The HI and P2 values are between 55 and 520 mg HC/g TOC and 1040 and 8380 ppm respectively, due to low maturity in some interval. The T_{max} (416–437°C) and SCI (4.5–6.0) values indicate that the unit is early mature (Table 2). Relatively high HI values may be due to low maturity of organic matter. Thus, the Miocene unit has been evaluated as immature potential source rock for oil and gas in the area.

GEOCHEMICAL ANALYSIS OF SEEPS AND OIL SHOWS

Rize Oil Seep

The only oil sample taken from the Eastern Pontides that has been recovered (at Rize) is biodegraded, as indicated by the absence of *n*-alkanes, a big hump on the gas chromatogram (Figure 3), and the presence of 17α(H)-25-norhopane (Seifert and Moldowan, 1979; Rullkötter and Wendisch, 1982). Higher amounts of rearranged steranes relative to normal (Rubinstein et al., 1975; Seiskind et al., 1979; Zumberge, 1984; McKirdy et al., 1984) (Figure 4) and the absence of benzothiophenes (Hughes, 1984) imply a shale source rock or a unit containing considerable amounts of clay.

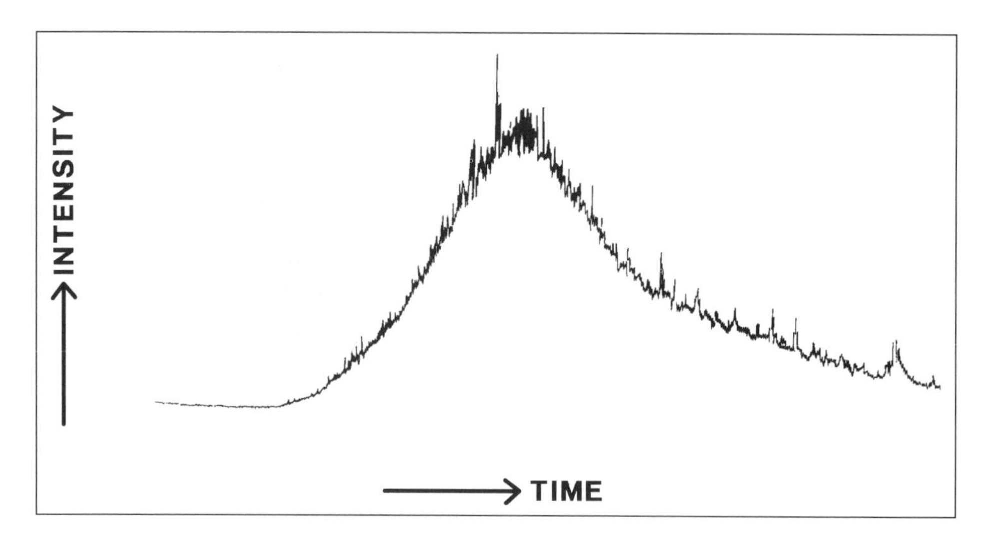

Figure 3. Gas chromatogram of Rize oil seep.

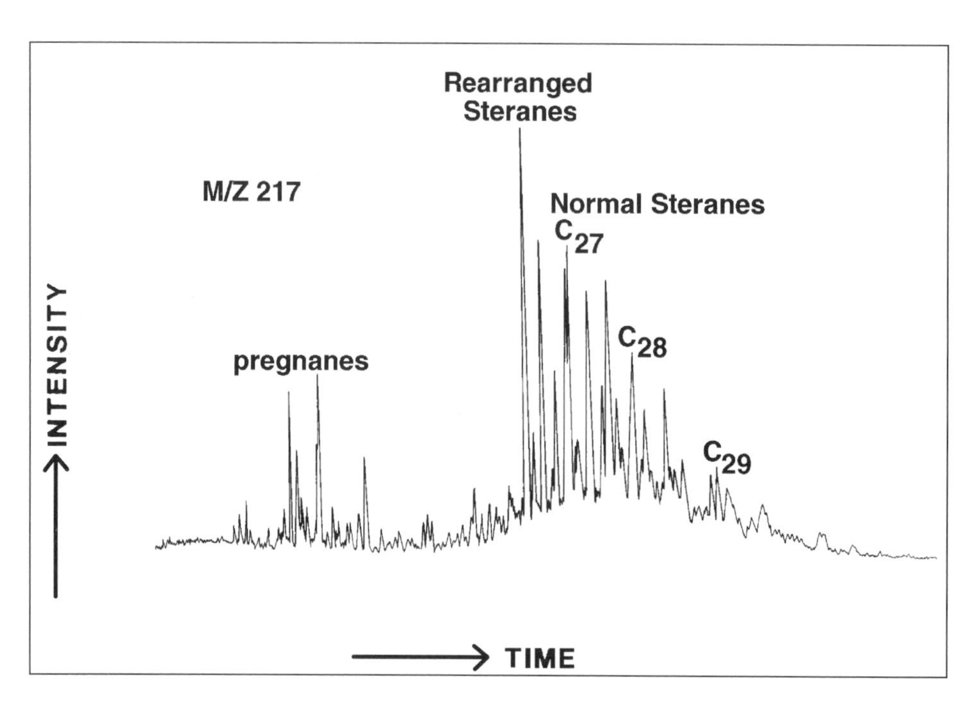

Figure 4. M/Z 217 mass fragmentogram showing the sterane distribution of Rize oil seep.

The presence of an oleanane peak on the terpane (M/Z 191) fragmentogram (Figure 5) of the oil has been interpreted as indicating the age of the source rock is Upper Cretaceous or younger (Philp and Gilbert, 1985; Taluktar et al., 1985). Low C_{32} 22S/22S + 22R terpane (0.48), low C_{29} 20S/20S+20R (0.46) sterane ratios, and low amounts of lower carbon number tri- and monoaromatic steranes (C_{20}–C_{22}) relative to the higher carbon number counterparts (C_{26}–C_{29}) suggest a low maturity level (Sofer et al., 1985) for the Rize oil (Figure 5). The most probable source rock for this oil is an upper Eocene (Robinson et al., 1996) and/or Maikopian (Oligocene–early Miocene) unit, which probably extends throughout the Black Sea.

Armutçuk Oil Seep

The Armutçuk oil sample was taken from the Alacaağzı Formation in a coal mine gallery near Zonguldak. No trace of biodegradation has been seen on the gas chromatogram (Figure 6). The presence of *n*-alkanes in substantial amounts, the absence of a baseline hump on the gas chromatogram, and C_{29} 20S/20S + 20R sterane ratio of 0.55 (Mackenzie et al., 1980) indicate that the Armutçuk oil is mature. High pristane/phytane (2.4) and Pr/*n*-C_{17} (1.0) and low Ph/*n*-C_{18} ratios imply a source rock deposited in an oxic (or suboxic) near-shore environment. Also, low tricyclic terpanes relative to pentacyclics (Philp and Gilbert, 1985), high C_{24} tetracyclic terpanes relative to tricyclics (Cassini et al., 1987) (Figure 7), and high C_{29} steranes relative to C_{27}, C_{28} counterparts (Huang and Meinshein, 1979; Hughes, 1984) (Figure 8) all support this suggestion. Low C_{29} norhopene/C_{30} hopane (Pym et al., 1975; Fan Pu and Claypool, 1987; ten Haven et al., 1988) and low C_{35}/C_{34} extended hopane (McKirdy et al., 1981) ratios imply a noncarbonate (shale) source rock for the Armutçuk oil

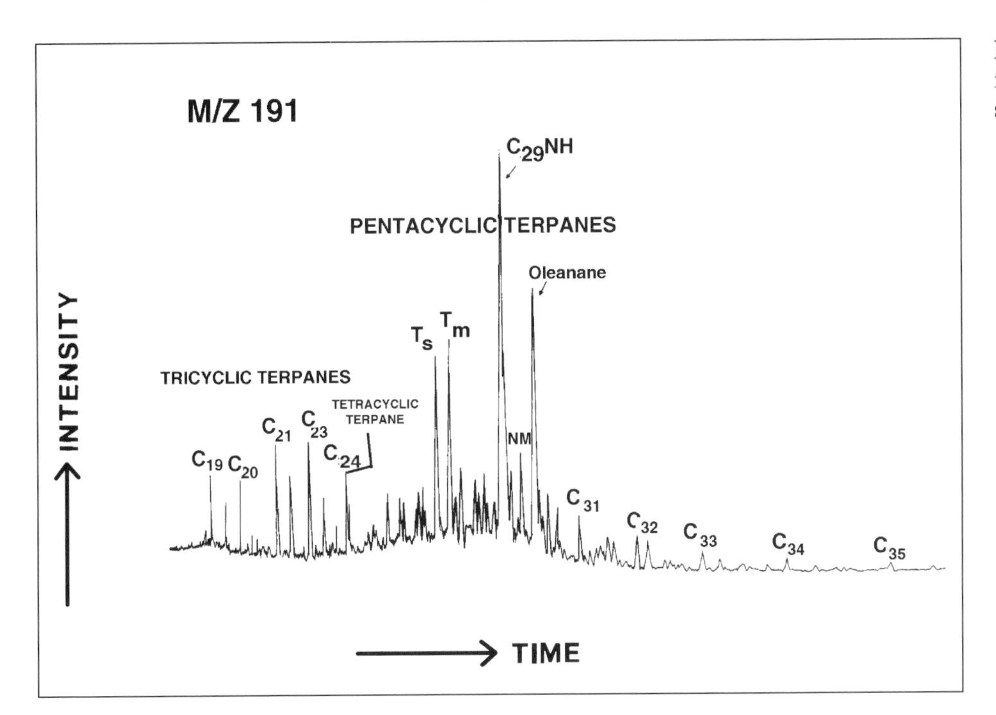

Figure 5. M/Z 191 terpane fragmentogram of Rize oil seep.

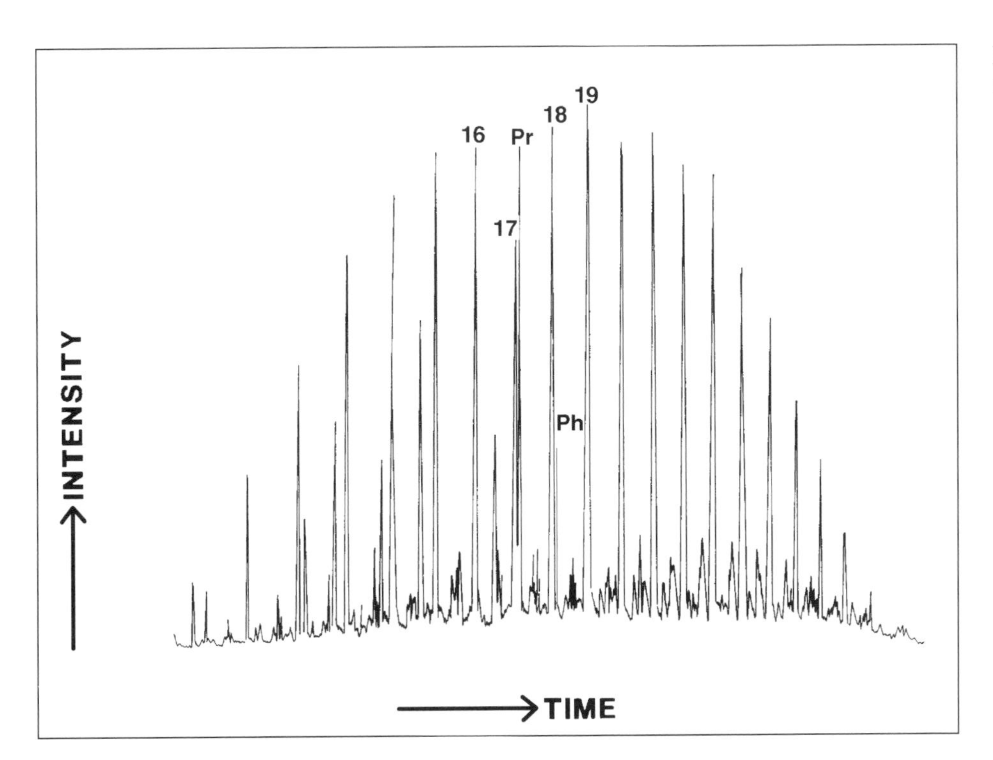

Figure 6. Gas chromatogram of Armutçuk oil seep.

seep. However, low amounts of rearranged steranes relative to normal suggest a carbonate- or clay-poor source rock, which is in contrast to the data above.

Zonguldak Oil Seep

The oil sample was recovered from the Devonian Yılanlı Formation near Zonguldak, which is composed of thick carbonate and thin shale alternations. High *n*-alkane concentrations on the gas chromatogram, high API gravity (42°), high saturate/aromatic ratios (Hughes, 1984; Palacas et al., 1984; Tissot and Welte, 1984), high T_s/T_m (two terpane molecules that are used as maturity and source rock parameters) (Seifert and Moldowan, 1978) ratios, low biomarker concentration (Robinson et al., 1985), high MPI (methyl phenontrane index)[1] value (0.71) (Radke and Weite, 1983), and high C_{29} 20S/20S + 20R ratio (Mackenzie et al., 1980) imply a high maturity level for the Zonguldak oil. High

1 MPI (Methyl Phenontrane Index) $= 1.5\left(\frac{2MP + 3MP}{P + 1MP + 9MP}\right)$

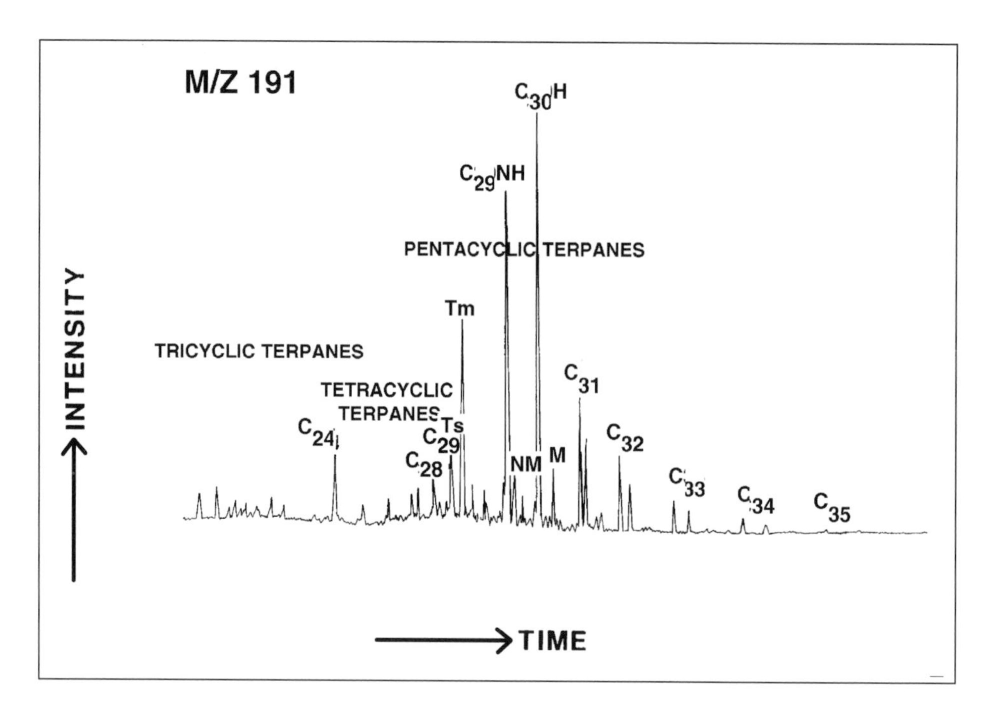

Figure 7. M/Z 191 terpane fragmentogram of Armutçuk oil seep.

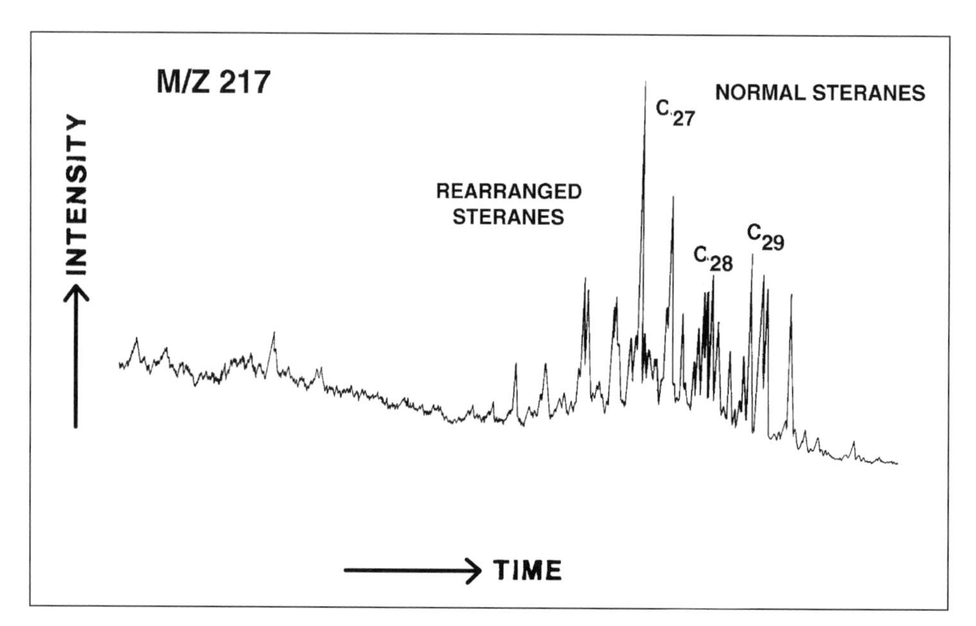

Figure 8. M/Z 217 sterane fragmentogram of Armutçuk oil seep.

extended tricyclic terpanes (Aquino Neto et al., 1982), higher C_{27} steranes relative to C_{28} and C_{29} steranes, and a carbon isotope ratio of the whole oil measurement of –27.4‰ PDB (TPAO, 1993, unpublished report) suggest marine organic matter input into the source sediments. However, the presence of C_{19} and C_{20} tricyclic terpanes (Reed, 1977; Simoneit, 1977; Palmer, 1981; Zumberge, 1987) shows that the organic matter also contains terrestrially derived plant material. Higher rearranged steranes relative to normal suggests shale (or clay-rich) source rock. High C_{24} tetracyclic terpane may be attributed to the higher maturity level of the oil (Aquino Neto et al., 1981) or to the terrestrial organic matter content of the source rock (Hughes and Hoiba, 1987).

Pusacik Oil Seep

The Pusacik oil seep, recovered from the Western Pontides, is biodegraded, as indicated by the absence of *n*-alkanes on the gas chromatograms. High peak concentration in the biomarker region (C_{20}–C_{30} interval on GC) implies low maturity (Ebukanson and Kinghorn, 1985). Additionally, high amounts of polar compounds (54%), low T_s/T_m (0.4), and low C_{32} 22S/22S + 22R ratios (0.56) (Mackenzie et al., 1980) support a low maturity level for the Pusacik oil. The presence of gammacerane (Fan Pu and Zhang Baisheng, 1987), a heavy carbon isotope ratio of the whole oil of –22.4‰ PDB (BP unpublished report) and a low abundance of rearranged steranes suggest a source rock deposited in

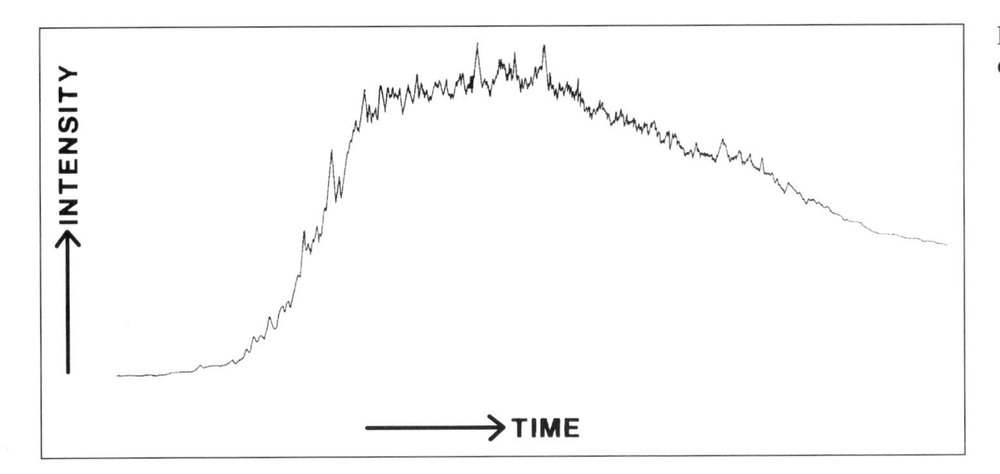

Figure 9. Gas chromatogram of Ekinveren oil seep.

a carbonate or possibly evaporitic environment. The sequence containing evaporite within the Pontide region is an unnamed unit of Cretaceous age underlying the Ülüs Formation in the Ülüs Basin. The unit containing evaporite in the area near the Pusacik oil seep is Oligo–Miocene formations in Çankırı-Çorum basin.

Ekinveren Oil Seep

The Ekinveren oil seep is located in the Central Pontides. It is strongly biodegraded, which is evidenced by the complete absence of *n*-alkanes and the presence of a huge hump on the gas chromatogram (Figure 9). High amounts of rearranged sterane (57%) relative to normal suggest a siliciclastic (shale) source rock. High T_s/T_m (2.5), high C_{29} 20S/20S+20R (0.64) ratios, and MPI value (0.59) indicate mature oil. The oil has been derived from a source rock deposited in a marine environment, evidenced by a heavier carbon isotope ratio (–25.6‰ PDB) and high amounts of C_{27} steranes (44%) relative to C_{28} (21%) and C_{29} (35%) counterparts. The most probable source rock candidate for the Ekinveren oil is the Çağlayan Formation, since it is a siliciclastic, marine, and mature unit that is exposed in a large area in the Central Pontides.

Oil Shows

İğneada-1 well was drilled at the westernmost part of the Black Sea (Figure 1). In this well, several hydrocarbon-rich intervals have been detected [production index (PI)[1] >0.80] between 1692 and 2007 m, which covers the Eocene–middle Miocene Badut Formation. Organic geochemical analyses indicate that this unit has no oil source potential due to its unsuitable organic matter type (Type III) and low maturity level (R_o = 0.25–0.55%; SCI = 2.0–5.0; T_{max} = 419–423°C). In order to characterize the oil, GC and GCMS analyses have been performed on the rock extracts from the oil-bearing interval. High *n*-alkane concentration (Figure 10), no odd-even predominance (CPI ≅ 1.0) (Bray and Evans, 1961), high-saturate HC/aromatic HC ratio (2.0), high T_s/T_m ratio (2.0), the presence of a hump in the tricyclic terpane region, and high tricyclic terpane content (Seifert and Moldowan, 1983) on the terpane chromatogram (M/Z 191) (Figure 11) suggest that the oil (extract) is mature. The source rock from which the oil has been derived must be a terrigeneous unit, evidenced by high amounts of rearranged sterane relative to normal amounts (Figure 12). High C_{27} steranes compared to C_{28} and C_{29} steranes imply a marine depositional environment for the source rock.

[1] Production Index = PI = $\frac{P1}{P1+P2}$

Aslancı Gas Seep

The Aslancı gas seep is in the Ülüs Basin in the Western Pontides (Figure 1). High amounts of C_{2+} hydrocarbons (13%) indicate that it is a wet gas. Geochemical analyses (Table 2) reported that several units (Alacaağzı, Zonguldak, and Ülüs formations and Tertiary rocks) are capable of producing gas. In the basin, >6000 m of sediments are present. Since Cretaceous sediments at the surface are not mature, Cretaceous and pre-Cretaceous units that have been buried deep enough can produce gas. Wet gas shows have also been encountered in Bartin-1 and Filyos-1 wells, which are located to the north and west of the Ülüs gas seep.

Akçakoca-1 Well

A gas show was also encountered in the Akçakoca-1 well (Figure 1); 2.5 MMCFGD has been tested. It cannot be determined whether it is biogenic or thermogenic in origin by using its chemical composition (~100% CH_4). Isotopic analysis has not been performed.

OIL SOURCE ROCK CORRELATION

In the Western Black Sea region, oil source rock correlation has been attempted between the Armutçuk oil seep and the Kartal, Alacaağzı, Zonguldak, and

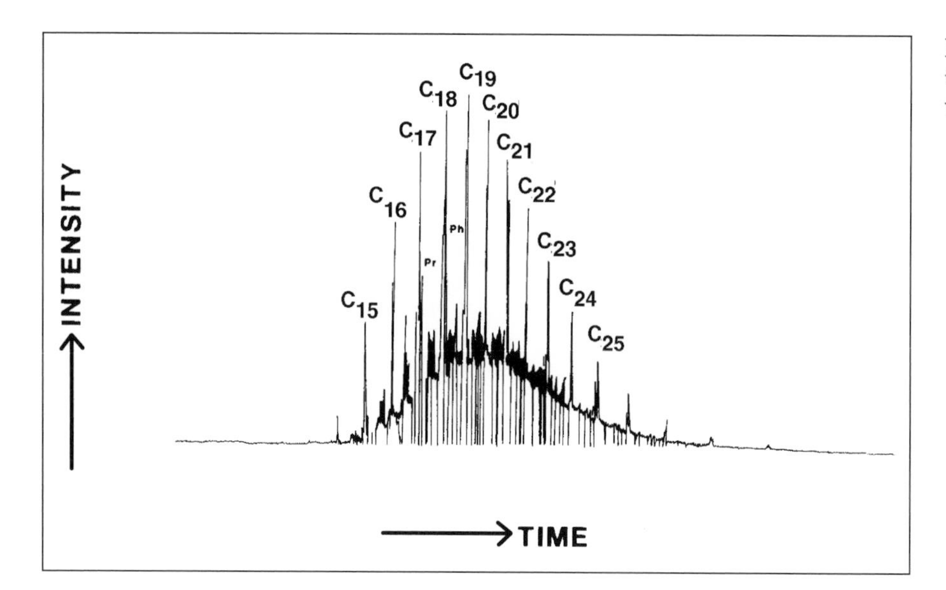

Figure 10. Gas chromatogram of the contaminant oil in İğneada-1 well.

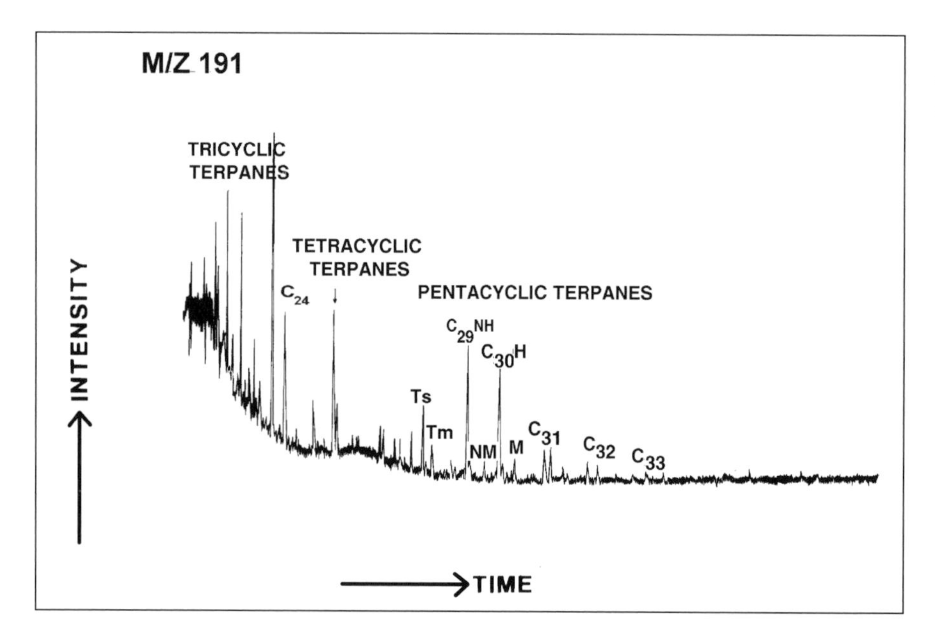

Figure 11. M/Z 191 terpane fragmentogram of the contaminant oil in İğneada-1 well.

Çağlayan formations—four possible source rocks in the area. The results of fingerprint analysis performed on several GCMS fragmentograms have shown that Lower Cretaceous Ülüs and Devonian Kartal formations cannot be the source of the Armutçuk oil. The fragmentograms of the shales of the Namurian Alacaağzı Formation are, however, similar to those of Armutçuk oil. Low amounts of tricyclic terpanes and low T_s/T_m, C_{29} norhopane/C_{30} hopane, C_{35}/C_{34} homohopane ratios are characteristic in the terpane fragmentograms of the Alacaağzı extracts and Armutçuk oil (Figure 13). In M/Z 218 sterane fragmentograms (ββ steranes), the Alacaağzı extract and Armutçuk oil have low amounts of rearranged steranes (Figure 14). Both fragmentograms contain a peak labeled *"x"* (C_{30} sterane?), which is not present in either the Ülüs or the Kartal formations. Small differences on the fragmentograms have been attributed to mixing from another source, probably from the coal measures in the same formation, which have also good source rock potential.

Maturity Evaluation

In the region, many basins, different in type and size, have developed from the Paleozoic through the Quaternary (Derman, 1995b). They have been affected by various tectonic processes and magmatic/volcanic activities, causing units to acquire different maturity levels.

There are two important trends in the maturity level of Devonian and Carboniferous rocks. First, maturity levels change from older (SCI of Kartal Formation varies between 7.5 and 10.0) to younger (SCI of the Zonguldak Formation varies between 5.5 and 7.5), which is probably related to burial history and paleogeothermal gradient in the region. Second, the maturity level decreases from south to north, which may be related to some other processes (e.g., presence of granitic intrusions of possibly Early or Middle Jurassic age in the south of the area). The Himmetpaşa Formation has almost the same maturity value as the Carboniferous, indicating that they have gone through similar burial histories, especially in the Cide area.

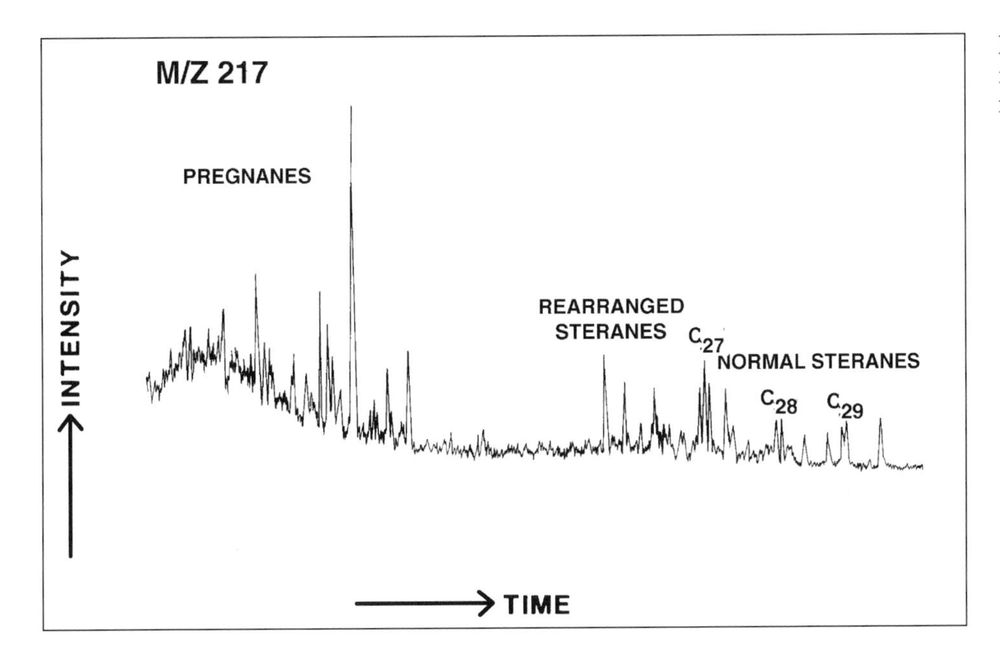

Figure 12. M/Z 217 sterane fragmentogram of the contaminant oil in İğneada-1 well.

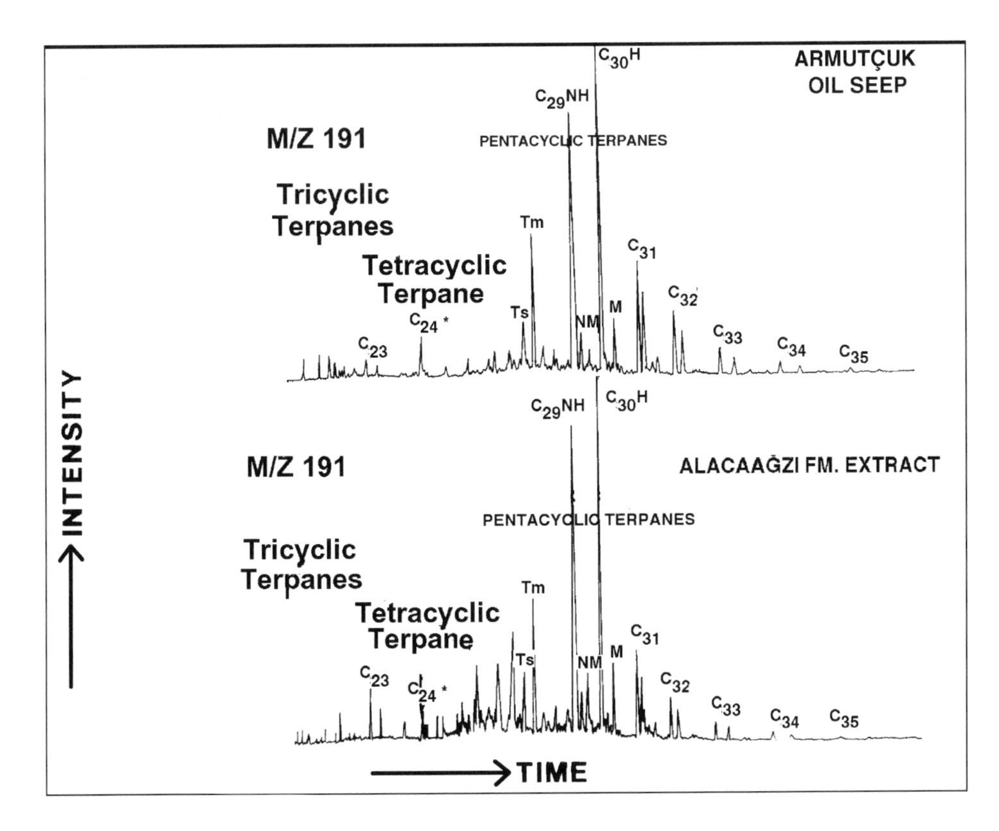

Figure 13. The comparison between M/Z 191 terpane fragmentograms of the extract of the Alacaağzı Formation and Armutçuk oil seep.

There is a jump in maturity level from the Himmetpaşa Formation (SCI = 6.0–7.5) to the Ülüs Formation (SCI = 4.0–10). As indicated, there is a large unconformity between the İnaltı and Ülüs formations. The large variation in the maturity level of the Ülüs and Çağlayan formations is striking. In the Ülüs Basin, maturity values increase from the margin of the basin toward the center. There are three reasons for this: (1) the Ülüs Formation is younger along the margin due to onlapping relations of the unit with the margin; (2) along the axis of the basin, the unit is buried deeper than the marginal areas; and (3) the presence of the volcanic rocks along the basin axis. In the Çağlayan Formation, abnormally high maturities are encountered where intrusions or volcanic rocks are present. These intrusions may have a local effect on the maturity of the organic matter. The best example of this is encountered in the Ekinveren-1 well. In this well, a lower maturity interval is encountered between higher maturity levels, although the sequence is uniformly conformable. The time of deposition of the Ülüs and Çağlayan formations is the rifting stage, when geothermal gradient was

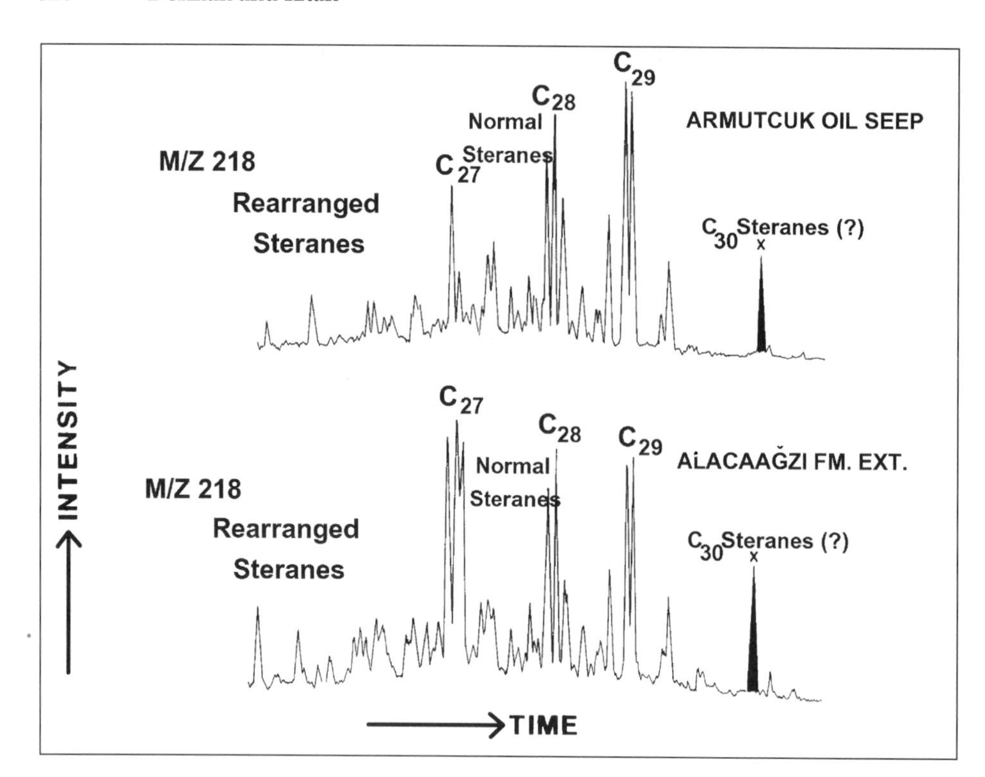

Figure 14. The comparison between M/Z 218 sterane fragmentograms of the extract of Alacaağzı Formation and Armutçuk oil seep.

possibly high (Derman, 1995b). The Tasmaca Formation, which was deposited in a relatively stable area, shows low scatter in data. The Yemişliçay Formation shows higher maturity values than the Tasmaca Formation, which can be attributed again to the volcanic activity in the region.

In the Eastern Pontides, there are no geochemical measurements from Paleozoic rocks. Measurements were made from Liassic sediments. Maturity values of Liassic units are variable in the region. In some areas, Liassic sediments have high maturity (SCI = 9.0); in Pukeyi Dağı section, maturity values are low (SCI = 4.5–6.0). Overlying units have a normal maturity gradient.

A jump in the maturity level between the Himmetpaşa Formation and the Ülüs Formation suggests that the Paleozoic sequence matured between the Middle Jurassic and the Cretaceous. The present thickness of Jurassic and Cretaceous sediments is not enough to bury Paleozoic rocks to reach their present maturity level. Besides, the decrease in the maturity level of the Paleozoic rocks from south to north suggests that some other causes may be present (e.g., granitic intrusions).

SUMMARY AND CONCLUSION

Occurrence of hydrocarbons has been indicated by oil and gas shows in the region. Geochemical studies also indicate that source rocks for oil and gas are present in the area, and that they are mature enough to generate hydrocarbons. The most important source rocks are the Alacaağzı and Tasmaca formations in the Western Pontides. Although the Tasmaca Formation is not mature in the onshore areas, it may be mature enough to generate hydrocarbon in the offshore area in the Western Pontides. The Çağlayan Formation is, however, the only source rock candidate among the formations sampled in the Central and Eastern Pontides. Although the Yemişliçay Formation is generally not considered to be a source rock in the region, the Filyos-1 well encountered a thick interval of the Yemişliçay Formation, suggesting that the unit may have good source rock quality locally.

Geochemical analyses of the five oil seeps from different localities in the Black Sea region indicate that they may have been derived from different units that have different lithologies, ages, and maturity levels. Fragmentograms of the Armutçuk oil and the Alacaağzı Formation, however, have similar signatures, suggesting that Armutçuk oil was derived from the Alacaağzı Formation.

There are many potential source rocks that show normal maturity gradients up to the Middle Jurassic. Surface samples of Paleozoic rocks have high R_o, suggesting that a thick sedimentary cover must have been removed from the area in order for Paleozoic rocks to reach their present maturity level, or there must have been some other cause for the maturity (e.g., intrusions). In Early Cretaceous sediments, however, maturity data are quite scattered, due to rifting and magmatic and volcanic activity during the Late Cretaceous.

Inconsistencies in the maturity levels of the organic matter, especially in Cretaceous sediments, suggest that there must have been causes for maturity other than burial. For instance, intrusions have complicated the geology of the Eastern Pontides, and may have an important impact on the maturation of the organic matter.

ACKNOWLEDGMENTS

The authors thank the management of Turkish Petroleum Corporation (TPAO) for permission to publish this paper.

REFERENCES CITED

Akdeniz, N., E. Timur, F. Akçören, and A. Elmas, 1992, Tectono-stratigraphic units of the southwestern part of Eastern Pontides (abs.): General Directorate of Mineral Research and Exploration and Chamber of Geological Engineers, International Symposium on the Geology of the Black Sea Region, Ankara, Turkey, September 7–11, 1992, p. 36.

Akyol, Z., E. Arpat, B. Erdoğan, E. Göger, Y. Güner, F. Saroğlu, I. Sentürk, K. Tütüncü, and P. ve Uysal, 1974, 1/50.000 ölçekli Türkiye Jeoloji Haritasy Serisi, Zonguldak E29 a, E29 b, E29 c, E29 d, Kastamonu E30 a, E30 d.: Maden Tetkik ve Arama Enstitüsü Yayinlari, Ankara, 2 sheets.

Alisan, C., and A.S. Derman, 1992, The first palinological age, sedimentological and stratigraphic data for Çakraz Group (Permo–Triassic), Western Black Sea (abs.): General Directorate of Mineral Research and Exploration and Chamber of Geological Engineers, International Symposium on the Geology of the Black Sea Region, Ankara, Turkey, September 7–11, 1992, p. 93–98.

Altınlı, I.E., N. Soytürk, and K. Saka, 1970, Geology of the Hereke-Tavsancil-Tavsanli-Tepecik area: Istanbul Üniversitesi Fen Fakültesi Mecmuasi, Seri B, Cilt XXXV, Sayi 1-2, Sayfa 69–75, with plates.

Aquino Neto, F.R., J.M. Trendel, A. Restle, P. Albrecht, and J. Connan, 1981, Occurrence and formation of tricyclic and tetracyclic terpanes in sediments and petroleum, *in* M. Bjory, P. Albrecht, C. Conford, K. de Grast, G. Erlington, E. Galinov, D. Leythueuser, R. Pelet, J. Rüllkotter, and G. Socers, eds., Advances in organic geochemistry: Chichester, J. Wiley and Sons, p. 659–667.

Aquino Neto, F.R., A. Restle, J. Connan, P. Albrecht, and G. Ourisson, 1982, Novel tricyclic terpanes (C_{19}–C_{20}) in sediments and petroleums: Tetrahedron Letters, v. 23, p. 2027–2030.

Arni, P., 1936, Azdavay ve Karafasil Taskömür mintikasi hakkynda rapor: Geologischer Bericht ber das Gebeit Azdavay 5.15 s. 2 Kesit 27 cm. Unpublished MTA Report no. 27.

Arpat, E., K. Tütüncü, S. Uysal, and E. ve Göğer, 1978, Safranbolu yöresinde Kambrian–Devonian istifi, Türkiye Jeoloji Kurumu 32: Bilimsel ve Teknik Kurultayi Bildiri özetleri, Ankara.

Aydın, M., Ö. Şahintürk, and Y.ve Özçelik, 1984, Araç-Daday-Karadere ve dolayinin jeolojisi ve petrol olanaklary: TPAO Unpublished Rapor. 1948.

Aydın, M., Ö. Şahintürk, H.S. Serdar, and Y. ve Özçelik, 1986, Ballıdağ-Çangaldağ (Kastamonu) arasindaki bölgenin Jeolojisi: TJK Bülteni, C. 29, s. 1–16.

Bray, E.E., and E.D. Evans, 1961, Distribution of *n*-paraffins as a clue to recognition of source beds: Geochimica et Cosmochimica Acta, v. 22, p. 2–5.

Cassini, F., O. Gallango, S. Talukdar, C. Vallejosi, and U. Ehrmann, 1987, Methylphenantrene maturity index of marine source rock extracts and crude oils from the Maracaibo Basin, *in* L. Matavelli and L. Novelli, eds., Advances in Organic Geochemistry: Oxford, Pergamon Press, p. 73–80.

Derman, A.S., 1985, Bati Karadeniz Bölgesi'ndeki Karbonifer istifinin gelisimi: Petrol isleri Genel Müdürlüğü Bülteni no. 29, Ankara.

Derman, A.S., 1990, Bati Karadeniz Bölgesinin Geç Jura-Erken Kretasedeki Jeolojik evrimi: Türkiye 8 Petrol Kongresi Bildiriler Kitaby, Ankara, p. 328–339.

Derman, A.S., 1995a, Megabreccias and other mass flow deposits in the Ülüs Basin: Ph.D. thesis, Middle East Technical University, Ankara, Turkey, 229 p.

Derman, A.S., 1995b, Poster, Evolution of the Western Black Sea, Türkiye: AAPG Convention, Nice, France September 10–13.

Derman, A.S., Y. Özçelik, S. Kirici, N.Y. Bragin, and F. Kuru, 1996, Bati Karadenizin Geç Jura Paleocoğrafyasi: Proceeding of Geology, Türkiye 11 Petrol Kongresi ve Sergisi, Ankara, p. 75–80.

Derman, A.S., A. Kilinç, Y. Özçelik, and R. ve Çokuğras, 1985, Bati Karadeniz Bölgesi Üst Paleozoik ve Üst Jura-Alt Kretase birimlerinin ortam yorumu ön çalysmasi, TPAO Unpublished Rapor. 2073.

Derman, A.S., and Y. Özçelik, 1991, Bati Karadeniz Bblgesindeki Paleozoik birimler ve muhtemel evrimi: Suat ERK Simpozyumu, Ankara.

Derman, A.S., and A. Sayılı, 1992, İnaltı Formation: a key unit for regional geology: General Directorate of Mineral Research and Exploration and Chamber of Geological Engineers, International Symposium on the Geology of the Black Sea Region, Ankara, Turkey, September 7–11, 1992, p. 104–108.

Derman, A.S., C. Alisan, and Y. Özçelik, 1992, Himmetpaşa Formation: new palinological age data and significance: General Directorate of Mineral Research and Exploration and Chamber of Geological Engineers, International Symposium on the Geology of the Black Sea Region, Ankara, Turkey, p. 99–103.

Ebukanson, E.J., and R.R.F. Kinghorn, 1985, Kerogen facies in the major Jurassic mudrock formations of southern England and the implication on the depositional environments of their precursors: Journal of Petroleum Geology, v. 48, no. 4, p. 435–462.

Egeman, R., 1945, Amasra taskömürü hakkinda jeolojik rapor/Rapport geologique sur la Carbonifere d'Amasra, 34.4 s. 4 harita, 4 kesit, 27 cm: Unpublished MTA Report no. 1636.

Fan Pu, J.D., and G.E. Claypool, 1987, Characteristics of biomarker compounds in Chinese crude oils, *in* R.K. Kumar, P. Dwiv'edi, V. Banorjie, and V. Gupta, eds., Petroleum geochemistry and exploration in the Afro-Asian Region: Balkema, Rotterdam, p. 197–202.

Fan Pu, J.D., and Z. Baisheng, 1987, Biomarker characteristics of nonmarine oils in China, *in* L. Matavelli and L. Novelli, eds., Advances in organic Geochemistry, 1987: Oxford, Pergamon Press, p. 627–632.

Fratschner, W.Th., 1956, Azdavay-Maksut-Dognuç-Kozcaviran ve Suğlayaylasi-Karafasil civarynda taskömür tasyian jeolojik strüktürlerde yapylan incelemelere dair nihai rapor 40.38 s. 1 cetvel, 8 kesit, 6 harita, 27 cm: Unpublished MTA Report no. 2407, Ankara.

Görür, N., 1988, Timing of opening of the Black Sea Basin: Tectonophysics, v. 47, p. 247–262.

Görür, N., and O, Tüysüz, this volume, Petroleum geology of the southern continental margin of the Black Sea, *in* A.G. Robinson, ed., Regional and petroleum geology of the Black Sea and surrounding region: AAPG Memoir 68, p. 241–254.

Görür, N., O. Tüysüz, A. Akyol, M. Sakinç, E. Yiğitbas, and R. Akkök, 1993, Cretaceous red pelagic carbonates of northern Turkey: their place in the opening of the Black Sea: Eclogea Geologicae Helveticae, v. 86/3, p. 819–838.

Graning, B., 1936, Azdavay ile Karafasil havzalari kömür arastirmalari: 2.6 s. 27 cm: Unpublished MTA Rapor 1130.

Güven, A., 1980, Karabük Formasyonunun Fasiyes Analizi: 50 Milyon Yil Önceki Bir Akarsu-Delta Kompleksinin izleri (Facies Analysis of the Karabük Formation: traces of a fluvio-deltaic complex of 50 million years ago): Türkiye Besinci Petrol Kongresi (Jeolojik-Jeofizik Bildirileri) Proceedings, Ankara, p. 95–110.

Harput, O.B., M. Aydın, O. Demir, Y. Özçelik, and A. Çaptuğ, 1993, Karadeniz bölgesi kaynak kaya ve olgunlasma değerlendirmesi: TPAO Research Center Report 3201, 336 p.

Huang, W.Y., and W.G. Meinshein, 1979, Sterols as ecological indicator: Geochimica et Cosmochimica Acta, v. 43, p. 739.

Hughes, W.B., 1984, Use of thiophenic organosulfur compounds in characterizing crude oils derived from carbonate versus siliciclastic sources, *in* J.G. Palacas, ed., Petroleum geochemistry and source rock potential of carbonate rocks: AAPG Studies in Geology, no. 18, p. 181–196.

Hughes, W.B., and A.G. Hoiba, 1987, Relationship between crude oils quality and biomarker patterns, *in* L. Matavelli and L. Novelli, eds., Advances in Organic Geochemistry: Oxford, Pergamon Press, p. 15–30.

Kaya, O., 1982, Ereğli, Yiğilca, Bolukuzeyi, Mengenalanlarinin Stratigrafisi ve Yapi Özellikleri: TPAO Report 1639, 62 p.

Kerey, E., 1982, Stratigraphical and sedimentological studies of Upper Carboniferous rocks in northwestern Turkey: Ph. D. thesis, Keele University, England, 232 p.

Ketin, I., and O. ve Gümüs, 1963, Sinop-Ayancik güneyinde üçüncü bölgeye dahil sahalarin jeolojisi hakkinda rapor, II. kisim Jura ve Kretase formasyonlarinin etüdü: Unpublished TPAO Rapor 288.

Ketin, I., 1965, Bartin bölgesindeki Paleozoyik ve buna bağli tesekküllerin jeolojik etüdü hakkinda rapor: Unpublished TPAO Report.

Konak, N., Y. Hakyemez, Z.R. Bilgin, T. Bilgiç, T. Ercan, Z. Öztürk, N. Hepsen, H. Mengi, and M. Bulut, 1992, Tectono-stratigraphic units of mesozoic age between Erzurum and Artvin (Eastern Pontides) (abs.): General Directorate of Mineral Research and Exploration and Chamber of Geological Engineers, International Symposium on the Geology of the Black Sea Region, Ankara, Turkey, September 7–11, p. 57.

Korkmaz, S., M. Er, A. Van, A. Musaoğlu, I. Keskin, and N. Tüysüz, 1992, Stratigraphy of the Eastern Pontides, NE Turkey (abs.): General Directorate of Mineral Research and Exploration and Chamber of Geological Engineers, International Symposium on the Geology of the Black Sea Region, Ankara, Turkey, September 7–11, p. 62.

Lucius, M., 1935, Amasra kömür havzasi hakkinda rapor/Rapport sur la bassin Houiller d'Amasra, 30, 29 s. 27 cm: Unpublished MTA Rapor 13.

Mackenzie, A.S., R.L. Patience, J.B. Maxwell, M. Wandenbrucke, and B. Durand, 1980, Molecular parameters of maturation in the Toarcian shales, Paris Basin, France. Changes in configuration of acyclic isoprenoid alkanes, steranes and triterpanes: Geochimica et Cosmochimica Acta, v. 44, p. 1709–1721.

McKirdy, D.M., A.K. Aldridge, and P.J.M. Ipma, 1981, A geochemical comparison of some crude oils from Pre-Ordovician carbonate rocks, *in* M. Bjory, P. Albrecht, C. Conford, K. de Grast, G. Erlington, E. Galinov, D. Leythueuser, R. Pelet, J. Rüllkotter, and G. Socers, eds., Advances in organic geochemistry: Chichester, John Wiley and Sons, p. 99–107.

McKirdy, D.M., A.S. Kantsler, J.K. Emmitt, and A.K. Aldridge, 1984, Hydrocarbon genesis and organic facies in Cambrian carbonates of the Eastern Officer Basin, South Australia: Tulsa, Oklahoma, AAPG Studies in Geology, no. 18, p. 13–32.

Norman, T.N., and M.E. Atabey, 1992, Sea floor gas escape features around Inceburun Peninsula, Northern Turkey (abs.): General Directorate of Mineral Research and Exploration and Chamber of Geological Engineers, International Symposium on the Geology of the Black Sea Region, Ankara, Turkey, September 7–11, p. 83.

Özdemir, Ü., 1971, Kocacli Yarimadasi, Tepekli Triyasi makrofaunasi ve Biyostratigrafisi: MTA Mecmuasi, Sayi. 77, Sayfa, p. 57–98.

Özdemir, Ü., 1975, Kocacli Triyasinin tipik belemnitleri hakkinda: MTA Dergisi, sayy 85, p. 149–160.

Özer, S., 1986, Bati Karadeniz Alt Kretase Rudist Faunasi ve Paleoekolojisi: TPAO Unpublished Report 1964, Ankara.

Palacas, J.G., E. Donald, and J. D. King, 1984, South Florida Basin—a prime example of carbonate source rocks of petroleum, *in* J.G. Palacas, ed.: Studies in Geology, no. 18, p. 71–96.

Palmer, S.E., 1981, Organic facies of the lacustrine Elko Formation (Eocene/Oligocene), northeastern Nevada (abs.): GSA Abstracts with Programs, v. 13, p. 525.

Patijn, R., 1953, The geology of the Zonguldak-Kozlu area of the North Anatolian coal field: Maden, Turkish Mining Engineer's Association Journal, p. 1–20.

Philp, R.P., and T.D. Gilbert, 1985, Biomarker distributions in Australian oils predominantly derived from terrigenous source material, *in* D. Leythaeuser and J. Rüllkotter, eds., Advances in organic geochemistry, 1985: Oxford, Pergamon Press, p. 73–84.

Pym, J.G., J.E. Ray, G.W. Simith, and E.V. Whitehead, 1975, Petroleum triterpane fingerprinting of crude oils: Analytical Chemistry, v. 47, no. 9, p. 1617–1622.

Radke, M., and D.H. Welte, 1983, The Methylphenantrene Index (MPI): a maturity parameter based on aromatic hydrocarbons, *in* M. Bjory, P. Albrecht, C. Conford, K. de Grast, G. Erlington, E. Galinov, D. Leythueuser, R. Pelet, J. Rüllkotter, and G. Socers, eds., Advances in organic geochemistry, 1981: Chichester, John Wiley and Sons, p. 504–512.

Ralli, G., 1933, Zonguldak-Ereğli havzasy kömür durumu/Franszca, Maden Dairesi: Tercüme Fatin, 7.9 s: Unpublished MTA Report no. 12.

Reed, W.E., 1977, Molecular composition of weathered petroleum and comparison with its possible source: Geochimica et Cosmochimica Acta, v. 41, p. 237–247.

Robinson, N., G. Eglinton, C. Brassell, A.P. Gowar, and J. Powell, 1985, Hydrocarbon compositions of bitumens associated with igneous intrusions and hydrothermal deposites in Britain, *in* D. Leythveser and J. Rüllkotter, eds., Advances in organic geochemistry, 1985: Oxford, Pergamon Press, p. 145–152.

Robinson, A.G., J.H. Rudat, C.J. Banks, and R.L.F. Wiles, 1996, Petroleum geology of the Black Sea: Marine and Petroleum Geology, v. 13, no. 2, p. 195–223.

Rubinstein, I., O. Sieskind, and P. Albrecht, 1975, Rearranged steranes in a shale: occurrence and simulated formation: Journal of the Chemical Society, Parkin Transaction 7, p. 1833–1836.

Rüllkotter, J., and D. Wendisch, 1982, Microbial alteration of 17(H) hopanes in Madagaskar asphalts: removal of C-10 methyl group and ring opening: Geochimica et Cosmochimica Acta, v. 46, p. 1545–1553.

Sahintürk, Ö., and Y. Özçelik, 1983, Zonguldak-Bartin-Amasra-Kurucasile-Cide dolaylarinin jeolojisi ve petrol olanaklari: Unpublished TPAO Report, Ankara.

Saner, S., I. Taner, Z. Aksoy, M. Siyako, and K.A. Bürkan, 1979, Karabük-Safranbolu bölgesinin Jeolojisi: Unpublished TPAO Rapor, Ankara.

Saner, S., M. Siyako, Z. Aksoy, K.A. Bürkan, and O. Demir, 1980, Zonguldak dolayinin jeolojisi ve petrol olanaklari: Unpublished TPAO Report, Ankara.

Sayılı, A., A.S. Derman, and S. Kirici, 1992, Sedimentology and diagenesis of Upper Jurassic İnaltı Formation in the Western Black Sea region: Proceedings "Geology" of the 9th Petroleum Congress and Exhibition of Türkiye, Ankara, p. 151–160.

Seifert, W.K., and J.M. Moldowan, 1978, Application of steranes, terpanes and monoaromatics to the maturation, migration, and source of crude oil: Geochimica et Cosmochimica Acta, v. 42, p. 77–95.

Seifert, W.K., and J.M. Moldowan, 1979, The effect of biodegradation and steranes and terpanes in crude oils: Geochimica et Cosmochimica Acta, v. 43, p. 11–26.

Seifert, W.K., and J.M. Moldowan, 1983, Use of biological markers in petroleum exploration, *in* Organic geochemistry of contemporaneous and ancient sediments: SEPM Great Lake Section Short Course Notes, p. 3-1–3-31.

Şengör, A.M.C., 1984, Türkiyenin tektonik tarihinin yapisal siniflamasi: T.J.K, Ketin simpozyumu, p. 37–62.

Şengör, A.M.C., and Y. Yılmaz, 1981, Tethyan evolution of Turkey: a plate tectonic approach: Tectonophysics, v. 75, p. 181–241.

Şengör, A.M.C., Y. Yılmaz, and O. Sungurlu, 1984, Tectonics of the Mediterranean Cimmerids, *in* J.E. Dixon and A.H.F. Robertson, eds., The geological evolution of the Eastern Mediterranean: Oxford, Blackwell, published for the Geological Society of London, p. 77–112.

Serdar, H.S., and O. Demir, 1983, Bolu, Mengen, Devrek dolayynyn Jeolojisi ve Petrol Olanaklary: Unpublished TPAO Report, Ankara.

Sieskind, O., Gb. Joly, and P. Albrecht, 1979, Simulation of the geochemical transformations: Geochimica et Cosmochimica Acta, v. 43, no. 10, p. 1675–1680.

Simoneit, B.R., 1977, Diterpenoid compound and other lipids in deep-sea sediments and their geochemical significance: Geochimica et Cosmochimica Acta, v. 41, p. 463–476.

Sofer, Z., J.E. Zumberge, and W. Lay, 1985, Stable carbon isotopes and biomarkers as tools for understanding genetic relationship, maturation, biodegradation and migration of crude oils in the northern Peruvian Oriente (Maranon) Basin, *in* D. Leythueuser and J. Rüllkotter, eds., Advances in organic geochemistry, 1985: Oxford, Pergamon Press, p. 377–389.

Spratt, T., 1877, Remarks on the coal bearing deposits near Erekli (the ancient Heraclea, Pontica, Brithynia): Quarterly Journal of Geological Society of London, v. 33, p. 524–533.

Taluktar, S., O. Gallango, A. Chin, and M. Lien, 1985, Generation and migration of hydrocarbons in the Maracaibo Basin, Venezuela: an integrated basin study, *in* D. Leythueuser and J. Rüllkotter, eds., Advances in organic geochemistry, 1985: Oxford, Pergamon Press, p. 261–279.

ten Haven, H.L., J.W. Dee Leeuw, J.S. Sinninghe Damste, P.A. Schenck, S.E. Palmer, and J.E. Zumberge, 1988, Application of biological markers in the recognition of paleo-hypersaline environments, *in* A.J. Fleet, K. Kelts, and M.R. Talbot, eds., Lacustrine petroleum source rocks: Oxford, Blackwell, Geological Society of London Special Publication 40, p. 123–130.

Tissot, B.P., G. Demaison, P. Mosson, J. R. Delteil, and A. Combaz, 1980, Paleoenvironment and petroleum potential of Middle Cretaceous black shales in Atlantic basins: AAPG Bulletin, v. 64, no. 11, p. 2051–2063.

Tissot, B.P., and D.H. Welte, 1984, Petroleum formation and occurrence: New York, Springer-Verlag, 699 p.

Wedding, H., 1967, Amasra-Cide-Ülüs bölgesindeki Karbon gaz etütleri, 1. Mevren ve Aritdere/Karbon gaz studien im raume Amasra-Cide-Ülüs. 1. Mevren und Aritdere, l c, 2h. 27 cm: Unpublished MTA Report 4004.

Wedding, H., 1969, Amasra-Cide-Ülüs bölgesinde Karbon gaz etüdleri, ümit verici sahanin bati kenari/Karbon gaz studien im Raume Amasra-Cide-Ülüs Der Westrand des Hoffnunges gebeites,

36.48 s. 1 harita, 1 kesit, 27 cm: Unpublished MTA Report 4280.

Yazman, K.M., and A.R. Çokuğras, 1983, Adapazary-Kandira-Düzce-Akçakoca yerlesim merkezleriyle synirli alanin Jeolojisi ve Hidrokarbon olanaklari: Unpublished TPAO Report 1747.

Zijlstra, G., 1952, Azdavay karbonifer tesekkülleri hakkinda rapor/Report on the Azdavay Carboniferous inlier, 25.19 s., 10 harita, 7 kesit, 27 cm: Unpublished MTA Report 2033.

Zumberge, J.E., 1984, Source rock of the La Luna Formation (U. Cretaceous) in the Middle Magdelena Valley, Colombia: Studies in Geology, no. 18, p. 127–134.

Zumberge, J.E., 1987, Prediction of source rock characteristics based on terpane biomarkers in crude oils: A multivariate statistical approach: Geochimica et Cosmochimica Acta, v. 51 , no. 6, p. 1625–1637.

Banks, C.J., A.G. Robinson, and M.P. Williams, 1997, Structure and regional tectonics of the Achara-Trialet fold belt and the adjacent Rioni and Kartli foreland basins, Republic of Georgia, *in* A.G. Robinson, ed., Regional and petroleum geology of the Black Sea and surrounding region: AAPG Memoir 68, p. 331–346.

Chapter 17

Structure and Regional Tectonics of the Achara-Trialet Fold Belt and the Adjacent Rioni and Kartli Foreland Basins, Republic of Georgia

Chris J. Banks
Royal Holloway University of London
Egham, Surrey, United Kingdom

Andrew G. Robinson
JKX Oil & Gas plc
Guildford, Surrey, United Kingdom

Math P. Williams
Robertson Research International Ltd.
Llanrhos, Llandudno, Gwynedd, United Kingdom

ABSTRACT

This chapter describes the geology of Georgia and the Georgian part of the Black Sea. It is based on geological maps and seismic interpretation, integrated with well data and outcrop studies. The geology of Georgia consists of two major thrust belts: the Greater Caucasus and the Achara-Trialet belt, separated by two foreland basins (Rioni and Kartli) with an intervening basement culmination, the Dziruli Massif. The Achara-Trialet belt comprises a thick Upper Cretaceous and Paleogene sequence that restores to a rift and postrift basin of probable Paleocene age, connecting to the Eastern Black Sea. The basin began to close by the Oligocene. Structures are detached at Aptian and Oligocene levels and are large and open. The Rioni Basin developed mainly during the Oligocene and the Miocene through loading by the Achara-Trialet belt folds. It dies out into the Eastern Black Sea as the foreland basin megasequence merges with the postrift fill of the latter. North of the Rioni Basin, the major thrust front is a large south-dipping monocline, in front of which there are extensive salients detached in Upper Jurassic evaporites. The Kartli Basin passes into the Kura Basin to the east, where the foreland basin is deformed by the Greater Caucasus south-vergent thrust structures.

INTRODUCTION

The Republic of Georgia (Sakhartvelo) lies at the far eastern end of the Black Sea (Figure 1). Its geology is dominated by two fold and thrust belts separated by a chain of Neogene foreland basins. The more northerly of these fold and thrust belts is the Greater Caucasus Mountains, which trend east-southeast and run from the Ukraine-Russia border at the Kerch straits as far as the Caspian coast in Dagestan and Azerbaijan. The Greater Caucasus do *not* extend into the Crimean Mountains, where the stratigraphy and structural style are quite different (Robinson and Kerusov, this volume). In eastern Georgia, the south-vergent frontal thrust structures of the Greater Caucasus converge with the north-vergent frontal structures of the Achara-Trialet belt. Between the two converging mountain ranges are two small low-land areas, the Rioni Basin in the west and the Kartli Basin in central Georgia. These are single, or double-sided flexural basins of Neogene age, separated by the Dziruli Massif, where the basement is exposed. The Kartli Basin is effectively the western end of the Kura Basin of Azerbaijan.

The Achara-Trialet belt is a mainly north-vergent fold belt trending east-west through southern Georgia. Other authors (e.g., Adamia et al., 1992) refer to the same area as the Transcaucasus, but this term is better dropped in this context because it can refer to a geographical area that includes a range of geological entities. To the west, the Achara-Trialet belt bends sharply to the southwest to link with the on- and offshore structures of the Eastern Pontides of Turkey (Robinson et al., 1995a; Okay and Şahinturk, this volume). To the east, it passes between the Armenian/Khrami and Dziruli massifs, outcrops of metamorphic and igneous rock, and becomes overridden by the frontal folds of the Caucasus.

The foreland basins and the frontal zones of both thrust belts contain oil and have attracted petroleum exploration activity (Robinson et al., this volume). There is thus fair coverage of reflection seismic lines in both western and central Georgia, which extends not only over the foreland basins but also over the frontal folds of the adjacent thrust belts. Seismic data quality deteriorates sharply in the thrust belts. There are also many oil exploration wells, including three deep stratigraphic tests in the center of the Kartli Basin. There is regional geological map coverage at 1:200,000 scale (which is published but sometimes problematic to obtain), and local mapping at scales up to 1:25,000 (Georgian Oil, unpublished data).

Previous published work on Georgian geology has dealt mostly with large-scale tectonics, involving attempts to create a plate-tectonic interpretation for the region (Khain, 1975; Adamia et al., 1981; Gamkrelidze, 1986, 1991; Kazmin, 1991), or has been focused on the structure of the Caucasus (Isayev et al., 1981; Tsagareli, 1984; Philip et al., 1989; Zonenshain et al., 1990). This chapter describes the results of a study of the structure of the fold and thrust belts and foreland basins, with particular emphasis on the Achara-Trialet belt. This belt is significant for understanding regional tectonics because of its relationship with the Eastern Black Sea and the Pontides in Turkey and the Kura Basin to the east.

Our results are based on our own interpretation of more than 2000 km of reflection seismic data tied to wells and outcrops, including some offshore lines; on geological map interpretation; and on field studies performed during 1995. We illustrate the structure of the thrust belts and foreland basins principally by regional cross sections and interpreted seismic lines, located on Figures 1 and 5. In the fold and thrust belts, the sections were constructed using geological maps on the most detailed available scale, together with field studies. The ages of samples collected were checked by biostratigraphic methods. In the foreland basins, the sections are based on seismic interpretations and well data. We begin the chapter with a summary of the geology of the Eastern Black Sea because of its importance for understanding the regional geology. We end with some speculations about the relationship between the Achara-Trialet belt and the Black and South Caspian seas.

EASTERN BLACK SEA REGIONAL STRUCTURE

A useful way of approaching the onshore geology of Georgia is from the regional structure of the Eastern Black Sea, where there are regional marine reflection seismic lines of fair quality, particularly in the Turkish and Russian sectors (Robinson et al., 1995a, 1996), and to lesser extent offshore Georgia (Gorshkov, 1983). Mapping of these lines shows the presence of a large rigid block gently tilted to the north, between the Caucasus front and the deep Eastern Black Sea Basin, characterized by approximately parallel seismic reflectors. This is called the Shatsky Ridge and is interpreted as the northern rift margin of the extensional Eastern Black Sea (Figure 1) (Robinson et al., 1996, their plate 10). Finetti et al. (1988) suggested a compressional origin for the Shatsky Ridge. The southern margin of the Shatsky Ridge trends ESE from offshore Crimea, runs approximately parallel to the Russian coast, and crosses the Georgian coast near Poti. It comprises a belt, ~20 km wide, of major normal faults downthrowing to the southwest, their overall listric shape resulting in small back-tilted terraces. To the south of this margin, the Eastern Black Sea Basin shows no evidence of the presence of the Shatsky Ridge basement and stratigraphy, and is likely to be oceanic or possibly highly extended continental crust. The deepest postrift seismic reflector in the Eastern Black Sea that can be plausibly tied to well data (top Eocene) is at a depth subsea of ≤9 km, with another 2–3 km of sediments below (Robinson et al., 1995b). The age of basin formation may be further constrained by the prerift stratigraphy within the Shatsky Ridge, which can be dated as young as Danian from onshore wells close to the Georgian coast (e.g., Ochamchira) (Figure 1). The basin appears therefore to be a Late Paleocene to Early Eocene rift

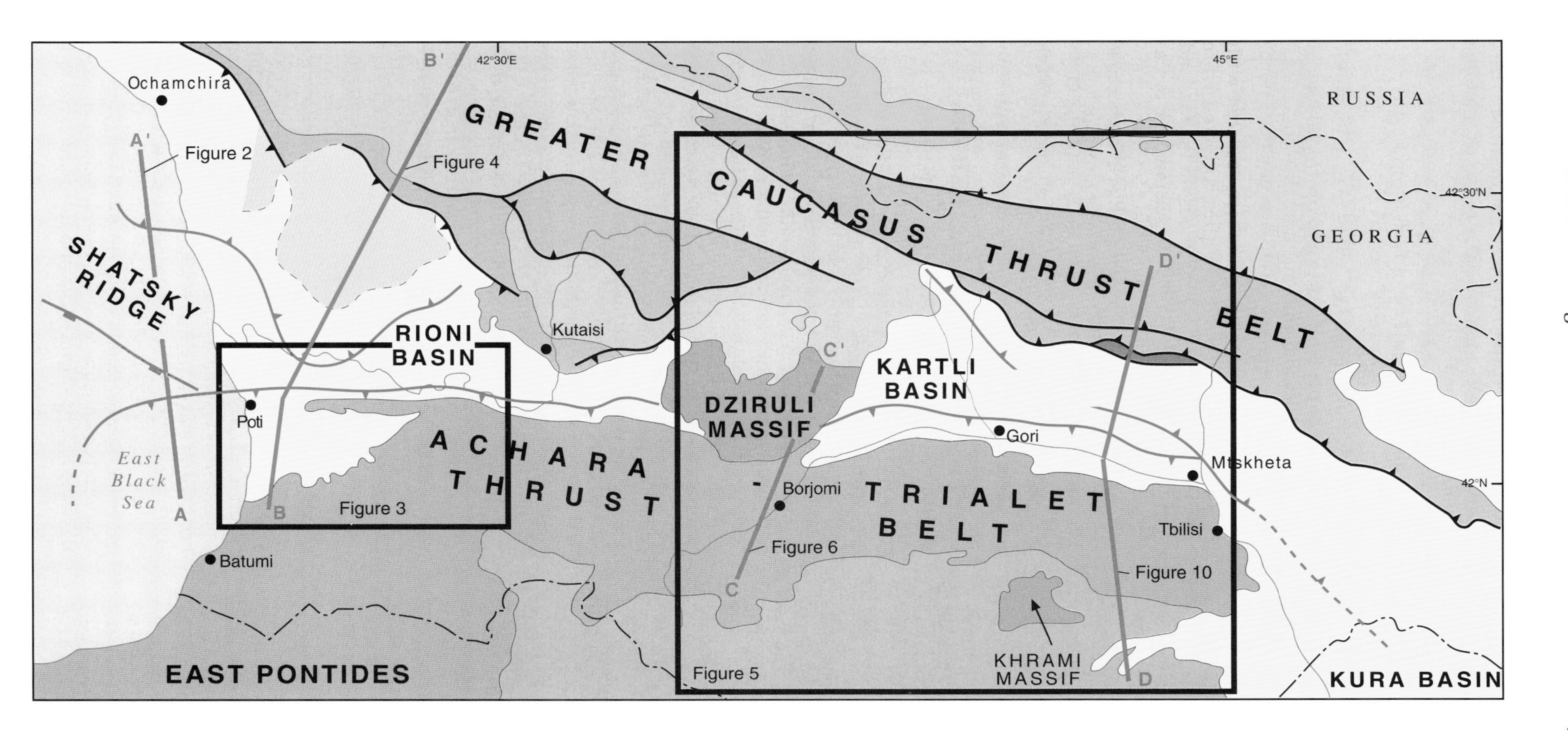

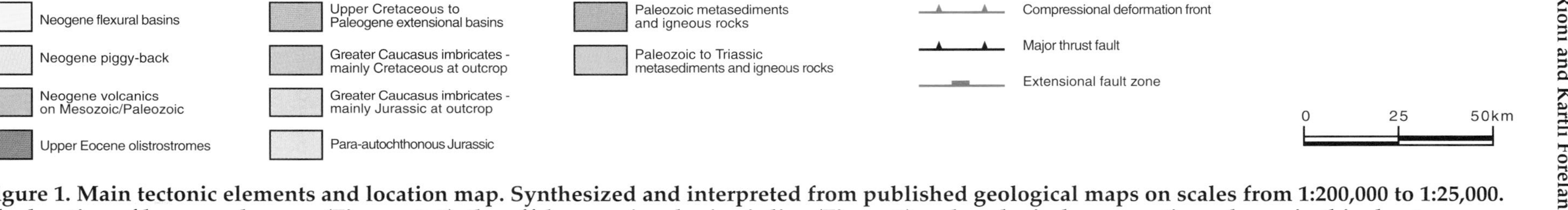

Figure 1. Main tectonic elements and location map. Synthesized and interpreted from published geological maps on scales from 1:200,000 to 1:25,000. The location of larger scale maps (Figures 3, 5), the offshore regional seismic line (Figure 2) and geological cross sections shown in this chapter (Figures 4, 6, and 10) are indicated. Sections CC′ and DD′ are located more precisely on Figure 5.

(unlike the Western Black Sea, which is mid-Cretaceous) (Görür, 1988, this volume).

The conjugate (SW) margin of the offshore part of the Eastern Black Sea is the Mid-Black Sea High, a complex ridge dominated by extensional roll-over of strata toward the basin, and north-south–trending cross-ridge faults (Robinson et al., 1996; Robinson, this volume). However, toward the southeast, the extensional southern margin of the Eastern Black Sea Basin is overridden by the Pontide thrust front a short distance north of the Turkish coast; its location farther east is not known (Robinson et al., 1995a).

We conclude, regarding the structure of Georgia, that the pre-Jurassic basement and its Jurassic–Cretaceous cover below most of the Rioni Basin (and probably also below the Kartli Basin and the Dziruli Massif) is an onshore continuation of the Shatsky Ridge.

WEST GEORGIA

Offshore: Achara-Trialet Belt–Rioni Basin–Shatsky Ridge

The structure beneath the Black Sea a few kilometers from the Georgian coast is illustrated by an interpreted regional seismic line that runs approximately north-south (Figure 2). In the south, the frontal compressional structures of the Achara-Trialet belt verge toward the north and override the Shatsky Ridge, which is flexed down to the south. The flexural depression created—the offshore extension of the Rioni Basin—is partly filled by Miocene to Quaternary sediments, which pass toward the west into the postrift fill of the Eastern Black Sea.

The more internal of the folds on the line show very little seismic character and, by analogy with onshore structures, are probably cored by deep marine Middle Eocene volcaniclastic sediments and volcanics (Figure 3). The more external (northerly) folds appear to be related to detachment faulting. Again by analogy with the onshore, they are likely to involve mainly upper Miocene to Pliocene sediments (the Pontian is clearly folded). The Rioni Basin includes a thick upper Miocene to Quaternary section that thickens southwards toward the Achara-Trialet fold belt, and onlaps the Mesozoic rocks of the Shatsky Ridge to the north. There are many unconformities within the sequence, related to the development of submarine canyons transferring sediment into the Black Sea. The Paleogene–middle Miocene is condensed to absent beneath the Rioni Basin, as it is generally above the Shatsky Ridge (Robinson et al., 1996). This may reflect both nondeposition and erosion during foreland basin development.

The Shatsky Ridge shows the characteristic thick sequence of approximately parallel reflectors, which can be tied to onshore wells (e.g., Ochamchira) and shown to be a basinal Jurassic to Danian sequence. The strong reflector that marks the top of the Danian–Cretaceous limestones appears to be faulted down to the south. This extensional faulting may be related both to Eastern Black Sea rifting (late Paleocene) and early flexure (Oligocene?–early Miocene). About 30 km from the northern end of the section, there is a small noncylindrical anticline involving the Mesozoic. These structures are quite common onshore and offshore and are described in more detail below.

Onshore: Achara-Trialet Belt–Rioni Basin–Greater Caucasus

Figure 3 is a summary geological map of the southwestern part of the Rioni Basin and the frontal folds of the Achara-Trialet belt. The structure of this area is illustrated by Figure 4, a geological cross section that extends from the Achara-Trialet belt through the Rioni Basin and as far as the axial part of the Greater Caucasus.

The area that we have studied in most detail is the northwest corner of the onshore Achara-Trialet belt, where the structural trend changes and the folds plunge into the sea (where the offshore seismic lines show that they continue without significant change). This area overlies the terraces on the south flank of the Shatsky Ridge that plunge below the frontal folds. Both footwalls and hangingwalls of the major thrusts are likely to comprise Eocene deep basinal sediments (as exposed a short distance to the south) and possibly oceanic crust. The frontal thrust at Supsa brings Sarmatian sediments to surface, over a thick pile of late Miocene to Recent sediments. Immediately south of Supsa, the Natanebi anticline is a tight pop-up structure with steep-dipping middle to upper Miocene sediments and north- and south-vergent thrusts. Oligocene to lower Miocene sediments (known locally as Maikop) outcrop repeatedly in the frontal fold belt and clearly represent a flat-prone unit, so the interpretation here shows surface structures as north-vergent and detaching in the Oligocene to lower Miocene formation. Below the frontal folds, there is a duplex with imbricates of thick Eocene volcanics and probably some Cretaceous volcanics. Erosion down to the middle Eocene volcanics during the Sarmatian is demonstrated by a major unconformity in the Choloki wells and by the presence of middle Eocene volcanic olistoliths within the Sarmatian on the south flank of the Natanebi anticline (Figure 3). All structures farther south are broader folds containing thick, mainly middle Eocene volcanics and volcanogenic sediments.

Along the remainder of the Achara-Trialet front to the east, Eocene volcanics and volcaniclastics predominate at outcrop. Upper Cretaceous limestones locally form the core to frontal antiforms, but no older rocks are exposed, suggesting a possible Cretaceous detachment.

The fill of the Rioni foreland basin is late Miocene to Quaternary in age, all units thickening southward toward the Achara-Trialet folds and onlapping the Shatsky Ridge (compare with Figure 2, offshore). Some 50 km south of the main Greater Caucasus deformation front, there is a highly arcuate salient of minor, distinctly noncylindrical anticlinal structures, similar to that shown in Figure 2. One of these—the Tsaishi anticline—has been studied in detail with several wells and a grid of seismic lines of good quality acquired in 1988. It is a simple ramp anticline with a thrust detaching at about the level of Upper Jurassic evaporites (which contain

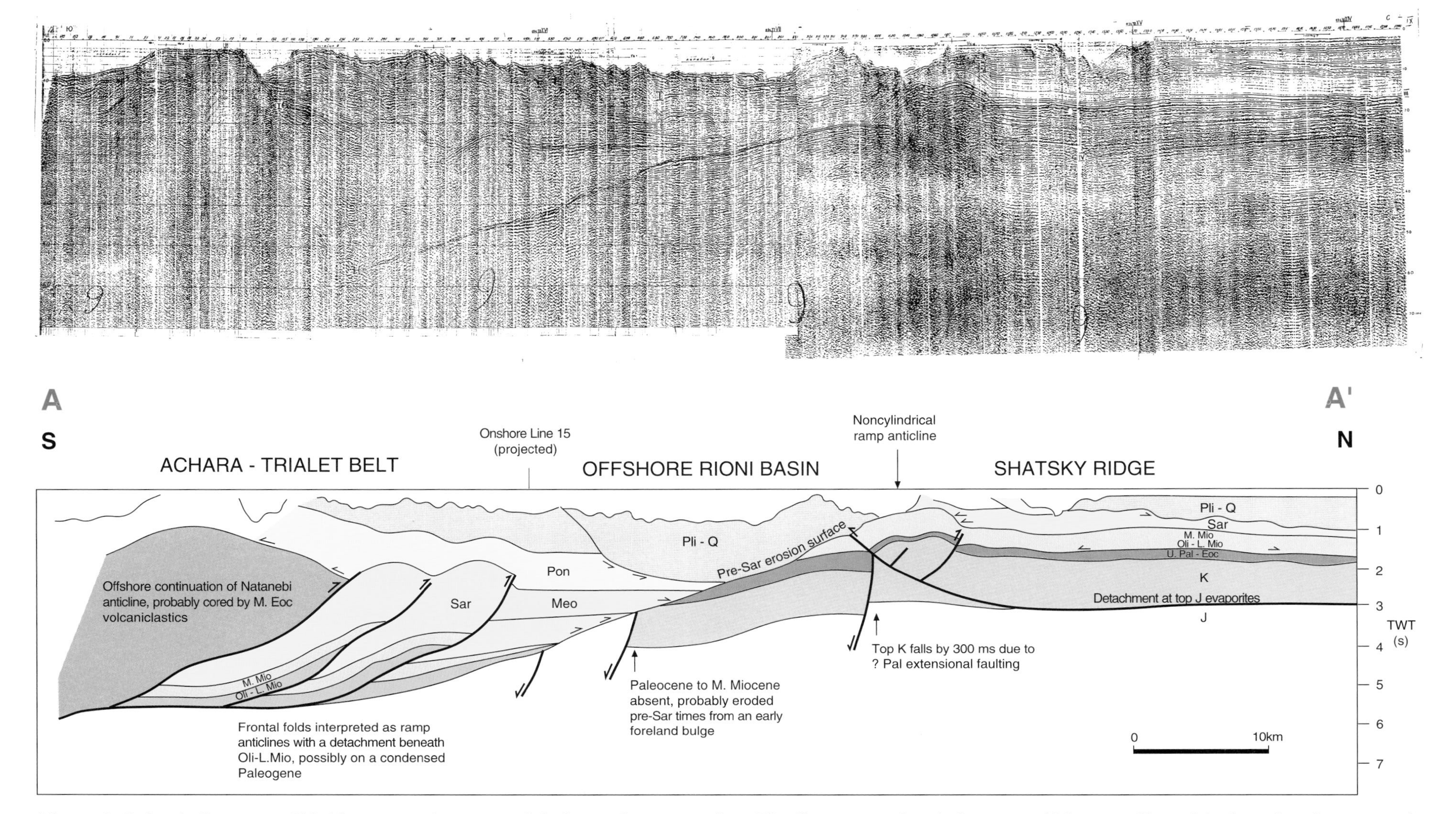

Figure 2. Seismic line 03477 IX. Above = uninterpreted; below = interpretation. The line cannot be tied to any offshore wells and is therefore interpreted using the following sources of data: A 10-km jump tie from onshore line 15, which ends at the coast and is tied to Lesa exploration well (projection of line 15 is indicated); a jump tie from the northern end of the line to the onshore Ochamchira-4 well, a distance of ~10 km; projection offshore of the onshore fold axes (Natanebi and Supsa anticlines) and exposed geology. Meo = Meotian; Sar = Sarmatian; Pon = Pontian.

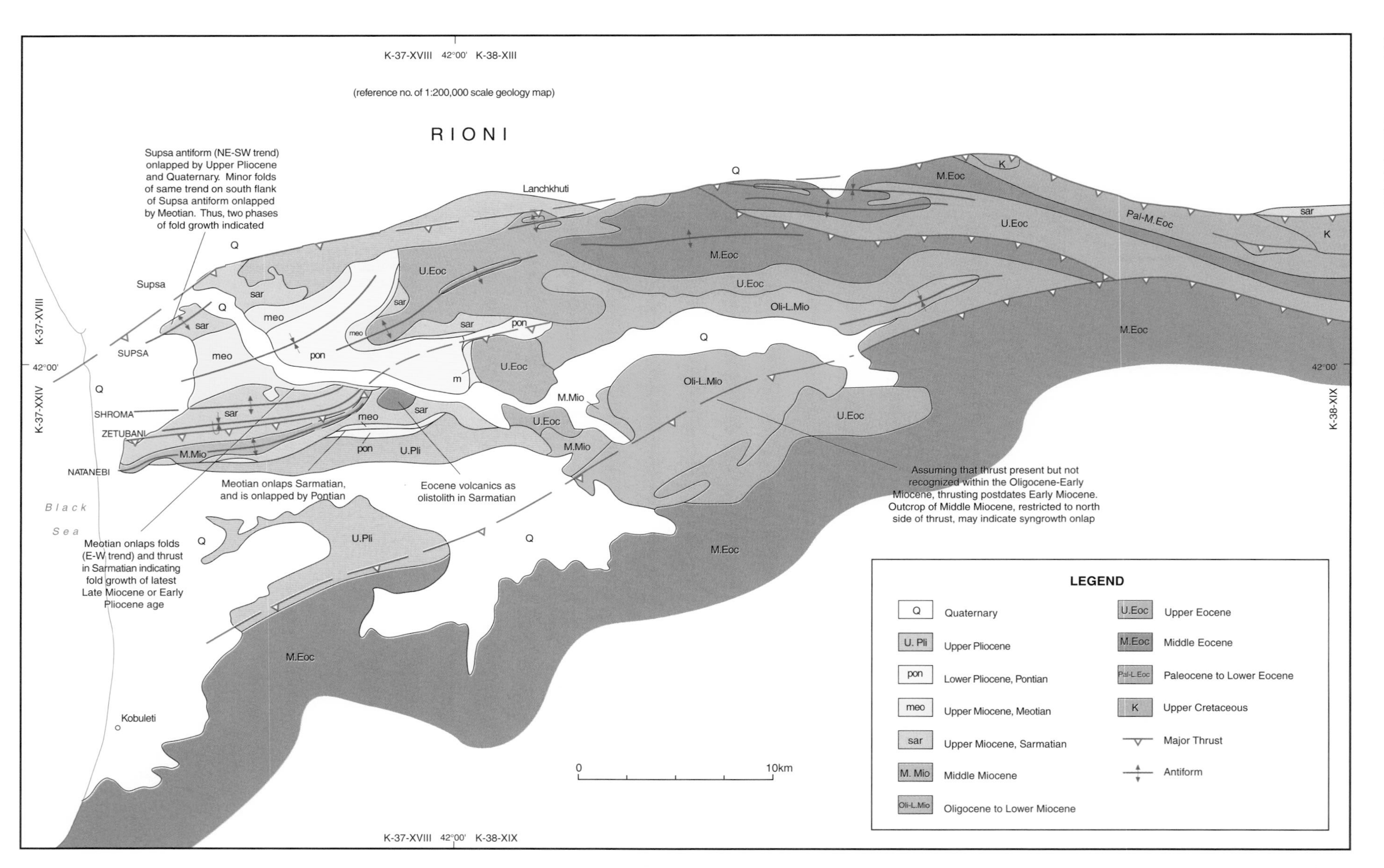

Figure 3. Structural elements, Southwest Georgia. Compiled from geological maps on scale of 1:25,000 (Georgian Oil, unpublished data) and field observations.

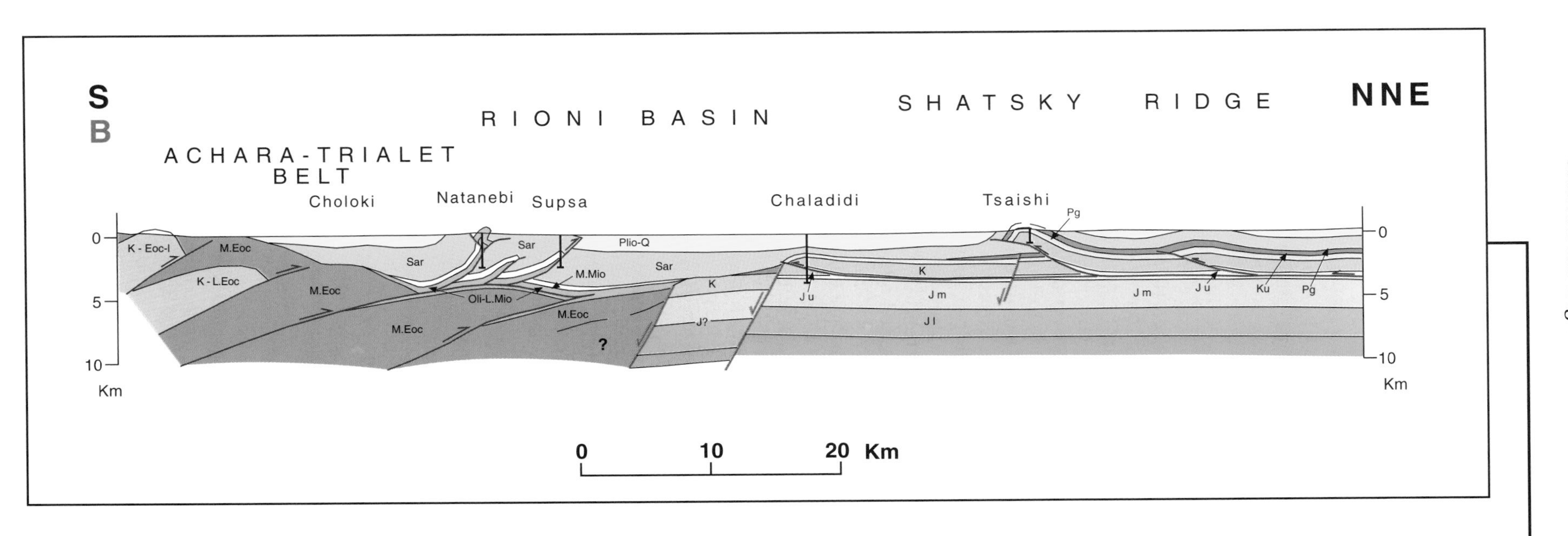

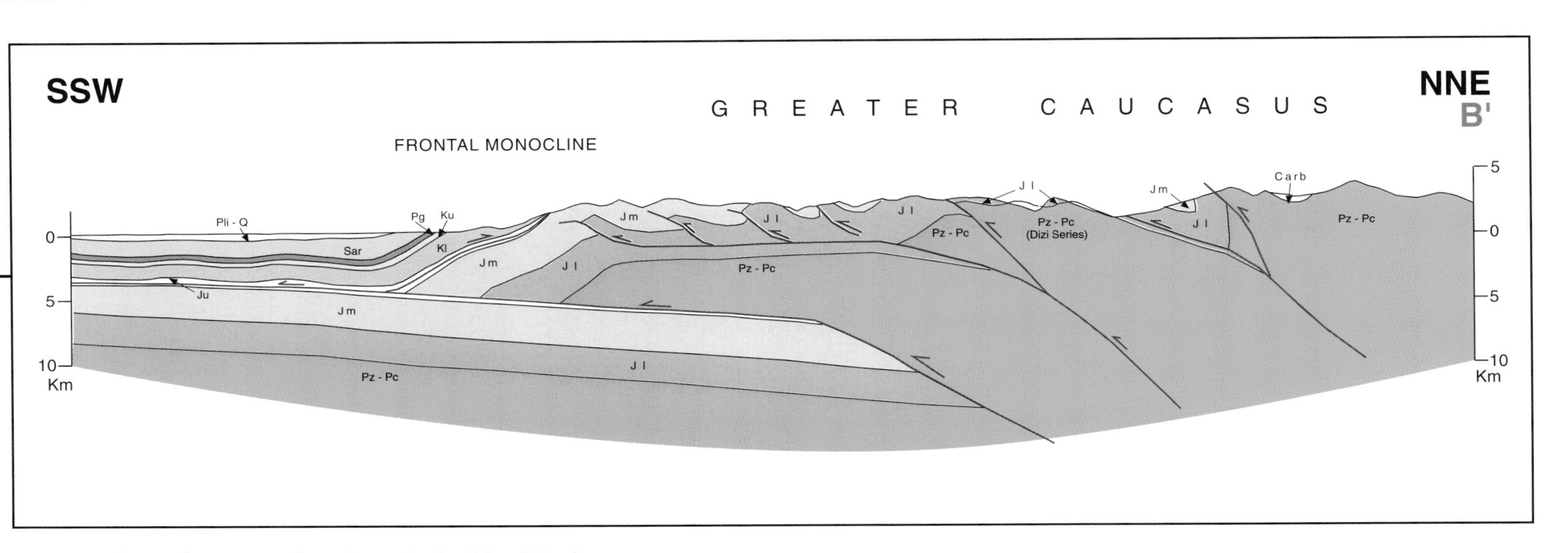

Figure 4. Geological cross section through the Rioni Basin.

halite). However, below the compressional anticlines, the seismic data show that the regional elevation of Danian and older strata (Shatsky Ridge) *falls* to the south by ~200 ms. This may be due to the presence of extensional faults that offset the Danian–Mesozoic and, in particular, the evaporite decollement; as a consequence, the extensional faults were able to control the location of the later compressional structures. Onlap relationships on the seismic lines and geological maps show that the Tsaishi anticline developed during the late Miocene (Sarmatian–Meotian). The total amount of shortening that can be accommodated by these anticlines is ~2 km.

North of the Rioni Basin and the Tsaishi anticline, the Greater Caucasus mountain front is dominated by a south-dipping monocline in which a Jurassic–Cretaceous stratigraphy closely similar to that in the Ochamchira wells on the Shatsky Ridge is exposed. Our interpretation of this frontal monocline involves a major compressional fault ramping, probably from within basement, up to the Upper Jurassic evaporites, where it goes flat. This is a ramp height of ~10 km, accounting for uplift of the Middle–Lower Jurassic outcrop belt by the same amount above its regional elevation. There may be additional uplift due to deformation within the Jurassic. Horizontal displacement of ~30 km on this fault is implied. This magnitude of displacement is not seen in front of the monocline, so a passive backthrust in the evaporites is needed.

To the north of the frontal monocline, there are two major culminations separated by a feature described previously as a flysch syncline (Borsuk and Sholpo, 1983). The first culmination exposes the Dizi Series, and the second is the main Caucasus axis, where metamorphic rocks are at surface. There are few thrusts or reverse faults shown on the geological maps despite the magnitude of deformation, suggesting the presence of major unmapped or blind thrusts, perhaps with a Lower Jurassic detachment.

The Jurassic and Cretaceous sequences of the axial zones of the Caucasus are thickly developed and mostly in flysch facies. Moving toward the frontal folds near the coast, the stratigraphy appears to thin, however, and becomes identical with that of the Shatsky Ridge (Robinson et al., 1996). The latter therefore seems to have been essentially the southwestern margin of the Mesozoic Greater Caucasus Basin, accumulating inner- to outer-shelf sediments during the phase of postrift subsidence as deep marine turbidites accumulated along the basin axis to the north and east. Paleozoic or Precambrian granitic metamorphics are exposed in the axis of the Greater Caucasus, in most places immediately below the Lower Jurassic. In a large area of the Russian Caucasus, there are outcrops of Paleozoic rocks, ranging from at least as old as Devonian to Permo–Triassic. Map patterns suggest that these strata were cut by extensional faults during the Triassic. The Dizi Series in northern Georgia includes clastic and carbonate rocks of the same age (as old as Silurian), but said to be very different, having a much lesser degree of compression and metamorphism (Adamia et al., 1992). Şengör (1984) suggests that the Dizi Series may be correlated with equivalent rocks in the Transcaucasus in Iran.

CENTRAL GEORGIA

Achara-Trialet Belt–Dziruli Massif

Pre-Jurassic basement outcrops in the Dziruli Massif that separates the Rioni and Kartli foreland basins (Figures 1, 5). It has probable Hercynian granitic metamorphics as its core, overlain in rare outcrops by Devonian phyllite, and tuffs said to be of Carboniferous age (Georgian Oil, unpublished data). Lower Jurassic terrestrial and shallow marine sediments including limestones outcrop around the margins. Most of the massif is intruded by granitoids and covered with tuffs and lavas of Middle Jurassic age. This indicates that Dziruli was part of the Middle Jurassic magmatic province seen throughout the Caucasus, thought to be related to northward subduction of a Paleotethys plate below the Black Sea region (Banks and Robinson, this volume). The volcanics were peneplaned and then overlain by a thin Upper Jurassic sequence containing evaporites. This is ~250 m thick in wells near Ochamchira, but pinches out to the east, so that it is absent on the Dziruli Massif. Marine limestones start to be deposited regionally in the Early Cretaceous, but did not cover the Dziruli Massif until the Barremian. Marls and limestones continued to be deposited over the platform until the end of the Danian, with the Upper Cretaceous to Danian comprising mainly chalks.

The frontal folds of the Achara-Trialet belt wrap around the southern flank of the Dziruli Massif, with north-vergent thrusts overriding the thin sedimentary cover. Figure 6 shows a geological cross section through the fold belt where this abuts the Dziruli Massif. Three subzones can be recognized in the Achara-Trialet belt: a frontal culmination interpreted to be an antiformal stack duplex, a central synformal zone, and a basement culmination. Deformation in the area is interpreted as the result of the emplacement of a major basement thrust slice onto the autochthonous basement block (Dziruli Massif), causing it to be depressed and to dip southward at an essentially constant 20°. Shortening propagates into the frontal zones on an assumed mid-Cretaceous (Aptian?) detachment (the deepest stratigraphic level exposed in the region).

Restoring the section shown in Figure 6 reveals a simple Paleogene basin with the geometry of a postrift sag basin (Figure 7). Successively younger stratigraphic intervals onlap progressively northward in a regular fashion along the northern margin of the Achara-Trialet Basin and can be traced some distance to the east (Figure 5). No extensional faults have yet been recognized in the now highly deformed fold belt; the dominant deformation style is detachment thrusting rather than inversion. Near Mokhisi, an anticlinal structure in the corner of the Kartli Basin, extensional faults can be seen on seismic data and these displace the Cretaceous (Figures 8, 9). However, it is difficult to be certain whether these faults are related to the formation of an extensional basin to the south (Paleocene?) or to later flexure of a foreland by the growing fold belt (Oligocene–Miocene). Some of them show evidence of limited reversal during the compressive deformation.

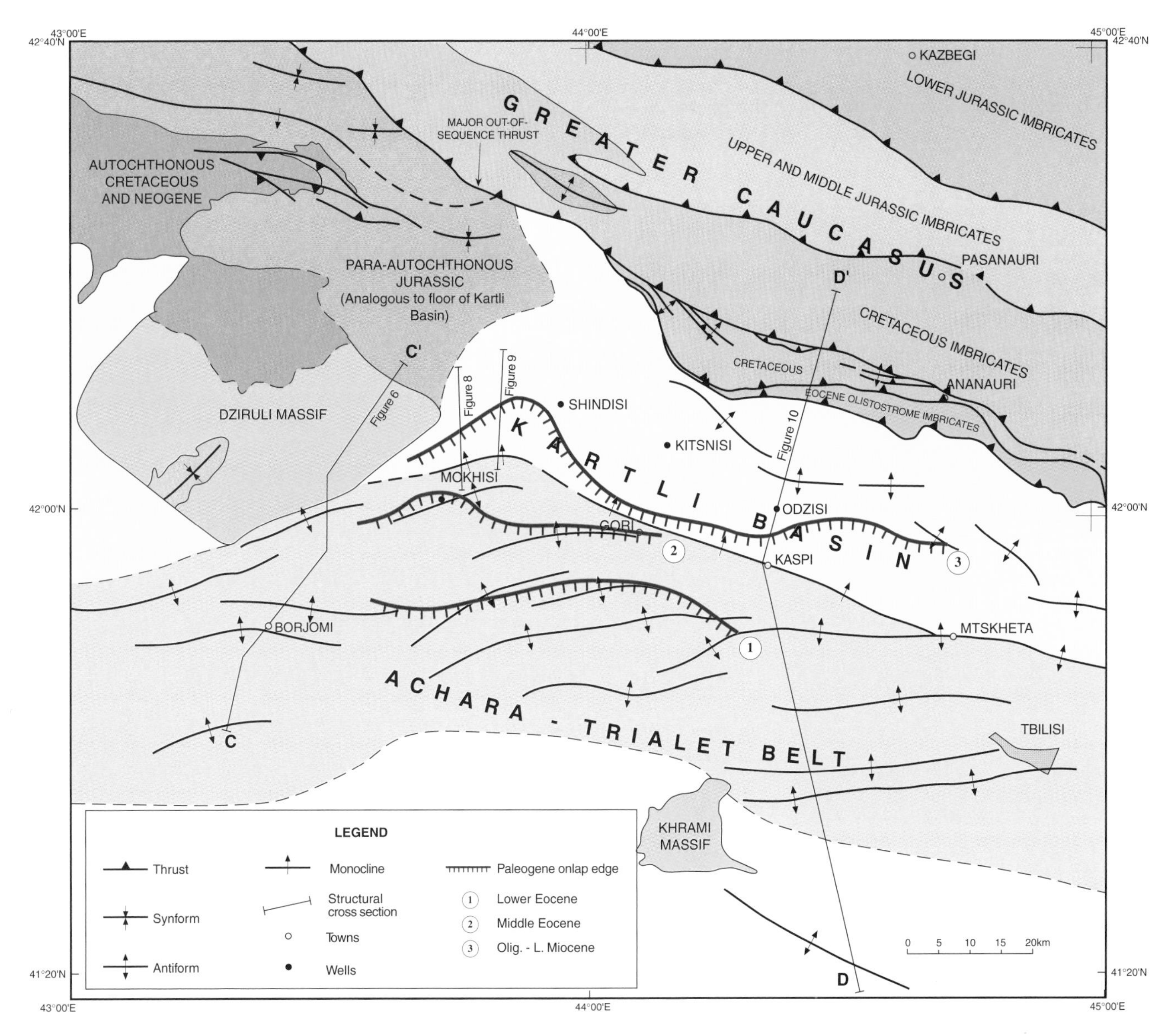

Figure 5. Structural elements, Central Georgia. Compiled from geological maps on scales of 1:200,000 and 1:25,000, reflection seismic lines, and field observations. The onlap edges of the Paleogene units are interpreted from mapped unconformities in the Achara-Trialet belt and from seismic interpretation beneath the Kartli Basin (Figures 8, 9).

Achara-Trialet Belt—Kartli Basin

Figure 10 is a geological cross section through the Achara-Trialet belt and the central portion of the Kartli Basin. The same three subzones can be recognized within the fold belt—a frontal culmination, a central synformal zone, and a basement culmination (Khrami Massif). As in the Borjomi section (Figure 6), deformation in the area is interpreted as the result of the emplacement of a basement thrust slice, represented at outcrop near the line of section by the Khrami Massif. The Khrami Massif links directly in a southeast direction with the Armenian Massif (Lesser Caucasus range) and may be related with other isolated outcrops of metamorphic rock along the southern flanks of the Eastern Pontides in Turkey (e.g., Bayburt/Pulur Massif) (Robinson et al., 1995a; Okay, 1996; Okay and Şahinturk, this volume). The geological map shows a core of Paleozoic granitoids covered by Carboniferous limestones and clastic sediments. There are some small remnants of Lower Jurassic shales and Upper Jurassic limestones (and in Armenia, Middle–Upper Jurassic volcanics). These are followed by Cenomanian limestones, which on the road section on the east of the massif lie nearly vertically and in unconformable contact with granitic basement. The remainder of the Upper Cretaceous consists of volcanics with red limestones in the Maastrichtian.

The frontal zone of the Achara-Trialet belt contains repeated thrust slices of Cretaceous to (at least) upper Eocene strata, enclosed at the front by a north-dipping panel of rocks of early Miocene and younger age. Between these two packages is the Oligocene–lower Miocene (Maykop), very poorly exposed because of its soft, muddy lithology. These factors are all characteristic

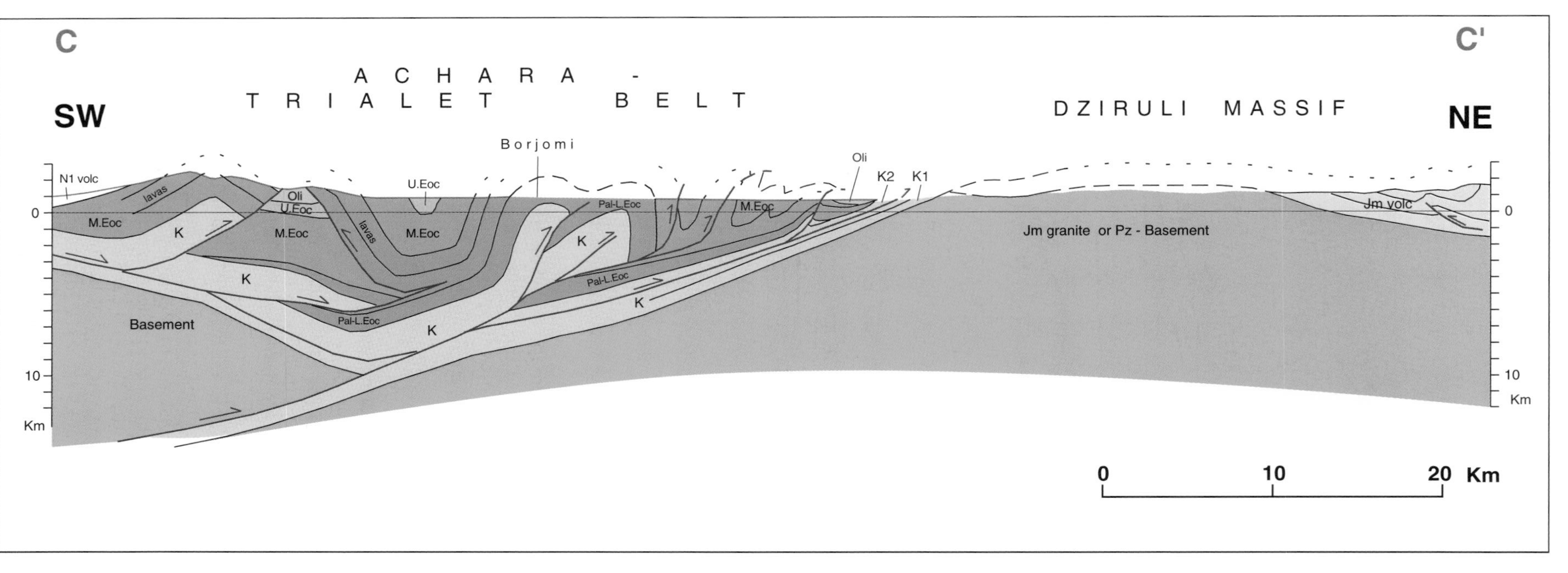

Figure 6. Geological cross section through the central Achara-Trialet belt and Dziruli Massif.

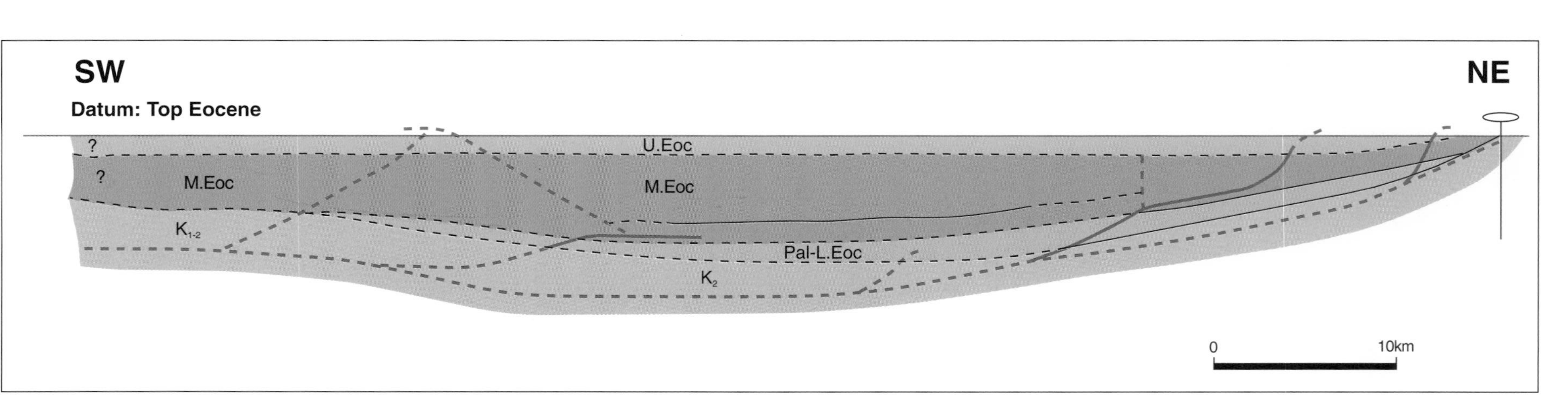

Figure 7. Section of Figure 6 restored to top-Eocene age.

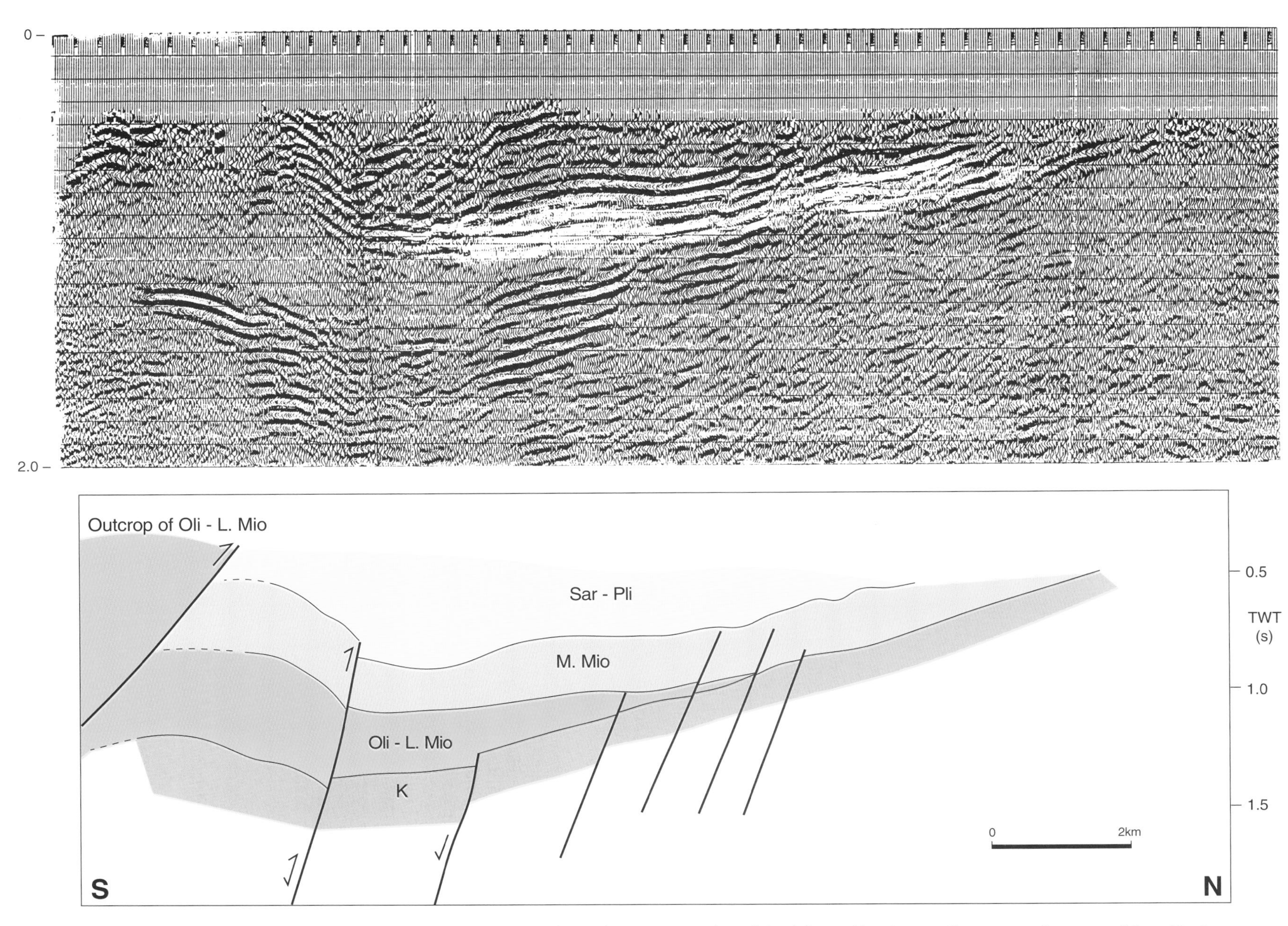

Figure 8. Seismic line 018704 (see Figure 5 for location). The line shows extensional faulting affecting sediments at least as old as Cretaceous and downthrowing to the south. Folding of Miocene strata above the extensional faults suggests limited inversion. Note thinning and onlap of the accoustically transparent Oligocene?–Lower Miocene to the north.

of frontal duplexes, in this case with a roof thrust in the Oligocene shales. Because deformation does not propagate into the basin, the roof thrust must be a passive backthrust (Figure 9). The timing of deformation is indicated by the age of tilted beds in the frontal monocline as post-Sarmatian, probably Pliocene. However, there is a small patch of sediments marked as Sarmatian on the geological maps unconformably overlying Cretaceous to Oligocene rocks of the third duplex slice. If the dating is correct, this would imply an earlier phase of deformation and erosion.

Reflection seismic lines show that the Dziruli Massif dips gently beneath the Kartli foreland basin, so that on the line of section of Figure 10, basement is at a depth of around 4 to 5 km. Deep stratigraphic wells within the basin (Figures 5, 10) penetrate as deep as Upper Cretaceous and show that between the Mesozoic and the thick Neogene foreland basin fill, the entire Paleogene is thin, with some units probably missing.

The frontal zone of the Greater Caucasus in this area consists of thrust imbricates of Sarmatian and Meotian foreland basin-fill sediments, deformed in the Pliocene. Going farther north, progressively older sediments are exposed as thrust imbricates, until in the core of the mountains, Lower Jurassic mudstones overlie metamorphic and igneous basement. Some of the main faults are suggested to be out of sequence. South of Ananuri, there are imbricates with a much thinner Cretaceous, and an olistostrome with a late Eocene muddy matrix and olistoliths of Jurassic–Neocomian limestone and Middle Jurassic volcanics (marked on 1:200,000 geological maps as Upper Jurassic) (Isayev et al., 1981). These cannot have been derived from the north because sediments of these ages to the north were turbidites in the deep Caucasus Basin. We suggest that the olistoliths were derived from the southern margin of the basin (Dziruli Massif), when foreland-bulge flexure and faulting of the autochthonous floor of the Kartli Basin exposed the Jurassic platform sediments (Bradley and Kidd, 1991). This implies that compressive deformation had started at least as early as the late Eocene, an interpretation supported by geological maps of the outer folds of the Greater Caucasus in both Russia and Georgia, where upper Eocene strata onlap folds.

East of Tbilisi, the Achara-Trialet Zone is overridden by the frontal folds of the Caucasus (Figure 1). The autochthonous basement of the Kartli Basin plunges eastward beneath the Kura Basin toward the deep South Caspian Sea.

CONCLUSIONS AND DISCUSSION

Relative to the stable East European plate, the Shatsky-Georgian block was extended and moved a short distance to the south, possibly in the Late Triassic, resulting in a Jurassic–Cretaceous postrift basin (not ocean), now in the southern flank of the Greater Caucasus. The Shatsky-Georgian block formed the southern margin of the postrift basin until the basin was compressed in the late Eocene–Neogene, leaving the Greater Caucasus in net compression. In the Achara-Trialet belt, the age of extension is not easy to define but could have occurred in the late Paleocene, synchronous with the age suggested for the opening of the Eastern Black Sea (Robinson et al., 1996). That the Achara-Trialet belt and Eastern Black Sea were originally one basin, now partly closed, is suggested by the disappearance of the thrust structures into the postrift fill of the Eastern Black Sea and by similarities between the interpreted Paleogene stratigraphy in the two areas, especially the thick Eocene sequence (Robinson et al., 1995b). Mid-Cretaceous extension (as in the Western Black Sea) cannot be ruled out by the exposed geology. There are, for example, no known extensional faults or characteristic synrift facies of either late Paleocene or Cretaceous age. [Robinson et al. (1995b) give a discussion of the reasons for the absence of synrift facies.]

Like the older Greater Caucasus Basin, the Achara-Trialet zone was recompressed from at least the Oligocene through the Pliocene, with some compression possibly as early as the late Eocene. This compression effected a complete switch in the location of sedimentary basins. The two older extensional basins became inverted, while the area that had previously formed the margin between them became a flexural basin and a locus of thick Neogene sedimentation. This floor of the Rioni and Kartli basins is a continental crustal block that continues directly into the Shatsky Ridge, the northern rift margin of the Eastern Black Sea. The Rioni Basin is not, therefore, a direct continuation of (or successor to) the deep Eastern Black Sea Basin, but is a younger foreland basin that developed through partial closure of the Eastern Black Sea and the consequent flexure of its northern margin.

The basement of the foreland basin system is arched transversally across the foreland basins because of loading by the two thrust belts. South of the Dziruli Massif the dip is as $\leq 20°$, and in the Kartli Basin dips are $>10°$. Such steep dips probably occur because the arch is in effect two superimposed flexural bulges, unable to migrate either north or south. The basement of the foreland basins is also arched latitudinally along the basin axis: a top-Middle Jurassic volcanics datum is at a depth of 3–4 km near the Black Sea coast but at ~3 km *above* sea level over the Dziruli Massif, and again at very great depth beneath the eastern part of the Kartli Basin. Why the Dziruli Massif is so high is not understood.

The northward push responsible for closing the old extensional basins was probably linked with the collision of Arabia with the Anatolide microplates (Gondwana fragments), and of these blocks with the subduction zone south of the Armenian Massif. The closure of the Tethys Ocean (along a suture that is now marked by the İzmir-Ankara-Erzincan-Sevan belt of ophiolites) nonetheless took place prior to the Middle Eocene (A. Okay, 1995, personal communication). The Armenian Massif (including the Khrami Massif) was probably a distal marginal block of Shatsky-Georgian basement that became obducted onto the platform margin, thus tilting it and transmitting compression to the sedimentary cover. All of the compressive deformation that we have observed is Alpide. In neither the Greater Caucasus nor the Achara-Trialet belt

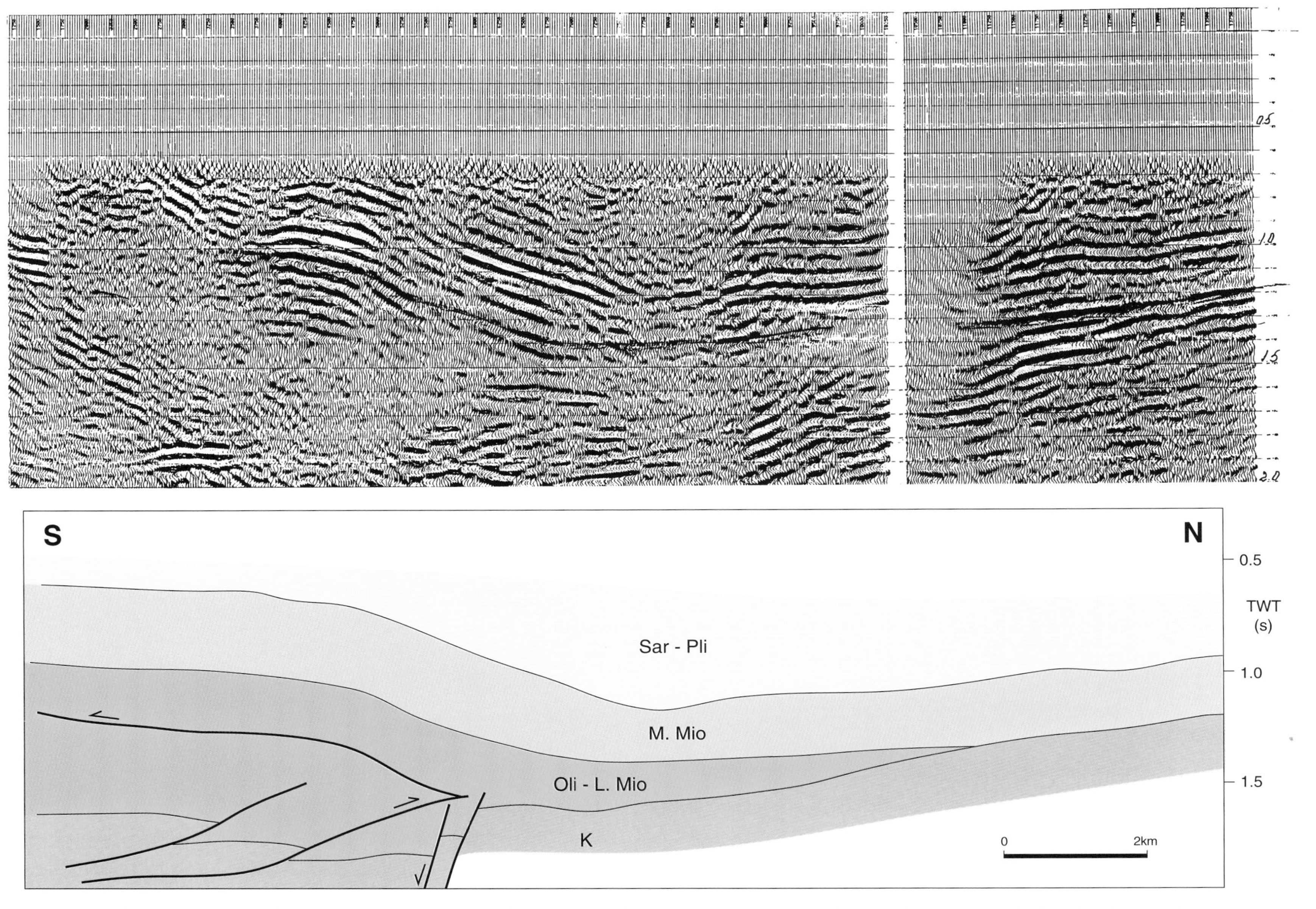

Figure 9. Seismic line 018707 (see Figure 5 for location). This line shows the frontal monocline of the Achara-Trialet belt. The frontal thrust tips out within the accoustically transparent Oligocene–lower Miocene, producing the north-dipping monocline. A passive roof duplex is developed within the Oligocene–lower Miocene. The interpretation suggests that the location of the thrust tip is influenced by the buttressing effect of a footwall to an extensional fault.

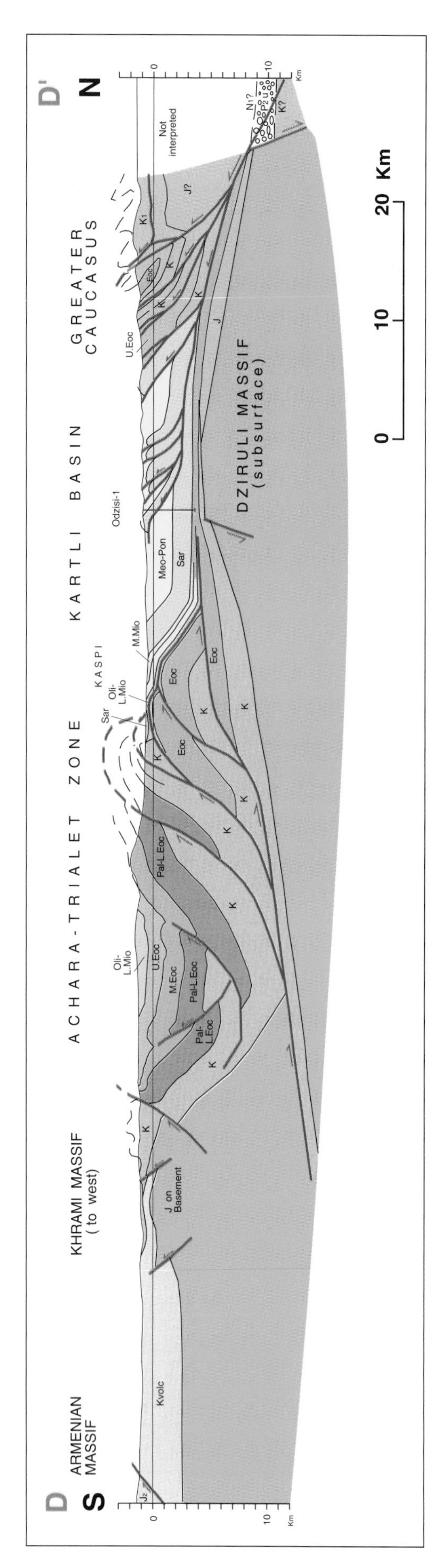

Figure 10. Geological cross section through the Achara-Trialet belt and central Kartli Basin.

have we discovered any evidence for Cimmeride (Late Triassic–Early Jurassic) deformation.

The interpretation of the Achara-Trialet thrust belt as the closed part of the Eastern Black Sea is significant because it effectively extends the original Eastern Black Sea extensional basin as far east as at least the Georgia–Azerbaijan border. What appears to be a similar Paleogene stratigraphy is also known from petroleum exploration wells to be present beneath the western part of the Kura Basin in Azerbaijan. Farther east, the Paleogene plunges to great depths beneath the huge thickness of Miocene to Pliocene sediments that eventually merge into the postrift fill of the South Caspian Sea. It is thus possible that the Eastern Black Sea and South Caspian Sea were formed as one extensional basin during the Paleocene, becoming separated only during the Miocene as the thrust structures emerged above sea level.

ACKNOWLEDGMENTS

We thank JKX Oil & Gas plc, Georgian British Oil Company, and Georgian Oil (Saknavtobi), especially Dito Papava, for providing us with geological maps, reflection seismic data, and the opportunity to participate in field excursions in much of Georgia during June and July 1995. Some of the seismic data interpretation was carried out by Alastair Gray.

REFERENCES CITED

Adamia, S.A., T. Chkhouta, M. Kekelia, M. Lordkipanidze, I. Shavishvili, and G. Zakariadze, 1981, Tectonics of the Caucasus and adjoining regions; implications for the evolution of the Tethys Ocean: Journal of Structural Geology, v. 3, p. 437–47.

Adamia, S.A., K.T. Akhvlediani, V.M. Kilasonia, A.E.M. Nairn, D. Papava, and D.K. Patton, 1992, Geology of the Republic of Georgia: a review: International Geology Review, v. 34/5, p. 447–476.

Banks, C.J., and A.G. Robinson, this volume, Mesozoic strike-slip back-arc basins of the Western Black Sea region, *in* A.G. Robinson, ed., Regional and petroleum geology of the Black Sea and surrounding region: AAPG Memoir 68, p. 53–62.

Borsuk, A.M., and V.N. Sholpo, 1983, Correlation of endogenous processes in the Alpine cycle of the Caucasus, *in* N. Rast and F.M. Delany, eds., Profiles of orogenic belts: American Geophysical Union and Geological Society of America, Geodynamics Series, v. 10, p. 97–143.

Bradley, D.C., and W.S.F. Kidd, 1991, Flexural extension of the upper continental crust in collisional foredeeps: Bulletin of the Geological Society of America, v. 103, p. 1416–1438.

Finetti, I., G. Bricchi, A. Del Ben, M. Pipan, and Z. Xuan, 1988, Geophysical study of the Black Sea area: Bolletino di Geofisica Teorica ed Applicata, v. 30, no. 117–118, p. 197–324.

Gamkrelidze, I.P., 1986, Geodynamic evolution of the Caucasus and adjacent areas in Alpine time:

Tectonophysics, v. 127, p. 261–277.

Gamkrelidze, I.P., 1991, Tectonic nappes and horizontal layering in the Earth's crust in the Mediterranean belt (Carpathians, Balkanides and Caucasus): Tectonophysics, v. 196, p. 385–396.

Gorshkov, A.S., 1983, The marine prolongation of the Adzhar-Trialet fold system: Geotectonics, v. 17, no. 4.

Görür, N., 1988, Timing of the opening of the Black Sea Basin: Tectonophysics, v. 147, p. 247–262.

Görür, N., this volume, Cretaceous syn- to postrift sedimentation on the southern continental margin of the Western Black Sea Basin, *in* A.G. Robinson, ed., Regional and petroleum geology of the Black Sea and surrounding region: AAPG Memoir 68, p. 227–240.

Isayev, B.M, T.D. Gadzhiyev, S.A. Ali-Zade, and T.N. Kengerli, 1981, Tectonic sheets and olistostrome complexes in the southeastern Caucasus: Geotectonics, v. 15, p. 45–53.

Kazmin, V.G, 1991, Collision and rifting in the Tethys Ocean: geodynamic implications: Tectonophysics, v. 196, p. 371–384.

Khain, V.E., 1975, Structure and main stages in tectono-magmatic development of the Caucasus: an attempt at geodynamic interpretation: American Journal of Science, v. 275A, p. 131–156.

Okay, A.I., 1996, Granulite facies gneisses from the Pulur region, Eastern Pontides: Turkish Journal of Earth Sciences, v. 5, p. 55–61.

Okay, A.I., and Ö. Şahintürk, this volume, Geology of the Eastern Pontides, *in* A.G. Robinson, ed., Regional and petroleum geology of the Black Sea and surrounding region: AAPG Memoir 68, p. 291–312.

Philip, H., A. Cisternas, A. Gvishiani, and A. Gorshkov, 1989, The Caucasus: an actual example of the initial stages of continental collision: Tectonophysics, v. 161, p. 1–21.

Rebai, S., H. Philip, L. Dorbath, B. Borissoff, H. Haessler, and A. Cisternas, 1993, Active tectonics in the Lesser Caucasus: coexistence of compressive and extensional structures: Tectonics, v. 12, p. 1089–1114.

Robinson, A.G., this volume, Introduction: tectonic elements of the Black Sea Region, *in* A.G. Robinson, ed., Regional and petroleum geology of the Black Sea and surrounding region: AAPG Memoir 68, p. 1–6.

Robinson, A.G., and E. Kerusov, this volume, Stratigraphic and structural development of the Gulf of Odessa, Ukrainian Black Sea: implications for petroleum exploration, *in* A.G. Robinson, ed., Regional and petroleum geology of the Black Sea and surrounding region: AAPG Memoir 68, p. 369–380.

Robinson, A.G., C.J. Banks, M.M. Rutherford, and J.P.P. Hirst, 1995a, Stratigraphic and structural development of the Eastern Pontides, Turkey: London, Journal of the Geological Society, v. 152, p. 861–872.

Robinson, A.G., G. Spadini, S.A.P.L. Cloetingh, and J. Rudat, 1995b, Stratigraphic evolution of the Black Sea: inferences from basin modelling: Marine and Petroleum Geology, v. 12, p. 821–835.

Robinson, A.G., J.H. Rudat, C.J. Banks, and R.L.F. Wiles, 1996, Petroleum geology of the Black Sea: Marine and Petroleum Geology, v. 13, p. 195–223.

Robinson, A.G., A. Gardiner, E.T. Griffith, and A. Home, this volume, Petroleum geology of the Georgian fold and thrust belts and foreland basins, *in* A.G. Robinson, ed., Regional and petroleum geology of the Black Sea and surrounding region: AAPG Memoir 68, p. 347–368.

Şengör, A.M.C., 1984, The Cimmeride orogenic system and the tectonics of Eurasia: Geological Society of America Special Paper 195, 82 p.

Tsagareli, A.L., 1984, Geology of Western Caucasus: Geotectonics, v. 8, no. 3. (English edition by the American Geophysical Union and the Geological Society of America, December 1994).

Zonenshain, L., M. Kuzmin, and L. Natapov, 1990, Geology of the USSR: a plate tectonic synthesis: Washington, DC, American Geophysical Union, 242 p.

Robinson, A.G., E.T. Griffith, A.R. Gardiner, and A.K. Home, 1997, Petroleum geology of the Georgian fold and thrust belts and foreland basins, *in* A.G. Robinson, ed., Regional and petroleum geology of the Black Sea and surrounding region: AAPG Memoir 68, p. 347–367.

Chapter 18

Petroleum Geology of the Georgian Fold and Thrust Belts and Foreland Basins

Andrew G. Robinson
Eric T. Griffith
JKX Oil & Gas plc
Guildford, United Kingdom

Andrew R. Gardiner
Andrew K. Home
Robertson Research International
Llandudno, Gwynedd, United Kingdom

ABSTRACT

Numerous, mainly small, oil discoveries have been made within the foreland basins and fold and thrust belts of Georgia. The largest field in Georgia (Samgori) contained ~200 MMbbl (million barrels) recoverable reserves reservoired in fractured middle Eocene volcaniclastics—the main proven reservoir in Georgia—trapped in a compressional fold of the Achara-Trialet belt. Where the Achara-Trialet deformation extended into the foreland basins, frontal folds with Miocene–Pliocene clastic reservoirs are known to be oil-bearing (e.g., Supsa field). Within the foreland basins in areas unaffected by Neogene compression, structural closures related to pre-Neogene extensional faulting may include draping lower Miocene and Mesozoic reservoirs: these are largely untested. The frontal folds of the Greater Caucasus have yielded small oil discoveries in lower Miocene fluvial to shallow marine clastic reservoirs. The widespread oil discoveries along the Achara-Trialet frontal folds demonstrate the presence of a working oil sourcing system from the Black Sea through to the Kura Basin. Gas chromatography–mass spectrometry and carbon isotope analyses indicate that a single source rock was responsible for generation of many of the oils in the foreland basins; oil source correlations suggest that this was late Eocene in age, deposited within the Paleogene Achara-Trialet Basin. Further, oil-prone source rocks appear to be present locally within the Greater Caucasus.

INTRODUCTION

The geology of Georgia is dominated by two Neogene foreland basins running from east to west through the center of the country and flanked to north and south by compressional fold belts, the Achara-Trialet belt and the Greater Caucasus (Figure 1) (Adamia et al., 1992; Banks et al., this volume, their figure 1). The Rioni Basin in West Georgia is a foreland basin to the Achara-Trialet thrust belt. The thrust belt represents an extensional basin that probably began to rift during the late Paleocene and was compressively deformed mainly during the Miocene. The Rioni Basin is separated from the Kartli Basin in Central Georgia by a basement high (the Dziruli Massif). The Kartli Basin is also a foreland basin, but was produced by loading by both thrust belts, to the north and south.

Oil seeps are widespread in Georgia, particularly along the northern margin of the Achara-Trialet thrust belt, but also farther north within the Rioni and Kartli foreland basins. Exploration in the country began during the 19th century by exploitation of the surface seeps and shallow drilling beneath them. The first substantive discovery was the Supsa field close to the Black Sea, discovered in 1889 by the Anglo-Belgian Oil Company and still producing small amounts of oil. Despite the drilling of many exploration wells in the foreland basins, exploration success has so far been limited, with the Samgori-Patardzeuli field (~200 MMbbl initial oil reserves) and its extension, Ninotsminda, being the only substantial discoveries. There has been no drilling offshore. Nonetheless, exploration interest in Georgia has been renewed during the 1990s following the independence of the country.

In this chapter, we give the first review of the petroleum geology of the country. Like its companion paper (Banks et al., this volume), the interpretations are based on original geological field studies, follow-up laboratory work, and petroleum exploration activities performed in Georgia during 1994 and 1995; on Georgian geological maps, mostly published (although difficult to obtain); on our own interpretation of Georgian seismic data; and on other mainly stratigraphic data provided by the state oil company, Saknavtobi. We first describe the context of the oil occurrences in Georgia by reviewing the geological setting and history of the Kartli and Rioni foreland basins and the Achara-Trialet thrust belt [covered in more detail by Banks et al. (this volume)]. We then describe the main proven plays in Georgia, including some original sedimentologic and stratigraphic work. This is followed by a discussion of the nature of working oil source systems based on a geochemical study of oils and potential source rocks. The locations of wells and discoveries referred to in the text are shown in Figure 1.

STRATIGRAPHIC AND STRUCTURAL EVOLUTION: A SUMMARY

The basins running through the central part of Georgia today—Rioni in the west and Kartli in the center—are flexural basins related principally to loading during the Neogene by the Achara-Trialet thrust belt that runs through southern Georgia and extends westwards into the undeformed Eastern Black Sea and into northern Turkey as the Eastern Pontides (Robinson et al., 1995; Banks et al., this volume; Okay and Şahinturk, this volume) (Figure 1). The Achara-Trialet belt apears to be a Paleogene extensional basin. Its prerift basement outcrops in central Georgia as the Dziruli Massif and in South Georgia as the Khrami Massif. Both of these areas include Upper Jurassic to Lower Cretaceous rocks resting unconformably on Middle Jurassic volcanics and high-level intrusives, and Hercynian metasedimentary and igneous basement. Lower Cretaceous to upper Eocene sediments progressively onlap the northern rift margin (Dziruli Massif–Shatsky Ridge). Virtually all of these sediments are basinal, possibly condensed during the Paleocene but including several kilometers of Eocene turbidites. The lower Eocene is mainly turbidites: the middle Eocene, volcaniclastic sediments and volcanics, also deposited in deep water; the upper Eocene, again turbidites, distal at the base and becoming generally coarser and more proximal upwards.

During the late Eocene or early Oligocene, postrift subsidence was augmented by flexural subsidence as the tectonic regime switched from extensional to compressional (related to final closure of the Tethys Ocean). Thrust faulting and folding in the outer parts of the belt began in the early Miocene and reached a peak during the late Miocene, bending the Shatsky Ridge–Dziruli Massif foreland down toward the south. By the late Oligocene–early Miocene, and possibly as early as the late Eocene, the foreland basins formed part of the extensive marginal basin system known as Paratethys and had limited links with the world's ocean systems (Jones and Simmons, this volume). At least as early as the early Miocene, the Dziruli Massif was emergent and formed a major watershed and sediment source area; sediments in the Kartli and Kura basins were shed eastward, toward the South Caspian Sea, while those in the Rioni Basin were shed westward, toward the Black Sea. Neogene strata are, accordingly, frequently coarse-grained and either nonmarine or restricted-marine, shallow water sediments.

The present structure of the Achara-Trialet belt is interpreted as resulting from the northward thrusting of a basement wedge, which now outcrops as the Khrami Massif. This imparts an overall synclinal form to the fold belt in which outcrop is dominated by Eocene sediments. Toward the north, the deformation is probably dominantly thin-skinned, with a major detachment running within the Upper Cretaceous and ramping up through the lower Eocene toward the northern part of the basin. Near the northern deformation front, duplexes are developed with a roof detachment (probably within the Oligocene) that outcrops as a major backthrust on the southern margin of the Kartli foreland basin (Banks et al., this volume).

During the Paleogene, while great thicknesses of deep marine sediment were accumulating in the Achara-Trialet Basin, the area to the north (now beneath the Kartli and Rioni foreland basins) formed the basin margin. The Paleogene sequence on this margin is only a few hundred meters thick. As flexural subsidence began

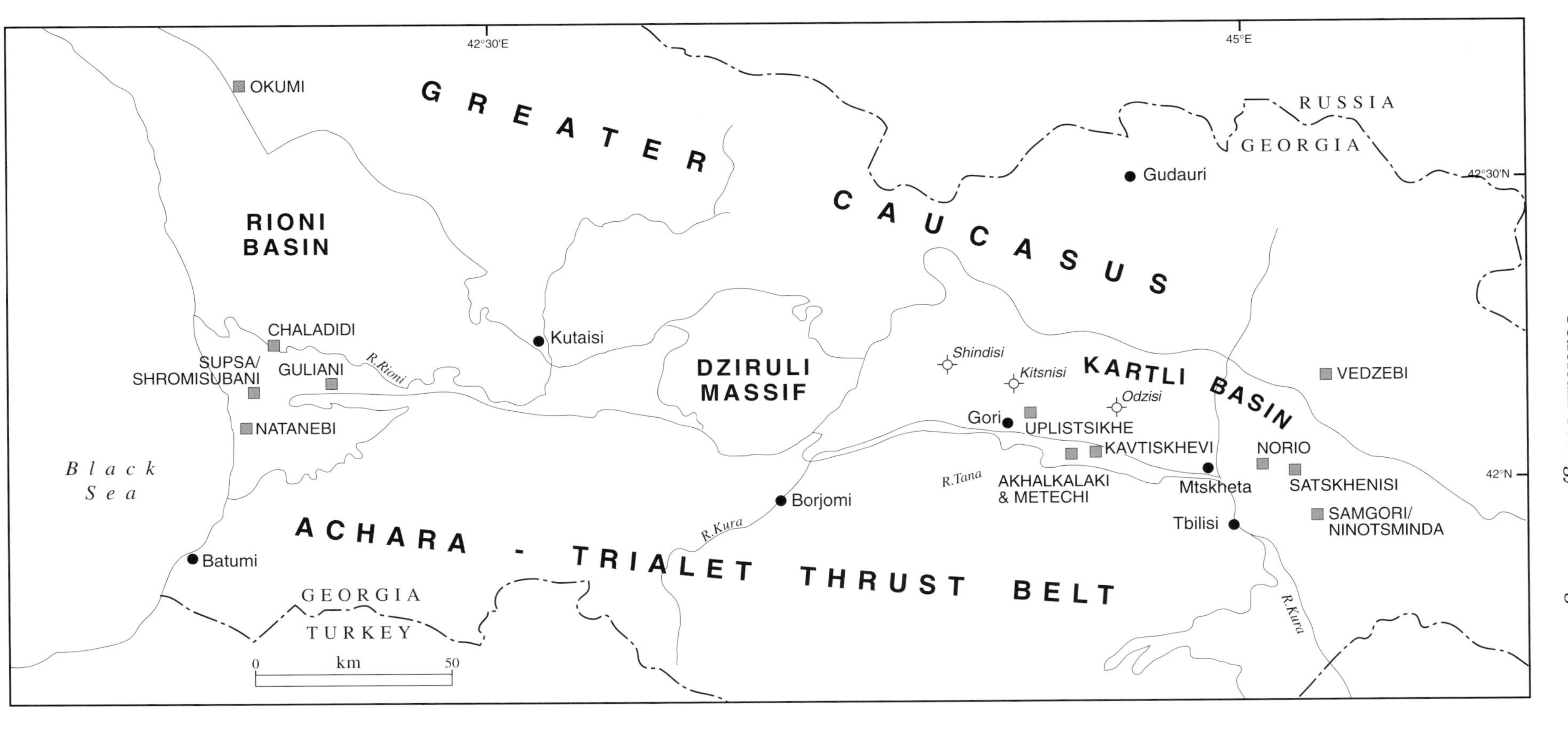

Figure 1. Location map showing distribution of oil occurrences in Georgia.

to affect the extensional basin margin, great thicknesses of Neogene clastic sediments accumulated, mainly during the late Miocene and Pliocene. The basement of the Kartli Basin plunges east toward the South Caspian Sea and passes into Azerbaijan below the Kura Basin. The northern part of the basin is strongly deformed by thin-skinned compressive folding related to the development of the Greater Caucasus. Loading by the Greater Caucasus, as well as by the Achara-Trialet belt, has imparted an overall symmetry that is unusual in flexural basins. Toward the east, the Greater Caucasus thrust belt has completely overridden the Achara-Trialet belt along a major south-vergent detachment, so the Paleocene rocks of the latter are not exposed east of Tbilisi (although they are known from the subsurface into Azerbaijan). The Rioni Basin plunges westward from the Dziruli Massif to eventually merge with the undeformed postrift fill of the Eastern Black Sea. The basement of the Rioni Basin has a pronounced southern dip due to loading by the Achara-Trialet folds. In the north, a major horizontal detachment propagates southward from the Greater Caucasus, along Upper Jurassic evaporites. Where this ramps up to surface, there are several noncylindrical anticlines involving Cretaceous to Tertiary sediments. Nonetheless, Greater Caucasus deformation has had very little influence on the geometry or structure of the Rioni Basin.

PLAYS AND TRAPPING MECHANISMS

Mesozoic

The Mesozoic has not been an important exploration target in Georgia. There are, nonetheless, two discoveries in West Georgia. The Chaladidi oil discovery is a small compressional ramp anticline that represents the southern deformation front of the Greater Caucasus, propagated horizontally along Upper Jurassic evaporites (Banks et al., this volume, their figure 4); Okumi was an accidental oil discovery, found during coal exploration beneath the backthrust of the frontal Greater Caucasus monocline, north of the Rioni foreland basin. The reservoir at Chaladidi is an Upper Cretaceous chalk, while the Okumi oil came from Upper Jurassic shallow marine limestones.

The lithostratigraphy of the Mesozoic in West Georgia is effectively that of the Shatsky Ridge, the northern passive margin of the Eastern Black Sea; it is known from onshore drilling to be a largely complete sequence of mainly deep water sediments from Lower Jurassic to Danian in age (Robinson et al., 1996). The distribution of potential reservoirs within this sequence is, however, poorly known. The Shatsky Ridge is not highly deformed either offshore or onshore, but there are a number of types of structural closures that might trap oil. Offshore, there are large low-amplitude closures cut by minor extensional faults (Gudauta, Ochamchira) that may be flexural features, related to loading by the Greater Caucasus. Onshore, there are gentle roll-over anticlines associated with the extensional (flexural?) faults that punctuate the otherwise monoclinal south-dip of the Shatsky Ridge beneath the Neogene Rioni Basin (Banks et al., this volume, their figures 2, 4). Both of these groups of structures affect the entire sedimentary sequence. In contrast, the detachment faults that propagate along the Upper Jurassic salt and produce small ramp anticlines where they ramp upward affect only Cretaceous and younger strata.

Beneath the Neogene Kartli foreland basin, Mesozoic sediments can be seen on seismic to form extensional tilted fault blocks beneath the foreland basin megasequence (Banks et al., this volume, their figures 8, 9). This stratigraphy has been drilled by two (dry) exploration wells (Shindisi and Kitsnisi), but very little information was collected from the Mesozoic section, so the implications from these wells for the distribution of reservoirs within the Mesozoic in Central Georgia remain unclear. Northeast of the Kartli foreland basin, there are small discoveries in the Mesozoic of the Greater Caucasus, notably in Lower Cretaceous turbidites (Vedzebi North). The reservoirs are immature thin sandstones, probably turbidites.

Middle Eocene

The middle Eocene has been the most productive play in Georgia (Vernik, 1990). It is the reservoir in the largest field in Georgia (Samgori), in the adjacent accumulation Ninotsminda, and in a number of small fields and discoveries in East Georgia, southeast of Tbilisi. There are also several small oil fields with middle Eocene reservoirs on the northern margin of the Achara-Trialet thrust belt, on the edge of the Kartli foreland basin (Akhalkalaki, Kavtiskhevi, Metechi). West of the Dziruli Massif in the Rioni foreland basin, the middle Eocene has been a target of exploration drilling, again along the northern margin of the thrust belt, but there have been no substantial discoveries. To the east, the play extends into the Kura Basin in Azerbaijan. The extent of the play to the south within the thrust belt is limited by the structural elevation of the Eocene. Samgori has produced >165 MMbbl of oil (Patton, 1993); Ninotsminda, which has not been fully developed, has produced 3 MMbbl of oil. Production from the other fields has been small.

The middle Eocene is dominated by interbedded volcaniclastic sandstones and siltstones (Figure 2) with subordinate submarine volcanic rocks (andesitic flows ≤30 m thick) and boulder beds (Figure 3). The sandstone-siltstone intervals show clear turbidite characteristics (graded bedding and Bouma sequences) and are similar to underlying Paleocene to lower Eocene turbidites, except that a high proportion of the grains is volcanogenic, especially plagioclase feldspar and mafic rock fragments. In the area around Tbilisi, the top 100 m of the middle Eocene is characterized by very coarse lithologies (Figure 3).

None of the middle Eocene lithologies has particularly high matrix porosity or permeability. Reservoir properties are reported to be best in tuffaceous rocks partly altered to laumontite (Grynberg et al., 1993). In Samgori, these have matrix porosities averaging 12% and matrix permeabilities averaging 15 mD. In Ninotsminda, while core plug He porosities may be ≤15%,

Figure 2. Middle Eocene volcanogenic turbidites, Tana Valley.

they are associated with matrix permeabilities typically <1 mD. Nonetheless, wells in Samgori completed openhole flowed at initial rates as high as 5000 bbl of oil per day (bopd) while even cased and perforated wells in Ninotsminda frequently flowed at ~700–800 bopd. The implication is that well performance is dependent upon fractures (Figure 4). Grynberg et al. (1993) identified two sets: microfractures within the laumontized zones, and tectonic subvertical fractures that link laumontized zones to one another. In outcrops west of Tbilisi, there is a clear relationship between sediment grain size and degree of fracturing: the finest grained turbidite beds are pervasively fractured, while coarser, sand-grade rocks are relatively unaffected by fracturing (Figure 5). A similar relationship has been observed in the Monterey Formation reservoirs, onshore and offshore California, where the bulk of the oil is stored in the finest grained sediments, in a stratigraphically controlled fracture porosity (Hornafius, 1994). This may be true also of the middle Eocene reservoirs in Georgia.

The middle Eocene volcaniclastic reservoirs are sealed by a thick sequence of upper Eocene mudstones (which probably also sourced the oil). The accumulations occur in ramp anticlines of the Achara-Trialet belt, particularly toward its northern margin. In East Georgia, the Achara-Trialet belt plunges east, disappearing just east of Tbilisi beneath a highly folded Oligocene to Miocene sequence. The latter appears to be thrust on top of earlier, previously eroded Achara-Trialet folds, so that the structures above the detachment as mapped at the surface bear no relationship to those in the underthrust (Figure 6). Most of the obvious anticlines with surface expressions have been drilled by the Georgian National Oil Company, Saknavtobi. Many are oil discoveries, although mainly small. However, there is potential to find further oil accumulations in thrust duplexes that have no obvious surface expression (other than in elevating the Paleogene sediments) and have not up to now been resolved by Georgian seismic reflection data. Such prospects would be very similar in structural setting to the giant Cusiana field in the Llanos foothills, Colombia (Cazier et al., 1995).

Lower Miocene

The lower Miocene includes a few small discoveries northeast of Tbilisi that have produced minor quantities of oil (Satskhenisi, Norio), but it has not been a major exploration target in either West or East Georgia. There are, however, excellent potential reservoirs at outcrop. Lower Miocene sediments outcrop along the southern margin of the Kartli foreland basin near Gori, where they rest apparently conformably on the Oligocene to lower Miocene Maikop unit (Figures 7, 8). Maikop siltstones and fine sandstones with abundant plant debris coarsen upward into medium to coarse sandstones considered to be of Burdigalian age. The general absence of primary sedimentary structures and the evidence for soft sediment deformation suggest that the thickly bedded lower Miocene sandstones in the lower part of the section were deposited rapidly by submarine gravity flows, probably in relatively shallow water at the front of a delta (Figure 9). Coarser cross-bedded sandstones above were probably deposited in a braided river system (Figure 10). The vertical transition from shallow marine to fluvial suggests deposition by a fan or braid delta that would have been prograding toward the southeast (paleocurrent data). Lower Miocene sandstones are very rich in quartz and feldspar and appear to have excellent reservoir properties (Figure 11).

Figure 3. Cliff of middle Eocene boulder beds beneath the Metechi church in the Kura River Gorge, Tbilisi. Boulders up to several meters across can be seen in the cliff below the church. These conglomerates, breccias, and boulder beds contain polymictic clasts of fine-grained porphyritic igneous rocks, mudstones, siltstones, sandstones, and rare limestones. The clasts are moderately rounded and the rocks appear to be clast supported with a matrix of mineralogically immature sand. These coarse sediments are interpreted as submarine debris flows, presumably active around submarine volcanic highs.

Samples from higher in the sequence also contain volcanogenic material. The sources of the quartz are presumably the Paleozoic metamorphic rocks and Middle Jurassic microgranites of the Dziruli Massif.

In the Kartli foreland basin, the lower Miocene appears to lie structurally above the major backthrust at the front of the Achara-Trialet fold belt (Banks et al., this volume). As a consequence, on the southern margin of the basin, it dips monoclinally northward. It does, however, become structured in the compressive folds that propagate southward from the Greater Caucasus fold belt (e.g., Norio, Satskhenisi discoveries).

Figure 4. Fractures in middle Eocene volcanogenic sediments, Tbilisi.

The lower Miocene also forms low-amplitude but potentially large drapes over (probably extensional) basement highs in the Kartli foreland basin that have never been tested by drilling. Seal could be provided by the silts and marls of the middle Miocene or, more distally to the east, by intraformational lower Miocene mudstones, but the presence of an effective seal is probably the main risk associated with this play. In the Rioni foreland basin, the lower Miocene has never been considered an exploration target; outcrop is poor and little is known about the unit.

Upper Miocene (Sarmatian and Meotian)

Sarmatian and Meotian clastics have been among the main exploration targets in the Rioni foreland basin. The Supsa field contains ~29 MMbbl oil in place in a number of stacked Sarmatian clastic units that form a fault-bend fold in the hanging wall of the frontal Achara-Trialet thrust (Banks et al., this volume, their figure 4). Beneath the thrust, the Shromisubani oil discovery is reservoired in Meotian clastics and may be a stratigraphic trap. Outcrop is very poor in this area and little sedimentological work has so far been done on

Figure 5. Relationship between grain size and degree of fracturing in middle Eocene volcanogenic turbidites west of Tbilisi.

well data. As a consequence, little is known about the depositional settings of these units. The wireline log data from the Meotian reservoir sands in Shromisubani-101 are interpreted as reflecting deposition in a fluvial to shallow marine setting. The abundance of Eocene foraminifera in these upper Miocene sediments and the abundant volcanogenic material indicate that the main source of the sediment was the Achara-Trialet folds growing to the south. Reservoir quality is adversely affected by abundant volcanogenic grains.

Sarmatian and Meotian sediments are folded into fault bend folds along the southern margin of the Rioni Basin east of Supsa. Marine seismic data show that the same geology continues unbroken offshore, with several frontal folds occurring close to the shoreline.

PETROLEUM SOURCE SYSTEMS

Oil Geochemistry

Eight oil and oil seep samples were collected (Table 1; Figure 1); four from West Georgia (Shromisubani, Natanebi, Guliani, and Okumi), two from the Kartli Basin (Uplistsikhe and Akhalkalaki), and two from East Georgia (Vedzebi North and Ninotsminda). Oils were analyzed by GC to identify major components, by GCMS to quantify specific biomarkers, and were also analyzed for carbon isotope ratios following standard liquid chromatographic separation into four fractions (Tissot and Welte, 1984).

Gas Chromatography

Figures 12 and 13 show whole oil- and saturate-fraction gas chromatograms for the analyzed oils. Three of the analyses show the raised background that is characteristic of biodegradation. This alteration is so severe for the Guliani and Akhalkalaki samples that little further information can be extracted from their gas chromatograms. Their biomarker contents may also have been altered. The Natanebi gas chromatogram has a raised background and a high ratio of pristane and phytane to *n*-alkanes, both indicating that the oil has suffered more moderate biodegradation. The whole oil–gas chromatogram also has a low content of $<C_{13}$ compounds, indicating evaporative loss. The Shromisubani oil has a broad, flat *n*-alkane envelope extending over the higher molecular weight range, including abundant isoprenoids and waxes, and a high content of biomarkers. It seems likely that this oil has been produced by mixing of two oils: (1) A biodegraded oil responsible for the relatively high biomarker content and possibly the elevated isoprenoid/*n*-alkane ratio. The GCMS biomarker analysis indicates that the source is mixed terrestrial and marine organic matter; and (2) A waxy oil supplying the high-molecular-weight *n*-alkanes, generated from a source rock with predominantly terrestrial organic matter.

The Okumi oil is little altered, although the absence of peaks below n-C_9 indicates evaporative loss. The remaining *n*-alkane envelope indicates a mixed marine-terrestrial source and the low isoprenoid/*n*-alkane ratio generation at a high level of maturity.

The Uplistsikhe oil is a light oil that has undergone very mild biodegradation, depleting the volatile compounds. The *n*-alkane envelope is typical of a clastic marine source rock, with minor terrestrial input; the high isoprenoid/*n*-alkane ratio indicates generation at a low level of maturity.

The oil from Ninotsminda has an *n*-alkane envelope characteristic of a middle mature oil that may have lost some light components through mild biodegradation,

Table 1. Oil and Source Rock Extract Samples.

Oil Sample	Reservoir	Pr/Phy	API Gravity	Alteration
West Georgia				
Shromisubani 42	Meotian	1.53	21.5	Moderate biodegradation
Natanebi 2	(well head seep)	1.53	*	Severe evaporative loss
Guliani 21	(well head seep)		14.7	Severe biodegradation
Okumi 1	Upper Jurassic	1.86	42.5	
Kartli				
Uplistsikhe 5	Middle Eocene(?)	0.96	41.3	
Akhalkalaki	(surface seep)		*	Severe biodegradation
East Georgia				
Ninotsminda 30	Middle Eocene	1.94	40.9	
Vedzebi North 1	Lower Cretaceous	1.99	30.4	
Extracts (upper Eocene)				
Kavtiskhevi 7 (1889.5 m)		2.30		
Kavtiskhevi 25 (1500 m)		2.55		

*Insufficient sample for analysis.

and was generated from a source rock containing mixed marine and terrestrial kerogen. The high isoprenoid content suggests that the oil was sourced from a middle mature kerogen. The Vedzebi North oil appears rather similar to that from Ninotsminda, but it seems to be more biodegraded.

Figure 14 shows pristane and phytane contents normalized to their *n*-alkane isomers (Shanmugam, 1985). The results indicate that all oils have mixed marine and terrestrial kerogen sources. The Okumi sample is notable for its high maturity.

Gas Chromatography–Mass Spectrometry

Figure 15 shows crossplots of C_{27}, C_{28}, and C_{29} steranes for the analyzed oils. The grouping is not particularly tight, probably reflecting at very least a variation in source rock organic facies and also in maturity. Note in particular how the Vedzebi North oil appears quite distinct from the others. The variation in C_{29}/C_{27} sterane content is consistent with mixed terrestrial-marine kerogen (Moldowan et al., 1985), while the relatively high C_{28} content (about the same as that of the other two steranes) is characteristic of oils derived from Tertiary or possibly Late Cretaceous source rocks. All of the oils contain oleanane, again suggesting a Tertiary or Upper Cretaceous higher plant component in the source organic matter (Riva et al., 1988; Ekweozor and Telnaes, 1990; Thomas, 1990).

Carbon isotopes

Figure 16 shows Galimov curves for the eight oils. The oils from Natanebi, Shromisubani, Uplistsikhe, Akhalkalaki, and Ninotsminda have very similar curves with alkane and whole oil ratios around –27‰, consistent with derivation from a single source rock. The curve for Vedzebi North oil is shifted by ~1.5–2‰ to heavier ratios; this is possibly in part a reflection of the higher maturity of this oil, but is also likely to be due to it having a different source rock. The Galimov curve for the Okumi oil is also very different, with alkanes and whole oil ratios between –31 and –32‰, suggesting that this was not derived from the same source rock as the oils from the Natanebi group either.

Source Rock Geochemistry

A total of 13 outcrop samples and 36 core samples of mudstone were analyzed to determine their potential as source rocks. These came from locations in Kartli and East Georgia; no samples were available from West Georgia, because mudstones do not outcrop well and because core was not available. Samples were analyzed for total organic carbon (TOC) content, and those with TOC >1% were analyzed further by Rock-Eval pyrolysis. Those demonstrated to have significant oil source potential were then extracted and analyzed by GC, GCMS, and stable isotope mass spectrometry. The results of the screening are listed in Table 2.

Only samples from the upper Eocene and, to a lesser extent, the Oligocene show significant source potential. Upper Eocene samples have TOCs ≤4.3%, and pyrolysis yields ≤17.9 kg/t. The HI (hydrogen index) between 70 and 416 indicates potential for generating oil and gas, but samples from the Kavtiskhevi wells in particular are distinctly oil-prone. The organic matter in these samples is predominantly marine sapropel. The Oligocene samples with elevated TOC and P_2 tend, in contrast, to be mainly gas-prone. There is just a single sample of uncertain Oligocene age from Kavtiskhevi-25, which has P_2 of 9.5 kg/t and HI of 588, indicating good oil source potential.

Oil Source Correlation

The GC, GCMS, and carbon isotope analyses of extracts from upper Eocene and Oligocene source rocks are plotted on Figures 14–16. Upper Eocene source rocks appear capable of sourcing all of the analyzed oils, with the exception of those from Okumi and Vedzebi North

Table 2. Source Rock Screening Analysis.

Position	Location	Depth (m)	TOC (%)	T_{max} (°C)	P_2 (kg/T)	HI	VR (%)	SCI
Upper Jurassic	Gudauri	*	0.38				0.35	4
Upper Jurassic	Mleti	*	1.02	426	.03	3		
Lower Cretaceous	Kavtiskhevi 8	3737	0.35					
Albian–Cenomanian	Kavtiskhevi 29	3318	0.47					
Lower–Upper Cretaceous	Kitsnisi 1	2788	0.48					
Upper Cretaceous	Mokhisi 2	1660	0.28					
Upper Cretaceous	Kavtiskhevi 8	3150	0.38					
Upper Cretaceous	Kavtiskhevi 26	3463	0.24					
Upper Cretaceous	Kavtiskhevi 26	3470	0.68					
Upper Cretaceous	Kavtiskhevi 29	2986	0.58					
Paleocene/ Lower Eocene	Kavtiskhevi 27	3495	0.25					
Lower Eocene	Borjomi	*	0.36				0.70	
Lower Eocene	Borjomi	*	0.11					
Lower Eocene	Tana valley	*	0.15					
Lower Eocene	Tana valley	*	0.04					
Lower Eocene	Tana valley	*	0.04					7.5
Middle Eocene	Kavtiskhevi 25a	3472	0.58					
Middle Eocene	Kavtiskhevi 26	2981	0.17					
Middle Eocene	Kavtiskhevi 26	3244	0.11					
Middle Eocene	Kavtiskhevi 26	3415	0.18					
Middle Eocene	Kavtiskhevi 27	3374	0.23					
Middle Eocene	Tbilisi	*	1.18	455	1.1	92	0.62	
Middle Eocene	Borjomi	*	0.09				0.34	3.5
Middle Eocene	Tana valley	*	1.56	444	1.6	248		
Upper Eocene	Metechi 3	2107	1.46	436	1.5	105		
Upper Eocene	Metechi 3	2959	1.04	441	0.7	70		
Upper Eocene	Kavtiskhevi 7	1888	4.30	417	17.9	416	0.31	2.5
Upper Eocene	Kavtiskhevi 23	1910	1.48	430	1.7	115		
Upper Eocene	Kavtiskhevi 25a	2670	1.34	429	2.4	176		
Upper Eocene	Kavtiskhevi 25a	2758	2.20	424	6.1	275	0.38	3.5
Upper Eocene	Kavtiskhevi 25a	2863	2.06	426	5.8	282		
Upper Eocene	Kavtiskhevi 25a	2975	1.16	433	1.4	122		
Upper Eocene	Kavtiskhevi 25a	3157	0.89					
Upper Eocene	Kavtiskhevi 25a	3446	1.99	425	6.2	314	0.43	3.5
Upper Eocene	Kavtiskhevi 26	2124	2.46	422	9.4	382	0.34	3.5
Upper Eocene	Kavtiskhevi 26	2655	1.49	434	2.1	141		
Upper Eocene	Kavtiskhevi 26	2774	1.24	434	1.7	133		
Upper Eocene	Kavtiskhevi 27	2644	0.09					
Oligocene	Metechi 3	1039	2.68	425	6.1	226		
Oligocene	Metechi 3	1305	1.53	435	1.6	107		
Oligocene	Kavtiskhevi 23	1688	1.27	431	1.5	115		
Oligocene(?)	Kavtiskhevi 25a	1234	1.67	431	1.8	107		
Oligocene(?)	Kavtiskhevi 25a	1500	1.62	423	9.5	588	0.34	3.5
Oligocene	Kavtiskhevi 25a	1706	1.66	429	2.8	166		
Oligocene	Khrami massif	*	1.12	429	0.71	63		
Oligocene	Tana valley	*	1.63	436	4.0	248	0.41	3.5
Oligocene	Tana valley	*	1.19	433	2.5	211		
Lower Miocene	Sartichala	*	0.57				0.44	3
Lower Miocene	Uplistsikhe	*	0.30					
Middle Miocene(?)	Udjarma	*	1.24	428	1.6	127	0.5	3.5
Sarmatian	Kitsnisi 1	2082	0.36					
Sarmatian	Odzisi 1	4035	0.47					

*Denotes sample collected at outcrop.

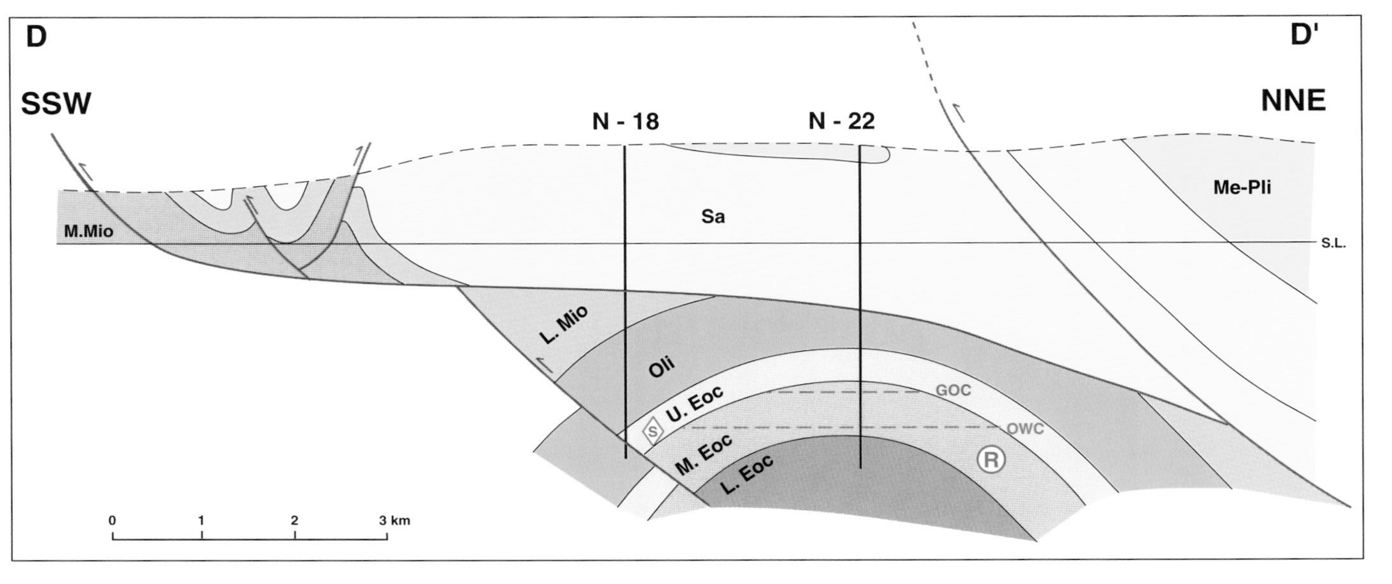

Figure 6. Geological cross section through Ninotsminda field, East Georgia. Sa = Sarmatian; Me = Meotian; Horizontal = vertical scale.

Figure 7. Lower Miocene clastic sequence of the Kartli foreland basin (Uplistsikhe, near Gori). Photograph taken looking east along the Kura Valley from the medieval cave town of Uplistsikhe. The cave dwellings are excavated in the lower part of a 650-m-thick series of lower Miocene sandstones, which are capped by middle Miocene marls and limestones (visible in distance). A log through part of this section is shown in Figure 8.

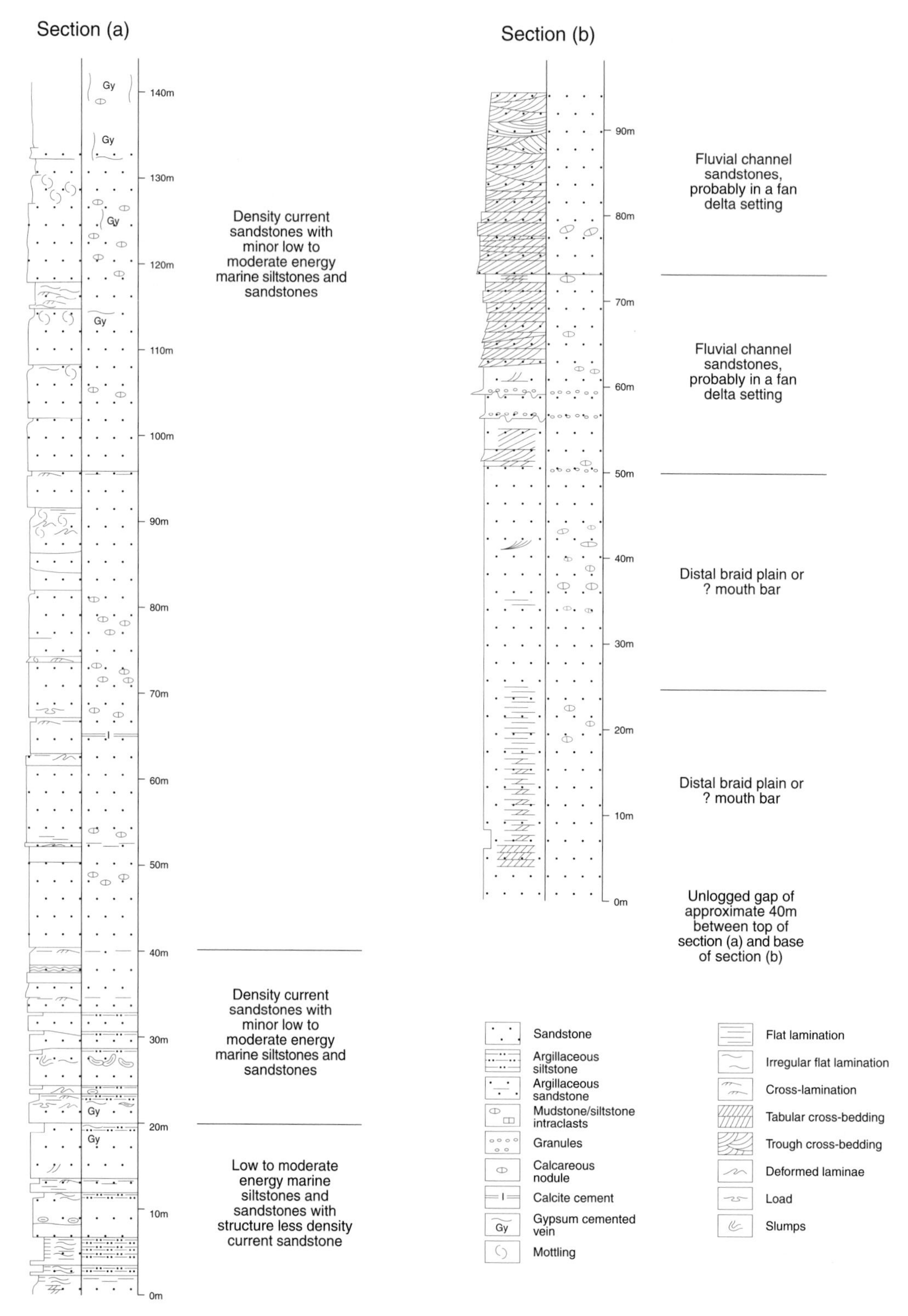

Figure 8. Summary sedimentary log through the lower part of the lower Miocene, Uplistsikhe. The sandstones on section (a) are sharp based and tabular; primary sedimentary structures are absent but there are occasional slumps. Individual sand beds are generally 1.5–6 m thick, but beds coalesce to form sandy units ≤10 m thick that are separated by thin (<0.5-m-thick) fine sandstones or siltstones. Farther up the section [lower part of section (b)], the sandstones are locally cross-bedded, with sets 10–25 cm thick, but indistinct horizontal bedding remains predominant. Paleocurrent directions obtained from the cross sets are unidirectional and to the southeast. Above 56 m on section (b), there are a number of erosive surfaces overlain by granule and pebble horizons; 73 m above the base of section (b), there is a pronounced color change from gray to orange, coinciding with a marked erosive contact, an increase in grain size, and in the proportion of volcanogenic grains. Above this point, the sandstones exhibit large-scale cross-bedding, with tabular sets 0.5–1.2 m thick overlain by trough cross sets ≤3 m thick. Some of the sands again show evidence of soft-sediment deformation.

Figure 9. Lower Miocene sandstones. Photograph taken at ~24–35 m on section (a), Figure 8. Individual sandstones are ≤4 m thick and are interpreted as sediment gravity flow (turbidity current or grain flow) deposits.

Figure 10. Trough cross-bedded lower Miocene sandstones east of Uplistsikhe. Sets are 1–3 m thick and 10–20 m wide and indicate paleocurrents toward the ESE (toward the camera). Note the local soft-sediment deformation. Equivalent to ~80–95 m on section (b), Figure 8.

Figure 11. Scanning election photomicrograph of lower Miocene sandstone, Uplistsikhe. The sandstones show abundant intergranular porosity, with minor grain-coating clays and zeolites.

(precluded by the stable carbon isotope data) and perhaps one of the components of the apparently mixed Shromisubani oil. Robinson et al. (1996) concluded that an upper Eocene source rock as exposed on the coast of the Russian Black Sea near Tuapse was probably responsible for generating oils over much of the Black Sea region, including the Lebada field, offshore Romania. Patton (1993) suggested that the source rock for the oil in Samgori was of lower Eocene age. However, he was unable to support this conclusion with geochemical data, basing it on burial history and thermal modeling alone.

Upper Eocene organic-rich black mudstones are exposed around the northern and eastern outcrop belt of the Achara-Trialet thrust belt (Figure 17), and are in stratigraphic contact with the most important reservoir in the region, the middle Eocene volcanogenic turbidites. They comprise several hundred meters of mainly distal turbidites, with relatively few fine sand and silt beds. The unit was deposited during the late postrift phase of the Achara-Trialet Basin and onlaps to the north toward the Neogene Kartli foreland basin (the northern basin margin during the Paleogene) (Banks et al., this volume, their figure 5). Beneath the Kartli basin, the upper Eocene is condensed to absent (in Shindisi and Kitsnisi wells), but it thickens again to the north toward the Caucasus Basin where upper Eocene sediments include spectacular olistostromes with blocks of Upper Jurassic limestone (Banks et al., this volume). On the other side of the Caucasus, where inversion of the Mesozoic basin began in the late Eocene, the unit presumably onlaps the Russian Platform to the north. As compressional deformation in the Black Sea region had begun by the late Eocene (related to closure of the Tethys Ocean to the south) (Robinson et al., 1996), it is possible that the organic-rich upper Eocene mudstones represent the first sediments deposited in the newly restricted chain of marginal basins north of the suture—Paratethys.

The Okumi oil remains somewhat enigmatic. Although the stable isotope data show that this oil is not cogenetic with the others, the presence of oleanane still suggests a Tertiary to Upper Cretaceous source rock. However, it is hard to see any physical connection or possible migration route between Okumi and a deeply buried sequence of this age that might contain a source rock (Banks et al., this volume). Note that Robinson et al. (1996) did not find oleanane in their analysis of the Okumi oil, possibly suggesting that some form of contamination has affected the present study. A Mesozoic source rock is probably necessary if Mesozoic plays are to prove oil (or gas) bearing in most of Georgia. Apart from the evidence of the Okumi discovery, however, there is the existence of Vedzebi North and other related small discoveries. Vedzebi North cannot, on geological grounds, have been sourced by the upper Eocene, and an alternative source rock is suggested by the geochemical data. The apparent presence of oleanane suggests that the source rock is probably Upper Cretaceous in age. Upper Jurassic mudstones exposed in the Greater Caucasus are graphitic, but the original nature of the organic matter and the extent of such rocks are not known.

One further source rock is probably responsible for the second component of the Shromisubani oil. The flat GC profile, rich in waxes, suggests the involvement of a locally mature Tertiary coal. Biostratigraphic data suggest that the wettest period during the Neogene—and, therefore, perhaps the most probable age for coal development—was during the early Miocene (Robertsons, 1996, unpublished data).

Maturation and Migration

Upper Eocene sediments are unlikely to have been covered by sufficient sediment to initiate oil generation prior to the initiation of compressional faulting and folding in the Achara-Trialet thrust belt, probably sometime during the Oligocene. Oil generation is likely to have been initiated by thrusting and consequent subsidence of the northern Achara-Trialet Basin margin during the Oligocene, with most generation probably taking place during the Miocene. Oil could then fill the middle Eocene volcaniclastic reservoirs

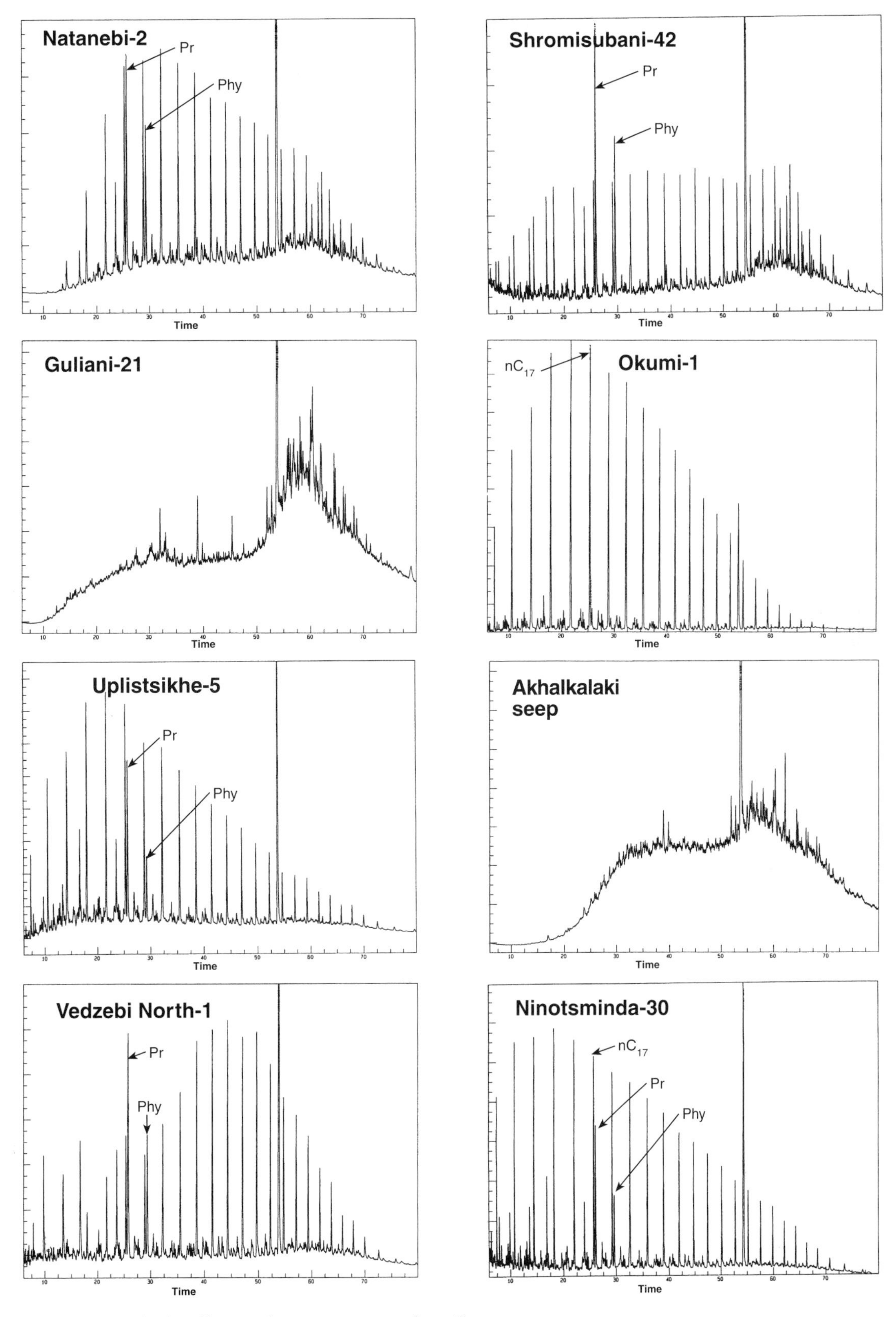

Figure 12. Whole oil–gas chromatograms for oils.

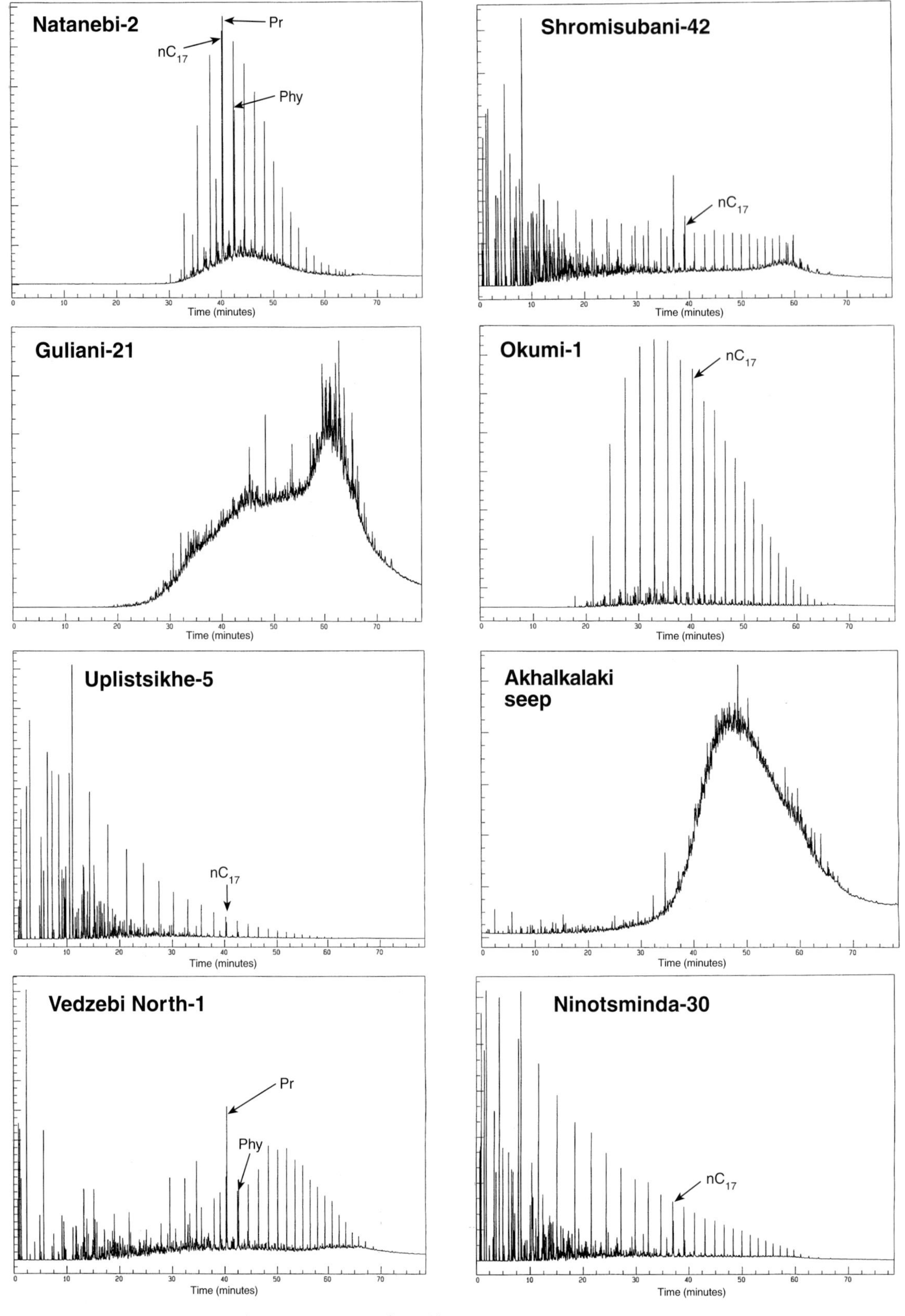

Figure 13. Saturate–gas chromatograms for oils.

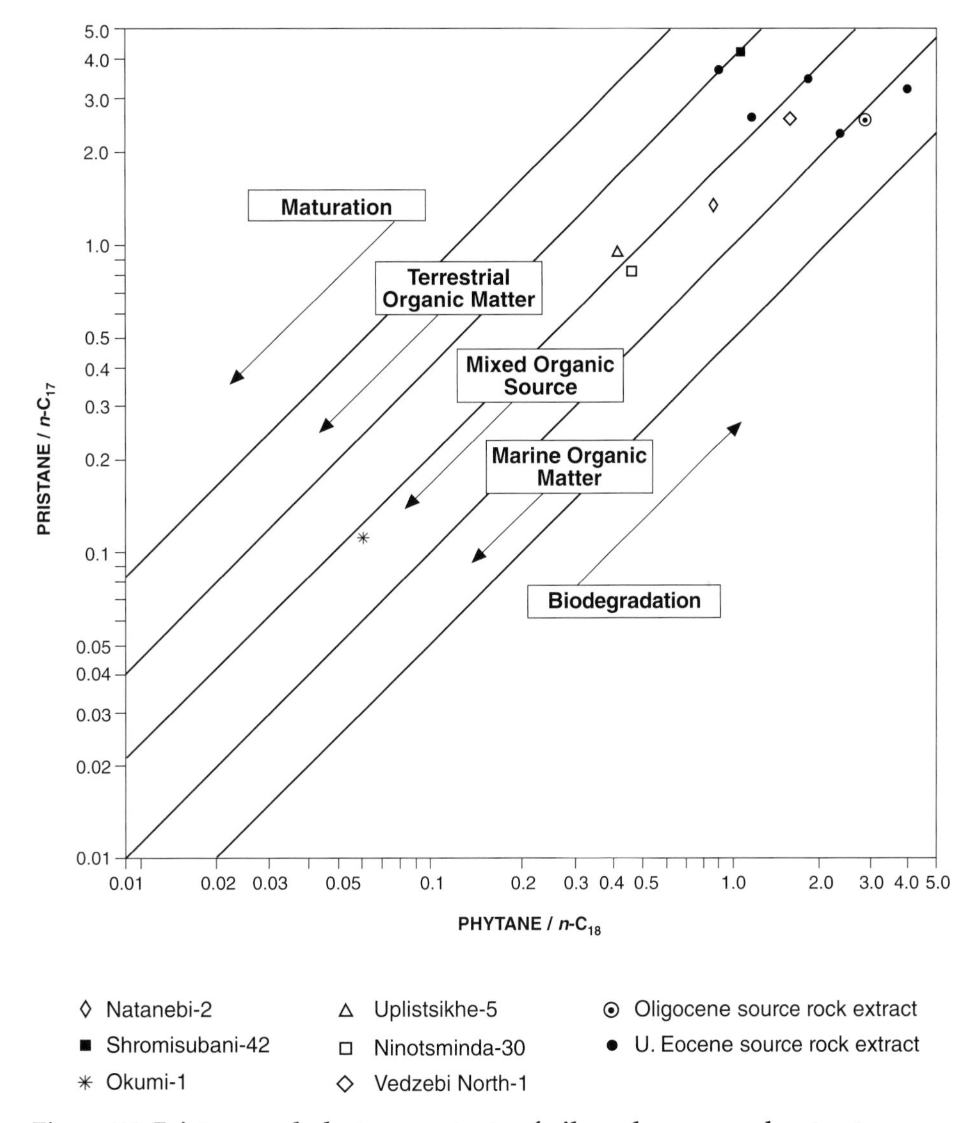

Figure 14. Pristane and phytane contents of oils and source rock extracts.

that are in stratigraphic contact with the upper Eocene, either from a locally mature source or by migration along faults from a more deeply buried duplex.

Few maturity measurements are available. At Kavtiskhevi in the Kartli Basin, the upper Eocene in contact with the middle Eocene reservoir is immature to just early mature (Table 2), and migration of oil from depth is implied. Vitrinite reflectance measurements for the upper Eocene in the Samgori field in East Georgia indicate an oil generation threshold at ~1200 m, with the main phase of oil generation (0.5–0.75% R_0) between 1800 and 2700 m (Patton, 1993). These maturity data indicate either that the geothermal gradient is high or that there is some section missing due to uplift and erosion. The oil from the adjacent Ninotsminda accumulation is a middle to late-mature oil, generated at R_0 of ~0.75% (see above), which would correspond to a present-day depth of ~2700 m. The flanks of the Ninotsminda structure today extend to this depth; it is therefore possible that at least some of the oil was locally sourced prior to regional uplift.

CONCLUSIONS

The basins that run through central Georgia form a coherent petroleum province characterized by (1) a common stratigraphic and structural history involving the development of a Paleogene extensional basin to the south (Achara-Trialet), its subsequent compression, and the consequent development of flexural foreland basins above the old rift margins (Shatsky Ridge and its extensions); and (2) the widespread presence of an upper Eocene oil-prone source rock matured during Neogene thrusting.

The widespread working source system alone suggests that despite many years of exploration with relatively modest success, there remains potential for new discoveries in Georgia. The middle Eocene play has been intensively explored, particularly around the margins of the foreland basins, but Georgian reflection seismic data have never been able to image deeper structures such as thrust duplexes; none of which, as a consequence, have been drilled. There is probably also

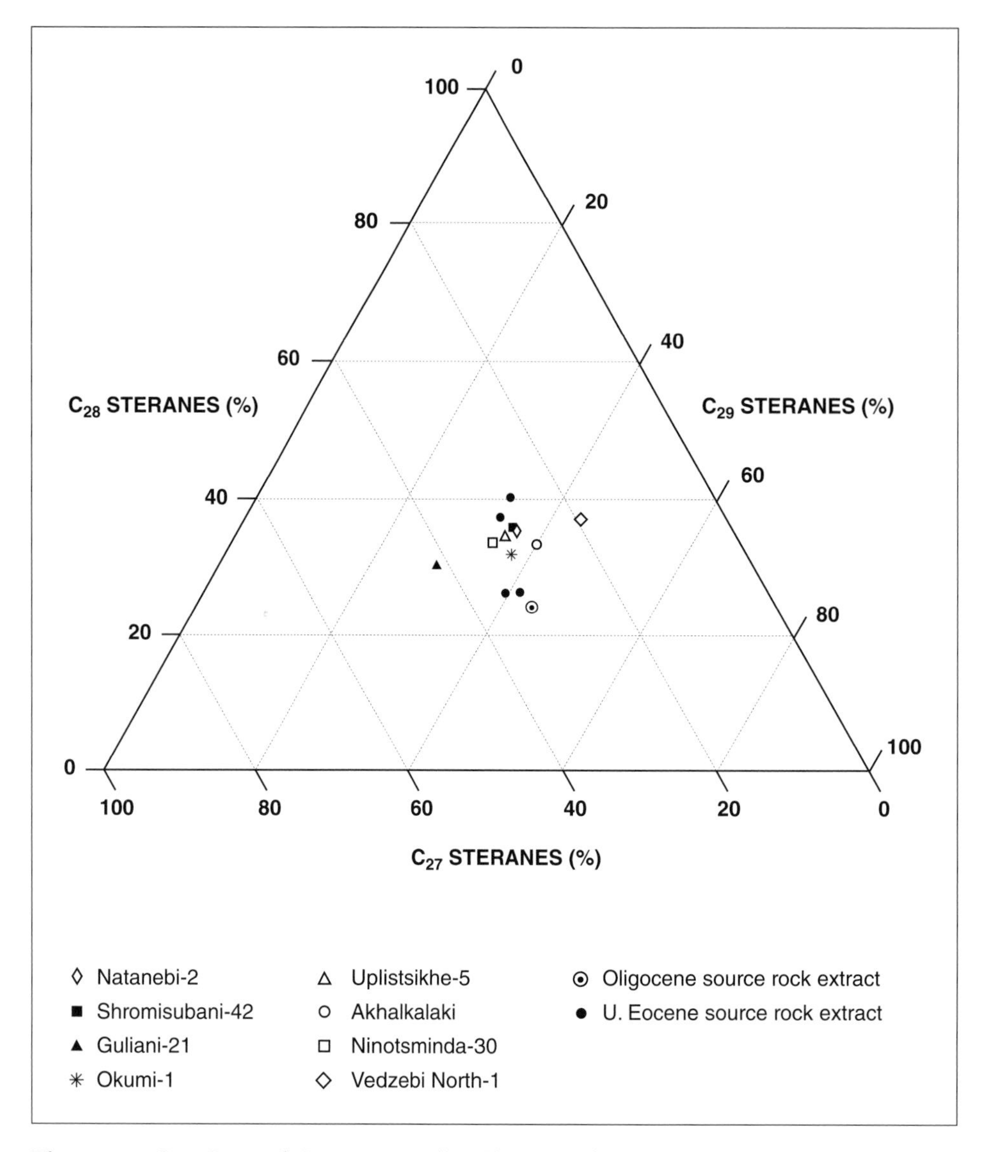

Figure 15. C_{27}, C_{28} and C_{29} sterane distributions for oils and source rock extracts.

potential in the effectively unexplored lower Miocene or poorly constrained Mesozoic plays in the central parts of the foreland basins. Structural closures have not been properly defined in these areas, particularly in the Kartli Basin, because of limited reflection seismic coverage of poor quality. The lower Miocene is of particular interest because of its good reservoir quality where observed at outcrop. Significant potential probably also exists offshore, where there has been no exploration drilling and reflection seismic data coverage is limited and of poor quality.

ACKNOWLEDGMENTS

We would like to thank Dito Papava and colleagues in Saknavtobi (Georgian Oil), especially Irakli Tavdumadze, for help in acquiring and obtaining data. Saknavtobi, Robertsons, and JKX Oil & Gas kindly gave permission to publish this study.

REFERENCES CITED

Adamia, S., K.T. Akhvlediani, V.M. Kilasonia, A.E.M. Nairn, D. Papava, and D.K. Patton, 1992, Geology of the Republic of Georgia: International Geology Review, v. 34, p. 447–476.

Banks, C.J., A.G. Robinson, and M.P. Williams, this volume, Structure and regional tectonics of the Achara-Trialet fold belt and the adjacent Rioni and Kartli foreland basins, Republic of Georgia, *in* A.G. Robinson, ed., Regional and petroleum geology of the Black Sea and surrounding region: AAPG Memoir 68, p. 331–346.

Cazier, E.C., A.B. Hayward, G. Espinoza, J. Velandia, J.-F. Mugniot, and W.G. Leel, Jr., 1995, Petroleum geology of the Cusiana field, Llanos Basin foothills, Colombia: AAPG Bulletin, v. 79, p. 1444–1463.

Ekweozor, C.M., and N. Telnaes, 1990, Oleanane parameter; verification by quantitative study of the

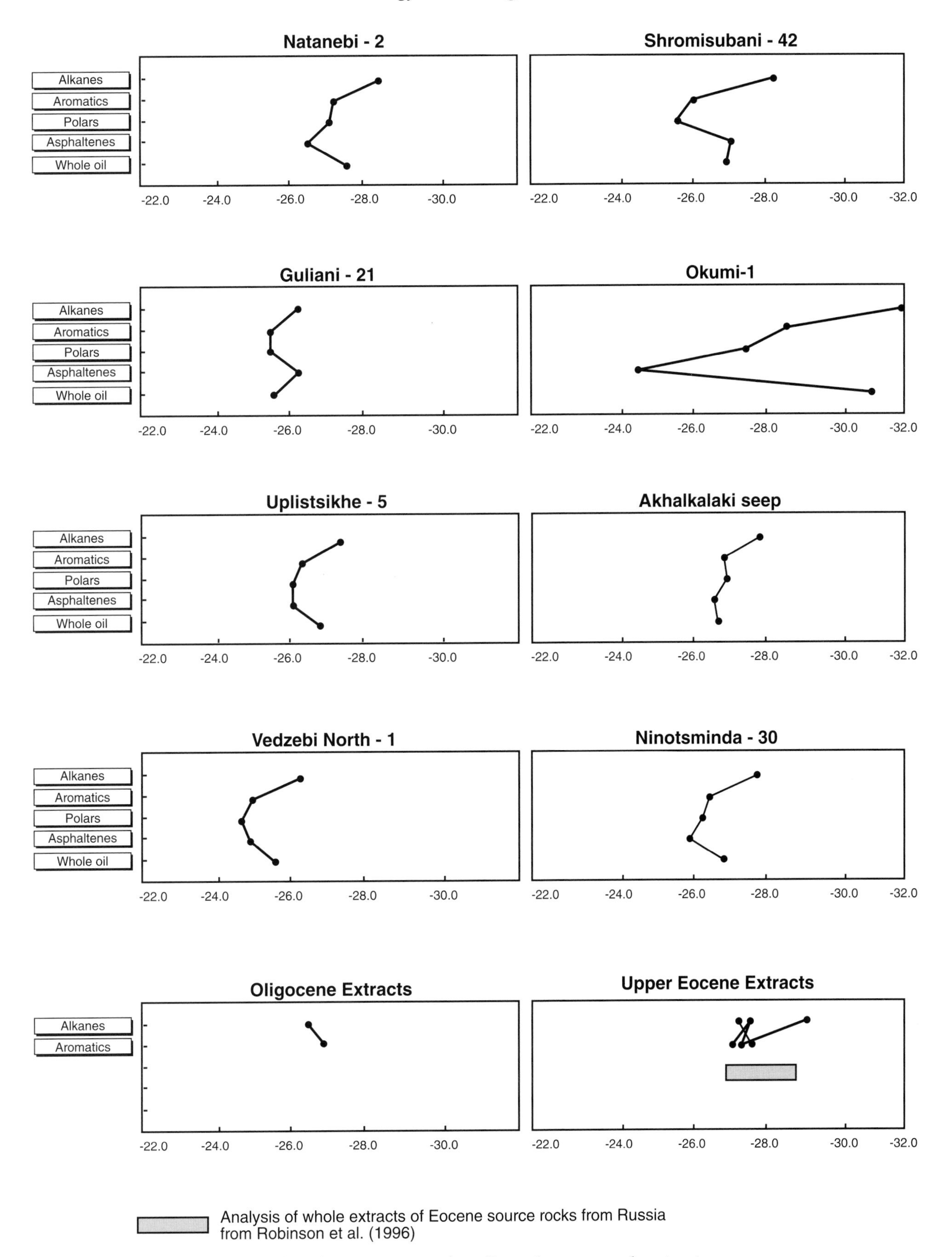

Figure 16. Galimov stable carbon isotope curves for oils and source rock extracts.

Figure 17. Outcrop of upper Eocene turbidites east of Tbilisi.

biomarker occurrence in sediments of the Niger Delta: Organic Geochemistry, v. 16, p. 401–413.
Grynberg, M.E., D. Papava, M. Shengelia, A. Takaishvili, A. Nanadze, and D.K. Patton, 1993, Petrophysical characteristics of the middle Eocene laumontite tuff reservoir, Samgori field, Republic of Georgia: Journal of Petroleum Geology, v. 16, p. 313–322.
Hornafius, J.S., ed., 1994, Field guide to the Monterey Formation between Santa Barbara and Gaviota, California: AAPG Pacific Section, 123 p.
Jones, R.W., and M.D. Simmons, this volume, A review of the stratigraphy of Eastern Paratethys (Oligocene–Holocene), with particular emphasis on the Black Sea, *in* A.G. Robinson, ed., Regional and petroleum geology of the Black Sea and surrounding region: AAPG Memoir 68, p. 39–52.
Moldowan, J.M., W.K. Seifert, and E.J. Gallegos, 1985, Relationship between petroleum composition and depositional environment of petroleum source rocks: AAPG Bulletin, v. 69, p. 1255–1268.
Okay, A.I., and Ö. Şahintürk, this volume, Geology of the Eastern Pontides, *in* A.G. Robinson, ed., Regional and petroleum geology of the Black Sea and surrounding region: AAPG Memoir 68, p. 291–312.
Patton, D.K., 1993, Samgori field, Republic of Georgia: critical review of island-arc oil and gas: Journal of Petroleum Geology, v. 16, p. 153–168.
Robinson, A.G., C.J. Banks, M.M. Rutherford and J.P.P. Hirst, 1995, Stratigraphic and structural evolution of the Eastern Pontides, Turkey: Journal of the Geological Society of London, v. 152, p. 861–872.
Robinson, A.G., J.H. Rudat, C.J. Banks, and R.L.F. Wiles, 1996, Petroleum geology of the Black Sea: Marine and Petroleum Geology, v. 13, p. 195–223.
Riva, A., P.G. Caccialanza, and F. Quagliaroli, 1988, Recognition of 18β(H)-oleanane in several crudes and Tertiary to Upper Cretaceous sediments: definition of a new maturity parameter: Organic Geochemistry, v. 13, p. 671–675.
Shanmugam G., 1985, Significance of coniferous rain forests and related organic matter in generating commercial quantities of oil, Gippsland Basin, Australia: AAPG Bulletin, v. 69, p. 1241–1254.
Thomas, J., 1990, Biological markers in sediments with respect to geological time: Ph.D. thesis, University of Bristol, U.K.
Tissot, B.P., and D.H. Welte, 1984, Petroleum formation and occurrence: New York, Springer-Verlag, 699 p.
Vernik, L., 1990, A new type of reservoir rock in volcaniclastic sequences: AAPG Bulletin, v. 74, p. 830–836.

Robinson, A.G., and E. Kerusov, 1997, Stratigraphic and structural development of the Gulf of Odessa, Ukrainian Black Sea: implications for petroleum exploration, *in* A.G. Robinson, ed., Regional and petroleum geology of the Black Sea and surrounding region: AAPG Memoir 68, p. 369–380.

Chapter 19

Stratigraphic and Structural Development of the Gulf of Odessa, Ukrainian Black Sea: Implications for Petroleum Exploration

Andrew G. Robinson
JKX Oil & Gas plc
Guildford, Surrey, United Kingdom

Edward Kerusov
Chernomorneftegas
Simferopol, Ukraine

ABSTRACT

The Gulf of Odessa forms the northern rift and passive margin of the extensional Western Black Sea. The prerift comprises the Scythian Proterozoic to Triassic platform in the north (which dips gently southward) and, in the south, a Triassic–Early Jurassic back-arc basin that closed during the Middle Jurassic (Tavric-Küre Series). Both of these units were covered by a Late Jurassic carbonate platform prior to the Aptian–Albian doming and rifting that preceded the opening of the Western Black Sea (Cenomanian). During the late Eocene to Oligocene, Aptian–Albian half-grabens suffered limited inversion related to closure of the Tethyan Ocean in Central Anatolia. The main play in the Gulf of Odessa has involved Lower Paleocene chalk in inversion-related anticlines formed during the late Eocene to Oligocene. The chalks are not significantly fractured, and permeabilities are of the order of a few millidarcys. The source rock for the wet gas has not been positively identified, but may be Paleozoic, possibly Devonian, or Albian in age. Extensional structures that formed prior to inversion may still contain the early oil charge from such a source. Adjacent to the deep Black Sea Basin, there is an east-west–trending extensional high (Kalamit Ridge) that extends into Romania and includes the Lebada oil field. The Lebada play, transgressional Albian sandstones draped over partly inverted extensional fault blocks and charged by a Tertiary (Upper Eocene?) source rock in the deep Black Sea Basin, extends into Ukrainian waters.

INTRODUCTION

The Gulf of Odessa is the northwestern shelf of the Black Sea and is in Ukrainian territorial waters. It is unusual in the Black Sea in that there is a large area of shelf beneath moderate water depths of <100 m and, as a result, there has been offshore exploration activity since 1962, when the first reflection seismic data were acquired offshore. Deep drilling commenced in 1971 with the Golitsyna-1 discovery well; there are now seven gas and gas-condensate discoveries: Odessa, Shtormavaya, Golitsyna, South Golitsyna, Schmidta Archangelsk, and Krym. The first three have Paleocene carbonate (chalk) reservoirs that contain wet gas; the last four have Oligocene siltstone reservoirs that contain dry gas (Palii and Tochkov, 1994). Shtormavaya is the largest accumulation known, with reserves of ~700 bcf; Golitsyna contained initial reserves of ~420 bcf but is now substantially depleted.

Many of the key features of the geology of the Gulf of Odessa are related to its status as the northern rift margin of the Western Black Sea (Robinson et al., 1996) (Figure 1). The Western Black Sea is an Aptian–Albian rift that opened into an oceanic basin during the Cenomanian, separating the Gulf of Odessa from the area that subsequently formed the Western and Central Pontides in North Turkey (Görür, 1988; Banks and Robinson, this volume). Both the Pontides and the Crimean Mountains underwent compression from the late Eocene, related to closure of the Tethys Ocean to the south. As a consequence, much stratigraphy that is relevant to the offshore Gulf of Odessa has been elevated and now outcrops.

In this chapter, we report the results of a study of well and offshore reflection seismic data that we have integrated with outcrop studies in both the Crimean Mountains and the Pontides in Turkey. We have adopted a seismic stratigraphic approach to interpretation of the offshore data and tried to understand it in terms of well data (often rather scanty), information from outcrop, and the regional geological setting of the area. The first part of the chapter covers the structural and stratigraphic evolution of the Gulf of Odessa, organized according to coherent seismic stratigraphic units we have identified that each relate to a phase of basin development (megasequences of Hubbard et al., 1985). This is illustrated with reference to a long regional seismic line (Figure 2). Each megasequence is defined in terms of its seismic stratigraphic characteristics and then interpreted with reference to onshore and offshore stratigraphic data. We then summarize the implications of the tectonostratigraphic interpretation for the development and distribution of petroleum reservoirs, proven and possible. Finally, there is a discussion of the petroleum source system responsible for the gas discoveries in the area.

GEOLOGICAL HISTORY

Prerift

Seismic Stratigraphy and Well Data

The prerift megasequence can be identified on reflection seismic data offshore as a coherent seismic stratigraphic package beneath a major erosional unconformity and cut by apparently planar extensional faults that do not generally cut the strata above the unconformity (Figure 2). The erosion and faulting that mark the top of the prerift are best developed in the southern and central parts of the Gulf of Odessa; extension does not appear to have affected the prerift stratigraphy too much in the north. In this northern zone, the prerift has a clearly sedimentary character and shows little truncation beneath the unconformity. South of about the Selskogo well on the Kalamit Ridge, the clear reflections within the prerift tend to become restricted to the upper 100–200 ms; beneath this, the unit is accoustically virtually transparent. In this zone, the top of the prerift is a very marked high-amplitude reflector.

The prerift has been drilled in a number of wells, including Desantnaya, Delphin, and Golitsyna-2, the results of which appear to reflect the seismic stratigraphic differences between north and south. Golitsyna-2 in the northeastern part of the Gulf of Odessa drilled into rocks of supposed Proterozoic age at a depth of 3695 m (although the basis of the dating is not known). On the Kalamit Ridge farther south, the prerift is a sequence of micaceous deep marine siltstones and sandstones characterized by chaotic dips on dipmeter logs, by quartz veining, and by an absence of microfauna or palynomorphs. The age of the prerift is known to be older than Albian from the Desantnaya well, but the interpretation of seismic lines away from the well to the north suggests that the prerift is, in fact, much older (Figure 2).

Analogies at Outcrop

Clues to the stratigraphic affinities of the offshore prerift can be found at outcrop in the Crimean Mountains and the Central Pontides, Turkey (the conjugate rift margin of the Western Black Sea) (Figure 3). In the Crimean Mountains and the Central Pontides, the oldest rocks exposed are a sequence of basinal turbiditic mudstones and siltstones. In the Central Pontides, these are known as the Akgöl Formation or Küre Series and include ophiolites at the town of Küre (Ustaömer, 1993; Ustaömer and Robertson, 1994, this volume). In Crimea, what appears on the basis of stratigraphic position, deformation, and lithology to be the same unit is known as the Tavric Series. Where exposed on the coast near Alyushta, these can be seen to be chevron-folded turbidites (Figure 4). Sea floor dredge samples collected off the southern Crimean coast have also been interpreted as Tavric (Shnyukov et al., 1990). The Tavric-Küre Series is interpreted in Turkey as the fill of a back-arc basin of Triassic–Early Jurassic age that was compressionally deformed by closure of the basin (with ophiolite emplacement) and eroded subareally during the Middle Jurassic (Ustaömer and Robertson, 1994). The series is notorious onshore for its lack of microfossils, and is dated by rare Triassic ammonites and Early Jurassic bivalves. Deformation of the Küre Series is dated in Turkey by cross-cutting granites at older than 165 Ma (pre-Early Bathonian) (Yılmaz and Boztug, 1986). North of the Crimean Mountains, the Mesozoic is known to be underlain by Riphean to Paleozoic sediments of the Scythian Platform.

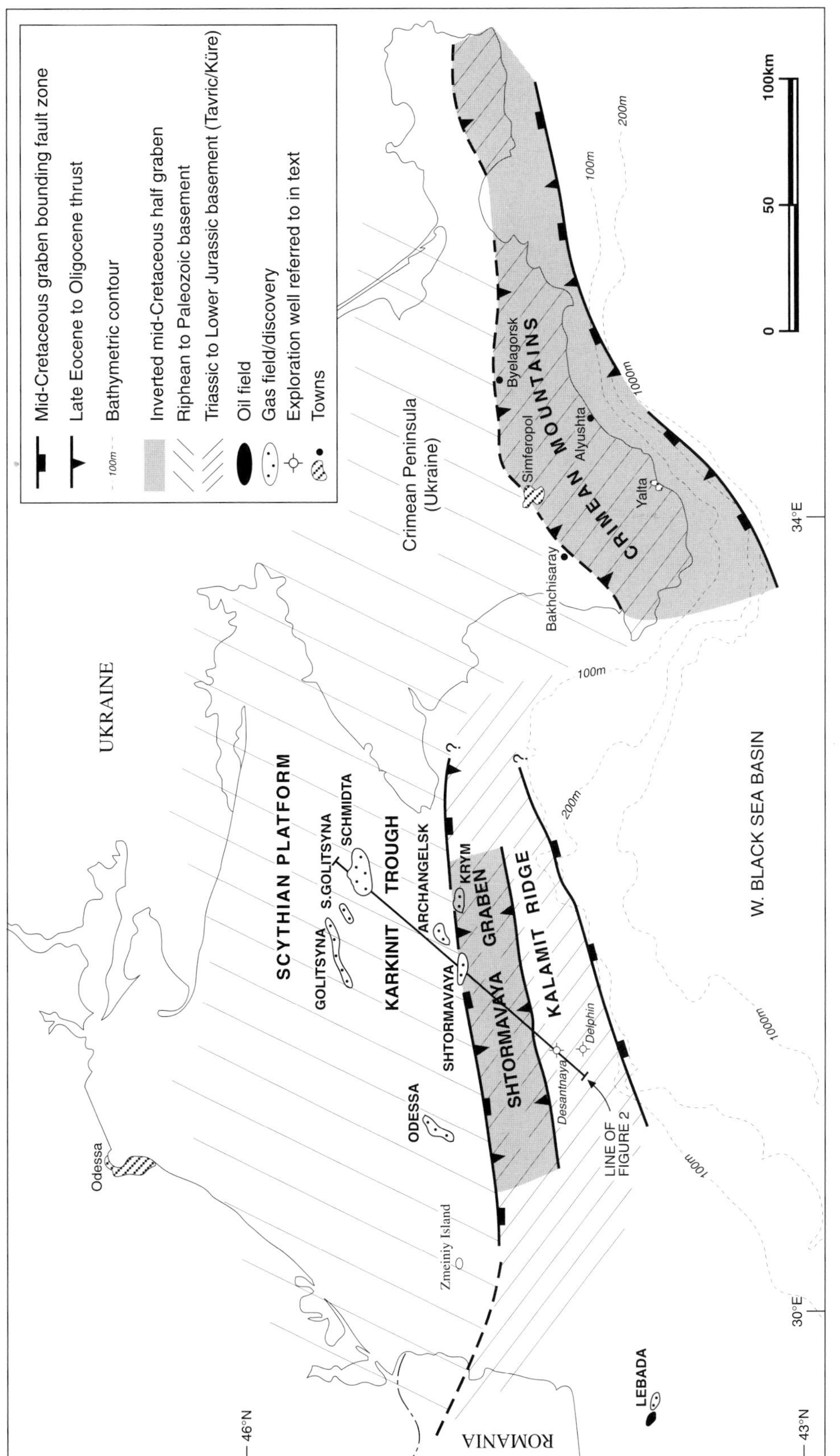

Figure 1. Location map with main tectonic features. The location of line 862045 is indicated.

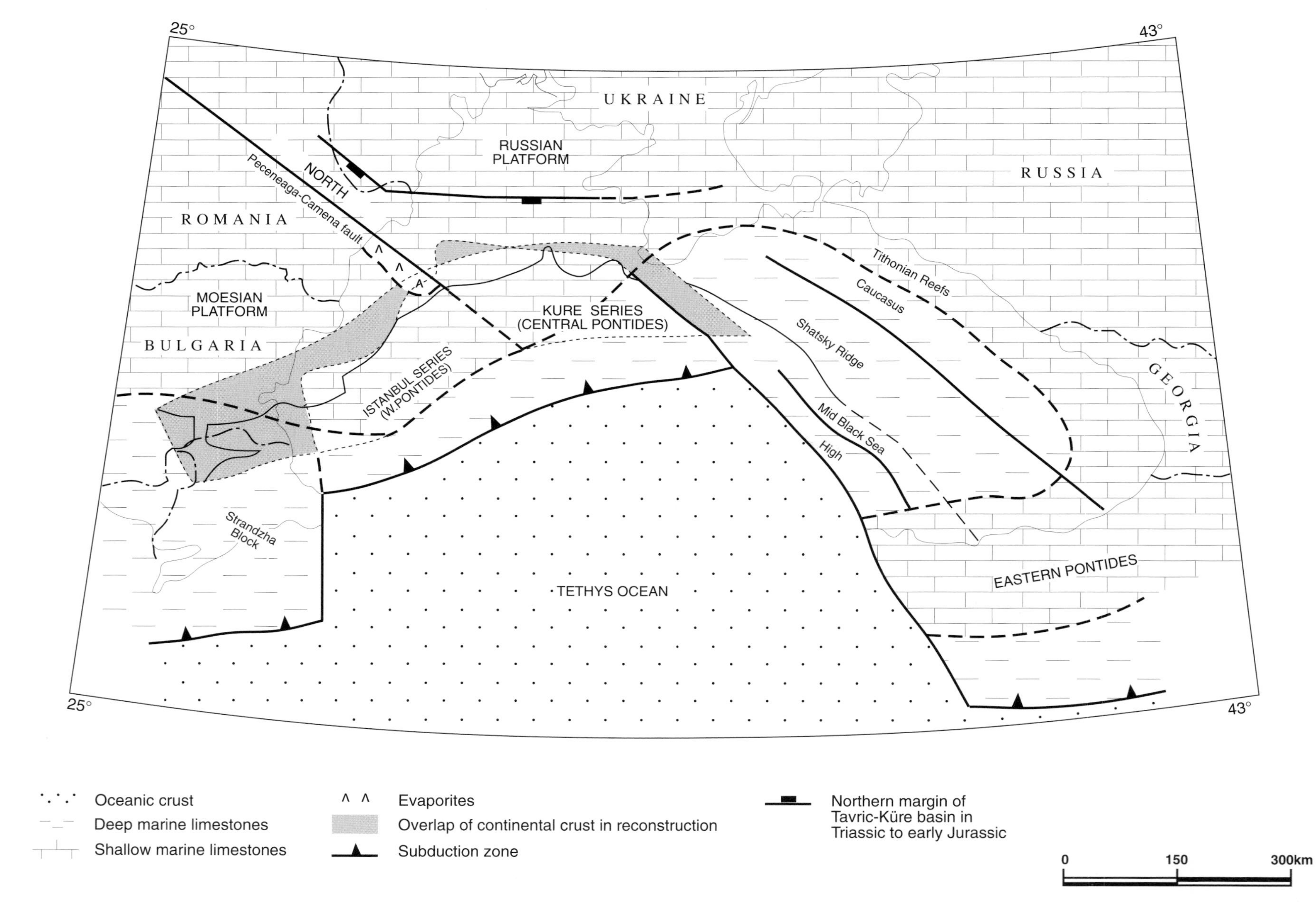

Figure 3. End-Jurassic plate reconstruction and paleogeography of the Western Black Sea area. The Western Black Sea is restored along two transform margins: one in the east, along the western margin of the Mid-Black Sea High; another in the east, which is obscured by the Balkanide deformation. This overriding of the transform margin in the east may be responsible for much of the overlap. The reconstruction shows how the Western and Central Pontides were adjacent to the Gulf of Odessa and Crimea prior to Aptian–Albian rifting and Cenomanian spreading in the Western Black Sea.

Figure 4. Tavric Series exposed on the Crimean coast near Alyushta.

In Turkey and Crimea, the folded and eroded Tavric-Küre Series is unconformably overlain first by continental to shallow marine strata of Middle Jurassic age, and then by shallow marine platform carbonates of approximate Late Jurassic to Neocomian age (Muratov, 1973). In Crimea, the oldest Middle Jurassic is dated as Bajocian and includes volcanogenic sediments and interbedded coals (once mined near Yalta), indicating a paralic environment. These are succeded apparently unconformably by red beds of Late Callovian age. In the Central Pontides, the Middle Jurassic is mainly continental to shallow marine red beds (Bürnük Formation); older volcanogenic sediments and coals are known only from the Eastern Pontides (Robinson et al., 1995; Okay and Şahinturk, this volume). In both areas, the red beds are overlain by limestones of a major south-facing carbonate platform. The oldest limestones in the Pontides appear to be of Callovian age, but those in the Crimea are Oxfordian and younger, indicating a general northward transgression. The Crimean Mountains and the Pontides are dominated by shallow marine facies, known in the latter as the İnaltı Formation; coarse sediments include occasional reefs but are more often grainstone banks, suggesting a carbonate ramp with occasional patch reef development (Harbury and Cohen, this volume). To the south of the Pontides, correlative limestones are distal ramp and eventually pelagic facies with an oceanic assemblage of volcanics and condensed strata (Ager, 1991). The youngest limestones in Crimea (and the Greater Caucasus) appear to be Tithonian, but in Turkey they are Barremian in age. In Crimea, the Berriasian is always missing and later Lower Cretaceous rocks are characterized by being thin and by rapid facies changes. These Hauterivian to Barremian facies get coarser toward the north and east and are shallow marine to possibly fluvial sediments. These relationships are consistent with an end-Jurassic regression, restricting the carbonate platform to the south (Pontides) in the Early Cretaceous.

Interpretation

The stratigraphic location, the lack of coherent internal reflections on seismic data, the lithology and structure, and the lack of microfauna suggest that the prerift drilled on the Kalamit Ridge offshore is equivalent to the Tavric-Küre Series. The strong reflections that appear locally at the top of the prerift are interpreted as representing a Callovian–Barremian sequence including volcanogenic sediments at the base, then shallow marine limestones, possibly overlain by shallow marine to fluvial sediments. The Upper Jurassic–Lower Cretaceous was completely eroded from much of the Kalamit Ridge during Aptian–Albian thermal doming and rifting.

In the northern part of the Gulf of Odessa, the prerift appears to be made up of the relatively undeformed Proterozoic sediments of the Scythian Platform, with a thin coating of Lower Cretaceous (Burakovskiy et al., 1970). The absence of the Paleozoic in Golitsyna-2 requires explanation, particularly as there is a thick Paleozoic sedimentary sequence onshore near Odessa (e.g., Saratskaya wells) and in the Western Pontides. One explanation may be that there was massive footwall uplift of the Western Black Sea northern rift margin during the mid-Cretaceous. Spadini et al. (1996, this volume) found that the Western Black Sea was initiated on a thick, cold lithosphere; this type of lithosphere is usually subjected to major rift flank erosion due to its high flexural rigidity. In the Western Pontides, even within the half-graben system, the mid-Cretaceous erosion cut down at least as far as the Devonian. A further possibility is that rift flank erosion is older, related to the development of the Triassic–early Jurassic Tavrik-Küre back-arc basin. Erosion during both rift phases might be the reason why so much section appears to be missing. The boundary between the Tavrik-Küre and Scythian Platform basement terranes is presumably the once-extensional margin of the back-arc basin (likely to have been inverted in the mid-Jurassic). It must be located somewhere between the Desantnaya and Golitsyna-2 wells; seismic stratigraphy suggests a boundary somewhere near the Shtormavaya field (Figures 1, 2).

Synrift to Early Postrift

Seismic Stratigraphy and Well Data

The synrift to early postrift is characterized on offshore seismic lines by major thickness changes across faults (Figure 2). Fanning reflector geometry toward faults has not been clearly observed. Both the top and bottom of the sequence are unconformities. The basal unconformity—the top of the prerift—is a dissected extensional fault-block topography onto which the basal synrift frequently downlaps or onlaps; the upper unconformity is not in contrast angular, with relatively gentle (although in places considerable) truncation of syn- to early postrift reflectors beneath it. The syn- to early postrift unit thickens markedly toward—and abruptly across—faults that, although inverted during the Tertiary, generally still display net extension. On line 862045, the most significant of these faults can be shown to delineate a major horst and graben geometry (Figure 2). There is a half graben, (Shtormavaya Graben) ~30 km across, south of the Shtormavaya gas field, with its boundary fault beneath the field downthrowing to the south. The Kalamit Ridge represents the footwall to the next graben to the south (which became part of the Western Black Sea passive margin and cannot be resolved on reflection seismic data).

A well tie to Desantnaya suggests that the upper part of this sequence (the only part that has been drilled) is of Albian age. Correlation to the north from Desantnaya suggests that a considerable part of the section is older (Figure 2).

Analogs from Outcrop

Sediments interpreted as deposited during the initial rifting of the Western Black Sea have been described from the Western and Central Pontides and are mainly of Aptian–Albian age, with some possibly as old as Late Barremian (Görür, 1988; Robinson et al., 1996; Görür et al., this volume). The Aptian–Albian in the Central Pontides includes thick, deep water turbidites and olistostromes with Upper Jurassic limestone blocks, deposited in half grabens, and shallow marine to beach facies above extensional fault-block footwalls, where it may even be absent (Figures 5, 6). These strata are collectively known as the Çağlayan Formation. The correlative Ülüs Formation incorporates thick marine debris flows. In the Crimean Mountains, the Albian is not well exposed. South of Simferopol, the Albian locally has a polymictic basal conglomerate with clasts of Upper Jurassic limestone, sandstone, quartzite, and vein quartz, but is mainly mudstones, siltstones, and sandstones that appear to be turbidites. There are also volcanics. Underlying Barremian mudstones are reported to contain olistoliths of Upper Jurassic limestone. The thickness of the Albian is from nothing to >1000 m, and the geological map suggests that the strata south of Simferopol fill a pre-Albian submarine valley.

Interpretation

The syn- to early postrift unit identified on offshore reflection seismic data is likely to be mainly of Aptian–Albian age, possibly with some sediments as old as Late Barremian. By analogy with the Aptian–Albian in the Pontides and Crimea and with synrift sequences in general, the unit is likely to be characterized by rapid facies, as well as thickness, variations. This is suggested to an extent by the seismic facies. The earliest reflectors in the Shtormavaya graben downlap strongly and prograde to the north, apparently reflecting a sediment source prograding from the hangingwall (the Kalamit Ridge), as is common in present-day East African rifts (Scholz, 1995). Higher reflectors in the unit tend to be more parallel and may represent deeper water sedimentation taking over as the graben further subsided and deepened. On the Kalamit Ridge, the oldest synrift strata are Albian and include a probably transgressive sandstone near the base.

Postrift

Seismic Stratigraphy

The postrift unit lies above the erosional unconformity that marks the top of the syn- to early postrift, and extends upward to a disconformity that marks the onset of compressional deformation (Figure 2). The unit thins slowly to the north (toward the Scythian Platform) and shows limited thickness changes related to the mid-Cretaceous half-graben system. In the Shtormovaya Graben, it thickens and appears to erode the synrift, whereas it thins substantially over the Kalamit Ridge. The earliest postrift sequence is a wedge of sediments in the northern part of the Gulf of Odessa that progrades toward the south. The remainder of the unit is characterized by parallel reflectors.

This main postrift unit is relatively well known from offshore exploration wells because it includes the main reservoirs for the gas and gas-condensate fields. The southward-prograding wedge has been drilled by Schmidta-6 and comprises rubbly, presumably shallow marine limestone of Cenomanian–Turonian age with reworked Albian fossils. In Shtormavaya, Desantnaya, and the remainder of the Gulf of Odessa, the younger parts of the postrift are known to comprise Santonian–Danian chalks and Upper Paleocene–middle Eocene mudstones and marls.

Analogs from Outcrop

Comparisons between the postrift sequences in the Pontides and in Crimea must be made with caution because of the Cenomanian spreading in the Western Black Sea and the consequent physical separation of the two areas. In the Western Pontides, Aptian–Albian sediments are overlain disconformably by Cenomanian–Santonian, often red, pelagic limestones and submarine volcanics and tuffs (Kapanboğazı and Yemişliçay formations) (Görür et al., 1993). These are overlain by Campanian–Maastrichtian terrigenous turbidites (the Görsükü Formation) and then by Maastrichtian chalks, often containing tuffaceous debris (the Akveren Formation). The Paleocene appears to be missing, and the Maastrichtian is unconformably overlain by terrigenous turbidites of the Kusuri Formation.

In the Crimean Mountains, the Upper Cretaceous–Danian is up to about 1500 m thick and, as in the offshore, is exclusively chalk (Figure 7). The chalk is overlain by an Upper Paleocene grainstone and then a sequence of lower Eocene marls.

Interpretation

The prograding system in the northern part of the Gulf of Odessa demonstrates a major transgression at the end of the Albian that reflects the breakup of

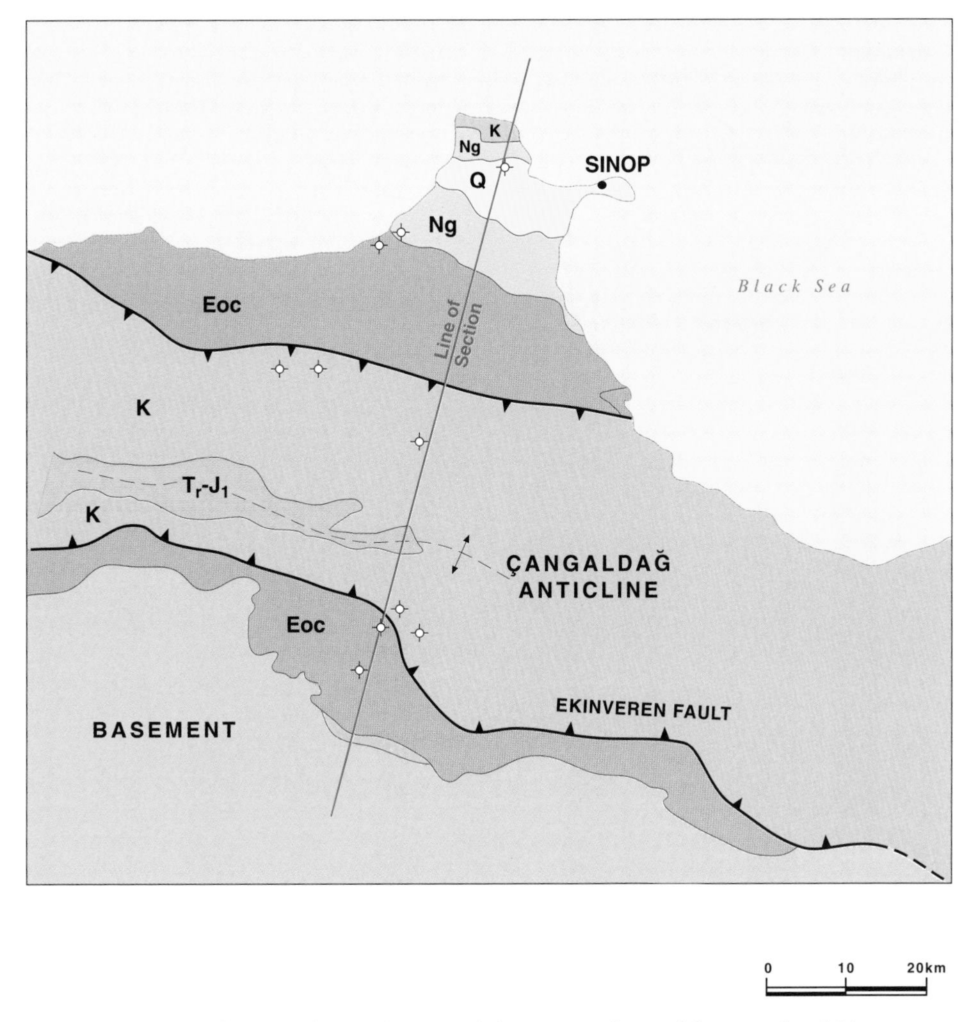

Figure 5. Simplified geological map of the Central Pontides south of Sinop. The map shows the line of section in Figure 6.

the Western Black Sea rift and the evolution of the area into the south-facing passive margin of the Western Black Sea. Far from sediment sources (Naidin et al., 1980), Upper Cretaceous facies farther south on the Kalamit Ridge are thin, becoming even condensed or absent through nondeposition, while chalks were deposited above the still-subsiding Shtormavaya graben. By the early Eocene, sufficient fine clastic material was able to enter the basins for marls to become deposited. The passive margin must have been filled close to sea level by the middle Eocene, as there is widespread development of nummulitic limestones, even over the Kalamit Ridge where middle Eocene carbonates rest directly above the deformed and eroded Tavric-Küre prerift. By the middle Eocene, the relief in the Gulf of Odessa that was inherited from the mid-Cretaceous rifting had largely disappeared.

Syncompression

Seismic Stratigraphy and Structure

Above the Upper Cretaceous to middle Eocene is a unit that shows different seismic geometry. Its principal characteristic is onlap of internal reflectors onto compressional folds; a sequence of such onlaps demonstrates that the unit was deposited during fold growth (Figure 2). This folding is well developed in the vicinity of the Shtormavaya gas-condensate field and is spatially linked to mid-Cretaceous extensional features. The regional elevation of the top of the middle Eocene is raised by ~200 ms above the mid-Cretaceous Shtormavaya graben; the boundaries of the elevated portion are marked in the south by a monocline and in the north by the anticlines of the Shtormavaya field. Thickness changes in the Aptian–Albian show that the field is directly above the old extensional bounding fault of the graben. The earliest seismic unit that was deposited during folding is characterized by parallel reflectors and gentle thickness changes, with most thickening evident into the Karkinit Trough; there are also reflectors that downlap in opposite directions that appear to be sediment fans. The overlying unit takes the form of a major prograding wedge that eventually reached the southern flank of the Kalamit Ridge (south of which equivalent facies are all toesets). It thickens markedly into the Karkinit Trough.

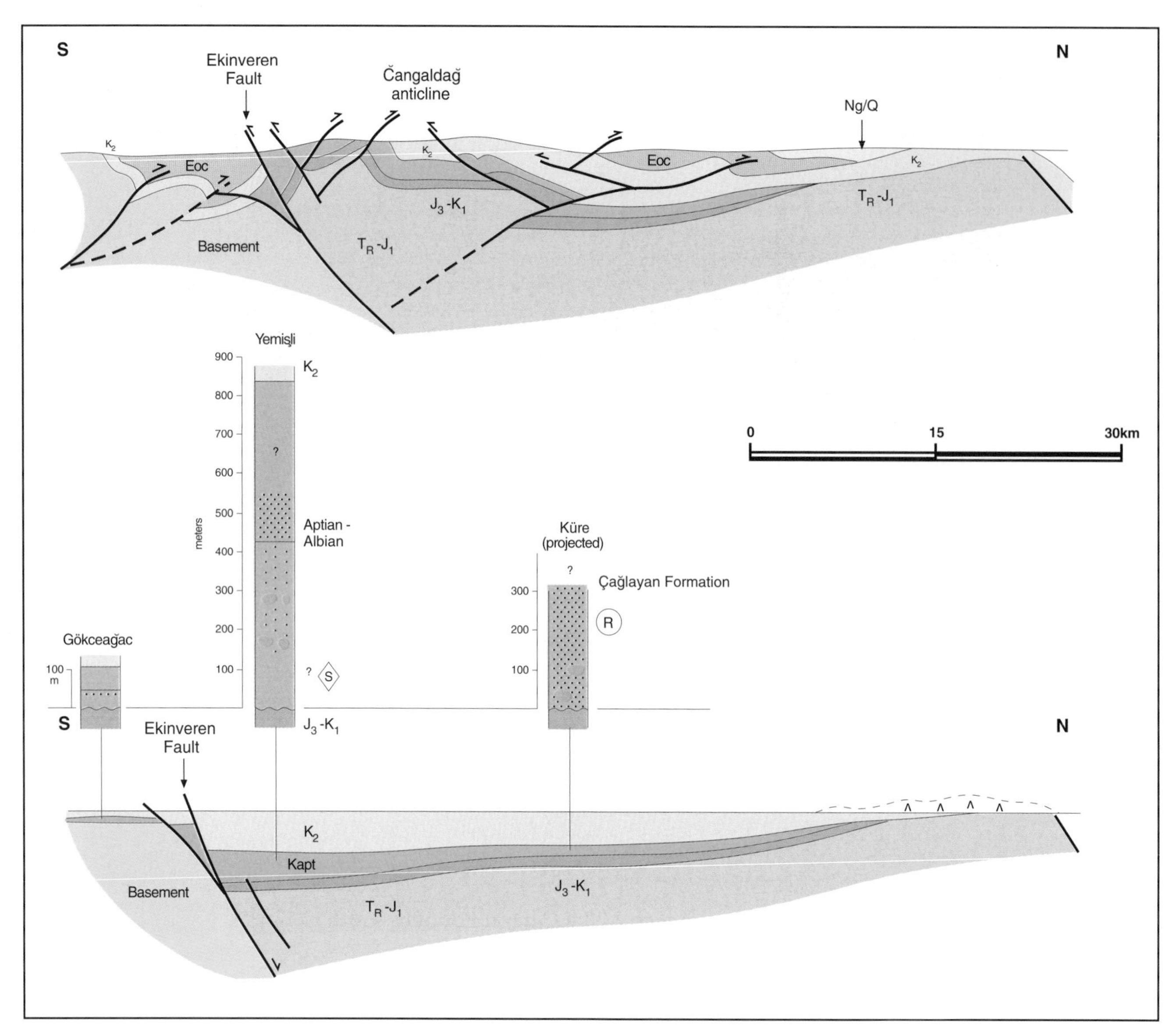

Figure 6. Structural section across the Central Pontides related to Aptian–Albian stratigraphy. Structure of the Çangaldağ anticline is interpreted as an inverted Mid-Cretaceous half graben. This interpretation is partly based on the thickness and facies changes observed in sections measured north and south of the Ekinveren fault. Measured sections are located on the section now restored to the end of the Cretaceous (below). Transgressive sands with reservoir potential are well developed tens of kilometers away from the graben-bounding faults (Küre Section), but not immediately adjacent to faults. On footwalls, the Aptian–Albian is condensed or absent through a combination of nondeposition and erosion (Gökceağac Section). On hangingwalls, near the bounding faults, the section is much thicker and mainly turbidites with occasional olistostromes (Yemişli Section).

Numerous wells penetrate the syncompression sequence offshore and show that it ranges from late Eocene–Oligocene and possibly early Miocene in age. The upper Eocene—the lower unit, characterized by parallel reflectors—is mainly mudstone. The southward prograding wedge is Oligocene and is known locally as the Maikop. It includes toeset mudstones, coarsening upward to topset sands.

Analogs at Outcrop

By the late Eocene, comparisons between the stratigraphy of the Gulf of Odessa and that of the Pontides tend to lose their significance because of the physical separation of the two areas and because their structural histories are not the same. In the Pontides, for example, the upper Eocene is missing; the only Oligocene sedimentary rocks exposed are in piggyback basins behind growing folds and are mainly fluvial (Cemalletin Formation). This at least demonstrates compressional fold growth in the Pontides during the Oligocene. In Crimea, the upper Eocene and Oligocene are not well exposed. Farther west, upper Eocene strata on the Russian Black Sea coast near Tuapse are distal turbidites with significant oil-prone source potential

Figure 7. Upper Cretaceous–middle Eocene section near Bakhchisaray. There is a complete section exposed from the Campanian–Upper Paleocene. Campanian and Maastrichtian chalks with a characteristic fauna of inoceramids and other burrowing bivalves and echinoderms pass upward into Danian chalks, which contain substantial quantities of quartz sand and glauconite, becoming essentially sandstones at the top. These are overlain apparently conformably by Upper Paleocene bioclastic grainstones, lower Eocene marls, and then middle Eocene nummulitic grainstones.

(Robinson et al., 1996). In the adjacent Greater Caucasus foothills, geological maps show evidence for onlap of upper Eocene–Oligocene strata onto compressional folds.

Interpretation

The regional elevation of the top middle Eocene shows that the folding that took place in the Gulf of Odessa from the late Eocene to the Oligocene or early Miocene was compressional. The restriction of the elevation to the older graben strongly suggests that the compression has caused inversion of the mid-Cretaceous extensional faults, and has caused the graben fill to pop up. These are classic features of the inversion of extensional half grabens (McClay and Buchanan, 1992). The fault interpretation shown in Figure 2 is based on this model. The graben is shown bounded to the north by an extensional fault (A) that has been inverted, leading to the development of footwall shortcut thrusts (B) and folding in the postrift and syn-inversion cover. These folds constitute the Shtormavaya gas-condensate field; the Golitsyna field is a similar inversion anticline. The monocline that marks the southern boundary of the elevated stratigraphy is interpreted as lying above a deep-seated fault, because there is no visible low-angle detachment running near the top of the prerift or through the graben fill.

The Karkinit Trough is a puzzling feature, representing a depocenter of principally late Eocene to Oligocene age (although possibly as old as Paleocene). As such, it cannot be related to decay of the mid-Cretaceous thermal dome associated with rifting. It is not a graben as suggested by Okay et al. (1994). Even though it developed largely during inversion of the old extensional faults, the amount of shortening hardly seems sufficient to have caused a flexural basin to develop.

The parallel reflectors, fans, and muddy lithologies that typify the upper Eocene in the Gulf of Odessa suggest that the unit was deposited in relatively deep water. Only during the Oligocene was sediment able to fill the basin. This is in accord with evidence from other areas that suggests that the late Eocene was a period of major transgression across most of the Black Sea and surrounding areas (Robinson et al., 1996).

Postcompression

The uppermost seismic stratigraphic unit downlaps on the top of the syncompressional unit. It forms a sediment wedge that thickens toward the present shelf margin, showing no thickness changes related to the older Karkinit Trough, Shtormavaya graben, or Kalamit Ridge. There are large doubly downlapping features on the basal downlap surface (Point 900-1000, Figure 2). Near the present shelf edge, the unit is characterized by chaotic internal reflectors, the results of slumping and gravity-induced faulting.

Well ties demonstrate that this wedge is clastic, including sandstones, siltstones, and mudstones, and of middle Miocene to Quaternary age. Correlative stratigraphy is very poorly exposed onshore in Crimea, and is in any case likely to comprise facies quite different from those offshore. A major transgression around the end of the middle Miocene is implied by the accommodation space created for the Neogene above, but it is unclear whether the fan shown in Figure 2 is a lowstand fan related to a preceding sea level fall or a highstand fan related to the transgression itself. The accommodation space created was filled during the remainder of the Neogene by a southward-prograding shelf that has built out to the present shelf margin.

RESERVOIR DEVELOPMENT

Prerift (Pre-Aptian)

The Tavric-Küre Series contains few sandstones and is intensely deformed, so it cannot be expected to contain viable petroleum reservoirs (despite the presence of gas shows in the Desantnaya well). Reservoirs may be present in the clastic and carbonate sequence that postdates the Middle Jurassic deformation but predates Western Black Sea rifting. Upper Jurassic carbonate grainstones are known from the Crimean Mountains and other areas around the Black Sea and constitute the reservoir in the Tyulenovo field, onshore Bulgaria (Harbury and Cohen, this volume). At outcrop, these carbonates contain very little remnant primary porosity, and the reservoir at Tyulenovo is dependent on karstification for secondary porosity development. Karstification is most likely on the footwalls of Aptian–Albian extensional faults. On many of these, however, the unit has clearly been completely eroded (e.g., Desantnaya and Delphin wells on the Kalamit Ridge). Some of the footwall anticlines have in addition been extensively modified by Tertiary inversion.

There may be potential for clastic reservoirs in the post-Berriasian Lower Cretaceous. Porous trough cross-bedded sandstones dated as Hauterivian to Barremian are exposed between Simferopol and Byelagorsk, but the facies and controls on the distribution of such sands are not known.

Synrift (Aptian–Albian)

Aptian–Albian synrift transgressive sandstones are known from the conjugate rift margin in Turkey (Çağlayan Formation); are the reservoir in the Lebada field offshore Romania; and have been drilled in Desantnaya, where they were permeable but tested water at a rate of 4150 bbl per day. The seal for a petroleum accumulation at this level would be provided intraformationally, by Albian mudstones. The Albian unit that includes the sands can identified on reflection seismic data at Desantnaya and onlaps the rift unconformity. Although the unit appears to drape some of the extensional fault blocks of the Kalamit Ridge, it does not extend over the highest part. This picture of the distribution of Albian sandstone is supported by the outcrop data from Turkey (Figure 6) and means that successful exploration for this play will be contingent on both the acquisition of high-quality reflection seismic data capable of imaging pinch-outs within the Albian, and on the erection of sophisticated sedimentological models.

Other synrift plays are possible, although none have as yet been explored. Fanlike geometries are suggested on line 862045 (Figure 2) adjacent to the southern bounding faults of the Shtormovaya graben. These may be eroding limestone and turbidites here, so reservoir quality would be a concern. Similar fans may be present adjacent to the northern bounding faults but are not imaged on seismic.

Postrift (Upper Cretaceous to Middle Eocene)

The gas-condensate fields in the Gulf of Odessa have Danian (and sometimes Maastrichtian) carbonate reservoirs folded in inversion anticlines. Although described locally as "reefs," cores are of pelagic coccolithic chalk, and thus outer-shelf deposits. No buildups are visible on reflection seismic. In the Shtormavaya gas-condensate field, the upper parts of the reservoir are probably reworked, and accordingly have rather higher porosity (up to ~10 mD in Shtormavaya-5). Other than in these reworked quartz-rich (possibly tuffaceous) zones, chalk permeability is very low (1 mD or less); nonetheless, gas flow rates of several million standard cubic feet of gas per day are commonly obtained from wells. Matrix permeabilities appear similar to those estimated from test data, so the chalk does not appear to be significantly fractured.

Syn-Inversion (Late Eocene to Oligocene)

Late Eocene–Oligocene inversion was crucial to the development of petroleum-bearing structures in the Gulf of Odessa, but was probably far less so from the point of view of reservoir development. Upper Maikop (upper Oligocene) siltstones are reservoirs in the South Golitsyna and Schmidta discoveries (Palii and Tochkov, 1994) and probably represent the topsets of the southerly prograding wedge observed on line 862045 (Figure 2). Flow rates of ~7 MMSCFD are reported (Palii and Tochkov, 1994).

PETROLEUM SOURCE SYSTEMS

Little is known about source systems in the Ukrainian Black Sea. Around much of the Black Sea, there is apparently an upper Eocene oil-prone source (Robinson et al., 1996, this volume). However, the source of the wet gas in the Gulf of Odessa cannot be within the upper Eocene for two reasons: (1) this unit cannot be mature for even oil generation in the area, and (2) Golitsyna condensate is geochemically distinct from other probable upper Eocene-sourced oils around the Black Sea (including Lebada) (Robinson et al., 1996). There are at least three other possible candidates for the source of the wet gas:

1. Devonian—Small oil discoveries in the Paleozoic onshore south of Odessa (Saratskaya and Limanskaya) suggest the presence of a Middle Devonian? source rock on the southern flank of the Scythian

Platform. This would be present only within the Scythian Platform: its southern limit would therefore correspond to the southern boundary of the Scythian Platform with the Triassic–Early Jurassic Tavric-Küre back-arc basin. The boundary may be close to Shtormavaya, in which case Shtormavaya could be sourced from the Devonian along extensional faults. Structures south of the northern margin of the Shtormavaya graben could not be easily charged from the Devonian, however. This would explain the absence of wet-gas discoveries south of Shtormavaya. A Devonian source rock could have begun to generate oil as early as the Cretaceous, before inversion anticlines were formed. The inversion anticlines could then only have been charged with late-generation products (wet gas). The oil generated may still be located within earlier structures that were not breached during inversion.

2. Upper Carboniferous—Coals are mined on the conjugate rift margin in Turkey (Zonguldak) and could source dry-gas discoveries such as the Odesskaya field. The distribution of coal measures would be similar to that of a Devonian source rock.
3. Aptian–Albian—Where exposed in Crimea, Aptian–Albian mudstones appear to be at best poor source rocks with low organic carbon contents and Type III *dry* gas-prone kerogen (Robinson et al., 1996). Albian mudstones would probably be localized within the thicker synrift sequences in the extensional basins. This could explain the gas at Shtormavaya (although perhaps not the condensate), but there is apparently no major Aptian–Albian extensional basin associated with the Golitsyna or Schmidta accumulations. Generation of gas would probably not have taken place until the Neogene, after the inversion anticlines had formed.

In the southern part of the Gulf of Odessa, there may be a second source system working that probably does involve the upper Eocene. The upper Eocene can be mature only some distance south of the Kalamit Ridge: migration of oil into structures such as Delphin and Komsamalskaya would therefore need to be updip over several kilometers. This appears to happen at Lebada, where oil migrates along an erosional unconformity at the base of a submarine canyon (Robinson et al., 1996). Generation would have begun during the Neogene.

In contrast to the gas accumulations in the lower Paleocene, those in the Oligocene are dry. It is possible that this gas is biogenic, or even that it is a later-generation product of the same source rock responsible for the Paleocene-reservoired gas (the folding of the Oligocene took place *after* that of the Paleocene).

CONCLUSIONS

During the late Paleozoic, the area now occupied by the Gulf of Odessa was near the southern passive margin of the Scythian Platform, north of a precursor of the Tethys Ocean. During the Triassic, an extensional back-arc basin opened, was filled with turbidites, and eventually closed during the Middle Jurassic, with local ophiolite emplacement. The folded Triassic–Lower Jurassic was peneplaned during the Middle Jurassic and eventually transgressed in the Oxfordian; this established a south-facing carbonate platform (ramp) that lasted until the end of the Jurassic in the area in question (but until the Barremian farther south). This carbonate platform was domed, eroded, and extensionally faulted during the Aptian and Albian, as the basin that was to form the Western Black Sea began to develop. Some of the major obvious tectonic features in the Gulf of Odessa were formed at this time: the Kalamit Ridge as a major extensional high and the Shtormavaya graben. The Cretaceous rift effectively reactivated the Triassic rift, splitting the Triassic to Lower Jurassic basin fill and its carbonate cover between the Pontides and the Gulf of Odessa and Crimean Mountains. From the Cenomanian to the middle Eocene, the Gulf of Odessa formed the subsiding northern passive margin of the Western Black Sea. During the late Eocene to Oligocene, however, this tranquility was interrupted by a phase of compression that inverted the Cretaceous extensional faults, squeezing out the synrift sediments and producing inversion anticlines in the postrift. Inversion offshore has not been particularly severe; the most impressive manifestations of the inversion of Aptian–Albian half-graben fills are the Pontide and Crimean Mountains. The Karkinit Trough is a depocenter related in some way to this period of inversion and is not an extensional structure.

The Gulf of Odessa is a fairly extensive proven gas province. The gas has been discovered to date in only one type of structure (inversion anticlines), and the total resources discovered are modest. The inversion anticlines are clear on even poor reflection seismic data and are mostly at moderate depths; these have, not surprisingly, virtually all been drilled. The future of the area as a petroleum province will therefore rely on the development of new play concepts. Recent developments in seismic data reprocessing and the acquisition of new reflection seismic data in the area have shown that there are indeed a number of other plays within the pre- and synrift, most of which have never been tested by drilling. Those involving structures that formed relatively early, before the late Eocene–Oligocene inversion anticlines, may have retained the early-generated oil rather than gas condensate. The main uncertainty associated with these new plays is probably reservoir distribution and quality. Some of the uncertainty can be reduced by studies of the correlative stratigraphy at outcrops on both sides of the present Black Sea. On the southern flank of the Kalamit Ridge, extensional structures may be linked to a mature upper Eocene oil-prone source rock in the Western Black Sea basin to the south; further discoveries like Lebada are possible in Ukrainian territorial waters.

ACKNOWLEDGMENTS

We thank Chernomorneftegas for permission to publish this study and are grateful to some of its employees for providing information, particularly Peter Melnichuk. Robertsons (Llandudno, U.K.) and

Odessmorgeologiya (Odessa, Ukraine) kindly allowed us to publish a reprocessed reflection seismic line. We also thank JKX Oil & Gas plc for supporting this work and for permission to publish.

REFERENCES CITED

Ager, D.V., 1991, Mesozoic brachiopod faunas from the Western Pontides, Turkey; their stratigraphical, paleogeographical, and paleoecological significance: Geologica Romana, v. 27, p. 237–243.

Banks, C.J., and A.G. Robinson, this volume, Mesozoic strike-slip back-arc basins of the Western Black Sea region, *in* A.G. Robinson, ed., Regional and petroleum geology of the Black Sea and surrounding region: AAPG Memoir 68, p. 53–62.

Burakovskiy, V.Ye., and B.L. Gurevich, 1970, Boundary of the East European Platform in the northwestern sector of the Black Sea and in the southern part of the Prut-Dniester interfluve: Doklady Akademii Nauk SSSR, v. 193, p. 45–47.

Görür, N., 1988, Timing of opening of the Black Sea Basin: Tectonophysics, v. 147, p. 247–262.

Görür, N., this volume, Cretaceous syn- to postrift sedimentation on the southern continental margin of the Western Black Sea Basin, *in* A.G. Robinson, ed., Regional and petroleum geology of the Black Sea and surrounding region: AAPG Memoir 68, p. 227–240.

Görür, N., O. Tüysüz, A. Aykol, M. Sakinç, E. Yeğitbaş, and R. Akkok, 1993, Cretaceous red pelagic carbonates of northern Turkey: their place in the opening history of the Black Sea: Eclogae Geologia Helvetica, v. 86, p. 819–838.

Harbury, N., and M. Cohen, this volume, Sedimentary history of the Late Jurassic–Paleogene of Northeast Bulgaria and the Bulgarian Black Sea, *in* A.G. Robinson, ed., Regional and petroleum geology of the Black Sea and surrounding region: AAPG Memoir 68, p. 129–168.

Hubbard, R.J., J. Pape, and D.G. Roberts, 1985, Depositional sequence mapping as a technique to establish tectonic and stratigraphic framework and evaluate hydrocarbon potential on a passive continental margin, *in* O.R. Berg and D.G. Woolverton, eds., Seismic stratigraphy II—an integrated approach: AAPG Memoir 39, p. 79–92.

McClay, K.R., and P.G. Buchanan, 1992, Thrust faults in inverted extensional basins, *in* K.R. McClay, ed., Thrust tectonics: London, Chapman and Hall, p. 93–104.

Muratov, M.V., 1973, Handbook for the student field geologist in the Crimea, Vol. 2, Geology of the Crimean Peninsula (in Russian): Moscow, Nedra, 192 p.

Naidin, D.P., I.G. Sasonova, Z.N. Pojarkova, M.R. Djalilov, G.N. Papulov, Yu. Senkovsky, V.N. Benjamovsky, and L.F. Kopaevich, 1980, Cretaceous transgressions and regressions on the Russian Platform, in Crimea and Central Asia: Cretaceous Research, v. 1, p. 375–387.

Okay, A.I., and Ö. Şahintürk, this volume, Geology of the Eastern Pontides, *in* A.G. Robinson, ed., Regional and petroleum geology of the Black Sea and surrounding region: AAPG Memoir 68, p. 291–312.

Okay, A.I., A.M.C. Şengor, and N. Görür, 1994, Kinematic history of the opening of the Black Sea and its effect on the surrounding regions: Geology, v. 22, p. 267–270.

Palii, A., and D. Tochkov, 1994, Oil and gas in the Cenozoic deposits of the Black Sea basin, *in* Proceedings of the Conference on Petroleum Geology and Hydrocarbon Potential of the Black Sea Area, October 16–18: Varna, p. 6–10.

Robinson, A.G., C.J. Banks, M.M. Rutherford, and J.P.P. Hirst, 1995, Stratigraphic and structural evolution of the Eastern Pontides, Turkey: Journal of the Geological Society of London, v. 152, p. 861–872.

Robinson, A.G., E.T. Griffith, A.R. Gardiner, and A.K. Home, this volume, Petroleum geology of the Georgian fold and thrust belts and foreland basins, *in* A.G. Robinson, ed., Regional and petroleum geology of the Black Sea and surrounding region: AAPG Memoir 68, p. 347–368.

Robinson, A.G., J.H. Rudat, C.J. Banks, and R.L.F. Wiles, 1996, Petroleum geology of the Black Sea: Marine and Petroleum Geology, v. 13, p. 195–223.

Scholz, C.A., 1995, Deltas of the Lake Malawi rift, East Africa: seismic expression and exploration implications: AAPG Bulletin, v. 79, p. 1679–1697.

Shnyukov, E.F., N.B. Maslun, Yu.E. Inozentsev, and Yu.Yu. Orovetskiy, 1990, Noviy danniy o geologicheskam straeniy kantinentalnava sklona yuzhnava Kryma (New information about the geological structure of the continental slope of southern Crimea): Geologicheskii Zhurnal, v. 3, p. 88–98.

Spadini, G., A.G. Robinson, and S.A.P.L. Cloetingh, 1996, Western versus eastern Black Sea tectonic evolution: prerift lithospheric controls on basin formation: Tectonophysics, v. 266, p. 139–154.

Spadini, G., A.G. Robinson, and S.A.P.L. Cloetingh, this volume, Thermomechanical modeling of Black Sea Basin formation, subsidence, and sedimentation, *in* A.G. Robinson, ed., Regional and petroleum geology of the Black Sea and surrounding region: AAPG Memoir 68, p. 19–38.

Ustaömer, T., 1993, Pre-Late Jurassic tectonic-sedimentary evolution of North Tethys: Central Pontides, North Turkey: Ph.D. thesis, Edinburgh University.

Ustaömer, T., and A.H.F. Robertson, 1994, Paleozoic marginal basin and subduction-accretion, the Palaeotethyan Küre Complex, Central Pontides, northern Turkey: Journal of the Geological Society of London, v. 151, p. 291–305.

Ustaömer, T., and A. Robertson, this volume, Tectonic-sedimentary evolution of the North-Tethyan margin in the Central Pontides of Northern Turkey, *in* A.G. Robinson, ed., Regional and petroleum geology of the Black Sea and surrounding region: AAPG Memoir 68, p. 255–290.

Yılmaz, O., and D. Boztuğ, 1986, Kastamonu granitoid belt of northern Turkey; first arc plutonism product related to the subduction of the Paleotethys: Geology, v. 14, p. 179–183.

Index